Doctor at Dienbienphu

PAUL GRAUWIN

Doctor
at Dienbienphu

The John Day Company

New York

Contents

List of Illustrations

PHOTOGRAPHS . (*All following page 104*)

Major Grauwin

Aerial view of the entrenched camp at Dienbienphu

Paratroops wounded on the last opening up of the road

Wounded crowded into one of the field hospital shelters during the Gabrielle attack

Wounded in the field hospital's main passage, waiting to go into the clearing station

The helicopter has just landed for another attempt to evacuate wounded.

A 105 delayed-action shell has exploded in the X-ray shelter. It is a total wreck.

View of the field hospital roof after the mid-March attacks

Doctor at Dienbienphu

There was a whistling, a dull thud, then four or five seconds' silence, followed by a sharp explosion—a crash like some great blow from a hammer on an anvil buried in the ground: more delayed-action shells.

Quickly I sprang to my feet. My throat was dry, and suddenly I was sweating. I put on my shorts, looked for my glasses, and began waiting. It was four in the morning.

Shells fell relentlessly, one a minute, and I was sickened by the sound they made as they plunged into the ground. Who was going to be covered in rubble in a few more seconds? Who would be brought to me, slung across the shoulders or on a stretcher, covered with blackish dust, blue in the face, with a leg broken, an open wound in the head, or the thorax gaping and puffing like a bellows?

There was a second explosion, muted this time, underground and close at hand. The walls quivered, and the whole shelter was shaken. Looking at the ceiling, I saw a piece of dry earth fall and crumble on my small metal table. At my feet, Phuc watched me. He was a medical orderly in the paratroops, and his right arm had been amputated.

"Major, I'm scared," he said. "I don't like that sort of shell."

"I don't like them either, my boy."

But I had one advantage in that I could move and have the feeling that I was dodging the shell which would crush my poor shelter in a matter of seconds.

I stepped over Yann, paratroop sergeant. He had no legs, and he was staring at something on the wall, which was made of earth.

I came out into the central passage. All was quiet; operating had been finished two hours ago. To right and left there were rows of stretchers where the wounded and the medical orderlies were sleeping, all jumbled together.

Here was N'Diaye, my chief orderly, a fine athletic African, a good man with plenty of courage.

Then came Sioni, a corporal in the Foreign Legion, ambulance driver, orderly, a colleague of Geneviève's, a man I used to admire, always unruffled yet full of daring. Next were two men with chest wounds, their breathing difficult and painful; but they were asleep now, as they had had morphine not long before. There was only just enough room to step between the stretchers and the walls, and in making your way along you had to lean against the earth wall.

My abdominal cases, fresh from their operations, were in the last shelter. The smell was one of damp sweat, urine, and feces. The convalescents were in another shelter, where Phu was on duty.

Laid out on their stretchers, revealing the great bandages around their abdomens, they looked up at me, each watching my face and my gestures for any indication which would relieve him or show that his case was hopeless.

Moret was the first of them, the son of a doctor and himself a medical orderly sergeant. "Better not make any mistake, major," he said, "my father's a doc too, and you'll have him to face."

He was a wonderful fellow. He had got a bullet in the

abdomen when for the third time he was bringing in the wounded under fire just below Dominique 3.

"If you make no mistake," he went on, "you'll be able to come and see me in Paris, and then you'll learn for yourself what a fine man my father is."

He had had a splenectomy; the liver and the large and small intestines were all affected by his wound. Three days later he died.

Next was Walter, another Legionnaire. He had an intestinal resection and a wound in the liver: he would get better all right.

"*Bitte, mein Kommandant. Ein Schluck Wasser.*" He asked me for a drink in his own tongue.

Then Corporal Thach, a Cambodian shock trooper. His skin was bronzed and covered with tattoo marks that had a religious significance. His dark eyes were large and anxious. He protested, "My stomach's hurting. Phu wouldn't let me have any water."

Bao, a Tonkinese scout, had undergone a laparotomy and amputation of the left arm. "Major, give me some." He did not die, but I never knew why.

Dechamp, a gunner, had the spleen and a kidney missing. There was considerable hemorrhage. "God, give me a drop of water, major, or I've had it. The guy on duty doesn't understand a thing. Tell him . . ."

Then I had to explain, "If you drink, then you've quite certainly had it. If you don't drink, you've got a chance to pull through. You're drinking all the time without realizing it. You see all those little bottles up there with rubber tubes tied to a log in the ceiling? That's the water you're making such a fuss about. Now do you get it?"

"Yes, I get it. All the same, it's tough."

Ben Moktar, a Moroccan rifleman. In the course of the morning water detail a shell had exploded and opened up his abdomen. He came out of it still standing, but with blood pouring down into his boots. Now his face was ashen, his lips like clay. Death was not far off. "Major, water, water."

Antoine, from Senegal, was his neighbor. Antoine was his Christian name. The nature of the wound in the large intestine obliged me to treat it by externalization. He would not see the point of this: "Why didn't you leave it inside, why make my guts stick out? Tomorrow, major, be a good guy and put my guts back in my stomach. After that, leave it to me."

The shells were terrible; I had counted a dozen already. Usually after about twenty of them it was over until the next day or the day after.

My abdominal cases never even heard them: for them the whole universe was concentrated in their accursed bellies, so vulnerable and unprotected. Their thoughts were on their abdominal cavities and the whitish tubes marked with stitches. They were conscious of the slow process of healing and the suffering in this complicated machinery which expressed itself in fearful colics and thirst.

"Hell, when is all this mess going to be cleared up?"

This shelter had already collapsed once on its occupants. That was March 15; a delayed-action 105 shell came through the earth and logs of the roof to explode on the ground. There were twelve wounded inside, who had received treatment and been provided with their discharge cards. Three of them were got out. The other nine were dead, suffocated, and they were taken out four days later by the engineers, who then restored the roof as well as they could. The walls were still striped with marks of the explosion.

I thought of the wards for abdominal cases in the hospitals in the rear, hygienic with their fresh paint and fresh air. My field hospital was much finer by reason of its simplicity; to me it seemed magnificent.

But I was a sentimental fool. There was no hygiene in this shelter, no comfort, no proper aseptic treatment; wounds couldn't help getting dirt in them. The death rate must, unhappily, be far higher than in hospital wards.

"No," Colonel Chippaux, our consulting surgeon, was to inform me, "your statistics compare well enough with them."

There must indeed have been a miracle—a miracle at Dienbienphu.

1.

My Last Assignment

Yes, I was really at Dienbienphu, and the events which had brought me there unrolled in my mind like a queer sort of film, simple though they were.

It was at Haiphong in the beginning of February, 1954. I had just left Namdinh, my favorite military post. Bitterness filled me as I sadly thought of the many true friends, among both the civilian and the military, the French and the Vietnam populations, whom I had left in the town. I had a case full of the presents they had given me on parting.

Among them was one from Nui, a Vietnamese. He had a rectangular wound which began in the sternum and disappeared in the hollow of the armpit. When I went to say good-by to him, he wanted me to have a last look under the dressing. "It's doing well," I told him. "You'll soon be out, somehow or other."

It was quite true, for the scar was white and clean, and the skin had regained its elasticity.

Then he handed me a statuette shaped out of a piece of orangewood, depicting an old peasant slightly bent, with a stick in his left hand; it was a simple enough piece of sculpture—and it was also magnificent. His mother had come nearly ten miles on foot along the little embankment between the rice fields to put it in his hands as a present for "Bac-sy Kim."

Bac-sy means doctor; Kim was my Vietnam surname, meaning "the man who stitches."

"Good-by, major, come back soon." He smiled faintly and sadly as he spoke, and his hand seemed painfully thin as my European paw grasped it.

Then there were presents from the doctor in charge, from nurses and orderlies and colleagues: a Parker fountain pen, a watch, lacquerwork, and embroidery. Among these pieces of embroidery one of the finest was given me by an engineer in the cotton factory.

Now I strolled through the streets of this town of Haiphong, for which I had no affection; I was serving part time at the hospital there while waiting for the boat which was to take me home: "Probable date of embarkation, March 13, 1954."

All the same, Haiphong hospital was agreeable. I had made friends with the wounded, and my medical colleagues were very pleasant; I was also made welcome in the mess.

One evening I met there a guest of Captain Vittori, doctor in charge of the air base of Catbi. A brilliant talker, he knew his subject and was very keen on flying, so we listened to him with great interest. He told us of many trips he had made; for professional reasons, he often accompanied bomber crews and reconnaissance, transport, and freight aircraft. He described one of these transport planes to us in detail, the C-119, the Packett, new to Indochina.

"It's sensational," he added. "Yesterday morning, I flew over Dienbienphu in a Packett; we dropped five tons of barbed wire in one run."

Dienbienphu! My thoughts began to take shape. Operation

Beaver! It was brilliant and famous. "They're making enough fuss about it," Julot used to say, while we were in the rice fields of Thaibinh with their icy water and mud. Ours was just a routine operation like so many others, a painful and exhausting business, killing, but with little to show for it, certainly with no publicity or glory attached to it.

Every day the words "Dienbienphu," "Operation Beaver," and "paratroops" recurred on the radio or in the daily communiqué. They got on our nerves.

We did not ask that the same fuss be made about our own activities, either on the radio or in the press, but we did feel that a little more restraint should have been used in describing that other operation; it was given too much the air of an excursion.

At Lanessan, the military hospital in Hanoi, few of the wounded were from down at Dienbienphu, only three or four a day. All the same, in November I had seen the body of Captain André of the medical service, who had been killed by a bullet when troops were first dropped.

All this led me now to ask, "And what does the famous hollow of Dienbienphu look like?"

"Oh, there's not much to see. I'll tell you quite frankly that I'm getting a little bored with what you see from the air. But if you want to take a look, you can, whenever you feel like it."

"How?"

"Packetts are dropping material on Dienbienphu every morning. Be at Catbi at eight o'clock tomorrow morning and introduce yourself, mentioning my name, at the office there."

The next morning, at eight o'clock, I was in the Packett office. A major in blue uniform was seated behind the usual military desk. Around him stood some fifteen men in flying uniform—pilots, co-pilots, radio operators, and men to do the unloading.

There were huge maps on the walls with red, blue, and yellow route markings, with arrows and large circles.

The major talked, and the others listened in silence. Everybody was smoking. The electric fans were not yet working, as it was still a little chilly in February.

When the briefing was over, I introduced myself to the major. "It's all right," he assured me, "the doctor in charge called me about you." He summoned one of the pilots, who moved slowly, leaning over to one side, a heavy optical appliance in his right hand. "This is the major in the medical service I told you about last night."

An open and friendly face was turned toward me, a hand extended: "Delighted. Follow us; we're leaving in ten minutes."

Trucks were waiting for us outside, and we drove swiftly alongside the huge runway, passing the black, sturdy-looking fighters, the silvery Dakotas, and a row of Privateers, impressive four-engined bombers. Then came the C-119; its outline has become well known, lines sharp and clear, yet graceful as an athlete bred to the job.

We climbed into the cabin. The pilot, whom I followed as if I were his shadow, told me, "We only make one run over Dienbienphu, only one drop—the barbed wire all tumbles out at once. If you like, you can go on another plane, the one carrying ammunition, which makes four runs over the place."

"Barbed wire, shells . . . Between ourselves, I really prefer the barbed wire." We both laughed.

I had my parachute harness fitted on and installed myself in a comfortable seat of rubber and steel tubing directly behind the pilot. It was a fine cabin, entirely transparent. At my feet was a panel covered with a number of black dials with pointers and figures in yellow, red, and green.

The pilot got the engine turning over. The plane hardly trembled, only a quiver as of muscles about to contract. Gently we began to move and take up our position on the runway. The lights changed color on the control tower, far to our left, and we pushed forcefully ahead. Then came the well-known feeling of taking off, and we rose in the air with the sense of exaltation which springs from irresistible power and absolute security. The fine sound of seven thousand horse-power echoed in my ears.

The sky was gray and cloudy, but it seemed that the mountain peaks rose above all that. In a few minutes we passed through the thick blanket of cloud and suddenly came out into a white and fleecy desert, while around and above us spread an intensely blue sky—and above all the warm welcome of the sun.

The pilot gave me headphones and pointed with his finger to three switches: "This one is music, French Union Radio. That one is simply operational—you'll hear the foot-sloggers down below chatting to one another."

This was the one for me, the men below:

"Hello. Alpha Polka Romeo calling Isidore. Reply."

"Hello. Isidore speaking. Getting you five on five. Answer."

"Hello. Alpha Polka Romeo speaking. We're in sight of Naples, 440 yards away. I'm deploying my companies on the eastern embankment. I'm waiting for the barrage to be started as arranged."

"Message received. Isidore speaking. Barrage begins in three minutes at 8:37. I repeat, at 8:37."

How far away all that seemed in the warm and comfortable cabin, flying through a universe of blue and white. Yet in three minutes hundreds of shells would fall on the village occupied by the Vietminhs. They had already gone to earth in their strong underground shelters, having forced the villagers to stay in the holes dug under their beds. In three minutes there would be dozens killed, dozens of civilians wounded. In ten minutes all the uproar of firing would break loose, tommy guns, machine guns, grenades, mortars. We would have ten killed, thirty wounded.

That was how morning began in the delta for the "operational battalion" put at the disposal of the colonels in command of the various sectors. And the evening communiqué at G.H.Q. would read: "There was some contact between our forces operating in the Thaibinh sector and a strong Vietminh group established on the outskirts north of the village of Loanloc. We suffered some casualties. The rebels left three dead and six wounded on the field. We took one prisoner."

Then came another message over the radio: "Hello, hello. Alpha Sun calling Gamma Sun. Your second child is missing on my right. I repeat: your second child is missing on my right." Hunched up, I listened to these calls which brought back so many cherished memories.

Suddenly the pilot turned toward me and made a sign, his thumb pointing downward. I realized that we were over Dienbienphu. We had to go down through the fleecy floor spread beneath us, a maneuver which I never enjoy much.

We kept on moving around in wide circles, waiting for orders from below. Waiting with us were four Packetts, two Dakotas, two Moranes. Suddenly we saw two Packetts dive into the clouds. Then it was our turn and we went down, with the engines turning over more slowly, down into a whiteness like wax.

Twenty seconds flashed by, and suddenly the plan of Dienbienphu spread out beneath us. What you saw first was the winding and silvery river, then a vast green plain surrounded by a classical landscape of tree-covered hills.

The plane dropped lower, and a dirty mark began to grow larger in the middle of this green plain; it was the color of ocher, something like ringworm, and the river passed across it. Toward the north this stain developed into a wide gray patch, which was the airfield; I could see the colored lights. The dirty mark, the color of ocher, was Dienbienphu.

Hills rose up a little to the east, northeast, and northwest. The hilltops were the same color as the mark in the middle of the plain.

Now we were between six and seven hundred feet up, and I could begin to make out the details: a complicated network of paths and roads encircling heaps of earth which I realized were shelters—there were any number of them. It came to me that the earthwork we were flying over was the exact center of the scene spread out below. The summits of the hills had been cleared of trees, and a whole series of shelters connected by very narrow paths were clearly visible. Farther away, a wider road left the green hills toward the northeast, beyond the last outpost, the road numbered "41" on the military maps. It stayed on the left bank of the Namyoum, crossed the whole length of the plain, and reached the southern support post, which had much the same appearance as the one in the center.

Trucks and jeeps were moving across this strange town lost among the mountains. All over the place clouds of thick dust were slowly dispersing.

Generally speaking, where earth showed was French, while the green parts belonged to the Viets. There was a certain amount of movement going on among our people, but none among the Viets, nothing at all, not even a puff of smoke to reveal a human presence. Somehow all that did not look very reassuring. I don't know why, but there was a shadow over my thoughts.

Having forgotten the function of the Packett in which I was a passenger, I was startled by the sudden jerk it made. After some tenths of seconds it was once more horizontal.

The pilot again gestured with his thumb, and below I saw five tons of barbed wire scattering like a shower of rain.

We regained height, and my last glance, before we once

more passed through the blanket of cloud, went to an ambulance which I recognized from the large red cross painted on its roof and the small flag waving to the right of the hood; it appeared to be going in the direction of the airfield.

The return to Haiphong took place without incident; three hours afterward I was with my friends again in the mess at the hospital.

"How did your trip to Dienbienphu turn out?" I was asked.

"It's grim," I told them. "I wonder how we will ever extricate ourselves, if one day the Vietminhs should attack in strength."

In the days that followed, this trip was often in my mind, and I questioned friends on the various staffs at the rear bases of the fighting units. From them I learned that many of my friends in the Foreign Legion were down there at Dienbienphu, colonial paratroopers, gunners, and others at the command post. My oldest friend there was certainly Captain Cabiro, whom I had known when he was still a second lieutenant, now company commander in the First Foreign Paratroops.

Then one day, February 16 it was, Captain Vittori of the medical corps stopped me in the central passage of the hospital to say, "I've just had a call from the chief: your assistant has to be sent to Dienbienphu at once. If you would like to speak to him, he's still on the line."

"Hello. Major Grauwin speaking. Greetings, Colonel. I've just spoken to Captain Vittori. You know, my assistant is on the young side—he only did his first abdominal operation yesterday evening."

"It's simply a question of finding a substitute for two weeks. Captain Thuriés, the surgeon, is sick and needs a little rest. In another two weeks I'll have found somebody else, or Thuriés will be better."

Two weeks! I was suddenly seized by a sort of giddiness. The boat went in another month. In a flash I saw in my mind's eye Touret, Lacoste, Violés, Barraud, Grand d'Esnon, who were all at Dieubienphu. I also saw the streets of Haiphong thronged with people who cared nothing about the war, the dull movies, the Commerce—a pretentious night club with faded girls—the foolish strolling from bar to bar.

"Colonel, I could go if that would suit you. Two weeks are soon gone."

"What? You're crazy! And what about your own rest?"

"Oh, my rest . . . I'll rest better down there in the sunshine with my friends."

"You know, speaking for myself, I would be glad to know that you were at Dienbienphu. But . . . you must think it over. If you really want to go, be here tomorrow morning at eight o'clock. Good-by."

Oddly enough, my spirits were rising. I would go. I gave up the whole evening to my preparations. But why did I lock up my cases as if I were going on a long journey, arrange my papers and settle my correspondence, when I would only take a small suitcase and the regulation pack with me to Dienbienphu?

At seven o'clock the next morning I was on my way into Haiphong after brief good-by's at the hospital. At ten I was in the medical service director's office. "You're a funny sort of fellow," he told me.

By one I was at the Gialam airport with other passengers waiting in the sunshine for the plane to Dienbienphu.

At two my name was called, and I climbed the ladder into the belly of a Stratoliner. No seats—everybody crouched on the metal floor. I came across Lieutenant Démézières. He was in the First Foreign Paratroops in 1949, and we recalled how the battalion was cut up between Caobang and Thatkhe in 1950. Now it had been reconstituted and was serving at Dienbienphu. He was on his way to rejoin it.

Two Vietnamese were seated in front of me: Phuc, a medical orderly, was being posted to the "Isabelle" strong

point; I knew his father, who was president of the mixed
tribunal in Hanoi. Do, a signal corporal, was returning to
his destination at the command post of the Fourth Battalion,
Seventh Algerian Rifles, which was holding the "Gabrielle"
hill. There were seventy more men strung out right to the
tail of the aircraft, soldiers of all races and colors, Frenchmen,
Legionnaires, Moroccans, Senegalese.

At four in the afternoon the four-engined machine landed
in an immense cloud of yellow dust. We got out one by one,
and immediately I recognized a jeep of the medical service.
Seeing me, its occupants jumped quickly out and came to
meet me: "I'm Captain Thuriés. Welcome, major." His face
was pale and his features were drawn.

Then came a voice I knew: "Major! What a surprise!"
It was Marant, a sergeant major whom I had known for eight
years. He had covered himself with glory in the heroic days
of December, 1946, in Hanoi. He was finishing his third tour
of service.

"We have to go through the air control office." This
proved to be a large rectangular hole surmounted with a sort
of shelter. Behind a rickety table rose the figure of Captain
Foucras, transport officer, formerly at Namdinh: "It's not
possible. You here . . ." A large smile and a handshake followed.

My attention was attracted to a piece of wood stuck on the
wall, on which some shell splinters had been arranged.
"What's that?" I inquired.

"Well, you know, some ten or so shells fell last week, so
I kept a few fragments as souvenirs."

After a glance at the fighters and the Morane planes squatting in their places, we climbed into the jeep and, constantly
surrounded with dust, followed the road—or rather the track
of dried earth—in the direction of the command post. The
driver's name was Sioni; he was a corporal in the Foreign
Legion. He was a small, broad-shouldered man with bright

eyes and thick red hair. We passed numbers of shelters covered with earth, the ones I had seen from the air the week before. Each of these shelters averaged nine feet by six; the roof was constructed of logs of wood pressed together, single or double in depth and covered with four feet of earth.

Soldiers moved among the shelters, bare-chested or in open shirts, good-natured, slow, and unruffled.

We reached the command post, placed exactly in the middle of this collection of human anthills. It was an earthwork sixty feet long covered with sandbags and a great arc of corrugated iron. A narrow passage with a concealed entrance led inside. On the left, going in, I ran into Major Léost and Captain Méhay, who had been in Intelligence at Namdinh. "What, you? I thought you were on the boat!"

So once more I said my piece. Two weeks would pass quickly. I introduced myself to the chief of staff and to Colonel de Castries, whom I had not seen since the days at Thaibinh. "Good, I hope you have a good stay. But don't hang around here too long."

I took a look around; the place had the usual appearance of an operational command post, but instead of a dugout there was an impressive collection of sandbags and tree trunks. On my way out I greeted Colonel Piroth, who was in command of the artillery, and in front of me I recognized Colonel Langlais, commanding officer of the Second Airborne, who exclaimed, "Good to see you, friend!"

"The same to you, colonel," I replied.

I had not seen him since December, 1947. Then he was commanding a battalion of the Sixth Colonial Infantry and was acting as chief of staff in a great campaign in which I also took part, the operations on the River Claire under the command of Colonel Communal. Another old friend with whom I shook hands was Captain Bonnal. "Glad to see you," he said, "but you make me a bit suspicious. Usually you turn up in places where there is going to be trouble."

We left the command post and went some thirty yards past the barbed-wire entanglement, turning right by a notice which said, "First-Aid Post No. 29," to reach a platform some forty yards by twenty, where to the right again were two ambulances and two jeeps belonging to the medical service, liberally supplied with red crosses and garaged in compartments banked with earth. To the left there were a row of shelters and a slope leading gently to the river, which was seventy yards beyond the barbed-wire network.

"Here's your new home, major. Would you like me to introduce the staff to you?"

"Look here, Thuriés, just let me have a quick glance over the chief points," I replied, "and rough me out some sort of plan. The chief insisted that you should return to Hanoi today. I'll see the staff for myself tomorrow morning, with Marant."

We were on the terrace which gave access to the whole outfit. In front of me was the roof of the shelter which served as a mess. I clambered up onto it, and nearly the whole area of the entrenched camp lay revealed. To the east, two-thirds of a mile beyond the river, rose a series of hills stretching north and south, the Elianes with their central peak, Eliane 2, and the Dominiques with their central peak, Dominique 3, held by the Moroccans and dominating the airfield. To the north, beyond the end of the runway, rose Gabrielle, held by the Fourth Battalion, Seventh Algerian Rifles. Much farther to the northeast, over three miles away, three little hills stood out at the foot of a high mountain; this position had the name of Anne-Marie and was held by Thais of the Third Thai Battalion.

Between the Dominiques and Gabrielle a kind of yellow ridge appeared above the green. This was Beatrice, or rather its main earthwork. It was nearly four miles away as the crow flies, a very strong position, even said to be impregnable, and held by Legionnaires of the Thirteenth Demi-Brigade.

To the south and west stretched the plain, earthy at first, covered with shelters and bristling with radio aerials, beyond which it swiftly changed into a thick network of barbed-wire entanglements. Then the plain became green and overgrown, bounded far off by mountains, real mountains, green like the nearer one behind dark and forbidding Dominique.

Everywhere there were logs and earth, earth and more logs. They created a genuine feeling of security, and the depressing ideas I had had in the Packett dissolved once I got to know this underground fortress better.

Below me, stretching from the road to the shelter which housed the mess, there were a dozen other shelters linked by deep, narrow trenches. This was a defensive position held by Legionnaires—so I would be well defended. Straight in front of me I saw a black hole indicating the entrance to an outpost. I went down into it and immediately came up against a wall of earth, so I turned right, groping my way, and found myself in a dark little cellar, square, dimly lit by a couple of candles placed in niches.

Four Legionnaires were standing at attention.

On each side there were a couple of canvas bunks, one above the other, and between them there was room for a man to pass. At the back, opposite the entry, I made out a gleaming black weapon, supported by a buttress of earth— a 12.7 machine gun, its barrel vanishing into a horizontal loophole, narrow and blocked by a kind of plank. A Legionnaire saw what I was looking at and removed the plank, revealing the field of fire, a rectangle not very great in extent: it covered a gentle incline, two networks of barbed wire, the bridge, and the opposite bank, which also disclosed the humps formed by a number of shelters. There were photographs nailed to the walls, the inevitable pin-ups, and a phonograph was tucked away in a little hole dug out of the wall.

I returned to the terrace above with Captain Thuriés.

Here, beyond the mess, extending in a curve, came the

The entrenched camp of DIEN BIEN PHU

sterilization shelter, then the men's eating and sleeping quarters, lightly roofed over, then the shelter housing the electric plants, one of which was working, as the lighting everywhere had to be taken care of day and night; finally came the entrance to the central passage. This passage was some forty yards long, about three feet wide, and a little over six feet high, open to the sky at the top. I knocked my fist against the wall and was surprised at the compactness of the earth; it was as hard as brick. Halfway up ran the electric and telephone wires, in a small channel cut into the wall.

On the left, beyond the entry to the main passage, was the shelter of the dentist, the young and athletic Captain Riccardi; a huge tooth outlined on a piece of cardboard attracted attention above the entrance to his shelter—no mistake possible there. Inside was all the usual apparatus of a dentist in the field, American in origin, simple enough but entirely adequate. The revolving chair was bracketed to a billet of wood fixed in the ground. There was a cot at the back.

We returned to the main passage. A few yards away to the right was the entrance to a typical shelter serving as a small hospital ward, measuring twelve feet by six. Recessed in each corner were three cots, or rather bunks, fixed one above another, making twelve in all; but the top one, which almost touched the logs in the roof, had little practical value, for it was quite impossible for an invalid or a wounded man to get into it without being helped. The one beneath the vent hole would be deluged when rain fell. The neighboring shelter was the same in every detail. A few more yards and we were in the N.C.O. shelter, much the same, with some sheeting on the walls to serve as wallpaper; there was a radio tucked away in a recess: "This is Radio Hirondelle, the voice of the French Union forces."

I entered the shelter of the chief medical officer, which was narrower; on the ground was a chest with an enameled basin on it. On the right was a small metal folding table with some books and files; there were a few shelves on the walls. The ceiling and walls were covered with a good brown holland which I learned later was the material used for shrouds.

Altogether it had an air of simplicity, austere and monastic, which was far from displeasing to me.

A few more yards brought me to the entrance of the last hospital shelter; after a right-angle turn there appeared the exit steps, which led straight onto the main track. Just beyond this track, some thirty yards away, was the shelter containing Colonel de Castries' command post.

I returned to the entrance of my little room; when I stood with my back to it I faced a crossway, open to the sky, which looked to me like the nerve center of the whole place. Straight in front was a trench some twelve feet long; going in, I found the emergency-treatment room on the left, the operating room on the right, while directly ahead was the X-ray shelter. The emergency-treatment room was the largest of these shelters, thirty feet by ten. There were fifteen cots here, ten of them in the form of bunks. Appliances and all the medical necessities for emergency treatment were spread out on a long table to the right. Between the beds, leaning against the wall, were oxygen cylinders with nickel handles.

The walls were covered with interlaced bamboos. The ceiling looked solid enough; great crossbeams supported a metal plate similar to those covering the runway on the airfield, and on this plate sandbags were heaped. Every six feet along the central axis, logs were driven into the ground to support the total weight, which was considerable.

A slight incline led down into the operating room, deeper underground. The ceiling was made up of enormous tree trunks, themselves also sustained by two central beams. There was six feet of earth above all this. It was a really solid affair.

The walls were all covered with white sheeting, and I saw set out in good order all the necessities of an operating room such as are usually given to a surgical unit on active service.

The X-ray room looked just as good. The apparatus was a modern American one of the improved sort, easy to use; it was the Laichau type, brought there by air. Baskets and chests were ranged on banks of earth along the walls, containing reserves of medicine and materials.

The whole setup of operating room, emergency-treatment room, and X-ray room, the three of them branching out from one passage, seemed to me a very ingenious one. I had never seen such perfection so close to the front. It was a pity that the crossway was open to the sky.

"Supposing you suddenly had a hundred wounded to cope with," I asked Captain Thuriés, who was still at my side, "what would you do? For so far I can only count forty-two beds."

"There's no difficulty about that. There are always the planes. The wounded can be taken to the airfield in groups of ten or twenty, which is the capacity of a Dakota. We can have three or four of them at our disposal whenever we like."

"And supposing the airfield were shelled or put out of action by the weather?"

"Then we would make use of the Airborne Commandos' quarters. If you would care to follow me . . ."

We went out once more and crossed the road, coming to a barbed-wire entanglement, got across it, and then went down a dark hole.

The Airborne Commandos' Group was a unit famous all over Indochina both for its commando activities and for its intelligence work. Its basis was French, first-class men who were war-tried veterans, serving with local troops who had also passed the test, Vietnamese, Thais, Muongs, and Nungs. But you had to shut your eyes to some of the dishes they cooked up. Their particular job gives them certain privileges —it's nothing out of the way!

The main passage in this section was also roofed with logs

and earth; every few yards, to right and left, were openings into shelters. Here and there were air vents.

"Altogether," I was told, "we can accommodate a hundred wounded, but preferably those who can walk, for the trench that leads in is not easy going for stretchers."

I groped my way along in the uncertain light. There were Thais with their families. When the need arose, their women helped in the intelligence work; their costumes were very becoming with their bright colors. The children were half-naked.

By now it was six o'clock in the evening. Captain Thuriés showed me a few more papers and made a few remarks about his recent cases, and then I went with him to the airfield.

The moment came to salute and shake hands. "Have no fear," I told him, "I'll look after things all right for you."

"Thanks. I expect to be back at the beginning of March, if I'm well enough."

"No, take a good three weeks. I'm not due to embark until March 13. I don't need to be back in Haiphong before the tenth."

A few more minutes and the plane vanished beyond the hills to the southeast. Now I was alone and happy at the prospect of making one more effort before my final departure, in the company of men who had won me over at first sight.

Evening was falling. Back in the field hospital, I found my new staff quietly getting busy. "When do we eat?" I inquired.

"Half-past seven, major," Marant replied.

"This evening I want to see the whole unit at table with me —all ranks."

"Just so, major. Anyhow, it's all set—you're well known here."

It was a marvelous, an astonishing meal! Sergeant Deudon, a flaxen giant from Flanders and a master cook, had surpassed himself.

Tomato soup, two entrées and a dessert, including a real Chateaubriand steak with fried potatoes and a chocolate custard—chilled, of all things—followed by first-class coffee. Also a glass of champagne. Spirits rose rapidly, and by the end of the meal all reserve had vanished. My new team was listening eagerly, having forced me "to tell the story of my life," as the saying goes.

No doubt the best pleased of all was Marant, our respected sergeant major.

We were served by former "Pims," Indochinese prisoners, smart and soldierly, silent and skillful. I was often aware of their glances resting on me. A few months ago they had been in the ranks of the Viets.

Toward ten o'clock another flaxen giant stooped with difficulty through the narrow entrance to the shelter—Captain Barraud, another doctor, from the Second Thai Battalion. Jean-Louis to his friends.

"Major, you were the only person missing here," he said.

Pierre was his real Christian name; he was a friend of mine. He had just left his peaceful job in the hospital at Namdinh, to finish his tour of duty as he began it, in the post of battalion doctor. Then along came Captain De Carfort, doctor in charge of the Eighth Assault, whose commanding officer was another of my friends. His infirmary was some hundred yards away. Next came sergeant major Buezek, also of the Eighth Assault, pioneer section. He was to be a great help to us, a most useful man.

Midnight found us sitting on the roof of the mess admiring the magnificent panorama spread out before us. To the southwest the moon was slowly rising from behind a high mountain; the great circle of hills was etched darkly against a sky luminous with shades of blue. From the northwest to the northeast the tops of the mountains were enveloped in flames; during the day our fighters had dropped napalm bombs, in order to prevent the Viets from erecting any forward positions or gun emplacements.

Barraud told me something about the sort of life led in the camp since he had arrived a month before. The garrison enjoyed good health on the whole: very little malaria, no dysentery, and none of the typhoid type of epidemics. One odd thing was that there were no mosquitoes and it was usual to sleep without a mosquito net—which is quite unheard-of in Indochina.

Every two or three days one or two battalions made a reconnaissance to a depth of three to six miles, always ending up by making contact with a Vietminh forward position or by getting into an ambush, luckily not too deadly. But the preceding week paratroops out on a night march had run into a Viet patrol also engaged in reconnoitering. The skirmish was short, but sharp; we had five killed and thirty wounded, all of whom were got back before dawn.

"So it's quite certain that the Viets are there in strength," Barraud told me, "but intelligence is difficult to get."

Every day, too, the road to Isabelle had to be opened up, and this often happened without incident.

The days were long, but seldom boring; work on the fortification went on without a break; every company and every section was improving its shelters and its forward position, helped by hundreds of coolies and four bulldozers when larger clearances had to be made. After six in the evening medicine balls were brought out in most places, and after that everybody bathed; and before going to sleep beneath woolen blankets the men had a few games of cards, often *belote*, by the light of a few candles; with the officers it was poker and bridge.

I suddenly jumped at the din our guns made, all firing at the same moment, achieving a "T on T," that is to say that at a given moment they all sent a shell to the same spot. Blinding violet-colored flames sprang into existence out in front, below Dominique, behind the command post, to the east of the airfield; and far to the south there were lights in the sky above Isabelle.

Then all was silent until, a few seconds later, a roll of thunder reached our ears, reverberating from mountain to mountain, repeating itself again and again and only slowly dying down.

The ground returned to darkness: there was no light allowed. The blackout regulations were severe. There must be no targets for snipers.

Very high up in the sky a green light was moving slowly, and the sound of aircraft engines could be heard. This was the *Firefly*, a Dakota which flew over the battle area during the night, looking for the headlights of trucks or any other revealing lights in Viet territory. It was also responsible for radio relays between Dienbienphu and Hanoi.

At eleven I withdrew into my little shelter hung with white, where the light was harsh. I wrote a letter to my family in which I had to pretend: "I am strolling through the streets of Haiphong waiting for the time to come when I can embark . . ."

Another letter went to Lieutenant Colonel Landrieu, adjutant to the director of medical services. This said, "Don't worry if you should have difficulty in finding a surgeon for Dienbienphu at once. I can stay here beyond the fortnight I promised."

The next morning I got a telegram with my coffee: "At ten o'clock there will be a visit from General Jeansotte, inspector of medical services, accompanied by Colonel Terramorsi, director of medical services to the French Union forces in Indochina." We had to clear for action at once. My official introduction to my staff would have to be put off a day. It could not be helped. First of all we had to get ready for the inspection. By nine everything was in order, the staff all in their proper uniforms, the shelters cleaned out, and the equipment correctly arranged.

By a quarter to ten I was at the airfield. The four-engined aircraft landed. General Navarre and General Cogny appeared. A company of troops presented arms, and a jeep, in charge of Colonel de Castries, took them swiftly away to the command post.

General Jeansotte then came into view, a tall man with graying hair, a fine old veteran. After the introductions had been correctly performed, I took him and Colonel Terramorsi off in a jeep to the field hospital. My men were all immaculate, lined up on the terrace outside; our vehicles were clean and gleaming in their compartments.

"At ease. Return to work . . ."

I introduced my unit to the general, as Captain Thuriés had introduced the men to me only the day before. In the main passage he raised his head and stopped in astonishment: "There's no roof over this. How's that?"

I had no answer to give. He went into each shelter, stopping some time; then he asked, "How thick is the roof?"

"There are one or two layers of logs and four or five feet of earth."

"H'm."

In the operating room he showed obvious signs of satisfaction. Behind me I heard Colonel Terramorsi talking to Marant: "Are you coming back with us? Don't forget that you are due to take the Skymaster soon."

"If you will give your permission, colonel, I would like to stay with Major Grauwin a little longer."

This reply came as a great relief to me, and I shook his hand behind the backs of the others.

At twelve the general went off to lunch at the command post, "with the V.I.P.'s," as Julot used to say.

By two we were back at the air transport office. The general drew me to one side and asked me the same questions as I had put to Captain Thuriés the day before: "What if the airfield is put out of action?"

"There are the Airborne Commandos' quarters, general, which you have seen. We could get a hundred wounded into them."

"And if you have three hundred?"

"In that case, general, I assume that a decision would be made higher up."

He took a few paces up and down, then paused frowning to gaze at the vast trenched camp, the hills with shelters on them, the networks of barbed wire, and the high mountains in the background which had such a gloomy and forbidding appearance.

He had been a battalion doctor throughout the 1914–18 war, which gave point to his next remark: "If things really get moving here, you'll be back to the warfare of forty years ago, and you won't be able to get out alone, without being relieved. Well, I hope that everything passes off all right and that the Viets will do no more here than at Nasan and Hoabinh. There they attacked one or two hills and then withdrew. First of all I'll send another surgical team to reinforce you; then you can wire me for anything you need. I rather think you'll need a good deal. No, you won't get out alone."

2.

The Field Hospital

At Dienbienphu I was not quite on my own.

No, because there was my team, lined up on the terrace in the fresh air of the morning, their trousers perfectly creased, the blue colonial forage cap at an angle over the left eyebrow. I already knew them, just from spending the previous evening with them. Marant stood a few yards in front, and as I came forward he turned and saluted.

Marant was a Parisian, twenty-six years old. He was a sergeant major in the medical service, expert in intravenous therapy, anesthetist, in charge of surgical instruments and the X-ray—the perfect medical orderly. The Tonkin health service regarded him as one of the best men they had. It was a pity that he had to leave me.

The next in rank was N'Diaye, a black-skinned and athletic sergeant, twenty-three years old. He had just been cited in regimental orders for his part in an action during Operation Seagull under the command of Colonel de Castries.

He seemed quiet enough, but his energy was tireless. He had charge of patients before and after they had undergone an operation. He had to see to the wounded, undress them, wash them, discover the nature of the wound, write out the necessary form, recording the first treatment they received, and help with the intravenous therapy Marant gave when there were serious signs of traumatic shock.

After the operation, the wounded man was installed in a cot and then it was also N'Diaye's job to see to the care and diet of the wounded man after his operation. Quite as a matter of course he also saw to the service as a whole, the cleaning of the quarters, general hygiene, maintenance of medical supplies; also the few elementary rules of discipline.

Sergeant Deudon, twenty-four years old, assisted during operations. He was the master cook who had prepared the excellent meal the evening before. He excelled in both these functions. He had his own private ways of securing provisions which extended to the most distant of the supporting positions; the bottle of vermouth which he got in the morning from some friendly airman had mysteriously transformed itself by the evening into two magnificent roast chickens. Chicken was the greatest of luxuries in this country, and it is an item not offered by the supply column.

"I was a medical student at Lille, major," he told me, "in my third year. I've prolonged my term as a draftee . . ."

He had extended his travels as well as his service. I was lucky to have this man who was almost a doctor. He would be a doctor before he got his degree, at least in experience.

Corporal Lachamp was a small, burly fellow of twenty-one, bright as a new penny. He was the office orderly who had just arrived from Hanoi. "I took part in the evacuation by air at Lanessan and I'm fed up with all this office work. I'm too young to be one of the chairborne; besides, that wasn't what I joined up for," he told me.

"Unfortunately, you're down to do the same thing here . . ." That disillusioned him. Well, we would have to see.

This office work consisted in keeping up to date the lists of wounded and sick, the intake and the discharges, also the surgical records, which was more important. The clerk had to make out lists of the medical supplies we required, having found out what was running short; he had to reply to service correspondence and get out the monthly reports on what was being done in the way of surgery.

I too had a holy terror of paper work. I should certainly find another job for him.

Pfc. Perez was small and thin, with very dark eyes. Two of his front teeth were missing; this gave him a boyish air when he smiled. He had become a sort of understudy of Marant's and followed him everywhere. On Marant's departure, Perez was due to replace him. Would he stick it out? It was true that he had a Mediterranean temperament; he was very quick and impulsive.

One evening after dinner he quarreled with Fleury of the Eighth Assault; Fleury was a flaxen Norman, large and placid, with ditch digger's arms very useful to us in digging shelters. Fleury only laughed, making fun of Perez and his size. Perez saw red, made as if to hurl himself at him, thought better of it, and came down the steps of the mess where I was sitting with a few friends: "Major, if you don't come at once, I'm afraid I shall do something desperate."

Next came my five North Africans.

Corporal Kabbour was in charge of the sterilizer. For work of this sort he had the use of two "Poupinels," apparatus which provided dry heat for sterilizing instruments, while damp heat was provided by a sterilizer for bandages, compresses, and other cloths used in the course of operations. Heating was done with a Primus, a metal lamp which vaporized gasoline by compression.

Kabbour liked to work alone. He would only put up with one assistant, Corporal Hoang. For three years he had been in charge of sterilization in a unit out there. He was a good man on whom I could rely.

Corporal Arriba was a tall man of thirty, a veteran with thirteen years' service to his credit. He had enlisted in the first medical battalion formed in Africa in 1943 and served in the Italian, French, and German campaigns. He worked with the others under the orders of Sergeant N'Diaye.

He was known for his good humor, and he was in charge of some twenty coolies, to whom he gave canned stuff and rice which he got from Sergeant Deudon. When groups of workers formed up at the coolies' camp in the morning, the one for the field hospital was always the largest.

Corporal Abbou was also tall, and thin; he had a splendid mustache like a kiss-curl, the right end of it always lower than the left. When I drew attention to this, he flushed, very much put out. He tried to get it right by rolling it between his thumb and forefinger, a gesture which seemed to have become a habit with him. Abbou, under N'Diaye, gave post-operative care. He was a first-class medical orderly, obedient and highly skilled.

Pfc. Lahcen was the *boudjadi* of the unit—that is, a recruit; he was only nineteen and as strong as a horse. He lent a hand everywhere with the utmost good humor. Under orders from Sergeant N'Diaye, his job was to receive the wounded.

The two ambulances were in the charge of Driver Ahmed and Driver Ben-Aissa. Ahmed was the veteran, Ben-Aissa the recruit. They were both of them born drivers, but you could not help being a little apprehensive when they raised the hood and got their hands on the engine, which to them was a sort of animal which now and then needed coaxing or calming down. If it stopped, there was no need to make a fuss. It only needed a little kindness or a few blows. If it still showed some reluctance, something had better be moved, perhaps just there where it seemed to be leaking a little. Probably there was some wire which was upsetting it, or a piece of metal had got turned back to front. Move that and it would go all right!

My North African drivers were the despair of the army

workshops. All the same, they were the best of fellows, and I ask for none better.

Two Legionnaires were assigned to the field hospital. I knew beforehand that they would be friends of mine. Sioni and Cortés, posted from the Thirteenth Demi-Brigade of the Foreign Legion, drove our two jeeps. There they were, side by side, one of them born in Italy, the other in Spain. Their faces bore the marks of those who have suffered from the day they were born; their eyes had seen too much, a great deal too much. But as those eyes gazed at me, I found something more in them than the resignation with which they accepted their lot; they were also looking for a little friendliness, which I did my best to give them in returning their glance.

Julot was the last of the Europeans, a small man with a very bright and lively eye. He was our signal man, responsible for communications. He told me he was from Roubaix, on the Belgian border.

Telephone operator and electrician as well as orderly, he also overhauled the electric plant, a serious matter to us. He tried to speak good French but found it difficult. Really he preferred his own local dialect, which is picturesque. Deudon and I were almost the only ones who could follow it. I replied to Julot in his own dialect, and we were soon friends.

In civilian life he had had "a little trouble with the cops." Well, after all, you've got to eat and live. There was a small wound on his left cheek. "I've been a steeplejack in my time," he said, "and one day I fell from the top of a factory chimney nearly seventy feet high into a pile of coal dust." He went nine feet in. Luckily the factory workers lost no time in digging him out. For a week afterward he was spitting out jet-black stuff.

Four Vietnamese ended the procession: Hoang, Minh, Muon, and Binh, all small and slight. Hoang had won the Croix de Guerre for his conduct during operations in the delta.

Their faces were impenetrable, their eyes a little veiled but with very quick and lively pupils. In the past seven years I had got to know these Vietnamese. There had been ten of them in my last team. Taking leave of them in February had been a most dramatic affair: each of them had given me a present exactly equivalent to his month's pay.

Hoang was on sterilizing, due to replace Kabbour, who was to embark in a month's time. Minh and Muon were under Marant for emergency treatment. They were very efficient orderlies, known for their gentleness and cleanliness. The wounded showed a decided preference for them.

Binh was sick. "Here, I've caught *quai-by* . . ." he said and showed me two swellings in front of his ears going down toward the neck. *Quai-by* means the handle of a basket, and the swellings did in fact curve rather like that. The next day he would be in the plane for Hanoi, for I had no wish to see this disease spread through the camp.

On the left, facing my team, were the coolies. They had put on clean shirts, newly ironed. There were twenty of them. The youngest was Jimmy, the dentist's boy, who was fifteen. The oldest was fifty-three. He had been born in a small village in Phu-Ly province; one day the French carried him off as a suspect.

They all reached Dienbienphu by plane from Laichau or from camps at Hanoi. Two years ago they were Viets or belonged to some semimilitary group such as *Du-Kich* (pronounced "zoo-key"). They worked in the field hospital quite freely, almost unguarded. In the evening they got together and returned to their camp of their own accord. Yet it was quite impossible to make out what they were thinking. For a moment they stared hard at me. What was the new boss going to be like?

This was the first time that I was not required to say, "Good morning, mademoiselle," on taking over command of a new surgical unit.

A few months before, the higher command had decided to abolish feminine staff in medical units at the front. No more nurses, no more girl ambulance drivers. In the last year military operations had become too hazardous, and the roads were strewn with mines. It was also embarrassing to have men and women constantly together under the conditions of camp life. There had to be tough fellows at the wheels of ambulances, prepared, when occasion arose—as it often did—to jump down from their seat, throw themselves full length, and use tommy guns.

The nurses were replaced by fully trained medical orderlies. In columns engaged in active service or stationed in rebel territory, also these orderlies were group or section leaders.

All this was the result of a war which grew daily more serious. It was tough luck for the wounded, and it was also tough luck for me!

When I used to say to one of my nurses, "You'll have to keep an eye on him all night," I could go off to bed and sleep soundly—and so could the wounded man.

Nothing can replace a woman at the bedside of a wounded man, not only at base hospitals, but more especially at the front. The year before, when a wounded man arrived at my field hospital, scared and in pain, he immediately found two girls dressed in white leaning over his bed. That was enough: his doubts and anxieties were over there and then. He felt he was safe the moment he saw a girl's quiet smile. After all, one has to smile back at an attractive face—it's only polite—and one has to brazen it out a bit too and pretend that there's nothing wrong even when one is ready to howl with pain. One has to show gratitude for so much gentleness and patience, for the mysterious feminine quality which appears even in the most professional actions. It acts like a charm.

When a medical orderly gives an injection, the soldier yells, "Watch out, you brute! You couldn't have chosen a blunter needle!" While to the nurse he politely answers, "You're being too gentle, mademoiselle; the needle's so sharp I hardly feel it."

Muller was a Legionnaire who had had a serious abdominal operation. Half of the large intestine had been taken away and the free end of the small intestine stitched to the left colon. The mechanism takes some time to settle down again. Muller had come out of it well; his life had been saved, and now he had to eat a little to regain his strength—or else . . . But he was not hungry. "No," was his answer to the orderly.

"Come now," said Mademoiselle Poupart, "do eat a little. I've made this soup specially for you. You're not being very nice to me . . ."

Muller cleaned the plate.

Yes, it's a pity. In the course of the last eight years, in the various units I've had under me, I've seen dozens of wonderful young women for whom such terms as "selflessness" and "sacrifice," or "professional duty" and "contempt for danger" were all concentrated in the single aim of giving everything to the service.

So, having reviewed the whole unit in my first parade, I gave the order to dismiss and told them, "Get to the place where you work. There you'll show me all the medical supplies for which you are personally responsible."

First of all I went into the sterilization section. This was a shelter just like the others. To the right was a cot; to the left, very clean and shining, were the two Poupinels and the sterilizer. At the back there was a table—or rather a large plank resting on four bamboos driven into the ground—supporting large rectangular boxes and barrels of compresses; everything was very clean and in its proper place. Over a hundred surgical instruments were heaped up together on a large enamel dish; they had been cleaned and dried and were waiting to be sterilized and put away in their cases. Some dozen jerry cans under the table held the fuel for the Primus.

Dressings used in operations were arranged in neat piles on shelves attached to the wall.

"You don't get too hot when you're working?" I asked.

"Oh, no. Hoang takes my place every now and then . . . but there's one thing I would like to ask you, sir: I think the snake who lives here with me ought to be killed. He comes out five or six times a day, just there were the logs of the ceiling touch the earth wall."

I left the place in a hurry. Snakes were almost the only creatures I was afraid of in that country. In 1949, at Vietri, when I was going over a field of raspberry canes which was to be turned into a landing ground for a Morane aircraft, I was bitten in the leg by a sort of rattlesnake which had yellow and black markings. Although the correct treatment was applied at once, my leg swelled to a huge size and was covered with blisters. I still have the shiny scar left by the bite.

Next we visited the cookhouse and the sleeping quarters, simply holes covered with tent poles. "Why isn't this better protected, Marant?" I asked.

"The engineers were short of materials, and they had to see to strengthening the forward positions first."

It was the usual story.

The next shelter housed the electric plants, one of five, one of three, and one of two kilowatts. This was Julot's department. Everything here was clean and clearly set out. On the wall to the left was a small plan, a real masterpiece of ingenuity. The large plant had a wire to Colonel de Castries' command post and could supply light to his entire quarters, in the event of a breakdown there.

We came up to ground level again, and before going down into the main passage, I realized that in going from one shelter to another you had to expose yourself completely to enemy fire on this sort of terrace. "Tomorrow morning, N'Diaye, we must have a trench dug linking up the shelters I have just seen and ending up at the entry into the main passage. You had better ask for twenty extra coolies."

We went down into the main passage. To the right was the dentist whom we had already met. Some fifteen soldiers were crouched down outside, waiting. Dentistry was confined to extractions and fillings. False teeth could only be got at Hanoi. When we were really pressed, the dentist helped in the surgery or gave the anesthetic.

The shelter bedrooms were unoccupied except for the one marked "For evacuation by air." There the sick and the superficially wounded were waiting for the last plane of the evening.

We turned right in front of the entrance to my shelter and came into the passage which ran at right angles to the main one, some eight feet long; then on the left we came into the emergency-treatment room, Marant's department.

To the right against the wall stood a long table laden with instruments, phials, and flasks. To the left was Lachamp's little office; along the walls or at right angles to them were fifteen cots. Close to the entrance, half sunk in the ground, were two refrigerators containing blood kept fresh on ice. A plane brought ice every morning. "How much blood is there here?" I asked.

"Always six pints. For urgent cases ten pints can be brought by air three hours after the call has been sent out. . . . There are also blood donors of every group in the camp, especially among the Legionnaires."

The service telephone was attached to the first upright log. "And saline and plasma?" I asked.

"We have a hundred flasks of dry plasma and a hundred of liquid; two hundred bottles of saline solution."

"Antibiotics?"

"Fifty million units of penicillin, fifty grams of streptomycin."

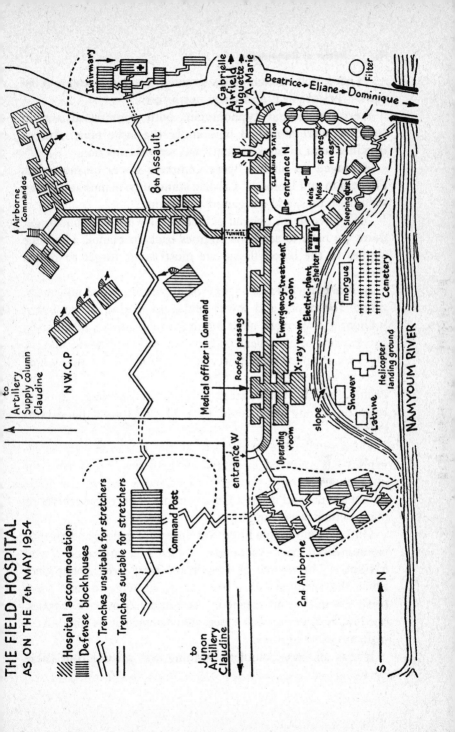

THE FIELD HOSPITAL
AS ON THE 7th MAY 1954

▨ Hospital accommodation
▦ Defense blockhouses
⌇ Trenches unsuitable for stretchers
═ Trenches suitable for stretchers

to
Artillery
Supply column
Claudine

N.W.C.P.

8th Assault

Airborne
Commandos

Infirmary

to Gabrielle
Airfield Huguette
A.-Marie

Beatrice → Eliane → Dominique →

Filter

CLEARING STATION

entrance N

stores
mess
Men's
Mess

Sleeping qurs.

TUNNEL

Medical officer in Command

Roofed passage

Emergency-treatment room

Electric-plant shelter

X-ray room

morgue

Cemetery

Operating room

slope

Shower

Latrine

Helicopter landing ground

NAMYOUM RIVER

entrance W

Command Post

2nd Airborne

to
Junon Artillery
Claudine

S
N

"That's not enough. This evening we must send out an order. Telegraph it and write out a form."

Aureomycin and typhomycin, both compressed and in solution, were stored in bins under the large table. Aureomycin is used in cases of acute and serious infection.

Arranged on shelves were complete boxes of morphine, Phenergan and Dolosal.* Cardiac stimulants, hemostatics, antitetanus serums, and antigangrene serums.

"We have seven oxygen cylinders," I was told, "but to get more we have to send the empties back to Hanoi. The same applies to the blood flasks; we must never forget to return them."

In one corner was a variety of apparatus, wood and metal splints for upper and lower limbs. In a kind of cupboard without a door were piled hundreds of bandages of all sizes, and packets of absorbent cotton. Around the second upright log were strapped some thirty rubber tourniquets. The whole place was well lit; there were ten bulbs hanging from the ceiling, which was covered with white sheeting. Another lamp on a long wire could be used to explore the darkest corner.

On a small table to the left of the entrance were intravenous kits arranged in dozens of small tins. To prepare for intravenous therapy you have to expose a vein of the ankle with a scalpel and insert a large cannula. There were thirty of them, which was enough.

On Lachamp's table there were pressure gauges and twenty medium-sized tins—vaculiters. "That's a nuisance," said Marant. "The people of Hanoi are very strict about that. Once the vaculiters have been used, we have to send them back, complete and cleaned." Vaculiters consist of nozzles, needles, and an expensive percolator which is as difficult to maintain as to sterilize.

It was all very complete, nothing was missing, but there

---

* An analgesic, comparable to pethidine. (Translator's note.)

were only fifteen beds, approximately the number of wounded requiring emergency treatment in an intake of a hundred and fifty. Where were the remaining hundred and thirty-five to be put? In the shelters off the main passage? They might take forty-two. There were the Airborne Commandos' quarters, but that meant crossing the road, which would be unhealthy under fire. What was needed was some place, easy to get at, where the men could be sorted out. That should be seen to.

A small sloping passage led to the operating room. In this passage, on the left, was a water tank with a tap to it; below was another tank for water that had been used. The water tank rested on iron bars driven into the wall. It held over thirty-five gallons of sterilized water. The whole thing was fixed up by the Legionnaires.

The operating room was nearly twelve feet by nine; the walls and ceiling were covered with white sheeting. The table was right in the middle, covered with white oilskin; there were two lighting systems, one at each end. To the right, side by side against the wall, were four collapsible metal tables with some twenty nickel boxes of all sizes, some used in abdominal cases, some in bone surgery, others for surgery of the head and of soft tissues. In smaller cases were knives, syringes, and accessories. Needles were immersed in alcohol in a glass bowl. On one side were barrels, big nickel cylinders, containing all the linen used in operations, overalls, aprons, sheets, and gloves. On a shelf on the wall were flasks of mercurochrome, Dakin's solution, ether, alcohol, and hydrogen peroxide.

On the left was the anesthetist's corner: a number of boxes of Pentothal, metal flasks of ether; a series of little compartments in a flat case holding phials with substances to inject into the patient while under the anaesthetic, according to the instructions of the doctor performing the operation. Coramine, Syncortyl, Adrenalin, morphine . . .

The ground was covered with sacking several layers thick; an oxygen cylinder was fixed to a metal support ready for use. On a small shelf was an electric aspirator for absorbing excessive blood caused by operating.

Once more, it was all very complete. I had never seen an operating room so well equipped in an area where fighting was in progress.

Next we went into the X-ray room. An American apparatus, for use on active service, black, massive, and nickeled, took up all the left side of the shelter. At the moment it was chiefly used to reveal any pulmonary tubercular infection among soldiers in the garrison. Every three months every man had to go behind its screen.

Civilians had heard about this process, and they came from villages in the plains and the mountains, showing their curiosity and their astonishment. They slipped behind the fluorescent screen with great respect, watching the white magician and having no doubt that they would be cured there and then. I have always noticed the remarkable effect which a radioscopic apparatus has in the villages and towns of Indochina. The inhabitants always come thronging, and in this way I have been able to discover hundreds and hundreds of tubercular infections in the early stages. If such attempts were multiplied by a hundred, they could be a real help to the country.

I had now made a complete tour of the field hospital proper. The annex, the Airborne Commandos' quarters, which could accommodate another hundred, was made up of shelters similar to our own. I would hand that over to the extra medical team that General Jeansotte had promised to send out.

The question of a clearing station, or rather shelter, was very much on my mind. We could not have the men cluttering up the main passage, whatever happened. So digging had to begin as soon as possible.

We were now on ground level once more, Marant, N'Diaye, and myself.

"The morgue is on the right here, major." The morgue was my pet aversion—a large square hole without a roof dug in the slope leading down to the river, only a few yards from the sterilization shelter. Empty coffins were piled up there.

Generally speaking, a man who is killed in battle still belongs to his unit, which is responsible for getting him back to the base. But that is out of the question in a war of movement. Fighting over rice fields or in the mountains, units are unable to transport their dead, and so they entrust them to the divisional command post or that of a mobile group. There an officer has to concern himself with the formalities, but meanwhile what is to be done with the body? Here there was a morgue, or at least a hole set apart; but what happens in a war of movement?

The body is always brought to the field hospital. How can one refuse? How can one neglect these mortal remains which, bloodstained and covered with mud, yet have their own claim to glory? The body has to be undressed, washed, covered in a white sheet, the hands joined, the eyes closed. This was a task for my orderlies and nurses. And when we had a little time to spare, so little was needed to make an altar of repose: some parachute material, a stretcher raised on two piles of bricks, some foliage and a few flowers, a red, white, and blue flag.

There was no doubt of the best spot for the clearing station, to the right of the terrace opposite the mess. The excavation had to run north and south, against the west side of the road. Then it would be in the line of my existing shelters; a trench would link it directly with the main passage.

What about a roof? We should have to see the engineers about that. Meanwhile we would cover it with American-type tent poles, which we had to order from Hanoi at once.

In a proper clearing station there is a sort of metal trestle on which the stretcher with the wounded man on it can at once be placed. I needed forty of them, but I knew that the Hanoi depot would have to get them from Saigon. It would be simpler and just as effective to cut banks of earth six feet by five and three and a half feet high—ten of them on either side of a central gangway three feet wide. Two stretchers could be placed side by side on each bank of earth. If we were crowded, we could get another in between these banks.

The excavation would be sixty feet by fifteen; but I should need the engineers, or at least coolies with picks and spades, and it had to be done quickly. I knew that I could rely on Major Touret, commanding the Eighth Assault. I rang him and got the reply, "Right, doc, I'll send you Buezek and Fleury."

Buezek was sergeant major of the pioneer section, a man of medium height, athletic, clear-eyed, and spruce. Fleury was the flaxen giant who had aroused the temper of Perez, my emergency-treatment assistant.

Next I rang Major Léost of the command post and told him of my scheme. "You're losing no time," he answered. "Right, I'll let you have twenty extra coolies in the morning."

Buezek was to work out the general plan, while Fleury would take charge of the coolies; Arriba would be responsible for the extra rations required. By the evening I was quite satisfied. N'Diaye and Marant were all for the idea. During dinner I got a telegram: "Following our conversation of February 18, 1954, the Forty-fourth Mobile Surgical Unit is coming to you with Lieutenant Gindrey of the medical service."

The next morning toward ten o'clock, an aircraft landed this unit. They were all smartly dressed in new uniforms, their forage caps worn in such a manner that we knew they were rookies. How wrong we were!

Lieutenant Gindrey wore glasses and had a toothbrush mustache; he was thin, fair, and blue-eyed. "I've done a spell of six months with the 415th at Saigon," he told me. "This is my first active service. I'm not pretending that I'm not a little scared!"

But whom did I see behind him? A smiling face, not very competently shaved, thick eyebrows—in other words a face covered with black hairs—the face of a small, slight man. Yes, that's who it was, my dear old Levasseur, my sergeant major from 1947 to 1950. Memories came crowding back: Namdinh, Backan, Vietri, the plains, and the plantations. This was really remarkable; there would be somebody to take Marant's place after all.

Then came Sergeant Bacus, red-haired and freckled. He had a fine head; he was a Breton. "I've already served with the Sixth Colonial Paratroops," he told me. The devil he had! Here was another useful man. His job was surgical instruments.

Corporal Bescond was another on the thin side, also rather timid, a real rookie. He had just passed his training tests. We would find a place for him in the new clearing station.

Then came four Vietnamese, holding back, awkward in their borrowed combat uniforms: Hoat, Thanh, Bong, and Khanh. They were to work with Bescond in the new clearing station.

Until we had something better for them, I asked N'Diaye to quarter all these people in the Airborne Commandos' place. We would put up a separate shelter for Lieutenant Gindrey, between the electric-plant shelter and the entrance to the main passage. It would be open to the north.

At the mess in the evening we had a very lively meal. We were very soon on the best of terms with the new unit. Levasseur in particular was anxious to celebrate our reunion. He had quite a headache the next day.

Of course Barraud was there, with his vast bulk, a lock of his yellow hair falling over his eyes. Gindrey talked and pronounced his satisfaction: "Bergeron told me about you, and I'm really very glad to be a colleague of yours." Bergeron was a young lieutenant, surgeon in a field hospital. He was my assistant for a number of months at Namdinh. I had great respect for him. He was at Nasan, and an explosion there had rather affected his right thigh.

I had already made contact on my arrival with the doctor in charge of the operational group. The next day I had a long talk with him on the health arrangements for the battalions in action and on the first-aid posts.

Every battalion holding a support post had a first-aid post which could also be called the battalion infirmary. The battalion doctor was nearly always a lieutenant who had four or five shelters in his charge: one of these was used for examining the men and for urgent cases; the others had beds improvised from stretchers fixed with strong cord to the logs in the roof, not more than ten of them all told. The medical lieutenant worked with a team of orderlies and stretcher bearers recruited from his own battalion. There were seven or eight of them to a first-aid post. In each company there was a small group composed of two medical orderlies and four stretcher bearers, ordinary infantrymen.

Any request to evacuate wounded had to be made to the field hospital, and it was for me to dispatch the vehicles required. Every first-aid post was linked by an automobile track to the chief roads in the entrenched camp.

I had only two ambulances and two medical-service jeeps on the terrace above my field hospital. That did not seem to me to be enough to serve eleven first-aid posts, some of them far apart, as was the case with the Isabelle support post's infirmary, which is over six miles from the central command post.

In the course of the next few days I had to make time to visit all the battalion doctors. I already knew Patrice de Carfort of the Eighth Assault and Barraud of the Second Thai Battalion. Rondy of the First Foreign Paratroops had already paid me a visit: he was a real fighting doctor, gifted with astonishing energy and extraordinary sang-froid. Being a camera fan, he smuggled a Leica with him wherever he went.

I still had to see Auber, doctor in charge of the Third Battalion, Thirteenth Demi-Brigade, Foreign Legion, which held the Beatrice post; Lieutenant Chauveau, doctor to the Fifth Algerian Infantry, which held Gabrielle; Lieutenant Prémilieu, doctor to the Second Moroccan Infantry, which held the Elianes; Leude, doctor in charge of another battalion of Moroccans which held the Dominiques; Verdaguet, who, with the Thais, was quartered on the distant hilltop Anne-Marie.

Nearer at hand there was Captain Stermann, with the First Battalion, Thirteenth Demi-Brigade, Foreign Legion, which was entrusted with the defense of the central command post; Lieutenant Déchelotte of the First Battalion, Second Foreign Infantry, commanded by one of my friends, Major Clémençon, a veteran of the Third Foreign Legion. This First Battalion held the positions west of the central support post, the Huguettes.

At the Isabelle support post, moreover, I had to see Captain Le Damany, doctor in charge of the Sixth Moroccan Group. In a few days he was to leave his post and take up the duties of doctor in charge of the operational group. His place was to be taken by Captain Calvet, doctor in charge of the Third Battalion, Third Algerian Infantry, who would himself be succeeded by a young lieutenant, Pons, newly arrived from Hanoi. I also had to see Lieutenant Aynié, doctor in charge of the Thirty-third Infantry Regiment, commanded by a friend of mine, Major Grand d'Esnon.

Taking into account the forty-two beds in my own unit and the ten beds in the battalion infirmaries, I was quite clear in my own mind that the whole medical system rested on the airfield and the evacuation of the wounded by air.

Every morning each battalion doctor sent me some five to ten sick or superficially wounded men to take the plane for Hanoi. The infirmaries only treated those likely to recover quickly; those suffering, for instance, from feverish exhaustion, bouts of malaria, or trench mouth.

In the field hospital itself we could treat only urgent cases, such as wounds in danger of becoming fatal; and even in such cases as these if the condition responded to preliminary treatment, if the blood pressure rose and remained steady, and if the pulse returned to normal, then evacuation should be attempted.

In the two hours the plane took to get from Dienbienphu to Hanoi, treatment would be continued by a flight nurse and an orderly belonging to the Air Service.

It is obvious that in the case of serious wounds, the chance of survival is much greater if the surgical work is done in an ultramodern operating room, air-conditioned and provided with the latest equipment, such as the one in the Lanessan hospital at Hanoi.

To sum up, the wounded picked up on the scene of fighting were looked after on the spot by the company orderly or the battalion doctor. Then they were taken to the battalion first-aid post and dispatched to the surgical unit, which treated and dressed their wounds and finally handed them over to the flight nurse on a Dakota of the medical service.

These flight nurses were old acquaintances of mine. I had known them in every theater of war in Tonkin. A good number of doctors in fighting units had asked for them to be abolished and replaced by orderlies who could handle stretch-

ers. It is true that it is hard work to take fourteen stretchers laden with wounded from the ambulances to the plane, and you cannot expect the same strength from a delicate young girl as you have a right to ask of a sturdy medical orderly.

The flight nurse used to reach Dienbienphu toward nine in the morning. The field hospital jeep took her to the mess, where she had her first cup of coffee. She had to wait for an urgent case to take back to Hanoi; and often this wait would last until seven in the evening, when the last plane went on which the ordinary evacuation cases were taken.

She had her midday meal with us, but often some young lieutenant would show up around half-past eleven and—"Ah, these lieutenants!"—would gallantly invite her in the name of his commanding officer to lunch in the battalion mess.

Sometimes she brought us things not to be found in Dienbienphu: apéritifs, beer, toothpaste, fresh fruit, books. . . .

One of them was particularly efficient and friendly. Her name was Geneviève de Galard.

3.

Surgery at the Front

"Above all, if he's restless don't hesitate to give him half a dose of Phenergan-Dolosal."

The plane was about to go off, and I had a last look at that pale face, the color of ivory, those decisive and virile features. With the long black lashes of his closed eyes he looked like some proud Italian noble, strayed from a Renaissance portrait.

The man was Cabiro—this time the Viets had really got him: a grenade rolled in the dust and the earth scattered. Both legs smashed, at least twenty fragmentation wounds. The left foot was warm, but the right foot was far from reassuring to me. I hoped the injury to the tibial artery was near its lower end . . . Otherwise . . .

Yet this lovely day had begun well enough, and we were in the best of humors. The coolie gangs, inspired by rum and a good ration of cigarettes, worked with a will. In six days all could be finished off, the trenches, the clearing station, and Gindrey's shelter.

We got plentiful replacements of medical supplies, then letters, and finally at ten o'clock the air attendant brought

us with an air of mystery a cylindrical object wrapped in newspaper—whisky, a present from a generous colleague in Hanoi.

Going down the gentle slope which began beside the mess, I had visited the area between the terrace above the field hospital and the barbed wire in front of the river. That was still part of our ground, beyond the morgue, the pit twelve feet square dug in the side of our slope. A little beyond that was the helicopters' landing ground, thirty yards square, shut in by barbed wire; and finally to the left were the outworks of the defense section.

On the spur of the moment, Marant, N'Diaye, and I had decided on a number of changes. First of all, vehicles should no longer be allowed to stay on the terrace; they were too exposed there, and they also got in the way of the work in progress. Now they would be parked below, near the morgue. A direct track to the road would have to be made, but this presented no difficulties; it was only a matter of taking up the barbed wire on the northern side and replacing it with a spiked fence. Then the latrines would be altered, re-erected a little farther off, near the barbed wire, and covered with sacking.

It was still cold in February, so that a warm shower would be welcome, and we agreed to make a place for one out of bamboos and sheeting at the bottom of the slope, not far from the cookhouse.

Then why not make the helicopters' landing place into a ground for volleyball? We could rig up a net on posts which could be moved easily. After getting into touch with the paratroops of the Second Airborne Group, Colonel Langlais' men, we at once set out to make our volleyball ground, fifty-four feet by twenty-seven, the side lines marked out by strips of cloth, which was one thing we were not short of in the field hospital. The posts would be two tall bamboos fixed in buried shell cases, but the net would also be needed. Who

had a net? "We have," came the answer from the N.C.O.'s and Vietnamese of the Second Airborne.

I had brought a volleyball with me from Hanoi, for I had learned to know the virtues of a well-inflated leather ball.

Now I must give this warning to any doctor who may venture into Vietnamese villages without previous experience: My friend, if you are wanting to make tests or to vaccinate, you will first of all be an object of suspicion. Doors will be closed on you, and people will avoid the questions you ask; children are well aware that you have needles or vaccine syringes in your pockets, and that you are almost alone with your little team in the middle of the village.

This is the moment for you to produce a fine new ball, bright yellow in color, from one of your baskets, throw it in the air, bounce it two or three times—and all the doors will open and the children and young people will rush toward you with shouts of joy. By evening you will be worn out, but you can get ready to do your vaccinating with an easy mind. Those doors will remain open.

In the course of my many moves on active service, I was often compelled to take up quarters in places that were quite unknown, remaining there with my men, cut off from the others, while our fighting units were in action some miles away. My net and volleyball did more than any amount of talking to help me to get to know the people in the place and to obtain from them anything that my own outfit happened to require.

So it came about that on this morning some of my hospital orderlies had got going with men of the Second Airborne, the Eighth Assault, and the command post and had almost finished fixing up our little sports ground, on the site of the helicopters' landing stage. We could have begun playing, but

Julot came to say, "Quick, major, the command post is on the phone, wanting you."

I hurried along. "Hello?"

"In half an hour the helicopter will be landing on your ground. There has been a severe clash in the mountains, not far from here. Five killed, a dozen wounded. You had better get ready for them."

I returned to the landing stage and ordered the removal of the net. It was disappointing, but it did not matter: the start had only to be put off to the next day. My orderlies went back to their place to get ready to receive the wounded.

That morning, around seven o'clock, I had seen two companies of the First Foreign Paratroops march past the field hospital, section by section, moving off in good heart to make a reconnaissance some distance away. Following the usual custom, they had crossed the bridge and vanished toward the east. A couple of days before I had been the guest of Major Guiraud—Lieutenant Rondy was the doctor serving with him —and chatted over old times with Captain Cabiro, who was in command of the second company.

Hell! Cabiro? The telephone was beside me, so I rang at once. "Hello, the Second Airborne? Can you tell me whether Captain Cabiro . . ."

"But he's wounded, didn't you know? Badly smashed up, according to a message from the doctor, who didn't sound very hopeful."

They had got him at last—it had to happen.

My thoughts went back to Namdinh. It was March in 1947 after the large-scale operation in Tonkin under the command of Colonel Grosjean which had freed the town, and reinforcements had been quartered in the country around, making a chain of outposts in the outlying villages.

Second Lieutenant Cabiro, section leader, was already well known for his energy and his astonishing contempt for danger, but the Viets had gone off, and he was like a young horse pawing the ground with impatience. He was in command of a section of Legionnaires who worshiped him—and he was not much older than his youngest corporal. The battalion left Namdinh in the course of the summer and was replaced by the First Colonial Infantry.

Then, toward the end of that term of service and after six months' leave, he returned with his paratroop wings in the First Foreign Paratroops, with whom he fought in Laos, Cambodia, Tonkin, and Annam. In 1953 he went home again for his second leave. After the usual six months he came back for his third term of service at Dienbienphu.

Yet he could quite well have stayed in Africa—what more did he want? Captain at the age of twenty-seven, officer of the Legion of Honor, he only had to wait; promotion was assured, and he had a brilliant career before him. He was already a great leader of men.

What was it that kept all these lieutenants at it? I have known dozens and dozens of them in every unit and in every branch of the service. Their first term of duty would see them section leaders and their second, company commanders, but the third often ended with the loss of a limb or in some military cemetery lost in the wilderness. How many are left now of the lieutenants who used to be with the Third Foreign Legion? Where are Benoistel, Hamacek, Guillemin, Palissère, and Fontaine buried . . . ?

In the spring of 1947, still at Namdinh, there were three cavalry officers who had their canteen where the hospital dispensary is now. I used to see them every evening, De Lassus, Mercier, and Monroe. They were buried at a year's interval from each other, but not far apart in the Namdinh cemetery, which has been extended now to the other side of the road, the airfield side.

Generals' sons have paid a heavy price for the privilege of carrying a famous name: Lieutenant Leclerc, Lieutenant Bernard de Lattre, Lieutenant Preau . . . why did they refuse a quiet post when they had more than done their duty as section leaders or company commanders? The fear that people would say, "Oh, he's the chief's son"? No, it was simply love for the profession of arms, in which they were no different from their comrades whose names were less well known.

One day at Ninhbinh in General Gilles' mess—he was commanding Operation Upper Alps—a tall young lieutenant, red-haired, rather shy and gentle in manner, came and sat down beside me. He told me that he was with the Third Foreign—just to hear that name always rouses memories of a period in my life that I shall never forget. We had a long chat. Then he went quietly off, after a salute and a handshake.

"Who is that lieutenant?" I asked a captain opposite.

"What? Don't you know him? He's Marshal Juin's son."

There was a purring sound in the sky. Soon the helicopter appeared and we heard the regular whistling of its propellers. It landed in an immense cloud of dust. It was a Sikorski, able to hold ten wounded, of whom three could lie down and five sit. The door opened and the less seriously wounded came out first; among them I noticed a sergeant major, with a field dressing around his right leg, leaning on a stretcher bearer. "Captain Cabiro's inside, major," he told me, "badly smashed up."

A stretcher was gently moved out by careful hands. My first glimpse was of two huge dressings attached to metal splints—yes, it was Cabiro, and he spotted me at once: "Hurry up, doc, I'm not feeling so good . . ."

His pulse was rapid and barely perceptible; his lips had lost their color. He did not complain or groan, but the masseters were violently contracted beneath the skin of the cheek.

His company had had orders to capture a hilltop from which the Viets were directing an accurate fire with their machine guns on our small operational group. As usual, he ordered a direct assault, with himself at the head of it, the whole company following him in an irresistible onslaught. But the Viets had skillfully camouflaged a strong blockhouse they had up there. Waiting until Cabiro was only a few yards away, they opened fire.

A grenade exploded against his legs; he collapsed and rolled down to the bottom of the slope. Fifteen men fell with him, four of whom were killed outright.

He was quickly laid on a cot and given emergency treatment. "You know, doc," he told me, "there are a good many more of them than we thought. It looks as if you're going to have plenty of work on your hands."

I had a look above the dressings; there was no tourniquet—that was all right. Pinned to his uniform was a little yellow card, as was usual with a wounded man evacuated from the front: "Compound fractures in both legs caused by a grenade, antitetanus toxoid, morphine, half a million units of penicillin. Rondy."

"Don't touch the dressing. Give an injection of Phenergan-Dolosal," I ordered. "Get out two flasks of blood."

"His blood pressure is 62," Marant told me.

We had to work quickly. Opening a vein at the ankle was out of the question. Luckily the veins in the hollow of the elbow will do very well. But chilled blood cannot be injected; it must be slightly warmed first. Meanwhile two flasks of plasma were flowing at the same time, a needle in each arm. "Not too quickly; we must be careful of the heart."

Needles were put into the thighs, which were undamaged. Coramine, Syncortyl, Kthrombyl, anti-gangrene serum, a million units of penicillin.

"Blood pressure is 83." The lips were not quite so pale, but the pulse was still barely perceptible.

Major Guiraud came in, anxiously asking for my opinion, but I could only shrug my shoulders. Calls came from the command post, from the Second Airborne, from Isabelle, while officers and men, comrades of his, thronged the passage; Cabiro was admired and respected throughout the camp.

"Blood pressure 40." It was the irreducible minimum.

Quick, the blood was warmed now . . . "Give two drops a second." I leaned over him; the nostrils were dilated, breathing was weak. Was he going to die? Then he stirred. "You're firing too much to the right." Then, thinking himself still in the fighting, he added: "Good God, look at your tripod!"

I ordered half a dose of Phenergan-Dolosal. Soon he was calm again. "Blood pressure 73." It was still not enough. "Get out two more flasks of blood." If the pressure fell again, I was ready to summon the chaplain. No, that could not happen, he could not die.

At last, after the third flask of blood, his blood pressure rose—90, 100, 110. It remained steady at 110. The lips were pinker now, and color was coming back into the cheeks. I raised an eyelid. There was a strong corneal reflex; under my finger the pulse was rapid, but firm.

Then I had to have a look at the legs. Undoing the dressing of a fractured leg is very dangerous and can produce a secondary shock which may prove fatal. Marant listened with the stethoscope, waiting for any sign of returning weakness. I myself cut the bandages soaked in blood; under the skin the bones were broken in several places. Blood was ebbing sluggishly from a vein. Good, there was no arterial blood, and so no lesion in the large vessels. There was hope that he might keep one leg, if not both. I sighed with relief.

With infinite precaution we managed to make a more permanent dressing and then a splint. Then it was enough to stabilize the pressure finally by helping it with injections of glucose, saline, and, now and then, a little cardiac stimulant. Camphor solution, strychnine . . .

To prevent any infection, which always comes very quickly when dirt gets into leg wounds, there was a final injection of penicillin and streptomycin.

Then at last, at six in the evening, Cabiro was in his stretcher on the way to the airfield. At half-past he was in the plane and the flight nurse had received her instructions; in a couple of hours he would be at Hanoi and the surgeon at the Lanessan Hospital would read my notes.

When the plane had gone off I was a little depressed. The warm atmosphere of the mess raised my spirits.

On the helicopter field, a game of volleyball was in progress, a match between the Eighth Assault and the Second Airborne's command post; I got an idea that the Eighth Assault were on the way to being beaten. But what was that? Yes, there was Colonel Langlais in shorts, Major de Pazzis, and a couple of other officers. So I too changed into my sports outfit and joined the Eighth Assault team; and I rather think that the command post's side were caught with their pants down on that occasion.

When the time came to sit down to our meal, we had Barraud with us, our permanent guest, and Hubert, a friend of Marant's, of mixed blood but French in his feeling as in his language. In 1947 he had a kidney removed and was no longer fit for active service. But now he was back in the service . . . a queer sort of service—Intelligence. He had long since won the respect of those who worked with him for his honesty and his reliability.

"Tomorrow," he informed us, "a vaccination party is off to Bancomy. I'm going with the doctor to take a few soundings in the village. Last night a priest was kidnapped with his catechists by the Viets."

Ever since I had come to Dienbienphu I had wanted to see a Thai village, and next morning we set off, Marant, Hubert, and I. The jeep raised clouds of dust on the road as it went along. Every hundred yards or so we passed a few soldiers squatting in the ditch with a machine gun turned on the scrubby plain. That was the process of opening up the road.

Every morning one or two companies of infantry, escorted

by two or three armored cars, tanks, or trucks mounting machine guns, left their post inside the barbed wire. One section marched in the middle of the road in Indian file, with five or six yards between them. Two other sections advanced cautiously two hundred yards to the left and right and a little in front, wading in the rice field or climbing hills, combing the thickets and the little villages; then behind the middle section the armor followed, ready to support the infantry with covering fire. This went on every morning on all the roads in Tonkin, according to a well-established formula which really involved a small-scale operation in itself.

It was a matter of destroying any possible enemy ambush and opening the way for both military and civilian traffic. These ambushes were sometimes very ugly affairs and ruthless in their effects on any officer, charged with opening up the road, who neglected a precaution or made the least blunder.

In 1953 a detachment engaged in one of these operations was attacked on one of the delta roads between Namdinh and Mycoi. Mycoi was a strong position perched on a small mountain which commanded the entire plain. The companies in question left these two places, nearly ten miles apart, at the same time and were to link up halfway. They were both ambushed at the same moment. Fortunately Intelligence had done a good job and reinforcements were at hand. I was with them. We had twenty killed and thirty wounded, but the Viets' casualties were four times as heavy as ours.

I will never forget the smashed-up front of the leading light-armored car, which had caught fire. Aided by my orderlies, I had to get the driver and the gunner out piece by piece; smoke was still rising from them.

A Viet had suddenly appeared in front of the armored car with an S.K.Z.—this is the Vietminhs' bazooka—in his hand. It was impossible for him to miss. At the same moment a hundred more Viets rose up from the small dikes and rushed to attack the second car and its escorting infantry. This second car executed a real massacre; the man with the bazooka was struck down where he stood. I remember that I had a good look at him.

Before long we had reached the village where the French lieutenant of the medical service was quartered in the chief house of the village and had started the vaccinations. The whole population were gathered around him, having left their houses of wood and bamboo covered with dried leaves of the fan palm and other palm trees. These houses were all built on piles, a precaution against snakes and wild beasts. Scattered haphazard, they each sheltered what almost amounted to a tribe, comprising twenty to twenty-five people. At night all members of the tribe slept together rolled up in a mat, side by side in the only room, which smelled of the stable and *nuoc-mam*, a sauce made from rotten fish. Buffaloes sheltered casually between the piles. Pigs, ducks, and chickens circulated freely, showing no fear, mixed up with naked children.

The men were dressed in grayish cloth with vertical stripes —baggy trousers and a blouse with a high, closed collar. The women and girls were really charming. Their black hair, which was lustrous and silky, was piled up and gave the right contrast to a skin which was astonishingly white and delicate. They were clothed in a sort of sheath of very dark and clinging material which molded a slender figure and breasts superior to any of our modern pin-ups. At the front, embroidery in many different colors relieved the apparent austerity of this costume. They always walked barefoot, carrying a little basket laden with fruits, which they perched on their heads with a delicate curve of the arm, emphasizing the usual graceful swaying of the hips.

The official ceremony of vaccination was a very gay occasion. With eight orderlies at work, it was all over inside an hour; they had got through eight hundred vaccinations.

We had earned our right to a little meal helped down with a glass of vermouth: cold chicken, plain cake, peanuts. The head man of the village, a charming old man with a white goatee, came to greet us. We thanked him and then returned at full speed.

There came to my mind a vaccination which had gone off infinitely less agreeably than this one: it was in the winter of 1951 at Tien-Yen, a small town in the coastal region, wedged between a number of green hills and inhabited by Nungs who were obviously Chinese by race.

Suddenly smallpox broke out; in a few weeks it had killed some fifty children and adolescents. It was my first experience of smallpox in its clinically pure condition, as described by old writers in times when vaccination had not yet been thought of.

It is a horrible thing. It begins with little pink spots spread over the entire body. Four days later, the whole body is nothing but a disgusting scab, which oozes and smells foul. The eyes are closed and the lids gummed up; and any form of nourishment, even liquid, is out of the question. Death comes at about the eighth day, after complications affecting the lungs, the kidneys, or the intestines, producing hemorrhages which nothing can check. Very acute cases which run their course within a few hours are not uncommon, and I remember a young Nung soldier who was struck down in the street with hemoptysis. He was taken at once to the field hospital and died two hours later, in spite of intensive treatment which was administered at once.

Naturally, I began vaccinating on the first day, but I was well aware that it was too late. Immunity is not acquired in a few days. Vaccination was given in the field hospital or in the little civilian hospital which was also under my control.

But how much ingenuity it took to reach the figure of ten thousand vaccinations in that month of December! The town had been put under a ban; nobody was allowed to leave or enter it. The market was open only to people armed with a vaccination certificate.

The worst difficulty came from the Nungs' religious beliefs. For them smallpox is a manifestation of Makoui, their devil, who is as with us the opposite of a benevolent God. To try to wipe out the epidemic was to arouse Makoui's anger and to prompt him to further manifestations of evil. Anybody with smallpox is regarded as a case of diabolical possession and must be pushed out of the family circle.

Then he is hidden in the darkest and farthest corner of the house and lies there, uncared for, on a mat, bathed in his own pus. From time to time he is given a jar of water with a scoop consisting of the dried half of a coconut.

If by chance the sick man should recover, he can only be received back into the family after weeks have passed, and before he is readmitted there is a purification ceremony which takes the form of an infernal din made up of cries and curses, the piercing notes of a flute, with heavy and repeated blows on a drum or a pot. At the same time the house is fumigated by burning a heap of consecrated herbs. The aim of all this is to frighten the Makoui so that he will leave the house once and for all.

In a couple of months all the delightful kids who used to make such a hullabaloo in the streets had vanished. I think our vaccinations had very little effect and the epidemic died down of its own accord.

A rich merchant, who was a well-read man, took me considerably aback when he made these remarks: "You French are a funny sort of people. Before you came here, whenever an epidemic of this type broke out, we dispersed far and wide, way off into the mountains, and didn't return to our own town for months afterward. In this way we avoided human contacts as far as possible, and the illness only affected very few people. But now you shut up the town and imprison us in a very limited area. I am not quite convinced that your science is always the best!"

His words led me to reflect; and I think he was right.

When I got back to my shelter, Marant reminded me that today, February 22, was the feast of St. Isabelle—and therefore of the support post which bore her name—and I was invited to lunch with them.

Alone in my jeep, I crossed the bridge over the Namyoum, took Road 41, and drove rapidly toward the south. The dusty road passed through three Thai villages, and a few miles before reaching my destination it ran alongside the emergency airfield. This airfield was the same length as the one at Dienbienphu, but it had no metaled surface.

The Isabelle support post looked just like the central support post at Dienbienphu. But it was more spread out, and the chief outworks were more on the right bank of the Namyoum. The immediate neighborhood was quite open; it was almost like a position in open country, as the nearest mountain was over six miles away. If the Viets attacked, they would have their work cut out. It was the Foreign Legion, not paratroops, that controlled the situation there—the Third Battalion, Third Foreign Infantry, supported by a North African battalion with replacements from a few Thai and Vietnamese companies.

I turned around by the 105 guns in the middle of the camp and reached the command post of the Sixth Group. Introductions, salutes, and handshakes followed. Lieutenant Colonel Lalande, a young commanding officer for the Legion but a veteran of warfare, surprised me by his ease of manner no less than by his decision, revealed in his energetic features, which could also relax into a smile. Colonel de Castries was to join us shortly.

I had not forgotten that I was the guest of the Third Battalion. There my old friend Major Grand d'Esnon was waiting for me. Thin and pale, with vivid blue eyes, he concealed beneath a rather slight appearance an astonishing amount of energy and still more strength of will, the intensity of which only appeared when he was preparing for battle and when fighting was actually in progress.

It was a copious meal, and sitting down to it were nearly all the Legion's majors who were at Dienbienphu. I was closely acquainted with Major Clémencon of the First Foreign Infantry, who asked me to lunch with him the next day; Majors Violés and Lacote, veterans of the Third Foreign; Major Guiraud, in command of the First Foreign Paratroops; Major Cheynel, of the Second Thai Battalion. Then the lieutenants—Lieutenant Rossini, whom I had known at Rachgia on the Gulf of Siam, Lieutenant Gambiez, son of General Gambiez who was in command at Namdinh in 1951, and Aynié, of the medical service with the Third Foreign Infantry.

The conversation turned on old memories shared and on the chance which had brought us together at Dienbienphu, rather than on politics, when suddenly the phone rang. It was for me: Marant was summoning me to attend to six wounded who had just come in.

Bitterly disappointed, I was obliged to take my leave. A captain, rather slender in figure and aristocratic in appearance, asked for a seat in my jeep, having to return to Dienbienphu on an urgent service matter. This was Captain Hervouet; he had all the armor in the camp under his command. We made good time on the way back. We chatted as we went and agreed to meet the following day.

The six wounded were not at all serious cases; I arranged with Marant for their evacuation by the last plane.

That evening, when Barraud, Marant, Levasseur, and I were playing a democratic game of *belote*, the command post rang to ask me to send an ambulance to Gabrielle to pick up a man who was seriously wounded. I telephoned to Chauveau and learned that it was an abdominal wound.

Some twenty-five minutes later, I was making an examination of a North African in the emergency-treatment room. He had been serving as an "alarm post" in the Thalweg, which is the northern boundary of the Gabrielle support post. "Alarm posts" are forward sentries who do their duty some three hundred yards in front of the last outwork, in the undergrowth. It is an odd sort of job. On reaching his observation post the poor fellow had run into a Viet who had got there before him and who shot him in the abdomen.

The face was completely bloodless, the lips white; the pulse could not be taken. His blood pressure was 73. Treatment was started at once, and blood, plasma, cardiac stimulant, penicillin, and streptomycin were injected into him.

It was at least an hour before the blood pressure rose to 100, and several times it fell suddenly; there were obvious signs of a serious intraperitoneal hemorrhage. So it was essential to operate on him without delay.

I got through to the command post and spoke to Major Guérin, who was in charge of air support: "Hello, this is the surgeon. Would you get the *Firefly* to come down here? I've got a wounded man, an urgent case, to evacuate to Hanoi."

"Wait a minute. I'll get through to Intelligence . . . Hello, it can't be done. The *Firefly* is out on a very important reconnaissance flight."

To fetch a plane from Hanoi and send it back would take about five hours. It would be too late, so I had to operate myself. Levasseur would see to the anesthetic, Deudon and Bacus would keep me supplied, and Dr. Gindrey would lend a hand, while Marant would continue his intravenous transfusion all the time. So I was going to embark on my first laparotomy at Dienbienphu.

To open an abdomen, examine it, and repair the organs affected is considered, perhaps wrongly, the most delicate of all operations under the pressing conditions of surgery at the front. It is also a decisive test for the young surgeon who is going to face an operation on his own.

It is also a matter of the most absorbing interest. With the last stitch suturing the abdominal wall, one's work is finished and sealed, and its success or failure will not become apparent until some days afterward. If a mistake has been made, it cannot be rectified and death will ensue. When intestinal peristalsis begins functioning again and the first stool makes its appearance, even veterans and high-ranking surgeons experience a secret thrill.

Whatever causes an abdominal wound, it seldom happens that only one organ is affected, and the results are very complex, entailing a long and difficult operation. If the spleen is affected, it has to be removed; and the same holds good for the kidney and pancreas. If the liver is damaged, one can only put in a few sutures in an attempt to stop the hemorrhage, which is complicated by the pouring of the bile into the peritoneum. If the large intestine is damaged it has to be externalized, and feces will pass by the sort of unnatural anus thus brought into being. A stomach wound has to be anastomosed. Segments of the small intestine torn by an explosion have to be resected. Then the two free ends have to be sutured, end to end—the intestinal suture which is the pet aversion of beginners. Surgeons in training practice dozens of intestinal sutures on an anatomical specimen before making one on a living body; they make sure that their work is watertight by injecting water under pressure into the intestinal cavity. If the bladder is damaged, a cystostomy has to be undertaken, which consists of putting a rubber drainage tube into the bladder, through the abdominal wall. Urine passes out by means of this new channel.

Once the wall of the abdomen is opened up, one has to make an examination, which is always hindered by the blood that fills the cavity, blood mixed with feces or bile. A tiny wound behind the spleen, a minute perforation of the stomach—these must not be overlooked; it must not be forgotten that perforations comprise two holes; a hole in the small intestine is often concealed by its mesentery. The cecum may have two large slits four inches apart. Is this a case for a hemicolectomy, a very serious matter indeed?

I remember Bergeron's first abdominal operation. "A fine abdomen," he called it. He had done an intestinal resection of ten inches and achieved a very fine anastomosis. In the three days following the operation, he went without food and sleep. He got to bed at two in the morning and was up again at six, seeing his patient twenty times a day, sounding him, encouraging him, coddling him. Finally on the morning of the fourth day peristalsis began once more. No doubt it was the happiest day of his life.

Lieutenant Robert, a medical colleague of Bergeron's, went off one day to Buichu with my surgical team and four days later sent me a man with a wound in the abdomen on whom he had operated. It was his first, or at least the first he had done all by himself. He had already opened an abdomen, but that was at the hospital and under my supervision; that didn't count.

With the man who had undergone the operation, the air attendant handed over to me a six-page letter from Robert in which he explained the whole case in detail, asking me at least ten times to take special care of what was really a very special case. . . .

When he came back a fortnight later, covered with mud and utterly worn out, his first question was: "How is my abdomen getting along?"

In the spring of 1939 I was not yet twenty-five. Thursday was the day for operations in the hospital where I was a student, and it was on this day that Professor Swynghedauw of Lille said to me, "Now, Grauwin, here's the knife. Operate. I'll help you." I was seized with a trembling which I was unable to control. I only had to do a simple appendectomy—but might I not clumsily puncture the large intestine? Would I be able to nip the little artery which always spurts the moment one cuts through the peritoneum? Would my stitches and my sutures hold?

I felt that the whole staff of the operating room had their eyes fixed on me; I also felt the chief's eyes, which were steel blue and severe behind his glasses. I raised my own eyes . . . No, his were gentle and kindly, and I guessed that there was a smile behind the white mask. Then all went well.

It was he who taught me to set about such an operation without losing my way in the maze of the abdominal cavity and to examine rapidly the most inaccessible corners; to make strong and equal overcast stitches, on three layers. And even today when I find an open abdomen in front of me and hesitate over the decision to be made, I think, "What would the chief have done?"

Unfortunately, the most brilliant operations do not always produce the results they deserve. In Indochina nearly half the abdominal cases die a few days or a few weeks after the operation. It is only to be expected when one remembers that the soldier has been wounded in the heat of battle and that his intestines, as is usual in tropical countries, are occupied by a considerable intestinal flora, and that it takes from two hours to a day to get him to a surgical unit. Finally it is well known that a European in this country is constantly in a state of lowered resistance to illness and infection.

In operating, moreover, there is something more than the simple application of an established technique which gives one a sense of personal satisfaction. There should also be some feeling for the patient.

In a civilian hospital, a man who is going to have an operation is prepared for it days beforehand; he is surrounded by his family, who are affectionate and kindly disposed, and he goes into the operating room without fear and without distrust.

It is easy to guess the feelings of a lad of twenty who gets a bullet in the abdomen, whether at Dienbienphu or elsewhere. He is brought in on a stretcher and put in a line behind others who are waiting for their turn. To right and left and above him he sees nothing but earth and the legs of those who have nothing wrong with them, passing by carefree and hurried: "The doctor is just coming, and then you'll be all right."

He hears cries and groans. In front of him and behind him are stretchers with men wounded just as he is. "But what are the orderlies up to? Where are they? Good God, my blood's running away and I'm in pain. I don't want to die out here! What about my parents and my home? To hell with this country!"

He becomes a little boy again, terribly scared. He is so frightened that he begins to cry. Then I turn up and ask, "What's the matter? You're crying. What is it?"

"No, I'm not crying, but I'm in such pain."

Now he is naked on the table, harshly lit by the lamp, his abdomen painted red.

"Now, have you ever been operated on for appendicitis?"

"Yes, when I was fifteen."

Suddenly he remembers his mother's gentle smile, kissing him before the anesthetist's mask goes over his face, a moment of peace before the darkness.

He is crying again. I put my hand on his forehead and smile at him. "Come on, you needn't worry; you won't feel anything. Everything will be all right. In another month you'll be running around like the rest of them."

Then I am entitled to a look which expresses his feeling of consolation and gratitude. It is all I ask for.

After some such reflections, I was tying the last of the bronze threads closing up the abdomen of Ben-Azzyz, infantryman, wounded while doing his "alarm post" duty in front of Gabrielle.

4.

The Attack

It was agreed: I was to embark on the *Claude-Bernard* about March 20. But how was I to leave the place, knowing that "something" was going to happen?

But Marant had to go. After a year in Thailand, he was entitled to some leave to recuperate. He was going to Vatchai, a seaside resort on the bay of Along. After that, he was to return home.

It was now March 11. We got news of Cabiro twice a day; he was out of danger and would keep both his legs.

Our excavations were completed: a deep and narrow trench went from the entrance to the mess, curving toward the men's quarters, passing in front of the electric-plant shelter and coming out to link up with the main passage.

The clearing station was finished, a fine piece of work, with ten banks of earth on either side of a central alley, a wide entrance to the north, and steps coming out where the terrace began. The wounded would only have a short distance to go to reach it. There was a way out to the south through a narrow passage which also linked up with the main passage of the field hospital proper.

Unfortunately there was still the question of roofing this area. The engineers had agreed to it, but they were waiting for materials from Hanoi, iron supports and metal plates. We would have to send men into the forest to cut down some thirty trees.

There was also the main passage, which was still open to the sky. I had been promised help, but the engineers had first of all to strengthen the forward positions and build others.

On the afternoon of the eleventh our guns went into action, and shells exploded a little beyond Beatrice. You could see the smoke of the explosions stretching like a mist far beyond the hills. Buezek said that the Viets had taken up positions in front of Beatrice in some strength. With glasses you could see them in broad daylight, moving quickly and vanishing, digging in and making emplacements for their mortars. Now and then our shells went whistling over and forced them back into their holes. Someone said something about trenches; they were making trenches. There was no doubt that the real trial of strength was coming, at least for the northern positions.

It was said that the advanced positions at Beatrice were already threatened and getting bursts of machine-gun fire and shells from mortars. Toward four in the afternoon, we saw a few companies of the First Paratroops and the Eighth Assault go off, crossing the bridge and vanishing toward Road 41, to the northeast. Then shelling started up again on the other side. Toward six we heard that the Viets had abandoned their positions, leaving numbers of dead and some automatic weapons on the field. Our paratroops had decided the matter in three-quarters of an hour. Optimism was the order of the day: the Viets had asked for a scrap, and now they would get it . . .

In response to a call from Auber, I sent him the ambulances and the jeeps, which returned half an hour later with Legionnaires, paratroops, and some Vietnamese infantry all bunched up together. We used the new clearing station for the first time. There was not too much damage: two Legionnaires needed intravenous therapy, one wounded in the chest, the other in the head. There were fifteen all told, and they would be evacuated to Hanoi in the evening all in one relay.

After dinner I went down to the command post. I made out Colonel de Castries in his compartment, the last on the right. Two or three telephones were all ringing at once. On the right of the entrance was the artillery command post, under Colonel Piroth. To the left were three compartments, with Major Léost and Captain Méhay in the first, the air support under Colonel Guérin in the second. The last faced Colonel de Castries' and was occupied by the chief of staff. At the back behind sheeting nailed to the logs in the ceiling was Intelligence, under Captain Drouin. You could hear the urgent tapping of the radio station.

"Well, Méhay, what's the news?"

"I think the great attack is going to start soon."

"Do you think it will be the same as it was at Nasan?"

"I hope so."

No details, hardly any intelligence reports. The Viets were there, sure enough, but how many of them? Were they going to attack Beatrice? Or was this only a feint, a diversion?

My N.C.O.'s were well informed. It is generally known that a garrison's N.C.O.'s form a sort of brotherhood and often know more than the officers about what is going on. But there is always an element of exaggeration or distortion.

Anyhow, Marant was definite enough: "There are certainly two divisions over there, sir. Hubert told me so."

"Well, you're going off. You'll be in the plane tomorrow. I don't want any complaints from the chief. The man there is waiting to replace you . . ."

"But I want to stay here, sir."

"Nothing doing. Go to the command post and get your papers signed."

That evening there was great excitement in the mess. There

were Barraud, de Carfort, Hubert and his chief, Lieutenant Bourreau, Marant, Gindrey, and myself. And then the rest of the team too, seated as well as they could manage on the ground. Spirits could not have been higher: "The Viets are going to attack." There were commentaries in plenty, and the mood was frankly one of optimism. De Carfort gave the Viets a week, not a day more. Barraud was more cautious: "I would rather they waited until I'm due to go home."

Levasseur recalled other evenings before an attack was launched which we had been through together in other years. Now it was once more the eve of battle. We could hear the constant coming and going of trucks outside and jeeps moving off in a hurry. Aircraft were ceaselessly landing and taking off. The beginning of the runway was not so very far from the field hospital, and to reach it they flew over us at less than a hundred and fifty feet.

Barraud and de Carfort talked to me about their medical supplies, which they considered inadequate. They asked me if I could let them have any more. Their requests were at once granted, and they went off laden with packages, boxes, and flasks.

At midnight we all returned to our shelters. As we crossed the platform we paused a moment to admire the flares going up to the east and the northeast, falling again in a graceful curve. The *Firefly* was constantly turning in the sky, every five minutes releasing a parachute flare which lit up the countryside for some time. Now and then our guns spat out some twenty or so shells, and in the distance we saw the momentary flash of the explosions shown up against the dark background of the mountain heights.

It was brilliant weather on the morning of the twelfth—a spring morning on the Côte d'Azur. By nine o'clock dozens of aircraft of every type had already come and gone. The rear bases at Hanoi and Haiphong were sending back men who had been on leave or convalescing. The ammunition dumps were being replenished, and I too received a dozen containers with medical supplies, combat uniforms, boots.

Toward one o'clock, while we were sipping some good coffee, there were suddenly some explosions rather close by. "Those are not our guns," I said to myself.

We jumped to our feet together and saw great columns of smoke and dust rising from the runway of the airfield. Hell, they were Viet shells, the first we had had! The mess was half a mile from the end of the runway as the crow flies; the shells were coming from the north, and you could not hear the whistle they made. Then there came six, seven, eight more explosions. Levasseur said, "That's a 105."

Suddenly there was the rumble of a heavier outbreak, more spaced out, and at once a twisting column of black smoke went up toward the sky, with a bright red glow at the base of it.

"They've hit the Packett."

Five or six days previously, a Packett aircraft had been forced to land with engine trouble; a party of mechanics had come at once from Hanoi, and it should have returned to its base about this time.

Now it had had it! For a first attempt, it was really masterly. One shell to the right, another to the left, and then bang on the target.

We noticed other explosions, a little to the right, and to the left, followed by a huge cloud of dust. Fighters took off, and in a few minutes they were turning above our heads, gaining height, going toward the northeast. A Morane on reconnaissance moved slowly at a great height. But what could it hope to see in the dense, close growth of the jungle? It could hardly make out the ribbon of the roads, which were at least a little clearer; that was its limit. As for the smoke which marks the firing of a shell, it disperses very quickly, and the flash is impossible to see when the emplacement is really well camouflaged.

The fighters dived, fired their guns, dropped their bombs. Our artillery went into action and the sounds echoed, reverberating in the mountains. That was our reply to the Viets, and it lasted for more than half an hour, followed by silence.

The phone rang: "Quick, send an ambulance to the runway. There are four wounded."

"Get going, Lahcen."

He was not very anxious to go; Sioni had better go with him.

A quarter of an hour later, the wounded were in the emergency-treatment room—two Moroccans, a coolie, and Lebon, a movie reporter. Two of these movie men had been out on the runway when the shells landed. The Packett was in flames: what a chance to get an action shot! They both darted out of the shelter in which they had taken refuge; then came a whistling sound and an explosion—Lebon got it in the leg, and the other man was killed outright.

Lebon was a tall, dark fellow. He was in great pain: "Oh, the swine, the swine!"

His foot was half off, the amputation more or less done already. It only needed tidying up, cutting a little of the bone sticking out through the shattered tendons. I put a tourniquet just above the wound as N'Diaye told me, "There's a plane for Hanoi in ten minutes, major." Lebon could go on that. We quickly fixed up a dressing and a splint and gave the usual injections. "Have the ambulance brought to the passage entrance."

Two hours later Lebon and the other wounded would be in the clearing station of Lanessan hospital.

The evening was taken up with preparations of every kind. I got as many supplies and medicines as possible into the emergency-treatment room, the X-ray room, and the operating room. My reserve supplies were kept in a hole covered over with a tarpaulin. I had another anxious look at my clearing station, which still had only sheeting over it.

I was back in my own shelter toward eleven, where I wrote to Lieutenant Colonel Landrieu at Hanoi: "I think the balloon is going up. You'd better get the supply people to have parachute containers ready, and plenty of them."

To my family I wrote: "I am still waiting in Haiphong for the boat which is going to bring me . . ."

At half-past eleven I lay down to sleep, but was roused almost at once by explosions similar to those of the afternoon. Suddenly realizing that my team were sleeping under canvas, I rushed outside.

It was the runway getting another salvo of 105 shells. But I had an idea that they were coming closer. They were falling on the quarters where the fighters were tucked away—for every evening the fighters returned to their own place, a wide circle surrounded by a little wall of earth some six feet high. Why did they stay there without making a move—why didn't they take off? They would be destroyed on the ground. I was a fool: flares would have to be lit to let them take off, and then the runway would be lit up like a city street, a fine target for the Viet guns.

I went along to my orderlies' quarters and roused them: "Get up! Shells are falling, and it may last or get worse. You'll have to sleep in the clearing station." Cross as children disturbed in their sleep, they went off to the trench. Perez was very put out.

But that was all for that night. When morning came, the weather was still glorious. As usual, I heard the men on fatigue duty trotting carelessly over my roof. The sound of the first aircraft came in through the ventilator.

Marant was getting ready his case and his pack. He went off for an hour and said good-by to his many friends. Everything was quiet, nobody even wanting medical advice. The flight nurse was late. She didn't arrive until nearly noon. Suddenly alarmed, I took the jeep to the airfield and met the plane. "Hello, this is a surprise!" she said.

"Oh, it's nothing, but this time yesterday the Viets sent a few shells over, and I don't want to have you on my operating table."

So we set off for the field hospital and had hardly reached the terrace when the first explosions reverberated around us. The flight nurse turned toward me; she was very pale.

Twenty minutes later my ambulances brought back some fifteen wounded. Lahcen and Larbi, the drivers, were a little out of breath. Gindrey sorted out the wounded and examined them. Only one case was serious. They would leave with the flight nurse in the evening.

I went down into the mess and rang Le Damany, doctor in charge of the Ninth Group. He was always in touch with the command post. "I think it will be this evening," he told me.

"Good. We're ready."

Lunch was soon over. Marant said good-by to me. I would very much have liked to keep him with me, but I could not assume such a responsibility.

Then Hubert turned up, pale with excitement: "I've come to say good-by, major. I've just had a telegram calling me back to Hanoi. I can't stay here."

"Why?"

"I'm not quite sure, but I rather think that things are going to get hotter than you expect; and you know I'm of mixed blood and in Intelligence, and if the Viets should get hold of me—perhaps it's just as well that I should be kept out of trouble . . ."

Hubert got in beside Marant. The jeep went off in a cloud of dust; I still saw a hand making a gesture of farewell. The ambulance laden with wounded was also making for the runway.

Back in the mess I rang Captain Foucras of the air transport office and said, "I'm sending you another lot to evacuate, Foucras. Be a good fellow and keep an eye on them if you can . . . by the way, I should think you've already added to your collection of shell fragments."

There was a laugh, and his voice came clearly: "Don't worry about that, major, and it's all right about your bandage party. It smells of powder around here . . . As for the shell fragments, I'm afraid the next collection may be made in my own body. But we'll lick them all the same."

I hung up and at the same moment heard the sound of some ten explosions. Hell, they were on the runway again . . . At five o'clock a Dakota took off and flew above us with all its engines revving. I learned later that Marant, Hubert, the flight nurse, and the wounded just had time to get on that Dakota.

In the little cookhouse the *bep*—the cook—and the coolies were happily preparing dinner: "There will be tripe." But we were fated never to eat that tripe!

It was also around five that the Huguette support post sent me four wounded, not serious cases. Déchellote was in high spirits: "The battalion's morale is terrific. Remember how long we've been waiting for this."

Suddenly Bacus came down the steps: "This time, major, I think it's our turn." Certainly the first shells were bursting loudly a hundred yards from us, to the right of the command post, and making me jump. A few seconds passed, then three, then four whistling sounds, followed by three, then four explosions.

I went out a little way into the trench. There was a fire in the direction of Beatrice, a constant red glow thrown into relief by the closer hills of the Dominiques, and against this glow there were sudden flashes which vanished abruptly. There could be no doubt of what it meant; it was the usual artillery barrage which precedes an attack. I had not seen one since 1944.

I went back into the mess. The coolies were motionless.

They looked at me, and one of them said, "Maybe Viet-Minh attack? Yes?"

I passed from the trench into the main passage and dispersed my staff in shelters and in the main block. The infernal bombardment had started and was intensified every minute. I had an idea that 105 shells were coming over in salvos of twelve to sixteen at a time. They were falling everywhere, on the center of the camp, on the command post, on the Eighth Assault, on the Ninth Group, and in front of us toward the bridge. The shorter bursts of 75's could be clearly made out.

My people were all as silent as statues. For most of them it was their first experience of an enemy bombardment.

N'Diaye was the first to get excited, then Lachamp, and of course Levasseur, and Bacus. You had to talk, say something or other. Sioni began joking and teasing Cortés.

The shells were still falling, about sixty a minute, almost as heavy a barrage as in the big attacks of 1944. I went off to my shelter, and at the moment when I reached the open crossways I heard the whistle of five shells which exploded near the command post, thirty yards away.

I brought back a bottle of rum and handed it around; then we started smoking. The atmosphere warmed up, and soon we forgot the whistle and explosion of shells. It was just what we needed, to refuse to listen or hear anything—to detach oneself from everything that is going on outside, to think only of the work that will have to be done soon.

Then there came a lull—which lasted. The phone rang: "Hello, major, Rondy speaking. A shell has fallen on one of our blockhouses, and I've got twelve wounded. Would you send an ambulance along?"

"Okay." I hung up. Another ring: "Hello, major, de Carfort here. A shell has exploded in one of our shelters. I've got five killed, five wounded. Have you an ambulance?"

So it went on: Stermann of the First Battalion, Thirteenth Foreign, Barraud of the Second Thai Battalion, Le Damany of the Ninth Group . . . "We have ten . . . seven . . . twelve wounded." The phone was ringing all the time.

N'Diaye had gone out. He returned out of breath: "Major, loads of wounded are coming into the main passage . . ."

"Get them into the shelters—it doesn't matter which. We'll have a look at them here afterward, one by one."

They came from all over the place, from neighboring units, from the supply column, from the workshops, from the Thai group. They had come direct to the field hospital, with their own field dressings hastily stuck on wounds, the blood soaking through the little squares of gauze.

They were all coming to the field hospital; even the wounded from battalions provided with an infirmary had not gone to their own doctor. So I rang one of these.

"But, major, what can be done? Our infirmary is full up."

There was no answer to that. Soon the shelters of the main passage were full to overflowing. The wounded came in and sank down groaning. They were all over the place, Frenchmen, Legionnaires, Moroccans, Vietnamese, coolies.

Shells were still falling, but less often, more spaced out. It could not be helped, we would have to use the clearing station. It was full in a moment. I prayed God to direct the Viet fire.

Father Heinrich had arrived and gone to work without a word. Julot was looking for me . . . Quick, the telephone: "Le Damany here. Colonel Gaucher has just been seriously wounded. I think he's going to die. Martinelli is also wounded, and four Legionnaires. Send one of your jeeps."

Sioni had heard and was already off. Colonel Gaucher was his regimental commander.

After a few minutes' wait, two grave-faced Legionnaires put down a stretcher in front of me on which lay Colonel

Gaucher. His legs and arms were all literally smashed, and his thorax was open; he was dying. "Father, here, quick . . ."

Father Heinrich had just time to perform the last rites, and Colonel Gaucher breathed his last.

A 105 shell had exploded in the command shelter, having blown in the entrance. Major Martinelli was not seriously wounded. He was the chief of staff of the Ninth Group. I had known him when he was in command of the Second Battalion of the Thirteenth Foreign, one of the operational battalions of the Fourth Group.

I took a white sheet from a basket and covered up the bleeding remains spread before me; the two Legionnaires took their commanding officer away to the morgue.

Ten more wounded arrived, from the other bank, the Second Thai Battalion and Claudine. Claudine was the position to the southwest, where Rondy was stationed. There was no more room in the clearing station; I gave orders for them to be put into the mess and the men's sleeping quarters. I also dashed into the sterilization shelter: "Kabbour, get the sterilizer going all out. We shall certainly be operating throughout the night."

I went back to the clearing station. Gindrey and his team had already sent three abdominal wounds and ten with tourniquets to the operating room. These ten would have to be operated on first, in the effort to save a limb and avoid gangrene at all costs. The abdomens could wait for an hour or two.

I made a rapid choice among the shelters, which were crammed. I had to step over bodies laid side by side, even on the ground. Most of the wounded were quite at ease, smoking, joking, and asking me for brandy.

"Fighting is over for me," said one of them, "tomorrow I'll be off to Hanoi to have a good time."

I had a look at his wound. One of his arms was completely pulped.

"Major, make a quick job of this," said another. "Now I've got an account to settle with those guys in the hills."

Then again: "Major, this will be the third time that you've done some butcher's work on me." I leaned down. It was quite true, for I recognized the man: "You were with the Colonial Infantry at Kaobang, and I operated on you at Backan in 1948."

"Yes, look." He pointed to the mark of my knife on his right thigh. "And now I'm a medic like one of your bunch."

"What battalion?"

"I was with the party to go to Isabelle; I only got here yesterday."

Isabelle: I had quite forgotten. What if Calvet sent me, either tonight or tomorrow morning, a hundred more wounded? Where was I to put them? I dashed to the phone: "Give me the chief of staff . . . Colonel, we must have a surgical unit parachuted to Isabelle, in case there is an attack on this position or the road is cut."

"Don't go . . . I'll talk to Colonel de Castries about it . . . Yes, that's agreed. We'll give it priority."

I thought of what General Jeansotte had said: "You'll never get out of this place alone."

I had counted up a hundred and fifty wounded. Seventy of them were superficially or at least not too seriously wounded and could go back to their battalion infirmary. Eighty would have to be examined more closely, and I considered that fifty of them would require an operation. I had spotted ten abdomens, fifteen fractured limbs, two head wounds, ten thorax cases. The rest were multiple injuries.

Lachamp followed me everywhere. An official medical card was tied to every man, as is the practice at the front, and on it was written the diagnosis, the immediate treatment he was to receive, and the decision whether to operate or not.

The whole team were hard at work, and I was glad to see

how active and enthusiastic they were. Inside an hour all the injections had been given—ten a minute, almost a record. The dressings were well advanced. N'Diaye had taken an orderly and a couple of coolies with him to carry drums of compresses and a tray of instruments. Bacus did the same with the Vietnamese in his team. Lachamp was writing all the time at my dictation both on the cards and on the record.

"Poor fellow," I said to him, "you never wanted office work."

"Oh, yes, major, it's all right when it's like this. And then you'll let me help in the emergency-treatment room or in getting the men away?"

"Surely."

Every two or three minutes, five or six shells fell almost simultaneously. As soon as the whistling was heard, the main passage emptied in a flash. I had given strict orders: "No wounded in the main passage."

I risked a glance outside in the direction of Beatrice. It was an extraordinary spectacle: there was a great fire, and you could hear the roll of thunder. I had no idea what time it was, but I realized that it was night; yet you could see as clearly as if it were broad daylight. Flares were springing up on all sides, from Claudine to well beyond Gabrielle.

The *Firefly* constantly dropped its parachute flares. All our guns were roaring: the 105's close at hand, the 155's beside the workshops. They produced a muffled sound as they fired, powerful enough to shake the earth around us. This great barrage put me in mind of the massive air bombardments at night in the north of France in 1943 and 1944.

The men in charge of the electric plant were hard at work, and I had a glance at the Morgue. The square hole was full up; outside, between the hole and the barbed wire, there were a hundred bodies, dropped there in confusion, either on stretchers or on the ground, fixed in grotesque or tragic attitudes. Some were sheeted in canvas, others were wearing their combat uniforms, motionless in the position in which death had caught them.

Julot summoned me to the telephone: "Hello, this is Gabrielle command post. Our doctor has been wounded in the abdomen. Send an ambulance—quick!" That would be Chauveau, a colleague of Gindrey's, promoted at the same time. Gindrey was badly upset when I gave him the news.

Chauveau was brought in a quarter of an hour later, and I examined him. The projectile had only wounded the abdominal wall and not perforated it, but the right forearm had a nasty compound fracture. On the next day we would try to evacuate him to Hanoi. I let Le Damany know: "We must find a replacement for Chauveau at Gabrielle."

"I'll send Déchelotte there. Stermann and I will look after the First Battalion, Second Foreign. You know, things are going badly at Beatrice."

The operating room was busy; Gindrey was finishing his first amputation and still had fourteen to do, and then ten abdomens to open. Operations had begun, and they were not to stop for fifty-seven days and fifty-seven nights.

After each operation, fresh arrivals had to be looked at, for they were coming in all the time. The strong light of the lamp hurt the eyes, sometimes dazzling them. One had to harden oneself. Then there is a terrible tiredness which creeps into the muscles of the forearm, into the back and the calves. Coffee with a drop of rum gives one a lift at such moments.

Someone in the main passage announced, "Beatrice has fallen." I paid no attention. Suddenly I became aware that my orderlies were looking at me to see how I took it. "Oh well," I said, "it's a hill just like any other. At Nasan too they captured one hill. It was recaptured the next day."

Hamel, an N.C.O. paratrooper, France's youngest holder of the Military Medal, had now lost his left arm.

Filoche, of the Eighth Assault, was one of the wounded that De Carfort sent me a little while ago. He had lost the lower half of both his legs. Before the operation, he was screaming with pain; but now he was quite calm and was smoking. He had just come to. "Bah, what are one's pins? They can be replaced."

Beatrice had fallen and a battalion of the Legion was gone.

The fourth amputation was in progress. In the shelters Deudon was sending a meal around. There was beer for all.

"Major, it's five in the morning. Would you like a little coffee?"

Five o'clock! The night had gone very quickly. The coffee burned my throat and did me good. Everybody had done well, and I was very pleased. But there were still fifteen poor devils to operate on: five abdomens, ten fractures which still had tourniquets on them. The tourniquets were loosened every ten minutes, but at the end of a dozen hours gangrene always sets in.

We had to inject penicillin on a large scale—a million units to each wounded man. That meant a total of a hundred and fifty million units, my entire supply. In a few hours it would all be gone, and I had to think of tomorrow's wounded. I restricted use to half a million units and ordered the distribution of sulfonamide tablets, one every two hours.

There was no more blood. The eight pints I had had in reserve were exhausted. Take it from one man and give it to another? Would that be right? Every fighting man needs all his strength at a time like this. We would have to use dry and liquid plasma.

I got through to the command post and asked for Signal: "Hello? Take a message: 'Extremely urgent, send by the Air Service or by parachute: blood, 20 pints; penicillin, 500 million units; streptomycin, 500 grams.'"

There were still a number of shortages. We would have to see to them later. It was a matter of getting the most important things first of all.

Now it was six in the morning. I went out on the terrace to take a little air, which was delightful and revived me. I breathed in as much as I could, even making an exercise of it. Everything was quiet, absolutely quiet. I saw shell holes all over the place: one crater in the roof of the last shelter, one in mine, two beside the emergency-treatment room, five or six on the road which ran alongside us and drew attention to the clearing station, covered with its green canvas.

The coolies, calm and relaxed, were sweeping and cleaning and carrying huge baskets full of bloodstained dressings to the refuse dump. The cookhouse was getting busy, its smoke going straight up into the sky.

I had a look at the command post, a little beyond our west exit. It was surrounded with a series of craters. The barbed wire had been torn up, and a jeep, garaged between small earth walls, had been blown to bits.

Then I went along to the command post to find out what was in the wind. Not a single member of the staff had had any sleep. The telephone had been ringing all the time, orderlies had been going to and fro with messages and still were; added to it all were the tap of typewriters and the noise of radios from the signal group and the artillery command post. But none of their faces showed any signs of exhaustion or discouragement.

Colonel de Castries was thoughtfully walking up and down the main passage off which the other compartments led. He was smoking nervously, wearing a combat uniform, his eternal red forage cap on his head.

I went up to Captain Méhay: "What about Beatrice?"

"Well, yes, it was a surprise. But look out—I rather think it may be Gabrielle's turn this evening."

Major Léost was by his side, so I asked, "Major, is there no way of getting my main passage covered?"

"I'm entirely agreed in principle, but last night eight shelters collapsed. The engineers have got their hands full. I'll send them to you as soon as they're free."

I returned to the field hospital, where some men with minor wounds had just arrived, having managed to escape from Beatrice. Their eyes were round with terror as they told of their experiences: "If you could have seen them, major, thousands and thousands of them, jumping over each other, over the ones who were already dead, mowed down by our fire. Then the thousands of shells—when they had finished falling, half our shelters had collapsed."

On a cot at the back of the emergency-treatment room there was a lieutenant with leg wounds. He called me to say, "I was a Viet prisoner for three hours. They released me with a note for Colonel de Castries."

I let the command post know, and they sent an officer along. In this note the Viets named an hour at which we could pick up our wounded, whom they had left at Beatrice. Toward noon, Le Damany, wearing a mauve cap and with an armlet bearing a red cross on his left arm, went off in one of the medical service's jeeps. But there were only two or three wounded to bring back. It was some kind of tryout, with what object we could not tell.

A few moments later, Méhay told me that the Third Field Surgical Unit was going to descend by parachute on the Isabelle emergency airfield toward three o'clock.

At three I was at the command post to follow the operation. I saw a Dakota spiraling slowly down. I got close to Major Guérin, who was talking to the pilot. Then our guns started firing, which would certainly provoke a counter-barrage from the Viets.

I could hear the pilot saying: "Hello, I'm coming down six hundred feet, and they're bailing out now."

"But the Surgical Unit is to drop at Isabelle, not here," I quickly intervened, but already it was too late.

Eight parachutes were in fact already opening and swinging slowly down, while at the same time the Viet counter-barrage had started. I stepped quickly back inside the command post. The eight figures dangling from the parachutes dropped right in the middle of the barbed wire, where shells were also falling. It would be sheer luck if they all managed to get out of there.

The first of them were only a few yards away. They got clear of their harness, saw us, and ran breathless into the command post.

Lieutenant Rézillot of the medical service was a tall, thin man, very likeable. Bergeron and Gindrey had already spoken very highly of him. I took him back to the field hospital, followed by two of his medical orderlies; the rest were due to arrive half an hour later. Among them was Jeannot, a sergeant major whom I had known for a long time, a veteran of field hospital work, a man who could not be bettered. His inflexible courage and strength of will were masked by an air of surprising youthfulness.

Twenty minutes more and the whole team was off in a truck which had brought me a load of wounded from Isabelle. There had been a sprinkling of shells there in the course of the night, but not quite so many as we had.

Gindrey was hard at work with his team in the operating room. He still had ten amputations to get through.

In the morning at eight o'clock, a Beaver had landed and brought twelve pints of blood, but no penicillin or streptomycin. So I went back to the command post to see Major Guérin, to ask if there was any hope of more planes that day.

"Out of the question," he told me. "The runway is smashed and has to be repaired. Besides, did you see how little room there was even for the Beaver this morning? Tomorrow, possibly."

Back in the field hospital, I had to consider how to make room for the evening's intake. Le Damany offered me ten beds in his place; Rondy had three. Déchelotte was not with his battalion; he was at Gabrielle. But his orderly told me he had room for ten. By five I was ready to take on some twenty wounded, but I dared not think of an influx on the scale of the night before.

I had already taken possession of two shelters belonging to the Airborne Commandos, but the scouts and agents they had out in the mountains had returned to their base after the attack began. I could hardly drive away these agents' families, who were quartered in other shelters. Where could they go?

Julot handed me the phone: "Hello, this is Gabrielle. Will you send an ambulance—Dr. Déchelotte has just been wounded."

Twenty minutes later he appeared, his head wrapped in dressings, fragments all over him—not serious, but it would mean an X-ray, as they had to be removed, and a few stitches. "You know," he said, "it's not very funny up there; you just can't stick your nose out of doors. That's what I tried to do, and you can see the results for yourself . . . The Viets have been making trenches all night, right up to our forward positions. There are a lot of them. I believe they're going to make a great effort tonight."

So there was no doctor left at Gabrielle. I got in touch with Le Damany, who could not spare another doctor but supplied a Legionnaire sergeant, an Austrian medical student. He would have to take up the duties of battalion doctor at Gabrielle.

Next I went down into the clearing station, where there were still two banks of earth unoccupied by stretchers. Everything had gone well. The Vietnamese orderlies had done a good job. Suddenly there were a series of whistlings over our heads, one after another, six explosions in a row, followed by more whistling. What was to be done? The orderlies and wounded turned their eyes in my direction, and although I would very much have liked to make my escape, I managed to have a look at one or two wounds and then go slowly out into the trench which led to the emergency-treatment room. But tomorrow the command post would really have to come to a decision about that roof.

Whistlings and explosions followed each other without respite; it was just like the day before. Orderlies, coolies, men with minor injuries who had been outside, quickly regained the shelters. In the clearing station nobody moved, because there was nowhere to go.

This barrage seemed to me worse than that of the day before; nor was I wrong. Our guns replied—the 155's, the 105's, the 120's, not far off on our right. Then the Viet counter-barrage answered back with a terrifying concentration of power. How many guns did they have, anyway? The din was fearful: ten projectiles exploded on our roof at the same moment, and suddenly I heard an unusual sound, a sharp crack followed by a muffled thud, a noise which put me in mind of a stone rebounding on the rocky bed of a river; then the ground beneath one's feet shook. I had never heard anything like it before.

The first wounded were not long in coming, as before, straight to us, without going to their own first-aid posts. What could be done? They came in and collapsed at once. My team got to work; already they had the gestures of medical orderlies who are veterans at the job.

Orders flowed from my lips like a litany: "Phenergan, Dolosal, Adrenoxyl, antitetanus toxoid, antigangrene." Lachamp was always beside me, using his book of counterfoils and keeping the record up to date.

The phone rang just as before with doctors informing me of eight, ten, forty wounded. The vehicles were all out, bringing back Legionnaires from Claudine and Huguette, paratroopers from the runway and more from Eliane, Thais from their Second Battalion, Algerian infantry. Once more they were piling up.

A long line of men came into the passage, ten coolies. A shell had exploded in the middle of a group of workers. Soon six stretchers arrived, revealing six creatures black with dust, with an arm or a leg literally torn off, terror in their eyes, a wide-open mouth struggling to articulate sounds, a hand feeling for something that wasn't there. The tall fellow with a black beard beneath his chin who came with them was a medical orderly, and I heard his calm voice saying, "I don't know what the trouble is, sir. They're a funny sort of shell, these, going down into the ground and only exploding six or seven seconds later." That was the noise I had heard a little while before.

"They're delayed-action shells," an artillery lieutenant explained to me. He too had had a shelter collapse on him, but had escaped with no more than severe bruising.

Next came paratroopers from the Eighth Assault and the First Foreign, North African engineers, Senegalese gunners, Vietnamese, Thais. The clearing station was full up. I had Major Martinelli put into Lieutenant Gindrey's shelter. But still they came, more and more of them, a lieutenant, a captain, a string of coolies, helping one another along. Shells were whistling, ten or more at a time, exploding all at once. The shelters were full, and fresh arrivals no longer even had room to lie down.

"Put them in the X-ray room—we can get four in there."

The next order was, "Put them in the emergency-treatment room—we can squeeze a few more in there."

Ten minutes later I found myself wedged between the phone and Lachamp's desk. A Vietnamese with the upper jaw broken had collapsed at my feet and was grasping my legs with his arms. Each time he breathed he spat blood, and his eyes reflected his terror.

Two paratroopers were sitting on the blood refrigerators. One of them had a wound in his left shoulder, where the white bone was visible in the crushed tissue. The other had his left arm smashed and was trying with his good hand to support the forearm, which was already dead and inert. If they were to lie down, we would be done for; it would be impossible to get in or out without stepping on them. So I passed a wide bandage in front of them and fixed it to the walls, hemming them in.

The next order was, "Use the operating room." I had to put a stop to operations. God help us!

The first thing was to protect the wounded from the shells, which were falling worse than ever.

The operating room was soon full up. Screams, cries, groans, and the ringing of the phone, all mingled with the unholy din outside, filling my ears so that I could no longer even think. From that moment I was no longer aware whether it was day or night, whether I was hungry or thirsty, whether I was a living human being or only a character in a nightmare.

On top of all this, there were at least fifty cases demanding immediate treatment, and I only had four pints of blood left. I needed three hundred million units of penicillin and had only fifty million left.

I remembered having heard someone say: "Gabrielle has fallen. Anne-Marie has been abandoned."

Was that important? What did strategy or the number of Viets killed in the barbed wire around Gabrielle matter to me? Because this little fellow from Montpellier lying on a stretcher in the X-ray room was going to die; because there was blood spurting up into my face from a hole in this thorax and I couldn't stop it; because this abdomen, which was as hard as stone, belonged to a Legionnaire who told me: *"Ich bin fertig, ich weiss"*—"I'm done for, I know"; because this little Vietnamese's dark eyes were full of reproach as he asked me why I had cut his leg off. . . .

I knew it was morning when Jimmy said gently, "You're very tired, major. Drink this coffee." There was silence all around—silence, because some were dead and others asleep. When I saw Gindrey's face as he appeared in front of me, I realized that I too must look just like that.

5.

The Days That Followed

The main passage was nothing but a long line of poor wretches piled up behind one another. In my own shelter four officers were sleeping like logs.

Laboriously, by taking great strides over the bodies spread on the ground, I made my way to the end of the passage. God had been merciful, for at least no shell had fallen in that. Gindrey's shelter was crammed, and a horrible stench emanated from it. In the shelter where the electric plants were you could see nothing, apart from the one engine which was working all the time, except bloodstained dressings showing up on dusty combat uniforms. Here and there I noticed a sorry figure with the mouth open and the eyes closed. The men's sleeping and eating quarters were just as crammed as everywhere else; so was the mess. In the trenches there were a row of men asleep, wrapped in mats or blankets.

The clearing station presented a similar spectacle; I considered the men crowded in there, beneath a canvas roof as full of holes as a strainer, all the way to the steps leading up to the north entry, close to the crossways.

Among this crowd I noticed a thigh open all the way with an absurd field dressing stuck over it; a head with the eyes bandaged and a couple of hands gesticulating in the air, searching for some human contact; a leg which stopped short suddenly just above the ankle; a naked torso, such as a sculptor might model, but as battered as a statue of Praxiteles' freshly dug up out of the rubble. There were no longer any screams of pain, but only slow, gentle groans like a song full of sadness.

When I went up to the terrace, I found that a coolie had deposited a bin of used dressings outside the passage, and sticking grotesquely out of this bin was a leg with its toes pointing toward the sky. Everything was quiet again, as on the previous morning, but there were lines of stretchers, the bearers bringing in wounded who had escaped from Gabrielle—yet few enough of them, not much over forty.

Suddenly, from Gabrielle itself, which I thought was quite dead, there sprang up a series of flashes and explosions, fresh signs of destruction, and the rattle of machine-gun fire. Our artillery went into action, making me think at once of the Viet counter-barrage.

In the emergency-treatment room I rang Le Damany to ask him, "Haven't you a place or two to spare? Here we've reached our limit; I can't admit another one."

"You can send me ten wounded. I'm just going to ask for the messes to be cleared. Then I can take another thirty."

"What's up in the Gabrielle direction? We thought they had had it."

"It's a counterattack, old man: the First Foreign Paratroops, the Eighth Assault, and the tanks."

I ordered the ambulances at once, to evacuate twenty wounded who had received treatment to the Ninth Group. I sent off those who had limbs in casts, thorax cases whose wounds had been sutured, and those with large superficial wounds.

Lahcen, Larbi, and Sioni were at the end of their tether. They had been driving over the tracks all day and all night, with shells bursting all around them. Sioni had done marvels with our jeep. From Eliane he went right across to Gabrielle, then to Huguette, just when the Viets were laying down their barrage. He was constantly straddled with fire, one shell to the right, another to the left, one in front. He smiled as he told me about it and was quite ready to set out again. Already numbers of wounded men owed their lives to him.

Next came soldiers injured in the course of the counter-attack; there was no more space in the emergency-treatment room, so they would have to go in the shelters. Not in the first ones, where the serious operated cases were, nor in the main passage, which was full. There was still room for three in the X-ray shelter, so I went with the stretchers and put them myself on the apparatus and to right and left of it. There were a North African, a coolie who was carrying ammunition, and a Legionnaire. I examined them and found one of them with a tourniquet; he would have to be put close to the operating room.

Then I went back to the emergency-treatment room. I was hardly inside when there was a muffled explosion, such as happens when you drop a lighted match into a pool of gaso-line; then the violence of the blast shook the walls. I caught hold of one of the logs in the shelter. Then a bluish smoke came from the direction of the X-ray room; it was blinding and had an infernal stench. The sink which was fixed to the wall of the operating room crashed to the ground.

I went forward to the crossways and found another huge cloud of smoke coming to meet the other, while shouts and cries were heard on all sides: "Help, help! Orderlies, this way!"

My orderlies left the wounds they were dressing, and our neighbors from the Second Group and the Eighth Assault came up at the double. Figures appeared like ghosts in the smoke.

Two delayed-action 105 shells had fallen at the same moment, one in the X-ray room, the other in the end shelter. The X-ray room was demolished, as if an earthquake had struck it; a huge beam had been flung right across to the entry of the operating room. Earth and rubble of every kind had covered up the three wounded men I had just been looking at. We tried to get them out with our hands, tearing our nails, tugging at the thick planks.

"Quick, or they'll be suffocated! Get a spade!"

One was still breathing; the second had had his forehead smashed down into his jaw—he was dead; the third had had his leg broken, as had the other survivor.

The same efforts to clear away the mass of rubble were going on in the end shelter, which presented an even more terrifying spectacle. Only three men had survived out of the twelve who had undergone operations; the others were all dead. I came upon a face wedged between a beam and the ground and raised the eyelid—no reflex. "Leave him, he's dead."

Another by his side in the rubble, who had had an operation on his head, also had a discharge card pinned to his dressing: EVACUATE TO HANOI—URGENT AND IMMEDIATE. He was dead. He was a young fellow from the North of France. We had agreed to meet someday at the Café Jean in Lille.

I had the search stopped, as it was no longer any use. Twenty more wounded came in from the north entrance to the passage. Those able to walk groped their way along the walls and without meaning to do so knocked against their comrades lying on the ground in the passage, causing groans, oaths, and cries of pain.

I was forced to sit down, for the simple reason that my legs gave way. I seemed to have reached the most acute point of a suffering greater than I had ever known before.

Father Heinrich was at hand. Since the thirteenth he had administered the last sacrament more than two hundred times. He put a hand on my shoulder. I was not sure I wasn't going to cry. No, I had to be off to the command post. Something had to be done; but as soon as I got inside, I realized that nothing could be done. All the same, I made the attempt: "Can't you get a truce? Or have a village declared neutral? Or let me have a section of engineers at once? And what about planes?"

"Planes? It may be possible this afternoon."

So I had to get back to the field hospital, where Gindrey and his team had not yet moved out of the operating room. I shuddered at the thought that the shell might have fallen on them instead of exploding in the X-ray room, and that consoled me a little. Then the phone rang to say, "At three this afternoon another surgical unit is going to make a parachute drop, the Seventh Unit."

At three o'clock there was a repetition of the previous day's scene with the Third Unit, the drop being made at six hundred feet, and I seemed to hear the whistle of bullets in the air at the same time—then they too tumbled into the barbed wire, with one shell to the right of them and another to the left.

Lieutenant Vidal was the first to reach the hospital, a burly and muscular man of medium height, fair-haired and blue-eyed. He was not at all out of breath and had a really splendid smile. Then came the rest of his team, seven altogether, all veterans. They increased the confidence of my own men, who were very pleased to see them. After I had briefly sketched the position up to date and introduced them to Gindrey, I went over to the command post to discuss quarters for Vidal and his men.

The staff wanted to put them in with my teams, which would mean three teams working on the orthodox pattern, one resting, one clearing cases, one in the operating room.

Major Grauwin

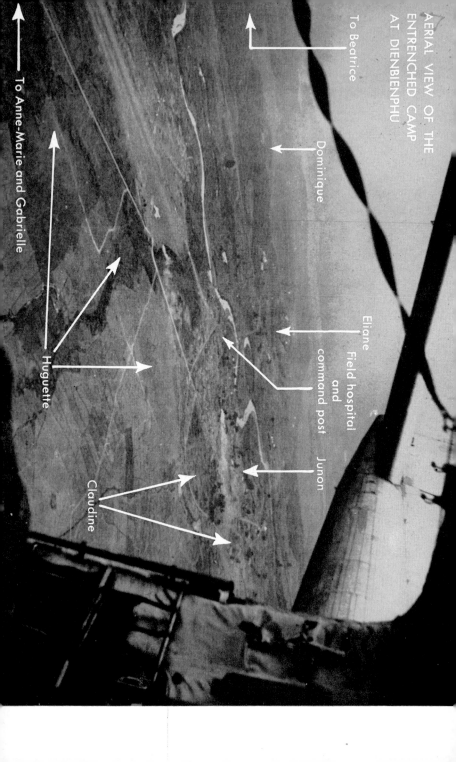

AERIAL VIEW OF THE ENTRENCHED CAMP AT DIENBIENPHU

To Beatrice

Dominique

Eliane

Field hospital and command post

Junon

To Anne-Marie and Gabrielle

Huguette

Claudine

Paratroops wounded on the last opening up of the road. In the foreground a Vietnamese killed in the fighting is being carried away.

Wounded crowded into one of the field hospital shelters during the Gabrielle attack

Wounded in the field hospital's main passage, waiting to go into the clearing station

The helicopter has just landed. An orderly is waving a Red Cross flag. For once, perhaps the Viets will not fire?

A 105 delayed-action shell has exploded in the X-ray shelter. It is a total wreck.

View of the field hospital roof after the mid-March attacks. Engineers are roofing the main passage.

But I wanted to have Vidal on the left bank of the Nam-youm. It was dangerous having to bring wounded across the bridge; and an attack on the Dominiques and the Elianes had also to be kept in mind. If there were numbers of wounded, the new team could act as a clearing station, which would very greatly ease matters for me. After a few minutes' discussion, my plan was agreed to.

Back in the field hospital, I rang Barraud and asked him to find a place for the unit. Some hundred and fifty yards from his infirmary there was a local command post which had been abandoned; it was covered with metal plates and sandbags, which was what we wanted. Vidal went off there with his team. The supplies dropped with him were picked up and would follow him in a few minutes. As Barraud was there, I had nothing to worry about, for Vidal would find him an admirable colleague, thoughtful and helpful. There would be a communication trench between the infirmary and the new operating unit. It was a pity that only thirty beds could be got into the old command post. But Barraud would have a few neighboring shelters cleared and alter his own infirmary to aid the work of the unit.

Julot called me to the phone; the shells were raining down again. "Hello, Grauwin? This is Guérin. There's a good deal of stuff being dropped by parachute for you—beginning now and going on tomorrow morning. Also you're to get ready a truckload of wounded to go to the airfield. A plane will be landing, as the runway is now repaired."

I could have shouted for joy. At last! I called to N'Diaye, Lachamp, and the regimental police who had been turned into stretcher bearers: "Follow me and I'll point out to you the forty wounded who will be on their way to Hanoi in a few minutes."

The work was done and the forms written out in a moment —Lachamp had never done his office work with such a will. Then the phone rang again. "As soon as the aircraft flies over,

you will give the order for your trucks to move off. In this
way the plane will land at the same moment as your wounded
reach the runway, we'll waste no time, and the Viets won't be
able to find the range."

The seriously wounded were put into the ambulance, the
less seriously into a truck. The Dakota appeared six hundred
feet up: "O.K., start!"

We had fixed up a huge Red Cross flag with sheets that we
had cut up and painted with mercurochrome, just like the
ones here on the roof of my field hospital. The largest was
close to the entrance.

The vehicles slowly moved off from the platform and got
a couple of hundred yards away when suddenly I saw shells
falling on the runway. What could be done? The trucks had
gone; how could they be called back? But N'Diaye was in
charge of the operation, and I had confidence in him. But
what would the plane do? I saw it describe a large arc and
regain height. I dashed to the phone: "Hello, air support?
What's the next move?"

"The pilot saw the explosions and was unable to land. I'm
telling him to go back . . ."

The pace of the explosions increased, and our vehicles
were on the airfield, in a cloud of dust and smoke. The walking wounded hurried to the trenches. A shell to the right, a
shell to the left, and then the blast; it was warming up. N'Diaye,
Lachamp, and Déry, one of the regimental police, looked up
at the sky and saw no sign of a plane. They told the wounded
to get back to the vehicles—and quick, for they had to return
to the field hospital.

I saw them come back straddled by the Viet shells, which
fell with terrible accuracy. When they reached the field hospital, I heard an explosion though there was no whistling,
then another, and another . . . They were firing at us. "Get
the wounded into the shelters," I called out.

The walking wounded were soon inside, but the ones on

stretchers were still in the vehicles. They had to be got out. It was then that I discovered how many brave men—I was going to say "heroes"—there were among my staff; my heart was filled with pride.

Half a dozen times this fearful operation had to be repeated. Roux was taken out of my shelter seven times, Major Martinelli four times. And taking stretchers along narrow trenches, where wounded men are lying on the ground, is killing work. The wounded themselves were at the end of their tether and had to be kept going with injections of camphor, morphine, and anything else we could think of.

The Viets waited diabolically for the ambulance to begin on its way to the plane and then began firing, for they too had heard the conversation between Major Guérin and the pilot.

"Here's the plane. Get the wounded into the vehicles."

But shells were falling on the road only a few yards away, on the morgue too, or rather on what had now become the field of the dead. Once more the wounded were reluctant to leave their shelters. The Dakota came down, but finding no ambulance, went off again. I was terribly discouraged.

"Just try once more," Major Guérin urged, "and we'll see how it goes. It will be the last time."

And then the miracle happened: forty wounded were taken off. A second plane had even succeeded in landing.

The departure of this second plane was highly dramatic. Straddled by shells, the plane was likely to be hit at any moment; loading up was almost finished, and the pilot had not slowed down his engines—and he took off. Wounded men who were clinging to the fuselage in a mad hope of escaping from this hell were flung to the ground by the suddenness of the departure.

Things like that could not be allowed to happen again. I rang Major Léost, who suggested a section of Legionnaires to police these evacuations the next time. There was no help for it; serious steps had to be taken.

I returned to the emergency-treatment room, where the beds were all occupied and in the stretchers on the ground there were bleeding bodies which gave vent to groans. Gindrey, with his team, was busy cutting, sawing, carving, nipping, and tying up. He had already done twenty-three amputations and operated on seven abdomens. Twenty-three amputations: that's about the number I did in the whole of 1950.

More wounded came; the stretcher bearers, N'Diaye, Bacus, and the Vietnamese orderlies got them into the clearing station and sent the more serious cases for immediate intravenous therapy.

From the main passage came a joyous shout, "Parachutes, major!" And there they were issuing out of the black hole in the Dakota, where the dispatcher was making large gestures in our direction, packages dangling on parachutes of every color. The Viets were resting and not a shell fell, which was most unusual; the packages were quickly got together and opened at once. The speed of Lachamp, Cortés, and Sioni had to be seen to be believed; they are a trio never to be forgotten.

We discovered penicillin, streptomycin, and blood—eight pints of blood packed in ice—morphine and plaster, in fact almost everything I had asked for. We congratulated one another and shook hands in our excitement. Some dozen wounded would be saved from death that evening.

Then I heard shouts from Levasseur. He had just unearthed from one container a large bottle full of a greenish liquid, with a label pasted on the side of it: "Best absinthe, from the staff here to the surgical unit at Dienbienphu."

But we still had another great trial before us. The shells had begun to fall again very close at hand, in salvos of from ten to fifteen at a time. They were 120's, as was evident both from their explosions and from the amount of blast which followed them; I could feel the earth quaking. Listen now, that one wasn't far off.

Suddenly N'Diaye appeared in front of me, eyes popping

out of his head, mouth open, as he tried in vain to speak, simply pointing toward the passage. He went off and I followed him: "It's the clearing station, major—a 120 shell."

When I reached the passage leading to the clearing station, I was confronted with a thick cloud of smoke, while on the ground, scattered in confusion, wounded men, naked, their dressings ripped open, crawled toward us. There were yells, curses, and cries for help, smoke which got into the throat, dust which got into the eyes—and in the clearing station itself there was a scene of real horror.

The whole of the canvas roof on the east side had been destroyed; the shell had burst just on the edge of the dugout where fifty wounded were confined, on the banks of earth and between them, and all along the central gangway. Sunshine poured in through the huge rent in the roof, revealing a heap of bloodstained parachutes, broken stretchers, limbs that had been torn off, and broken flasks. All over the place there were splashes, pools, and spurts of blood; it was a massacre.

Near the actual crater no movement was visible. They were all dead; I counted fourteen of them. At the southern exit the heap was stirring: "Help! Help! Major!"

N'Diaye and the men with him, Sioni, Cortés, Bacus, my whole staff, rushed forward and began the work of rescue. The Eighth Assault and other friends close at hand sent reinforcements. The survivors were taken toward the emergency-treatment room—but where were they going to be housed?

Among the dead was one of my orderlies, Bong, killed outright. I leaned over him and closed his eyes. Clasped in his fist there was a glass syringe, the needle still in it. There were two more orderlies among the wounded.

As soon as the last survivor had been extricated from the cataclysm, I called a halt to the search. Other shells might soon be falling.

Back in the emergency-treatment room the whole staff had

stopped work, overcome, paralyzed. Some were quietly crying. Minh, who had been Bong's friend, was sobbing on Father Heinrich's shoulder. Some of them stared at me, others at the ground, dulled by the shock. Suddenly I felt a surge of rebellion and despair engulfing me. No—that wouldn't do.

"Now then, can't you see that man's bleeding?" I called out. "Good God, Perez, why aren't you replacing that empty bottle of plasma? Minh, have you given an injection of streptomycin to that cranial case? Get a move on!"

They all fell back into their routine, like toys that start moving again once their spring has been wound up.

I had to go to the command post, where there was the usual bustle. Colonel de Castries was silently smoking with his back to the door. I told Major Léost and Captain Méhay of what had been happening with us, which caused consternation. Méhay gripped my hand as he said, "Cheer up, doc, we've still got a lot of work coming your way."

Major Léost promised me the engineers the very next day, and I went back to the field hospital with this comforting news. Intravenous therapy had given good results, and Perez reported the blood pressures to me. I asked Deudon to make a special effort with the dinner. I decided to have some rum issued. I phoned the supply column, where a lieutenant was a friend of mine: there would be beer for the wounded that evening and thirty cases of Vinogel.*

Julot told me, "There's hardly any gas left for the electric plant." So I rang Major Léost and learned that there was some at the workshops. Sioni went off for it at once.

We had to operate all night, right on to dawn, cutting away, sawing off above the knee or below it, slicing into the biceps, making the saw grate on the humerus, disjointing a hand; a chest wound, which wheezed and gurgled, had to be sutured; and the lucky ones who could keep their arms and legs had to be encased in plaster. So the calls went out:

* A tonic wine. (Translator's note.)

"Catgut 1, catgut 2."

"An injection of Reverdin."

"Take care of his breathing."

"Quick, some strychnine there."

"A little oxygen here."

"Wipe my forehead."

"Bring me some coffee."

Shells were exploding from time to time, ten or twenty of them in a salvo. But we no longer heard anything. In the shadows around the entrance I could make out the faces of friends from the Second Airborne, the Eighth Assault, the command post.

They were staring, but what were they thinking about? At times I was aware of their eyes on the back of my neck. Then when I raised my eyes I saw a spark, a sudden warmth of sympathy in theirs.

We stopped at five in the morning for an hour's rest. Jimmy brought us some excellent coffee, boiling hot. Sioni and his orderlies took it around to the wounded. Since the day before we had taken over four of the Airborne Commandos' shelters; thirty wounded were quartered there, but they were cut off from us and the way over there had its dangers.

Then someone said, "The engineers have turned up." They proved to be a complete section of Moroccans under the command of Lieutenant Maury, whose face showed signs of fatigue; he was another who had not had much sleep. While the shells were still falling, he had repaired more than ten shelters which had collapsed. When I showed him mine, he was unable to control a gesture of horror; then I showed him the passage which was open to the sky.

"Tomorrow, major," he told me, "it will all be finished."

He got to work at once, and I put all my coolies under his orders. The first thing to be done was to get out the poor men who were buried in the ruins. The heat of the sun had already half rotted them, and the stench was appalling. They were quickly wrapped in shrouds and given discharge cards, with their names penciled on them—discharge to the morgue.

But the morgue presented an even more frightful spectacle. By now there were nearly three hundred corpses littering the whole area in front of the helicopter, which was still there on its landing stage with a propeller broken. Flies swarmed by the thousands, huge purple ones.

The men who brought the bodies here, under shellfire, were in a hurry to get away and dumped their burdens as best they could. Some were on the roof of the mess, some on that of the sterilizer shelter, some in the men's sleeping quarters.

So I rang Major Léost, who said, "Yes, doc, I get it. I'll send a fatigue party along." A couple of hours later, I got a standing order, issued to all units: "In future men killed in battle will be buried where they fall."

At two in the afternoon a team of coolies came along and took the dead off to long trenches which had been opened up by a bulldozer some six hundred yards away. While this task of burial was going on, the Viets were finding the range with their 75's, which meant more dead and more wounded.

When I got back, I rang Vidal, who told me, "Everything is going fine, major. Barraud is a good guy. If you've got too much on your hands, send some along to me."

Next I rang Le Damany to ask for fifteen more beds at his place. "Okay," he agreed, "but I suggest that you send the wounded back to their battalion doctors once they've been operated on and are out of danger."

So I got into touch with all the battalion doctors. They agreed to ask the commanding officer of their battalion to give up messes and depots which had a proper shelter roof.

At four I got a call from Major Guérin: "We're fixing up an evacuation by air with Dakotas and helicopters. Two helicopters are coming down, one at your place and one at Le

Damany's. And there may be one at Vidal's. I'll ring you again."

The main passage was to be covered with a sheet of metal taken from where the fighters were, supported by logs, the whole to be covered with four feet of earth. We would have an electric bulb every five or six yards.

The fighters were nearly all destroyed. One or two had got away. There was nothing left of the Moranes to the east of the runway except one blackened hulk. One Dakota had been torn to shreds. The helicopter, which had been parked near the fighters, was lying on its side. The Vietminh artillery had sounded the knell for aviation at Dienbienphu.

A series of whistlings and explosions echoed around us, and the engineers dashed to the shelters. They had already repaired the end shelter, and the X-ray room had been rebuilt with sections from a Bailey bridge; now its roof was really reassuring. It would be our supply room and dispensary. Cortés and Sioni would stock it up with as many supplies and medicines as we could get in.

There was a ring from Major Guérin to say, "The first helicopter is on its way and will land at your place."

I got the ten wounded men ready in the main passage with stretcher bearers to rush them to the airfield.

Le Damany suggested that I should put a man out a few seconds before the machine came down to wave a red cross flag, which the Viets could see with their field glasses. Possibly they wouldn't fire then.

The helicopter came down. Julot waved the flag as hard as he could. "Quick now, you stretcher bearers. The ones who have to lie down first, then those who can sit."

Filoche was at last aboard, Filoche who had lost both his feet and who had already been taken to the airfield seven times.

Suddenly there was a whistle and an explosion on the river bank. "Hurry," I called out. There was another whistle and an explosion on the ridge where the men acting as police were. The pilot revved up his engine, the propellers turned more rapidly, raising a cloud of dust, and the machine gained height, gliding along the river. It was high time, for a few seconds later five shells burst exactly on the spot he had just left. We dashed back into the shelters.

The machine which was due to land at the Ninth Group was less lucky. The Viets got the range of the landing stage and he had to go off without landing; one of the wounded, waiting on a stretcher, was killed.

Soon it was evening; the engineers had already covered half the passage. There were twelve operations to be done, which would keep us busy until daybreak. Some one said, "Tomorrow, the road to Isabelle is going to be opened up." Rézillot was to send us fifty wounded who had been treated and operated on, in the hope of getting them evacuated to Hanoi. Opening the road would mean more wounded.

This prophecy was justified. At ten in the morning some thirty stretchers appeared, men from the Third Foreign, whom it was easier to send here. Among them was a medical orderly who had had both clavicles fractured by a bullet, a wound which I had not come across before. When the débridement and the tidying up had been finished, there were no clavicles left at all. His reaction was, "Oh, well, at least I can still walk."

The trucks laden with the wounded from Isabelle were able to get through. These told us: "Shells by the hundreds, but no serious infantry attack. One helicopter was damaged; a shell exploded under it just as it was taking off. Lieutenant Gambiez, who was one of the wounded being evacuated in it, was killed; and the pilot, Lieutenant Bartier, had to have his leg taken off."

Bartier was another veteran. I had known him long ago when he was piloting a Morane of the medical service. He was a sergeant then, and he had evacuated hundreds. He knew all the landing grounds in Indochina. He was lodged in one of the command post shelters while waiting to be evacuated.

N'Diaye called me outside to say, "Look, major, your jeep is full of shell splinters."

Our vehicles, which were parked at the bottom of the slope, had been brought back to the terrace because the "mortuary field" down below had taken up all the available space. The upper parts of the trucks and ambulances were riddled like sieves, but fortunately the engines were still untouched. But we had to find another place to park them or they would be destroyed.

I rang up Le Damany, and we agreed that the medical-service vehicles should park behind the earth walls at the Ninth Group's quarters, where they would be out of view. I would only keep one jeep, which we could camouflage behind the mess.

Major Guérin rang up in the afternoon to ask me to get ready for another evacuation similar to the one of the day before. The plane was due at four; if all went well, six more planes were to follow. The section of the Legion down to police the evacuation was held in readiness.

At four we were ready and waiting, the ambulances with their engines running. The wounded had been selected and given their cards, and everything was ready for a speedy get-away. We heard a purring in the air, and there came a ring from Major Guérin: "Here you are—jump to it."

But the Viets were on the watch, and they missed nothing. They waited until the plane was on the ground, and then some thirty shells fell in thirty seconds. With its engines roaring, the plane moved along the runway and took off at record speed. The walking wounded had scattered to the trenches. They had to be picked up one by one and brought back under shellfire. N'Diaye and Lachamp asked for a respite—and so did the wounded: "Major, it's no longer a practical proposition."

Major Guérin summoned me to the command post. "We won't try any more evacuations in daylight," he told me. "But this evening and tomorrow evening we'll try evacuation under cover of darkness. We'll take the wounded in turn from you, from Le Damany, and from Vidal."

The idea was that a Dakota should fly over Dienbienphu six hundred feet up. While it was doing this, another Dakota, with its engines more muffled, was to land on the runway, aided by beacons at a few points which would be camouflaged from view of the Viets. Midnight was the hour agreed on.

Le Damany had the job of coordinating evacuations from the three different points. We learned from him that a helicopter had succeeded in landing at the Ninth Group in the course of the afternoon and had managed to take away ten wounded.

At the hour arranged we listened for the purring noise which should be joining the sound made by the *Firefly*, which we trusted would abandon the dropping of its flares for the occasion. Then suddenly we distinguished the noise we were waiting for; and a few minutes later a truck and an ambulance, without lights, pulled up outside our west exit. They were quickly filled with wounded, and then I heard the sound of their engines die down in the darkness. Suddenly we were aware of something gliding over our heads—the Dakota. Then we waited in anxious silence: if everything turned out well, the whole business should be over in four or five minutes. The decoy plane did its job in the sky until suddenly, more immediately above us, we heard the characteristic sound of a Dakota gaining height: the trick had worked, and we had pulled it off. Then came a call from Major Guérin: "You heard it all, doctor? It went off perfectly. We'll do it again tomorrow."

The next day forty wounded were evacuated in this way, and the day after that forty more. And one evening Le

Damany told me that six planes were expected, which was wonderful. So forty wounded went off every evening, but twenty more were brought in during the night and morning. With six planes, however, something could really be done, and we were all filled with the wildest hopes.

At midnight we were once more on the alert. The first time, the second, and again the third, everything went according to plan, as in a film where every detail had been properly worked out. But on the fourth occasion there was a catastrophe: Huguette 6, the support post at the end of the runway, discharged a flare which revealed to the Viets the whole of the stratagem which we had constructed with such care. Thirty seconds later, shells were raining down on the runway. A fifth and a sixth plane were out of the question.

Could we go on with this dangerous game, now that the Viets had got wind of our scheme—would we be able to take them in again? The attempt had to be made anyhow.

One evening Le Damany wanted to make direct contact with the pilot, and he set off with a load of wounded, stretcher bearers, and a few Legionnaires. The plane came down, passing over us with the gliding motion which we had now learned to recognize—when suddenly there were loud explosions close at hand and the rattle of automatic weapons. What was going on? We soon knew when a man in flying uniform was brought to the emergency-treatment room on a stretcher; a large-caliber bullet had shattered both his knees. The Viets had simply arranged an ambush, and the radio operator had been killed. A bullet had gone right through the cabin, and there was some damage which had not yet been properly assessed. Our wounded man was the co-pilot. His wounds were serious, and he had to have an operation at once. Half an hour later, I found that both the joints were done for and would remain ankylosed.

There was also a flight nurse in the plane. Surprised and scared, she said, "I didn't know it was going to be like that."

At daybreak it was found that the damage to the cabin was not very serious and the plane took off, under cover of a morning mist and in the teeth of the Viets, carrying with it its killed or wounded crew and fifteen of my wounded as well.

I spent the rest of the night getting all those who had been operated on into the same shelter, aided by a few stretcher bearers and coolies. I tried to place together all those in casts and those who had undergone operations in the abdomen or limbs. This enabled me to free some fifteen beds; I now had thirty cleared, which was a great thing.

For the first time I gave Gindrey's team a rest by stopping work in the operating room at midnight. They lay down and were asleep in a tenth of a second.

In the morning we were greatly relieved to have the main passage entirely covered, from the west to the north entry. Now we could get to all our shelters without any difficulty, and the wounded could wait outside the rooms in which we were working. The sorting out could be done in the passage itself, as nothing was left of the clearing station. Now at least we were free from the dread of an explosion in that damnable passage.

I walked through it with great satisfaction; it was a joy to see the metal plates on the ceiling. The entrance would be covered up at night, and then we would be able to have an electric bulb at the end. But suddenly a man with a wound in the face rushed up to me and feverishly grasped my right hand. He was a tall man, fair-haired, in the uniform of a paratrooper. A great bloody hole had taken the place of his mouth.

Through the blood I could make out the two bars indicating his rank of lieutenant. His right hand still clasped mine, while his other pointed to the terrifying mess beneath his nose; he gurgled, but could not speak, and there is no word for the expression in his eyes.

"Come along." I took him off to the emergency-treatment

room. He was undressed on a cot, and needles went quickly into his thighs and arms. He calmed down but continued to watch me intently. I ought to know those eyes. Then Lachamp made out the card, "Lieutenant Démèzières, First Foreign Paratroops."

God, yes, I ought to have recognized him. He had sat beside me in the plane, the very plane which had brought me here, to Dienbienphu. In 1949 he had been at Major Secretin's mess, on a free evening when I was a guest. This was a fine beginning to his second term of service. "I've recognized you," I assured him. "Forgive me—but with all that blood . . ." He pressed my hand, and his expression was more peaceful; then his eyes closed.

The blood pressure was satisfactory; there was no immediate danger. But I did not like the gurgling sound in his throat; he was spitting long threads of bloody mucus. Drugs had little effect; he was still spitting and his forehead had the tinge of suffocation. "Quick, oxygen!" The gas was passed in by a rubber tube slipped into the nostril—no time for the inhaler. This brought a few minutes' respite, then signs of suffocation reappeared. It was evident that there was some obstruction in the larynx.

"Quick, get everything ready for a tracheotomy," was my next order. I made an incision in the skin at the base of the throat, between the two rings of cartilage, and seized the curved silver tube ending in a sharp trocar. I exerted pressure . . . that was it. Air drove along the new passage and forced out a great clot of coagulated blood, which was flung against my chest. Breathing became easier—and we breathed more easily too.

"Don't worry, all's well," I assured him. "You'll take the plane this evening, and in Paris they'll fix you up with a new face. You need have no anxiety. I'll meet you for a drink in the Champs Elysées in a month or so."

His eyes expressed the extent of his gratitude, and then he fell asleep.

Yes, the road to Isabelle had been opened up—and so had Démèzières' jaw.

Then there were more wounded, three Legionnaires, six paratroopers, fifteen engineers. Once more I was oblivious of time and space; at a given moment, Deudon might say, "Your meal is ready." Then I came out and swallowed a few sardines and a cup of hot coffee, but plunged back at once into my own universe, which was made up of shattered bone and blood.

Toward midnight Le Damany gave me a call: "The trucks are on their way to your place; the Dakota will be here in half an hour's time." So we got Démèzières onto a stretcher, an immense dressing over his shattered face.

I heard the plane come down and held my breath as I listened to it gliding past. Some seconds later came the sound of explosions—the Viets were still lying in wait. I could count about twenty shells falling. What was going to happen? Would the plane turn back? Then we would have to begin all over again. No, I could hear the Dakota's engines roaring over us, using all their power. How I thanked God for that!

The rest of the night was a bad dream, marked off by explosions every few minutes; but this nightmare had now become a habit, and it was prolonged into the day that followed, the day after, and the night.

Then toward eleven Le Damany rang: "Get sixteen wounded ready for half-past eleven."

Everything went smoothly—the truck, the loading, the plane gliding down, and the inevitable explosions. But we missed the triumphant sound of the engines exerting all their power. We were never to hear it again, not the next day, nor the day after, nor in all the days that were to come.

A quarter of an hour later a stretcher was brought into the passage escorted by airmen in flying uniform or in their blue uniform. On the stretcher lay a wounded Legionnaire, one of those policing the evacuation. "A splinter in the knee," he told me.

With him was Dupouich, a medical sergeant helping to convoy the wounded.

And in the background there was a young girl in blue, with a wing in gold on her breast, the flight nurse. It was not the one who had come a few days earlier. I recognized this one—her name was Geneviève de Galard.

6.

The Dominique Positions

There were to be no more planes: Major Guérin held out no hope of them. Never again would an aircraft land on the runway. The last machine, which had fallen into the trap last night, had caught fire this morning, and in a few seconds its fate was sealed.

At daybreak the crew had tried to repair it a little, but the morning mist dispersed earlier than usual and the mechanics had to scatter, chased by the Viet shells.

One wounded member of the crew was fated to remain with me until the end of the fighting. Now it was essential to prepare and organize additional hospital accommodation.

Le Damany already had a hundred wounded in his place, half of them on cots, half on stretchers. He had taken over the messes in his group and was slowly spreading into all neighboring shelters which were not actual fighting posts.

Battalion doctors had also enlarged their hospital accommodations by taking over messes and the men's rest quarters —which did not matter, as there was no longer any rest. Men slept when they could, beside their weapons, where they fought. Officers gave up individual shelters and spent the night on a mat on the ground in the command post.

Vidal only had room for thirty in his shelter, but he could also use the Second Thai Battalion's infirmary and some neighboring shelters; it was further understood that if he had too many, as often happened, he could send them on either to me or to Le Damany.

I too had to invade my neighbors' quarters. Colonel Langlais made it very simple: "Send me any officers who can walk; they can eat at my table, and perhaps they will be able to do a little work for me?"

His people were just the same. His N.C.O.'s said: "Send us any wounded N.C.O.'s. We'll squeeze up a bit and make room for them." And it was the same with the privates, so that the paratroop group made room for twenty-five altogether.

The central command post gave me its individual shelters. The staff there, officers and men, took their meals on their office tables.

I had already moved into five shelters of the Airborne Commandos. The Thais quartered in the main passage there were packed like sardines in a can. But I still had not enough room and needed more shelters cleared for my wounded.

De Carfort had got his battalion pioneers to build an extra infirmary. He could take fifty wounded under his own direct supervision, and another fifty in neighboring shelters under the supervision of his medical orderlies.

I visited all our shelters with N'Diaye, one by one, and we made room for another ten by arranging some cots like bunks on top of one another. While making this inspection we had a look at the roof, and then I realized how inadequate was the amount of earth heaped on the crossbeams and metal plates.

There was a huge heap of earth on the terrace which had come from the excavation of the clearing station and, if only the engineers could let us have a few thick planks, we could use this to strengthen our roof considerably.

I still had Fleury and my coolies, nor was there any lack of picks and shovels. Buezek supplied the heavy planks, and work began at once, to last until the thirtieth and the Dominique attack.

I often wondered where Fleury got the strength of character which made him such a reliable man. I have never seen anybody so cool and so contemptuous of danger. Day and night he would stand up on our roof, urging the coolies to work. He had no sympathy for laggards, sluggards, or cowards; he calmly watched shells explode without blinking.

Shells fell on the road, near the mess, on the Second Airborne, our neighbors; and every living creature vanished into some hole—except Fleury, who still stood erect, quite without fear. "Where are my coolies?" he would say. "Are you on leave? Come on there, snap out of it."

Then the coolies would emerge, giving him a frightened look such as one might direct to some powerful god who is superior to all earthly wounds.

After a few days the example he gave them produced its effect and, while the shells were falling, I could still make out the sounds of wheelbarrows, picks, and shovels at work on our roof.

An extra three feet of earth was spread on top, over and above the earth already there. Fleury would go off with Buezek at night toward the airfield runway and would return carrying on his back, apparently without effort, metal plates of a staggering weight.

He found crossbeams and thick planks in the ruins of shattered shelters, and trunks of trees on the river bank which nobody had dared to touch, believing them to be mined.

The main passage, the crossways of the central block, the emergency-treatment room, the operating room, all were covered with a double layer of rubble, separated by nearly six

feet of earth. This gave us an assurance of safety, at least for
the vital central section of our field hospital.

I realized that I owed a great deal to Fleury and that a considerable number of us, both the wounded and the medical
staff, owed our lives to him. When I was able to eat at normal
times I invited him to eat with me, and he stayed by my side,
calm as ever, not saying a word. Then one day I had an idea:
"When you've finished, Fleury, I would like to give you a
present." At once he began to protest. "No," I went on, "it's
not a present, it's simply a souvenir. I know you're alone in
the world, and I wouldn't like you to forget, in days to come,
that you've won our friendship and our respect. I'm going to
give you my signet ring."

I saw him flush with pleasure, but he did not utter a word.

Every morning we had a visit from a very remarkable person, Sergeant Stetter, from the Moroccan battalion which
held the central hill of the Dominique position. He came
down through the trenches on his hill, joined the road, crossed
the bridge, came to the field hospital, and then went on to
the command post to pick up his battalion's mail, with as
much ease and nonchalance as some stroller on a boulevard in
Paris. He was always gay and smiling, always in a good temper, spreading optimism wherever he went. Every morning
at eight o'clock I would hear his voice in the main passage:
"And the next morning, at eight o'clock, the duck was still
alive."

He could recite all Robert Lamoureux's stories without forgetting a single word, and the moment he arrived there would
be shouts of laughter from the wounded and the orderlies. His
visit meant a great deal to me, and I told Deudon always to
keep half a pint of wine for him, our issue of Vinogel it often
was.

There was also Sergeant Lasserre of Intelligence. He knew
all the little secrets and took part in the questioning of prisoners. We had nicknamed him "Lemmy Caution" after the

celebrated detective-story hero; his spirits were unfailing and his optimism unshakable, while his prophecies were very odd indeed.

When he said: "At two in the morning, there is to be an attack on such and such a hill," we could be quite sure of a peaceful night; and whenever he forecast a quiet night, then there would be a most hideous din.

Every day he would declare that the 308th Division was badly mauled, that the 312th Division had been wiped out, or that two Viet batteries had been destroyed. Every time he passed the shelters of the wounded, they never failed to call him over, and I am sure that more than one of the poor fellows went to sleep with optimism in his heart after hearing him. The next day they were disillusioned, but they had got a few hours' good sleep out of it. That is always a gain from a medical point of view.

Then there were the fellows of the Second Airborne, those close to Colonel Langlais, Patrice de Carfort's orderlies, Le Damany's Legionnaires, and "Julot's pal," Jupiter, of the command post message center.

All these men gave us a warmth of feeling which was frank and wholehearted; and their presence was a constant refreshment to us, buried alive in our hospital shelters.

Then a great day came, the twenty-eighth of March. The Viets from their hills to the east and west had advanced a trench toward the Isabelle road which had become a matter of grave concern for those in command. It was essential to gain control of this trench and reopen the road, which involved an operation in itself. It began at dawn.

I saw the armored cars go off, the Eighth Assault, the First Foreign Paratroops, and the battalions dropped by parachute to reinforce them a few days before, the Sixth Colonial Paratroops.

The barrage was terrific, and the Viets, surprised by a

clever move, forgot to send us their usual morning shells. There was tremendous confidence in the attack; it seemed that there had never been such an assault in Indochina before! In spite of our losses, the battalion commanding officers were in raptures about the way our men had fought.

The first wounded to reach us told us about the fighting: there had been a frontal attack, an encirclement, and then the trench was cut off, so that the Viets were caught like rats in a trap. Then the paratroops had delivered an assault which nothing could resist; two Viet battalions were wiped out and a considerable number of arms captured. By noon optimism had reached its height. Hope swept through the whole garrison.

On my side, I had some reason to be satisfied too. This battle cost us more than a hundred wounded. Vidal took the first brunt of it, acting as a clearing station, then swiftly evacuating to us the wounded, who had been provided with cards giving a valuable diagnosis in his own hand, which saved us a great deal of time and labor.

My ambulance drivers performed miracles; my orderlies worked indefatigably. The superficially wounded and less serious cases were passed on to Le Damany and the battalion infirmaries. All those seriously wounded received intravenous therapy and were got ready for surgery.

An hour after the last of the wounded had been brought in, the position was clearly defined and we knew exactly what operations had to be done. Gindrey and his team stood the test and performed sixteen major operations within twenty hours.

Our losses, though not numerous, were serious because they included some of our best men, and it was decided that in future the Isabelle road would have to remain closed . . . until there was a real change. Bloodshed on that scale could not happen every day, for the battles yet to come had also to be taken into account. Everyone was aware of that.

Rézillot had been able to send us some wounded to whom he had already given treatment. Through them I learned of the death of Lieutenant Rossini, who was killed by an anti-aircraft shell. Rossini had been on Major Grand d'Esnon's staff.

Ack-ack had in fact made its first appearance at Dienbienphu. While I was watching the planes in the sky, I had already heard whistlings in the distance caused by projectiles of some larger caliber. "A sniper," the orderlies used to say, but I had my doubts. Then one morning the ack-ack made its presence felt in a very tragic way.

Major Guérin had warned me that a considerable amount of material was to be dropped, including a number of containers destined for the medical service. So from daybreak we were straining our ears for the usual purring—and suddenly the sky was full of it, for a whole group of planes was taking part in the delivery. The packages began to fall briskly, and the company charged with getting them together was dashing all over the place. Sioni, at the wheel of the jeep, and Cortés with him brought back everything that was marked "Red Cross." Then the ack-ack got going. From north, east, and west a stream of bullets went up into the sky and a sudden flash ringed with black puffs of smoke showed up between the aircraft—the bursting of 37-millimeter shells.

This first ack-ack demonstration hardly lasted more than ten minutes, but one of the Dakotas flying between three and six hundred feet up was hit and crashed in flames a little beyond the Claudine positions. The crew, who had been burned, were afterward given a proper funeral. Meanwhile the rest of the planes went on with the drop, right down to the last package.

Sioni and Cortés had brought back thirty packages, which were a pleasant surprise to us, for they contained the complete equipment of an American field hospital, a real luxury:

three hundred pairs of blue pajamas, three hundred sheets, very light and delicate; pillows, folding cots, and every type of surgical instrument; hundreds of flasks of various anti-biotics; and a considerable quantity of hospital supplies which we had been without, as three hundred wounded are not normally provided for in the equipment of a surgical unit.

Julot went into rhapsodies over the magnificent white woolen blankets, the pearl buttons of the pajamas, and also the bottles of champagne which our Director had added to the consignment.

The champagne was at once given to those who had under-gone serious operations. In the evening we had our usual visitors, and after the last operation had been finished, they challenged Levasseur and Bacus to a game of *belote*, which took place in the main passage. This challenge cost the two lads from the Second Airborne something, for the stake was a bottle of brandy.

Everything seemed quiet enough outside, and Levasseur was just voicing a shout of triumph when suddenly some fifteen explosions echoed above our heads; then a few sec-onds' pause, then fifteen more, followed by a few which were more spaced out.

This trick of the Viets was a very effective one.

In the evening, toward ten o'clock, they stopped their harassing fire; people stayed in their shelters, but after twenty minutes risked having a glance outside; that tempted them to take a step or two as well as a glance, and those steps led them toward some neighboring shelter, and then their friends came out too. Why not smoke a cigarette together and chat over the events of the day? You could also profit by adding a few more sandbags to your roof, getting some supplies from your company command post, and making all those contacts which had not been made in the course of the day. Then suddenly from the horizon to the northeast would spring a series of flashes. Those who had kept close to their shelters had time to take cover. It was tough luck for the others.

And every time, in the half-hour afterward, some ten to fifteen wounded would show up in the passage:

"I was just making myself a cup of coffee."

"I had found three batteries for my torch."

"I was only washing my shirt."

"I had just come back from the canteen."

Levasseur, the most hard-boiled member of the team, used to say, "It's too quiet this evening. I'm not going out."

When he had to go out, he used to wait until a few shells had fallen, then pick up his steel helmet and go calmly off.

This evening this firing out of the blue had once more accounted for some wounded. I heard footsteps and gaspings coming at the same time from the west and north entrances. On the left I saw Foucras coming in, very pale and spitting blood, supported by men from the command post.

"It was only a few yards away," he said. "I was standing just in front of my shelter. Lieutenant Dutour was killed."

On the right I saw Boisbouvier, a young paratroop lieutenant with a large dressing on his right thigh.

We got Foucras half-seated on a bed in the emergency-treatment room. His breathing was difficult and halting; blood issued from his nose and the corners of his mouth. But his blood pressure was good.

"There you are, major," he said with a smile. "I've added to my collection of shell fragments—I've got them here." It is true that I found ten or more holes in the walls of his thorax. In a few minutes he was having the usual injections and going off to sleep under their influence.

Boisbouvier had been wounded that morning, a little hole on the inner side of the thigh. Rondy had fixed him up with a dressing which was not too constricting and sent him back to his company. His company commander was Lieutenant Bertrand, who had been killed beside him.

Then in the evening, only half an hour before, Boisbouvier had suddenly felt warm blood flowing down his leg. Lieutenant Rondy had said to him, "Get over to the field hospital at once."

Carefully I undid the dressing. The arterial pulse in the foot was beating regularly, just as well as in the other foot. It would be surprising if the femoral artery was affected. Rondy would have fixed a tourniquet; perhaps the femoral vein . . . ? That could wait; so I put on a tight dressing.

He was to keep it like that for three days; then I had another look. It had all cleared up. It was simply a superficial vein, and Boisbouvier was able to go back to his post on his own two legs. But he was to be back again, three more times.

While he was under observation, he had been put in with my N.C.O.'s, beside Lieutenant Rollin, from Boisbouvier's battalion, who had come in five days before with a compound fracture of the right leg, the projectile being still imbedded in it. I decided not to operate but to evacuate him to Hanoi, as the operation needed to be done with the aid of an X-ray screen. But an end had been put to all evacuations by air a couple of days before, and I had been obliged to operate. I had found no splinter, and the leg was slowly swelling, which caused me great anxiety.

Then Vidal was on the phone: "Major, I'm doing no more operations at the moment, as I have nothing sterilized at hand, and it will take another hour to get it all done. But I have an abdominal case which has been waiting since eight this morning. His blood pressure is good. May I send him along?"

"Why don't you come along yourself and operate on him with me?"

"Really? I didn't like to ask. I'd be particularly glad of your opinion too, as it's rather a difficult case."

Sioni went off with the jeep, returning a few minutes later with the wounded man, Vidal, and two of his orderlies. We went into the emergency-treatment room, where Gindrey joined us.

The wounded man was a little chap from the Paris district. His eyes were frightened, but the words which came to his lips were the typical chaff of the Paris suburbs. He was trying to be impudent: "Now they're messing around with my guts as if they were a bit of veal bought cheap at the market."

He brazened it out like a little tough—or rather, he pretended to be tough. He was quite right, for this was the only way he could face it. An officer would know how to be cool and phlegmatic; he could not manage that, so he did the best he could.

There was a little hole in the hypochondrium, the ill-defined region at the junction of the ribs and the abdomen. I palpated the abdomen, which remained soft, but there was pain, for I could feel the muscles contract. "I want to vomit," our patient said. He coughed and spat a little blood. The lung was certainly affected, but what about the abdomen? Was it necessary to open it and look?

A laparotomy which fails to show up any lesion can be done in a proper operating room, but here it was a luxury best avoided. It was at this moment that Patrice came in. He always looked in during the course of the evening or the night, always quiet, silent, and distinguished in his manner. I called him Patrice because "De Carfort" was too formal and "Carfort" too familiar, so I could only say "Patrice." But I wondered why I went out of my way to be as familiar as that.

At the end of ten minutes, we were all four agreed. Another ten minutes and Vidal and Gindrey were operating, while Patrice and I looked on.

"Wound in the pleura and the lung, wound in the spleen, injury to the small intestine, a slit in the stomach."

Then when I think that this extraordinary creature was pretending that he felt no pain!

And I have never seen a war wound operated on with so much skill and care, with so much tenderness—yes, that is the only word for it, tenderness!

While Gindrey was tying up the last of the bronze threads on the wall of the abdomen, there came a rumbling of explosions from the direction of Dominique. Five minutes later, the phone was ringing urgently, Vidal's orderly sergeant to say: "Lieutenant, you must come back at once; the Viets are shelling Dominique and Eliane 4. There are twenty wounded waiting right now."

Then, all of a sudden, between two explosions, I heard the sound of some automatic weapon which was new to me, a sound very easily distinguished, dying down slowly in a rhythmical reverberation. It was not the usual sound of an automatic weapon projecting from a shelter.

"It's a four-barreled affair," Lieutenant Rollin told me, "set up on the edge of the road leading to the airfield. Its four barrels are out in the open, and the man who fires it is lower down than with the ordinary type of automatic weapon. If it's firing now, it can only mean that the Viets are stirring around Dominique."

The Viets' harassing fire and the echoing reply to it made by our guns did not prevent me from snatching a few hours' sleep. But at six I was wakened by steps in the passage and a murmur: "There was some stuff parachuted down in the night. I've brought the mail."

"Couldn't you have waited until seven?"

But it was too late by then, for the word "mail" had flashed down the passage and into the shelters.

"A green envelope, that's for me, major."

"There should be at least ten for me . . ."

"That's my wife, I can tell her writing."

Julot too had a letter, an official one in a yellow envelope. In the upper left-hand corner I read, "Police Headquarters,

Roubaix." It was a fine which he had forgotten to pay when he was in France. It made him furious!

When I had finished distributing the letters, there were still six official ones left for me. The first was from Haiphong to say: "Please let me know whether you wish to receive your monthly pay where you are at the moment or whether you wish me to credit you with it here . . ."

Homeric laughter burst from my orderlies and my wounded men.

The second letter said: "Please send Corporal Mohamed Ben Kabbour to his depot at Haiphong without further delay. He is due to embark for home on the thirtieth of March."

That caused more Homeric laughter.

The two letters were put up on the wall outside the emergency-treatment room. There was no doubt that we were in the hands of people who took their jobs seriously.

In the course of the afternoon I returned to my shelter and banged my head against the beams of the ceiling. Ty and Yann roared with laughter. They were two paratroop N.C.O.'s, one Vietnamese, the other Chinese. Both had had their legs taken off above the knee. I had put them in my own shelter. They were not too much in the way, and they enjoyed any visitors I got, while Bacus had not far to go to renew their dressings. During the night I acted as their orderly:

"Major, I'm thirsty—let me have some water."

"Major, I want to piss."

"Major, give me a cigarette."

Levasseur was calling me. Gindrey wanted me in the operating room. Coming out, I once more knocked my head against a beam. No, it did not happen every day . . . Other days I used to come straight into my room without any trouble. So I quickly tore the white sheeting which hid the ceiling from me and saw to my surprise that three of the logs were cracked down the middle and that my roof was on the verge of collapsing.

I darted outside and called to N'Diaye: "Come here at once; we've got to get Ty and Yann out."

Then cautiously we went inside my shelter, keeping close to the walls, and removed the sheeting. The flimsy construction suddenly became evident to me, and it was something of a shock. There was certainly a metal plate, but only supported by bamboos, one every seven inches.

"Why wasn't this properly built like the other shelters, N'Diaye?" I asked.

"Captain Thuriés wanted the operational block strengthened first. This was going to be done last."

"Get hold of Fleury."

His figure was soon taking up the whole of the entrance. He had a look around, touched the roof here and there, made a few calculations, and went off, to return half an hour later with a dozen coolies. He had also managed to find half a dozen props in the form of great logs and was soon wielding his hammer, digging and urging on his workers. He put in three props to support the crossbeam and three more along the left wall. Space was very much reduced, but all the same I felt a little more comfortable.

With some maneuvering we managed to get Ty and Yann back in their respective places. Fleury, assuring me that he had nothing on hand that afternoon took off the old torn sheeting and got to work on a brand-new piece, spotlessly clean.

Then suddenly we heard some dull thuds and explosions, and rapid whistlings which got nearer. It was not the usual harassing fire. The uproar went on without a respite. The dentist turned up to say, "Dominique is getting it."

It was an artillery barrage, paving the way for an attack. In another hour there would be a great influx, probably, and we would have to go through the nights we had endured when it was the turn of Beatrice and Gabrielle.

Buezek arrived, out of breath: "Quick, Fleury, you've got

to go back to your section. You're wanted at the end of the trench with your flame thrower."

Fleury got up, dropped his tools on the ground, saluted, shook hands, and made off at the double.

I was never to see him again.

The shells were coming down even more than before the attacks on Beatrice and Gabrielle.

Still, at least the paralyzing interval of waiting was over, and every man went calmly about his business. Perez got flasks of plasma and blood ready; Bacus got his sterilized cases back for use; N'Diaye put the stretchers ready, piled against the walls of the passage. Deudon poured lemon powder and sugar into jugs of filtered water and added a few pieces of ice.

The first of the wounded to come in was the twelve-year-old son of a Thai partisan, hit in an open trench of the Airborne Commandos, only a few yards from us. His abdomen had been opened right up, and he was dead in a matter of seconds.

Now both the north and west entries echoed to the sound of more and more trampling feet, and there was a constant procession of men, bleeding, limping, and groaning.

The passage was filled in a flash: the emergency-treatment room, which should only take fifteen wounded, got twenty-five, between the beds, on the ground, and under the table; the hospital shelters were thronged all over again—stretchers were slipped inside, under beds, on the floor. You can get two Vietnamese on one stretcher, as they weigh about 175 pounds between them, which is the weight of the average Legionnaire. The dentist took a dozen poor lads, who could stoop down, into his shelter.

Nobody could be left outside; there were deafening explosions on our roof, and clods of dried earth tumbled down the vent holes; I had one wounded man put in the passage to the X-ray room, another under the sink, two in the little passage leading to the crossways. That was accomplished—and now the difficulty was to find somewhere to put your feet.

What effort it must have cost those two paratroopers of the Sixth Colonial to get through here with their lieutenant, who had a leg completely torn off! They were bathed in sweat and were standing in the entrance to the emergency-treatment room, holding the stretcher, looking for a place to put it. There was only one place left—the operating table.

Putting their lieutenant down there, they told me, "The Viets are storming Dominique . . . and they're attacking Eliane."

Once more calls for help, moans, explosions, and the whistle of shells fell on our ears, but we were past hearing—we refused to hear any more.

So, for hours and hours which were timeless, I plunged once more into my closed universe, where nothing existed beyond shattered bodies, gleaming instruments, plaster, and blood.

"Major, over here . . . don't you recognize me?"

A bronzed face with dark eyes and a broken nose in the middle of it which could only belong to one man. His name was Lanzac.

"It's really you, Lanzac?"

"Yes, it's me—I'm one of the parachute reinforcements."

In 1947 Lanzac was a corporal in the Sixth Colonial Infantry at Hanoi. I extracted a bullet from one of his thighs. In 1949 he was sergeant in the Colonial Infantry at Backan. I took a nasty shell splinter out from behind his left ear; the bone suppurated for a long time. In 1953 he was warrant officer in a battalion of paratroops. I opened up his abdomen at that stage of his career. Now in 1954 he was a company sergeant major, and his left leg was shattered just at the junction with the pelvis.

This time the shock was irreversible, and in five minutes he was dead.

The fourth time it was for good and all; I was unable to beat the record I had achieved with Vandenberghe in 1951, for I had also operated on him three times at intervals of a year. But for him too the fourth wound was the last.

Lemmy Caution came along, and the men from the Second Airborne: "Dominique has fallen, and Eliane is cut off. But there's going to be a counterattack."

During the attacks on Gabrielle and Beatrice, we heard little in our quarters of the tommy guns and rifles, but to-night we were spared nothing. The rattle from them and from the machine guns was constant and excruciating, never stopping.

Bullets passed over our vent holes with an angry whistle. My friend the four-barreled affair fired in short bursts, which reverberated, went on and on . . .

Suddenly there came a deafening explosion, and at the same moment we were plunged into darkness. The wires which brought us our light had been cut; it was not the first time, though they were under three feet of earth. I called out to Julot, "Quick, phone the command post."

Our own plant was out of action and we were getting light from them. Julot went on cranking the phone, again and again, without result. The telephone wires were also cut.

"Take your steel helmet, Julot, and run along to Signal." Without a murmur he went off, using the feeble light of his pocket flash to pick his way over the masses of bleeding tissue laid out on the stretchers.

The wounded were suddenly scared of the dark and started calling out. They had to be talked to and calmed down. The pool of light from our torches passed rapidly, as in some film designed to curdle the blood, over a squashed face, an open knee, the bloody stump of a foot, a dangerous hole in an abdomen from which blood issued, eyes with dilated pupils, hands grasping half a pint of some cooling drink.

The flight nurse, the girl who had joined our ranks a few days before, moved through this fantastic world, gentle and efficient, silent.

A voice spoke out of the shadows in the passage: "The control tower is on fire. No more radio control. How will they be able to direct the fighters?"

There was also a great cloud of smoke coming from the direction of the gasoline dump.

The lights went up again. Julot came back, flushed and out of breath. Some more Moroccans were brought in, and there was no more room. Shells were still falling all the time.

Lachamp told me: "There are at least ten in Lieutenant Gindrey's shelter, and as many in the other shelters, and they are crowding in the trenches outside, all herded together . . ."

One shell had fallen on the sterilizer room, and a stretcher had got covered with earth . . . N'Diaye was trying to free it . . .

The flight nurse took her helmet from the nail where it was hanging, put it on her head, and went toward the exit picking a zigzag course in order to avoid the wounded.

"Mademoiselle, where are you going? Stay here."

"But, major, I must go outside. I'm sure I'm needed there."

She turned away and, resuming her zigzag course, vanished at the crossways.

Bacus, Levasseur, and Gindrey had succeeded in clearing the operating room a little, as ten or more wounded had been so considerate as to die.

"No, I don't want to die, I don't want . . . Major, come here, here, listen to me, I don't want to die." He was a little paratroop corporal, one more of them. His back was nothing but a great breathing wound. Why had he not died the moment he was hit?

Then there came into my mind a scene in a film that I had seen when I was twenty. Beside me, a priest was weeping; it was a scene from *All Quiet on the Western Front*. A simple church in a country village and hundreds of wounded men, as there were here, moaning and miserable, attended by medical orderlies and nurses. A chaplain was saying mass at the altar on a Sunday morning. Standing by a pillar was a soldier with a tragic face, Pierre Blanchard, with his expressive eyes; and quietly in the background a voice was singing Schubert's marvelous *Ave Maria*. The soldier stared at the Christ above the altar and said: "Lord, give me days without bread and water, give me poverty, give me danger . . . But spare me suffering, I implore you, spare me that. Lord, spare me from dying . . ."

Later I learned that three days and three nights had gone by.

After the last operation I staggered, half conscious, toward the rectangle of gray light, down there at the end of the passage. There, with my back to the wall, I watched the indifferent clouds passing in the sky, the clouds which were so peaceful and which knew no fear.

Then I heard a small voice whispering somewhere behind me: "Oh, I would so like to go to sleep and never, never wake up again."

I turned and saw Geneviève, leaning against the wall behind me. She was quietly crying.

7.

Geneviève

We called her Geneviève now. It had been "Mademoiselle" until the day came when one of the wounded —Courtade, I think it was—said, "May I call you Geneviève?"

The evening she came, Sioni broke out, "Another girl— how are we going to make room for her? Anyhow, I'm not giving up my stretcher."

But she found a stretcher for herself, one that was very dirty and damp. She opened it out and put it on the ground between the beds of Rollin and Deflinne, two lieutenants who were wounded. There she went peacefully off to sleep.

At the end of March the wounded were being evacuated day and night and the medical orderlies used to come back from the airfield raging against the medical service and the air crews and anything else which came to mind.

"There was another girl in the plane . . . more of these girls who're not even strong enough to lift a stretcher. That means that we have to mess around and climb up into the plane."

Le Damany and I made no reply to all this. We knew that there is always a bit of jealousy in these affairs. It's always the same story.

Before the attack which took place on March 13, the nurse who accompanied the wounded used to wait all day for the evening plane which was to return to Hanoi with the sick and wounded. In the middle of the day she was often invited to eat in the officers' mess. My orderlies used to say, "Why can't she eat in our mess? Why must it always be the officers?"

The evening she arrived she came shyly up to me in my quarters to say, "'As I can't go back, I've come to place myself under your orders."

I put her in charge of a shelter which contained ten of the most serious cases. They had to be given their dressings, their injections, their food; they needed help in making the least movement. They had lost an arm or a leg or even both; or a piece of the large intestine protruded from the wall of the abdomen so that feces issued out there.

I used to watch her when the shells were falling, and I was astonished to see how calm she was. She continued to go from one wounded man to another, as if nothing were happening. She always did exactly what was needed; she had a woman's gentleness, and her fresh young voice found just the right things to say:

"Here we are, another injection. Did I hurt you?

"You want something to drink? Wait a minute, I'll get you some fruit juice.

"A cigarette? I don't smoke, but the major is sure to let me have one."

My orderlies watched her and scowled.

Why did she want to make hot soup every evening? What was she trying to do? And then she wanted all the Vinogel, saying, "It's for the wounded"—as if they didn't know that!

And she was such a nuisance to the major: it was always,

"Major, will you look at this?" or "Major, could you attend to that?" It was a good thing that the chief knew all about women—otherwise she would certainly have got around him.

"Major, Heinz is in pain. Oughtn't he to have some morphine?

"Rondeau is really bad—will you come and have a look at him?

"While you're here, just have a look at the man with burns in the other shelter; there's something he wants to ask you . . ."

Every evening, when we got the chance, we used to eat bunched up together in the N.C.O. shelter. It had to be done in three shifts, as there was only room for eight and our full strength was over thirty. We sat on the edge of two cots around a table which consisted of an upturned box. At the end of the meal there was usually a bit of cheese, some jam, and a cracker or two left over.

Geneviève used to collect these fragments, saying, "I'll give this to the coolie who's lost an arm; there was no rice this evening."

The day after she came, she said to me, "But where are the rest of the wounded?"

"There are some everywhere," I told her, "with the Second Airborne, the command post, the Ninth Group, and the Eighth Assault."

"Can I go and see them?"

"Yes, but you're only to visit the wounded with the Second Airborne, which is next to us. You will report to Colonel Langlais and have a look at the wounded. There are Captain Hervouet, Lieutenant Le Boudec, and N.C.O.'s from the Sixth Colonial Paratroops. I haven't seen them since they were wounded three days ago . . . You'll let me know how they are."

It was nearly two hours before she came back, flushed and out of breath, covered with mud and, to judge from her face, in the best of spirits, on top of the world. "I saw the wounded with the Second Airborne," she told me. "They'll come and see you tomorrow, all those who can walk."

"You've taken your time about it."

"Yes, I took the opportunity of going on to the Thai Group and the Ninth Group; then I went to the supply column and the Airborne Commandos—and the Eighth Assault."

She had almost made a complete circuit of the main camp. Shells had been falling all the time, and she had to take a very complicated route, going out of the trenches across paths in the open under fire, jumping over shell holes, and forcing a way through barbed wire.

"And you didn't think what would happen if a shell had exploded in front of you?"

"Oh, no! If only you could have seen how happy they were and how pleased I was! Everywhere they were saying, 'Mademoiselle, who are you? A nurse—that's marvelous . . . You must come and see us often.' "

When they saw her they were all the same—white, black, yellow, and North African troops—they all emerged for a moment from the evil dream which existence had become for them.

Colonel Langlais had given her some cigarettes, and she had distributed them in the shelters that were farthest away—even in one I had never seen, near the supply column and close to the 155 guns.

"All the same, you could very easily have been wounded," I told her, "and brought back here on a stretcher."

"Oh no—you see, I had my helmet with me . . ."

It was then I realized that she was entitled to a place in the great procession of extraordinary young women which went on without a break for more than eight years in Indochina.

Geneviève de Galard was just such another as "la Dêche," the one they called the beggar girl because the day after she got her pay it all went into the pockets of the fellows she looked after. For years "la Dêche" was welfare assistant to a battalion of the Ninth Colonial Infantry Division, tireless in her work, adored by the whole battalion, ranking next to the major—whose name was Langlais. Once she walked into the hospital at Lanessan—it was midnight—at the head of a string of buffaloes, bulls as well as cows, and a huge squad of ducks, saying, "To supplement the diet of the wounded."

Geneviève was just such another as Suzy Poirier, who got a bullet wound in the head while at the wheel of her ambulance on the Caobang road.

Another was Aline Lerouge, a fearless ambulance-driver, who once plunged with her vehicle into an icy river in Tonkin. She was to be seen on every road in the country. In the course of an operation along the Phuly dike in 1947, the half-track in front of her was attacked by a sniper and the driver killed. Immediately she handed over the wheel of her ambulance to the girl with her, jumped into the half-track, and drove off. Some hundred yards farther on there was more shooting from the direction of the rice field. She got out on the embankment, threw herself down, and emptied her rifle at the enemy. A Viet bullet went through her lung.

Another was Marguerite, Aline's colleague, who had taken her degree in philosophy—and she was certainly very calm and serene. When the Caobang convoys were being attacked, she was to be seen strolling to the head of the column with a cigarette in her mouth, while the escorting troops took refuge in the ditches.

Another was Odette, in the winter of 1947, in the River Claire country. When she was with me she did over a hundred and sixty miles on foot, from Tuyenquang to Hanoi.

Others of this great company were Mathy, Poupart, Baugé, Sage, Sorin, all nurses, full of devotion and tenderness for the wounded, in a service extending over eight years in Indochina.

They would come on duty at midnight or two in the morning just to see if the chest case they had attended earlier was still bleeding. No, it wasn't really that—they came simply to say, "It's all right, don't worry, I'm here, and I'll be back soon, at half-past seven."

Another of them was Minouche, of the ambulance service, who also handed over her pay to the fellows she drove. She was known and loved all over Tonkin and Cochin China, from north to south and from east to west. Once at Buichu the telephone rang to give news that some men had been badly wounded four miles away. It was dawn, and the road had not yet been opened up. That didn't worry her; she forced her way through and opened it up herself!

Another of them was Robinet, an anesthetist. She had sent thousands of soldiers to sleep, in North Africa, in Italy, in Germany and, of course, in Indochina. She fell in 1953 on the deck of a river transport at Quangtri; a Viet bullet had gone right through her.

One day I was asked to scribble "a few words" in the album of the girls who drove the Caobang ambulances. This is what I wrote: "A man who is wounded in battle becomes for you a sort of demigod, and nothing is too good for him."

Julot was the first to give Geneviève a dress; then N'Diaye gave her a dicky. It was Levasseur who gave up his boots to her. After all, she could not keep on wearing the same navy-blue suit and women's shoes.

One evening Deudon had a soup made that was thick and hot; the smell of it brought comfort to all the wounded men. After that it was Sioni who came to ask me if he could work with her: "She's always running back and forth; I can fetch what she needs—cotton, gauze, instruments . . ."

Then Lachamp, being a scrounger with the gift of gab, brought her a pile of cigarettes to distribute.

Then an N.C.O. of the Second Airborne made her a present of his paratroop uniform, which had a zip-fastener.

One day I said to Bacus, "You know what the roof of my shelter is like; I really can't make her sleep under that." So he offered her the cot to which he was so attached, but she refused. Then a white sheet was found for her, and a soft pillow, and a stretcher that was at least clean. Now at last she was one of the team, once and for all.

Colonel Langlais invited her to lunch one day. His men had concocted a marvelous chocolate custard. It was also the first time that I saw the paratroops all present in full strength.

"Well, what's she like, this nurse of yours?" he asked me.

"You remember 'la Dêche,' colonel? She's just such another."

He smiled at once and his clear eyes grew thoughtful. "But where can she sleep?"

"She has a stretcher on the ground, among the wounded."

"Oh, no, we can't have that!"

The next morning, Colonel Langlais had a small shelter cleared out at one end of the Airborne Commandos' quarters. Before noon he had presented Geneviève with a delightful little bed covered with white parachute silk, and a real mattress also covered with white silk. There were a little table and a chair from his command post.

No other girl in the world ever had the happiness which filled her heart that evening.

There was only one more incident. The idea of the shelter-bedroom had come from outside, not from a member of the "team," with the result that my men were seized with a bad attack of jealousy: "Why should the ones over there interfere? Geneviève belongs to us, not to them. How could we offer her a shelter to herself, considering that we haven't got one?"

Sioni didn't want to go on working with her any longer: "That's the way it is; you're like the rest of the girls that used to come here. You'll be going off to dine with the officers every day . . . You'll drop us now."

One evening she entered my shelter in tears, overwrought, bewildered, exhausted, sobbing in her desperation: "What should I do? I just don't understand."

I comforted her as well as I could, telling her that she must forgive the poor fellows any remarks they had made, that the whole incident really showed how strong and sincere their feelings for her were: "They love you now and would willingly die for you."

I got my orderlies together and said the few words that the occasion demanded. The reconciliation took place half an hour later. They hugged one another until Geneviève, delighted, brushed away her tears, all smiles again.

Each day had its moments of anxiety for me. There were two reasons, in particular, for this. The first was delayed-action shells, the 105's. When I heard a shell bury itself in the ground without exploding, I immediately had a vision of my shelters all sent flying and my wounded men suffocated by earth in their mouths and nostrils. My other reason for anxiety was supplied by Geneviève when she picked up her helmet and went out along the passage without saying a word. She was only going to the little hut surrounded with sacks near the barbed wire, just beyond the morgue. Normal bodily functions, which cannot be postponed, made this necessary.

For us it was easy enough, as there were empty flasks everywhere. You had only to turn toward the wall, and later it was thrown into the barbed wire beside the road.

Usually when she took her helmet she told me, "I'm going to the Second Airborne" or "I'm going to the Airborne Commandos." When she was only going for the other reason, she said nothing, and she always reappeared quite at ease—and always smiling.

I had put a ban on the use of fresh water for washing, at least for my own orderlies. Water was kept for the operating room and for drinking purposes. Every evening we washed with a little denatured alcohol, which was good enough. But an exception was made in the case of Geneviève; she was entitled to a basin of water a day, filtered but not sterilized.

One day a very nasty boil appeared on her right shoulder, and it rapidly developed into a carbuncle. It caused her great pain and made her feverish, until one morning while changing the dressing I told her, "We'll have to operate on this; it's a case for the knife." Of course I intended to use an anesthetic, Pentothal. But she utterly refused this, because it would put her out of action for some hours while it wore off: "I'm not going to be off duty for a whole day just because I've got a little boil."

Then I suggested a local anesthetic, Novocain, but I had no phials of it left, so that I had to have some procaine dissolved in a little saline. The anesthetic effect of this mixture was extremely uncertain; I had already seen its effect on some of the wounded, who had protested vigorously. So I said, "If I hurt you and make you cry out, it doesn't matter—you're fully entitled to Pentothal, and Levasseur will be at hand to administer it. The syringe will be all ready."

She said, "Okay!" and laughed.

The carbuncle was as big as the palm of the hand. I must have hurt a great deal, but she never uttered a word. She did not move a muscle, and her eyes, opened wide, were fixed on the ceiling. But her hands, clenched on the sides of the operating table, contracted so strongly that the knuckles went absolutely white.

As soon as the dressing was finished, she went back to her duties.

At least twice a day it was her task to change the dressings on six abdominal cases with colostomies. This meant that twice a day her delicate hands were immersed in bundles of gauze soiled with feces, and she always did this with a smile, a joke, or some gentle teasing. Then she carefully washed her hands, rinsed them in alcohol, and went on to the next case. Another task which fell to her was renewing the dressings on the amputations: Heinz, for instance, had three stumps; both arms and a leg were missing. As a good deal of dirt had got into the wounds in the first place and our antiseptics were not always effective, the stumps had not healed—they still gaped.

At first each dressing produced a real crisis in Heinz, and for hours afterward he lay in a coma, overcome with the pain. Half an hour had to be taken over each stump, very slowly unsticking the old dressing and putting on the new one with extreme care and patience. Geneviève was the only person to achieve the miracle of doing this without making Heinz cry out.

Another Legionnaire, Müller, had a compound fracture high up in the left thigh and an enormous wound in the buttocks and loins, making it impossible to use plaster. Normally with a wound of this kind the procedure would be to put a splint along the tibia and adjust a metal ring around it—a sort of stirrup—from which is suspended a weight of between twenty and forty pounds. This forces the ends of the bones into position and eliminates the pain, which is always acute when a fracture is not held rigid. At the same time the wounded man would be placed on a large bed with straps and a system of cords and pulleys enabling him to be raised, providing access to the wound underneath and making the dressing of it a comparatively simple matter. But a bed of that size and all that apparatus of pulleys could hardly have been got into the shelter which had to contain not only Müller but the ten other wounded men who were lying there.

An attempt had been made to secure traction by winding bands of adhesive tape around the leg, but the constant trickle of sweat had made this come unstuck, and in a few minutes the whole affair had collapsed. Müller then had to be content with a large splint which was obliged to stop exactly at the point where the break was, at the top of the thigh where it joined the body; and it became necessary to turn him on his side in order to reach the wound underneath. This operation forced screams of pain from him each time.

It took two hours to renew the dressing, with Müller asking for a rest every five minutes. A cardiac stimulant was injected, and he was given a little fruit juice to drink. It took all Geneviève's infinite patience to bring this exhausting task to a satisfactory conclusion.

The full story of Müller and his wound was a long martyrdom—first getting him into the emergency-treatment room, then operating on him and dressing the wounds afterward, then the ten days spent in the Viet field hospital, followed by his final evacuation to Hanoi.

When he was at last placed on a proper hospital bed in Hanoi, he remained grim and silent, unable to forget all that he had been through. But his face lit up with a really splendid smile when Geneviève appeared at his bedside—she had just been liberated.

Then there was Courtade. A bullet had got his spinal cord and produced paralysis in both legs. His cot was in the shelter which had to be crossed in going to the Airborne Commandos' quarters, and Geneviève had to pass by ten or fifteen times a day. Each time, it was: "Geneviève, help me to move my right foot. I've got pins and needles." Then: "Geneviève, put a little cotton under my knee; it's hurting." Then: "Geneviève, there's a bug under my right calf, I'm sure there is. Do look." Then: "Geneviève . . . I'm thirsty . . . I can't sleep . . ."

Always serene and smiling, Geneviève would move the foot which refused to move, slip some cotton under the knee, rub the lifeless calf with a little alcohol, give him something to drink, or get him a sleeping pill.

Nearly every day we had packages dropped by parachute inscribed with red letters "For the Wounded." These contained everything which they wanted most—cigarettes, mild and full strength, cans of every sort of fruit, condensed milk, oranges, and apples. Real oranges and real apples.

Geneviève was responsible for distributing all these things, from the first shelter, close to mine, to the last one away off at the far end of the Airborne Commandos' trench. To reach it, you had to climb out of our passage, do twenty-five yards over open ground, and then go down again. There were not enough apples and oranges for everybody, and they had to be cut in half. There were five cigarettes for each man and a can of milk for four. She was the only one who could get the wounded to be content with five cigarettes a day without grumbling. Five cigarettes are few enough when you have nothing to do except keep on staring through the gloom at the same log of wood in the ceiling or listen to shells whistling and exploding and all the other sounds of battle.

"I'm not hungry today, so I'll take my soup along to that coolie who can't use his jaws," Geneviève would say.

The man's lower jaw was in fact fractured in several places and was held in position against the upper jaw with fine steel wire. Liquid food had to be passed between his broken teeth in a teaspoon, a spoonful at a time. Or a feeding tube could be inserted in the nostrils which would take fluid down into the stomach; then some form of liquid nourishment could be introduced into the tube by means of a syringe. This task took half an hour to accomplish, and it had to be done three times a day.

Colonel Langlais often paid us a visit.

"Greetings, colonel," I would say, to which he would reply, "Confound your greetings . . . They're all right when you've got nothing better to do . . ."

He was always bareheaded. He wore a cap on parade or on the barracks square. When a battle was being fought, he always went bareheaded; it was a permanent gesture of defiance.

"And how's the little girl getting along?" he asked.

"I can only repeat what I said before, colonel—it's 'la Dêche' all over again."

"Good, good, then we must do something to help her, or at least sustain her morale. It's obvious that she must be suffering, even though she never lets it appear. Doc, you must write a few lines about her and we'll see what can be done . . ."

That evening, in my shelter, I applied myself to this—but how difficult it is to find words which are worthy of the men, of all those I saw daily around me. "She has more than proved her value as a nurse . . . exceptional achievements . . . universally admired . . . her courage . . ."

How commonplace the phrases are: it is so much simpler and more "military" to add nothing to the magnificent and concise phrase which has the ring of a bugle call: "For distinguished service under fire."

I knew that some sort of decoration was being considered, but I was caught unawares when, one evening, she was away some time and reappeared, smiling as ever, but now flushed and radiant: "Oh, just look what they have given me; really, you know, it's much too much, I simply haven't deserved it . . ."

I saw the red ribbon of the Legion of Honor bright against the green of her blouse. Beside it was the Croix de Guerre with a palm in gold. The matter had been settled in less than an hour over the radio to Hanoi.

We all hugged her fervently; Julot, I'm quite sure, embraced her twice, and even the austere Bacus remarked: "I've never known a decoration to be so well deserved."

It was a first attempt to repay a little of what we owed her. She had given so much, not only her very presence there, which was itself a consolation, but all the pains she had taken, all the thousand and one little sacrifices she had made and had passed off with an unaffected laugh, all the immense weariness which her ceaseless activity cost her, her devotion, which was endless, and all that she had to endure—and then there was the tenderness of a woman which appeared in her lightest gesture.

I urged her to show herself to the wounded with the decorations themselves pinned on, not just the ribbons, but she refused: "No, I've been given all that, but what have they had? When they get their reward, then I'll be able to stand in line with them and show my decorations."

April 30 came around, a day which the Foreign Legion always celebrates, for it is the anniversary of the Cameroons. I also took part in these celebrations, since I was an honorary Legionnaire, first class, in the Third Regiment. I never missed a single year; the celebrations were very simple, yet striking. It was their very simplicity which made them so sincere.

Geneviève had been summoned to the Command Post at six o'clock. She returned toward eleven and appeared before me, saying, "Look, major, I'm like you now."

She turned, and I saw on her left sleeve the green and black shield of the Legion; the Thirteenth Demi-Brigade had just made her an honorary Legionnaire, first class.

She agreed to pay an immediate visit to the wounded, and there was an endless chorus of approval and congratulations. She was proud now to account herself one of those for whom she had so much affection.

I had ten bottles of champagne in reserve. Soon the ten corks had popped in the air, and she herself took every wounded man his share in the festivity. It was a splendid evening!

When at the end of May the Viets decided to set her free and send her to Hanoi, I accompanied her to the airfield with Sioni and Buezek.

After the simple but moving good-by's had been said, we did an about-face, Sioni, Buezek and I. For a long time she watched us returning to our prison tent, where I rejoined my group of orderlies. They were sad and depressed, and I couldn't help saying to them, "We've lost our mascot. Get your gear ready, we'll soon be on our way to the prison camp."

Five days later we were on Road 41, going in the direction of Tuangiao.

8.

April

The network of trenches was now well organized; you could go from the command post to the field hospital and from there to the Second Group or to the Eighth Assault without having to sprint across open ground, as was the case before. And at last there was some sort of tunnel passing under the road and linking the Second Airborne with the central command post.

I had taken over half the Airborne Commandos' shelters, and getting stretchers between them and the field hospital was still a very dangerous affair, for you had to leave the passage by the north entrance, go along the road, which was constantly under fire, and go down again into the gloomy entrance to the Airborne Commandos' quarters. When the wounded man on the stretcher was moaning with pain, you could hardly run.

I was afraid there would be trouble—and there was. One day a Thai N.C.O. who was helping us was killed outright while engaged in this work. So then I asked Colonel Langlais if I could have a covered trench, where stretchers could pass, under the road, similar to the one which already linked his command post with the central one. He gave his consent and put me in touch with Lieutenant Maury. The job was simple enough: two teams would be engaged, one on the Airborne Commandos' side, the other on ours. They would start digging at the same moment and finally meet in the middle of the road. Then the trench, once it had been dug, would need to be covered with large beams and metal plates. It would only take a quarter of an hour to make the road fit for traffic again.

"Okay, major," Maury told me, "just let me know when you want it done. At night would be better of course . . . It's out of the question by day."

I decided to have the work started the same evening, but at ten o'clock a support post at Huguette was attacked. Trucks kept on going by, and nothing could be allowed to get in their way.

The next evening, when I was about to ring Lieutenant Maury, the Vietminhs started laying down an artillery barrage.

At last the evening came when the two camps got to work. It was a pitch-dark night, and everything went well; the ground under the road was as hard as stone, and when I had a few minutes off I took the engineers some hot coffee and rum; every now and then the Viets sent up a flare; everybody crouched down, and for a few minutes bursts from automatic weapons and shells whistled over our heads.

Since the fall of Dominique 3, there was danger everywhere, for it was now enemy territory. Its heights menaced all that remained to us. The Viets had observation posts there and had set up numbers of mortars on the slopes, and here and there you could make out cleverly concealed loopholes.

I was in a great hurry to get the work finished; all my coolies lent a hand, and even a few of my orderlies. Everything was ready to cover over the gap in the road; at nightfall a truck had brought over six large beams of wood and iron.

It was about two in the morning when a salvo of mortars exploded on our roof and on the road. Then what I had feared happened. An engineer N.C.O. came to see me in the emergency-treatment room, where I was taking a look around, to say, "One of my men has been hit."

A few minutes later my orderlies brought a Moroccan engineer in on a stretcher. A mortar shell had exploded only two or three yards behind him. There was a huge hole in the middle of his back: his vertebrae were shattered, and the spinal cord was destroyed. In the few seconds before he died, I seemed to read a reproach to me in his eyes.

I gave orders to suspend work on the road, as I was responsible for the death of this man; the work could be left to the next day.

An engineer N.C.O. phoned his major. In a few moments, he was on the scene: "No, no, doctor, it's all in the day's work. Don't you worry . . . When a battalion commander gives the order to attack, he knows that he is going to lose men . . . that's how it is."

Work started again and was finished by dawn. It was now possible to pass directly from the field hospital to the Airborne Commandos. The wounded and the orderlies no longer ran any risks.

I still had only six of the Airborne Commandos' shelters, and I needed them all; then I would have two hundred and fifty beds in my main field hospital, without counting those in many neighboring shelters.

Here again Colonel Langlais was a great help to me and gave orders for all the remaining shelters to be evacuated. The Thais began digging cells and holes alongside their trenches and in the walls of their fighting outposts and came to resemble a large family of rats.

But the roofing of the main trench was weaker than ours, and in places there was no cover at all. This aroused fresh anxieties. In the walls of this main trench my orderlies dug some fifteen little recesses, each one of which would take a wounded man full length.

In the end Colonel Langlais had still more shelters cleared, but they were not linked to my main group. They came from the northwest command post, which was now useless, and from the paratroop operational command and an intelligence section, which were now also out of action.

This gave me fifty more places, but only for walking wounded. I planned to put there those with arm wounds, those who had lost an eye, and those with chest or head wounds which were well on the way to being cured.

I would have needed Fleury to get all this work carried out to perfection. But Fleury had been killed on the night of March 30, an hour after he left us under fire from the Viets.

His fighting outpost was a trench at the extreme west of the airfield. In the course of the attack on the Dominique positions, the Viets infiltrated and reached him. His flame thrower transformed them into living torches for a few minutes, but he ran out of fuel and once more a wave of them advanced. He started firing with his tommy gun, but he could not see too well . . . He would do better standing up. He climbed out of the trench, and his huge figure emerged erect to confront the Viets. He emptied two magazines and suddenly went down, facing the enemy; he was killed instantly, pierced by a hundred bullets.

So my signet ring remains on my finger.

Gone too was our delightful "Duck"—Sergeant Stetter. With the fall of Dominique he was lost to us, which made Bacus say with a wry smile when day broke on March 31: "It's eight o'clock, and there's no 'Duck.' "

I was now quite used to the sound of the four-barreled machine gun and the rhythm of its reverberation. It went on day and night, its four barrels aimed at Dominique, where every sign of life had vanished. But you could just make out molehills, narrow trenches, camouflaged loopholes.

One of the men who fired this gun was wounded by a shell splinter, luckily not a serious wound, and while dressing it I talked to him about this weapon of his. "Oh, major," he said, "if you only knew what a beauty she is. If we had twenty of them here, we'd have no trouble."

He spoke of "her" lovingly, as a sportsman speaks of a racehorse. So I too developed an affection for her, and I often used to listen to her when I had a chance to lie on my bed, beneath the vent hole. She fired up to the last minute.

After the surrender, I made a pilgrimage to her. For twenty square yards around her there was a carpet of empty shell cases some three feet thick. And hundreds of craters, superimposed on one another. The weapon was lying on the ground, the barrels pointing uselessly to the sky. She made me think of a wounded stag lying on the ground overwhelmed by the fight made before accepting defeat.

I also recognized the sound of the 155 gun, the only one left. That too fired up to the last minute. It went off with a dull shock, so forcible that it made the ground shake.

I went there too after the fall of Dienbienphu. The hollow in which it was still standing was like the huge crater made by a one-ton bomb, and for a hundred and fifty yards around the earth had an apocalyptic aspect, not a square inch of it intact —no insect, no worm would have been able to live there. You had to look hard to find the entrances to shelters around the hollow to which the gunners crawled back after firing.

Dominique having fallen, the problem of water had become even more pressing.

The water detail—it was my daily terror, precise in its movements as those of a ballet. I felt the time slip by, six o'clock and the trampling on my roof, the sound of empty cans knocking against one another, half-past six and the explosions, seven and the arrival at the north entrance of the five or six wounded who were still able to walk: "Major, you're wanted in the emergency-treatment room."

The water-purification unit had been set up near the bridge and was now under fire from Dominique. To get there, we had to have new trenches dug; one of them went zigzagging from the Second Airborne's blockhouses, crossed the barbed-wire entanglement, went along the river bank, and ended by the bridge. This was the way my water carriers went. When they reached the bridge, they had to come out into the open, run to the purifier, and fill the jerry cans with water.

It was a problem. I had five jerry cans, and my coolies made the journey twice a day, in the morning at six, and in the evening at five. That brought in fifty gallons; it was not much, but it had to suffice.

I had to send the water detail to the purifier during the day. At night nobody was allowed to leave his post, and at six in the morning the carriers went off to the trench while there was still a slight mist to hide the ground from the Viets, but they had to be quick about it, for a 105 and mortars had long kept the bridge and its immediate neighborhood under fire.

Toward the middle of April, with only two journeys a day, I had already lost three of my coolies, but often, after a great influx of wounded, the water tank was dry and I had to order a third journey.

In the last two weeks, the mud in the passages leading to the river reached a depth of three feet, and my water carriers came back enveloped in mud up to the waist and above, out of breath and exhausted. At the beginning of April the journey took ten minutes; at the end, two hours.

So every morning boys with jerry cans on their shoulders went down from the Elianes, the Eighth Assault, the Second Thai Battalion, and the artillery, and came out at the purifier. All of a sudden, without a word of warning, twenty shells would explode around them, and many companies have waited in vain for their water, until my phone informed them: "Take the names of three of your people who have just been wounded by the bridge."

Chevalier had just died when Boisbouvier came in, his second experience of a stretcher.

Chevalier was a lieutenant; a bullet had gone right through the back of his neck and had severed the spinal cord just below the medulla oblongata. If the medulla had been hit, he would have been killed instantly.

It was quite out of the question to undress him; when he was touched he did not cry out, but moaned softly, like a child. The moment he saw me, he said: "Major, I've had it, I know."

It was true too.

The nervous tissues degenerated daily. Daily, paralysis gained control of the legs, the abdomen, the thorax, the arms; but the respiratory and cardiac centers situated in the brain were only affected a few minutes before death, and he remained terribly conscious up to the last minute.

Sensitivity to pain persisted and became more acute; he also remained conscious of hunger and thirst. Twice a day Geneviève gave him soup with a teaspoon. The chaplain was often with him, and they had whispered conversations together which lasted some minutes.

I tried the whole range of sedatives: Dolosal, Phenergan, morphine, sedol, and gardenal. Nothing had any effect; he remained conscious up to the moment of his death.

He died after six days of it, still wearing his combat uniform. The chaplain was still talking to him when his heart stopped.

Boisbouvier was in for the second time, with some ten shell splinters in him, but examination showed that none of them were serious. But the shock must have been severe, for he presented all the characteristics of a technical knockout. After a few injections and a shot of rum, he got up and shook himself like a dog emerging from the water: "Really, nothing broken? Well, good-by till the next time."

So he went off, covered with dressings and adhesive tape. Yes, I was to see him for a third time—but that would be the last.

It was hot in our shelters now. Covering the main passage had been an excellent idea, but as a result there was not enough ventilation.

The weather at the beginning of April was brilliant; winter was over, and spring was like summer in Provence. Stripped to the waist in the trenches, the men got sunburned during the lulls in the fighting.

But in the overheated field hospital the heat became unbearable—the heat of the roof baked by the sun, the heat of fifty electric bulbs, the heat of the lamp in the operating room, the heat of two hundred living creatures constantly moving around, the heat which encouraged the growth of mushrooms and algae all over the walls and roof beams.

At the end of April, when the rains came, it was even worse. Water was trickling everywhere and only evaporating very slowly. The heat became damp and smelly. Blood, vomit, and feces mixed with the mud made up a frightful compound which stuck to the boots in thick layers.

Shorts were the only possible uniform. Sweat poured constantly over the forehead and the back, dripping from the armpits to the hands and from the chest to the stomach. You kept drinking all the time, no matter what—water mixed with lemon, orange, or aniseed powder, or with a little sugar or coffee.

At the end of twenty-four hours the wounded all had their dressings damp and dirty; they had to be changed more often than that. With those in casts, sweat caused terrible skin irritations which developed into running sores which made sleep out of the question. The casts had to be removed and fresh ones supplied—which refused to dry in this humid atmosphere.

This extra disaster had to be endured with the others.

Visitors coming inside our west or north entrance soon found themselves perspiring from head to foot; the hot air interfered with their normal breathing; first they unbuttoned their uniform blouse, then took it off. At every opening in the passage there was always a group of people trying to get a breath of fresh air.

I shall never forget the martyrdom endured by men wounded in the thorax, trying in vain to get into their lungs the air and oxygen on which their lives depended; my oxygen cylinders were emptied at a prodigious rate. If I did not want them to die of suffocation, I had to put them in the farthest of the Airborne Commandos' shelters, where the main passage was not covered over; but I was not able to give them the same supervision there and ended by overlooking them. When I saw them again a pleural effusion was gently taking them to their death. Or if I put them in our main passage, they were constantly jostled by visitors and the constant procession of wounded from right and left.

The terrace in front of the field hospital was now continually swept by Viet bullets and mortars. The wounded had to be rushed to me, and a good many stretcher bearers were themselves wounded doing this, while some of those they were carrying received another injury.

Only the west entrance remained relatively easy of access, but toward the middle of April it shared the same fate as the one to the north.

Two Sherman tanks, camouflaged with nets and branches, were tucked away between walls of earth on each side of the Second Airborne's shelters. But the Viets had spotted them and every five or six hours sent over a salvo of 105's, 75's, and mortars of every caliber. The second tank was in a compartment exactly six feet to the left of our west entrance.

This led Le Damany to say: "You need a suicide squad to send stretcher bearers to your place now."

Lahcen and Larbi, my two ambulance drivers, had long been lying helpless in a shelter, stuffed with shell splinters. Two Legionnaires were driving the ambulances, which to my mind are the most heroic vehicles the medical service has ever had.

They were two very remarkable men, these, both of them Germans, and even the wounded who were themselves returning from the scene of fighting could not help regarding them with deep admiration. I always kept a little rum or brandy for them or a pack of cigarettes.

The first ambulance ended its career on the first of May; a shell scored a direct hit on it while it was passing in front of the entrance to our terrace; all the wounded in it were killed. The driver had a miraculous escape, and the next day I saw him at the wheel of a command jeep which had been turned over to the medical service and looked as if it had issued from the gates of hell.

Stretcher bearing by day became impossible. As for vehicles, they were as easy a target as rabbits during harvest in the cornfields of the Beauce. It was tough luck to be wounded in the morning, for you had to wait until evening to receive surgical treatment; and that was how battalion doctors were also obliged to become surgeons.

Patrice hadn't far to go; he came over to me to discuss the numbers of wounded who were constantly reaching him. He could not send them to the field hospital, for to get through himself he had to use the narrow trench which zigzagged and was out of the question for stretchers. When it was absolutely necessary to operate on a serious case, an abdomen, for instance, in my operating room, the stretcher bearers took up their positions in the trench and held the stretcher at arm's length above their heads. Then the stretcher seemed to float above the passage and the earth itself like a ship adrift in a storm, while bullets whistled and shells exploded around it.

Le Damany, Verdaguet, Rondy, and Stermann were farther off, and so we had recourse to the phone: "Hello, major, Rondy speaking. I've got a wounded man to send you—compound fracture in the leg—and he can't be got to you."

"Describe the lesions to me."

"The calf muscles are destroyed, the tibia fractured. The nerves seem whole, but the tibial arteries are cut; I've had to apply a tourniquet. What's to be done?"

"You must amputate it."

"But I've nothing to operate with."

"Send an orderly over to me . . ."

Rondy came himself, bringing orderlies with bags. I gave him some forceps, a knife, and an amputating saw, Pentothal, penicillin, linen thread—in short, everything needed for an operation. "Don't forget to introduce Novocain into the nerve," I added. "Tie the artery with linen thread, twice. Don't worry about the bone . . . The first thing is to save the man's life."

Verdaguet had a man with a wound in the thorax; he was spitting blood—a great wheezing hole in the chest. "What's to be done?" he asked.

"Suture the hole somehow, very widely, after a slight débridement . . . Then in three days you can begin to drain it and inject penicillin and streptomycin."

"But I haven't a thing."

He too came with his orderlies, and I gave him Reverdin needles, scissors, forceps, material for the ligature, and antibiotics.

Every morning, too, there was a line of orderlies in my dispensary from all the battalions, begging for surgical equipment, dressings, essential medicines, bandages, and plaster.

I had to watch my reserves diminishing at a terrifying rate.

My requests for supplies to be dropped by parachute were piling up on the command post's radio desk.

Then came the day when a mortar shell fell on Vidal's reserve supplies. In a few seconds, they had all gone up in flames. Earlier, these reserves had been in a shelter, but this had to be cleared to make room for the wounded, and the cases, baskets, and bottles of ether and alcohol had simply been stored in a hole in the ground. Vidal was in the position of a man who has been held up and robbed of all he possessed.

His orderlies came through the trenches, over the bridge, across the barbed wire. I gave him half of all that I had so that his team could get to work again.

During the attacks on the Dominique and Eliane positions, Vidal had been really a marvel; for three days and three nights he had operated without a break and quite alone. From time to time, Barraud had gone to see and help him, but he had his own men to look after, as a battalion doctor. Nor had Vidal's place either the size or the strength of ours. He had only one small electric plant, and the time came when he had to put this in his operating room to get it out of the way of shells. He operated with smoke rising around him and the infuriating sound of a two-stroke engine in his ears.

After these three days, he came back to me at night, as before, to operate on those seriously wounded in the course of the day, and once more we lived through nights never to be forgotten in the company of Gindrey and Patrice. The operating room was turned into a real consulting room, and there were fruitful discussions over a difficult case; the operation which followed was like a scientific demonstration.

Then Vidal was prevented from coming. The tanks which had been camouflaged out of sight had to come out into the open to reply to the Viet fire. A tank could no longer go toward the airfield, nor toward Huguette, nor could it serve as support to infantry around the Dominique position. From time to time, Eliane asked for help from them, and the distance which they had to traverse became increasingly limited.

The preferred site for firing on the Dominique position was the entrance to our terrace, which was a little raised and commanded a good field of fire to the east. Every couple of hours, day and night, I heard one or other of the tanks starting up and the sound of metal tracks crunching into the ground; this slowly increased in volume, reaching its maximum when passing close to our vent holes, then diminishing toward the crossway. Then you would hear the roar of its gun and its machine guns.

The reply was not long delayed: the Viets at once sent a salvo of 75's, 105's, and mortar shells which fell all around it, and of course a large number of them landed on our roof.

When it had finished firing, the tank turned and went back to its place, followed by a series of explosions which only stopped many minutes later.

The result was that Vidal and his orderlies, with the wounded entrusted to them, could no longer be risked on the way to the field hospital, nor on our terrace, which was constantly under fire from shells of every caliber.

Then I could only talk to him over the phone; we spoke often, ten times a day on occasion, especially when we were counterattacking and his inadequately equipped post would receive fifty wounded at a time.

For the Viets were constantly attacking and always being reinforced. Their network of trenches developed infinite ramifications, enveloping our forward positions and hilltops as in a spider's web. Our paratroops and Legionnaires would storm a trench or so by day or night and fill it in with picks and spades, under constant fire from mortars. But the next day they would be opened up again, and others would have appeared, branching this way and that like the ramifications of a genealogical table.

We could tell when a support post was going to be attacked because a Viet trench would be advanced to the edge of our

PART ONE: CONTENTS

Certificate of Price

I, Juan Gallo de Andrada, scrivener of the Chamber of our master the King, in behalf of those who reside in his Council, do hereby certify and affirm that, those lords having seen a book entitled *The Ingenious Gentleman of La Mancha*, composed by Miguel de Cervantes Saavedra, they have estimated the value of each sheet of the said book at three and a half maravedis, and inasmuch as it contains eighty-three sheets, the value of the paper in the said book amounts to two-hundred-ninety maravedis and a half, at which price they have licensed it to be sold; and they have commanded that this certificate of price be placed in the front of the book, which may not be sold without it. As witness these presents, in Valladolid, on the twentieth day of the month of December of the year one-thousand-six-hundred-and-four.

JUAN GALLO DE ANDRADA

Certificate of Errata

THIS book contains nothing worthy of note that does not correspond to the original. In witness of the corrections made, in the College of the Mother of God of the Theologians of the University of Alcalá, on the first of December of the year one-thousand-six-hundred-and-four.

THE LICENTIATE FRANCISCO MURCIA DE LA LLANA

Royal Privilege

THE KING

INASMUCH as we have been informed, Miguel de Cervantes, that you have composed a book entitled *The Ingenious Gentleman of La Mancha*, which book has cost you much labor and is a very useful and profitable work; and inasmuch as you have petitioned and entreated us to grant you the license and authority to have it printed, along with a

Privilege for such time as we in our good grace might see fit to specify; and inasmuch as the said book has been duly scrutinized by our Council in accordance with our recent decree regarding the printing of books, it has been decided that we should grant you this scroll for the said purpose, the which we right willingly do.

With this object in view, by way of showing you grace and favor, we do hereby grant you, or the person you shall employ and none other, license and authority to print the said book entitled *The Ingenious Gentleman of La Mancha,* of which mention has been made above, in all these our realms of Castile, throughout the time and space of ten years current from the day of the date of this our scroll. It is further provided that any person or persons who without your permission shall print or sell the said book or cause it to be printed or sold shall lose the printing which he has made of it along with the type and the forms and shall in addition incur the penalty of a fine of fifty thousand maravedis for each such offense, one third of the said fine to go to the plaintiff, one third to our Chamber, and the remaining third to the judge who shall sentence him.

Withal, each time that you shall have the said book printed in the course of the said ten years, you shall bring it before our Council that each page may be endorsed and the work signed at the end by Juan Gallo de Andrada, our scrivener of the Chamber, in behalf of those in residence; this by way of seeing that the said printing conforms to the original; or you shall take public oath that the said printing has been seen and corrected by the reader appointed by us and has been found to be in conformity with the original; and there shall be printed also a list of the errata pointed out by him for each of the books published; and, finally, the price of each volume shall be duly fixed as provided by law.

And we do hereby command the printer who shall print the said book that he shall not print the beginning nor the first sheet of it nor deliver more than a single book along with the original to the person who pays the cost of the printing or any other person whomsoever until, first and foremost, the said book shall have been corrected and its price fixed by our Council. Only when this shall have been done and under no other circumstances may the beginning and the first sheet be printed, and after it shall be printed this our scroll and approbation, together with the certificate of price and the errata; this under pain of incurring those penalties provided in the laws and regulations of these our realms.

And we do hereby command the members of our Council and all others whomsoever charged with enforcing their decrees, to keep and observe this our scroll and that which is contained therein.

Done in Valladolid, on the twenty-sixth day of the month of September of the year one-thousand-six-hundred-and-four.

I, THE KING

By command of our master, the King,

JUAN DE AMEZQUETA

To the Duke of Béjar

MARQUIS OF GIBRALEÓN, COUNT OF BENALCÁZAR AND BENARES, VISCOUNT OF LA PUEBLA, LORD OF THE BOROUGHS OF CAPILLA, CURIEL, AND BURGUILLOS.

TRUSTING in that good reception and those marks of honor that your Excellency is in the habit of according to books of every sort, being a prince so inclined by nature to favor the fine arts, especially those works that by their nobility do not lower themselves to the service and profit of the vulgar, I have resolved to bring to light THE INGENIOUS GENTLEMAN, DON QUIXOTE OF LA MANCHA under the shelter of your Excellency's most illustrious name; and with that respect that I owe to one so great I do hereby beseech you to receive it and graciously to take it under your protection. Thus, even though barren of those precious ornaments of elegance and erudition in which works composed in the houses of the learned are accustomed to go clad, in your august shadow it may safely dare to appear before the judgment of those who, not content to confine themselves within the bounds of their own ignorance, are wont to condemn with much severity and less justice all writings that are strange to them. If your Excellency in your wisdom will but deign to look upon my worthy desire, I feel sure that you will not disdain this offering by reason of the scant service that it renders you.

MIGUEL DE CERVANTES SAAVEDRA

Prologue

IDLING READER, you may believe me when I tell you that I should have liked this book, which is the child of my brain, to be the fairest, the sprightliest, and the cleverest that could be imagined; but I have not been able to contravene the law of nature which would have it that like begets like. And so, what was to be expected of a sterile and uncultivated wit such as that which I possess if not an offspring that was dried up, shriveled, and eccentric: a story filled with thoughts that never occurred to anyone else, of a sort that might be engendered in a prison where every annoyance has its home and every mournful sound its habitation? [1] Peace and tranquillity, the pleasures of the countryside, the serenity of the heavens, the murmur of fountains, and ease of mind can do much toward causing the most unproductive of muses to become fecund and bring forth progeny that will be the marvel and delight of mankind.

It sometimes happens that a father has an ugly son with no redeeming grace whatever, yet love will draw a veil over the parental eyes which then behold only cleverness and beauty in place of defects, and in speaking to his friends he will make those defects out to be the signs of comeliness and intellect. I, however, who am but Don Quixote's stepfather, have no desire to go with the current of custom, nor would I, dearest reader, beseech you with tears in my eyes as others do to pardon or overlook the faults you discover in this book; you are neither relative nor friend but may call your soul your own and exercise your free judgment. You are in your own house where you are master as the king is of his taxes, for you are familiar with the saying, "Under my cloak I kill the king." [2] All of which exempts and frees you from any kind of respect or obligation; you may say of this story whatever you choose without fear of being slandered for an ill opinion any more than you will be rewarded for a good one.

I should like to bring you the tale unadulterated and unadorned, stripped of the usual prologue and the endless string of sonnets, epigrams, and eulogies such as are commonly found at the beginning of books. For I may tell you that, although I expended no little labor upon the work itself, I have found no task more difficult than the composition of this preface which you are now reading. Many times I took up my pen

and many times I laid it down again, not knowing what to write. On one
occasion when I was thus in suspense, paper before me, pen over my
ear, elbow on the table, and chin in hand, a very clever friend of mine
came in. Seeing me lost in thought, he inquired as to the reason, and I
made no effort to conceal from him the fact that my mind was on the
preface which I had to write for the story of Don Quixote, and that it
was giving me so much trouble that I had about decided not to write
any at all and to abandon entirely the idea of publishing the exploits of
so noble a knight.

"How," I said to him, "can you expect me not to be concerned over
what that venerable legislator, the Public, will say when it sees me, at
my age, after all these years of silent slumber, coming out with a tale
that is as dried as a rush, a stranger to invention, paltry in style, impoverished in content, and wholly lacking in learning and wisdom,
without marginal citations or notes at the end of the book when other
works of this sort, even though they be fabulous and profane, are so
packed with maxims from Aristotle and Plato and the whole crowd of
philosophers as to fill the reader with admiration and lead him to regard
the author as a well read, learned, and eloquent individual? Not to speak
of the citations from Holy Writ! You would think they were at the very
least so many St. Thomases and other doctors of the Church; for they
are so adroit at maintaining a solemn face that, having portrayed in one
line a distracted lover, in the next they will give you a nice little Christian sermon that is a joy and a privilege to hear and read.

"All this my book will lack, for I have no citations for the margins, no
notes for the end. To tell the truth, I do not even know who the authors
are to whom I am indebted, and so am unable to follow the example of
all the others by listing them alphabetically at the beginning, starting
with Aristotle and closing with Xenophon, or, perhaps, with Zoilus or
Zeuxis, notwithstanding the fact that the former was a snarling critic,
the latter a painter. This work will also be found lacking in prefatory
sonnets by dukes, marquises, counts, bishops, ladies, and poets of great
renown; although if I were to ask two or three colleagues of mine, they
would supply the deficiency by furnishing me with productions that
could not be equaled by the authors of most repute in all Spain.

"In short, my friend," I went on, "I am resolved that Señor Don
Quixote shall remain buried in the archives of La Mancha until Heaven
shall provide him with someone to deck him out with all the ornaments
that he lacks; for I find myself incapable of remedying the situation,
being possessed of little learning or aptitude, and I am, moreover, ex-

tremely lazy when it comes to hunting up authors who will say for me what I am unable to say for myself. And if I am in a state of suspense and my thoughts are woolgathering, you will find a sufficient explanation in what I have just told you."

Hearing this, my friend struck his forehead with the palm of his hand and burst into a loud laugh.

"In the name of God, brother," he said, "you have just deprived me of an illusion. I have known you for a long time, and I have always taken you to be clever and prudent in all your actions; but I now perceive that you are as far from all that as Heaven from the earth. How is it that things of so little moment and so easily remedied can worry and perplex a mind as mature as yours and ordinarily so well adapted to break down and trample underfoot far greater obstacles? I give you my word, this does not come from any lack of cleverness on your part, but ra.her from excessive indolence and a lack of experience. Do you ask for proof of what I say? Then pay attention closely and in the blink of an eye you shall see how I am going to solve all your difficulties and supply all those things the want of which, so you tell me, is keeping you in suspense, as a result of which you hesitate to publish the history of that famous Don Quixote of yours, the light and mirror of all knight-errantry."

"Tell me, then," I replied, "how you propose to go about curing my diffidence and bringing clarity out of the chaos and confusion of my mind?"

"Take that first matter," he continued, "of the sonnets, epigrams, or eulogies, which should bear the names of grave and titled personages: you can remedy that by taking a little trouble and composing the pieces yourself, and afterward you can baptize them with any name you see fit, fathering them on Prester John of the Indies or the Emperor of Trebizond, for I have heard tell that they were famous poets; and supposing they were not and that a few pedants and bachelors of arts should go around muttering behind your back that it is not so, you should not give so much as a pair of maravedis for all their carping, since even though they make you out to be a liar, they are not going to cut off the hand that put these things on paper.

"As for marginal citations and authors in whom you may find maxims and sayings that you may put in your story, you have but to make use of those scraps of Latin that you know by heart or can look up without too much bother. Thus, when you come to treat of liberty and slavery, jot down:

Non bene pro toto libertas venditur auro.[3]

And then in the margin you will cite Horace or whoever it was that
said it. If the subject is death, come up with:

>*Pallida mors aequo pulsat pede pauperum tabernas*
>*Regumque turres.*[4]

If it is friendship or the love that God commands us to show our enemies,
then is the time to fall back on the Scriptures, which you can do by
putting yourself out very little; you have but to quote the words of God
himself:

>*Ego autem dico vobis: diligite inimicos vestros.*

If it is evil thoughts, lose no time in turning to the Gospels:

>*De corde exeunt cogitationes malae.*[5]

If it is the instability of friends, here is Cato for you with a distich:

>*Donec eris felix multos numerabis amicos;*
>*Tempora si fuerint nubila, solus eris.*[6]

With these odds and ends of Latin and others of the same sort, you can
cause yourself to be taken for a grammarian, although I must say that is
no great honor or advantage these days.

"So far as notes at the end of the book are concerned, you may safely
go about it in this manner: let us suppose that you mention some giant,
Goliath let us say; with this one allusion which costs you little or nothing, you have a fine note which you may set down as follows: *The giant
Golias or Goliath. This was a Philistine whom the shepherd David slew
with a mighty cast from his slingshot in the valley of Terebinth, according to what we read in the Book of Kings*, chapter so-and-so where you
find it written.[7]

"In addition to this, by way of showing that you are a learned humanist and a cosmographer, contrive to bring into your story the name of
the River Tagus, and there you are with another great little note: *The
River Tagus was so called after a king of Spain; it rises in such and such
a place and empties into the ocean, washing the walls of the famous city
of Lisbon; it is supposed to have golden sands*, etc. If it is robbers, I will
let you have the story of Cacus,[8] which I know by heart. If it is loose
women, there is the Bishop of Mondoñedo,[9] who will lend you Lamia,
Laïs, and Flora, an allusion that will do you great credit. If the subject is cruelty, Ovid will supply you with Medea; or if it is enchantresses
and witches, Homer has Calypso and Vergil Circe. If it is valorous captains, Julius Caesar will lend you himself, in his *Commentaries*, and Plutarch will furnish a thousand Alexanders. If it is loves, with the ounce
or two of Tuscan that you know you may make the acquaintance of
Leon the Hebrew,[10] who will satisfy you to your heart's content. And

in case you do not care to go abroad, here in your own house you have Fonseca's *Of the Love of God*,[11] where you will encounter in condensed form all that the most imaginative person could wish upon this subject. The short of the matter is, you have but to allude to these names or touch upon those stories that I have mentioned and leave to me the business of the notes and citations; I will guarantee you enough to fill the margins and four whole sheets at the back.

"And now we come to the list of authors cited, such as other works contain but in which your own is lacking. Here again the remedy is an easy one; you have but to look up some book that has them all, from A to Z as you were saying, and transfer the entire list as it stands. What if the imposition is plain for all to see? You have little need to refer to them, and so it does not matter; and some may be so simple-minded as to believe that you have drawn upon them all in your simple unpretentious little story. If it serves no other purpose, this imposing list of authors will at least give your book an unlooked-for air of authority. What is more, no one is going to put himself to the trouble of verifying your references to see whether or not you have followed all these authors, since it will not be worth his pains to do so.

"This is especially true in view of the fact that your book stands in no need of all these things whose absence you lament; for the entire work is an attack upon the books of chivalry of which Aristotle never dreamed, of which St. Basil has nothing to say, and of which Cicero had no knowledge; nor do the fine points of truth or the observations of astrology have anything to do with its fanciful absurdities; geometrical measurements, likewise, and rhetorical argumentations serve for nothing here; you have no sermon to preach to anyone by mingling the human with the divine, a kind of motley in which no Christian intellect should be willing to clothe itself.

"All that you have to do is to make proper use of imitation in what you write, and the more perfect the imitation the better will your writing be. Inasmuch as you have no other object in view than that of overthrowing the authority and prestige which books of chivalry enjoy in the world at large and among the vulgar, there is no reason why you should go begging maxims of the philosophers, counsels of Holy Writ, fables of the poets, orations of the rhetoricians, or miracles of the saints; see to it, rather, that your style flows along smoothly, pleasingly, and sonorously, and that your words are the proper ones, meaningful and well placed, expressive of your intention in setting them down and of what you wish to say, without any intricacy or obscurity.

"Let it be your aim that, by reading your story, the melancholy may be moved to laughter and the cheerful man made merrier still; let the simple not be bored, but may the clever admire your originality; let the grave ones not despise you, but let the prudent praise you. And keep in mind, above all, your purpose, which is that of undermining the ill-founded edifice that is constituted by those books of chivalry, so abhorred by many but admired by many more; if you succeed in attaining it, you will have accomplished no little."

Listening in profound silence to what my friend had to say, I was so impressed by his reasoning that, with no thought of questioning them, I decided to make use of his arguments in composing this prologue. Here, gentle reader, you will perceive my friend's cleverness, my own good fortune in coming upon such a counselor at a time when I needed him so badly, and the profit which you yourselves are to have in finding so sincere and straightforward an account of the famous Don Quixote de la Mancha, who is held by the inhabitants of the Campo de Montiel region [12] to have been the most chaste lover and the most valiant knight that had been seen in those parts for many a year. I have no desire to enlarge upon the service I am rendering you in bringing you the story of so notable and honored a gentleman; I merely would have you thank me for having made you acquainted with the famous Sancho Panza, his squire, in whom, to my mind, is to be found an epitome of all the squires and their drolleries scattered here and there throughout the pages of those vain and empty books of chivalry. And with this, may God give you health, and may He be not unmindful of me as well. VALE.

PREFATORY POEMS

Urganda the Unknown

FOR THE BOOK OF DON QUIXOTE DE LA MANCHA[1]

If to win the worthy be thine ambition,
O book, then let the foolish chatter
As much as they please, it will not matter,
For thy desire has had fruition.
To bake bread for fools is not thy mission:
Hand raised to mouth, they're hungry still,
But taste thee the dunces surely will,
And each his fingers will greedily lick
To prove he appreciates the trick
Of such fine fare and would eat his fill.

Experience shows that he who reaches
A tree that's goodly, fair, and thriving,
Is bound to find there, upon arriving,
A pleasing shade; let none impeach
This lesson life itself would teach.
Draw near; thy star benign is showing
A regal tree in Béjar[2] that's growing.
In way of fruit this tree doth bear
One who a princely crown doth wear;
'Tis an Alexander his shade bestowing.

Thou shalt relate the high emprises
Of a Manchegan[3] gentleman whose reading
Had turned his head with tales of bleeding
Knights-errant, damsels, love's surprises,
And all of chivalry's disguises.
By deeds of valor he sought to gain
His lady's love, and ease his pain;
His model Orlando Furioso,
And Dulcinea del Toboso
Was the one whose favor he would obtain.

No hieroglyphs upon thy shield,[4]
No pictures to display thy pride;

Better by far a humbler stride,
Then envy's weapon none can wield
By saying all that thou dost yield
Is an old story quite banal
Of Alvaro de Luna [5] or Hannibal
Or of King Francis his fate bemoaning
As at Madrid he lies a-groaning. [6]
So, close the door on their cabal.

Seeing it was not Heaven's pleasure
To make thee learned as black John, [7]
Do not the cloak of learning don
By quoting Latin in over-measure,
Displaying thy philosophic treasure
In long and windy argument,
Until some fellow irreverent,
Twisting his mouth at thine ear shall say:
"Why give me flowers, anyway?
On me such bounty is misspent."

Seek not to know or to portray
The lives of others; mind thine own
And leave thy neighbor's life alone.
Be wise in this and in the play
Thou givest thy wit—there may come a day
When the word spoken in lightsome jest
Will come winging home with thee to rest;
And ever seek an honest fame,
For he is doomed to perpetual blame
Who nonsense prints and calls it best.

Remember, 'tis a foolish thing,
Dwelling beneath a roof of glass,
To stone thy neighbors as they pass,
For they likewise may pebbles fling.
Seek rather to please in everything
The man of taste and judgment fine,
That he may ponder every line;
If damsels be thy audience,
Thou shalt be spurned by those with sense,
To fools thou dost thyself consign.

Amadis of Gaul
TO DON QUIXOTE DE LA MANCHA [8]

SONNET

Thou who didst imitate my own sad life,
So full of loneliness and love's disdain
As on the Poor Rock [9] I endured my pain—
My days once joyful now with sorrow rife,
To pay love's penance was my constant strife—
Thou knowest the taste of tears; for thee most vain
Were silver, tin, or copper plate; thou wert fain
To make of the earth thy table and chatelaine.
But rest assured, thou livest eternally,
Or as long as blond Apollo in that fourth sphere
Doth guide on their heavenly course his fiery steeds.
Thy fame and valor shall unsullied be,
Thy fatherland remain without a peer,
And peerless the chronicler of thy brave deeds.

Don Belianís of Greece [10]

TO DON QUIXOTE DE LA MANCHA

SONNET

In slashing, smashing, bruising, in word and deed,
I was the foremost knight of errantry,
In pride, in valor, in dexterity.
A myriad wrongs I righted, did ever heed
The call of those who were in direst need;
My famed exploits shall endure eternally.
Deep-versed was I in love and ecstasy,
And on the field of honor I did bleed.
A giant for me was but a dwarf. No boon
Luck did deny me; I was ever wise
And brought her by the forelock to my feet.
But though my fortune rides the horn o' the moon,
I envy still thy deeds of high emprise,
O great Quixote, who dost with me compete!

The Lady Oriana [11]

TO DULCINEA DEL TOBOSO

O lovely Dulcinea, could I with thee
But exchange my Miraflores [12] of such renown,
London for El Toboso, thy little town,
How great a comfort and relief 'twould be!
Could I but once my soul and body see
Dressed in thy love as in a daily gown,
And behold that famous knight (thy love his crown)
Performing some brave feat of chivalry!
Ah, then, I might remain fully as chaste
With Amadis [13] as thou with thy lover bold,
The gallant Don Quixote without blame!
Then I'd not envy, but envied be, nor waste
My life in sorrow for the time that's told;
Joy would be mine, no cost to my good name!

Gandalin, Squire to Amadis of Gaul,

TO SANCHO PANZA, DON QUIXOTE'S SQUIRE

Hail, celebrated one, Fortune was kind
When she did set thee to the squire's trade,
And wise as well—ah, she no blunder made;
No great calamity e'er came to find
Thee out, but men still fondly call to mind
That thou didst erstwhile leave sickle and spade
For the pursuit of arms, all unafraid;
Thy squire's simplicity puts far behind
The haughty pride that would defy the moon.
I envy thee thine ass, thy name, thy sense,
And those saddlebags that thou didst wisely stuff.
Sancho, hail once again! And very soon
May our Spanish Ovid [14] do thee reverence
By giving thee a famous kick-and-cuff. [15]

Donoso, Interlarded Poet,[16]

TO SANCHO PANZA AND ROCINANTE

TO SANCHO PANZA

I am Sancho Panza, squi—	(squire)
Of the Manchegan Don Quixo—	(Quixote)
Who did withdraw to a place remo—	(remote)
That I might from his service reti—.	(retire)
Villadiego [17] known as the Si—	(Silent)
Is said to have found that the real se—	(secret)
Of a good life was a pleasant re—;	(retreat)
His words you'll find if in that divine boo—,	(book)
The *Celestina*,[18] you choose to loo—,	(look)
Or 'twould be divine if more discree—.	(discreet)

TO ROCINANTE

I am Rocinante, the famous stee—,	(steed)
Great Babieca's [19] great grandso—.	(grandson)
'Twas the sin of leanness that for me wo—	(won)
My master (I met his every nee—),	(need)
Don Quixote of far-famed dee—.	(deed)
I ran my race in my own good ti—,	(time)
And can say no stable mate of mi—	(mine)
Ever stole my barley by dint of hoo—;	(hoof)
From Lazarillo [20] I learned, in soo—	(sooth)
With a straw to take the blind man's wi—.	(wine)

Orlando Furioso

TO DON QUIXOTE DE LA MANCHA

SONNET [21]

If thou art not a Peer,[22] no peer hast thou,
But amongst a thousand Peers, a peer thou art,
When thou art present, thou dost stand apart.
Victor invincible, unvanquished up to now.

Quixote, I am Orlando. Hast heard how
I sailed far seas for her who held my heart?
Love for Angelica [23] my course did chart;
My valor on Fame's altar laid its vow,
Held back oblivion. It is not meet
To rival thee in prowess or in fame,
E'en though our loss of sense be a common bond;
But thou mayest very well with me compete,
Though neither Moor nor Scythian didst tame:
In our ill-fated loves we correspond.

The Knight of the Sun [24]

TO DON QUIXOTE DE LA MANCHA

My sword, though valiant, did never equal thine,
Phoebus of Spain, O thou most courteous knight,
Nor was my arm as powerful in the fight,
Though it lightning-flashed all while the sun did shine.
Empires I wanted not. I did decline
The rosy Orient's crown for the countenance bright
Of Claridiana, filled with dawn's own light,
For she was my Aurora blest, divine.
Miraculous my love for her and rare;
And banished by her decree, my mighty arm
Caused hell in all its fury to fear my rage.
But thou, Gothic Quixote, shinest everywhere
Immortal, thanks to Dulcinea's charm,
While she is ever famous, honored, sage.

Solisdan [25]

TO DON QUIXOTE DE LA MANCHA

Señor Quixote, your fancies turned your head,
But none shall reprehend your lack of guile
Or take you for a man that's base and vile;
Your deeds speak for themselves when all is said.

You went about the world in knightly style,
Undoing wrongs and suffering the while
A myriad drubbings; but be comforted.
If the beauteous Dulcinea did prolong
Love's agony and pitied not your pain,
In such a case there's one thing you may do:
Reflect that Sancho Panza was not strong
As a go-between a lady's love to gain;
He was a dunce, she cruel, no lover you.

DIALOGUE BETWEEN BABIECA [26] AND ROCINANTE

SONNET

B. How comes it, Rocinante, you are so lean?
R. From working overmuch and eating never.
B. But straw and barley they must give you ever?
R. Not one mouthful, my master is so mean.
B. Come, come, sir, you are quite ill bred, I ween.
  You talk like an ass; our acquaintance we must sever.
R. A lifelong ass is he—at least not clever—
  And in love the biggest ass was ever seen.
B. To love is foolish, then? R. It is not wise.
B. You grow metaphysical. R. From lack of food.
B. Why not complain of the squire? R. Ah, what's the use?
  How in my sorrow can I sermonize
  When master and man are of the selfsame brood
  And both are hacks like me,[27] fit for abuse?

The Ingenious Gentleman

DON QUIXOTE

DE LA MANCHA

Part One

CHAPTER I. *Which treats of the station in life and the pursuits of the famous gentleman, Don Quixote de la Mancha.*

IN A village of La Mancha the name of which I have no desire to recall,[1] there lived not so long ago one of those gentlemen who always have a lance in the rack, an ancient buckler, a skinny nag, and a greyhound for the chase. A stew with more beef than mutton in it, chopped meat for his evening meal, scraps[2] for a Saturday, lentils on Friday, and a young pigeon as a special delicacy for Sunday, went to account for three-quarters of his income. The rest of it he laid out on a broadcloth greatcoat and velvet stockings for feast days, with slippers to match, while the other days of the week he cut a figure in a suit of the finest homespun. Living with him were a housekeeper in her forties, a niece who was not yet twenty, and a lad of the field and market place who saddled his horse for him and wielded the pruning knife.

This gentleman of ours was close on to fifty, of a robust constitution but with little flesh on his bones and a face that was lean and gaunt. He was noted for his early rising, being very fond of the hunt. They will try to tell you that his surname was Quijada or Quesada—there is some

difference of opinion among those who have written on the subject—
but according to the most likely conjectures we are to understand that
it was really Quejana. But all this means very little so far as our story
is concerned, providing that in the telling of it we do not depart one
iota from the truth.

You may know, then, that the aforesaid gentleman, on those occasions
when he was at leisure, which was most of the year around, was in the
habit of reading books of chivalry with such pleasure and devotion as to
lead him almost wholly to forget the life of a hunter and even the ad-
ministration of his estate. So great was his curiosity and infatuation in
this regard that he even sold many acres of tillable land in order to be
able to buy and read the books that he loved, and he would carry home
with him as many of them as he could obtain.

Of all those that he thus devoured none pleased him so well as the ones
that had been composed by the famous Feliciano de Silva,[3] whose lucid
prose style and involved conceits were as precious to him as pearls; especially when he came to read those tales of love and amorous challenges
that are to be met with in many places, such a passage as the following,
for example: "The reason of the unreason that afflicts my reason, in such
a manner weakens my reason that I with reason lament me of your comeliness." And he was similarly affected when his eyes fell upon such lines
as these: ". . . the high Heaven of your divinity divinely fortifies you
with the stars and renders you deserving of that desert your greatness
doth deserve."

The poor fellow used to lie awake nights in an effort to disentangle
the meaning and make sense out of passages such as these, although
Aristotle himself would not have been able to understand them, even if
he had been resurrected for that sole purpose. He was not at ease in his
mind over those wounds that Don Belianís [4] gave and received; for no
matter how great the surgeons who treated him, the poor fellow must
have been left with his face and his entire body covered with marks
and scars. Nevertheless, he was grateful to the author for closing the
book with the promise of an interminable adventure to come; many a
time he was tempted to take up his pen and literally finish the tale as
had been promised, and he undoubtedly would have done so, and would
have succeeded at it very well, if his thoughts had not been constantly
occupied with other things of greater moment.

He often talked it over with the village curate, who was a learned man,
a graduate of Sigüenza,[5] and they would hold long discussions as to who
had been the better knight, Palmerin of England or Amadis of Gaul; but

Master Nicholas, the barber of the same village, was in the habit of saying that no one could come up to the Knight of Phoebus, and that if anyone *could* compare with him it was Don Galaor, brother of Amadis of Gaul, for Galaor was ready for anything—he was none of your finical knights, who went around whimpering as his brother did, and in point of valor he did not lag behind him.

In short, our gentleman became so immersed in his reading that he spent whole nights from sundown to sunup and his days from dawn to dusk in poring over his books, until, finally, from so little sleeping and so much reading, his brain dried up and he went completely out of his mind. He had filled his imagination with everything that he had read, with enchantments, knightly encounters, battles, challenges, wounds, with tales of love and its torments, and all sorts of impossible things, and as a result had come to believe that all these fictitious happenings were true; they were more real to him than anything else in the world. He would remark that the Cid Ruy Díaz had been a very good knight, but there was no comparison between him and the Knight of the Flaming Sword,[6] who with a single backward stroke had cut in half two fierce and monstrous giants. He preferred Bernardo del Carpio, who at Roncesvalles had slain Roland despite the charm the latter bore, availing himself of the stratagem which Hercules employed when he strangled Antaeus, the son of Earth, in his arms.

He had much good to say for Morgante who, though he belonged to the haughty, overbearing race of giants, was of an affable disposition and well brought up. But, above all, he cherished an admiration for Rinaldo of Montalbán,[7] especially as he beheld him sallying forth from his castle to rob all those that crossed his path, or when he thought of him overseas stealing the image of Mohammed which, so the story has it, was all of gold. And he would have liked very well to have had his fill of kicking that traitor Galalón,[8] a privilege for which he would have given his housekeeper with his niece thrown into the bargain.

At last, when his wits were gone beyond repair, he came to conceive the strangest idea that ever occurred to any madman in this world. It now appeared to him fitting and necessary, in order to win a greater amount of honor for himself and serve his country at the same time, to become a knight-errant and roam the world on horseback, in a suit of armor; he would go in quest of adventures, by way of putting into practice all that he had read in his books; he would right every manner of wrong, placing himself in situations of the greatest peril such as would redound to the eternal glory of his name. As a reward for his valor and the might of his arm, the poor fellow could already see himself crowned Emperor of Trebizond at the very least; and so, carried away by the strange pleasure that he found in such thoughts as these, he at once set about putting his plan into effect.

The first thing he did was to burnish up some old pieces of armor, left him by his great-grandfather, which for ages had lain in a corner, moldering and forgotten. He polished and adjusted them as best he could, and then he noticed that one very important thing was lacking: there was no closed helmet, but only a morion, or visorless headpiece, with turned up brim of the kind foot soldiers wore. His ingenuity, however, enabled him to remedy this, and he proceeded to fashion out of cardboard a kind of half-helmet, which, when attached to the morion, gave the appearance of a whole one. True, when he went to see if it was strong enough to withstand a good slashing blow, he was somewhat disappointed; for when he drew his sword and gave it a couple of thrusts, he succeeded only in undoing a whole week's labor. The ease with which he had hewed it to bits disturbed him no little, and he decided to make it over. This time he placed a few strips of iron on the inside, and then, convinced that it was strong enough, refrained from putting it to any further test; instead, he adopted it then and there as the finest helmet ever made.

After this, he went out to have a look at his nag; and although the animal had more *cuartos*, or cracks, in its hoof than there are quarters in a real,[9] and more blemishes than Gonela's steed which *tantum pellis et ossa fuit*,[10] it nonetheless looked to its master like a far better horse than Alexander's Bucephalus or the Babieca of the Cid. He spent all of four days in trying to think up a name for his mount; for—so he told himself—seeing that it belonged to so famous and worthy a knight, there was no reason why it should not have a name of equal renown. The kind of name he wanted was one that would at once indicate what the nag had been before it came to belong to a knight-errant and what its present status was; for it stood to reason that, when the master's worldly condition changed, his horse also ought to have a famous, high-sounding appellation, one suited to the new order of things and the new profession that it was to follow.

After he in his memory and imagination had made up, struck out, and discarded many names, now adding to and now subtracting from the list, he finally hit upon "Rocinante," a name that impressed him as being sonorous and at the same time indicative of what the steed had been when it was but a hack,[11] whereas now it was nothing other than the first and foremost of all the hacks in the world.

Having found a name for his horse that pleased his fancy, he then desired to do as much for himself, and this required another week, and by the end of that period he had made up his mind that he was henceforth to be known as Don Quixote,[12] which, as has been stated, has led the authors of this veracious history to assume that his real name must undoubtedly have been Quijada, and not Quesada as others would have it. But remembering that the valiant Amadis was not content to call himself that and nothing more, but added the name of his kingdom and fatherland that he might make it famous also, and thus came to take the name Amadis of Gaul, so our good knight chose to add his place of origin and become "Don Quixote de la Mancha"; for by this means, as he saw it, he was making very plain his lineage and was conferring honor upon his country by taking its name as his own.

And so, having polished up his armor and made the morion over into a closed helmet, and having given himself and his horse a name, he naturally found but one thing lacking still: he must seek out a lady of whom he could become enamored; for a knight-errant without a lady-love was like a tree without leaves or fruit, a body without a soul.

"If," he said to himself, "as a punishment for my sins or by a stroke of fortune I should come upon some giant hereabouts, a thing that very commonly happens to knights-errant, and if I should slay him in a hand-to-hand encounter or perhaps cut him in two, or, finally, if I should vanquish and subdue him, would it not be well to have someone to whom I may send him as a present, in order that he, if he is living, may come in, fall upon his knees in front of my sweet lady, and say in a humble and submissive tone of voice, 'I, lady, am the giant Caraculiambro, lord of the island Malindrania, who has been overcome in single combat by that knight who never can be praised enough, Don Quixote de la Mancha, the same who sent me to present myself before your Grace that your Highness may dispose of me as you see fit'?"

Oh, how our good knight reveled in this speech, and more than ever when he came to think of the name that he should give his lady! As the story goes, there was a very good-looking farm girl who lived near by, with whom he had once been smitten, although it is generally believed that she never knew or suspected it. Her name was Aldonza Lorenzo, and it seemed to him that she was the one upon whom he should bestow the title of mistress of his thoughts. For her he wished a name that should

not be incongruous with his own and that would convey the suggestion
of a princess or a great lady; and, accordingly, he resolved to call her
"Dulcinea del Toboso," she being a native of that place. A musical
name to his ears, out of the ordinary and significant, like the others he
had chosen for himself and his appurtenances.

CHAPTER II. *Which treats of the first sally that
the ingenious Don Quixote made from his native heath.*

HAVING, then, made all these preparations, he did not wish to lose
any time in putting his plan into effect, for he could not but blame himself for what the world was losing by his delay, so many were the wrongs
that were to be righted, the grievances to be redressed, the abuses to
be done away with, and the duties to be performed. Accordingly, without informing anyone of his intention and without letting anyone see
him, he set out one morning before daybreak on one of those very hot
days in July. Donning all his armor, mounting Rocinante, adjusting his
ill-contrived helmet, bracing his shield on his arm, and taking up his
lance, he sallied forth by the back gate of his stable yard into the open
countryside. It was with great contentment and joy that he saw how
easily he had made a beginning toward the fulfillment of his desire.

No sooner was he out on the plain, however, than a terrible thought
assailed him, one that all but caused him to abandon the enterprise he had
undertaken. This occurred when he suddenly remembered that he had
never formally been dubbed a knight, and so, in accordance with the
law of knighthood, was not permitted to bear arms against one who
had a right to that title. And even if he had been, as a novice knight he
would have had to wear white armor,[1] without any device on his shield,
until he should have earned one by his exploits. These thoughts led him
to waver in his purpose, but, madness prevailing over reason, he resolved
to have himself knighted by the first person he met, as many others had
done if what he had read in those books that he had at home was true.
And so far as white armor was concerned, he would scour his own the

first chance that offered until it shone whiter than any ermine. With this he became more tranquil and continued on his way, letting his horse take whatever path it chose, for he believed that therein lay the very essence of adventures.

And so we find our newly fledged adventurer jogging along and talking to himself. "Undoubtedly," he is saying, "in the days to come, when the true history of my famous deeds is published, the learned chronicler who records them, when he comes to describe my first sally so early in the morning, will put down something like this: 'No sooner had the rubicund Apollo spread over the face of the broad and spacious earth the gilded filaments of his beauteous locks, and no sooner had the little singing birds of painted plumage greeted with their sweet and mellifluous harmony the coming of the Dawn, who, leaving the soft couch of her jealous spouse, now showed herself to mortals at all the doors and balconies of the horizon that bounds La Mancha—no sooner had this happened than the famous knight, Don Quixote de la Mancha, forsaking his own downy bed and mounting his famous steed, Rocinante, fared forth and began riding over the ancient and famous Campo de Montiel.' " [2]

And this was the truth, for he was indeed riding over that stretch of plain.

"O happy age and happy century," he went on, "in which my famous exploits shall be published, exploits worthy of being engraved in bronze, sculptured in marble, and depicted in paintings for the benefit of posterity. O wise magician, whoever you be, to whom shall fall the task of chronicling this extraordinary history of mine! I beg of you not to forget my good Rocinante, eternal companion of my wayfarings and my wanderings."

Then, as though he really had been in love: "O Princess Dulcinea, lady of this captive heart! Much wrong have you done me in thus sending me forth with your reproaches and sternly commanding me not to appear in your beauteous presence. O lady, deign to be mindful of this your subject who endures so many woes for the love of you."

And so he went on, stringing together absurdities, all of a kind that his books had taught him, imitating insofar as he was able the language of their authors. He rode slowly, and the sun came up so swiftly and with so much heat that it would have been sufficient to melt his brains if he had had any. He had been on the road almost the entire day without anything happening that is worthy of being set down here; and he was on the verge of despair, for he wished to meet someone at once with whom he might try the valor of his good right arm. Certain authors say that his first adventure was that of Puerto Lápice, while others state that it was that of the windmills; ³ but in this particular instance I am in a position to affirm what I have read in the annals of La Mancha; and that is to the effect that he went all that day until nightfall, when he and his hack found themselves tired to death and famished. Gazing all around him to see if he could discover some castle or shepherd's hut where he might take shelter and attend to his pressing needs, he caught sight of an inn ⁴ not far off the road along which they were traveling, and this to him was like a star guiding him not merely to the gates, but rather, let us say, to the palace of redemption. Quickening his pace, he came up to it just as night was falling.

By chance there stood in the doorway two lasses of the sort known as "of the district"; they were on their way to Seville in the company of some mule drivers who were spending the night in the inn. Now, everything that this adventurer of ours thought, saw, or imagined seemed to him to be directly out of one of the storybooks he had read, and so, when he caught sight of the inn, it at once became a castle with its four turrets and its pinnacles of gleaming silver, not to speak of the drawbridge and moat and all the other things that are commonly supposed to go with a castle. As he rode up to it, he accordingly reined in Rocinante and sat there waiting for a dwarf to appear upon the battlements and blow his trumpet by way of announcing the arrival of a knight. The dwarf, however, was slow in coming, and as Rocinante was anxious to reach the stable, Don Quixote drew up to the door of the hostelry and surveyed the two merry maidens, who to him were a pair of beauteous damsels or gracious ladies taking their ease at the castle gate.

And then a swineherd came along, engaged in rounding up his drove of hogs—for, without any apology, that is what they were. He gave a blast on his horn to bring them together, and this at once became for Don Quixote just what he wished it to be: some dwarf who was heralding his coming; and so it was with a vast deal of satisfaction that he presented himself before the ladies in question, who, upon beholding a man in full armor like this, with lance and buckler, were filled with fright and made as if to flee indoors. Realizing that they were afraid, Don Quixote raised his pasteboard visor and revealed his withered, dust-covered face.

"Do not flee, your Ladyships," he said to them in a courteous manner and gentle voice. "You need not fear that any wrong will be done you, for it is not in accordance with the order of knighthood which I profess to wrong anyone, much less such highborn damsels as your appearance shows you to be."

The girls looked at him, endeavoring to scan his face, which was half hidden by his ill-made visor. Never having heard women of their profession called damsels before, they were unable to restrain their laughter, at which Don Quixote took offense.

"Modesty," he observed, "well becomes those with the dower of beauty, and, moreover, laughter that has not good cause is a very foolish thing. But I do not say this to be discourteous or to hurt your feelings; my only desire is to serve you."

The ladies did not understand what he was talking about, but felt more than ever like laughing at our knight's unprepossessing figure. This increased his annoyance, and there is no telling what would have happened if at that moment the innkeeper had not come out. He was very fat and very peaceably inclined; but upon sighting this grotesque personage clad in bits of armor that were quite as oddly matched as were his bridle, lance, buckler, and corselet, mine host was not at all indisposed to join the lasses in their merriment. He was suspicious, however, of all this paraphernalia and decided that it would be better to keep a civil tongue in his head.

"If, Sir Knight," he said, "your Grace desires a lodging, aside from a bed—for there is none to be had in this inn—you will find all else that you may want in great abundance."

When Don Quixote saw how humble the governor of the castle was— for he took the innkeeper and his inn to be no less than that—he replied, "For me, Sir Castellan, anything will do, since

> *Arms are my only ornament,*
> *My only rest the fight,* etc."

The landlord thought that the knight had called him a castellan because he took him for one of those worthies of Castile,[5] whereas the truth was, he was an Andalusian from the beach of Sanlúcar, no less a thief than Cacus himself, and as full of tricks as a student or a page boy.

"In that case," he said,

> *"Your bed will be the solid rock,*
> *Your sleep: to watch all night.*[6]

This being so, you may be assured of finding beneath this roof enough to keep you awake for a whole year, to say nothing of a single night."

With this, he went up to hold the stirrup for Don Quixote, who encountered much difficulty in dismounting, not having broken his fast all day long. The knight then directed his host to take good care of the steed, as it was the best piece of horseflesh in all the world. The innkeeper looked it over, and it did not impress him as being half as good as Don Quixote had said it was. Having stabled the animal, he came back to see what his guest would have and found the latter being relieved of his armor by the damsels, who by now had made their peace with the new arrival. They had already removed his breastplate and backpiece but had no idea how they were going to open his gorget or get his improvised helmet off. That piece of armor had been tied on with green ribbons which it would be necessary to cut, since the knots could not be undone, but he would not hear of this, and so spent all the rest of that night with his headpiece in place, which gave him the weirdest, most laughable appearance that could be imagined.

Don Quixote fancied that these wenches who were assisting him must surely be the chatelaine and other ladies of the castle, and so proceeded to address them very gracefully and with much wit:

> "*Never was knight so served*
> *By any noble dame*
> *As was Don Quixote*
> *When from his village he came,*
> *With damsels to wait on his every need*
> *While princesses cared for his hack . . .*[7]

"By hack," he explained, "is meant my steed Rocinante, for that is his name, and mine is Don Quixote de la Mancha. I had no intention of revealing my identity until my exploits done in your service should have made me known to you; but the necessity of adapting to present circumstances that old ballad of Lancelot has led to your becoming acquainted with it prematurely. However, the time will come when your Ladyships shall command and I will obey and with the valor of my good right arm show you how eager I am to serve you."

The young women were not used to listening to speeches like this and had not a word to say, but merely asked him if he desired to eat anything.

"I could eat a bite of something, yes," replied Don Quixote. "Indeed, I feel that a little food would go very nicely just now."

He thereupon learned that, since it was Friday, there was nothing to be had in all the inn except a few portions of codfish, which in Castile is called *abadejo*, in Andalusia *bacalao*, in some places *curadillo*, and elsewhere *truchuella* or small trout. Would his Grace, then, have some small trout, seeing that was all there was that they could offer him?

"If there are enough of them," said Don Quixote, "they will take the place of a trout, for it is all one to me whether I am given in change eight reales or one piece of eight. What is more, those small trout may be like veal, which is better than beef, or like kid, which is better than goat. But however that may be, bring them on at once, for the weight and burden of arms is not to be borne without inner sustenance."

Placing the table at the door of the hostelry, in the open air, they brought the guest a portion of badly soaked and worse cooked codfish and a piece of bread as black and moldy as the suit of armor that he wore. It was a mirth-provoking sight to see him eat, for he still had his helmet on with his visor fastened,[8] which made it impossible for him to put anything into his mouth with his hands, and so it was necessary for one of the girls to feed him. As for giving him anything to drink, that would have been out of the question if the innkeeper had not hollowed out a reed, placing one end in Don Quixote's mouth while through the other end he poured the wine. All this the knight bore very patiently rather than have them cut the ribbons of his helmet.

At this point a gelder of pigs approached the inn, announcing his arrival with four or five blasts on his horn, all of which confirmed Don Quixote in the belief that this was indeed a famous castle, for what was this if not music that they were playing for him? The fish was trout, the bread was of the finest, the wenches were ladies, and the innkeeper was the castellan. He was convinced that he had been right in his resolve to sally forth and roam the world at large, but there was one thing that still distressed him greatly, and that was the fact that he had not as yet been dubbed a knight; as he saw it, he could not legitimately engage in any adventure until he had received the order of knighthood.

Wearied of his thoughts, Don Quixote lost no time over the scanty repast which the inn afforded him. When he had finished, he summoned the landlord and, taking him out to the stable, closed the doors and fell on his knees in front of him.

"Never, valiant knight," he said, "shall I arise from here until you have courteously granted me the boon I seek, one which will redound to your praise and to the good of the human race."

Seeing his guest at his feet and hearing him utter such words as these, the innkeeper could only stare at him in bewilderment, not knowing what to say or do. It was in vain that he entreated him to rise, for Don Quixote refused to do so until his request had been granted.

"I expected nothing less of your great magnificence, my lord," the latter then continued, "and so I may tell you that the boon I asked and which you have so generously conceded me is that tomorrow morning you dub me a knight. Until that time, in the chapel of this your castle, I will watch over my armor, and when morning comes, as I have said, that which I so desire shall then be done, in order that I may lawfully go to the four corners of the earth in quest of adventures and to succor the needy, which is the chivalrous duty of all knights-errant such as I who long to engage in deeds of high emprise."

The innkeeper, as we have said, was a sharp fellow. He already had a suspicion that his guest was not quite right in the head, and he was now convinced of it as he listened to such remarks as these. However, just for the sport of it, he determined to humor him; and so he went on to assure Don Quixote that he was fully justified in his request and that such a desire and purpose was only natural on the part of so distinguished a knight as his gallant bearing plainly showed him to be.

He himself, the landlord added, when he was a young man, had followed the same honorable calling. He had gone through various parts of the world seeking adventures, among the places he had visited being the Percheles of Málaga, the Isles of Riarán, the District of Seville, the Little Market Place of Segovia, the Olivera of Valencia, the Rondilla of Granada, the beach of Sanlúcar, the Horse Fountain of Cordova, the Small Taverns of Toledo, and numerous other localities [1] where his nimble feet and light fingers had found much exercise. He had done many wrongs, cheated many widows, ruined many maidens, and swindled not a few minors until he had finally come to be known in almost all the courts and tribunals that are to be found in the whole of Spain.

At last he had retired to his castle here, where he lived upon his own income and the property of others; and here it was that he received all knights-errant of whatever quality and condition, simply out of the great affection that he bore them and that they might share with him their possessions in payment of his good will. Unfortunately, in this castle there was no chapel where Don Quixote might keep watch over his arms, for the old chapel had been torn down to make way for a new one; but in case of necessity, he felt quite sure that such a vigil could be maintained anywhere, and for the present occasion the courtyard of the castle would do; and then in the morning, please God, the requisite ceremony could be performed and his guest be duly dubbed a knight, as much a knight as anyone ever was.

He then inquired if Don Quixote had any money on his person, and the latter replied that he had not a cent, for in all the storybooks he had never read of knights-errant carrying any. But the innkeeper told him he was mistaken on this point: supposing the authors of those stories had not set down the fact in black and white, that was because they did not deem it necessary to speak of things as indispensable as money and a clean shirt, and one was not to assume for that reason that those knights-errant of whom the books were so full did not have any. He looked upon it as an absolute certainty that they all had well-stuffed purses, that they might be prepared for any emergency; and they also carried shirts and a little box of ointment for healing the wounds that they received.

For when they had been wounded in combat on the plains and in desert places, there was not always someone at hand to treat them, unless they had some skilled enchanter for a friend who then would succor them, bringing to them through the air, upon a cloud, some damsel or dwarf bearing a vial of water of such virtue that one had but to taste a drop of it and at once his wounds were healed and he was as sound as if he had never received any.

But even if this was not the case, knights in times past saw to it that their squires were well provided with money and other necessities, such as lint and ointment for healing purposes; and if they had no squires—which happened very rarely—they themselves carried these objects in a pair of saddlebags very cleverly attached to their horses' croups in such a manner as to be scarcely noticeable, as if they held something of greater importance than that,[2] for among the knights-errant saddlebags as a rule were not favored. Accordingly, he would advise the novice before him, and inasmuch as the latter was soon to be his godson, he might even command him, that henceforth he should not go without money and a supply of those things that have been mentioned, as he would find that they came in useful at a time when he least expected it.

Don Quixote promised to follow his host's advice punctiliously; and so it was arranged that he should watch his armor in a large barnyard at one side of the inn. He gathered up all the pieces, placed them in a horse trough that stood near the well, and, bracing his shield on his arm, took up his lance and with stately demeanor began pacing up and down in front of the trough even as night was closing in.

The innkeeper informed his other guests of what was going on, of Don Quixote's vigil and his expectation of being dubbed a knight; and, marveling greatly at so extraordinary a variety of madness, they all went out to see for themselves and stood there watching from a distance. For a while the knight-to-be, with tranquil mien, would merely walk up and down; then, leaning on his lance, he would pause to survey his armor, gazing fixedly at it for a considerable length of time. As has been said, it was night now, but the brightness of the moon, which well might rival that of Him who lent it, was such that everything the novice knight did was plainly visible to all.

At this point one of the mule drivers who were stopping at the inn came out to water his drove, and in order to do this it was necessary to remove the armor from the trough.

As he saw the man approaching, Don Quixote cried out to him, "O bold knight, whoever you may be, who thus would dare to lay hands upon the accouterments of the most valiant man of arms that ever girded on a sword, look well what you do and desist if you do not wish to pay with your life for your insolence!"

The muleteer gave no heed to these words—it would have been better for his own sake had he done so—but, taking it up by the straps, tossed the armor some distance from him. When he beheld this, Don Quixote rolled his eyes heavenward and with his thoughts apparently upon his Dulcinea exclaimed, "Succor, O lady mine, this vassal heart in this my first encounter; let not your favor and protection fail me in the peril in which for the first time I now find myself."

With these and other similar words, he loosed his buckler, grasped his lance in both his hands, and let the mule driver have such a blow on the head that the man fell to the ground stunned; and had it been followed by another one, he would have had no need of a surgeon to treat him. Having done this, Don Quixote gathered up his armor and resumed his pacing up and down with the same calm manner as before. Not long afterward, without knowing what had happened—for the first muleteer was still lying there unconscious—another came out with the same intention of watering his mules, and he too was about to remove the armor from the trough when the knight, without saying a word or asking favor of anyone, once more adjusted his buckler and raised his lance, and if he did not break the second mule driver's head to bits, he made more than three pieces of it by dividing it into quarters. At the sound of the fracas everybody in the inn came running out, among them the innkeeper; whereupon Don Quixote again lifted his buckler and laid his hand on his sword.

"O lady of beauty," he said, "strength and vigor of this fainting heart of mine! Now is the time to turn the eyes of your greatness upon this captive knight of yours who must face so formidable an adventure."

By this time he had worked himself up to such a pitch of anger that if all the mule drivers in the world had attacked him he would not have taken one step backward. The comrades of the wounded men, seeing the plight those two were in, now began showering stones on Don Quixote, who shielded himself as best he could with his buckler, although he did not dare stir from the trough for fear of leaving his armor unprotected. The landlord, meanwhile, kept calling to them to stop, for he had told them that this was a madman who would be sure to go free even though he killed them all. The knight was shouting louder than ever, calling them knaves and traitors. As for the lord of the castle, who allowed knights-errant to be treated in this fashion, he was a lowborn villain, and if he, Don Quixote, had but received the order of knighthood, he would make him pay for his treachery.

"As for you others, vile and filthy rabble, I take no account of you; you may stone me or come forward and attack me all you like; you shall see what the reward of your folly and insolence will be."

He spoke so vigorously and was so undaunted in bearing as to strike terror in those who would assail him; and for this reason, and owing also to the persuasions of the innkeeper, they ceased stoning him. He then permitted them to carry away the wounded, and went back to watching his armor with the same tranquil, unconcerned air that he had previously displayed.

The landlord was none too well pleased with these mad pranks on the part of his guest and determined to confer upon him that accursed order of knighthood before something else happened. Going up to him, he begged Don Quixote's pardon for the insolence which, without his knowledge, had been shown the knight by those of low degree. They, however, had been well punished for their impudence. As he had said, there was no chapel in this castle, but for that which remained to be done there was no need of any. According to what he had read of the ceremonial of the order, there was nothing to this business of being dubbed a knight except a slap on the neck and one across the shoulder, and that could be performed in the middle of a field as well as anywhere else. All that was required was for the knight-to-be to keep watch over his armor for a couple of hours, and Don Quixote had been at it more than four. The latter believed all this and announced that he was ready to obey and get the matter over with as speedily as possible. Once dubbed a knight, if he were attacked one more time, he did not think that he would leave a single person in the castle alive, save such as he might command be spared, at the bidding of his host and out of respect to him.

Thus warned, and fearful that it might occur, the castellan brought out the book in which he had jotted down the hay and barley for which the mule drivers owed him, and, accompanied by a lad bearing the butt of a candle and the two aforesaid damsels, he came up to where Don Quixote stood and commanded him to kneel. Reading from the account book—as if he had been saying a prayer—he raised his hand and, with the knight's own sword, gave him a good thwack upon the neck and another lusty one upon the shoulder, muttering all the while between his teeth. He then directed one of the ladies to gird on Don Quixote's sword, which she did with much gravity and composure; for it was all they could do to keep from laughing at every point of the ceremony, but the thought of the knight's prowess which they had already witnessed was sufficient to restrain their mirth.

"May God give your Grace much good fortune," said the worthy lady as she attached the blade, "and prosper you in battle."

Don Quixote thereupon inquired her name, for he desired to know to whom it was he was indebted for the favor he had just received, that he might share with her some of the honor which his strong right arm was sure to bring him. She replied very humbly that her name was Tolosa and that she was the daughter of a shoemaker, a native of Toledo who lived in the stalls of Sancho Bienaya.[3] To this the knight replied that she would do him a very great favor if from then on she would call herself Doña Tolosa, and she promised to do so. The other girl then helped him on with his spurs, and practically the same conversation was repeated. When asked her name, she stated that it was La Molinera and added that she was the daughter of a respectable miller of Antequera. Don Quixote likewise requested her to assume the "don" and become Doña Molinera and offered to render her further services and favors.

These unheard-of ceremonies having been dispatched in great haste, Don Quixote could scarcely wait to be astride his horse and sally forth on his quest for adventures. Saddling and mounting Rocinante, he embraced his host, thanking him for the favor of having dubbed him a knight and saying such strange things that it would be quite impossible to record them here. The innkeeper, who was only too glad to be rid of him, answered with a speech that was no less flowery, though somewhat shorter, and he did not so much as ask him for the price of a lodging, so glad was he to see him go.

CHAPTER IV. *Of what happened to our knight when he sallied forth from the inn.*

DAY was dawning when Don Quixote left the inn, so well satisfied with himself, so gay, so exhilarated, that the very girths of his steed all but burst with joy. But remembering the advice which his host had given him concerning the stock of necessary provisions that he should carry with him, especially money and shirts, he decided to turn back home and supply himself with whatever he needed, and with a squire as well; he had in mind a farmer who was a neighbor of his, a poor man and the father of a family but very well suited to fulfill the duties of squire to a man of arms. With this thought in mind he guided Rocinante toward the village once more, and that animal, realizing that he was homeward bound, began stepping out at so lively a gait that it seemed as if his feet barely touched the ground.

The knight had not gone far when from a hedge on his right hand he heard the sound of faint moans as of someone in distress.

"Thanks be to Heaven," he at once exclaimed, "for the favor it has shown me by providing me so soon with an opportunity to fulfill the obligations that I owe to my profession, a chance to pluck the fruit of my worthy desires. Those, undoubtedly, are the cries of someone in distress, who stands in need of my favor and assistance."

Turning Rocinante's head, he rode back to the place from which the cries appeared to be coming. Entering the wood, he had gone but a few paces when he saw a mare attached to an oak, while bound to another tree was a lad of fifteen or thereabouts, naked from the waist up. It was he who was uttering the cries, and not without reason, for there in front of him was a lusty farmer with a girdle who was giving him many lashes, each one accompanied by a reproof and a command, "Hold your tongue and keep your eyes open"; and the lad was saying, "I won't do it again, sir; by God's Passion, I won't do it again. I promise you that after this I'll take better care of the flock."

When he saw what was going on, Don Quixote was very angry. "Discourteous knight," he said, "it ill becomes you to strike one who is powerless to defend himself. Mount your steed and take your lance in hand"—for there was a lance leaning against the oak to which the mare was tied—"and I will show you what a coward you are."

The farmer, seeing before him this figure all clad in armor and brandishing a lance, decided that he was as good as done for. "Sir Knight," he said, speaking very mildly, "this lad that I am punishing here is my servant; he tends a flock of sheep which I have in these parts and he is so careless that every day one of them shows up missing. And when I punish him for his carelessness or his roguery, he says it is just because I am a miser and do not want to pay him the wages that I owe him, but I swear to God and upon my soul that he lies."

"It is you who lie, base lout," said Don Quixote, "and in my presence; and by the sun that gives us light, I am minded to run you through with this lance. Pay him and say no more about it, or else, by the God who rules us, I will make an end of you and annihilate you here and now. Release him at once."

The farmer hung his head and without a word untied his servant. Don Quixote then asked the boy how much his master owed him. For nine months' work, the lad told him, at seven reales the month. The knight did a little reckoning and found that this came to sixty-three reales; whereupon he ordered the farmer to pay over the money immediately, as he valued his life. The cowardly bumpkin replied that, facing death as he was and by the oath that he had sworn—he had not sworn any oath as yet—it did not amount to as much as that; for there were three pairs of shoes which he had given the lad that were to be deducted and taken into account, and a real for two blood-lettings when his servant was ill.

"That," said Don Quixote, "is all very well; but let the shoes and the blood-lettings go for the undeserved lashes which you have given him; if he has worn out the leather of the shoes that you paid for, you have taken the hide off his body, and if the barber [1] let a little blood for him when he was sick, you have done the same when he was well; and so far as that goes, he owes you nothing."

"But the trouble is, Sir Knight, that I have no money with me. Come along home with me, Andrés, and I will pay you real for real."

"I go home with him!" cried the lad. "Never in the world! No, sir, I would not even think of it; for once he has me alone he'll flay me like a St. Bartholomew."

"He will do nothing of the sort," said Don Quixote. "It is sufficient for me to command, and he out of respect will obey. Since he has sworn to me by the order of knighthood which he has received, I shall let him go free and I will guarantee that you will be paid."

"But look, your Grace," the lad remonstrated, "my master is no knight; he has never received any order of knighthood whatsoever. He is Juan Haldudo, a rich man and a resident of Quintanar."

"That makes little difference," declared Don Quixote, "for there may well be knights among the Haldudos,[2] all the more so in view of the fact that every man is the son of his works." [3]

"That is true enough," said Andrés, "but this master of mine—of what works is he the son, seeing that he refuses me the pay for my sweat and labor?"

"I do not refuse you, brother Andrés," said the farmer. "Do me the favor of coming with me, and I swear to you by all the orders of knighthood that there are in this world to pay you, as I have said, real for real, and perfumed at that." [4]

"You can dispense with the perfume," said Don Quixote; "just give him the reales and I shall be satisfied. And see to it that you keep your oath, or by the one that I myself have sworn I shall return to seek you out and chastise you, and I shall find you though you be as well hidden as a lizard. In case you would like to know who it is that is giving you this command in order that you may feel the more obliged to comply with it, I may tell you that I am the valorous Don Quixote de la Mancha, righter of wrongs and injustices; and so, God be with you, and do not

fail to do as you have promised, under that penalty that I have pronounced."

As he said this, he put spurs to Rocinante and was off. The farmer
watched him go, and when he saw that Don Quixote was out of the wood
and out of sight, he turned to his servant, Andrés.

"Come here, my son," he said. "I want to pay you what I owe you as
that righter of wrongs has commanded me."

"Take my word for it," replied Andrés, "your Grace would do well
to observe the command of that good knight—may he live a thousand
years; for as he is valorous and a righteous judge, if you don't pay me
then, by Roque,[5] he will come back and do just what he said!"

"And I will give you my word as well," said the farmer; "but seeing
that I am so fond of you, I wish to increase the debt, that I may owe you
all the more." And with this he seized the lad's arm and bound him to the
tree again and flogged him within an inch of his life. "There, Master
Andrés, you may call on that righter of wrongs if you like and you will
see whether or not he rights this one. I do not think I have quite finished
with you yet, for I have a good mind to flay you alive as you feared."

Finally, however, he unbound him and told him he might go look for
that judge of his to carry out the sentence that had been pronounced.
Andrés left, rather down in the mouth, swearing that he would indeed
go look for the brave Don Quixote de la Mancha; he would relate to
him everything that had happened, point by point, and the farmer would
have to pay for it seven times over. But for all that, he went away weeping, and his master stood laughing at him.

Such was the manner in which the valorous knight righted this particular wrong. Don Quixote was quite content with the way everything had
turned out; it seemed to him that he had made a very fortunate and
noble beginning with his deeds of chivalry, and he was very well satisfied with himself as he jogged along in the direction of his native village,
talking to himself in a low voice all the while.

"Well may'st thou call thyself fortunate today, above all other women
on earth, O fairest of the fair, Dulcinea del Toboso! Seeing that it has
fallen to thy lot to hold subject and submissive to thine every wish and
pleasure so valiant and renowned a knight as Don Quixote de la Mancha
is and shall be, who, as everyone knows, yesterday received the order
of knighthood and this day has righted the greatest wrong and grievance
that injustice ever conceived or cruelty ever perpetrated, by snatching
the lash from the hand of the merciless foeman who was so unreasonably
flogging that tender child."

At this point he came to a road that forked off in four directions, and at once he thought of those crossroads where knights-errant would pause to consider which path they should take. By way of imitating them, he halted there for a while; and when he had given the subject much thought, he slackened Rocinante's rein and let the hack follow its inclination. The animal's first impulse was to make straight for its own stable. After they had gone a couple of miles or so Don Quixote caught sight of what appeared to be a great throng of people, who, as was afterward learned, were certain merchants of Toledo on their way to purchase silk at Murcia. There were six of them altogether with their sunshades, accompanied by four attendants on horseback and three mule drivers on foot.

No sooner had he sighted them than Don Quixote imagined that he was on the brink of some fresh adventure. He was eager to imitate those passages at arms of which he had read in his books, and here, so it seemed to him, was one made to order. And so, with bold and knightly bearing, he settled himself firmly in the stirrups, couched his lance, covered himself with his shield, and took up a position in the middle of the road, where he paused to wait for those other knights-errant (for such he took them to be) to come up to him. When they were near enough to see and hear plainly, Don Quixote raised his voice and made a haughty gesture.

"Let everyone," he cried, "stand where he is, unless everyone will confess that there is not in all the world a more beauteous damsel than the Empress of La Mancha, the peerless Dulcinea del Toboso."

Upon hearing these words and beholding the weird figure who uttered them, the merchants stopped short. From the knight's appearance and his speech they knew at once that they had to deal with a madman; but they were curious to know what was meant by that confession that was demanded of them, and one of their number who was somewhat of a jester and a very clever fellow raised his voice.

"Sir Knight," he said, "we do not know who this beauteous lady is of whom you speak. Show her to us, and if she is as beautiful as you say, then we will right willingly and without any compulsion confess the truth as you have asked of us."

"If I were to show her to you," replied Don Quixote, "what merit would there be in your confessing a truth so self-evident? The important thing is for you, without seeing her, to believe, confess, affirm, swear, and defend that truth. Otherwise, monstrous and arrogant creatures that you are, you shall do battle with me. Come on, then, one by one, as the order of knighthood prescribes; or all of you together, if you will have it so, as is the sorry custom with those of your breed. Come on, and I will await you here, for I am confident that my cause is just."

"Sir Knight," responded the merchant, "I beg your Grace, in the name of all the princes here present, in order that we may not have upon our consciences the burden of confessing a thing which we have never seen nor heard, and one, moreover, so prejudicial to the empresses and queens of Alcarria and Estremadura,[6] that your Grace will show us some portrait of this lady, even though it be no larger than a grain of wheat, for by the thread one comes to the ball of yarn;[7] and with this we shall remain satisfied and assured, and your Grace will likewise be content and satisfied. The truth is, I believe that we are already so much of your way of thinking that though it should show her to be blind of one eye and distilling vermilion and brimstone from the other, nevertheless, to please your Grace, we would say in her behalf all that you desire."

"She distills nothing of the sort, infamous rabble!" shouted Don Quixote, for his wrath was kindling now. "I tell you, she does not distill what you say at all, but amber and civet wrapped in cotton;[8] and she is neither one-eyed nor hunchbacked but straighter than a spindle that comes from Guadarrama.[9] You shall pay for the great blasphemy which you have uttered against such a beauty as is my lady!"

Saying this, he came on with lowered lance against the one who had spoken, charging with such wrath and fury that if fortune had not caused Rocinante to stumble and fall in mid-career, things would have gone badly with the merchant and he would have paid for his insolent gibe. As it was, Don Quixote went rolling over the plain for some little distance, and when he tried to get to his feet, found that he was unable to do so, being too encumbered with his lance, shield, spurs, helmet, and the weight of that ancient suit of armor.

"Do not flee, cowardly ones," he cried even as he struggled to rise. "Stay, cravens, for it is not my fault but that of my steed that I am stretched out here."

One of the muleteers, who must have been an ill-natured lad, upon hearing the poor fallen knight speak so arrogantly, could not refrain from giving him an answer in the ribs. Going up to him, he took the knight's lance and broke it into bits, and then with a companion proceeded to belabor him so mercilessly that in spite of his armor they milled him like a hopper of wheat. The merchants called to them not to lay on so hard, saying that was enough and they should desist, but the mule driver by this time had warmed up to the sport and would not stop until he had vented his wrath, and, snatching up the broken pieces of the lance, he began hurling them at the wretched victim as he lay there on the ground. And through all this tempest of sticks that rained upon him Don Quixote never once closed his mouth nor ceased threatening Heaven and earth and these ruffians, for such he took them to be, who were thus mishandling him.

Finally the lad grew tired, and the merchants went their way with a good story to tell about the poor fellow who had had such a cudgeling. Finding himself alone, the knight endeavored to see if he could rise; but if this was a feat that he could not accomplish when he was sound and whole, how was he to achieve it when he had been thrashed and pounded to a pulp? Yet nonetheless he considered himself fortunate; for as he saw it, misfortunes such as this were common to knights-errant, and he put all the blame upon his horse; and if he was unable to rise, that was because his body was so bruised and battered all over.

CHAPTER V. *In which is continued the narrative of the misfortune that befell our knight.*

SEEING, then, that he was indeed unable to stir, he decided to fall back upon a favorite remedy of his, which was to think of some passage or other in his books; and as it happened, the one that he in his madness now recalled was the story of Baldwin and the Marquis of Mantua, when Carloto left the former wounded upon the mountainside,[1] a tale that is known to children, not unknown to young men, celebrated and believed in by the old, and, for all of that, not any truer than the miracles of Mohammed. Moreover, it impressed him as being especially suited to the straits in which he found himself; and, accordingly, with a great show of feeling, he began rolling and tossing on the ground as he feebly gasped out the lines which the wounded knight of the wood is supposed to have uttered:

> *"Where art thou, lady mine,*
> *That thou dost not grieve for my woe?*
> *Either thou art disloyal,*
> *Or my grief thou dost not know."*

He went on reciting the old ballad until he came to the following verses:

> *"O noble Marquis of Mantua,*
> *My uncle and liege lord true!"*

He had reached this point when down the road came a farmer of the same village, a neighbor of his, who had been to the mill with a load of wheat. Seeing a man lying there stretched out like that, he went up to him and inquired who he was and what was the trouble that caused him to utter such mournful complaints. Thinking that this must undoubtedly be his uncle, the Marquis of Mantua, Don Quixote did not answer but went on with his recitation of the ballad, giving an account of the Marquis' misfortunes and the amours of his wife and the emperor's son, exactly as the ballad has it.

The farmer was astounded at hearing all these absurdities, and after removing the knight's visor which had been battered to pieces by the blows it had received, the good man bathed the victim's face, only to discover, once the dust was off, that he knew him very well.

"Señor Quijana," he said (for such must have been Don Quixote's real name when he was in his right senses and before he had given up the life of a quiet country gentleman to become a knight-errant), "who is responsible for your Grace's being in such a plight as this?"

But the knight merely went on with his ballad in response to all the questions asked of him. Perceiving that it was impossible to obtain any information from him, the farmer as best he could relieved him of his breastplate and backpiece to see if he had any wounds, but there was no blood and no mark of any sort. He then tried to lift him from the ground, and with a great deal of effort finally managed to get him astride the ass, which appeared to be the easier mount for him. Gathering up the armor, including even the splinters from the lance, he made a bundle and tied it on Rocinante's back, and, taking the horse by the reins and the ass by the halter, he started out for the village. He was worried in his mind at hearing all the foolish things that Don Quixote said, and that individual himself was far from being at ease. Unable by reason of his bruises and his soreness to sit upright on the donkey, our knight-errant kept sighing to Heaven, which led the farmer to ask him once more what it was that ailed him.

It must have been the devil himself who caused him to remember those tales that seemed to fit his own case; for at this point he forgot all about Baldwin and recalled Abindarráez, and how the governor of Antequera, Rodrigo de Narváez, had taken him prisoner and carried him off captive to his castle.[2] Accordingly, when the countryman turned to inquire how he was and what was troubling him, Don Quixote replied with the very same words and phrases that the captive Abindarráez used in answering Rodrigo, just as he had read in the story *Diana* of Jorge de Montemayor,[3] where it is all written down, applying them very aptly to the present circumstances as the farmer went along cursing his luck for having to listen to such a lot of nonsense. Realizing that his neighbor was quite mad, he made haste to reach the village that he might not have to be annoyed any longer by Don Quixote's tiresome harangue.

"Señor Don Rodrigo de Narváez," the knight was saying, "I may inform your Grace that this beautiful Jarifa of whom I speak is not the lovely Dulcinea del Toboso, in whose behalf I have done, am doing, and shall do the most famous deeds of chivalry that ever have been or will be seen in all the world."

"But, sir," replied the farmer, "sinner that I am, cannot your Grace see that I am not Don Rodrigo de Narváez nor the Marquis of Mantua, but Pedro Alonso, your neighbor? And your Grace is neither Baldwin nor Abindarráez but a respectable gentleman by the name of Señor Quijana."

"I know who I am," said Don Quixote, "and who I may be, if I choose: not only those I have mentioned but all the Twelve Peers of France and the Nine Worthies as well; for the exploits of all of them together, or separately, cannot compare with mine."

With such talk as this they reached their destination just as night was falling; but the farmer decided to wait until it was a little darker in order that the badly battered gentleman might not be seen arriving in such a condition and mounted on an ass. When he thought the proper time had come, they entered the village and proceeded to Don Quixote's house, where they found everything in confusion. The curate and the barber were there, for they were great friends of the knight, and the housekeeper was speaking to them.

"Señor Licentiate Pero Pérez," she was saying, for that was the manner in which she addressed the curate, "what does your Grace think could have happened to my master? Three days now, and not a word of him, nor the hack, nor the buckler, nor the lance, nor the suit of armor. Ah, poor me! I am as certain as I am that I was born to die that it is those cursed books of chivalry he is always reading that have turned his head; for now that I recall, I have often heard him muttering to himself that he must become a knight-errant and go through the world in search of adventures. May such books as those be consigned to Satan and Barabbas, for they have sent to perdition the finest mind in all La Mancha."

The niece was of the same opinion. "I may tell you, Señor Master Nicholas," she said, for that was the barber's name, "that many times my uncle would sit reading those impious tales of misadventure for two whole days and nights at a stretch; and when he was through, he would toss the book aside, lay his hand on his sword, and begin slashing at the walls. When he was completely exhausted, he would tell us that he had just killed four giants as big as castle towers, while the sweat that poured off him was blood from the wounds that he had received in battle. He would then drink a big jug of cold water, after which he would be very calm and peaceful, saying that the water was the most precious liquid which the wise Esquife, a great magician and his friend, had brought to him. But I blame myself for everything. I should have advised your Worships of my uncle's nonsensical actions so that you could have done something about it by burning those damnable books of his before things came to such a pass; for he has many that ought to be burned as if they were heretics."

"I agree with you," said the curate, "and before tomorrow's sun has set there shall be a public *auto de fe*, and those works shall be condemned to the flames that they may not lead some other who reads them to follow the example of my good friend."

Don Quixote and the farmer overheard all this, and it was then that the latter came to understand the nature of his neighbor's affliction.

"Open the door, your Worships," the good man cried. "Open for Sir Baldwin and the Marquis of Mantua, who comes badly wounded, and for Señor Abindarráez the Moor whom the valiant Rodrigo de Narváez, governor of Antequera, brings captive."

At the sound of his voice they all ran out, recognizing at once friend, master, and uncle, who as yet was unable to get down off the donkey's back. They all ran up to embrace him.

"Wait, all of you," said Don Quixote, "for I am sorely wounded through fault of my steed. Bear me to my couch and summon, if it be possible, the wise Urganda to treat and care for my wounds."

"There!" exclaimed the housekeeper. "Plague take it! Did not my heart tell me right as to which foot my master limped on? To bed with your Grace at once, and we will take care of you without sending for that Urganda of yours. A curse, I say, and a hundred other curses, on those books of chivalry that have brought your Grace to this."

And so they carried him off to bed, but when they went to look for his wounds, they found none at all. He told them it was all the result of a great fall he had taken with Rocinante, his horse, while engaged in combating ten giants, the hugest and most insolent that were ever heard of in all the world.

"Tut, tut," said the curate. "So there are giants in the dance now, are there? Then, by the sign of the cross, I'll have them burned before nightfall tomorrow."

They had a thousand questions to put to Don Quixote, but his only answer was that they should give him something to eat and let him sleep, for that was the most important thing of all; so they humored him in this. The curate then interrogated the farmer at great length concerning the conversation he had had with his neighbor. The peasant told him everything, all the absurd things their friend had said when he found him lying there and afterward on the way home, all of which made the licentiate more anxious than ever to do what he did the following day, when he summoned Master Nicholas and went with him to Don Quixote's house.

CHAPTER VI. *Of the great and diverting scrutiny which the curate and the barber made in the library of our ingenious gentleman.*

As Don Quixote was still sleeping, the curate asked the niece for the keys to the room where those books responsible for all the trouble were, and she gave them to him very willingly. They all went in, the housekeeper too, and found more than a hundred large-sized volumes very well bound and a number of smaller ones. No sooner had the housekeeper laid eyes on them than she left the room, returning shortly with a basin of holy water and a sprinkling-pot.

"Here, Señor Licentiate," she said, "take this and sprinkle well, that no enchanter of the many these books contain may remain here to cast a spell on us for wishing to banish them from the world."

The curate could not but laugh at her simplicity as he directed the barber to hand him the volumes one by one so that he might see what their subject matter was, since it was possible that there were some there that did not deserve a punishment by fire.

"No," said the niece, "you must not pardon any of them, for they are all to blame. It would be better to toss them out the window into the courtyard, make a heap of them, and then set fire to it; or else you can take them out to the stable yard and make a bonfire there where the smoke will not annoy anyone."

The housekeeper said the same thing, both of them being very anxious to witness the death of these innocents, but the curate would not hear of this until he had read the titles. The first that Master Nicholas handed him was *The Four Books of Amadis of Gaul.*

"There seems to be some doubt about this one," he said, "for according to what I have heard, it was the first romance of chivalry to be printed in Spain and is the beginning and origin of all the others; but for that very reason I think that we should condemn it to the flames without any mercy whatsoever as the work that supplied the dogmas for so vile a sect."

"No, my dear sir," said the barber, "for I have heard that it is better than all the other books of this sort that have been composed, and inasmuch as it is unique of its kind, it ought to be pardoned."

"True enough," said the curate, "and for that reason we will spare its life for the present. Let us see the one next to it."

"It is the *Exploits of Esplandián*,[1] legitimate son of Amadis of Gaul."

"Well, I must say," the curate replied, "that the father's merits are not to be set down to the credit of his offspring. Take it, Mistress Housekeeper; open that window and throw it out into the stable yard; it will make a beginning for that bonfire of ours."

The housekeeper complied with a great deal of satisfaction, and the worthy Esplandián went flying out into the yard to wait as patiently as anyone could wish for the threatened conflagration.

"Let's have some more," said the curate.

"This one coming next," said the barber, "is *Amadis of Greece*;[2] in fact, all those on this side, so far as I can see, are of the same lineage—descendants of Amadis."

"Then out with them all," was the curate's verdict; "for in order to be able to burn Queen Pintiquinestra and the shepherd Darinel and his elegies and the author's diabolic and involved conceits, I would set fire, along with them, to the father that bore me if he were going around in the guise of a knight-errant."

"I agree with you on that," said the barber.

"And I also," put in the niece.

"Well, since that is the way it is," said the housekeeper, "to the stable yard with them."

They handed her a whole stack of them, and, to avoid the stair, she dumped them out the window into the yard below.

"What is that tub there?" inquired the curate.

"That," replied the barber, "is *Don Olivante de Laura.*" [3]

"The author of this book," observed the curate, "was the same one who composed the *Garden of Flowers,* and, in truth, there is no telling which of the two is the truer, or, to put it better, less filled with lies; I can only say that this one is going out into the yard as an arrogant braggart."

"The next," announced the barber, "is *Florismarte of Hircania.*" [4]

"So, Señor Florismarte is with us, is he? Then, upon my word, he is due in the yard this minute, in spite of his strange birth and imaginary adventures, for the stiffness and dryness of his style deserve nothing better. Out with him, and with the other as well, Mistress Housekeeper."

"With great pleasure," she said, and she gleefully carried out the order that had been given her.

"This," said the barber, "is *Platir the Knight.*" [5]

"A very old book," said the curate, "and I find nothing in it deserving of clemency. Let it accompany the others without appeal."

Once again sentence was carried out. They opened another volume and saw that its title was *The Knight of the Cross.*[6]

"Out of respect for a name so holy as the one this book bears, one might think that its ignorance should be pardoned; but you know the old saying, 'The devil takes refuge behind the cross,' so to the fire with it."

"And this," said the barber, taking up yet another, "is *The Mirror of Chivalry.*" [7]

"Ah, your Grace, I know you," said the curate. "Here we have Sir

Rinaldo of Montalbán with his friends and companions, bigger thieves than Cacus, all of them, and the Twelve Peers along with the veracious historian Turpin.[8] To tell you the truth, I am inclined to sentence them to no more than perpetual banishment, seeing that they have about them something of the inventiveness of Matteo Boiardo,[9] and it was out of them, also, that the Christian poet Ludovico Ariosto wove his tapestry —and by the way, if I find him here speaking any language other than his own, I will show him no respect, but if I meet with him in his own tongue, I will place him upon my head." [10]

"Yes," said the barber, "I have him at home in Italian, but I can't understand him."

"It is just as well that you cannot," said the curate. "And for this reason we might pardon the Captain [11] if he had not brought him to Spain and made him over into a Castilian, depriving him thereby of much of his native strength, as happens with all those who would render books of verse into another language; for however much care they may take, and however much cleverness they may display, they can never equal the original. I say, in short, that this work and all those on French themes ought to be thrown into, or deposited in, some dry well until we make up our minds just what should be done with them, with the exception of one *Bernardo del Carpio*, which is going the rounds, and another called *Roncesvalles;* [12] for these books, if they fall into my hands, shall be transferred to those of the housekeeper at once, and from there they go into the fire without any reprieve whatever."

The barber thoroughly approved of everything, being convinced that the curate was so good a Christian and so honest a man that he would not for anything in the world utter an untruth. Opening another book, he saw that it was *Palmerin de Oliva,* and next to it was one entitled *Palmerin of England.*[13]

The curate took one look at them. "Let this olive," he said, "be sliced to bits and burned until not even the ashes are left; but let this palm of England be guarded and preserved as something unique, and let there be made for it another case such as Alexander found among the spoils of Darius and set aside for the safekeeping of the works of the poet Homer. This book, my good friend, is deserving of respect for two reasons: first, because it is very good; and second, because it is reputed to have been composed by a wise and witty king of Portugal. All the adventures at Miraguarda's castle are excellently contrived, and the dialogue is clear and polished, the character and condition of the one who is speaking being observed with much propriety and understanding. And so, saving your good pleasure, Master Nicholas, I say that this book and *Amadis of Gaul* should be spared the flames, but all the others without more ado about it should perish."

"No, my friend," replied the barber, "for this one that I hold here in my hand is the famous *Don Belianís*." [14]

"Well," said the curate, "the second, third, and fourth parts need a little rhubarb to purge them of an excess of bile, and we shall have to relieve them of that Castle of Fame and other worse follies; but let them have the benefit of the overseas clause,[15] and, providing they mend their ways, they shall be shown justice and mercy. Meanwhile, friend, take them home with you and see to it that no one reads them."

"I shall be glad to do so," the barber assented. And not wishing to tire himself any further by reading these romances of knighthood, he told the housekeeper to take all the big ones and throw them into the yard. This was not said to one who was deaf or dull-witted, but to one who took more pleasure in such a bonfire than in the largest and finest tapestry that she could have woven. Snatching them up seven or eight at a time, she started flinging them out the window; but taking too big an armful, she let one of them fall at the barber's feet. Curious to see what it was, he bent over and picked it up. It was *The History of the Famous Knight, Tirant lo Blanch*.[16]

"Well, bless my soul!" cried the curate, "if that isn't *Tirant lo Blanch!* Let me have it, my friend, for I cannot but remember that I have found in it a treasure of contentment and a mine of recreation. Here we have Don Quirieleison de Montalbán, that valiant knight, and his brother, Tomás de Montalbán, and the knight Fonseca, along with the combat which brave Tirant waged with the mastiff, as well as the witty sayings of the damsel Placerdemivida and the amours and deceits of the Empress, who was enamored of Hipólito, her squire. Tell the truth, friend, and admit that in the matter of style this is the best book in the world. Here knights eat and sleep and die in their beds and make their wills before they die and do other things that are never heard of in books of this kind. But for all that, I am telling you that the one who needlessly composed so nonsensical a work deserves to be sent to the galleys for the rest of his life. Take it along home with you and read it and see if what I say is not so."

"That I will," said the barber, "but what are we going to do with these little ones that are left?"

"Those, I take it," replied the curate, "are not romances but poetry." Opening one of them, he saw that it was Jorge de Montemayor's *Diana*, and being under the impression that all the rest were of the same sort, he added, "These do not deserve to be burned like the others, for they are not harmful like the books of chivalry; they are works of imagination such as may be read without detriment."

"Ah, but Señor!" exclaimed the niece, "your Grace should send them to be burned along with the rest; for I shouldn't wonder at all if my uncle, after he has been cured of this chivalry sickness, reading one of these books, should take it into his head to become a shepherd and go wandering through the woods and meadows singing and piping, or, what is worse, become a poet, which they say is an incurable disease and one that is very catching."

"The young lady is right," said the curate. "It would be just as well to remove this stumbling block and temptation out of our friend's way. And so, to begin with Montemayor's *Diana*, I am of the opinion that it should not be burned, but rather that we should take out of it everything that has to do with that enchantress Felicia and her charmed potion, together with nearly all the longer verse pieces, while we willingly leave it the prose and the honor of being first and best among books of its kind."

"This one coming up now," said the barber, "is *The Second Part of La Diana*, 'by the Salamancan'; and here is yet another bearing the same title, whose author is Gil Polo." [17]

"As for the Salamancan's work," said the curate, "let it go to swell the number of the condemned out in the stable yard, but keep the Gil Polo as if it were from Apollo's own hand. Come, my friend, let us hurry, for it is growing late."

"This," said the barber as he opened another volume, "is *The Ten Books of the Fortunes of Love*, composed by Antonio de Lofraso, the Sardinian poet." [18]

"By the holy orders that I have received," the curate declared, "since Apollo was Apollo, since the Muses were Muses and poets were poets, so droll and absurd a book as this has not been written; in its own way it is unique among all those of its kind that have seen the light of day, and he who has not read it does not know what he has missed. Give it to me, my friend, for I am more pleased at having found it than if they had presented me with a cassock of Florentine cloth."

Saying this, he laid the book aside with great glee as the barber went on, "Those that we have here are *The Shepherd of Iberia, The Nymphs of Henares,* and *The Disenchantments of Jealousy.*" [19]

"Well," said the curate, "there is nothing to do with those but to turn them over to the housekeeper's secular arm; and do not ask me why, or we shall never be finished."

"And this is *Filida's Shepherd*." [20]

"He is no shepherd but a polished courtier. Guard him as you would a precious jewel."

"And this big one that I am handing you now is called *Treasury of Various Poems*." [21]

"If there were not so many of them," remarked the curate, "they would be held in greater esteem. This is a book that must be weeded out and cleansed of certain trivialities among the many fine things that it contains. Keep it, for the reason that its author is my friend and out of respect for other more heroic and lofty works that he has produced."

"This," said the barber, "is the *Song Book* of López de Maldonado." [22]

"Another great friend of mine; and when he himself recites or, better, sings his verses, all who hear them are filled with admiration for the charm and sweetness of his voice. His eclogues are a bit too long; for that which is good never did exist in great abundance.[23] Put it with the others that we have laid aside. But what is that one next to it?"

"*La Galatea* of Miguel de Cervantes," said the barber.

"Ah, that fellow Cervantes and I have been friends these many years, but, to my knowledge, he is better versed in misfortune than he is in verses. His book has a fairly good plot; it starts out well and ends up nowhere. We shall have to wait for the second part which he has promised us, and perhaps when it has been corrected somewhat it will find the favor that is now denied it.[24] Meanwhile, keep it locked up in your house."

"That I will gladly do," replied the barber. "And here we have three more—I will hand them to you all together: the *Araucana* of Don Alonso de Ercilla; the *Austriada* of Juan Rufo, magistrate of Cordova; and the *Monserrate* of Cristóbal de Virués, the poet of Valencia." [25]

"These three books," said the curate, "are the best that have been written in heroic verse in the Castilian tongue and may well compete with the most famous of Italy; keep them as the richest jewels of poetry that Spain has to show."

By this time his Reverence was too tired to look at any more books and accordingly decided that the rest should be burned without further inspection. The barber, however, had already opened one called *The Tears of Angélica*.[26]

"I should have wept myself," said the curate when he heard the title, "if I had sent that one to the flames; for its author was one of the most famous poets in the world, and not in Spain alone, and he was most happy in the translation that he made of certain of the fables of Ovid." [27]

CHAPTER VII. *Of the second sally of our good knight, Don Quixote de la Mancha.*

AT THAT instant Don Quixote began shouting, "Here! here! good knights, now is the time to show the strength of your mighty arms, for they of the court are gaining the better of the tourney!"

Called away by this noise and uproar, they went no further with the scrutinizing of those books that remained; and as a consequence it is believed that *La Carolea* and the *León of Spain* [1] went to the fire unseen and unheard, along with *The Deeds of the Emperor* as set down by Don Luis de Avila, [2] for these undoubtedly must have been among the works that were left, and possibly if the curate had seen them he would not have passed so severe a sentence upon them.

When they reached Don Quixote's side, he had already risen from his bed and was shouting and raving, laying about him on all sides with slashes and back-strokes, as wide awake as if he had never been asleep. Seizing him with their arms, they forced him into bed.

When he had quieted down a little he turned to the curate and said, "Most certainly, Señor Archbishop Turpin, it is a great disgrace for us who call ourselves the Twelve Peers so carelessly to allow the knights of the court to gain the victory in this tournament, seeing that previously we adventurers had carried off the prize for three days running."

"Be quiet, my friend," said the curate, "for, God willing, luck may change, and that which is lost today shall be won tomorrow. For the present, your Grace should look after your health, for you must be very tired, if not, perhaps, badly wounded."

"Wounded, no," said Don Quixote, "but bruised to a pulp, there is no doubt of that; for that bastard of a Don Orlando flayed me with the trunk of an oak, and all out of envy, because he knows that I am his only rival in feats of valor. But my name is not Rinaldo of Montalbán if on arising from this couch I do not make him pay for it in spite of all his enchantments. In the meantime, you may bring me something to eat, for I think that would do me more good than anything else. I will see to avenging myself in due course."

They did as he asked, brought him a bite of supper, and he once more fell asleep, while the others wondered at the strange madness that had laid hold of him. That night the housekeeper burned all the books there were in the stable yard and in all the house; and there must have been some that went up in smoke which should have been preserved in everlasting archives, if the one who did the scrutinizing had not been so indolent. Thus we see the truth of the old saying, to the effect that the innocent must sometimes pay for the sins of the guilty.

One of the things that the curate and the barber advised as a remedy for their friend's sickness was to wall up the room where the books had been, so that, when he arose, he would not find them missing —it might be that the cause being removed, the effect would cease— and they could tell him that a magician had made away with them, room and all. This they proceeded to do as quickly as possible. Two days later, when Don Quixote rose from his bed, the first thing he did was to go have a look at his library, and, not finding it where he had left it, he went from one part of the house to another searching for it. Going up to where the door had been, he ran his hands over the wall and rolled his eyes in every direction without saying a word; but after some little while he asked the housekeeper where his study was with all his books.

She had been well instructed in what to answer him. "Whatever study is your Grace talking about?" she said. "There is no study, and no books, in this house; the devil took them all away."

"No," said the niece, "it was not the devil but an enchanter who came upon a cloud one night, the day after your Grace left here; dismounting from a serpent that he rode, he entered your study, and I don't know what all he did there, but after a bit he went flying off through the roof, leaving the house full of smoke; and when we went to see what he had done, there was no study and not a book in sight. There is one thing, though, that the housekeeper and I remember very well: at the time that wicked old fellow left, he cried out in a loud voice that it was all on account of a secret enmity that he bore the owner of those books and that study, and that was why he had done the mischief in this house which we would discover. He also said that he was called Muñatón the Magician."

"Frestón, he should have said," remarked Don Quixote.

"I can't say as to that," replied the housekeeper, "whether he was called Frestón or Fritón; [3] all I know is that his name ended in a *tón*."

"So it does," said Don Quixote. "He is a wise enchanter, a great enemy of mine, who has a grudge against me because he knows by his arts and learning that in the course of time I am to fight in single combat with a knight whom he favors, and that I am to be the victor and he can do nothing to prevent it. For this reason he seeks to cause me all the trouble that he can, but I am warning him that it will be hard to gainsay or shun that which Heaven has ordained."

"Who could doubt that it is so?" said the niece. "But tell me, uncle, who is responsible for your being involved in these quarrels? Would it not be better to remain peacefully here at home and not go roaming through the world in search of better bread than is made from wheat, without taking into consideration that many who go for wool come back shorn?" [4]

"My dear niece," replied Don Quixote, "how little you understand of these matters! Before they shear me, I will have plucked and stripped the beards of any who dare to touch the tip of a single hair of mine."

The niece and the housekeeper did not care to answer him any further, for they saw that his wrath was rising.

After that he remained at home very tranquilly for a couple of weeks, without giving sign of any desire to repeat his former madness. During that time he had the most pleasant conversations with his two old friends, the curate and the barber, on the point he had raised to the effect that what the world needed most was knights-errant and a revival of chivalry. The curate would occasionally contradict him and again would give in, for it was only by means of this artifice that he could carry on a conversation with him at all.

In the meanwhile Don Quixote was bringing his powers of persuasion to bear upon a farmer who lived near by, a good man—if this title may be applied to one who is poor—but with very few wits in his head. The short of it is, by pleas and promises, he got the hapless rustic to agree to ride forth with him and serve him as his squire. Among other things, Don Quixote told him that he ought to be more than willing to go, because no telling what adventure might occur which would win them an island, and then he (the farmer) would be left to be the governor of it. As a result of these and other similar assurances, Sancho Panza forsook his wife and children and consented to take upon himself the duties of squire to his neighbor.

Next, Don Quixote set out to raise some money, and by selling this thing and pawning that and getting the worst of the bargain always, he finally scraped together a reasonable amount. He also asked a friend of his for the loan of a buckler and patched up his broken helmet as well as he could. He advised his squire, Sancho, of the day and hour when they were to take the road and told him to see to laying in a supply of those things that were most necessary, and, above all, not to forget the saddlebags. Sancho replied that he would see to all this and added that he was also thinking of taking along with him a very good ass that he had, as he was not much used to going on foot.

With regard to the ass, Don Quixote had to do a little thinking, trying to recall if any knight-errant had ever had a squire thus asininely mounted. He could not think of any, but nevertheless he decided to take Sancho with the intention of providing him with a nobler steed as soon as occasion offered; he had but to appropriate the horse of the first discourteous knight he met. Having furnished himself with shirts and all the other things that the innkeeper had recommended, he and Panza rode forth one night unseen by anyone and without taking leave of wife and children, housekeeper or niece. They went so far that by the time morning came they were safe from discovery had a hunt been started for them.

Mounted on his ass, Sancho Panza rode along like a patriarch, with saddlebags and flask, his mind set upon becoming governor of that island that his master had promised him. Don Quixote determined to take the same route and road over the Campo de Montiel that he had followed on his first journey; but he was not so uncomfortable this time, for it was early morning and the sun's rays fell upon them slantingly and accordingly did not tire them too much.

"Look, Sir Knight-errant," said Sancho, "your Grace should not forget that island you promised me; for no matter how big it is, I'll be able to govern it right enough."

"I would have you know, friend Sancho Panza," replied Don Quixote, "that among the knights-errant of old it was a very common custom to make their squires governors of the islands or the kingdoms that they won, and I am resolved that in my case so pleasing a usage shall not fall into desuetude. I even mean to go them one better; for they very often, perhaps most of the time, waited until their squires were old men who had had their fill of serving their masters during bad days and worse nights, whereupon they would give them the title of count, or marquis at most, of some valley or province more or less. But if you live and I live, it well may be that within a week I shall win some kingdom with others dependent upon it, and it will be the easiest thing in the world to crown you king of one of them. You need not marvel at this, for all sorts of unforeseen things happen to knights like me, and I may readily be able to give you even more than I have promised."

"In that case," said Sancho Panza, "if by one of those miracles of which your Grace was speaking I should become king, I would certainly send for Juana Gutiérrez, my old lady, to come and be my queen, and the young ones could be infantes."

"There is no doubt about it," Don Quixote assured him.

"Well, I doubt it," said Sancho, "for I think that even if God were to rain kingdoms upon the earth, no crown would sit well on the head of Mari Gutiérrez,[5] for I am telling you, sir, as a queen she is not worth two maravedis. She would do better as a countess, God help her."

"Leave everything to God, Sancho," said Don Quixote, "and he will give you whatever is most fitting; but I trust you will not be so pusillanimous as to be content with anything less than the title of viceroy."

"That I will not," said Sancho Panza, "especially seeing that I have in your Grace so illustrious a master who can give me all that is suitable to me and all that I can manage."

CHAPTER VIII. *Of the good fortune which the valorous Don Quixote had in the terrifying and never-before-imagined adventure of the windmills, along with other events that deserve to be suitably recorded.*

AT THIS point they caught sight of thirty or forty windmills which were standing on the plain there, and no sooner had Don Quixote laid eyes upon them than he turned to his squire and said, "Fortune is guiding our affairs better than we could have wished; for you see there before you, friend Sancho Panza, some thirty or more lawless giants with whom I mean to do battle. I shall deprive them of their lives, and with the spoils from this encounter we shall begin to enrich ourselves; for this is righteous warfare, and it is a great service to God to remove so accursed a breed from the face of the earth."

"What giants?" said Sancho Panza.

"Those that you see there," replied his master, "those with the long arms some of which are as much as two leagues in length."

"But look, your Grace, those are not giants but windmills, and what appear to be arms are their wings which, when whirled in the breeze, cause the millstone to go."

"It is plain to be seen," said Don Quixote, "that you have had little experience in this matter of adventures. If you are afraid, go off to one side and say your prayers while I am engaging them in fierce, unequal combat."

Saying this, he gave spurs to his steed Rocinante, without paying any heed to Sancho's warning that these were truly windmills and not giants that he was riding forth to attack. Nor even when he was close upon them did he perceive what they really were, but shouted at the top of his lungs, "Do not seek to flee, cowards and vile creatures that you are, for it is but a single knight with whom you have to deal!"

At that moment a little wind came up and the big wings began turning.

"Though you flourish as many arms as did the giant Briareus," said Don Quixote when he perceived this, "you still shall have to answer to me."

He thereupon commended himself with all his heart to his lady Dulcinea, beseeching her to succor him in this peril; and, being well covered with his shield and with his lance at rest, he bore down upon them at a full gallop and fell upon the first mill that stood in his way, giving a thrust at the wing, which was whirling at such a speed that his lance was broken into bits and both horse and horseman went rolling over the plain, very much battered indeed. Sancho upon his donkey came hurrying to his master's assistance as fast as he could, but when he reached the spot, the knight was unable to move, so great was the shock with which he and Rocinante had hit the ground.

"God help us!" exclaimed Sancho, "did I not tell your Grace to look well, that those were nothing but windmills, a fact which no one could fail to see unless he had other mills of the same sort in his head?"

"Be quiet, friend Sancho," said Don Quixote. "Such are the fortunes of war, which more than any other are subject to constant change. What is more, when I come to think of it, I am sure that this must be the work of that magician Frestón, the one who robbed me of my study and my books, and who has thus changed the giants into windmills in order to deprive me of the glory of overcoming them, so great is the enmity that he bears me; but in the end his evil arts shall not prevail against this trusty sword of mine."

"May God's will be done," was Sancho Panza's response. And with the aid of his squire the knight was once more mounted on Rocinante, who stood there with one shoulder half out of joint. And so, speaking of the adventure that had just befallen them, they continued along the Puerto Lápice highway; for there, Don Quixote said, they could not fail to find many and varied adventures, this being a much traveled thoroughfare. The only thing was, the knight was exceedingly down-cast over the loss of his lance.

"I remember," he said to his squire, "having read of a Spanish knight by the name of Diego Pérez de Vargas, who, having broken his sword in battle, tore from an oak a heavy bough or branch and with it did such feats of valor that day, and pounded so many Moors, that he came to be known as Machuca,[1] and he and his descendants from that day forth have been called Vargas y Machuca. I tell you this because I too intend to provide myself with just such a bough as the one he wielded, and with it I propose to do such exploits that you shall deem yourself fortunate to have been found worthy to come with me and behold and witness things that are almost beyond belief."

"God's will be done," said Sancho. "I believe everything that your Grace says; but straighten yourself up in the saddle a little, for you seem to be slipping down on one side, owing, no doubt, to the shaking-up that you received in your fall."

"Ah, that is the truth," replied Don Quixote, "and if I do not speak of my sufferings, it is for the reason that it is not permitted knights-errant to complain of any wound whatsoever, even though their bowels may be dropping out."

"If that is the way it is," said Sancho, "I have nothing more to say; but, God knows, it would suit me better if your Grace did complain when something hurts him. I can assure you that I mean to do so, over the least little thing that ails me—that is, unless the same rule applies to squires as well."

Don Quixote laughed long and heartily over Sancho's simplicity, tell-ing him that he might complain as much as he liked and where and when he liked, whether he had good cause or not; for he had read nothing to the contrary in the ordinances of chivalry. Sancho then called his master's attention to the fact that it was time to eat. The knight replied that he himself had no need of food at the moment, but his squire might eat whenever he chose. Having been granted this permission, Sancho seated himself as best he could upon his beast, and, taking out from his saddle-bags the provisions that he had stored there, he rode along leisurely behind his master, munching his victuals and taking a good, hearty swig now and then at the leather flask in a manner that might well have caused the biggest-bellied tavernkeeper of Málaga to envy him. Between draughts he gave not so much as a thought to any promise that his master might have made him, nor did he look upon it as any hardship, but rather as good sport, to go in quest of adventures however hazardous they might be.

The short of the matter is, they spent the night under some trees, from one of which Don Quixote tore off a withered bough to serve him as a lance, placing it in the lance head from which he had removed the broken one. He did not sleep all night long for thinking of his lady Dulcinea; for this was in accordance with what he had read in his books, of men of arms in the forest or desert places who kept a wakeful vigil, sustained by the memory of their ladies fair. Not so with Sancho, whose stomach was full, and not with chicory water. He fell into a dreamless slumber, and had not his master called him, he would not have been awakened either by the rays of the sun in his face or by the many birds who greeted the coming of the new day with their merry song.

Upon arising, he had another go at the flask, finding it somewhat more flaccid than it had been the night before, a circumstance which grieved his heart, for he could not see that they were on the way to remedying the deficiency within any very short space of time. Don Quixote did not wish any breakfast; for, as has been said, he was in the habit of nourishing himself on savorous memories. They then set out once more along the road to Puerto Lápice, and around three in the afternoon they came in sight of the pass that bears that name.

"There," said Don Quixote as his eyes fell upon it, "we may plunge our arms up to the elbow in what are known as adventures. But I must warn you that even though you see me in the greatest peril in the world, you are not to lay hand upon your sword to defend me, unless it be that those who attack me are rabble and men of low degree, in which case you may very well come to my aid; but if they be gentlemen, it is in no wise permitted by the laws of chivalry that you should assist me until you yourself shall have been dubbed a knight."

"Most certainly, sir," replied Sancho, "your Grace shall be very well obeyed in this; all the more so for the reason that I myself am of a peaceful disposition and not fond of meddling in the quarrels and feuds of others. However, when it comes to protecting my own person, I shall not take account of those laws of which you speak, seeing that all laws, human and divine, permit each one to defend himself whenever he is attacked."

"I am willing to grant you that," assented Don Quixote, "but in this matter of defending me against gentlemen you must restrain your natural impulses."

"I promise you I shall do so," said Sancho. "I will observe this precept as I would the Sabbath day."

As they were conversing in this manner, there appeared in the road in front of them two friars of the Order of St. Benedict, mounted upon dromedaries—for the she-mules they rode were certainly no smaller than that. The friars wore travelers' spectacles and carried sunshades, and behind them came a coach accompanied by four or five men on horseback and a couple of muleteers on foot. In the coach, as was afterwards learned, was a lady of Biscay, on her way to Seville to bid farewell to her husband, who had been appointed to some high post in the Indies. The religious were not of her company although they were going by the same road.

The instant Don Quixote laid eyes upon them he turned to his squire. "Either I am mistaken or this is going to be the most famous adventure that ever was seen; for those black-clad figures that you behold must be, and without any doubt are, certain enchanters who are bearing with them a captive princess in that coach, and I must do all I can to right this wrong."

"It will be worse than the windmills," declared Sancho. "Look you, sir, those are Benedictine friars and the coach must be that of some travelers. Mark well what I say and what you do, lest the devil lead you astray."

"I have already told you, Sancho," replied Don Quixote, "that you know little where the subject of adventures is concerned. What I am saying to you is the truth, as you shall now see."

With this, he rode forward and took up a position in the middle of the road along which the friars were coming, and as soon as they appeared to be within earshot he cried out to them in a loud voice, "O devilish and monstrous beings, set free at once the highborn princesses whom you bear captive in that coach, or else prepare at once to meet your death as the just punishment of your evil deeds."

The friars drew rein and sat there in astonishment, marveling as much at Don Quixote's appearance as at the words he spoke. "Sir Knight," they answered him, "we are neither devilish nor monstrous but religious of the Order of St. Benedict who are merely going our way. We know nothing of those who are in that coach, nor of any captive princesses either."

"Soft words," said Don Quixote, "have no effect on me. I know you for what you are, lying rabble!" And without waiting for any further parley he gave spur to Rocinante and, with lowered lance, bore down upon the first friar with such fury and intrepidity that, had not the fellow tumbled from his mule of his own accord, he would have been hurled to the ground and either killed or badly wounded. The second religious, seeing how his companion had been treated, dug his legs into his she-mule's flanks and scurried away over the countryside faster than the wind.

Seeing the friar upon the ground, Sancho Panza slipped lightly from his mount and, falling upon him, began stripping him of his habit. The two mule drivers accompanying the religious thereupon came running up and asked Sancho why he was doing this. The latter replied that the friar's garments belonged to him as legitimate spoils of the battle that his master Don Quixote had just won. The muleteers, however, were lads with no sense of humor, nor did they know what all this talk of spoils and battles was about; but, perceiving that Don Quixote had ridden off to one side to converse with those inside the coach, they pounced upon Sancho, threw him to the ground, and proceeded to pull out the hair of his beard and kick him to a pulp, after which they went off and left him stretched out there, bereft at once of breath and sense.

Without losing any time, they then assisted the friar to remount. The good brother was trembling all over from fright, and there was not a speck of color in his face, but when he found himself in the saddle once more, he quickly spurred his beast to where his companion, at some little distance, sat watching and waiting to see what the result of the encounter would be. Having no curiosity as to the final outcome of the fray, the two of them now resumed their journey, making more signs of the cross than the devil would be able to carry upon his back.

Meanwhile Don Quixote, as we have said, was speaking to the lady in the coach.

"Your beauty, my lady, may now dispose of your person as best may please you, for the arrogance of your abductors lies upon the ground, overthrown by this good arm of mine; and in order that you may not pine to know the name of your liberator, I may inform you that I am Don Quixote de la Mancha, knight-errant and adventurer and captive of the peerless and beauteous Doña Dulcinea del Toboso. In payment of the favor which you have received from me, I ask nothing other than that you return to El Toboso and on my behalf pay your respects to this lady, telling her that it was I who set you free."

One of the squires accompanying those in the coach, a Biscayan, was listening to Don Quixote's words, and when he saw that the knight did not propose to let the coach proceed upon its way but was bent upon having it turn back to El Toboso, he promptly went up to him, seized his lance, and said to him in bad Castilian and worse Biscayan,[2] "Go, *caballero*, and bad luck go with you; for by the God that created me, if you do not let this coach pass, me kill you or me no Biscayan."

Don Quixote heard him attentively enough and answered him very mildly, "If you were a *caballero*, which you are not, I should already have chastised you, wretched creature, for your foolhardiness and your impudence."

"Me no *caballero*?" cried the Biscayan.[3] "Me swear to God, you lie like a Christian. If you will but lay aside your lance and unsheath your sword, you will soon see that you are carrying water to the cat![4] Biscayan on land, gentleman at sea, but a gentleman in spite of the devil, and you lie if you say otherwise."

" ' "You shall see as to that presently," said Agrajes,' " Don Quixote quoted.[5] He cast his lance to the earth, drew his sword, and, taking his buckler on his arm, attacked the Biscayan with intent to slay him. The latter, when he saw his adversary approaching, would have liked to dismount from his mule, for she was one of the worthless sort that are let for hire and he had no confidence in her; but there was no time for this, and so he had no choice but to draw his own sword in turn and make the best of it. However, he was near enough to the coach to be able to snatch a cushion from it to serve him as a shield; and then they fell upon each other as though they were mortal enemies. The rest of those present sought to make peace between them but did not succeed, for the Biscayan with his disjointed phrases kept muttering that if they did not let him finish the battle then he himself would have to kill his mistress and anyone else who tried to stop him.

The lady inside the carriage, amazed by it all and trembling at what she saw, directed her coachman to drive on a little way; and there from a distance she watched the deadly combat, in the course of which the Biscayan came down with a great blow on Don Quixote's shoulder, over the top of the latter's shield, and had not the knight been clad in armor, it would have split him to the waist.

Feeling the weight of this blow, Don Quixote cried out, "O lady of my soul, Dulcinea, flower of beauty, succor this your champion who out of gratitude for your many favors finds himself in so perilous a plight!" To utter these words, lay hold of his sword, cover himself with his buckler, and attack the Biscayan was but the work of a moment; for he was now resolved to risk everything upon a single stroke.

As he saw Don Quixote approaching with so dauntless a bearing, the Biscayan was well aware of his adversary's courage and forthwith determined to imitate the example thus set him. He kept himself protected with his cushion, but he was unable to get his she-mule to budge to one side or the other, for the beast, out of sheer exhaustion and being, moreover, unused to such childish play, was incapable of taking a single step. And so, then, as has been stated, Don Quixote was approaching the wary Biscayan, his sword raised on high and with the firm resolve of cleaving his enemy in two; and the Biscayan was awaiting the knight in the same posture, cushion in front of him and with uplifted sword. All the bystanders were trembling with suspense at what would happen as a result of the terrible blows that were threatened, and the lady in the coach and her maids were making a thousand vows and offerings to all the images and shrines in Spain, praying that God would save them all and the lady's squire from this great peril that confronted them.

But the unfortunate part of the matter is that at this very point the author of the history breaks off and leaves the battle pending, excusing himself upon the ground that he has been unable to find anything else in writing concerning the exploits of Don Quixote beyond those already set forth.[6] It is true, on the other hand, that the second author of this work could not bring himself to believe that so unusual a chronicle would have been consigned to oblivion, nor that the learned ones of La Mancha were possessed of so little curiosity as not to be able to discover in their archives or registry offices certain papers that have to do with this famous knight. Being convinced of this, he did not despair of coming upon the end of this pleasing story, and Heaven favoring him, he did find it, as shall be related in the second part.[7]

CHAPTER IX. *In which is concluded and brought to an end the stupendous battle between the gallant Biscayan and the valiant Knight of La Mancha.*

IN THE first part of this history we left the valorous Biscayan and the famous Don Quixote with swords unsheathed and raised aloft, about to let fall furious slashing blows which, had they been delivered fairly and squarely, would at the very least have split them in two and laid them wide open from top to bottom like a pomegranate; and it was at this doubtful point that the pleasing chronicle came to a halt and broke off, without the author's informing us as to where the rest of it might be found.

I was deeply grieved by such a circumstance, and the pleasure I had had in reading so slight a portion was turned into annoyance as I thought of how difficult it would be to come upon the greater part which it seemed to me must still be missing. It appeared impossible and contrary to all good precedent that so worthy a knight should not have had some scribe to take upon himself the task of writing an account of these unheard-of exploits; for that was something that had happened to none of the knights-errant who, as the saying has it, had gone forth in quest of adventures, seeing that each of them had one or two chroniclers, as if ready at hand, who not only had set down their deeds, but had depicted their most trivial thoughts and amiable weaknesses, however well concealed they might be. The good knight of La Mancha surely could not have been so unfortunate as to have lacked what Platir and others like him had in abundance. And so I could not bring myself to believe that this gallant history could have remained thus lopped off and mutilated, and I could not but lay the blame upon the malignity of time, that devourer and consumer of all things, which must either have consumed it or kept it hidden.

On the other hand, I reflected that inasmuch as among the knight's books had been found such modern works as *The Disenchantments of Jealousy* and *The Nymphs and Shepherds of Henares*, his story likewise must be modern, and that even though it might not have been written down, it must remain in the memory of the good folk of his village and the surrounding ones. This thought left me somewhat confused and more than ever desirous of knowing the real and true story, the whole story, of the life and wondrous deeds of our famous Spaniard, Don Quixote, light and mirror of the chivalry of La Mancha, the first in our age and in these calamitous times to devote himself to the hardships and exercises of knight-errantry and to go about righting wrongs, succoring widows, and protecting damsels—damsels such as those who, mounted upon their palfreys and with riding-whip in hand, in full possession of their virginity, were in the habit of going from mountain to mountain and from valley to valley; for unless there were some villain, some rustic with an ax and hood, or some monstrous giant to force them, there were in times past maiden ladies who at the end of eighty years, during all which time they had not slept for a single day beneath a roof, would go to their graves as virginal as when their mothers had borne them.

If I speak of these things, it is for the reason that in this and in all other respects our gallant Quixote is deserving of constant memory and praise, and even I am not to be denied my share of it for my diligence and the labor to which I put myself in searching out the conclusion of this agreeable narrative; although if heaven, luck, and circumstance had not aided me, the world would have had to do without the pleasure and the pastime which anyone may enjoy who will read this work attentively for an hour or two. The manner in which it came about was as follows:

I was standing one day in the Alcaná, or market place, of Toledo when a lad came up to sell some old notebooks and other papers to a silk weaver who was there. As I am extremely fond of reading anything, even though it be but the scraps of paper in the streets, I followed my natural inclination and took one of the books, whereupon I at once perceived that it was written in characters which I recognized as Arabic. I recognized them, but reading them was another thing; and so I began looking around to see if there was any Spanish-speaking Moor near by who would be able to read them for me. It was not very hard to find such an interpreter, nor would it have been even if the tongue in question had been an older and a better one.[1] To make a long story short, chance brought a fellow my way; and when I told him what it was I wished and placed the book in his hands, he opened it in the middle and began reading and at once fell to laughing. When I asked him what the cause of his laughter was, he replied that it was a note which had been written in the margin.

I besought him to tell me the content of the note, and he, laughing still, went on, "As I told you, it is something in the margin here: 'This Dulcinea del Toboso, so often referred to, is said to have been the best hand at salting pigs of any woman in all La Mancha.'"

No sooner had I heard the name Dulcinea del Toboso than I was astonished and held in suspense, for at once the thought occurred to me that those notebooks must contain the history of Don Quixote. With this in mind I urged him to read me the title, and he proceeded to do so, turning the Arabic into Castilian upon the spot: *History of Don Quixote de la Mancha, Written by Cid Hamete Benengeli, Arabic Historian.* It was all I could do to conceal my satisfaction and, snatching them from the silk weaver, I bought from the lad all the papers and notebooks that he had for half a real; but if he had known or suspected how very much I wanted them, he might well have had more than six reales for them.

The Moor and I then betook ourselves to the cathedral cloister, where I requested him to translate for me into the Castilian tongue all the books that had to do with Don Quixote, adding nothing and subtracting nothing; and I offered him whatever payment he desired. He was content with two arrobas of raisins and two fanegas [2] of wheat and promised to translate them well and faithfully and with all dispatch. However, in order to facilitate matters, and also because I did not wish to let such a find as this out of my hands, I took the fellow home with me, where in a little more than a month and a half he translated the whole of the work just as you will find it set down here.

In the first of the books there was a very lifelike picture of the battle between Don Quixote and the Biscayan, the two being in precisely the same posture as described in the history, their swords upraised, the one covered by his buckler, the other with his cushion. As for the Biscayan's mule, you could see at the distance of a crossbow shot that it was one for hire. Beneath the Biscayan there was a rubric which read: "Don Sancho de Azpeitia," which must undoubtedly have been his name; while beneath the feet of Rocinante was another inscription: "Don Quixote." Rocinante was marvelously portrayed: so long and lank, so lean and flabby, so extremely consumptive-looking that one could well understand the justness and propriety with which the name of "hack" had been bestowed upon him.

Alongside Rocinante stood Sancho Panza, holding the halter of his ass, and below was the legend: "Sancho Zancas." The picture showed him with a big belly, a short body, and long shanks, and that must have been where he got the names of Panza y Zancas [3] by which he is a num-

ber of times called in the course of the history. There are other small
details that might be mentioned, but they are of little importance and
have nothing to do with the truth of the story—and no story is bad so
long as it is true.

If there is any objection to be raised against the veracity of the present
one, it can be only that the author was an Arab, and that nation is known
for its lying propensities; but even though they be our enemies, it may
readily be understood that they would more likely have detracted from,
rather than added to, the chronicle. So it seems to me, at any rate; for
whenever he might and should deploy the resources of his pen in praise
of so worthy a knight, the author appears to take pains to pass over the
matter in silence; all of which in my opinion is ill done and ill conceived,
for it should be the duty of historians to be exact, truthful, and dispassionate, and neither interest nor fear nor rancor nor affection should
swerve them from the path of truth, whose mother is history, rival of
time, depository of deeds, witness of the past, exemplar and adviser to
the present, and the future's counselor. In this work, I am sure, will be
found all that could be desired in the way of pleasant reading; and if
it is lacking in any way, I maintain that this is the fault of that hound of
an author rather than of the subject.

But to come to the point, the second part, according to the translation, began as follows:

As the two valorous and enraged combatants stood there, swords upraised and poised on high, it seemed from their bold mien as if they
must surely be threatening heaven, earth, and hell itself. The first to let
fall a blow was the choleric Biscayan, and he came down with such force
and fury that, had not his sword been deflected in mid-air, that single
stroke would have sufficed to put an end to this fearful combat and to
all our knight's adventures at the same time; but fortune, which was reserving him for greater things, turned aside his adversary's blade in such
a manner that, even though it fell upon his left shoulder, it did him no
other damage than to strip him completely of his armor on that side,
carrying with it a good part of his helmet along with half an ear, the
headpiece clattering to the ground with a dreadful din, leaving its wearer
in a sorry state.

Heaven help me! Who could properly describe the rage that now
entered the heart of our hero of La Mancha as he saw himself treated in
this fashion? It may merely be said that he once more reared himself in
the stirrups, laid hold of his sword with both hands, and dealt the Biscayan such a blow, over the cushion and upon the head, that, even so

good a defense proving useless, it was as if a mountain had fallen upon his enemy. The latter now began bleeding through the mouth, nose, and ears; he seemed about to fall from his mule, and would have fallen, no doubt, if he had not grasped the beast about the neck, but at that moment his feet slipped from the stirrups and his arms let go, and the mule, frightened by the terrible blow, began running across the plain, hurling its rider to the earth with a few quick plunges.

Don Quixote stood watching all this very calmly. When he saw his enemy fall, he leaped from his horse, ran over very nimbly, and thrust the point of his sword into the Biscayan's eyes, calling upon him at the same time to surrender or otherwise he would cut off his head. The Biscayan was so bewildered that he was unable to utter a single word in reply, and things would have gone badly with him, so blind was Don Quixote in his rage, if the ladies of the coach, who up to then had watched the struggle in dismay, had not come up to him at this point and begged him with many blandishments to do them the very great favor of sparing their squire's life.

To which Don Quixote replied with much haughtiness and dignity, "Most certainly, lovely ladies, I shall be very happy to do that which you ask of me, but upon one condition and understanding, and that is that this knight promise me that he will go to El Toboso and present himself in my behalf before Doña Dulcinea, in order that she may do with him as she may see fit."

Trembling and disconsolate, the ladies did not pause to discuss Don Quixote's request, but without so much as inquiring who Dulcinea might be they promised him that the squire would fulfill that which was commanded of him.

"Very well, then, trusting in your word, I will do him no further harm, even though he has well deserved it."

CHAPTER X. *Of the pleasing conversation that took place between Don Quixote and Sancho Panza, his squire.*

BY THIS time Sancho Panza had got to his feet, somewhat the worse for wear as the result of the treatment he had received from the friars' lads. He had been watching the battle attentively and praying God in his heart to give the victory to his master, Don Quixote, in order that he, Sancho, might gain some island where he could go to be governor as had been promised him. Seeing now that the combat was over and the knight was returning to mount Rocinante once more, he went up to hold the stirrup for him; but first he fell on his knees in front of him and, taking his hand, kissed it and said, "May your Grace be pleased, Señor Don Quixote, to grant me the governorship of that island which you have won in this deadly affray; for however large it may be, I feel that I am indeed capable of governing it as well as any man in this world has ever done."

To which Don Quixote replied, "Be advised, brother Sancho, that this adventure and other similar ones have nothing to do with islands; they are affairs of the crossroads in which one gains nothing more than a broken head or an ear the less. Be patient, for there will be others which will not only make you a governor, but more than that."

Sancho thanked him very much and, kissing his hand again and the skirt of his cuirass, he assisted him up on Rocinante's back, after which the squire bestraddled his own mount and started jogging along behind his master, who was now going at a good clip. Without pausing for any further converse with those in the coach, the knight made for a near-by wood, with Sancho following as fast as his beast could trot; but Rocinante was making such speed that the ass and its rider were left behind, and it was necessary to call out to Don Quixote to pull up and wait for them. He did so, reining in Rocinante until the weary Sancho had drawn abreast of him.

"It strikes me, sir," said the squire as he reached his master's side, "that it would be better for us to take refuge in some church; for in view of the way you have treated that one with whom you were fighting, it would be small wonder if they did not lay the matter before the Holy Brotherhood [1] and have us arrested; and faith, if they do that, we shall have to sweat a-plenty before we come out of jail."

"Be quiet," said Don Quixote. "And where have you ever seen, or read of, a knight being brought to justice no matter how many homicides he might have committed?"

"I know nothing about omecils," [2] replied Sancho, "nor ever in my life did I bear one to anybody; all I know is that the Holy Brotherhood has something to say about those who go around fighting on the highway, and I want nothing of it."

"Do not let it worry you," said Don Quixote, "for I will rescue you from the hands of the Chaldeans, not to speak of the Brotherhood. But answer me upon your life: have you ever seen a more valorous knight than I on all the known face of the earth? Have you ever read in the histories of any other who had more mettle in the attack, more perseverance in sustaining it, more dexterity in wounding his enemy, or more skill in overthrowing him?"

"The truth is," said Sancho, "I have never read any history whatsoever, for I do not know how to read or write; but what I would wager is that in all the days of my life I have never served a more courageous master than your Grace; I only hope your courage is not paid for in the place that I have mentioned. What I would suggest is that your Grace allow me to do something for that ear, for there is much blood coming from it, and I have here in my saddlebags some lint and a little white ointment."

"We could well dispense with all that," said Don Quixote, "if only I had remembered to bring along a vial of Fierabrás's balm, a single drop of which saves time and medicines."

"What vial and what balm is that?" inquired Sancho Panza.

"It is a balm the receipt for which I know by heart; with it one need have no fear of death nor think of dying from any wound. I shall make some of it and give it to you; and thereafter, whenever in any battle you see my body cut in two—as very often happens—all that is necessary is for you to take the part that lies on the ground, before the blood has congealed, and fit it very neatly and with great nicety upon the other part that remains in the saddle, taking care to adjust it evenly and exactly. Then you will give me but a couple of swallows of the balm of which I have told you, and you will see me sounder than an apple in no time at all."

"If that is so," said Panza, "I herewith renounce the governorship of the island you promised me and ask nothing other in payment of my many and faithful services than that your Grace give me the receipt for this wonderful potion, for I am sure that it would be worth more than two reales the ounce anywhere, and that is all I need for a life of ease and honor. But may I be so bold as to ask how much it costs to make it?"

"For less than three reales you can make something like six quarts," Don Quixote told him.

"Sinner that I am!" exclaimed Sancho. "Then why does your Grace not make some at once and teach me also?"

"Hush, my friend," said the knight, "I mean to teach you greater secrets than that and do you greater favors; but, for the present, let us look after this ear of mine, for it is hurting me more than I like."

Sancho thereupon took the lint and the ointment from his saddlebags; but when Don Quixote caught a glimpse of his helmet, he almost went out of his mind and, laying his hand upon his sword and lifting his eyes heavenward, he cried, "I make a vow to the Creator of all things and to the four holy Gospels in all their fullness of meaning that I will lead from now on the life that the great Marquis of Mantua did after he had sworn to avenge the death of his nephew Baldwin: not to eat bread off a tablecloth, not to embrace his wife, and other things which, although I am unable to recall them, we will look upon as understood—all this until I shall have wreaked an utter vengeance upon the one who has perpetrated such an outrage upon me."

"But let me remind your Grace," said Sancho when he heard these words, "that if the knight fulfills that which was commanded of him, by going to present himself before my lady Dulcinea del Toboso, then he will have paid his debt to you and merits no further punishment at your hands, unless it be for some fresh offense."

"You have spoken very well and to the point," said Don Quixote, "and so I annul the vow I have just made insofar as it has to do with any further vengeance, but I make it and confirm it anew so far as leading the life of which I have spoken is concerned, until such time as I shall have obtained by force of arms from some other knight another headpiece as good as this. And do not think, Sancho, that I am making smoke out of straw; there is one whom I well may imitate in this matter, for the same thing happened in all literalness in the case of Mambrino's helmet which cost Sacripante so dear." [3]

"I wish," said Sancho, "that your Grace would send all such oaths to the devil, for they are very bad for the health and harmful for the conscience as well. Tell me, please: supposing that for many days to come we meet no man wearing a helmet, then what are we to do? Must you still keep your vow in spite of all the inconveniences and discomforts, such as sleeping with your clothes on, not sleeping in any town, and a thousand other penances contained in the oath of that old madman of a Marquis of Mantua, an oath which you would now revive? Mark you, sir, along all these roads you meet no men of arms but only muleteers and carters, who not only do not wear helmets but quite likely have never heard tell of them in all their livelong days."

"In that you are wrong," said Don Quixote, "for we shall not be at these crossroads for the space of two hours before we shall see more men of arms than came to Albraca to win the fair Angélica."

"Very well, then," said Sancho, "so be it, and pray God that all turns out for the best so that I may at last win that island that is costing me so dearly, and then let me die."

"I have already told you, Sancho, that you are to give no thought to that; should the island fail, there is the kingdom of Denmark or that of Sobradisa,[4] which would fit you like a ring on your finger, and you ought, moreover, to be happy to be on *terra firma*.[5] But let us leave all this for some other time, while you look and see if you have something in those saddlebags for us to eat, after which we will go in search of some castle where we may lodge for the night and prepare that balm of which I was telling you, for I swear to God that my ear is paining me greatly."

"I have here an onion, a little cheese, and a few crusts of bread," said Sancho, "but they are not victuals fit for a valiant knight like your Grace."

"How little you know about it!" replied Don Quixote. "I would inform you, Sancho, that it is a point of honor with knights-errant to go for a month at a time without eating, and when they do eat, it is whatever may be at hand. You would certainly know that if you had read the histories as I have. There are many of them, and in none have I found any mention of knights eating unless it was by chance or at some sumptuous banquet that was tendered them; on other days they fasted. And even though it is well understood that, being men like us, they could not go without food entirely, any more than they could fail to satisfy the other necessities of nature, nevertheless, since they spent the greater part of their lives in forests and desert places without any cook to prepare their meals, their diet ordinarily consisted of rustic viands such as those that you now offer me. And so, Sancho my friend, do not be grieved at that which pleases me, nor seek to make the world over, nor to unhinge the institution of knight-errantry."

"Pardon me, your Grace," said Sancho, "but seeing that, as I have told you, I do not know how to read or write, I am consequently not familiar with the rules of the knightly calling. Hereafter, I will stuff my saddlebags with all manner of dried fruit for your Grace, but inasmuch as I am not a knight, I shall lay in for myself a stock of fowls and other more substantial fare."

"I am not saying, Sancho, that it is incumbent upon knights-errant to eat only those fruits of which you speak; what I am saying is that their ordinary sustenance should consist of fruit and a few herbs such as are to be found in the fields and with which they are well acquainted, as am I myself."

"It is a good thing," said Sancho, "to know those herbs, for, so far as I can see, we are going to have need of that knowledge one of these days."

With this, he brought out the articles he had mentioned, and the two of them ate in peace, and most companionably. Being desirous, however, of seeking a lodging for the night, they did not tarry long over their humble and unsavory repast. They then mounted and made what haste they could that they might arrive at a shelter before nightfall; but the sun failed them, and with it went the hope of attaining their wish. As the day ended they found themselves beside some goatherds' huts, and they accordingly decided to spend the night there. Sancho was as much disappointed at their not having reached a town as his master was content with sleeping under the open sky; for it seemed to Don Quixote that every time this happened it merely provided him with yet another opportunity to establish his claim to the title of knight-errant.

CHAPTER XI. Of what happened to Don Quixote in the company of certain goatherds.

HE WAS received by the herders with good grace, and Sancho having looked after Rocinante and the ass to the best of his ability, the knight, drawn by the aroma, went up to where some pieces of goat's meat were simmering in a pot over the fire. He would have liked then and there to see if they were done well enough to be transferred from pot to stomach, but he refrained in view of the fact that his hosts were already taking them off the fire. Spreading a few sheepskins on the ground, they hastily laid their rustic board and invited the strangers to share what there was of it. There were six of them altogether who belonged to that fold, and after they had urged Don Quixote, with rude politeness, to seat himself upon a small trough which they had turned upside down for the purpose, they took their own places upon the sheep hides round about. While his master sat there, Sancho remained standing to serve him the cup, which was made of horn. When the knight perceived this, he addressed his squire as follows:

"In order, Sancho, that you may see the good that there is in knight-errantry and how speedily those who follow the profession, no matter what the nature of their service may be, come to be honored and esteemed in the eyes of the world, I would have you here in the company of these good folk seat yourself at my side, that you may be even as I who am your master and natural lord, and eat from my plate and drink from where I drink; for of knight-errantry one may say the same as of love: that it makes all things equal."

"Many thanks!" said Sancho, "but if it is all the same to your Grace, providing there is enough to go around, I can eat just as well, or better, standing up and alone as I can seated beside an emperor. And if the truth must be told, I enjoy much more that which I eat in my own corner without any bowings and scrapings, even though it be only bread and onions, than I do a meal of roast turkey where I have to chew slowly, drink little, be always wiping my mouth, and can neither sneeze nor cough if I feel like it, nor do any of those other things that you can when you are free and alone.

"And so, my master," he went on, "these honors that your Grace would confer upon me as your servant and a follower of knight-errantry —which I am, being your Grace's squire—I would have you convert, if you will, into other things that will be of more profit and advantage to me; for though I hereby acknowledge them as duly received, I renounce them from this time forth to the end of the world."

"But for all that," said Don Quixote, "you must sit down; for whosoever humbleth himself, him God will exalt." And, laying hold of his squire's arm, he compelled him to take a seat beside him.

The goatherds did not understand all this jargon about squires and knights-errant; they did nothing but eat, keep silent, and study their guests, who very dexterously and with much appetite were stowing away chunks of meat as big as your fist. When the meat course was finished, they laid out upon the sheepskins a great quantity of dried acorns and half a cheese, which was harder than if it had been made of mortar. The drinking horn all this while was not idle but went the rounds so often—now full, now empty, like the bucket of a water wheel [1]—that they soon drained one of the two wine bags that were on hand. After Don Quixote had well satisfied his stomach, he took up a handful of acorns and, gazing at them attentively, fell into a soliloquy.

"Happy the age and happy those centuries to which the ancients gave the name of golden, and not because gold, which is so esteemed in this iron age of ours, was then to be had without toil, but because those who lived in that time did not know the meaning of the words 'thine' and 'mine.' In that blessed era all things were held in common, and to gain his daily sustenance no labor was required of any man save to reach forth his hand and take it from the sturdy oaks that stood liberally inviting him with their sweet and seasoned fruit. The clear-running fountains and rivers in magnificent abundance offered him palatable and transparent water for his thirst; while in the clefts of the rocks and the hollows of the trees the wise and busy honey-makers set up their republic so that any hand whatever might avail itself, fully and freely, of the fertile harvest which their fragrant toil had produced. The vigorous cork trees of their own free will and grace, without the asking, shed their broad, light bark with which men began to cover their dwellings, erected upon rude stakes merely as a protection against the inclemency of the heavens.

"All then was peace, all was concord and friendship; the crooked plowshare had not as yet grievously laid open and pried into the merciful bowels of our first mother, who without any forcing on man's part yielded her spacious fertile bosom on every hand for the satisfaction, sustenance, and delight of her first sons. Then it was that lovely and unspoiled young shepherdesses, with locks that were sometimes braided, sometimes flowing, went roaming from valley to valley and hillock to hillock with no more garments than were needed to cover decently that which modesty requires and always has required should remain covered. Nor were their adornments such as those in use today—of Tyrian purple and silk worked up in tortured patterns; a few green leaves of burdock or of ivy, and they were as splendidly and as becomingly clad as our ladies of the court with all the rare and exotic tricks of fashion that idle curiosity has taught them.

"Thoughts of love, also, in those days were set forth as simply as the simple hearts that conceived them, without any roundabout and artificial play of words by way of ornament. Fraud, deceit, and malice had not yet come to mingle with truth and plain-speaking. Justice kept its own domain, where favor and self-interest dared not trespass, dared not impair her rights, becloud, and persecute her as they now do. There was no such thing then as arbitrary judgments, for the reason that there was no one to judge or be judged. Maidens in all their modesty, as I have said, went where they would and unattended; whereas in this hateful age of ours none is safe, even though she go to hide and shut herself up in some new labyrinth like that of Crete; for in spite of all her seclusion, through chinks and crevices or borne upon the air, the amorous plague with all its cursed importunities will find her out and lead her to her ruin.

"It was for the safety of such as these, as time went on and depravity increased, that the order of knights-errant was instituted, for the protection of damsels, the aid of widows and orphans, and the succoring of the needy. It is to this order that I belong, my brothers, and I thank you for the welcome and the kindly treatment that you have accorded to me and my squire. By natural law, all living men are obliged to show favor to knights-errant, yet without being aware of this you have received and entertained me; and so it is with all possible good will that I acknowledge your own good will to me."

This long harangue on the part of our knight—it might very well have been dispensed with—was all due to the acorns they had given him, which had brought back to memory the age of gold; whereupon the whim had seized him to indulge in this futile harangue with the goatherds as his auditors. They listened in open-mouthed wonderment, saying not a word, and Sancho himself kept quiet and went on munching acorns, taking occasion very frequently to pay a visit to the second wine bag, which they had suspended from a cork tree to keep it cool.

It took Don Quixote much longer to finish his speech than it did to put away his supper; and when he was through, one of the goatherds addressed him.

"In order that your Grace may say with more truth that we have received you with readiness and good will, we desire to give you solace and contentment by having one of our comrades, who will be here soon, sing for you. He is a very bright young fellow and deeply in love, and what is more, you could not ask for anything better than to hear him play the three-stringed lute."

Scarcely had he done saying this when the sound of a rebec was heard, and shortly afterward the one who played it appeared. He was a good-looking youth, around twenty-two years of age. His companions asked him if he had had his supper, and when he replied that he had, the one who had spoken to Don Quixote said to him, "Well, then, Antonio, you can give us the pleasure of hearing you sing, in order that this gentleman whom we have as our guest may see that we of the woods and mountains also know something about music. We have been telling him how clever you are, and now we want you to show him that we were speaking the truth. And so I beg you by all means to sit down and sing us that love-song of yours that your uncle the prebendary composed for you and which the villagers liked so well.

"With great pleasure," the lad replied, and without any urging he seated himself on the stump of an oak that had been felled and, tuning up his rebec, soon began singing, very prettily, the following ballad:

THE BALLAD THAT ANTONIO SANG [2]

> *I know well that thou dost love me,*
> *My Olalla, even though*
> *Eyes of thine have never spoken—*
> *Love's mute tongues—to tell me so.*
> *Since I know thou knowest my passion,*
> *Of thy love I am more sure:*
> *No love ever was unhappy*
> *When it was both frank and pure.*
> *True it is, Olalla, sometimes*
> *Thou a heart of bronze hast shown,*
> *And it seemed to me that bosom,*
> *White and fair, was made of stone.*

Yet in spite of all repulses
And a chastity so cold,
It appeared that I Hope's garment
By the hem did clutch and hold.

For my faith I ever cherished;
It would rise to meet the bait;
Spurned, it never did diminish;
Favored, it preferred to wait.

Love, they say, hath gentle manners:
Thus it is it shows its face;
Then may I take hope, Olalla,
Trust to win a longed for grace.

If devotion hath the power
Hearts to move and make them kind,
Let the loyalty I've shown thee
Plead my cause, be kept in mind.

For if thou didst note my costume,
More than once thou must have seen,
Worn upon a simple Monday
Sunday's garb so bright and clean.

Love and brightness go together.
Dost thou ask the reason why
I thus deck myself on Monday?
It is but to catch thine eye.

I say nothing of the dances
I have danced for thy sweet sake;
Nor the serenades I've sung thee
Till the first cock did awake.

Nor will I repeat my praises
Of that beauty all can see;
True my words but oft unwelcome—
Certain lasses hated me.

One girl there is, I well remember—
She's Teresa on the hill—
Said, "You think you love an angel,
But she is a monkey still.

"Thanks to all her many trinkets
And her artificial hair
And her many aids to beauty,
Love's own self she would ensnare."

She was lying, I was angry,
And her cousin, very bold,
Challenged me upon my honor;
What ensued need not be told.

   Highflown words do not become me;
I'm a plain and simple man.
Pure the love that I would offer,
Serving thee as best I can.

   Silken are the bonds of marriage,
When two hearts do intertwine;
Mother Church the yoke will fasten;
Bow your neck and I'll bow mine.

   Or if not, my word I'll give thee,
From these mountains I'll come down—
Saint most holy be my witness—
Wearing a Capuchin gown.

With this the goatherd brought his song to a close, and although Don Quixote begged him to sing some more, Sancho Panza would not hear to this as he was too sleepy for any more ballads.

"Your Grace," he said to his master, "would do well to find out at once where his bed is to be, for the labor that these good men have to perform all day long does not permit them to stay up all night singing."

"I understand, Sancho," replied Don Quixote. "I perceive that those visits to the wine bag call for sleep rather than music as a recompense."

"It tastes well enough to all of us, God be praised," said Sancho.

"I am not denying that," said his master; "but go ahead and settle yourself down wherever you like. As for men of my profession, they prefer to keep vigil. But all the same, Sancho, perhaps you had better look after this ear, for it is paining me more than I like."

Sancho started to do as he was commanded, but one of the goatherds, when he saw the wound, told him not to bother, that he would place a remedy upon it that would heal it in no time. Taking a few leaves of rosemary, of which there was a great deal growing thereabouts, he mashed them in his mouth and, mixing them with a little salt, laid them on the ear, with the assurance that no other medicine was needed; and this proved to be the truth.

CHAPTER XII. *Of the story that one of the goatherds told to Don Quixote and the others.*

JUST then, another lad came up, one of those who brought the goatherds their provisions from the village.

"Do you know what's happening down there, my friends?" he said.

"How should we know?" one of the men answered him.

"In that case," the lad went on, "I must tell you that the famous student and shepherd known as Grisóstomo died this morning, muttering that the cause of his death was the love he had for that bewitched lass of a Marcela, daughter of the wealthy Guillermo—you know, the one who's been going around in these parts dressed like a shepherdess."

"For love of Marcela, you say?" one of the herders spoke up.

"That is what I'm telling you," replied the other lad. "And the best part of it is that he left directions in his will that he was to be buried in the field, as if he were a Moor, and that his grave was to be at the foot of the cliff where the Cork Tree Spring is; for, according to report, and he is supposed to have said so himself, that is the place where he saw her for the first time. There were other provisions, which the clergy of the village say cannot be carried out, nor would it be proper to fulfill them, seeing that they savor of heathen practices. But Grisóstomo's good friend, the student Ambrosio, who also dresses like a shepherd, insists that everything must be done to the letter, and as a result there is great excitement in the village.

"Nevertheless, from all I can hear, they will end by doing as Ambrosio and Grisóstomo's other friends desire, and tomorrow they will bury him with great ceremony in the place that I have mentioned. I believe it is going to be something worth seeing; at any rate, I mean to see it, even though it is too far for me to be able to return to the village before night-fall."

"We will all do the same," said the other goatherds. "We will cast lots to see who stays to watch the goats."

"That is right, Pedro," said one of their number, "but it will not be necessary to go to the trouble of casting lots. I will take care of the flocks for all of us; and do not think that I am being generous or that I am not as curious as the rest of you; it is simply that I cannot walk on account of the splinter I picked up in this foot the other day."

"Well, we thank you just the same," said Pedro.

Don Quixote then asked Pedro to tell him more about the dead man and the shepherd lass; to which the latter replied that all he knew was that Grisóstomo was a rich gentleman who had lived in a near-by village. He had been a student for many years at Salamanca and then had returned to his birthplace with the reputation of being very learned and well read; he was especially noted for his knowledge of the science of the stars and what the sun and moon were doing up there in the heavens, "for he would promptly tell us when their clips was to come."

"*Eclipse*, my friend, not *clips*," said Don Quixote, "is the name applied to the darkening-over of those major luminaries."

But Pedro, not pausing for any trifles, went on with his story. "He could also tell when the year was going to be plentiful or estil—"

"*Sterile*, you mean to say, friend—"

"*Sterile* or *estil*," said Pedro, "it all comes out the same in the end. But I can tell you one thing, that his father and his friends, who believed in him, did just as he advised them and they became rich; for he would say to them, 'This year, sow barley and not wheat'; and again, 'Sow chickpeas and not barley'; or, 'This season there will be a good crop of oil, but the three following ones you will not get a drop.' "

"That science," Don Quixote explained, "is known as astrology."

"I don't know what it's called," said Pedro, "but he knew all this and more yet. Finally, not many months after he returned from Salamanca, he appeared one day dressed like a shepherd with crook and sheepskin jacket; for he had resolved to lay aside the long gown that he wore as a scholar, and in this he was joined by Ambrosio, a dear friend of his and the companion of his studies. I forgot to tell you that Grisóstomo was a great one for composing verses; he even wrote the carols for Christmas Eve and the plays that were performed at Corpus Christi by the lads of our village,[1] and everyone said that they were the best ever.

"When the villagers saw the two scholars coming out dressed like shepherds, they were amazed and could not imagine what was the reason for such strange conduct on their part. It was about that time that Grisóstomo's father died and left him the heir to a large fortune, consisting of land and chattels, no small quantity of cattle, and a considerable sum of money, of all of which the young man was absolute master; and, to tell the truth, he deserved it, for he was very sociable and charitably inclined, a friend to all worthy folk, and he had a face that was like a benediction. Afterward it was learned that if he had changed his garments like this, it was only that he might be able to wander over the wastelands on the trail of that shepherdess Marcela of whom our friend was speaking, for the poor fellow had fallen in love with her. And now I should like to tell you, for it is well that you should know, just who this lass is; for it may be—indeed, there is no maybe about it—you will never hear the like in all the days of your life, though you live to be older than Sarna." [2]

"You should say *Sarah*," Don Quixote corrected him; for he could not bear hearing the goatherd using the wrong words all the time. [3]

"The itch," said Pedro, "lives long enough; and if, sir, you go on interrupting me at every word, we'll never be through in a year."

"Pardon me, friend," said Don Quixote, "it was only because there is so great a difference between Sarna and Sarah that I pointed it out to you; but you have given me a very good answer, for the itch does live longer than Sarah; and so go on with your story, and I will not contradict you any more."

"I was about to say, then, my dear sir," the goatherd went on, "that in our village there was a farmer who was richer still than Grisóstomo's father. His name was Guillermo, and, over and above his great wealth, God gave him a daughter whose mother, the most highly respected woman in these parts, died in bearing her. It seems to me I can see the good lady now, with that face that rivaled the sun and moon; [4] and I remember, above all, what a friend she was to the poor, for which reason I believe that her soul at this very moment must be enjoying God's presence in the other world.

"Grieving for the loss of so excellent a wife, Guillermo himself died, leaving his daughter Marcela, now a rich young woman, in the custody of one of her uncles, a priest who holds a benefice in our village. The girl grew up with such beauty as to remind us of her mother, beautiful as that lady had been. By the time she was fourteen or fifteen no one looked at her without giving thanks to God who had created such comeliness, and almost all were hopelessly in love with her. Her uncle kept her very closely shut up, but, for all of that, word of her great beauty spread to such an extent that by reason of it, as much as on account of the girl's wealth, her uncle found himself besought and importuned not only by the young men of our village, but by those for leagues around who desired to have her for a wife.

"But he, an upright Christian, although he wished to marry her off as soon as she was of age, had no desire to do so without her consent, not that he had any eye to the gain and profit which the custody of his niece's property brought him while her marriage was deferred. Indeed, this much was said in praise of the good priest in more than one circle of the village; for I would have you know, Sir Knight, that in these little places everything is discussed and becomes a subject of gossip; and you may rest assured, as I am for my part, that a priest must be more than ordinarily good if his parishioners feel bound to speak well of him, especially in the small towns."

"That is true," said Don Quixote, "but go on. I like your story very much, and you, good Pedro, tell it with very good grace."

"May the Lord's grace never fail me, for that is what counts. But to go on: Although the uncle set forth to his niece the qualities of each one in particular of the many who sought her hand, begging her to choose and marry whichever one she pleased, she never gave him any answer other than this: that she did not wish to marry at all, since being but a young girl she did not feel that she was equal to bearing the burdens of matrimony. As her reasons appeared to be proper and just, the uncle did not insist but thought he would wait until she was a little older, when she would be capable of selecting someone to her taste. For, he said, and quite right he was, parents ought not to impose a way of life upon their children against the latters' will. And then, one fine day, lo and behold, there was the finical Marcela turned shepherdess; and without paying any attention to her uncle or all those of the village who advised against it, she set out to wander through the fields with the other lasses, guarding flocks as they did.

"Well, the moment she appeared in public and her beauty was uncovered for all to see, I really cannot tell you how many rich young bachelors, gentlemen, and farmers proceeded to don a shepherd's garb and go to make love to her in the meadows. One of her suitors, as I have told you, was our deceased friend, and it is said that he did not love but adored her. But you must not think that because Marcela chose so free and easy a life, and one that offers little or no privacy, that she was thereby giving the faintest semblance of encouragement to those who would disparage her modesty and prudence; rather, so great was the vigilance with which she looked after her honor that of all those who waited upon her and solicited her favors, none could truly say that she had given him the slightest hope of attaining his desire.

"For although she does not flee nor shun the company and conversation of the shepherds, treating them in courteous and friendly fashion, the moment she discovers any intentions on their part, even though it be the just and holy one of matrimony, she hurls them from her like a catapult. As a result, she is doing more damage in this land than if a plague had fallen upon it; for her beauty and graciousness win the hearts of all who would serve her, but her disdain and the disillusionment it brings lead them in the end to despair, and then they can only call her cruel and ungrateful, along with other similar epithets that reveal all too plainly the state of mind that prompts them. If you were to stay here some time, sir, you would hear these uplands and valleys echo with the laments of those who have followed her only to be deceived.

"Not far from here is a place where there are a couple of dozen tall beeches, and there is not a one of them on whose smooth bark Marcela's name has not been engraved; and above some of these inscriptions you will find a crown, as if by this her lover meant to indicate that she deserved to wear the garland of beauty above all the women on the earth. Here a shepherd sighs and there another voices his lament. Now are to be heard amorous ballads, and again despairing ditties. One will spend all the hours of the night seated at the foot of some oak or rock without once closing his tearful eyes, and the morning sun will find him there, stupefied and lost in thought. Another, without giving truce or respite to his sighs, will lie stretched upon the burning sands in the full heat of the most exhausting summer noontide, sending up his complaint to merciful Heaven.

"And, meanwhile, over this one and that one, over one and all, the beauteous Marcela triumphs and goes her own way, free and unconcerned. All those of us who know her are waiting to see how far her pride will carry her, and who will be the fortunate man who will succeed in taming this terrible creature and thus come into possession of a beauty so matchless as hers. Knowing all this that I have told you to be undoubtedly true, I can readily believe this lad's story about the cause of Grisóstomo's death. And so I advise you, sir, not to fail to be present tomorrow at his burial; it will be well worth seeing, for he has many friends, and the place is not half a league from here."

"I will make a point of it," said Don Quixote, "and I thank you for the pleasure you have given me by telling me so delightful a tale."

"Oh," said the goatherd, "I do not know the half of the things that have happened to Marcela's lovers; but it is possible that tomorrow we may meet along the way some shepherd who will tell us more. And now it would be well for you to go and sleep under cover, for the night air may not be good for your wound, though with the remedy that has been put on it there is not much to fear."

Sancho Panza, who had been sending the goatherd to the devil for talking so much, now put in a word with his master, urging him to come and sleep in Pedro's hut. Don Quixote did so; and all the rest of the night was spent by him in thinking of his lady Dulcinea, in imitation of Marcela's lovers. As for Sancho, he made himself comfortable between Rocinante and the ass and at once dropped off to sleep, not like a lovelorn swain but, rather, like a man who has had a sound kicking that day.

CHAPTER **XIII**. *In which is brought to a close the story of the shepherdess Marcela, along with other events.*

DAY had barely begun to appear upon the balconies of the east when five or six goatherds arose and went to awaken Don Quixote and tell him that if he was still of a mind to go see Grisóstomo's famous burial they would keep him company. The knight, desiring nothing better, ordered Sancho to saddle at once, which was done with much dispatch, and then they all set out forthwith.

They had not gone more than a quarter of a league when, upon crossing a footpath, they saw coming toward them six shepherds clad in black sheepskins and with garlands of cypress and bitter rosebay on their heads. Each of them carried a thick staff made of the wood of the holly, and with them came two gentlemen on horseback in handsome traveling attire, accompanied by three lads on foot. As the two parties met they greeted each other courteously, each inquiring as to the other's destination, whereupon they learned that they were all going to the burial, and so continued to ride along together.

Speaking to his companion, one of them said, "I think, Señor Vivaldo, that we are going to be well repaid for the delay it will cost us to see this famous funeral; for famous it must surely be, judging by the strange things that these shepherds have told us of the dead man and the homicidal shepherdess."

"I think so too," agreed Vivaldo. "I should be willing to delay our journey not one day, but four, for the sake of seeing it."

Don Quixote then asked them what it was they had heard of Marcela and Grisóstomo. The traveler replied that on that very morning they had fallen in with those shepherds and, seeing them so mournfully trigged out, had asked them what the occasion for it was. One of the fellows had then told them of the beauty and strange demeanor of a shepherdess by the name of Marcela, her many suitors, and the death of this Grisóstomo, to whose funeral they were bound. He related, in short, the entire story as Don Quixote had heard it from Pedro.

Changing the subject, the gentleman called Vivaldo inquired of Don Quixote what it was that led him to go armed in that manner in a land that was so peaceful.

"The calling that I profess," replied Don Quixote, "does not permit me to do otherwise. An easy pace, pleasure, and repose—those things were invented for delicate courtiers; but toil, anxiety, and arms—they are for those whom the world knows as knights-errant, of whom I, though unworthy, am the very least."

No sooner had they heard this than all of them immediately took him for a madman. By way of assuring himself further and seeing what kind of madness it was of which Don Quixote was possessed, Vivaldo now asked him what was meant by the term knights-errant.

"Have not your Worships read the annals and the histories of England that treat of the famous exploits of King Arthur, who in our Castilian balladry is always called King Artús? According to a very old tradition that is common throughout the entire realm of Great Britain, this king did not die, but by an act of enchantment was changed into a raven; and in due course of time he is to return and reign once more, recovering his kingdom and his scepter; for which reason, from that day to this, no Englishman is known to have killed one of those birds. It was, moreover, in the time of that good king that the famous order of the Knights of the Round Table was instituted; and as for the love of Sir Lancelot of the Lake and Queen Guinevere, everything took place exactly as the story has it, their confidante and go-between being the honored matron Quintañona; [1] whence comes that charming ballad that is such a favorite with us Spaniards:

> Never was there a knight
> So served by maid and dame
> As the one they call Sir Lancelot
> When from Britain he came— [2]

to carry on the gentle, pleasing course of his loves and noble deeds.

"From that time forth, the order of chivalry was passed on and propagated from one individual to another until it had spread through many and various parts of the world. Among those famed for their exploits was the valiant Amadis of Gaul, with all his sons and grandsons to the fifth generation; and there was also the brave Felixmarte of Hircania,[3] and the never sufficiently praised Tirant lo Blanch; and in view of the fact that he lived in our own day, almost, we came near to seeing, hearing, and conversing with that other courageous knight, Don Belianís of Greece.

"And that, gentlemen, is what it means to be a knight-errant, and what I have been telling you of is the order of chivalry which such a knight professes, an order to which, as I have already informed you, I, although a sinner, have the honor of belonging; for I have made the same profession as have those other knights. That is why it is you find me in these wild and lonely places, riding in quest of adventure, being resolved to offer my arm and my person in the most dangerous undertaking fate may have in store for me, that I may be of aid to the weak and needy."

Listening to this speech, the travelers had some while since come to the conclusion that Don Quixote was out of his mind, and were likewise able to perceive the peculiar nature of his madness, and they wondered at it quite as much as did all those who encountered it for the first time. Being endowed with a ready wit and a merry disposition and thinking to pass the time until they reached the end of the short journey which, so he was told, awaited them before they should arrive at the mountain where the burial was to take place, Vivaldo decided to give him a further opportunity of displaying his absurdities.

"It strikes me, Sir Knight-errant," he said, "that your Grace has espoused one of the most austere professions to be found anywhere on earth—even more austere, if I am not mistaken, than that of the Carthusian monks."

"Theirs may be as austere as ours," Don Quixote replied, "but that it is as necessary I am very much inclined to doubt. For if the truth be told, the soldier who carries out his captain's order does no less than the captain who gives the order. By that I mean to say that the religious, in all peace and tranquility, pray to Heaven for earth's good, but we soldiers and knights put their prayers into execution by defending with the might of our good right arms and at the edge of the sword those things for which they pray; and we do this not under cover of a roof but under the open sky, beneath the insufferable rays of the summer sun and the biting cold of winter. Thus we become the ministers of God on earth, and our arms the means by which He executes His decrees. And just as war and all the things that have to do with it are impossible without toil, sweat, and anxiety, it follows that those who have taken upon themselves such a profession must unquestionably labor harder than do those who in peace and tranquility and at their ease pray God to favor the ones who can do little in their own behalf.

"I do not mean to say—I should not think of saying—that the state of knight-errant is as holy as that of the cloistered monk; I merely would imply, from what I myself endure, that ours is beyond a doubt the more laborious and arduous calling, more beset by hunger and thirst, more wretched, ragged, and ridden with lice. It is an absolute certainty that the knights-errant of old experienced much misfortune in the course of their lives; and if some by their might and valor came to be emperors, you may take my word for it, it cost them dearly in blood and sweat, and if those who rose to such a rank had lacked enchanters and magicians to aid them, they surely would have been cheated of their desires, deceived in their hopes and expectations."

"I agree with you on that," said the traveler, "but there is one thing among others that gives me a very bad impression of the knights-errant, and that is the fact that when they are about to enter upon some great and perilous adventure in which they are in danger of losing their lives, they never at that moment think of commending themselves to God as every good Christian is obliged to do under similar circumstances, but, rather, commend themselves to their ladies with as much fervor and devotion as if their mistresses were God himself; all of which to me smacks somewhat of paganism."

"Sir," Don Quixote answered him, "it could not by any means be otherwise; the knight-errant who did not do so would fall into disgrace, for it is the usage and custom of chivalry that the knight, before engaging in some great feat of arms, shall behold his lady in front of him and shall turn his eyes toward her, gently and lovingly, as if beseeching her favor and protection in the hazardous encounter that awaits him, and even though no one hears him, he is obliged to utter certain words between his teeth, commending himself to her with all his heart; and of this we have numerous examples in the histories. Nor is it to be assumed that he does not commend himself to God also, but the time and place for that is in the course of the undertaking."

"All the same," said the traveler, "I am not wholly clear in this matter; for I have often read of two knights-errant exchanging words until, one word leading to another, their wrath is kindled; whereupon, turning their steeds and taking a good run up the field, they whirl about and bear down upon each other at full speed, commending themselves to their ladies in the midst of it all. What commonly happens then is that one of the two topples from his horse's flanks and is run through and through with the other's lance; and his adversary would also fall to the ground if he did not cling to his horse's mane. What I do not understand is how the dead man would have had time to commend himself to God in the course of this accelerated combat. It would be better if the words he wasted in calling upon his lady as he ran toward the other knight had been spent in paying the debt that he owed as a Christian. Moreover, it is my personal opinion that not all knights-errant have ladies to whom to commend themselves, for not all of them are in love."

"That," said Don Quixote, "is impossible. I assert there can be no knight-errant without a lady; for it is as natural and proper for them to be in love as it is for the heavens to have stars, and I am quite sure that no one ever read a story in which a loveless man of arms was to be met with, for the simple reason that such a one would not be looked upon as a legitimate knight but as a bastard one who had entered the fortress of chivalry not by the main gate, but over the walls, like a robber and a thief."

"Nevertheless," said the traveler, "if my memory serves me right, I have read that Don Galaor, brother of the valorous Amadis of Gaul, never had a special lady to whom he prayed, yet he was not held in any the less esteem for that but was a very brave and famous knight."

Once again, our Don Quixote had an answer. "Sir, one swallow does not make a summer. And in any event, I happen to know that this knight was secretly very much in love. As for his habit of paying court to all the ladies that caught his fancy, that was a natural propensity on his part and one that he was unable to resist. There was, however, one particular lady whom he had made the mistress of his will and to whom he did commend himself very frequently and privately; for he prided himself upon being a reticent knight."

"Well, then," said the traveler, "if it is essential that every knight-errant be in love, it is to be presumed that your Grace is also, since you are of the profession. And unless it be that you pride yourself upon your reticence as much as did Don Galaor, then I truly, on my own behalf and in the name of all this company, beseech your Grace to tell us your lady's name, the name of the country where she resides, what her rank is, and something of the beauty of her person, that she may esteem herself fortunate in having all the world know that she is loved and served by such a knight as your Grace appears to me to be."

At this, Don Quixote heaved a deep sigh. "I cannot say," he began, "as to whether or not my sweet enemy would be pleased that all the world should know I serve her. I can only tell you, in response to the question which you have so politely put to me, that her name is Dulcinea, her place of residence El Toboso, a village of La Mancha. As to her rank, she should be at the very least a princess, seeing that she is my lady and my queen. Her beauty is superhuman, for in it are realized all the impossible and chimerical attributes that poets are accustomed to give their fair ones. Her locks are golden, her brow the Elysian Fields, her eyebrows rainbows, her eyes suns, her cheeks roses, her lips coral, her teeth pearls, her neck alabaster, her bosom marble, her hands ivory, her complexion snow-white. As for those parts which modesty keeps covered from the human sight, it is my opinion that, discreetly considered, they are only to be extolled and not compared to any other."

"We should like," said Vivaldo, "to know something as well of her lineage, her race and ancestry."

"She is not," said Don Quixote, "of the ancient Roman Curtii, Caii, or Scipios, nor of the modern Colonnas and Orsini, nor of the Moncadas and Requesenses of Catalonia, nor is she of the Rebellas and Villanovas of Valencia, or the Palafoxes, Nuzas, Rocabertis, Corellas, Lunas, Alagones, Urreas, or Gurreas of Aragon, the Cerdas, Manriques, Mendozas, or Guzmanes of Castile, the Alencastros, Pallas, or Menezes of Portugal; but she is of the Tobosos of La Mancha, and although the line is a modern one, it well may give rise to the most illustrious families of the centuries to come. And let none dispute this with me, unless it be under the conditions which Zerbino has set forth in the inscription beneath Orlando's arms:

> These let none move
> Who dares not with Orlando his valor prove." [4]

"Although my own line," replied the traveler, "is that of the Gachupins [5] of Laredo, I should not venture to compare it with the Tobosos of La Mancha, in view of the fact that, to tell you the truth, I have never heard the name before."

"How does it come that you have never heard it!" exclaimed Don Quixote.

The others were listening most attentively to the conversation of these two, and even the goatherds and shepherds were by now aware that our knight of La Mancha was more than a little insane. Sancho Panza alone thought that all his master said was the truth, for he was well acquainted with him, having known him since birth. The only doubt in his mind had to do with the beauteous Dulcinea del Toboso, for he knew of no such princess and the name was strange to his ears, although he lived not far from that place.

They were continuing on their way, conversing in this manner, when they caught sight of some twenty shepherds coming through the gap between two high mountains, all of them clad in black woolen garments and with wreaths on their heads, some of the garlands, as was afterward learned, being of cypress, others of yew. Six of them were carrying a bier covered with a great variety of flowers and boughs.

"There they come with Grisóstomo's body," said one of the goatherds, "and the foot of the mountain yonder is where he wished to be buried."

They accordingly quickened their pace and arrived just as those carrying the bier had set it down on the ground. Four of the shepherds with sharpened picks were engaged in digging a grave alongside the barren rock. After a courteous exchange of greetings, Don Quixote and his companions turned to look at the bier. Upon it lay a corpse covered with flowers, the body of a man dressed like a shepherd and around thirty years of age. Even in death it could be seen that he had had a handsome face and had been of a jovial disposition. Round about him upon the bier were a number of books and many papers, open and folded.

Meanwhile, those who stood gazing at the dead man and those who were digging the grave—everyone present, in fact—preserved an awed silence, until one of the pallbearers said to another, "Look well, Ambrosio, and make sure that this is the place that Grisóstomo had in mind, since you are bent upon carrying out to the letter the provisions of his will."

"This is it," replied Ambrosio; "for many times my unfortunate friend told me the story of his misadventure. He told me that it was here that he first laid eyes upon that mortal enemy of the human race, and it was here, also, that he first revealed to her his passion, for he was as honorable as he was lovelorn; and it was here, finally, at their last meeting, that she shattered his illusions and showed him her disdain, thus bringing to an end the tragedy of his wretched life. And here, in memory of his great misfortune, he wished to be laid in the bowels of eternal oblivion."

Then, turning to Don Quixote and the travelers, he went on, "This body, gentlemen, on which you now look with pitying eyes was the depository of a soul which heaven had endowed with a vast share of its

riches. This is the body of Grisóstomo, who was unrivaled in wit, un-
equaled in courtesy, supreme in gentleness of bearing, a model of friendship, generous without stint, grave without conceit, merry without
being vulgar—in short, first in all that is good and second to none in
the matter of misfortunes. He loved well and was hated, he adored and
was disdained; he wooed a wild beast, importuned a piece of marble,
ran after the wind, cried out to loneliness, waited upon ingratitude, and
his reward was to be the spoils of death midway in his life's course—a
life that was brought to an end by a shepherdess whom he sought to
immortalize that she might live on in the memory of mankind, as those
papers that you see there would very plainly show if he had not commanded me to consign them to the flames even as his body is given to
the earth."

"You," said Vivaldo, "would treat them with greater harshness and
cruelty than their owner himself, for it is neither just nor fitting to carry
out the will of one who commands what is contrary to all reason. It
would not have been a good thing for Augustus Caesar to consent to
have them execute the behests of the divine Mantuan in his last testa-
ment. And so, Señor Ambrosio, while you may give the body of your
friend to the earth, you ought not to give his writings to oblivion. If out
of bitterness he left such an order, that does not mean that you are to
obey it without using your own discretion. Rather, by granting life to
these papers, you permit Marcela's cruelheartedness to live forever and
serve as an example to the others in the days that are to come in order
that they may flee and avoid such pitfalls as these.

"I and those that have come with me know the story of this lovesick
and despairing friend of yours; we know the affection that was between
you, and what the occasion of his death was, and the things that he
commanded be done as his life drew to a close. And from this lamentable
tale anyone may see how great was Marcela's cruelty; they may behold
Grisóstomo's love, the loyalty that lay in your friendship, and the end
that awaits those who run headlong, with unbridled passion, down the
path that doting love opens before their gaze. Last night we heard of
your friend's death and learned that he was to be buried here, and out
of pity and curiosity we turned aside from our journey and resolved to
come see with our own eyes that which had aroused so much compassion
when it was told to us. And in requital of that compassion, and the desire
that has been born in us to prevent if we can a recurrence of such tragic
circumstances, we beg you, O prudent Ambrosio!—or, at least, I for

my part implore you—to give up your intention of burning these papers and let me carry some of them away with me."

Without waiting for the shepherd to reply he put out his hand and took a few of those that were nearest him.

"Out of courtesy, sir," said Ambrosio when he saw this, "I will consent for you to keep those that you have taken; but it is vain to think that I will refrain from burning the others."

Vivaldo, who was anxious to find out what was in the papers, opened one of them and perceived that it bore the title "Song of Despair."

Hearing this, Ambrosio said, "That is the last thing the poor fellow wrote; and in order, sir, that you may see the end to which his misfortunes brought him, read it aloud if you will, for we shall have time for it while they are digging the grave."

"That I will very willingly do," said Vivaldo.

And since all the bystanders had the same desire, they gathered around as he in a loud clear voice read the following poem.

CHAPTER **XIV**. *In which are set down the despairing verses of the deceased shepherd, with other unlooked-for happenings.*

GRISÓSTOMO'S SONG[1]

Since thou desirest that thy cruelty
Be spread from tongue to tongue and land to land,
The unrelenting sternness of thy heart
Shall turn my bosom's hell to minstrelsy
That all men everywhere may understand
The nature of my grief and what thou art.
And as I seek my sorrows to impart,
Telling of all the things that thou hast done,
My very entrails shall speak out to brand

Thy heartlessness, thy soul to reprimand,
Where no compassion ever have I won.
Then listen well, lend an attentive ear;
This ballad that thou art about to hear
Is not contrived by art; 'tis a simple song
Such as shepherds sing each day throughout the year—
Surcease of pain for me, for thee a prong.

Then let the roar of lion, fierce wolf's cry,
The horrid hissing of the scaly snake,
The terrifying sound of monsters strange,
Ill-omened call of crow against the sky,
The howling of the wind as it doth shake
The tossing sea where all is constant change,
Bellow of vanquished bull that cannot range
As it was wont to do, the piteous sob
Of the widowed dove as if its heart would break,
Hoot of the envied owl,² ever awake,
From hell's own choir the deep and mournful throb—
Let all these sounds come forth and mingle now.
For if I'm to tell my woes, why then, I vow,
I must new measures find, new modes invent,
With sound confusing sense, I may somehow
Portray the inferno where my days are spent.

The mournful echoes of my murmurous plaint
Father Tagus ³ shall not hear as he rolls his sand,
Nor olive-bordered Betis; ⁴ my lament shall be
To the tall and barren rock as I acquaint
The caves with my sorrow; the far and lonely strand
No human foot has trod shall hear from me
The story of thine inhumanity
As told with lifeless tongue but living word.
I'll tell it to the valleys near at hand
Where never shines the sun upon the land;
By venomous serpents shall my tale be heard
On the low-lying, marshy river plain.
And yet, the telling will not be in vain;
For the reverberations of my plight,
Thy matchless austerity and this my pain,
Through the wide world shall go, thee to indict.

Disdain may kill; suspicion false or true

May slay all patience; deadliest of all
Is jealousy; while absence renders life
Worse than a void; Hope lends no roseate hue
Against forgetfulness or the dread call
Of death inevitable, the end of strife.
Yet—unheard miracle!—with sorrows rife,
My own existence somehow still goes on;
The flame of life with me doth rise and fall.
Jealous I am, disdained; I know the gall
Of those suspicions that will not be gone,
Which leave me not the shadow of a hope,
And, desperate, I will not even grope
But rather will endure until the end,
And with despair eternally I'll cope,
Knowing that things for me will never mend.

   Can one both hope and fear at the same season?
Would it be well to do so in any case,
Seeing that fear, by far, hath the better excuse?
Confronting jealousy, is there any reason
For me to close my eyes to its stern face,
Pretend to see it not? What is the use,
When its dread presence I can still deduce
From countless gaping wounds deep in my heart?
When suspicion—bitter change!—to truth gives place,
And truth itself, losing its virgin grace,
Becomes a lie, is it not wisdom's part
To open wide the door to frank mistrust?
When disdain's unveiled, to doubt is only just.
O ye fierce tyrants of Love's empery!
Shackle these hands with stout cord, if ye must.
My pain shall drown your triumph—woe is me!

   I die, in short, and since nor life nor death
Yields any hope, to my fancy will I cling.
That man is freest who is Love's bond slave:
I'll say this with my living-dying breath,
And the ancient tyrant's praises I will sing.
Love is the greatest blessing Heaven e'er gave.
What greater beauty could a lover crave
Than that which my fair enemy doth show
In soul and body and in everything?

E'en her forgetfulness of me doth spring
From my own lack of grace, that I well know.
In spite of all the wrongs that he has wrought,
Love rules his empire justly as he ought.
Throw all to the winds and speed life's wretched span
By feeding on his self-deluding thought.
No blessing holds the future that I scan.

Thou whose unreasonableness reason doth give
For putting an end to this tired life of mine,
From the deep heart wounds which thou mayest plainly see,
Judge if the better course be to die or live.
Gladly did I surrender my will to thine,
Gladly I suffered all thou didst to me;
And now that I'm dying, should it seem to thee
My death is worth a tear from thy bright eyes,
Pray hold it back, fair one, do not repine,
For I would have from thee no faintest sign
Of penitence, e'en though my soul thy prize.
Rather, I'd have thee laugh, be very gay,
And let my funeral be a festive day—
But I am very simple! knowing full well
That thou art bound to go thy blithesome way,
And my untimely end thy fame shall swell.

Come, thirsting Tantalus from out Hell's pit;
Come, Sisyphus with the terrifying weight
Of that stone thou rollest; Tityus, bring
Thy vulture and thine anguish infinite;
Ixion with thy wheel, be thou not late;
Come, too, ye sisters ever laboring;
Come all, your griefs into my bosom fling,
And then, with lowered voices, intone a dirge,
If dirge be fitting for one so desperate,
A body without a shroud, unhappy fate!
And Hell's three-headed gateman, do thou emerge
With a myriad other phantoms, monstrous swarm,
Beings infernal of fantastic form,
Raising their voices for the uncomforted
In a counterpoint of grief, harmonious storm.
What better burial for a lover dead?

Despairing song of mine, do not complain,

Nor let our parting cause thee any pain,
For my misfortune is not wholly bad,
Seeing her fortune's bettered by my demise.
Then, even in the grave, be thou not sad.

Those who had listened to Grisóstomo's poem liked it well enough, but the one who read it remarked that it did not appear to him to conform to what had been told him of Marcela's modesty and virtue, seeing that in it the author complains of jealousy, suspicion, and absence, all to the prejudice of her good name. To this Ambrosio, as one who had known his friend's most deeply hidden thoughts, replied as follows:

"By way of satisfying, sir, the doubt that you entertain, it is well for you to know that when the unfortunate man wrote that poem, he was by his own volition absent from Marcela, to see if this would work a cure; but when the enamored one is away from his love, there is nothing that does not inspire in him fear and torment, and such was the case with Grisóstomo, for whom jealous imaginings, fears, and suspicions became a seeming reality. And so, in this respect, Marcela's reputation for virtue remains unimpaired; beyond being cruel and somewhat arrogant, and exceedingly disdainful, she could not be accused by the most envious of any other fault."

"Yes, that is so," said Vivaldo.

He was about to read another of the papers he had saved from the fire when he was stopped by a marvelous vision—for such it appeared—that suddenly met his sight; for there atop the rock beside which the grave was being hollowed out stood the shepherdess Marcela herself, more beautiful even than she was reputed to be. Those who up to then had never seen her looked on in silent admiration, while those who were accustomed to beholding her were held in as great a suspense as the ones who were gazing upon her for the first time.

No sooner had Ambrosio glimpsed her than, with a show of indignation, he called out to her, "So, fierce basilisk of these mountains, have you perchance come to see if in your presence blood will flow from the wounds of this poor wretch whom you by your cruelty have deprived of life? Have you come to gloat over your inhuman exploits, or would you from that height look down like another pitiless Nero upon your Rome in flames and ashes? Or perhaps you would arrogantly tread under foot this poor corpse, as an ungrateful daughter did that of her father Tarquinius? Tell us quickly why you have come and what it is that you want most; for I know that Grisóstomo's thoughts never failed to obey you in life, and though he is dead now, I will see that all those who call themselves his friends obey you likewise."

"I do not come, O Ambrosio, for any of the reasons that you have mentioned," replied Marcela. "I come to defend myself and to demonstrate how unreasonable all those persons are who blame me for their sufferings and for Grisóstomo's death. I therefore ask all present to hear me attentively. It will not take long and I shall not have to spend many words in persuading those of you who are sensible that I speak the truth.

"Heaven made me beautiful, you say, so beautiful that you are compelled to love me whether you will or no; and in return for the love that you show me, you would have it that I am obliged to love you in return. I know, with that natural understanding that God has given me, that everything beautiful is lovable; but I cannot see that it follows that the object that is loved for its beauty must love the one who loves it. Let us suppose that the lover of the beautiful were ugly and, being ugly, deserved to be shunned; it would then be highly absurd for him to say, 'I love you because you are beautiful; you must love me because I am ugly.'

"But assuming that two individuals are equally beautiful, it does not mean that their desires are the same; for not all beauty inspires love, but may sometimes merely delight the eye and leave the will intact. If it were otherwise, no one would know what he wanted, but all would wander vaguely and aimlessly with nothing upon which to settle their affections; for the number of beautiful objects being infinite, desires similarly would be boundless. I have heard it said that true love knows no division and must be voluntary and not forced. This being so, as I believe it is, then why would you compel me to surrender my will for no other reason than that you say you love me? But tell me: supposing that Heaven which made me beautiful had made me ugly instead, should I have any right to complain because you did not love me? You must remember, moreover, that I did not choose this beauty that is mine; such as it is, Heaven gave it to me of its grace, without any choice or asking on my part. As the viper is not to be blamed for the deadly poison that it bears, since that is a gift of nature, so I do not deserve to be reprehended for my comeliness of form.

"Beauty in a modest woman is like a distant fire or a sharp-edged sword: the one does not burn, the other does not cut, those who do not come near it. Honor and virtue are the adornments of the soul, without which the body is not beautiful though it may appear to be. If modesty is one of the virtues that most adorn and beautify body and soul, why should she who is loved for her beauty part with that virtue merely to satisfy the whim of one who solely for his own pleasure strives with all his force and energy to cause her to lose it? I was born a free being, and in order to live freely I chose the solitude of the fields; these mountain trees are my company, the clear-running waters in these brooks are my mirror, and to the trees and waters I communicate my thoughts and lend them of my beauty.

"In short, I am that distant fire, that sharp-edged sword, that does not burn or cut. Those who have been enamored by the sight of me I have disillusioned with my words; and if desire is sustained by hope, I gave none to Grisóstomo or any other, and of none of them can it be said that I killed them with my cruelty, for it was rather their own obstinacy that was to blame. And if you reproach me with the fact that his intentions were honorable and that I ought for that reason to have complied with them, I will tell you that when, on this very spot where his grave is now being dug, he revealed them to me, I replied that it was my own intention to live in perpetual solitude and that only the earth should enjoy the fruit of my retirement and the spoils of my beauty; and if he with all this plain-speaking was still stubbornly bent upon hoping against hope and sailing against the wind, is it to be wondered at if he drowned in the gulf of his own folly?

"Had I led him on, it would have been falsely; had I gratified his passion, it would have been against my own best judgment and intentions; but, though I had disillusioned him, he persisted, and though I did not hate him, he was driven to despair. Ask yourselves, then, if it is reasonable to blame me for his woes! Let him who has been truly deceived complain; let him despair who has been cheated of his promised hopes; if I have enticed any, let him speak up; if I have accepted the attentions of any, let him boast of it; but let not him to whom I have promised nothing, whom I have neither enticed nor accepted, apply to me such terms as cruel and homicidal. It has not as yet been Heaven's will to destine me to love any man, and there is no use expecting me to love of my own free choice.

"Let what I am saying now apply to each and every one of those who would have me for their own, and let it be understood from now on that if any die on account of me, he is not to be regarded as an unfortunate victim of jealousy, since she that cares for none can give to none the occasion for being jealous; nor is my plain-speaking to be taken as disdain. He who calls me a wild beast and a basilisk, let him leave me alone as something that is evil and harmful; let him who calls me ungrateful cease to wait upon me; let him who finds me strange shun my acquaintance; if I am cruel, do not run after me; in which case this wild beast, this basilisk, this strange, cruel, ungrateful creature will not run after them, seek them out, wait upon them, nor endeavor to know them in any way.

"The thing that killed Grisóstomo was his impatience and the impetuosity of his desire; so why blame my modest conduct and retiring life? If I choose to preserve my purity here in the company of the trees, how can he complain of my unwillingness to lose it who would have me keep it with other men? I, as you know, have a worldly fortune of my own and do not covet that of others. My life is a free one, and I do not wish to be subject to another in any way. I neither love nor hate anyone; I do not repel this one and allure that one; I do not play fast and loose with any. The modest conversation of these village lasses and the care of my goats is sufficient to occupy me. Those mountains there represent the bounds of my desire, and should my wishes go beyond them, it is but to contemplate the beauty of the heavens, that pathway by which the soul travels to its first dwelling place."

Saying this and without waiting for any reply, she turned her back and entered the thickest part of a near-by wood, leaving all present lost in admiration of her wit as well as her beauty. A few—those who had felt the powerful dart of her glances and bore the wounds inflicted by her lovely eyes—were of a mind to follow her, taking no heed of the plainly worded warning they had just had from her lips; whereupon Don Quixote, seeing this and thinking to himself that here was an opportunity to display his chivalry by succoring a damsel in distress, laid his hand upon the hilt of his sword and cried out, loudly and distinctly, "Let no person of whatever state or condition he may be dare to follow the beauteous Marcela under pain of incurring my furious wrath. She has shown with clear and sufficient reasons that little or no blame for Grisóstomo's death is to be attached to her; she has likewise shown how far she is from acceding to the desires of any of her suitors, and it is accordingly only just that in place of being hounded and persecuted she should be honored and esteemed by all good people in this world as the only woman in it who lives with such modesty and good intentions."

Whether it was due to Don Quixote's threats or because Ambrosio now told them that they should finish doing the things which his good friend had desired should be done, no one stirred from the spot until the burial was over and Grisóstomo's papers had been burned. As the body was laid in the grave, many tears were shed by the bystanders. Then they placed a heavy stone upon it until the slab which Ambrosio was thinking of having made should be ready, with an epitaph that was to read:

> Here lies a shepherd by love betrayed,
> His body cold in death,
> Who with his last and faltering breath
> Spoke of a faithless maid.
> He died by the cruel, heartless hand
> Of a coy and lovely lass,
> Who by bringing men to so sorry a pass
> Love's tyranny doth expand.

They then scattered many flowers and boughs over the top of the grave, and, expressing their condolences to the dead man's friend, Ambrosio, they all took their leave, including Vivaldo and his companions. Don Quixote now said good-by to the travelers as well, although they urged him to come with them to Seville, assuring him that he would find in every street and at every corner of that city more adventures than are to be met with anywhere else. He thanked them for the invitation and the courtesy they had shown him in offering it, but added that for the present he had no desire to visit Seville, not until he should have rid these mountains of the robbers and bandits of which they were said to be full.

Seeing that his mind was made up, the travelers did not urge him further but, bidding him another farewell, left him and continued on their way; and the reader may be sure that in the course of their journey they did not fail to discuss the story of Marcela and Grisóstomo as well as Don Quixote's madness. As for the good knight himself, he was resolved to go seek the shepherdess and offer her any service that lay in his power; but things did not turn out the way he expected, as is related in the course of this veracious history, the second part of which ends here.

CHAPTER XV. *In which is related the unfortunate adventure that befell Don Quixote when he encountered certain wicked Yanguesans.*

THE learned Cid Benengeli tells us that, upon taking leave of their hosts and all those who had attended the shepherd Grisóstomo's funeral, Don Quixote and his squire entered the same wood into which they had seen the shepherdess Marcela disappear, and that, having journeyed in the forest for more than two hours, looking for her everywhere without being able to discover her, they finally came to a meadow covered with fresh young grass, alongside the cool and placid waters of a mountain stream which irresistibly invited them to pause there during the noontide heat, for the sun was now beating down upon them. The two of them accordingly dismounted and, turning Rocinante and the ass out to feed upon the plentiful pasturage, proceeded to investigate the contents of the saddlebags, after which, without further ceremony, master and man sat down together very peaceably and sociably to eat what they had found there.

Now, Sancho had not taken the trouble to put fetters on Rocinante, knowing the hack to be so tame and so little inclined to lust that, he felt certain, all the mares in the Cordovan meadowlands would not be able to tempt him to an indiscretion. But fate and the devil—who is not always sleeping—had ordained that a herd of Galician ponies belonging to some carters of Yanguas[1] should be feeding in this same valley; for it was the custom of these men to stop for their siesta in some place where grass and water were to be had for their teams, and as it happened, the spot the Yanguesans had chosen on this occasion was not far from where Don Quixote was.

Then it was that Rocinante suddenly felt the desire to have a little sport with the ladies. The moment he scented them, he abandoned his customary gait and staid behavior and, without asking his master's leave, trotted briskly over to them to acquaint them with his needs. They, however, preferred to go on eating, or so it seemed, for they received him with their hoofs and teeth, to such good effect that they broke his girth and left him naked and without a saddle. But the worst of it was when the carters, seeing the violence that he was offering their mares, came running up with poles and so belabored him that they left him lying there badly battered on the ground.

At this point Don Quixote and Sancho, who had witnessed the drubbing that Rocinante received, also ran up, panting. It was the master who spoke first.

"So far as I can see, friend Sancho," he said, "those are not knights but low fellows of ignoble birth; and so you may very well aid me in wreaking a deserved vengeance upon them for the wrong they have done to Rocinante in front of our very eyes."

"What the devil kind of vengeance are we going to take," asked Sancho, "seeing there are more than twenty of them and not more than two of us, or maybe only one and a half?"

"I," replied Don Quixote, "am worth a hundred." Without saying anything more, he drew his sword and fell upon the Yanguesans, and, moved and incited by his master's example, Sancho Panza did the same.

At the first slashing blow he dealt, the knight laid open the leather jacket that the man wore along with a good part of one shoulder. Seeing themselves assaulted like this by two lone individuals while they were so many in number, the Yanguesans again ran up with their poles and, surrounding their assailants, began flaying them with great ardor and vehemence. The truth is that the second blow sufficed to lay Sancho low, and the same thing happened with Don Quixote, all his dexterity and high courage availing him not at all. As luck would have it, he fell at Rocinante's feet, for the animal had not yet been able to rise; all of which goes to show what damage poles can do when furiously wielded by angry rustics. When the Yanguesans saw what mischief they had wrought, they lost no time in loading their teams and were soon off down the road, leaving the two adventurers in a sorry plight and a worse mood.

The first to recover his senses was Sancho Panza. Finding himself beside his master, he called out to him in a weak and piteous voice, "Señor Don Quixote! Ah, Señor Don Quixote!"

"What do you want, brother Sancho?" said the knight in the same feeble, suffering tone that the squire had used.

"I'd like, if possible," said Sancho, "for your Grace to give me a couple of draughts of that ugly Bras,[2] if you happen to have any of it at hand. Perhaps it would be as good for broken bones as it is for wounds."

"If I only did have some of it, wretch that I am," said Don Quixote, "what more could we ask for? But I swear to you, Sancho Panza, on the word of a knight-errant, that before two days have passed, unless fortune should rule otherwise, I shall have it in my possession, or else my hands will have failed me."

"But how many days do you think it will be, your Grace, before we are able to move our feet?" Sancho wanted to know.

"For my part," said his well-cudgeled master, "I must confess that I cannot answer that question. I hold myself to blame for everything. I had no business putting hand to sword against men who had not been dubbed knights and so were not my equals. Because I thus violated the laws of knighthood, the God of battles has permitted this punishment to be inflicted upon me. For which reason, Sancho, you should pay attention to what I am about to say to you, for it may have much to do with the safety of both of us. Hereafter, when you see a rabble of this sort committing some offense against us, do not wait for me to draw my sword, for I shall not do so under any circumstances, but, rather, draw your own and chastise them to your heart's content. If any knights come to their aid and defense, I will protect you by attacking them with all my might; and you already know by a thousand proofs and experiences the valor of this, my strong right arm."

For the poor gentleman was still feeling puffed up as a result of his victory over the valiant Biscayan. His advice, however, did not strike Sancho as being so good that he could let it pass without an answer.

"Sir," he said, "I am a peaceful man, calm and quiet, and I can put up with any insult because I have a wife and young ones to support and bring up; and so let me advise your Grace, since it is not for me to lay down the law, that under no consideration will I draw my sword, either against rustic or against knight, but from now on, as God is my witness, I hereby pardon all wrongs that have been done or may be done to me by any person high or low, rich or poor, gentleman or commoner, without excepting any rank or walk in life whatsoever."

"I wish," said his master, "that I had a little breath so that I could speak to you without so much effort; I wish the pain in this rib would subside somewhat so that I might be able, Sancho, to show you how wrong you are. Come now, you sinner, supposing that the wind of fortune, which up to now has been so contrary a one, should veer in our favor, filling the sails of our desire so that we should certainly and without anything to hinder us be able to put into port at one of those islands that I have promised you, what would happen to you if, winning the victory, I were to make you the ruler of it? You will have rendered that impossible by not being a knight nor caring to become one, and by having no intention of avenging the insults offered you or defending your seignorial rights.

"For you must know that in newly conquered kingdoms and provinces the minds of the inhabitants are never tranquil, nor do they like their new lord so well that there is not to be feared some fresh move on their part to alter the existing state of affairs and, as the saying goes, see what their luck will bring. And so it is necessary that the new ruler possess the ability to govern and the valor to attack or defend himself as the case may be."

"Well, in the present case," said Sancho, "I can only wish I had that ability and that valor of which your Grace speaks; but I swear to you on the word of a poor man that I need a poultice more than I do an argument. If your Grace will try to rise, we will help Rocinante up, although he does not deserve it, seeing that he is the principal cause of this thrashing we have received. I never would have thought it of him; I always took him to be as chaste and peaceful as I am. Oh, well, they say it takes a lot of time to get to know a person and nothing in this life is certain. Who would have thought that those mighty slashes your Grace gave that poor knight-errant would be followed posthaste by such a tempest of blows as they let fall upon our shoulders?"

"Your shoulders, at any rate," observed Don Quixote, "ought to be used to such squalls as that, but mine, accustomed to fine cambric and Dutch linen, naturally feel more acutely the pain of this misfortune that has befallen us. And if I did not imagine—why do I say imagine?— if I did not know for a certainty that all these discomforts are the inevitable accompaniment of the profession of arms, I should straightway lay me down and die of pure vexation."

"Sir," replied the squire, "seeing that these mishaps are what one reaps when one is a knight, I wish your Grace would tell me if they happen very often or only at certain times; for it seems to me that after two such harvests, there will not be much left of us for the third, unless God in His infinite mercy sees fit to succor us."

"Be assured, friend Sancho," said Don Quixote, "that the life of knights-errant is subject to a thousand perils and misadventures. At the same time, it is within the power of those same knights to become at almost any moment kings and emperors, as experience has shown in the case of many different ones whose histories I know well. If this pain of mine permitted me, I could tell you right now of some who merely by the might of their arm have risen to the highest stations such as I have mentioned; yet these very ones, both before and after, endured various troubles and calamities.

"There was the valorous Amadis of Gaul, who fell into the power of his mortal enemy, Arcalaus the enchanter, who, after he had taken him prisoner and had bound him to a pillar in the courtyard, is known for a fact to have given him more than two hundred lashes with his horse's reins. And there is a certain author of no little repute, though his name is not widely known, who tells us how the Knight of the Sun, in a certain castle, was caught in a trapdoor that opened beneath his feet; on falling through the trap, he found himself in a deep underground pit, bound hand and foot, and they gave him one of those so-called clysters of sand and snow-water that all but finished him. Indeed, if in this great peril a magician who was a great friend of his had not come to his aid, it would have gone very badly with the poor knight.

"And so I well may suffer in the company of such worthy ones; for the indignities that they endured are worse than those that we have had to suffer. I would inform you, Sancho, that those wounds that are inflicted by any instruments that chance to be in the assailant's hand do not constitute an affront, as is expressly laid down in the dueling code. Thus, if the shoemaker strike another with the last that he holds, although it is really of wood, it cannot for that reason be said that the one attacked with it has been cudgeled. I tell you this in order that you may not think that, because we have been beaten to a pulp in this combat, an affront has thereby been offered us; for the arms that those men bore and with which they pommeled us were nothing other than stakes, and none of them, so far as I can recall, carried a rapier, sword, or dagger."

"They did not give me time to see what they carried," said Sancho, "for I had no sooner laid hands on my blade than they made the sign of the cross over my shoulder with their clubs, taking away the sight of my eyes and the strength of my feet, after which they went off and left me lying here where I am now, and I am not taking the trouble to think whether or not those blows they gave me with their poles were an affront; all I can think of is the pain they have caused me, which is as deeply imprinted on my memory as it is on my shoulders."

"But with all that, brother Panza," said Don Quixote, "I must remind you that there is no memory to which time does not put an end and no pain that death does not abolish."

"Well," said Panza, "what greater misfortune could there be than that of having to wait on time and death? If this trouble of ours were one of those that are cured with a couple of poultices, it would not be so bad. But I am beginning to think that all the plasters in a hospital will not be enough to put us in shape again."

"Leave all that," said Don Quixote, "and draw strength from weakness as I propose to do. Come, let us see how Rocinante is; for, it appears to me, the poor beast has had the worst of this mishap."

"I am not surprised at that," said Sancho, "in view of the fact that he is a knight-errant also. What does astonish me is that my donkey should have gone free and without costs while we have come off without our ribs." [3]

"Fortune," said Don Quixote, "always leaves a door open in adversity as a means of remedying it. What I would say is, this little beast may take the place of Rocinante now by carrying me to some castle where I may be healed of my wounds. And I may add that I do not look upon it as a disgrace to go mounted like that, for I recall having read that good old Silenus, the tutor and instructor of the merry god of laughter, when he entered the city of the hundred gates,[4] was pleased to do so mounted upon a very handsome ass."

"That may very well be," said Sancho, "but there is a big difference between going mounted and being slung across the animal's flanks like a bag of refuse."

"Wounds received in battle," replied Don Quixote, "confer honor, they do not take it away; and so, friend Sancho, say no more, but, as I have already told you, lift me up the best you can and place me on the ass in any fashion that pleases you, and we will then be on our way before night descends upon us here in this wilderness."

"But I thought I heard your Grace say," remarked Panza, "that it is very fitting for knights-errant to sleep out in the cold wastes and desert places the better part of the year, and that they esteem it a great good fortune to be able to do so."

"That," said Don Quixote, "is when they have no choice in the matter or when they are in love; and, it is true, there have been knights who for two years' time have remained upon a rock, in sun and shade and through all the inclemencies of the heavens, without their ladies knowing anything about it. One of these was Amadis, who, under the name of Beltenebros, took up his lodging on the rock known as Peña Pobre, remaining there either eight years or eight months, I am not quite certain as to the exact length of time; what matters is that he was there doing penance for some slight offense that he had given to his lady Oriana. But let us quit this talk, Sancho, and make haste before something happens to the ass as it did to Rocinante."

"There will be the devil to pay in that case," said Sancho; and venting himself of thirty "Ohs" and "Ahs" and sixty sighs and a hundred-twenty imprecations of various sorts, with curses for the one who had got him into this, he arose, pausing halfway like a Turkish bow bent in the middle, without the power to straighten himself. It was with the greatest difficulty that he succeeded in saddling his ass, which, making use of the unwonted freedom it had enjoyed that day, had wandered off some little distance. He then managed to get Rocinante on his feet, and if that animal had possessed the power to complain, you may be sure that he would have been an equal for Sancho and his master.

The end of the matter was, Sancho seated Don Quixote upon the donkey, tying Rocinante on behind, and then started off leading the ass by the halter, proceeding more or less in the direction in which he thought the main highway ought to be; and as chance was now guiding their affairs from good to better, he had gone but a short league when there before them was the road—not only the road but an inn, which greatly to Sancho's disgust and his master's delight had, of course, to be a castle. The squire stubbornly insisted that it was not a castle but a hostelry, while his master maintained the contrary. The argument lasted so long that they had reached the inn before it was ended, and with the point still unsettled, Sancho entered the gateway, followed by his cavalcade.

CHAPTER XVI. *Of what happened to the ingenious gentleman in the inn which he imagined was a castle.*

UPON seeing Don Quixote thus slung across the ass, the innkeeper inquired of Sancho what was wrong. The squire replied that it was nothing; his master had fallen from a cliff and bruised a few ribs, that was all. Now, the innkeeper had a wife who was not the kind one would expect to find among women of her calling, for she was naturally of a charitable disposition and inclined to sympathize with those of her neighbors who were in trouble. She accordingly came running up to take care of her injured guest and called upon her daughter, who was young and very good-looking, to lend her a helping hand.

Serving in the inn, also, was a lass from Asturia, broad-faced, flat-headed, and with a snub nose; she was blind in one eye and could not see very well out of the other. To be sure, her bodily graces made up for her other defects: she measured not more than seven palms from head to foot, and, being slightly hunchbacked, she had to keep looking at the ground a good deal more than she liked. This gentle creature in turn aided the daughter of the house, and the two made up a very uncomfortable bed for Don Quixote in an attic which gave every evidence of having formerly been a hayloft and which held another lodger, a mule driver, whose bed stood a little beyond the one they had prepared for our friend.

The muleteer's couch was composed of the packsaddles and blankets from his beasts, but it was a better one for all of that. The other consisted merely of four smooth planks laid upon two trestles of uneven height, and had a mattress so thin that it looked more like a counterpane, with lumps which, had they not been seen through the rents to be of wool, might from the feel of them have been taken for pebbles. To cover him, the knight had a pair of sheets made of the kind of leather they use on bucklers and a quilt whose threads anyone who chose might have counted without missing a single one.

On this wretched pallet Don Quixote stretched himself out, and then the innkeeper's wife and daughter proceeded to cover him from top to toe with plasters while Maritornes (for that was the Asturian girl's name) held the light. As she applied the poultices, the mistress of the house remarked that he was so black-and-blue in spots that his bruises looked more like the marks of blows than like those caused by a fall.

"They were not blows," said Sancho, adding that the rock had many sharp points and jutting edges and each one had left its imprint. "If your Ladyship," he went on, "can manage to save a little of that tow, it will come in handy, for my loins also hurt me a little."

"So, then," replied the innkeeper's wife, "you must have fallen too."

"I did not fall," said Sancho Panza, "but the shock I had at seeing my master take such a tumble makes my body ache as if I had received a thousand whacks."

"That may very well be," said the daughter, "for I have often dreamed that I was falling from a tower and yet I never reached the ground, and when I awoke from my dream I would feel as bruised and broken as if I had really fallen."

"The point is, lady," Sancho explained, "that I was not dreaming at all, but was more wide awake than I am at this minute, and yet I find myself with scarcely less bruises than my master, Don Quixote."

"What did you say the gentleman's name was?" asked Maritornes, the Asturian.

"Don Quixote de la Mancha," replied Sancho, "and he is a knightly adventurer and one of the best and bravest that the world has seen for a long time."

"What is a knightly adventurer?" the girl wished to know.

"Are you so unused to the ways of the world that you don't know that?" he said. "Then let me inform you, my sister, that it is something that can be summed up in two or three words: well thrashed and an emperor; today, he is the most wretched and needy creature that there is, and tomorrow he will have the crowns of two or three kingdoms to give to his squire."

"If that is so," said the innkeeper's wife, "how does it come that you, being this worthy gentleman's squire, have not so much as an earldom, to judge by appearances?"

"It is early yet," was Sancho's answer. "We have been looking for adventures for only a month now, and so far have not fallen in with what could rightly be called one. Sometimes you look for one thing and you find another. The truth is, once my master Don Quixote is healed of this wound or fall, providing I am none the worse for it all, I would not exchange my expectations for the best title in all Spain."

The knight had been following this conversation very closely; and at this point, raising himself up in the bed as well as he was able, he took the landlady's hand and said to her, "Believe me, beautiful lady, you well may call yourself fortunate for having given a lodging in this your castle to my person. If I myself do not tell you of my merits, it is for the reason that, as the saying goes, self-praise is degrading; but my squire can inform you as to who I am. I will only say that I have written down in my memory for all eternity the service which you have rendered me, that I may give you thanks as long as life endures. And I would to high Heaven that love did not hold me so captive and subject to its laws, and to the eyes of that beauteous but ungrateful one whose name I mutter between my teeth;[1] for then the orbs of this lovely damsel here would surely be the mistress of my liberty."

The landlady, her daughter, and the worthy Maritornes were very much bewildered by these remarks of the knight-errant; they understood about as much of them as if he had been speaking Greek, although they were able to make out that he was offering them flattery and compliments. Being wholly unused to such language, they could but stare at him in amazement, for he seemed to them a different kind of man than any they had known. And so, thanking him in their own idiom, which was that of a wayside tavern, they left him, while Maritornes looked after Sancho, who had no less need of attention than did his master.

The mule driver had arranged with the Asturian to have a little sport with her that night, and she had given him her word that, as soon as the guests were quiet and her master and mistress asleep, she would come to him and let him have his way. It was commonly said of the good lass that she never made such a promise without keeping it, even though it was in a forest and without witnesses, for she prided herself greatly upon being a lady and did not look upon it as any disgrace to be a servant in an inn, for, as she was in the habit of saying, it was misfortunes and ill luck that had brought her to such a state.

Don Quixote's hard, narrow, cramped, makeshift bed stood in the middle of this starry stable [2] and was the first that one encountered upon entering the room. Next to it was that of his squire, Sancho, which consisted solely of a cattail mat and a blanket that looked as if it was of shorn canvas rather than of wool. And beyond these two was that of the mule driver, made up, as has been said, of packsaddles and all the trappings of his two best mules, although he had twelve of them altogether, sleek, fat, and in fine condition; for he was one of the richest carters of Arévalo, according to the author of this history who knew him well and makes special mention of him—some say they were related in one way or another. In any event, Cid Hamete Benengeli was a historian who was at great pains to ascertain the truth and very accurate in everything, as is evident from the fact that he did not see fit to pass over in silence those details that have been mentioned, however trifling and insignificant they may appear to be.

All of which might serve as an example to those grave chroniclers who give us such brief and succinct accounts that we barely get a taste, the gist of the matter being left in their inkwells out of carelessness, malice, or ignorance. Blessings on the author of the *Tablante de Ricamonte* [3] and the one who wrote that other work in which are related the deeds of Count Tomillas—with what exactitude they describe everything!

But to go on with our story, the mule driver, after he had looked in on his beasts and had given them their second feeding, came back and stretched out on his packsaddles to await that model of conscientiousness, Maritornes. Sancho, having been duly poulticed, had also lain down and was doing his best to sleep, but the pain in his ribs would not let him. As for Don Quixote, he was suffering so much that he kept his eyes open like a rabbit. The inn was silent now, and there was no light other than from a lantern which hung in the middle of the gateway.

This uncanny silence, and our knight's constant habit of thinking of incidents described at every turn in those books that had been the cause of all his troubles, now led him to conceive as weird a delusion as could well be imagined. He fancied that he had reached a famous castle—for, as has been said, every inn where he stopped was a castle to him—and that the daughter of the lord (innkeeper) who dwelt there, having been won over by his gentle bearing, had fallen in love with him and had promised him that she would come that night, without her parents' knowledge, to lie beside him for a while. And taking this chimerical fancy which he had woven out of his imagination to be an established fact, he then began to be grieved at the thought that his virtue was thus being endangered, and firmly resolved not be false to his lady Dulcinea del Toboso, even though Queen Guinevere with her waiting-woman Quintañona should present themselves in person before him.

As he lay there, his mind filled with such nonsense as this, the hour that had been fixed for the Asturian's visit came, and an unlucky one it proved to be for Don Quixote. Clad in her nightgown and barefoot, her hair done up in a fustian net, Maritornes with silent, cautious steps stole into the room where the three were lodged, in search of the muleteer. She had no sooner crossed the threshold, however, than the knight became aware of her presence; and, sitting up in bed despite his poultices and the pain from his ribs, he held out his arms as if to receive the beautiful maiden. The latter, all doubled up and saying nothing, was groping her way to her lover's cot when she encountered Don Quixote. Seizing her firmly by the wrists, he drew her to him, without her daring to utter a sound.

Forcing her to sit down upon the bed, he began fingering her nightgown, and although it was of sackcloth, it impressed him as being of the finest and flimsiest silken gauze. On her wrists she wore some glass beads, but to him they gave off the gleam of oriental pearls. Her hair, which resembled a horse's mane rather than anything else, he decided was like filaments of the brightest gold of Araby whose splendor darkened even that of the sun. Her breath without a doubt smelled of yesterday's stale salad, but for Don Quixote it was a sweet and aromatic odor that came from her mouth.

The short of it is, he pictured her in his imagination as having the same appearance and manners as those other princesses whom he had read about in his books, who, overcome by love and similarly bedecked, came to visit their badly wounded knights. So great was the poor gentleman's blindness that neither his sense of touch nor the girl's breath nor anything else about her could disillusion him, although they were enough to cause anyone to vomit who did not happen to be a mule driver. To him it seemed that it was the goddess of beauty herself whom he held in his arms.

Clasping her tightly, he went on to speak to her in a low and amorous tone of voice. "Would that I were in a position, O beauteous and high-born lady, to be able to repay the favor that you have accorded me by thus affording me the sight of your great loveliness; but Fortune, which never tires of persecuting those who are worthy, has willed to place me in this bed where I lie so bruised and broken that, even though my desire were to satisfy yours, such a thing would be impossible. And added to this impossibility is another, greater one: my word and promise given to the peerless Dulcinea del Toboso, the one and only lady of my most secret thoughts. If this did not stand in the way, I should not be so insensible a knight as to let slip the fortunate opportunity which you out of your great goodness of heart have placed in my way."

Maritornes was extremely vexed and all a-sweat at finding herself held fast in Don Quixote's embrace, and without paying any heed to what he was saying she struggled silently to break away. Meanwhile, the mule driver, whose evil desires had kept him awake, had been aware of his wench's presence ever since she entered the door and had been listening attentively to everything that Don Quixote said. Jealous because the Asturian lass, as he thought, had broken her word and deserted him for another, he came up to the knight's cot and, without being able to make head or tail of all this talk, stood there waiting to see what the outcome would be.

When he saw that the girl was doing her best to free herself and Don Quixote was trying to hold her, he decided that the joke had gone far enough; raising his fist high above his head, he came down with so fearful a blow on the gaunt jaws of the enamored knight as to fill the poor man's mouth with blood. Not satisfied with this, the mule driver jumped on his ribs and at a pace somewhat faster than a trot gave them a thorough going-over from one end to the other. The bed, which was rather weak and not very firm on its foundations, was unable to support the mule-teer's added weight and sank to the floor with a loud crash. This awoke the innkeeper, who imagined that Maritornes must be involved in some brawl, since he had called twice to her and had received no answer. Sus-picious of what was going on, he arose, lighted a lamp, and made his way to the place from which the sound of the scuffle appeared to be coming. Frightened out of her wits when she heard her master, for she knew what a terrible temper he had, the girl took refuge beside Sancho Panza, who was still sleeping, and huddled herself there like a ball of yarn.

"Where are you, whore?" cried the landlord as he came in; "for I am certain that this is all your doing."

At that moment Sancho awoke and, feeling a bulky object almost on top of him and thinking it must be a nightmare, began throwing his fists about on one side and the other, giving Maritornes no telling how many punches. Feeling the pain, the wench cast all modesty aside and let him have so many blows in return that he very soon emerged from his sleepy state. When he saw himself being treated like this by an unknown assail-ant, he rose the best way he could and grappled with her, and there then began between the two of them the prettiest and most stubbornly fought skirmish that ever you saw.

When the muleteer perceived by the light of the lamp what was hap-pening to his lady, he left Don Quixote and went to her assistance. The innkeeper also came over to her, but with different intentions, for he meant to punish the girl, thinking that, undoubtedly, she was the cause of all the disturbance that prevailed. And so, then, as the saying goes, it was "the cat to the rat, the rat to the rope, the rope to the stick." [4] There was the mule driver pounding Sancho, Sancho and the wench flaying each other, and the landlord drubbing the girl; and they all laid on most vigorously, without allowing themselves a moment's rest. The best part of it was, the lamp went out, leaving them in darkness, whereupon there ensued a general and merciless melee, until there was not a hand's breadth left on any of their bodies that was not sore and aching.

As chance would have it, there was lodged at the inn that night a patrolman of the old Holy Brotherhood of Toledo,[5] who, hearing all this uproar and the sounds of a struggle, at once snatched up his staff of office and the tin box containing his warrants and went groping his way through the darkness to the room above, as he cried, "Hold, in the name of the law! Hold, in the name of the Holy Brotherhood!" The first one whom he encountered was the well-pommeled Don Quixote, who lay flat on his back and senseless on his broken-down bed. Grasping the knight's beard, the officer cried, "I charge you to aid the law!" But when he perceived that the one whom he thus held did not budge nor stir, he concluded that the man must be dead and the others in the room his murderers. Acting upon this suspicion, he called out in a booming voice, "Close the gateway of the inn! See that no one leaves, for someone here has killed a man!"

This cry startled them all, and each one left off his pommeling at the point where he was. The innkeeper then retired to his room, the mule driver to his packsaddles, and the wench to her stall, the poor unfortunate Don Quixote and Sancho being the only ones that could not move. The officer now let go of our friend's beard and left the room to go look for a light, that he might arrest the offenders. He did not find any, however, for the innkeeper had taken care to put out the lantern when he retired to his room, and the representative of the Holy Brotherhood was accordingly compelled to have recourse to the hearth, where with a great deal of time and trouble he finally succeeded in lighting another lamp.

CHAPTER XVII. *Wherein is continued the account of the innumerable troubles that the brave Don Quixote and his good squire Sancho Panza endured in the inn, which, to his sorrow, the knight took to be a castle.*

HAVING by this time recovered from his swoon, Don Quixote called to his squire in the same tone of voice that he had used the day before as they lay stretched out in the "vale of stakes." [1] "Sancho, my friend, are you asleep? Are you asleep, friend Sancho?"

"How do you expect me to sleep, curses on it?" replied the squire, who was filled with bitterness and sorrow. "I think all the devils in Hell must have been after me tonight."

"You are undoubtedly right about that," said his master; "for either I know little about it or this castle is an enchanted one. I may as well tell you—but first you must swear that you will keep it a secret until after I am dead."

"I swear," said Sancho.

"I ask that," Don Quixote went on, "because I hate taking away anyone's good name."

"I told you," Sancho repeated, "that I will say nothing about it until your Grace has reached the end of his days; and please God I may be able to reveal it tomorrow."

"Do I treat you so harshly, Sancho, that you wish to see me die so soon?"

"It is not for that reason," said Sancho. "It is just that I am opposed to keeping things too long—I don't like them to spoil on my hands."

"Be that as it may," said Don Quixote, "I am willing to trust your friendship and your courtesy. And so I may tell you that one of the weirdest adventures happened to me that I could possibly describe. To make a long story short, you must know that, a short while ago, the daughter of the lord of this castle came to me. She is the most genteel and lovely damsel to be found in many a land. How can I describe to you the grace of her person, her sprightly wit, or all those other hidden charms which, in order to keep faith with my lady Dulcinea, I must leave untouched and pass over in silence? I can only say that Heaven was envious of this gift that fortune had placed in my hands—or it may be (and this is more likely) that this castle, as I have remarked to you, is enchanted; at any rate, just as I was engaged with her in most sweet and amorous parley, without my seeing him or knowing whence he came, a monstrous giant seized me by the arm and gave me such a blow on the jaw that my mouth was bathed in blood; and after that he flayed me in such a manner that I am even worse off today than yesterday, when those carters on account of Rocinante's excesses did us that wrong with which you are acquainted. I therefore can only conjecture that the treasure of this damsel's beauty must be in the keeping of some enchanted Moor, and that it is not for me."

"Nor for me either," said Sancho; "for more than four hundred Moors have been mauling me and have made such a job of it that the thrashing those fellows gave me with their poles was but cakes and gingerbread by comparison. But tell me, sir, what name do you give to this fine and rare adventure which has left us where we are now? Your Grace, it is true, did not have quite so bad a time of it, with that incomparable beauty in your arms that you have been telling me about; but what was there in it for me except the worst beating that I hope to receive in all my born days? Pity me and the mother that bore me, for I am not a knight-errant nor ever expect to be, yet I always get the worst of whatever's coming!"

"So, you were beaten too, were you?" said Don Quixote.

"Did not I tell you I was, curses on it?" said Sancho.

"Well, do not let it worry you, my friend," said the knight; "for I will now make some of that precious balm and we shall both of us be healed in the blink of an eye."

The officer of the Brotherhood had lighted his lamp by this time and now came in to have a look at the one he thought was dead. The moment Sancho caught sight of him, in his nightgown, with a lamp in his hand, a towel around his head, and an evil-looking face, the squire turned to his master and said, "Could this be the enchanted Moor coming back to give us some more punishment, if there is any left in the inkwell?"

"No," replied Don Quixote, "it cannot be; for those who are under a spell do not let themselves be seen by anyone."

"If they do not let themselves be seen," remarked Sancho, "they certainly make themselves felt; if you do not believe it, let my ribs speak for me."

"Mine," said Don Quixote, "could tell the same story; but that is not a sufficient reason for believing that he whom we see here is the enchanted Moor."

Upon seeing them talking together so calmly, the officer did not know what to make of it, although the knight, true enough, was still flat on his back and unable to move, on account of his plasters and because he was still so stiff and sore.

"Well," said the officer coming up to him, "and how goes it, my good man?"

"If I were you," said Don Quixote, "I would speak a little more politely. Is it the custom in this country to address knights-errant in such a fashion, you dunce?"

Unable to bear being treated so ill by one whose appearance was so unimpressive, the patrolman raised his lamp with all the oil that was in it and let him have it over the head, a good stiff blow at that; after which, in the darkness, he slipped out of the room.

"Undoubtedly, sir," said Sancho, "that must be the enchanted Moor. He must be keeping the treasure for others, seeing all that he gives us is punches with his fist and blows with the lamp."

"Yes," said Don Quixote, "that is it; but no notice is to be taken of such things where enchantments are concerned, nor should one be angry or annoyed by them. Since these are invisible and fanciful beings, we should find no one on whom to take revenge even if we were to go looking for him. Arise, Sancho, if you can, summon the governor of this fortress, and tell him to let me have a little oil, wine, salt, and rosemary that I may make that health-giving balm. I think that truly I have need of it now, for there is much blood coming from the wound which that phantom gave me."

His bones aching all over, Sancho got to his feet and went out into the darkness to look for the landlord. On the way he met the officer, who was listening to find out what happened to his enemy.

"Sir," said the squire, "whoever you may be, kindly do us the favor of giving us a little rosemary, oil, salt, and wine, for they are needed to heal one of the most gallant knights-errant that ever walked the earth; he lies now in that bed, badly wounded at the hands of the enchanted Moor who is lodged in this inn."

Hearing this, the officer thought the man must be out of his senses, but inasmuch as day was already dawning, he threw open the inn door and told the proprietor what it was that Sancho required. The innkeeper provided all the things mentioned, and Sancho then took them to Don Quixote, who was lying there with his hands to his head, complaining of the pain from the blow that had been dealt him with the lamp, although the fact of the matter was that it had done him no more harm than to raise a couple of rather large bumps, while what he fancied to be blood was in reality nothing other than sweat, due to the anxiety he felt over the tempest that had but recently subsided.

Taking the ingredients, he now made a compound of them, mixing them all together and boiling them for some little while until he thought they were properly steeped. He then asked for a small vial into which he might pour the liquid, but as there was none to be had, he resolved to make use of an oil flask made of tinplate which the innkeeper presented to him free of charge. Above this flask he muttered more than eighty Our Fathers and as many Hail Marys and other prayers, each word being accompanied by the sign of the cross in way of benediction. All of which was witnessed by Sancho, the landlord, and the officer of the Holy Brotherhood. As for the carter, he had quietly gone out to look after his mules.

Having done this, the knight wished to try out the virtues of this precious balm, as he fancied it to be, and so he drank what remained in the pot, amounting to nearly half a quart. No sooner had he swallowed it than he at once began to vomit and kept it up until there was absolutely nothing left in his stomach; and with all his anxiety and the agitation of vomiting, a most copious sweat broke out upon him, whereupon he asked them to throw some covering over him and leave him alone. They did so, and he slept for more than three hours, at the end of which time he awoke, feeling greatly relieved in body and especially in his much battered bones. This led him to believe that he had been cured and that he had indeed discovered Fierabrás's balm; from now on he would be able to face with no fear whatsoever any kind of destruction, battle, or combat, no matter how perilous the undertaking.

Marveling at the change for the better that had been wrought in his master, Sancho Panza asked that what remained in the pot, which was no small quantity, be given to him. Don Quixote consented; and, taking the kettle in both hands, with good faith and right good will, the squire gulped down only a trifle less than his master had taken. Now, Sancho's stomach was not so delicate as the knight's, for he did not vomit at first but suffered such cramps and nausea, perspired so freely, and felt so faint, that he thought surely his last hour had come; and, finding himself in such misery and affliction, he cursed the balm and the thief who had given it to him.

"It is my opinion, Sancho," said Don Quixote, "that all this comes of your not having been dubbed a knight, for which reason this liquor is not suited to you."

"If your Grace knew that all the time," replied his squire, "then, curse me and all my kin, why did you let me taste it?"

At this point the beverage took effect and poor Sancho began to discharge at both ends and with such force that neither the cattail mat on which he had dropped down nor the coarse linen coverlet that had been tossed over him was of much use afterward. The sweat poured off him in such abundance, accompanied by such spasms and convulsions, that not only he but all who saw him thought that he was dying. This untoward squall kept up for nearly two hours, and when it was over he was not left in better condition as his master had been, but was so tired and weak that he was not able to stand.

But Don Quixote, who, as has been said, felt greatly relieved and quite himself again, was all for setting out at once in search of adventures; for, as he saw it, every moment that he tarried he was cheating the world and the needy ones in it of his favor and assistance—especially in view of the sense of security and confidence which the possession of his balm now afforded him. Accordingly, impelled by this desire, he himself saddled Rocinante and the ass and then aided his squire to clothe himself and straddle his beast, after which the knight mounted his steed and prepared to ride away. As he passed a corner of the inn, he seized a pike that was standing there to serve him as a lance.

All the guests in the hostelry, more than twenty persons, stood around watching, among them the innkeeper's daughter, and the knight in turn could not keep his eyes off the lass; every so often he would heave a sigh which it seemed must come from the depths of his entrails, but the others thought it must be from the pain in his ribs—at least, those who had seen him covered with plasters as he had been the night before were of this opinion.

As the two rode up to the gateway of the inn, Don Quixote called to his host and said to him, gravely and calmly, "Many and great are the favors, Sir Governor, which I have received in this your castle, and I shall be under obligations to you all the days of my life. If I can repay you by avenging the wrong done you by some haughty foe, you know that my profession is none other than that of helping those who cannot help themselves, avenging those who have been wronged, and chastising traitors. Search well your memory, and if you find anything of this sort with which to entrust me, you have but to speak, and I promise you by the order of chivalry which I have received to see that you are given satisfaction and are paid in accordance with your wishes."

The innkeeper's manner was equally tranquil as he replied, "Sir Knight, I have no need of your favor nor that you should avenge me of any wrong; for I can take such vengeance as I see fit when the need arises. The only thing needed in this case is for your Grace to pay me what you owe me for last night, including straw and barley for the two animals, your supper, and beds."

"Then this is an inn, is it?" said Don Quixote.

"And a very respectable one," replied the innkeeper.

"In that case I have been laboring under a mistake all this time," said the knight; "for the truth is, I thought it was a castle, and not a bad one at that. However, seeing it is not a castle but an inn, the only thing for you to do is to overlook the payment, since I cannot contravene the rule of knights-errant, none of whom, I am sure—at least, up to now, I have read nothing to the contrary—ever paid for his lodging or anything else when he stopped at an inn; for any hospitality that is offered to knights is only their just due, in return for all the hardships they suffer as they go in quest of adventures day and night, in summer and in winter, on horseback and on foot, enduring hunger and thirst and heat and cold, being subject to all the inclemencies of Heaven and all the discomforts of earth."

"I have little to do with all that," said the landlord. "Pay me what you owe me and let us hear no more of these accounts of chivalry. The only accounts that interest me are those that are due me."

"You are but a stupid, evil-minded tavernkeeper," was Don Quixote's answer; and, putting spurs to Rocinante and bringing his lance into position, he sallied out of the inn with no one to stop him. Without looking back to see if his squire was following him, he rode along for some distance. The innkeeper, meanwhile, seeing him leave like this without settling his account, straightway made for Sancho Panza, who said that since his master would not pay, neither would he, for being squire to a knight-errant as he was, he came under the same rule with regard to inns and taverns.

The landlord grew very indignant at this and began to threaten him, telling him that if he did not pay he would regret it. But Sancho replied that, by the law of knighthood which his master had received, he would not part with a single coronado,[2] even though it cost him his life; for if the worthy and ancient custom of knights-errant was to be violated, it would not be by him, nor would the squires of those knights who were yet to come into the world have any cause to complain of him or to reproach him for breaking so just a code.

As poor Sancho's ill luck would have it, stopping at the inn that day were four wool carders of Segovia, three needlemakers from the vicinity of the Horse Fountain of Cordova, and a couple of lads from the Fair of Seville,[3] merry fellows all of them, well intentioned, mischievous, and playful. They now, as if moved and instigated by one and the same impulse, came up to Sancho and pulled him off his donkey, and then one of them entered the inn to get the blanket off the host's bed. Throwing Sancho into it, they glanced up and saw that the roof was a little too low for the work in hand; so they went out into the stable yard, which was bounded only by the sky above. Placing the squire in the middle of the blanket, they began tossing him up and down, having as much sport with him as one does with a dog at Shrovetide.

The cries of the poor wretch in the blanket were so loud that they reached his master's ears. Reining in his steed to listen attentively, Don Quixote at first thought that it must be some new adventure that awaited him, until he came to distinguish clearly the voice of his squire. Turning about then, he returned to the inn at a painful gallop and, finding it closed, started circling the hostelry to see if he could find an entrance of some sort. The moment he reached the walls of the stable yard, which were not very high, he saw the scurvy trick that was being played on Sancho. He saw the latter going up and down in the air with such grace and dexterity that, had the knight's mounting wrath permitted him to do so, it is my opinion that he would have laughed at the sight.

He then endeavored to climb down from his horse onto the wall, but he was so stiff and sore that he was unable to dismount; whereupon, from his seat in the saddle he began hurling so many insults and maledictions at those who were doing the tossing that it would be quite impossible to set them all down here. The men in the yard, however, did not for this reason leave off their laughing sport, nor did the flying Sancho cease his lamentations, mingled now with threats and now with entreaties, all of which were of no avail until his tormentors saw fit to stop from pure exhaustion. After that, they brought his ass and set him upon it, bundling him in his greatcoat. Seeing him so done in, Maritornes felt sorry for him and, in order to refresh him, brought him a jug of water which she got from the well that it might be cooler. Taking the jug and raising it to his mouth, Sancho paused at sound of his master's words.

"Sancho, my son, do not drink that water. Do not drink it, my son, for it will kill you. Do you not see? I have here the most blessed balm"— and he showed him the vial containing the beverage—"of which you have but to imbibe two drops and you shall be healed without a doubt."

At this, Sancho rolled his eyes and cried out in a voice that was even louder than his master's, "Can it be your Grace has forgotten that I am not a knight, or do you want me to vomit up what guts I have left from last night? Keep your liquor and to the devil with it; just leave me alone, that's all."

Even as he finished saying this he started to take a drink; but perceiving at the first swallow that it was only water, he stopped and asked Maritornes to bring him some wine instead. She complied right willingly, paying for it out of her own money; for it is said of her that, although she occupied so lowly a station in life, there was something about her that remotely resembled a Christian woman. When he had drunk his fill, Sancho dug his heels into his ass's flanks, and the gate of the inn having been thrown wide open for him, he rode away quite well satisfied with himself because he had not had to pay anything, even though it had been at the expense of those usual bondsmen, his shoulders.

The truth is, the innkeeper had kept his saddlebags, but Sancho was so excited when he left that he did not notice they were gone. Once the two unwelcome guests were safely outside, the landlord was all for barring the gate; but the blanket-tossers would not hear of this, for they were fellows to whom it would not have made a penny's worth of difference if Don Quixote had really been one of the Knights of the Round Table.

CHAPTER **XVIII**. *In which is set forth the conversation that Sancho Panza had with his master, Don Quixote, along with other adventures deserving of record.*

BY THE time Sancho reached his master, he was so exhausted and felt so faint that he was not even able any longer to urge on his beast.

"Well, Sancho," said Don Quixote when he saw him, "I am now convinced that yonder castle or inn is without a doubt enchanted; for what sort of creatures could they be who had such atrocious sport with you if not phantoms from another world? The thing that confirms me in this belief is the fact that, when I was alongside the stable-yard wall, witnessing the acts of that sad tragedy, it was not possible for me to climb it or even so much as get down off Rocinante, and that shows they must have cast a spell on me. But I swear to you, by the sword of a knight, that if I had been able to dismount and come over that wall, I should have wreaked such vengeance in your behalf that those villainous knaves would never have forgotten their little jest; and I should have done this even though it be against the laws of knighthood; for as I have told you many times, it is not permitted that a knight raise his hand against one who is not of his calling, save it be in defense of his own life and person in a case of great and urgent necessity."

"I would have avenged myself, if I had been able," said Sancho, "whether I had been dubbed a knight or not; although it is my opinion that those who had such sport with me were not phantoms or human beings under a spell as your Grace says, but flesh-and-blood men like us. They all had names, for I heard them calling one another by them as they were tossing me. There was one who was called Pedro Martínez, and another Tenorio Hernández, and the innkeeper's name was Juan Palomeque the Left-Handed. And so, Señor, your not being able to leap over the stable-yard wall or even get down off your horse was due to something other than enchantments. What I make out of it all is that these adventures that we go looking for will end by bringing us so many misadventures that we shan't know which is our right foot. The best and most sensible thing to do, in my judgment, would be for us to return home, now that it is harvest time, and stop running about from Ceca to Mecca and from pail to bucket, as the saying goes." [1]

"How little you know, Sancho, about the matter of chivalry!" Don Quixote replied. "Hush, and have patience; the day shall come when you will see with your own eyes how honorable a calling it is that we follow. For tell me, if you will: what greater pleasure or satisfaction is to be had in this world than that of winning a battle and triumphing over one's enemy? None, undoubtedly none."

"That may be," said Sancho; "I cannot say as to that; but one thing I know is that since we have been knights-errant, or since your Grace has been one, for I am not to be counted among that honored number, we have not won a single battle, unless it was with the Biscayan, and even there your Grace came out with half an ear and half a helmet the less. Since then, all that we have had has been poundings, punches, and more poundings; and over and above that, I got the blanketing at the hands of certain persons who were under a spell, and so I do not know what that pleasure of conquering an enemy, of which your Grace speaks, is like."

"That," said Don Quixote, "is the thing that vexes me, and I can understand that it should vex you as well, Sancho. But from this time forth I shall endeavor to have at hand some sword made by so masterful an art that anyone who carries it with him cannot suffer any manner of enchantment. It may even be that fortune will procure for me the blade of Amadis,[2] the one he bore when he was called the Knight of the Flaming Sword. It was one of the best that ever a knight had in this world, for in addition to the aforesaid virtue which it possessed, it cut like a razor, and there was no suit of armor, however strong or enchanted it might be, that could withstand it."

"It would be just my luck," said Sancho, "that if your Grace did find a sword like that, it would be of use only to those who had been dubbed knights; as for the squires, they are out of luck."

"Never fear, Sancho," said his master, "Heaven will do better by you than that."

As they went along conversing in this manner, Don Quixote caught sight down the road of a large cloud of dust that was drawing nearer.

"This, O Sancho," he said, turning to his squire, "is the day when you shall see the boon that fate has in store for me; this, I repeat, is the day when, as well as on any other, shall be displayed the valor of my good right arm. On this day I shall perform deeds that will be written down in the book of fame for all centuries to come. Do you see that dust cloud rising there, Sancho? That is the dust stirred up [3] by a vast army marching in this direction and composed of many nations."

"At that rate," said Sancho, "there must be two of them, for there is another one just like it on the other side."

Don Quixote turned to look and saw that this was so. He was overjoyed by the thought that these were indeed two armies about to meet and clash in the middle of the broad plain; for at every hour and every moment his imagination was filled with battles, enchantments, nonsensical adventures, tales of love, amorous challenges, and the like, such as he had read of in the books of chivalry, and every word he uttered, every thought that crossed his mind, every act he performed, had to do with such things as these. The dust clouds he had sighted were raised by two large droves of sheep coming along the road in opposite directions, which by reason of the dust were not visible until they were close at hand, but Don Quixote insisted so earnestly that they were armies that Sancho came to believe it.

"Sir," he said, "what are we to do?"

"What are we to do?" echoed his master. "Favor and aid the weak and needy. I would inform you, Sancho, that the one coming toward us is led and commanded by the great emperor Alifanfarón, lord of the great isle of Trapobana. This other one at my back is that of his enemy, the king of the Garamantas, Pentapolín of the Rolled-up Sleeve, for he always goes into battle with his right arm bare." [4]

"But why are they such enemies?" Sancho asked.

"Because," said Don Quixote, "this Alifanfarón is a terrible pagan and in love with Pentapolín's daughter, who is a very beautiful and gracious lady and a Christian, for which reason her father does not wish to give her to the pagan king unless the latter first abjures the law of the false prophet, Mohammed, and adopts the faith that is Pentapolín's own."

"Then, by my beard," said Sancho, "if Pentapolín isn't right, and I am going to aid him all I can."

"In that," said Don Quixote, "you will only be doing your duty; for to engage in battles of this sort you need not have been dubbed a knight."

"I can understand that," said Sancho, "but where are we going to put this ass so that we will be certain of finding him after the fray is over? As for going into battle on such a mount, I do not think that has been done up to now."

"That is true enough," said Don Quixote. "What you had best do with him is to turn him loose and run the risk of losing him; for after we emerge the victors we shall have so many horses that even Rocinante will be in danger of being exchanged for another. But listen closely to what I am about to tell you, for I wish to give you an account of the principal knights that are accompanying these two armies; and in order that you may be the better able to see and take note of them, let us retire to that hillock over there which will afford us a very good view."

They then stationed themselves upon a slight elevation from which they would have been able to see very well the two droves of sheep that Don Quixote took to be armies if it had not been for the blinding clouds of dust. In spite of this, however, the worthy gentleman contrived to behold in his imagination what he did not see and what did not exist in reality.

Raising his voice, he went on to explain, "That knight in the gilded armor that you see there, bearing upon his shield a crowned lion crouched at the feet of a damsel, is the valiant Laurcalco, lord of the Silver Bridge; the other with the golden flowers on his armor, and on his shield three crowns argent on an azure field, is the dread Micocolembo, grand duke of Quirocia. And that one on Micocolembo's right hand, with the limbs of a giant, is the ever undaunted Brandabarbarán de Boliche, lord of the three Arabias. He goes armored in a serpent's skin and has for shield a door which, so report has it, is one of those from the temple that Samson pulled down, that time when he avenged himself on his enemies with his own death.

"But turn your eyes in this direction, and you will behold at the head of the other army the ever victorious, never vanquished Timonel de Carcajona, prince of New Biscay, who comes with quartered arms— azure, vert, argent, and or—and who has upon his shield a cat or on a field tawny, with the inscription *Miau*, which is the beginning of his lady's name; for she, so it is said, is the peerless Miulina, daughter of Alfeñiquén, duke of Algarve. And that one over there, who weights down and presses the loins of that powerful charger, in a suit of snow-white armor with a white shield that bears no device whatever—he is a novice knight of the French nation, called Pierres Papin, lord of the baronies of Utrique. As for him you see digging his iron spurs into the flanks of that fleet-footed zebra courser and whose arms are vairs azure, he is the mighty duke of Nervia, Espartafilardo of the Wood, who has for device upon his shield an asparagus plant with a motto in Castilian that says 'Rastrea mi suerte.' " [5]

In this manner he went on naming any number of imaginary knights on either side, describing on the spur of the moment their arms, colors, devices, and mottoes; for he was completely carried away by his imagination and by this unheard-of madness that had laid hold of him.

Without pausing, he went on, "This squadron in front of us is composed of men of various nations. There are those who drink the sweet waters of the famous Xanthus; woodsmen who tread the Massilian plain; those that sift the fine gold nuggets of Arabia Felix; those that are so fortunate as to dwell on the banks of the clear-running Thermodon, famed for their coolness; those who in many and diverse ways drain the golden Pactolus; Numidians, whose word is never to be trusted; Persians, with their famous bows and arrows; Medes and Parthians, who fight as they flee; Scythians, as cruel as they are fair of skin; Ethiopians, with their pierced lips; and an infinite number of other nationalities whose visages I see and recognize although I cannot recall their names.

"In this other squadron come those that drink from the crystal currents of the olive-bearing Betis; [6] those that smooth and polish their faces with the liquid of the ever rich and gilded Tagus; those that enjoy the beneficial waters of the divine Genil; [7] those that roam the Tartessian plains with their abundant pasturage; [8] those that disport themselves in the Elysian meadows of Jerez; [9] the men of La Mancha, rich and crowned with golden ears of corn; others clad in iron garments, ancient relics of the Gothic race; those that bathe in the Pisuerga, noted for the mildness of its current; [10] those that feed their herds in the wide-spreading pasture lands along the banks of the winding Guadiana, celebrated for its underground course; [11] those that shiver from the cold of the wooded Pyrenees or dwell amid the white peaks of the lofty Apennines—in short, all those whom Europe holds within its girth."

So help me God! How many provinces, how many nations did he not mention by name, giving to each one with marvelous readiness its proper attributes; for he was wholly absorbed and filled to the brim with what he had read in those lying books of his! Sancho Panza hung on his words, saying nothing, merely turning his head from time to time to have a look at those knights and giants that his master was pointing out to him; but he was unable to discover any of them.

"Sir," he said, "may I go to the devil if I see a single man, giant, or knight of all those that your Grace is talking about. Who knows? Maybe it is another spell, like last night."

"How can you say that?" replied Don Quixote. "Can you not hear the neighing of the horses, the sound of trumpets, the roll of drums?"

"I hear nothing," said Sancho, "except the bleating of sheep."

And this, of course, was the truth; for the flocks were drawing near.

"The trouble is, Sancho," said Don Quixote, "you are so afraid that you cannot see or hear properly; for one of the effects of fear is to disturb the senses and cause things to appear other than what they are. If you are so craven as all that, go off to one side and leave me alone, and I without your help will assure the victory to that side to which I lend my aid."

Saying this, he put spurs to Rocinante and, with his lance at rest, darted down the hillside like a flash of lightning.

As he did so, Sancho called after him, "Come back, your Grace, Señor Don Quixote; I vow to God those are sheep that you are charging. Come back! O wretched father that bore me! What madness is this? Look you, there are no giants, nor knights, nor cats, nor shields either quartered or whole, nor vairs azure or bedeviled. What is this you are doing, O sinner that I am in God's sight?"

But all this did not cause Don Quixote to turn back. Instead, he rode on, crying out at the top of his voice, "Ho, knights, those of you who follow and fight under the banners of the valiant Pentapolín of the Rolled-up Sleeve; follow me, all of you, and you shall see how easily I give you revenge on your enemy, Alifanfarón of Trapobana."

With these words he charged into the middle of the flock of sheep and began spearing at them with as much courage and boldness as if they had been his mortal enemies. The shepherds and herdsmen who were with the animals called to him to stop; but seeing it was no use, they unloosed their slings and saluted his ears with stones as big as your fist.

Don Quixote paid no attention to the missiles and, dashing about here and there, kept crying, "Where are you, haughty Alifanfarón? Come out to me; for here is a solitary knight who desires in single combat to test your strength and deprive you of your life, as a punishment for that which you have done to the valorous Pentapolín Garamanta."

At that instant a pebble [12] from the brook struck him in the side and buried a couple of ribs in his body. Believing himself dead or badly wounded, and remembering his potion, he took out his vial, placed it to his mouth, and began to swallow the balm; but before he had had what he thought was enough, there came another almond,[13] which struck him in the hand, crushing the tin vial and carrying away with it a couple of grinders from his mouth, as well as badly mashing two of his fingers. As a result of these blows the poor knight tumbled from his horse. Believing that they had killed him, the shepherds hastily collected their flock and, picking up the dead beasts, of which there were more than seven, they went off down the road without more ado.

Sancho all this time was standing on the slope observing the insane things that his master was doing; and as he plucked savagely at his beard he cursed the hour and minute when luck had brought them together. But when he saw him lying there on the ground and perceived that the shepherds were gone, he went down the hill and came up to him, finding him in very bad shape though not unconscious.

"Didn't I tell you, Señor Don Quixote," he said, "that you should come back, that those were not armies you were charging but flocks of sheep?"

"This," said Don Quixote, "is the work of that thieving magician, my enemy, who thus counterfeits things and causes them to disappear. You must know, Sancho, that it is very easy for them to make us assume any appearance that they choose; and so it is that malign one who persecutes me, envious of the glory he saw me about to achieve in this battle, changed the squadrons of the foe into flocks of sheep. If you do not believe me, I beseech you on my life to do one thing for me, that you may be undeceived and discover for yourself that what I say is true. Mount your ass and follow them quietly, and when you have gone a short way from here, you will see them become their former selves once more; they will no longer be sheep but men exactly as I described them to you in the first place. But do not go now, for I need your kind assistance; come over here and have a look and tell me how many grinders are missing, for it feels as if I did not have a single one left."

Sancho went over and almost put his eyes into his master's mouth. Now, as it happened, this was just the moment when the balm in Don Quixote's stomach began to work, and he promptly discharged its entire contents with more force than a musket straight into the beard of his good-hearted squire.

"Holy Mary!" exclaimed Sancho, "and what is this that has happened now? This sinner must surely be mortally wounded, for he is vomiting blood from the mouth."

When he investigated a little more closely, however, he discovered from the color, taste, and smell that this was not blood but balm from the vial from which he had seen his master drinking; and so great was the disgust he felt that, his stomach turning over, he now vomited up his insides all over Don Quixote and both of them were in a fine state indeed. Sancho then made for his saddlebags to get something with which to wipe the vomit off them, and when he found the bags were missing, it was more than he could do to contain himself. Cursing himself anew, he made up his mind that he would leave the knight and return home, even though he did lose what was coming to him for his services, along with all hope of becoming governor of that promised island.

Don Quixote then rose and, with his left hand to his mouth to keep his teeth from popping out, grasped Rocinante's reins in the other hand—for the animal had not stirred from his side, so loyal and well trained was he—and went over to where the squire was bending above his donkey with his hand to his cheek like one lost in thought.

Seeing him so downcast, his master said to him, "Bear in mind, Sancho, that one man is worth no more than another unless he does more. All these squalls that we have met with are merely a sign that the weather is going to clear and everything will turn out for the best; for it is impossible that either good or evil should be lasting; and from this it follows that, the evil having lasted so long, the good must be near at hand. And so you should not grieve for the misfortunes that have befallen me, since you have had no part in them."

"How is that?" replied Sancho. "I suppose the one they tossed in a blanket yesterday was somebody else than my father's son? And my saddlebags, which are gone now, did they belong to some other person?"

"You mean to say your saddlebags are missing, Sancho?"

"Yes," replied the squire, "that they are."

"Well, in that case, we shan't have anything to eat today," said Don Quixote.

"Not unless these meadows have some of those herbs which your Grace was saying he knows so well, with which unfortunate knights-errant like your Grace are in the habit of supplying their needs."

"So far as that goes," said his master, "right now I would rather have a quarter of a loaf or a loaf of bread and a couple of pilchards' heads than all the herbs that Dioscorides describes, even with Dr. Laguna's commentary.[14] But, nevertheless, Sancho, mount your ass and follow me; for inasmuch as God is the provider of all things, He will not fail us, especially seeing that we are so active in His service; for gnats never lack the air, grubs the earth, nor polliwogs the water; and He is so merciful that He causes His sun to shine on the good and the bad and the rain to fall on the just and the unjust."

"It strikes me," said Sancho, "that your Grace is better fitted to be a preacher than a knight-errant."

"Knights-errant," was Don Quixote's rejoinder, "have always known, and have to know, everything; for they might be called upon to deliver a sermon or make a speech in the middle of the open country, just as if they were graduates of the University of Paris; from which it may be deduced that the lance never yet blunted the pen nor the pen the lance." [15]

"That may all very well be as your Grace says," replied Sancho, "but let us leave here at once and go look for a lodging for tonight; and God grant it may be someplace where there are no blankets or blanket-tossers, nor phantoms nor enchanted Moors, for if I come upon any of those, I'll have nothing whatever to do with them." [16]

"Pray God, then, my son," said Don Quixote, "and lead the way where you will; for this time I will leave the lodging to your choice. But, first, put your finger in my mouth and feel how many teeth and grinders are missing on this right side of my upper jaw, for that is where the pain is."

Sancho did as he was told. "How many grinders did your Grace have on this side?"

"Four besides the double tooth and all of them whole and healthy."

"Mind what you are saying, your Grace," Sancho warned.

"I am telling you: four, if not five," said Don Quixote; "for in all my life I have never had a tooth or grinder pulled, nor has any fallen out or been destroyed by decay or abscess."

"Well, in this lower jaw," Sancho went on, "your Grace has not more than two grinders and a half left; and in the upper jaw, there is not even a half, there is none at all—it is all as smooth as the palm of your hand."

"How unfortunate I am!" cried Don Quixote as he heard this sad news from his squire. "I would rather they had robbed me of an arm so long as it was not my sword arm. For I must tell you, Sancho, that a mouth without grinders is like a mill without a millstone, and a tooth is more to be prized than a diamond. But to all this we are subject, those of us who follow the arduous profession of knighthood. So mount, my friend, and lead on, and I will follow at whatever pace you will."

Sancho obeyed, heading in the direction in which he thought they might be able to find a lodging without leaving the highway, which at this point was a much-traveled stretch of road. They went along slowly, for Don Quixote's jaws were hurting him so much that he could think of nothing else and was in no mood to make haste. Perceiving this, Sancho sought to divert him and to take his mind off his troubles by small talk of one kind or another; and some of the things he said to him are set forth in the chapter that follows.

CHAPTER XIX. *Of the shrewd things that Sancho Panza said to his master and the adventure that happened to him in connection with a dead body, along with other famous events.*

"IT SEEMS to me, sir, that all these misadventures that have happened to us of late are without any doubt a punishment for the sin your Grace committed against the order of knighthood by failing to keep the vow that you made not to eat bread off a tablecloth, or embrace the queen, and all the rest of it; your Grace swore not to do any of these things until you had taken a helmet from that Moor Malandrino [1] or whatever his name is, I don't rightly remember."

"There is much in what you say, Sancho," replied Don Quixote, "but to tell you the truth, I had forgotten about it; and you may be sure that it was because you had failed to remind me in time that the business of the blanket occurred. But I will see to making amends for it all; for in knighthood there are ways of adjusting everything."

"Why," said Sancho, "did I take some kind of oath, then?"

"It makes no difference whether you did or not," said Don Quixote. "It appears to me that you are not wholly clear of complicity in this matter, and so it will not be a bad thing to provide ourselves with a remedy."

"In that case," said his squire, "will your Grace please be sure not to forget the remedy as you did the vow? For who knows, the phantoms may take it into their heads to have sport with me again, and with your Grace as well, if they see you so stubborn."

While they were engaged in this and similar talk, night descended upon them as they were going along the highway, before they had as yet found a lodging; and what made matters worse, they were very hungry, for with their saddlebags they had lost their entire pantry and store of provisions. And on top of all their misfortunes, they now had an experience which, if it was not a real adventure, certainly had all the earmarks of one. Although it was already quite dark, they continued on their way, for Sancho was sure that, since this was a main highway, they would have to go but a league or two before they came upon some kind of inn. And as they were riding along through the darkness like that, the squire hungry and the master with a great desire to eat, they suddenly saw coming toward them a great number of lights which looked exactly like moving stars. Sancho was stunned by the sight, while Don Quixote did not feel altogether easy about it, and the one pulled on the halter of his ass, the other on his horse's reins. They sat there watching closely, trying to make out what these lights could be, which were all the time coming nearer—and the nearer they came, the bigger they seemed. Sancho was shaking like someone who had had a dose of mercury, and his master's hair was standing on end. Then Don Quixote managed to pluck up a little courage.

"There can be no doubt, Sancho," he said, "that this is going to be a very great and perilous adventure in which it will be necessary for me to display all my strength and valor."

"Poor me!" said his squire. "If by any chance this is to be another adventure with phantoms, where am I going to find the ribs to bear it?"

"Phantoms or not," said the knight, "I will not permit them to touch the nap of your garments. If they had sport with you last time, it was only because I was unable to get over the stable-yard wall; but here we are in the open where I can wield my sword as I like."

"And what if they enchant and benumb you as they did before, what difference will it make whether or not you are in the open?"

"Nonetheless," replied Don Quixote, "I beg of you, Sancho, to keep up your courage; for experience will teach you what mine is."

"Very well, I will keep it up, God willing," was Sancho's answer.

Retiring then to one side of the road, the two of them continued watching attentively to see what those moving lights could be; and it was not long before they caught sight of a large number of white-shirted figures,[2] a vision so frightening that Sancho lost what courage he had.

His teeth began chattering like those of a person who has the quartan fever, and they chattered more than ever as the apparition came near enough to be distinguishable; for there were some twenty of those shirted figures, all mounted on horseback and with lighted torches in their hands, and behind them came a litter covered with mourning, followed by six other riders all in black down to the feet of their mules, for it was obvious from their leisurely gait that these animals were not horses. As the cavalcade approached, it could be seen that the shirted ones were muttering something to themselves in a low and mournful tone of voice.

This weird vision, at such an hour and in so out-of-the-way a place, was sufficient to strike terror to Sancho's heart, and his master would have felt the same way had he been anyone else than Don Quixote. As it was, the former had by now reached the end of his strength, but not so the latter, whose vivid imagination was already at work and who saw here another adventure out of his storybooks. The litter had to be a bier, bearing some knight either dead or badly wounded, and it was for him, Don Quixote, and him alone, to exact vengeance; and so, without another word, he rested his lance, settled himself well in the saddle, and, with highborn mettle and intrepid bearing, took up his stand in the middle of the road along which the shirted figures had to pass.

When they were close upon him, he raised his voice and cried, "Halt, knight, or whoever you may be, and give an account of yourself; tell me whence you come and whither you are bound, and who it is that you bring with you on that bier; for to all appearances either you have done some wrong or some wrong has been done to you, and it is fitting and necessary that I should know of it, either to punish you for your evil deeds or to avenge you for the misdoings of another."

At this point, one of the figures spoke up. "We are in a hurry," he said, "and the inn is far, and we cannot stop to give you the information that you seek." And, so saying, he spurred his mule forward.

Don Quixote was greatly put out at such a reply and, seizing the mule by the bridle, he repeated, "Halt, I say, and show a little better breeding by giving me an answer to my questions. Otherwise, you shall all do battle with me."

Now, the mule as it happened was a little shy, and when Don Quixote laid hold of the bridle, it reared on its hind legs and threw its master to the ground. A lad who was on foot, upon seeing the shirted one fall, began reviling the knight; but our friend's wrath was up, and without further delay he brought his lance into position and bore down upon one of those who were clad in mourning, wounding him badly and tumbling him from his mount. Then he turned upon the others, and it was something to see the dexterity with which he attacked and routed them. It seemed as if at that moment Rocinante had sprouted wings, so proud-stepping and light-footed did he show himself to be.

All these shirt-wearers were timid folk, without arms, and so, naturally enough, they speedily quit the fray and started running across the fields, still bearing their lighted torches in their hands, which gave them the appearance of masked figures darting here and there on some night when a fiesta or other celebration is being held. Those who wore the mourning, on the other hand, wrapped and swathed in their skirts and gowns, were unable to move; and, accordingly, with no risk to himself, Don Quixote smote them all and drove them off against their will; for they thought that this surely was no man but a devil straight out of Hell who had come to rob them of the body that they carried on the litter.

Sancho watched it all, greatly admiring his master's ardor. "No doubt about it," he told himself, "he is as brave and powerful as he says he is."

There was a flaming torch that had been stuck in the ground near the first one who had fallen from his mule; and by its light Don Quixote could be seen coming up to the fellow, sticking the point of his lance in his face, and calling upon him to surrender as he valued his life.

"I am prisoner enough as it is," the man said; "for my leg is broken and I cannot stir. I beg your Grace, if you are a Christian knight, not to slay me; if you were to do so, you would be committing a great sacrilege, for I am a licentiate and have already taken my first orders."

"Well," said Don Quixote, "what in the devil brings you here if you are a churchman?"

"What, sir?" said the man on the ground. "My bad luck, that's all."

"Still worse luck awaits you," said Don Quixote, "if you do not answer to my satisfaction all those questions that I put to you in the first place."

"Your Grace shall be easily satisfied as to all that," replied the licentiate. "To begin with, I may tell your Grace that, although I said I was a licentiate, I am really but a bachelor, and my name is Alonso López, a native of Alcobendas. I come from the city of Baeza with eleven other priests, the ones that are carrying the torches. We are on our way to the city of Segovia, accompanying the corpse that is in that litter, the body of a gentleman who died in Baeza, where he was first interred; and now we are taking his bones to their last resting place in Segovia, where he was born."

"And who killed him?" demanded Don Quixote.

"God," said the bachelor, "by means of a pestilential fever that took him off."

"In that way," said the knight, "Our Lord has absolved me of the trouble of avenging him, as I should have had to do had he met his death at the hands of another; but He who slew him having slain him, there is nothing to do but be silent and shrug one's shoulders, and I should do the same if it were I whom He was slaying. I would have your reverence know that I am a knight of La Mancha, Don Quixote by name, and it is my calling and profession to go through the world righting wrongs and redressing injuries."

"I do not know what you mean by righting wrongs, seeing that you found me quite all right and left me very wrong indeed, with a broken leg which will not be right again as long as I live; [3] and if you have redressed any injury in my case, it has been done in such a way as to leave me injured forever. It was a great misadventure for me to fall in with you who go hunting adventures."

"Everything," replied Don Quixote, "does not occur in the same manner. The big mistake you made, Sir Bachelor Alonso López, was in coming as you did, by night, dressed in those surplices, bearing lighted torches and praying, all of which gave the appearance of something evil and of the other world. I accordingly could not fail to fulfill my obligation by attacking you, and I would have done so even though I knew for a certainty that you were devils out of Hell; for such I took you to be all the time."

"Since that is the way fate has willed it," said the bachelor, "I beseech your Grace, Sir Knight-errant—whose errantry has done me so bad a turn—I beseech you to help me up from under this mule, for one of my legs is caught between the stirrup and the saddle."

"Why," exclaimed Don Quixote, "I might have talked on until tomorrow! How long were you going to wait to tell me of your distress?"

He then called to Sancho to come, but the squire did not see fit to do so, being engaged at that moment in robbing a sumpter mule of the larder which these gentlemen were carrying with them and which was well stocked with things to eat. Having made a sack of his greatcoat, he dumped into it all that it would hold and threw it across his ass's back; and then, and only then, did he answer his master's call to come and help get the bachelor out from under the mule. Setting the fellow on his beast once more, they gave him his torch, and Don Quixote told him to follow in the track of his companions and beg their pardon on his behalf for the wrong which he had not been able to avoid doing them.

"And if," said Sancho, "those gentlemen wish to know who the valiant one was who did this to them, your Grace may inform them that he is the famous Don Quixote de la Mancha, otherwise known as the Knight of the Mournful Countenance."

At this the knight inquired of his squire what had led him to call him by such a title at that particular moment.

"I can tell you," said Sancho. "I was looking at you for a time by the light of the torch that poor fellow carried; and truly, your Grace now has the worst-looking countenance that I have ever seen, whether due to exhaustion from this combat or the lack of teeth and grinders, I cannot say."

"It is not that," said Don Quixote; "it is simply that the sage who is to write the history of my exploits must have thought that it would be a good thing for me to take another appellation as all knights of the past have done. Thus one was called the Knight of the Flaming Sword; another the Knight of the Unicorn; one the Knight of Damsels, and one the Knight of the Phoenix; another the Knight of the Griffin; and still another the Knight of Death: and by these names and insignia were they known all the world over. And so, I tell you, it must have been that sage of whom I was speaking who put it into your mind and on your tongue to dub me the Knight of the Mournful Countenance. This title I mean to adopt as my own from now on; and in order that it may better fit me, I propose, as soon as opportunity offers, to have painted on my shield a very sad-looking face."

"There is no necessity of wasting time and money on having a face made for you," said Sancho. "All that your Grace has to do is to uncover your own to those who look at you, and without need of any image or shield they will call you that. This is the truth I speak; for I assure your Grace—not meaning any harm—that hunger and the lack of grinders have given you so ill a countenance that you can very well do without the painted one."

Don Quixote laughed heartily at Sancho's wit, but still he could not give up the idea of calling himself by that name and having a suitable device painted on his buckler or shield just as he had conceived it.

At this point the bachelor prepared to take his departure.[4] "I neglected to warn your Grace," he said, "that you are hereby excommunicated for having laid violent hands on a holy thing: *Iuxta illud, si quis, suadente diablo*, etc." [5]

"I do not understand that Latin of yours," said Don Quixote, "but I am quite sure that I did not lay my hands on anything; I laid on with this lance. What is more, I did not realize that I was insulting priests or sacred things of the Church, which I respect and revere as the good Catholic and loyal Christian that I am; I thought, rather, that it was phantoms and monsters from the other world that I was attacking. But, even so, I cannot but recall what happened to Cid Ruy Díaz when he broke the chair of the royal ambassador in the presence of his Holiness the Pope, that day when the worthy Rodrigo de Vivar showed himself to be a brave and honored knight." [6]

Having listened to this speech, the bachelor went his way without saying a word in reply.

Don Quixote then wanted to see whether it really was bones they had in that litter or not; but Sancho would not consent.

"Sir," he said, "your Grace has concluded this adventure in the safest manner of any yet. But those fellows whom you overcame and routed may come to realize that it was, after all, only one individual who conquered them; and being thoroughly ashamed of themselves, they may pluck up courage and return to look for us, in which case they could give us plenty of trouble. The ass is ready, the mountains near by, and we are hungry; there is nothing for us to do but to retire as decently as may be, and as the saying goes, 'To the grave with the dead and the living to the bread.' " [7]

Urging his ass forward, he begged his master to follow him, and the latter, deciding that his squire was right, made no reply but fell in behind. After going a short distance they found themselves between two small mountains, in a broad and hidden valley. Here they dismounted, and Sancho relieved the donkey of its burden; after which, stretched upon the green grass and with hunger as a sauce, they breakfasted, lunched, dined, and supped at one and the same time, satisfying their stomachs with more than one cold cut which the gentlemen of the clergy attending the deceased—who seldom stint themselves in this regard—had brought along in their well-stocked larder upon the back of their sumpter mule.

But they still had one misfortune to endure, which for Sancho was the worst of all: they had no wine, nor even water, to drink, and so were harassed by thirst. Whereupon, noting the green young grass of the meadow round about, he conceived an idea which will be set forth in the following chapter.

CHAPTER XX. *Of an adventure such as never was seen nor heard of, which was completed by the valorous Don Quixote de la Mancha with less peril than any famous knight in all the world ever incurred in a similar undertaking.*

"It is not possible, sir," said Sancho, "that this grass should not betoken the presence near by of some spring or brook that provides it with moisture; and so, it would be a good thing if we were to go a little farther, for I am sure we should be able to find someplace where we might quench this terrible thirst that is consuming us and that, undoubtedly, is more painful to bear than hunger."

This impressed Don Quixote as being good advice; and after they had placed upon the ass what was left of their dinner, he took Rocinante's rein and Sancho took the halter of his beast and they started feeling their way up the meadow, for the night was so dark that they were unable to see anything at all. They had not gone two hundred paces when they heard a roaring sound, which appeared to be that of water falling from great, high cliffs. This cheered them enormously; but as they paused to determine the direction from which it came, another and terrible din fell upon their ears, watering down the satisfaction they had felt at the thought of finding water,[1] especially for Sancho, who was by nature timid and lacking in spirit. What they heard, I am telling you, was the sound of measured blows, together with the rattling of iron chains, accompanied by so furious a thunder of waters as to strike terror in any other heart than that of Don Quixote.

It was night, as has been stated, and they now chanced to reach a cluster of tall trees, whose leaves, stirred by the mild wind that was blowing, rustled with a soft and gentle murmur. The solitude, the place, the darkness, the din of the water, the rustling of the leaves—all this was frightful, horror-inspiring, especially when they found that the blows did not cease, nor did the wind fall asleep or morning come; and added to it all was the fact that they had no idea where they were. Don Quixote, however, with his own intrepid heart to keep him company, leaped upon Rocinante's back and, bracing his buckler on his arm, brought his lance into play.

"Sancho, my friend," he said, "you may know that I was born, by Heaven's will, in this our age of iron, to revive what is known as the Golden Age. I am he for whom are reserved the perils, the great exploits, the valiant deeds. I am—I say it again—he who is to revive the Knights of the Round Table, the Twelve Peers of France, and the Nine Worthies. I am he who is to cast into oblivion the Platirs, the Tablantes, the Olivantes, and the Tirants, the Knights of the Sun and the Belianises, together with the entire throng of famous knights-errant of times past, by performing in this age in which I live such great and wonderful feats of arms as shall darken the brightest of their achievements. Note well, my rightful and my loyal squire, the shades of night that lie about us; this uncanny silence; the low and indistinct rustling of those trees; the frightful sound made by that water that we came to seek, which appears to be falling precipitously from the tall mountains of the moon; those unceasing blows that grieve and wound our ears; all of which things together, and each one singly, are sufficient to strike fear, dread, and terror in the breast of Mars himself, not to speak of him who is not accustomed to such happenings and adventures.

"Well, all these things that I have been describing are for me but the incentives and awakeners of my courage, causing the heart within my bosom to burst with the desire of entering upon this adventure, however difficult it may be. And so, tighten Rocinante's girth a bit if you will, and God be with you. Wait for me here three days, no longer. If at the end of that time I have not returned, you may go back to our village; and then, as a special favor to me, you will go to El Toboso, where you will tell that incomparable lady, my Dulcinea, how her captive knight died, undertaking things that would render him worthy of being called hers."

Hearing his master speak these words, Sancho began weeping as if his heart would break. "Sir," he said, "I do not know why your Grace is so bent upon this fearful undertaking. It is night now, no one can see us, and we can easily turn about and take ourselves out of danger's path, even though we do not drink for the next three days. Since there is none here to see us, the fewer will there be to call us cowards. What's more, I have often heard the curate of our village say in his sermons— your Grace knows him very well—that whoever goes looking for danger will perish by it.[2] It is not good to tempt God by entering upon some monstrous undertaking from which you can escape only by a miracle, and Heaven has performed enough of them for your Grace by saving you from being tossed in a blanket as I was and by bringing you out the victor, safe and free, over all those enemies who were accompanying that corpse.

"And if all this does not suffice to move or soften that hard heart of yours, let it be moved by the thought, the certain knowledge, that no sooner will you have left this spot than I out of fear will yield my soul to any that cares to take it. I have left my native land, my wife and young ones, to come and serve your Grace, believing that by so doing I would better my lot, not make it worse; but as avarice always bursts the bag,[3] so has it torn my hopes to shreds. Just when they are brightest and I seem nearest to obtaining that wretched island, that cursed island, which your Grace so many times has promised me, I perceive that, in place of fulfilling that hope, you are about to go away and leave me in a place like this, so far from any human beings.

"In God's name, sir, do me not this wrong. If your Grace will not wholly desist from this enterprise, at least put it off until morning; for according to that knowledge of the heavens that I acquired as a shepherd, it should not be as much as three hours from now until dawn, seeing that the mouth of the Horn is directly overhead and midnight is in line with the left arm."[4]

"How, Sancho," said Don Quixote, "can you see that line or where the mouth of the Horn or your own head is, when it is so dark and there is not a star in the sky?"

"That," replied Sancho, "is because fear has many eyes and can see things under the earth and much more in the heavens above; and anyway, it stands to reason that daybreak cannot be far off."

"Far off or near," said his master, "it shall not be said of me, either now or at any other time, that tears and entreaties kept me from fulfilling my duties as a knight; and so, Sancho, I beg you to be quiet; for God, who has put it into my heart to undertake this dread adventure such as never before was heard of—God will see to my well-being and will comfort you in your sorrow. The thing for you to do is to tighten Rocinante's girth and remain here, and I shall return soon, either living or dead."

Perceiving his master's firm resolve, and seeing of how little avail were his own tears, advice, and entreaties, Sancho determined to have resort to his ingenuity in compelling him, if he could, to wait until daylight. Accordingly, when he went to tighten Rocinante's girth, he very deftly and without being observed slipped the halter of his ass over the hack's two front feet so that, when Don Quixote started to ride away, he found that his steed was unable to move except by little hops and jumps.

"Ah, sir," Sancho said to his master when he saw that his trick had worked, "Heaven itself, moved by my tears and supplications, has ordained that Rocinante should not stir; and if you stubbornly insist upon spurring and whipping him, you will merely be angering fortune and, so to speak, kicking against the prick."

Don Quixote was truly in despair now; for the more he dug his legs into his horse's flanks the less inclined that animal was to budge; and without noticing that the hack's feet had been bound, the knight decided there was nothing for him to do but be calm and wait until daylight should come or Rocinante should see fit to move; for he was convinced that all this came of something other than his squire's cleverness.

"Since Rocinante will not go," he said, "I am content, Sancho, to wait until dawn shall smile, even though I myself may weep that she is so long in coming."

"There is no occasion for weeping," replied Sancho, "for I will entertain your Grace by telling stories from now until daybreak, unless you care to dismount and lie down to sleep for a little while upon this green grass, as knights-errant are accustomed to do, so that you may be rested when day comes and fit to undertake this unlikely adventure that awaits you."

"Why," said Don Quixote, "do you call upon me to dismount or to sleep? Am I, perchance, one of those knights who take their repose amid dangers? Sleep, then, if you will, for you were born to sleep, or do whatever you like, and I shall do that which best befits my knightly character."

"Sir," said Sancho, "let not your Grace be angry, for I did not mean it in that way."

Coming up to his master, then, he laid both hands on the saddletree in such a manner that he stood embracing Don Quixote's left leg; and he did not stir an inch from there, so great was his fear of those blows which were still to be heard in regular cadence. Don Quixote then remarked that his squire might tell him a story by way of amusing him as he had promised; to which Sancho replied that he would be glad to do so if the fear which that sound inspired in him would only let him.

"But, in spite of all that," he said, "I will try to tell you a story which, if it does not escape me in the telling, and nobody stops me, is one of the best there is; and pay attention, your Grace, for I am about to begin. Let bygones be bygones; and may the good come to all and the evil to him who goes to look for it. For your Grace must know that when the ancients began their fables the beginning was by no means left to the choice of the one who told the tale; instead, they always began with a maxim from Cato Zonzorino,[5] the Roman, who uttered the words that I have quoted, '. . . and the evil to him who goes to look for it,' a saying that fits like the ring on your finger, signifying that your Grace should remain here and not go hunting trouble anywhere else, and that we should return by another road since there is no one to compel us to keep following this one where there are so many frightful things to startle us."

"Go on with your story, Sancho," said Don Quixote, "and as for the road that we are to follow, leave that to me."

"I will tell you, then," continued Sancho, "that in a village of Estremadura there lived a certain goat shepherd—I mean, one who tended goats—and this shepherd or goatherd of my story was named Lope Ruiz; and this Lope Ruiz was in love with a shepherd lass whose name was Torralba, which shepherd lass called Torralba was the daughter of a wealthy cattle-raiser, and this wealthy cattle-raiser—"

"If that is the way you are going to tell your story, Sancho, saying everything over twice, you will not be finished in a couple of days. Tell it in a straightforward manner, like a man of good sense, or otherwise do not tell it at all."

"In my country," said Sancho, "they tell all fables just the way I am telling this one, and I cannot tell it any other way, nor is it right for your Grace to ask me to adopt new customs."

"As you like, then," said Don Quixote, "and since fate has willed that I must listen, proceed with it."

"And so, then, my dear master, as I was saying, this shepherd was in love with Torralba, the shepherd lass, who was sturdy of figure, wild in her ways, and somewhat mannish— I can see yet those little mustaches of hers."

"You knew her, then?" asked Don Quixote.

"I did not know her, but the one who told me the story described her for me so truly and faithfully that, when I go to tell it to another, I could swear and affirm that I have seen her with my own eyes. And so, as days and days went by, the devil, who never sleeps but sweeps everything up into his pile, saw to it that the shepherd's love for the shepherd lass turned into hatred and ill will. The reason for this, according to the gossiping tongues, was that she had given him certain grounds for jealousy, which crossed the line and reached forbidden territory. And as a result of all this, the shepherd hated her from then on, so much, that in order not to have to see her again, he made up his mind to leave his native land and go where his eyes would never behold her. Finding herself thus spurned, La Torralba, who had never loved him before, became enamored of him."

"That is the way with women," said Don Quixote; "they spurn those that care for them and love those that hate them. But go on, Sancho."

"The shepherd then proceeded to do as he had resolved; and, getting together his goats, he set out through the countryside of Estremadura on his way to the kingdom of Portugal. Learning of this, La Torralba set out after him, following him, barefoot, from afar, a shepherd's staff in her hand and a knapsack around her neck, in which, so it is said, she carried a broken mirror, a piece of a comb, and some kind of paint or other for her face; but whatever it was she carried, I am not going to take the trouble to find out. I will merely tell you that the shepherd with his flock had by this time crossed the Guadiana River, which in that season was swollen and almost out of its banks; and at the point where he was, there was neither boat nor bark to be had, nor anyone to ferry him and his goats to the other side; all of which grieved him sorely, for he could now see La Torralba close on his heels and knew that she would be bound to annoy him greatly with her tears and pleas.

"As he was looking about, he saw a fisherman alongside a boat so small that it would hold only one person and a goat, but, nevertheless, he spoke to the man, who agreed to take the shepherd and his flock of three hundred to the opposite bank. The fisherman would climb into the boat and row one of the animals across and then return for another, and he kept this up, rowing across with a goat and coming back, rowing across and coming back— Your Grace must be sure to keep count of the goats that the fisherman rowed across the stream, for if a single one of them escapes your memory, the story is ended and it will not be possible to tell another word of it.

"I will go on, then, and tell you that the landing place on the other side was full of mud and slippery, and it took the fisherman a good while to make the trip each time; but in spite of that, he came back for another goat, and another, and another—"

"Just say he rowed them all across," said Don Quixote; "you need not be coming and going in that manner, or it will take you a year to get them all on the other side."

"How many have gone across up to now?" Sancho demanded.

"How the devil should I know?" replied Don Quixote.

"There, what did I tell you? You should have kept better count. Well, then, by God, the story's ended, for there is no going on with it."

"How can that be?" said the knight. "Is it so essential to know the exact number of goats that if I lose count of one of them you cannot tell the rest of the tale?"

"No, sir, I cannot by any means," said Sancho; "for when I asked your Grace to tell me how many goats had been rowed across and you replied that you did not know, at that very instant everything that I was about to say slipped my memory; and you may take my word for it, it was very good and you would have liked it."

"So," said Don Quixote, "the story is ended, is it?"

"As much ended as my own mother is," Sancho replied.

"Well, then," said Don Quixote, "I can assure you that you have told me one of the most novel fables, stories, or histories that anyone in the world could possibly conceive.[6] And I may add that such a way of telling and ending it has never been nor will be heard of in the course of a lifetime; although I expected nothing else from one with a wit like yours. However, I do not marvel at it, for it is possible that those ceaseless blows we hear have disturbed your understanding."

"Anything may be," said Sancho; "but in the matter of my story, I know that there is nothing more to be told, for it ends where you begin to lose count of the number of goats that have crossed."

"Let it end where it will, and well and good. But come, let us see if Rocinante can carry me now." With this, he applied the spurs once more, and the hack once again gave a start, but without budging from the spot, so well was he shackled.

At this juncture, whether it was the cool of the morning which was coming on, or something laxative he had eaten at supper, or—which is most likely—merely a necessity of nature, Sancho felt the will and desire to do that which no one else could do for him;[7] but so great was the fear that had lodged in his heart that he did not dare stir by so much as the tip of a fingernail from his master's side. It was, however, out of the question not to satisfy the need he felt; and what he did, accordingly, in order to have a little peace, was to remove his right hand which held the back of the saddle, and with this hand he very adroitly and without making any noise unloosed the slip-knot which alone sustained his breeches, thus letting them drop to the ground, where they lay like fetters about his feet; after which, he lifted his shirt and bared his behind, no small one by any means.

Having done this—and he thought it was all he needed to do in order to be rid of his agonizing cramps—he encountered another difficulty: how was he to vent himself without making some noise or sound? Gritting his teeth and huddling his shoulders, he held his breath as best he could; but despite all these precautions, the poor fellow ended by emitting a little sound quite different from the one that had filled him with such fear.

"What noise was that, Sancho?" said Don Quixote.

"I do not know, sir," he replied. "It must be something new; for adventures and misadventures never come singly."

He then tried his luck again and succeeded so well that, without any more noise or disturbance than the last time, he found himself free of the load that had given him so much discomfort. But Don Quixote's sense of smell was quite as keen as his sense of hearing, and Sancho was so close upon him that the fumes rose in almost a direct line, and so it is not surprising if some of them reached the knight's nostrils, whereupon he came to the aid of his nose by compressing it between two fingers.

"It strikes me, Sancho," he said in a somewhat snuffling tone of voice, "that you are very much frightened."

"That I am," replied his squire, "but how does your Grace happen to notice it, now more than ever?"

"Because you smell now more than ever, and it is not of ambergris."

"That may well be," said Sancho, "but I am not to blame; it is rather your Grace, for keeping me up at such hours and putting me through such unaccustomed paces."

"Retire, if you will, three or four paces from here, my friend," said Don Quixote, without taking his fingers from his nose; "and from now on, see to it that you take better care of your person and show more respect for mine. It is my familiarity with you that has bred this contempt."

"I'll wager," said Sancho, "your Grace thinks I have done something with my person that I ought not to have done."

"It only makes it worse to stir it, friend Sancho," Don Quixote answered him.

In talk such as this master and man spent the rest of the night; and when Sancho saw that morning was near he very cautiously removed the fetters from Rocinante and tied up his breeches. Finding himself free, although he was by no means a mettlesome animal, the hack appeared to be in high spirits and began pawing the earth, since—begging his pardon—he was not capable of leaping and prancing. When he beheld his steed in motion, Don Quixote took it for a good sign, a sign that he should begin that dread adventure.

It was light now and things could be clearly seen, and he discovered that they were in a grove of chestnut trees that cast a very deep shade. He was aware, also, that the sound of blows continued, although he could see no cause for it; and so, without any further delay, he dug his spurs into Rocinante and, turning to Sancho to bid him good-by, commanded him to wait three days at the most, as he had told him before. If at the end of that time he had not returned, his squire would know for a certainty that it had pleased God to have him end his life's span in this perilous undertaking.

Once again he reminded Sancho of the mission which the latter was to fulfill by bearing a message on his master's behalf to the lady Dulcinea. As to pay for his services, Sancho was not to let that worry him, as the knight before leaving home had made out his will in which his squire would find himself recompensed in full for all the wages due him in accordance with the time he had served. If, on the other hand, God should bring him, Don Quixote, safe, sound, and unscathed out of this peril, then his faithful servitor might be more than certain of obtaining that promised island. At hearing these sad words from his good master, Sancho again fell to weeping and resolved not to leave him until the final outcome and end of the business.

These tears and this noble resolve on the part of Sancho Panza are duly recorded by the author of the history, who must have been well bred and at the very least an old Christian.[8] Such a display of sentiment somewhat softened his master's heart. Not that Don Quixote showed any weakness, however; on the contrary, hiding his feelings as well as he could, he rode away in the direction from which the noise of water and the sound of blows appeared to be coming, with Sancho following on foot, leading his ass by the halter as usual, for that beast was his constant companion in good fortune or adversity.

When they had gone quite a way through the dense shade of the chestnut trees, they came out upon a little meadow at the foot of some tall cliffs over which poured a huge stream of water. Down below were a number of rude huts which looked more like ruins than houses, and it was from here that the hammering noise which never ceased was coming. Rocinante was frightened by the din of the waters and the sound of the blows, but Don Quixote quieted him and gradually made his way to where the huts stood, commending himself with all his heart to his lady and begging her favor in this dread enterprise; and as he went, he likewise commended himself to God, praying that He would not forget him. Sancho, meanwhile, never left his master's side but kept stretching his neck as far as he could between Rocinante's legs to see if the thing that had caused him so much fear and suspense was at last visible.

They had gone perhaps a hundred yards farther when, upon turning a corner, they discovered the obvious, unmistakable cause of that horrendous and, for them, terror-inspiring noise that all night long had so bewildered and alarmed them. And that cause was—if, O reader! you will not be too disappointed and disgusted—six fulling hammers which with their alternating strokes produced the clangor that resembled the sound of blows.

When Don Quixote saw what it was, he was speechless and remained as if paralyzed from head to foot. Gazing at him, Sancho saw that his head was on his bosom, as if he were abashed. The knight then glanced at his squire and perceived that his cheeks were puffed with laughter as if about to explode, and in spite of the melancholy that possessed him he in turn could not help laughing at the sight. Thus encouraged, Sancho gave in to his mirth and laughed so hard that he had to hold his sides to keep from bursting. He would stop for a while and then begin all over again, any number of times, laughing as hard as he had at first.

Don Quixote was furious at this, especially when he heard his squire saying, as if to mock him, " 'Sancho, my friend, you may know that I was born by Heaven's will, in this our age of iron, to revive what is known as the Golden Age. I am he for whom are reserved the perils, the great exploits, the valiant deeds . . .' " And he went on repeating all the other things that Don Quixote had said the first time they heard those frightening blows.

At seeing himself thus made sport of, the knight was so exceedingly wroth that he raised his lance and let Sancho have a couple of whacks, which, had they been received upon the head instead of across the shoulders, would have freed Don Quixote from the necessity of paying his wages, unless it had been to his heirs. The jest was becoming serious, and Sancho was afraid things might go further. He was very humble now.

"Calm yourself, your Grace," he said. "In God's name, I was only joking."

"Well, you may be joking, but I am not," said Don Quixote. "Come over here, my merry gentleman, I want to ask you a question. Supposing that, in place of fulling hammers, this had really been another dangerous adventure, did not I display the requisite courage for undertaking and carrying it through? Am I obliged, being a gentleman as I am, to recognize and distinguish sounds and know whether they come from fulling hammers or not? Especially when I may never before have laid eyes on such things, as happens to be the case, whereas you, rude bumpkin that you are, were born and brought up among them. But turn these six hammers into six giants and beard me with them one by one, or with all of them together, and if I do not cause them all to turn up their toes, then you may make as much sport of me as you like."

"I shall do so no more, sir," replied Sancho, "for I admit that I carried the joke a little too far. But tell me, your Grace, now that there is peace between us—and may God in the future bring you out of all adventures as safe and sound as He has brought you out of this one—tell me if it was not truly a laughing matter, and a good story as well, that great fright of ours? For I, at least, was afraid, although I am well aware that your Grace does not know what fear is."

"I do not deny," said Don Quixote, "that what happened to us has its comical aspects; but it is best not to tell the story, for not everyone is wise enough to see the point of the thing."

"Well, at any rate," said Sancho, "your Grace saw the point when you pointed your lance at my head—but it fell on my shoulders, thank God, and thanks also to my quickness in dodging it. But never mind, it will all come out in the wash; [9] and I have heard it said, 'He loves you well who makes you weep.' [10] It is the custom of great lords, after they have scolded a servant, to give him a pair of breeches; although I am sure I do not know what they would give him after a good clubbing, unless they happened to be knights-errant, and then perhaps they would give him a few islands or some kingdoms on *terra firma*." [11]

"The dice may so fall," replied Don Quixote, "that everything you say will come true. But let us overlook the past; for you are shrewd enough to know that the first instinctive movements a man makes are not within his control. Be advised of one thing for the future, however: you are to abstain and refrain from conversing with me so much; for in all the books of chivalry that I have read, and they are infinite in number, I have never heard of any squire talking so much to his master as you do to me. The truth is, I look upon it as a great fault, on your part and on mine: on your part because it shows that you have little respect for me; and on mine because I do not make myself more respected.

"There was, for example, Gandalín, squire to Amadis of Gaul, who was count of Firm Island. I have read of him that he never spoke to his master save with cap in hand, with lowered head and body bent double *more turquesco*. [12] Then, what shall we say of Gasabal, squire to Don

Galaor, who was so very silent that, by way of indicating how excellent a thing such taciturnity on his part was, the author of that history, which is as voluminous as it is veracious, sees fit to mention his name only once?

"From all this that I have told you, Sancho, you are to infer that it is necessary that there be a difference between master and man, lord and servant, a knight and his squire. And so, from now on, we must treat each other with more respect and less bantering; for in whatever way I may become annoyed with you, it will be bad for the pitcher.[18] The favors and benefits that I have promised you will all come in due time; and if they should not, your wages at least are safe as I have told you."

"That is all well and good," said Sancho, "but what I should like to know of your Grace is, if by any chance the time for the granting of favors does not come and it is necessary to think of the wages, how much did the squire of a knight-errant earn in those times, and was it reckoned by months, or by days as in the case of bricklayers?"

"I do not think," said Don Quixote, "that the squires of old received wages, but only favors; and if I have provided a wage for you, in the sealed will which I have left at home, it was in view of what might happen; as yet I do not know how chivalry will work out in these calamitous times in which we live, and I do not wish my soul in the other world to have to suffer on account of trifles; for I may tell you, Sancho, that there is no calling anywhere more dangerous than that of adventurer."

"That is the truth," said Sancho, "seeing that the mere sound of fulling hammers can disturb and agitate the heart of so valiant a knightly adventurer as is your Grace. But you may be sure that from now on I will not open my mouth to make light of what concerns your Grace, but will speak only to honor you as my liege lord and master."

"By so doing," replied Don Quixote, "you will live long upon the face of the earth; for after parents, masters are to be respected as if they were the ones that bore us."

CHAPTER XXI. *Which treats of the high and richly rewarded adventure of Mambrino's helmet, together with other things that happened to our invincible knight.*

At this point it began to rain a little, and Sancho suggested that they enter the fulling mill; but Don Quixote had conceived such a dislike for the place by reason of the offensive joke [1] associated with it that he would not hear of their setting foot inside it; and so, turning to the right, they came out into another road like the one they had traveled the day before.

They had not gone far before Don Quixote sighted a man on horseback wearing something on his head that gleamed like gold, and no sooner had he laid eyes upon him than he said to his squire, "It is my opinion, Sancho, that there is no proverb that is not true; for they are all drawn from experience itself, mother of all the sciences, and especially that saying that runs, 'Where one door closes another opens.' By this I mean to say that if, last night, fortune closed the door on what we were seeking by deceiving us with those fulling hammers, she is now opening another upon a better and more assured adventure, and if I do not embark upon that undertaking the fault will be mine, and I shall not be able to blame it upon those hammers or the darkness of night. I tell you this for the reason that, if I am not mistaken, there comes toward us now one who wears upon his head that helmet of Mambrino concerning which, as you know, I have taken a vow."

"But, your Grace," said Sancho, "mark well what I say and even better what you do; for I should not like to have any more fulling hammers fulling and finishing us off and cudgeling our brains."

"To the devil with the fellow!" exclaimed Don Quixote. "What has the helmet to do with fulling mills?"

"I know nothing about that," replied Sancho, "but upon my word, if I were free to talk as I used to, I could give you such reasons that your Grace would see he was mistaken in what he just said."

"How could I be mistaken in what I said, you unbelieving traitor? Tell me, do you not see that knight coming toward us, mounted on a dappled gray steed and with a golden helmet on his head?"

"What I see and perceive," said Sancho, "is a man upon an ass, a gray ass like mine, with something or other on his head that shines."

"Well," said Don Quixote, "that is Mambrino's helmet. Go off to one side and let me meet him singlehanded; and you shall see me end this adventure without wasting a word in parley, and when it is ended, the helmet which I have so greatly desired shall be mine."

"I will take care to go to one side, right enough," said Sancho; "but— I say again—I only pray God that it may turn out to be marjoram and not fulling hammers." [2]

"I have told you, brother," said Don Quixote, "not to think of mentioning those hammers to me again; and if you do, I vow—I need say no more—that I will full your very soul."

Sancho was silent, for he was afraid that his master would carry out this vow which he had hurled at him like a bowling ball.

The truth concerning that helmet and the horse and horseman that Don Quixote had sighted was this: in these parts there were two villages, one so small that it had neither apothecary nor barber, whereas the other had both; and as a consequence, the barber of the larger village served the smaller one, in which, as it happened, there was a sick man who had need of a blood-letting and another individual who needed to have his beard trimmed; and so the barber was on his way now, carrying with him a brass basin, and as it had started to rain and he did not wish to have his hat spoiled (it was probably a new one), he had placed the basin on his head, and since it was very clean it could be seen glittering half a league away. He was riding on an ass, a gray one as Sancho had remarked, and it was all this that had given Don Quixote the impression of a knight, a dappled steed, and a helmet of gold, for he readily fitted all the things that he saw to his own mad, ill-errant [3] thoughts of chivalry.

As he saw the poor fellow whom he took to be a knight approaching, without pausing for any exchange of words he bore down upon him with lowered lance at the best speed that Rocinante could make, with intent to run him through with his pike. As he drew near, without abating his fury in the least, he cried out, "Defend yourself, vile wretch, or else render to me of your own free will that which is so justly my due!"

The barber who, without any thought or fear of what was about to happen, had seen this apparition descending upon him, now had no other recourse by way of protecting himself from the lance blow than to slide down off his ass's back, and he had no more than touched the earth when he was up and running away across the fields faster than the wind, leaving his basin behind him upon the ground. Don Quixote was content with this, observing that the heathenish fellow had been wise in imitating the beaver, which, when it finds itself hard pressed by the hunters, bites and tears off [4] with its teeth that for which it knows it is being pursued. He commanded Sancho to pick up the helmet for him.

"By God," said the squire, taking it in his hands, "if it isn't a very good basin and worth a piece of eight if it's worth a maravedi."

With this, he handed it to his master, and Don Quixote at once placed it on his head, turning it round and round in search of the visor.

"Undoubtedly," he said when he failed to find one, "the pagan to whose measure this helmet was originally made must have had a very large head. The regrettable part of it is, half of it is missing."

Upon hearing the basin called a helmet, Sancho could not help laughing, but mindful of his master's ire, he stopped short.

"What are you laughing at, Sancho?" said Don Quixote.

"I was just thinking what a big pate that pagan had who owned it, for this helmet looks exactly like a barber's basin."

"Do you know what I think, Sancho? I think that this famous piece of that enchanted helmet must by some strange accident have fallen into the hands of someone who did not know, and was incapable of estimating, its worth, and who, seeing that it was of the purest gold and not realizing what he was doing, must have melted down the other half for what he could get for it, while from the remaining portion he fashioned what appears, as you have said, to be a barber's basin. But be that as it may; I recognize its value, and the transformation that it has undergone makes no difference to me; the first village that we come to where there is a blacksmith, I will have it repaired in such a manner that the helmet which the god of smithies made and forged for the god of battles shall not surpass or even come up to it. In the meanwhile, I will wear it the best way I can, for something is better than nothing at all,[5] especially seeing that it will serve quite well to protect me from stones."

"That is," said Sancho, "providing it is not a stone from a slingshot of the kind they let you have in the battle of the two armies, that time they made the sign of the cross on your Grace's grinders and broke the vial which held that blessed potion that made me vomit up my guts."

"I am not greatly grieved over having lost it," said Don Quixote, "for as you know, Sancho, I have the receipt in my memory."

"So have I," replied Sancho, "but if I ever in all my life make it or try it again, may this be my last hour on earth. What is more, I do not expect to have any occasion to use it, for I mean to see to it with all my five senses that I neither wound anybody nor am wounded by anyone else. As to being tossed in a blanket, I say nothing about that. Troubles of that kind are hard to foresee, and if they come, there is nothing to do but shrug your shoulders, hold your breath, shut your eyes, and let yourself go where luck and the blanket take you."

"You are a bad Christian, Sancho," said his master when he heard this, "for you never forget an injury that once has been done you. You should know that it is characteristic of noble and generous hearts to pay no attention to trifles. You have no lame leg, no fractured rib, no broken head to show for it; so why can you not forget that bit of buffoonery? For when you look at it closely, that is all it was: a jest and a little pastime; for had I not regarded it in that light, I should have returned and, in avenging you, should have wrought more damage than those Greeks did who stole Helen of Troy—who, you may be sure, if she had lived in these times or my Dulcinea had lived in those, would not have been so famed for her beauty as she now is." With this, he breathed a sigh and wafted it heavenward.

"Let it pass for a jest," said Sancho, "seeing that it cannot be avenged in earnest; but I know what jest and earnest mean, and I further know that this joke will never slip from my memory any more than it will from my shoulders. But leaving all that aside, tell me, your Grace, what are we to do with this dappled gray steed that looks like a gray-colored ass, which that fellow Martino [6] whom your Grace just routed has left here? For judging by the way he took to his heels, I don't think he ever means to come back for it; and by my beard, but the gray is a good one!"

"It is not my custom," said Don Quixote, "to despoil those whom I conquer, nor is it in accordance with the usages of knighthood to deprive one's enemy of his steed and leave him to go away on foot, unless it be that the victor has lost his own mount in the fray, in which case it is permitted to take that of the vanquished as something that has been won in lawful warfare. And so, Sancho, leave this horse, or ass, or whatever you choose to call him; for as soon as its master sees that we are gone, he will come back for it."

"God knows I'd like to take it," said Sancho, "or at least exchange it for this one of mine, which does not strike me as being a very good one. Surely the laws of knighthood must be pretty strict if they cannot be stretched far enough to permit you to exchange one ass for another. Could I not at least exchange trappings?"

"I am none too certain as to that," replied Don Quixote; "but being in doubt and until I am better informed, I should say that you might exchange them in case of extreme necessity."

"The necessity," said Sancho, "is so extreme that I could not need them more if they were for my own person."

Having been granted permission to do so, he now effected the *mutatio capparum*,[1] trigging his own beast out in great style, in such a manner as to alter its appearance most advantageously. This being done, they made their lunch on what was left over from the spoils of the sumpter mule, drinking water from the brook where the fulling hammers were but without turning their heads to look at them, for they still could not forget the fright which those distasteful objects had given them.

At length, all anger and melancholy gone, they mounted again and without taking any definite direction, as was the custom of knights-errant, they let Rocinante follow his own will, his master's inclinations and those of the ass falling in behind; for the ass followed wherever the hack led, very sociably and affectionately. Proceeding in this manner, they came back to the highway and continued riding along, leaving everything to chance and with no plan whatsoever.

Finally Sancho spoke up and addressed the knight. "Sir," he said, "would your Grace grant me permission to have a word with you? Ever since you gave me that order to be silent, a number of things in my stomach have gone to rot, and I have one now on the tip of my tongue that I do not want to see wasted."

"Say what you have to say," said Don Quixote, "and be brief about it, for there is no pleasure in listening to long speeches."

"Very well, sir," replied Sancho. "I just wanted to tell you that for some days now I have been thinking how little gain or profit there is in your Grace's going in search of adventures in these wasteland and cross-road places; for even if you come out the victor in the most dangerous of them, there is no one to witness them or know about them, and as a result, nothing will ever be heard of them, which is contrary to what your Grace had in mind and what they deserve. And, accordingly, it seems to me that it would be better—saving, always, your Grace's better judgment—for us to go serve some emperor or other great prince who has some war on his hands and in whose service your Grace would have an opportunity to display the valor of your person, the great feats of which you are capable, and your superior understanding. For when the lord we served beheld all this, being obliged to reward each according to his merits, he could not fail to have your Grace's exploits set down in writing, that they might never be forgotten. Of my own I say nothing, for they do not go beyond the bounds of what is becoming in a squire; although I may say this much: that if it were the custom of knighthood to record squirely achievements, I do not think mine would be left out."

"There is something in what you say, Sancho," replied Don Quixote; "but before we come to that, it is necessary for a knight to roam the world in quest of adventures and, so to speak, serve a period of probation, in order that, having brought a number of those adventures to a success-ful conclusion, he may win such name and fame as will render him well known for his accomplishments by the time he arrives at the court of some great monarch. He must be so well known that, when he enters the gate of the city, all the young lads will follow and surround him, shouting, 'There goes the Knight of the Sun,' or of the Serpent, or what-ever insignia it was under which he performed his feats of valor. 'He,' they will say, 'is the one who overcame singlehanded the giant Broca-bruno of the Mighty Strength; he it was who freed the Mameluke of Persia of the spell under which he had been for nearly nine hundred years.'

"Thus from mouth to mouth his fame will spread, until at last, aroused by the tumult of the lads and the throng that will have gathered, the king of that realm will appear at the windows of his royal palace, and as soon as he sees the knight, recognizing him by his armor or by the device on his shield, he will be certain to cry, 'What, ho! Up, all ye knights that be in my court and go forth to receive the flower of chivalry who cometh hither.' At this command, they will all come out, and the monarch him-self, descending the stair halfway, will welcome the new arrival, giving him a warm embrace and a kiss on the cheek, after which he will conduct him to the apartment of my lady the queen, and in her company the knight will be presented to her daughter, who will be one of the most beautiful and faultless damsels to be met with anywhere in the known world. And then it will come to pass that she will rest her eyes on the knight and he will rest his on her, and each will appear to the other as something that is nearer divine than human; and, without knowing how or why it comes about, they will find themselves caught and entangled in love's inextricable net, with a deep pain in their hearts at not being able to put into words their longings and desires.

"After that, they undoubtedly will take him to some room in the palace that is richly fitted out, and there, having relieved him of his armor, they will bring him a sumptuous scarlet cloak to wear; and if he presented a handsome appearance in his suit of armor, he will be even handsomer in a doublet. When night comes, he will sup with the king, queen, and infanta, and he will never take his eyes off the princess but will steal glances at her without the others seeing him, and she with equal cunning will do the same, for, as I have said, she is a very circumspect young lady. And then, when the tables have been cleared, through the door of the great hall there will at once enter a small and ugly dwarf, followed by a beautiful duenna between two giants, who comes to propose a certain adventure [8] conceived by a wise man of very long ago; and whoever carries it through is to be looked upon as the best knight in the world.

"The king will thereupon command all those present to undertake the adventure, and none will bring it to an end and conclusion except the knight who is their guest. This will greatly add to his fame, and the infanta will be very happy and feel well recompensed for having placed her affections upon so exalted a personage. But the best part of it is, this king or prince or whoever he may be is engaged in a bitter war with another monarch who is quite as powerful as he; and the stranger knight —after a few days spent at court—will then beg his royal host's permission to go serve him in the said war. His Majesty will grant this request with right good grace, and the knight will courteously kiss the king's hand in return for the favor shown him.

"That night, he will take leave of his lady the infanta through the grating of her chamber overlooking the garden where he has already conversed with her many times, the go-between and confidante in the affair being a maid-in-waiting whom the princess greatly trusts. He will sigh and she will swoon, and the damsel will bring water to revive her. He will be very much distressed at this, for morning is near, and for the sake of his lady's honor he would not have them discovered. Finally the infanta will come to herself and will hold out her white hands through the bars to her knight, who will kiss them thousands upon thousands of times, bathing them with his tears.

"It will be arranged between them how they are to keep each other informed as to the good or ill that befalls them, and the princess will entreat him not to remain away any longer than need be. He will give her this promise, with many oaths to bind it, and then he will kiss her hands once more and depart, so deeply moved that he is on the verge of dying. Going to his apartment, he will cast himself down upon his bed, but will be unable to sleep from the pain of parting. In the morning, very early, he will go to bid adieu to the king, queen, and infanta; but after he has paid his respects to the royal pair, he is informed that the princess is indisposed and cannot receive any visitors. The knight will think that she too must be suffering at prospect of their separation, his heart will be transfixed, and it will be all he can do to hide his feelings.

"But the damsel who is the go-between will be there; she will take note of everything and will go to report it all to her mistress, who will receive her with tears. The princess will then tell her maid-in-waiting that one of the things that causes her most sorrow is the fact that she does not know who her knight is, or whether he is of royal lineage or not. The damsel will assure her that so much courtesy, gentleness of bearing, and valor could be displayed only by a grave and royal personage, and with such words as these she will endeavor to assuage her mistress's grief. The princess will then seek to compose herself so as not to make a bad impression upon her parents, and after a couple of days she will appear in public once more.

"Meanwhile, the knight has left for the wars; he conquers the king's enemy, takes many cities, is victorious in many battles, returns to court, meets his lady in the accustomed place, and they agree that he is to ask her father for her hand in payment of his services. The king is unwilling to grant this request, for he does not know who the knight is; but, nevertheless, whether she is carried off or however it happens, she becomes his bride, and her father in the end comes to look upon it as a piece of great good fortune, for he has learned that the knight is the son of the valiant king of some realm or other which I do not think you will find on the map. The king then dies, the infanta inherits the throne, and, in a couple of words, the knight becomes king.[9]

"And here is where the bestowal of favors comes in, as he rewards his squire and all those who have assisted him in rising to so exalted a state. He marries the squire to one of the infanta's damsels, undoubtedly the one who was the go-between in his courting of the princess, and who is the daughter of a very great duke."

"That's what I want, and no mistake about it," said Sancho. "That is what I'm waiting for. All of this, word for word, is bound to happen to your Grace now that you bear the title Knight of the Mournful Countenance."

"Do not doubt it, Sancho," Don Quixote assured him; "for in this very manner and by these very steps of which I have told you, many come, and have come, to be kings and emperors. It only remains to find out what king of the Christians or the pagans is at war and has a beautiful daughter. But there will be time to think of all that; for, as I have said, one must achieve fame elsewhere before repairing to court. There is one other thing: supposing that I find a king with a war and with a beautiful daughter, and supposing that I have won an incredible amount of fame throughout the universe, I do not know how I am going to make myself out to be of royal line or even second cousin to an emperor; for the king will not wish to give me his daughter's hand unless he is first thoroughly satisfied on this point, however much my deeds may merit the honor; and for this reason I fear losing that which my good right arm has so well earned for me. It is true that I am a gentleman property-holder with a country house and estate, and am entitled to an income of five hundred sueldos; [10] and it may further be that the learned scribe who writes my history will so clear up my relationships and ancestry that I shall be found to be the descendant, fifth or sixth in line, of some king.

"For I would have you know, Sancho," he went on, "that there are in this world two kinds of ancestral lines. In the one case, there are those who trace their descent from princes and monarchs whom time has little by little reduced until they come to end in a point like a pyramid upside down; and in the other case, there are those who spring from the lower classes and who go upward, one step after another, until they come to be great lords; the difference being that the former were what they no longer are, while the latter are what they formerly were not. And I may be one of those who, after it has been ascertained that they are of great and famous origin, are accepted for what they are, and the king, my father-in-law, in that case will be content; but should he not be, the infanta will love me so much that, in spite of her father's wishes and even though she definitely knows me to be a water carrier's son, she still will insist upon my being received as a gentleman and her consort. And if everything else fails, then it will come to my abducting and carrying her off wherever I see fit; for time or death must eventually put an end to her parents' wrath."

"It comes to something else as well," said Sancho. "For I am reminded here of what certain wicked ones say: 'Never beg as a favor what you can take by force'; although they might better say: 'An escape from the slaughter is worth more than good men's prayers.' [11] I tell you this because if the king, your Grace's father-in-law, will not condescend to give you my lady the infanta, then, as your Grace says, there is nothing for it but to abduct and carry her off. But the trouble is that until you make your peace and come into the tranquil enjoyment of your kingdom, your poor squire can whistle for his favors—that is, unless the damsel who was the go-between and who is to be his wife accompanies the

princess and shares her ill fortune with her until Heaven ordains otherwise; for I take it that his master will give her to him at once as his lawful
spouse."

"No one can deny him that," said Don Quixote.

"Well, then," replied Sancho, "if that is so, we have nothing to do
but to commend ourselves to God and let fortune take whatever course
it will."

"May God fulfill my desires and your needs, Sancho," said Don
Quixote; "and let him be vile who looks upon himself as such." [12]

"In God's name, so let him be," said Sancho. "I am an old Christian, and
that in itself is enough to make me a count." [13]

"Enough and more than enough for you," said Don Quixote; "and
even if you were not, it would make no difference; for once I am king,
I can very well make a noble of you without any purchase price or
service on your part; and in making you a count, I make a gentleman
of you at the same time, and then let them say what they will, upon my
word they will have to call you 'my lordship' whether they like it or
not."

"And I would lend dignity to the tittle!" [14] said Sancho.

"*Title*, you mean to say, not *tittle*," his master corrected him.

"So be it," said Sancho. "I'd know how to behave myself properly; for
there was a time in my life when I was the beadle of a confraternity, and
the beadle's gown sat so well upon me that everybody said I ought to
be the steward. So what will it be when I put a ducal robe on my back
or dress myself out in gold and pearls like one of those foreign counts?
I think, myself, that folks will be coming to see me for a hundred leagues
around."

"You will cut a fine figure," said Don Quixote, "but it will be necessary
for you to shave your beard quite often, for it is so thick and unkempt
that unless you use the razor on it every other day at the least, people will
be able to see what you are at the distance of a musket shot."

"What more have I to do," said Sancho, "than to hire a barber and
keep him in the house? If necessary, I can even have him walk behind me
like a nobleman's equerry."

"How do you know," asked Don Quixote, "that noblemen have
equerries walking behind them?"

"I will tell you about that," Sancho replied. "Years ago I spent a month
near the court, and there I saw a very small gentleman who, they told
me, was a very great lord. [15] He was out for a stroll, and there was a man
on horseback following him at every turn he took just as if he had been

his tail. I asked why it was this man did not join the other one but always rode along behind him, and they replied that he was an equerry and that such was the custom of the nobility. I have known it ever since then, for I have never forgotten it."

"You are right," said Don Quixote, "and you may take your barber with you in the same manner; for all customs did not come into use, nor were they invented, at one and the same time; and so you may be the first count to be followed by his barber, for shaving the beard is a more intimate matter than saddling a horse."

"Just leave the barber to me," said Sancho, "while your Grace sees to becoming a king and making a count of me."

"So shall it be," said Don Quixote; and, raising his eyes, he saw something that will be related in the following chapter.

CHAPTER XXII. *Of how Don Quixote freed many unfortunate ones who, much against their will, were being taken where they did not wish to go.*

CID HAMETE BENENGELI, the Arabic and Manchegan [1] author, in the course of this most grave, high-sounding, minute, delightful, and imaginative history, informs us that, following the remarks that were exchanged between Don Quixote de la Mancha and Sancho Panza, his squire, as related at the end of Chapter xxi, the knight looked up and saw coming toward them down the road which they were following a dozen or so men on foot, strung together by their necks like beads on an iron chain and all of them wearing handcuffs. They were accompanied by two men on horseback and two on foot, the former carrying wheel-lock muskets while the other two were armed with swords and javelins.

"That," said Sancho as soon as he saw them, "is a chain of galley slaves, people on their way to the galleys where by order of the king they are forced to labor."

"What do you mean by 'forced'?" asked Don Quixote. "Is it possible that the king uses force on anyone?"

"I did not say that," replied Sancho. "What I did say was that these are folks who have been condemned for their crimes to forced labor in the galleys for his Majesty the King."

"The short of it is," said the knight, "whichever way you put it, these people are being taken there by force and not of their own free will."

"That is the way it is," said Sancho.

"Well, in that case," said his master, "now is the time for me to fulfill the duties of my calling, which is to right wrongs and come to the aid of the wretched."

"But take note, your Grace," said Sancho, "that justice, that is to say, the king himself, is not using any force upon, or doing any wrong to, people like these, but is merely punishing them for the crimes they have committed."

The chain of galley slaves had come up to them by this time, whereupon Don Quixote very courteously requested the guards to inform him of the reason or reasons why they were conducting these people in such a manner as this. One of the men on horseback then replied that the men were prisoners who had been condemned by his Majesty to serve in the galleys, whither they were bound, and that was all there was to be said about it and all that he, Don Quixote, need know.

"Nevertheless," said the latter, "I should like to inquire of each one of them, individually, the cause of his misfortune." And he went on speaking so very politely in an effort to persuade them to tell him what he wanted to know that the other mounted guard finally said, "Although we have here the record and certificate of sentence of each one of these wretches, we have not the time to get them out and read them to you; and so your Grace may come over and ask the prisoners themselves, and they will tell you if they choose, and you may be sure that they will, for these fellows take a delight in their knavish exploits and in boasting of them afterward."

With this permission, even though he would have done so if it had not been granted him, Don Quixote went up to the chain of prisoners and asked the first whom he encountered what sins had brought him to so sorry a plight. The man replied that it was for being a lover that he found himself in that line.

"For that and nothing more?" said Don Quixote. "And do they, then, send lovers to the galleys? If so, I should have been rowing there long ago."

"But it was not the kind of love that your Grace has in mind," the prisoner went on. "I loved a wash basket full of white linen so well and hugged it so tightly that, if they had not taken it away from me by force, I would never of my own choice have let go of it to this very minute. I was caught in the act, there was no need to torture me, the case was soon disposed of, and they supplied me with a hundred lashes across the shoulders and, in addition, a three-year stretch [2] in the *gurapas*, and that's all there is to tell."

"What are *gurapas*?" asked Don Quixote.

"*Gurapas* are the galleys," replied the prisoner. He was a lad of around twenty-four and stated that he was a native of Piedrahita.

The knight then put the same question to a second man, who appeared to be very downcast and melancholy and did not have a word to say. The first man answered for him.

"This one, sir," he said, "is going as a canary—I mean, as a musician and singer."

"How is that?" Don Quixote wanted to know. "Do musicians and singers go to the galleys too?"

"Yes, sir; and there is nothing worse than singing when you're in trouble."

"On the contrary," said Don Quixote, "I have heard it said that he who sings frightens away his sorrows." [3]

"It is just the opposite," said the prisoner; "for he who sings once weeps all his life long."

"I do not understand," said the knight.

One of the guards then explained. "Sir Knight, with this *non sancta* tribe, to sing when you're in trouble means to confess under torture.[4] This sinner was put to the torture and confessed his crime, which was that of being a *cuatrero*, or cattle thief, and as a result of his confession he was condemned to six years in the galleys in addition to two hundred lashes which he took on his shoulders; and so it is he is always downcast and moody, for the other thieves, those back where he came from and the ones here, mistreat, snub, ridicule, and despise him for having confessed and for not having had the courage to deny his guilt. They are in the habit of saying that the word *no* has the same number of letters as the word *sí*,[5] and that a culprit is in luck when his life or death depends on his own tongue and not that of witnesses or upon evidence; and, in my opinion, they are not very far wrong."

"And I," said Don Quixote, "feel the same way about it." He then went on to a third prisoner and repeated his question.

The fellow answered at once, quite unconcernedly. "I'm going to my ladies, the *gurapas*, for five years, for the lack of five ducats."

"I would gladly give twenty," said Don Quixote, "to get you out of this."

"That," said the prisoner, "reminds me of the man in the middle of the ocean who has money and is dying of hunger because there is no place to buy what he needs. I say this for the reason that if I had had, at the right time, those twenty ducats your Grace is now offering me, I'd have greased the notary's quill and freshened up the attorney's wit with them, and I'd now be living in the middle of Zocodover Square in Toledo instead of being here on this highway coupled like a greyhound. But God is great; patience, and that's enough of it."

Don Quixote went on to a fourth prisoner, a venerable-looking old fellow with a white beard that fell over his bosom. When asked how he came to be there, this one began weeping and made no reply, but a fifth comrade spoke up in his behalf.

"This worthy man," he said, "is on his way to the galleys after having made the usual rounds clad in a robe of state and on horseback." [6]

"That means, I take it," said Sancho, "that he has been put to shame in public."

"That is it," said the prisoner, "and the offense for which he is being punished is that of having been an ear broker, or, better, a body broker. By that I mean to say, in short, that the gentleman is a pimp, and besides, he has his points as a sorcerer."

"If that point had not been thrown in," said Don Quixote, "he would not deserve, for merely being a pimp, to have to row in the galleys, but rather should be the general and give orders there. For the office of pimp is not an indifferent one; it is a function to be performed by persons of discretion and is most necessary in a well-ordered state; it is a profession that should be followed only by the wellborn, and there should, moreover, be a supervisor or examiner as in the case of other offices, and the number of practitioners should be fixed by law as is done with brokers on the exchange. In that way many evils would be averted that arise when this office is filled and this calling practiced by stupid folk and those with little sense, such as silly women and pages or mountebanks with few years and less experience to their credit, who, on the most pressing occasions, when it is necessary to use one's wits, let the crumbs freeze between their hand and their mouth [7] and do not know which is their right hand and which is the left.

"I would go on and give reasons why it is fitting to choose carefully those who are to fulfill so necessary a state function, but this is not the place for it. One of these days I will speak of the matter to someone who is able to do something about it. I will say here only that the pain I felt at seeing those white hairs and this venerable countenance in such a plight, and all for his having been a pimp, has been offset for me by the additional information you have given me, to the effect that he is a sorcerer as well; for I am convinced that there are no sorcerers in the world who can move and compel the will, as some simple-minded persons think, but that our will is free and no herb or charm can force it. All that certain foolish women and cunning tricksters do is to compound a few mixtures and poisons with which they deprive men of their senses while pretending that they have the power to make them loved, although, as I have just said, one cannot affect another's will in that manner." [8]

"That is so," said the worthy old man; "but the truth is, sir, I am not guilty on the sorcery charge. As for being a pimp, that is something I cannot deny. I never thought there was any harm in it, however, my only desire being that everyone should enjoy himself and live in peace and quiet, without any quarrels or troubles. But these good intentions on my part cannot prevent me from going where I do not want to go, to a place from which I do not expect to return; for my years are heavy upon me and an affection of the urine that I have will not give me a moment's rest."

With this, he began weeping once more, and Sancho was so touched by it that he took a four-real piece from his bosom and gave it to him as an act of charity.

Don Quixote then went on and asked another what his offense was. The fellow answered him, not with less, but with much more, briskness than the preceding one had shown.

"I am here," he said, "for the reason that I carried a joke too far with a couple of cousins-german of mine and a couple of others who were not mine, and I ended by jesting with all of them to such an extent that the devil [9] himself would never be able to straighten out the relationship. They proved everything on me, there was no one to show me favor, I had no money, I came near swinging for it, they sentenced me to the galleys for six years, and I accepted the sentence as the punishment that was due me. I am young yet, and if I live long enough, everything will come out all right. If, Sir Knight, your Grace has anything with which to aid these poor creatures that you see before you, God will reward you in Heaven, and we here on earth will make it a point to ask God in our prayers to grant you long life and good health, as long and as good as your amiable presence deserves."

This man was dressed as a student, and one of the guards told Don Quixote that he was a great talker and a very fine Latinist.

Back of these came a man around thirty years of age and of very good appearance, except that when he looked at you his eyes were seen to be a little crossed. He was shackled in a different manner from the others, for he dragged behind him a chain so huge that it was wrapped all around his body, with two rings at the throat, one of which was attached to the chain while the other was fastened to what is known as a keep-friend or friend's foot, from which two irons hung down to his waist, ending in handcuffs secured by a heavy padlock in such a manner that he could neither raise his hands to his mouth nor lower his head to reach his hands.

When Don Quixote asked why this man was so much more heavily chained than the others, the guard replied that it was because he had more crimes against him than all the others put together, and he was so bold and cunning that, even though they had him chained like this, they were by no means sure of him but feared that he might escape from them.

"What crimes could he have committed," asked the knight, "if he has merited a punishment no greater than that of being sent to the galleys?"

"He is being sent there for ten years," replied the guard, "and that is equivalent to civil death. I need tell you no more than that this good man is the famous Ginés de Pasamonte, otherwise known as Ginesillo de Parapilla."

"Señor Commissary," spoke up the prisoner at this point, "go easy there and let us not be so free with names and surnames. My just name is Ginés and not Ginesillo; and Pasamonte, not Parapilla as you make it out to be, is my family name. Let each one mind his own affairs and he will have his hands full."

"Speak a little more respectfully, you big thief, you," said the commissary, "unless you want me to make you be quiet in a way you won't like."

"Man goes as God pleases,[10] that is plain to be seen," replied the galley slave, "but someday someone will know whether my name is Ginesillo de Parapilla or not."

"But, you liar, isn't that what they call you?"

"Yes," said Ginés, "they do call me that; but I'll put a stop to it, or else I'll skin their you-know-what. And you, sir, if you have anything to give us, give it and may God go with you, for I am tired of all this prying into other people's lives. If you want to know anything about my life, know that I am Ginés de Pasamonte whose life story has been written down by these fingers that you see here."

"He speaks the truth," said the commissary, "for he has himself written his story, as big as you please, and has left the book in the prison, having pawned it for two hundred reales."

"And I mean to redeem it," said Ginés, "even if it costs me two hundred ducats."

"Is it as good as that?" inquired Don Quixote.

"It is so good," replied Ginés, "that it will cast into the shade *Lazarillo de Tormes* [11] and all others of that sort that have been or will be written. What I would tell you is that it deals with facts, and facts so interesting and amusing that no lies could equal them."

"And what is the title of the book?" asked Don Quixote.

"*The Life of Ginés de Pasamonte.*"

"Is it finished?"

"How could it be finished," said Ginés, "when my life is not finished as yet? What I have written thus far is an account of what happened to me from the time I was born up to the last time that they sent me to the galleys."

"Then you have been there before?"

"In the service of God and the king I was there four years, and I know what the biscuit and the cowhide are like. I don't mind going very much, for there I will have a chance to finish my book. I still have many things to say, and in the Spanish galleys I shall have all the leisure that I need, though I don't need much, since I know by heart what it is I want to write."

"You seem to be a clever fellow," said Don Quixote.

"And an unfortunate one," said Ginés; "for misfortunes always pursue men of genius."

"They pursue rogues," said the commissary.

"I have told you to go easy, Señor Commissary," said Pasamonte, "for their Lordships did not give you that staff in order that you might mistreat us poor devils with it, but they intended that you should guide and conduct us in accordance with his Majesty's command. Otherwise, by the life of— But enough. It may be that someday the stains made in the inn will come out in the wash. Meanwhile, let everyone hold his tongue, behave well, and speak better, and let us be on our way. We've had enough of this foolishness."

At this point the commissary raised his staff as if to let Pasamonte have it in answer to his threats, but Don Quixote placed himself between them

and begged the officer not to abuse the man; for it was not to be wondered at if one who had his hands so bound should be a trifle free with
his tongue. With this, he turned and addressed them all.

"From all that you have told me, my dearest brothers," he said, "one
thing stands out clearly for me, and that is the fact that, even though it
is a punishment for offenses which you have committed, the penalty you
are about to pay is not greatly to your liking and you are going to the
galleys very much against your own will and desire. It may be that the
lack of spirit which one of you displayed under torture, the lack of
money on the part of another, the lack of influential friends, or, finally,
warped judgment on the part of the magistrate, was the thing that led to
your downfall; and, as a result, justice was not done you. All of which
presents itself to my mind in such a fashion that I am at this moment
engaged in trying to persuade and even force myself to show you what
the purpose was for which Heaven sent me into this world, why it was
it led me to adopt the calling of knighthood which I profess and take the
knightly vow to favor the needy and aid those who are oppressed by the
powerful.

"However, knowing as I do that it is not the part of prudence to do
by foul means what can be accomplished by fair ones, I propose to ask
these gentlemen, your guards, and the commissary to be so good as to
unshackle you and permit you to go in peace. There will be no dearth of
others to serve his Majesty under more propitious circumstances; and it
does not appear to me to be just to make slaves of those whom God
created as free men. What is more, gentlemen of the guard, these poor
fellows have committed no offense against you. Up there, each of us will
have to answer for his own sins; for God in Heaven will not fail to
punish the evil and reward the good; and it is not good for self-respecting
men to be executioners of their fellow-men in something that does not
concern them. And so, I ask this of you, gently and quietly, in order
that, if you comply with my request, I shall have reason to thank you;
and if you do not do so of your own accord, then this lance and this
sword and the valor of my arm shall compel you to do it by force."

"A fine lot of foolishness!" exclaimed the commissary. "So he comes
out at last with this nonsense! He would have us let the prisoners of the
king go free, as if we had any authority to do so or he any right to command it! Be on your way, sir, at once; straighten that basin that you
have on your head, and do not go looking for three feet on a cat." [12]

"You," replied Don Quixote, "are the cat and the rat and the rascal!"

And, saying this, he charged the commissary so quickly that the latter had no chance to defend himself but fell to the ground badly wounded by the lance blow. The other guards were astounded by this unexpected occurrence; but, recovering their self-possession, those on horseback drew their swords,[13] those on foot leveled their javelins, and all bore down on Don Quixote, who stood waiting for them very calmly. Things undoubtedly would have gone badly for him if the galley slaves, seeing an opportunity to gain their freedom, had not succeeded in breaking the chain that linked them together. Such was the confusion that the guards, now running to fall upon the prisoners and now attacking Don Quixote, who in turn was attacking them, accomplished nothing that was of any use.

Sancho for his part aided Ginés de Pasamonte to free himself, and that individual was the first to drop his chains and leap out onto the field, where, attacking the fallen commissary, he took away that officer's sword and musket; and as he stood there, aiming first at one and then at another, though without firing, the plain was soon cleared of guards, for they had taken to their heels, fleeing at once Pasamonte's weapon and the stones which the galley slaves, freed now, were hurling at them. Sancho, meanwhile, was very much disturbed over this unfortunate event, as he felt sure that the fugitives would report the matter to the Holy Brotherhood, which, to the ringing of the alarm bell, would come out to search for the guilty parties. He said as much to his master, telling him that they should leave at once and go into hiding in the near-by mountains.

"That is all very well," said Don Quixote, "but I know what had best be done now." He then summoned all the prisoners, who, running riot, had by this time despoiled the commissary of everything that he had, down to his skin, and as they gathered around to hear what he had to say, he addressed them as follows:

"It is fitting that those who are wellborn should give thanks for the benefits they have received, and one of the sins with which God is most offended is that of ingratitude. I say this, gentlemen, for the reason that you have seen and had manifest proof of what you owe to me; and now that you are free of the yoke which I have removed from about your necks, it is my will and desire that you should set out and proceed to the city of El Toboso and there present yourselves before the lady Dulcinea del Toboso and say to her that her champion, the Knight of the Mournful Countenance, has sent you; and then you will relate to her, point by point, the whole of this famous adventure which has won you your longed-for freedom. Having done that, you may go where you like, and may good luck go with you."

To this Ginés de Pasamonte replied in behalf of all of them, "It is absolutely impossible, your Grace, our liberator, for us to do what you have commanded. We cannot go down the highway all together but must separate and go singly, each in his own direction, endeavoring to hide ourselves in the bowels of the earth in order not to be found by the Holy Brotherhood, which undoubtedly will come out to search for us. What your Grace can do, and it is right that you should do so, is to change this service and toll that you require of us in connection with the lady Dulcinea del Toboso into a certain number of Credos and Hail Marys which we will say for your Grace's intention, as this is something that can be accomplished by day or night, fleeing or resting, in peace or in war. To imagine, on the other hand, that we are going to return to the fleshpots of Egypt, by which I mean, take up our chains again by setting out along the highway for El Toboso, is to believe that it is night now instead of ten o'clock in the morning and is to ask of us something that is the same as asking pears of the elm tree." [14]

"Then by all that's holy!" exclaimed Don Quixote, whose wrath was now aroused, "you, Don Son of a Whore, Don Ginesillo de Parapilla, or whatever your name is, you shall go alone, your tail between your legs and the whole chain on your back."

Pasamonte, who was by no means a long-suffering individual, was by this time convinced that Don Quixote was not quite right in the head, seeing that he had been guilty of such a folly as that of desiring to free them; and so, when he heard himself insulted in this manner, he merely gave the wink to his companions and, going off to one side, began raining so many stones upon the knight that the latter was wholly unable to protect himself with his buckler, while poor Rocinante paid no more attention to the spur than if he had been made of brass. As for Sancho, he took refuge behind his donkey as a protection against the cloud and shower of rocks that was falling on both of them, but Don Quixote was not able to shield himself so well, and there is no telling how many struck his body, with such force as to unhorse and bring him to the ground.

No sooner had he fallen than the student was upon him. Seizing the basin from the knight's head, he struck him three or four blows with it across the shoulders and banged it against the ground an equal number of times until it was fairly shattered to bits. They then stripped Don Quixote of the doublet which he wore over his armor, and would have taken his hose as well, if his greaves had not prevented them from doing so, and made off with Sancho's greatcoat, leaving him naked; after which, dividing the rest of the battle spoils amongst themselves, each of them went his own way, being a good deal more concerned with eluding the dreaded Holy Brotherhood than they were with burdening themselves with a chain or going to present themselves before the lady Dulcinea del Toboso.

They were left alone now—the ass and Rocinante, Sancho and Don Quixote: the ass, crestfallen and pensive, wagging its ears now and then, being under the impression that the hurricane of stones that had raged about them was not yet over; Rocinante, stretched alongside his master, for the hack also had been felled by a stone; Sancho, naked and fearful of the Holy Brotherhood; and Don Quixote, making wry faces at seeing himself so mishandled by those to whom he had done so much good.

CHAPTER **XXIII**. *Of what happened to the famous Don Quixote in the Sierra Morena, which is one of the rarest adventures related in this true history.*

SEEING himself so mistreated, Don Quixote remarked to his squire, "Always, Sancho, I have heard it said that to do good to boors is to pour water into the sea.[1] Had I believed what you told me, this would not have happened; but it is done now. Patience, and let us be warned from now on."

"If your Grace takes warning," said Sancho, "then I am a Turk; but since you say that all this might have been avoided if you had believed me, why not believe me now and so avoid a worse misfortune? For I must inform you that the Holy Brotherhood does not observe the customs of chivalry; they would not give a couple of maravedis for all the knights-errant that there are—do you know, I think I can already hear their arrows whizzing past my ears."

"You, Sancho," said Don Quixote, "are a natural-born coward; but in order that you may not be able to say that I am obstinate and never do what you advise, for this once I am going to take your advice and withdraw to a place where that fury you so dread cannot reach us. Upon one condition, however: you are never, in life or in death, to say to any-one that I retired and withdrew from this danger out of fear, but only by way of yielding to your entreaties. If you say anything else, you will be lying, and from now until then and from then until now I shall give you the lie, and say that you lie and will lie, every time that you think or say anything of the sort. Give me no further words; for at the very thought that I am withdrawing and retiring from some danger, and es-pecially from this present one, which, I admit, does carry with it the shadow of fear—at the very thought of such a thing, I am all for remain-ing here and waiting alone, not only for that terrible Holy Brotherhood of which you are all the time talking, but for the twelve tribes of Israel and the seven Maccabees and for Castor and Pollux and all the brothers and brotherhoods that there are in this world."

"Sir," replied Sancho, "to retire is not to flee, nor would remaining here be an act of prudence on your part. Where danger outweighs hope, wise men save themselves for the morrow and do not venture all upon a single day. For you may know that, although I am but an ignorant countryman, I have a little of what they call good sense. And so, do not repent of hav-ing taken my advice, but mount Rocinante if you can, and if you cannot I will help you, and then follow me. My noodle tells me that we have more need of feet than we do of hands just now."

Without another word Don Quixote mounted his hack, and with Sancho leading the way upon his donkey they set out in the direction of the near-by Sierra Morena, it being Sancho's intention to cross the range and come out at El Viso or Almodóvar del Campo, where they would hide for a few days among the crags, in case the Brotherhood came look-ing for them. He was encouraged in this purpose when he discovered that the stock of provisions they carried with them upon the ass's back had emerged safely from the fray with the galley slaves, and this he looked upon as little less than a miracle in view of the manner in which they had pillaged and plundered everything else.

[By the time darkness fell [2] they had reached the heart of the highlands, where Sancho thought it would be a good thing for them to spend the night and a few days as well, at least as long as their supplies held out. And so they came to a halt in a dense cork-tree grove between two cliffs; and it was then that fate took a hand, fate which, according to those who are not enlightened by the true gospel, directs everything. Fate now directed and arranged things after its own fashion by ordaining that Ginés de Pasamonte, the famous rogue and thief who had been freed from his chains by Don Quixote's mad but kindly whim, should come their way again. Dreading the Holy Brotherhood, which he had good reason to fear, Pasamonte, also, had decided to hide out in these mountains, and fate and his fear brought him to the very same part of the highlands where the knight and Sancho Panza were.

Arriving while it was light enough to recognize them, he let them fall asleep; for as evildoers are always ungrateful, necessity prompting them to misdeeds and with present advantage outweighing future gains, Ginés, who was neither grateful nor well intentioned, had made up his mind to steal Sancho Panza's ass, not caring to bother with Rocinante since the hack could neither be pawned nor sold with profit. Accordingly, while Sancho slept, he drove the beast off, and by the time daylight came was too far away to be found.

The dawn brought cheer to the earth but sadness to the heart of Sancho Panza, who, when he discovered that his gray ass was missing, began weeping so plaintively that Don Quixote was awakened by the sound.

"O son of my loins, born in my very house," he heard his squire exclaiming. "My children's playmate, joy of my wife, envy of my neighbors, solace in my cares, and, finally, half-supporter of my person, since the twenty-six maravedis that you earned each day met half of my expenses!"

Hearing the weeping and learning the cause, the knight did what he could to console Sancho. Begging him to be patient, he promised to give him a letter directing that three out of five ass-colts [3] that he had at home be turned over to his squire to make up for the loss. Sancho was consoled by this and, drying his tears and repressing his sobs, thanked his master for this favor.]

Upon entering the mountains, Don Quixote felt glad at heart, for it seemed to him that this was a place admirably adapted to the adventures that he sought. It brought back to mind all the marvelous things which in similar solitudes, amid surroundings such as these, had happened to knights-errant of old, and he became so lost in thought and carried away by his imaginings that he paid no heed to anything else. Nor did Sancho have any other care—now that it seemed to him they were safe from harm—than that of satisfying his stomach with what remained of the clerical spoils; and so he came behind his master with all that the ass carried,[4] emptying the bag and stuffing his paunch at the same time, and he would not have given a penny for another adventure while he could go along like that.

Glancing up and perceiving that the knight, having come to a halt, was endeavoring to lift with the tip of his lance some bulky object that lay on the ground, he at once hastened to offer his assistance in case it should be needed. He arrived at Don Quixote's side just as the latter was raising the object in question, which proved to be a saddle pad with a valise attached to it, both of them half or wholly rotten and falling to pieces. They weighed so much, however, that it was necessary for Sancho to dismount and take them in his hands. The knight then told him to see what was in the valise. Although it was secured by a chain and padlock, it had so rotted away that its contents were visible through the rents in the side, which revealed four fine cambric shirts and a number of other curious articles made of linen and all very clean, while wrapped in a handkerchief was a small pile of gold crowns.

"Thank Heaven," cried Sancho, "for providing us at last with a profitable adventure!" Looking further, he came upon a memorandum book, richly bound. Don Quixote asked to have this but told his squire to keep the money for himself. Out of gratitude for this favor, Sancho kissed his master's hand; after which he removed the linen and stored it away in the bag with the provisions.

"Do you know, Sancho," said Don Quixote, "it is my opinion—and it cannot be otherwise—that some traveler must have lost his way in these mountains and been set upon by robbers, who must have slain him and then brought his body to this isolated spot to bury it."

"It can't be that," said Sancho, "for if they had been robbers, they would not have left this money behind them."

"That is true," agreed Don Quixote; "and in that case I am sure I cannot guess, nor have I any idea, what all this may mean. But wait a moment. Let us see if in this little memorandum book there may not be something written down that will enable us to make out what we wish to know."

He opened the book and the first thing he found in the way of writing was the rough draft of a sonnet, in a very good hand; and in order that Sancho might hear it, he read it aloud:

> "Either Love, 'twould seem, lacks sensibility,
> Or else 'tis over-cruel, or my poor heart
> Is all unequal to its painful part,
> Condemned to the direst torment there can be.
> If Love is God, why, it is certain He

> *Knows all—that takes no casuistic art—*
> *And He's not cruel. Where, then, does my grief start,*
> *That grief I cherish so persistently?*
> *To say that it is thou, Phyllis, were wrong;*
> *So much of good and ill cannot abide*
> *In the same body, nor is Heaven to blame.*
> *One thing I know: I am not here for long;*
> *He's a sick man indeed cannot decide*
> *The Nature of his ill or whence it came."*

"There is nothing much to be learned from that ballad," said Sancho, "unless this thread leads to the yarn-ball of the whole matter." [5]

"What thread is that?" asked Don Quixote.

"I thought," said Sancho, "that your Grace said *hilo*." [6]

"No, I did not say *hilo*, but *Fili*," [7] replied Don Quixote. "That is undoubtedly the name of the lady to whom this author addresses his lament; and, upon my word, he must be a very fair poet or else I know nothing about the art." [8]

"So," said Sancho, "your Grace knows something of ballad-making too?"

"More than you think," said Don Quixote. "You will see that I do when you carry a letter, written in verse from beginning to end, to my lady Dulcinea del Toboso. For you must know, Sancho, that all or nearly all knights-errant in ages past were great troubadours and musicians, both these accomplishments, or, better, graces, being characteristic of love-lorn and wandering men of arms, though I must admit that the verses of those knights of old indicate more spirit than rhyming ability."

"Read on, your Grace, until you find something that will throw some light on this matter."

"This," said Don Quixote, turning a page, "is prose and appears to be a letter."

"A regular letter?" asked Sancho.

"The beginning seems to be all about love."

"Well, then, read it aloud, your Grace, for I am very fond of love stories."

"With pleasure," said Don Quixote; and he read the following:

"Your false promise and my certain misfortune are taking me to a place whence will come to your ears the news of my death. You have rejected me, O ungrateful creature! for one who has more but is not worth more than I. If virtue were esteemed wealth, I should not envy the fortune of

others nor weep for my own. That which your beauty raised up your deeds have laid low. By reason of the former I believed you to be an angel, and by reason of the latter I know you to be a woman. Be at peace, you who have sent me to war, and may Heaven grant that the deceits of your husband remain ever hidden, that you may not repent of what you have done, and I take a vengeance that I do not desire.

"This," said Don Quixote, as he finished reading the letter, "throws even less light on the subject than do the verses, beyond the fact that the one who wrote it was a rejected lover."

Leafing nearly all the way through the little book, he came upon other verses and letters, some of which he was able to read while others he could not. They were filled, all of them, with complaints, laments, misgivings, expressions of joy and sadness, talk of favors granted and a suit rejected. Some were exalted in tone, others mournful. While Don Quixote was going through the book, Sancho was doing the same with the valise; there was not a corner of it, or of the saddle pad, that he did not search, scrutinize, and pry into, not a seam that he did not rip out, not a tuft of wool that he did not unravel, being determined to let nothing escape him from want of care and proper pains, so great was the covetousness that had been awakened in him by the crowns he had discovered, a hundred or more of them all told. And although he found nothing more, he still felt that the tossings in the blanket, the potion that he had drunk, the benediction of the stakes, the mule driver's punches, the loss of his saddlebags, the theft of his greatcoat,[9] and all the hunger, thirst, and weariness that he had known in his good master's service, had been amply repaid by the finding of this treasure.

The Knight of the Mournful Countenance was extremely desirous of knowing who the owner of the valise was; for from the sonnet and the letter, the gold coins and the shirts of such good quality, he conjectured that this must be an important personage, very much in love, who had been led by the disdain his lady showed him and the ill treatment received at her hands to commit some desperate act. But seeing that in this rugged, uninhabitable place there was no one who might be able to give him the information that he wanted, his only concern now was to go on, letting Rocinante as usual choose the road to be followed, with the idea in mind always that by so doing he could not fail to meet with some extraordinary adventure there in those wilds.

As he rode along thinking of these things, he caught sight of a man on top of a small mountain facing him who went leaping from cliff to cliff and one tuft of underbrush to another with great agility. He had the appearance of being naked or nearly so, with a thick black beard and long tangled hair, his feet and lower legs bare, while his thighs were covered with a pair of trousers which seemed to be of tawny-colored velvet but which were so ragged that in many places the flesh was visible. He wore nothing on his head, and although his movements, as has been stated, were extremely swift, the Knight of the Mournful Countenance had a chance to observe and make note of all the details mentioned. Although he tried to follow the man, he was not able to do so, for Rocinante was too weak to traverse such rough ground as that, being, moreover, by nature slow-paced and phlegmatic.

At once Don Quixote conceived the idea that this must be the owner of the saddle pad and valise, and he made up his mind that he would hunt him down even if he had to spend a year in these mountains. And so he directed Sancho to get down off his donkey [10] and look on one side of the mountain while he would look on the other, until they should meet, and in this way it might be that they would be able to come upon the individual who had fled so hastily from in front of their eyes.

"I could not do that," protested Sancho, "for when I leave your Grace's side fear assaults me with a thousand different kinds of starts and visions. And let what I am saying serve as a notice, for from now on I do not intend to stir an inch from your presence."

"So be it," said the Knight of the Mournful Countenance. "I am very glad that you wish to avail yourself of my courage, for it shall not fail you even though your soul fails your body. Follow me closely, then, or as best you can, and make lanterns of your eyes. Let us circle this ridge, and perhaps we shall meet the one of whom we had a glimpse and who, undoubtedly, cannot be any other than the owner of that treasure."

"It would be much better," said Sancho, "not to go looking for him; for if we do find him and the money turns out to be his, I, of course, will have to give it back to him; but it would be better, without all this fruitless search, for me just to keep it until by some other less meddlesome and prying means we discover who the true owner is. And who knows, by that time I may have spent it and the king will then cancel the debt for me."

"You are wrong about that, Sancho," said Don Quixote; "for since we already have in advance a well-founded suspicion as to who the real owner is, we are obliged to seek him out and return the money. If we do not do this, the strong suspicion that we have of his being the owner renders us as guilty as if he were. And so, Sancho, do not let our search for him give you any anxiety, for it will relieve mine if we find him."

So saying, he spurred Rocinante and rode off, followed by Sancho on foot and heavily loaded down, thanks to Ginesillo de Pasamonte.[11] When they had rounded a part of the mountain, they came upon a mule, saddled and bridled, lying dead in a brook and half devoured by dogs and jack-daws; all of which confirmed them in the suspicion that the one who had fled them was the owner of the mule and the saddle pad.

As they stood there looking at the mule they heard a whistle, as of a shepherd tending his flock, and immediately thereafter, on their left hand, there appeared a large number of goats. Behind the flock, on top of the mountain, the figure of the goatherd, a very old man, now appeared. Don Quixote called him to come down where they were. He replied by shouting back at them the question as to what had brought them to this one spot which was almost never trodden by any feet but those of goats or wolves and other wild beasts. Sancho answered him, saying that, if he would come down, they would give him an account of everything.

The goatherd did so, and as he approached Don Quixote, he said, "I'll wager that you are looking at that hack mule that lies dead in that hollow. Upon my word, it's been there for six months now. Tell me, did you meet its owner anywhere?"

"We have met no one," replied Don Quixote. "All that we found was a saddle pad and a small valise not far from here."

"I found it too," said the goatherd, "but I never wanted to pick it up or go near it from fear of some bad luck or other, lest they charge me with having stolen it; for the devil is a sly one, and from under a man's feet things rise up to cause him to stumble and fall without knowing how it comes about."

"That is what I say," Sancho told him. "I also found it and I wouldn't come within a stone's throw of it; I left it there, and there it remains just as it was. I don't want a dog with bells." [12]

"Tell me, my good man," said Don Quixote, "do you know who the owner is?"

"All I know," said the old man, "is that six months ago, more or less, there came to a sheepfold which is some three leagues from here a youth of well-bred manners and appearance, mounted upon that same mule that lies dead there and with the same saddle pad and valise which you say you found and did not touch. He inquired of us which part of these highlands was the most rugged and inaccessible, and we told him that it was this part where we are now; which is indeed the truth, for if you go half a league farther in, you will not be able to find your way out. I am wondering how you two ever came here, seeing that there is no road or footpath that leads to this spot. But as I was saying, the youth upon hearing our answer turned about and made for the site that we had pointed out to him, leaving us all well pleased with the impression which he by his appearance had made upon us, while at the same time we were astonished at his question and the haste with which we had seen him turn toward the mountains and ride away.

"We saw no more of him after that until a few days ago, when without saying a word he fell upon one of our shepherds and began beating and kicking him severely, after which he went up to the ass that carried our supplies and took all the bread and cheese that he found there. Having done this, with amazing swiftness he darted back to his mountain hiding place. When some of us goatherds learned of what had happened, we spent nearly two whole days in looking for him through the most densely wooded part of this region, and at last we found him in the hollow of a thick and sturdy cork tree. He came out and greeted us very mildly, his clothing now in rags and his face burned and scarred by the sun to such an extent that we should scarcely have recognized him if his garments, which were familiar to us even though they were in shreds, had not served to convince us that he was the man we sought.

"His greeting was a courteous one. In a few well-chosen words he told us that we should not marvel at seeing him in this condition, for it was by way of fulfilling a certain penance that had been laid upon him for his many sins. We asked him if he would tell us who he was, but we did not succeed in finding out his name. We also requested him, when he was in need of food, which of course he must have, to let us know where we would find him and we would be only too glad to bring it to him; or if he did not care to do this, he should at least come and ask us for it and not take it by force from the shepherds. He thanked us for our offer, begged forgiveness for the assault he had committed, and promised that from then on he would ask for what he wanted in the name of God, without giving offense to anyone.

"As for his place of abode, he assured us that he had none, save such as chance might offer when night overtook him; and he ended by weeping so bitterly that we who heard him must have been made of stone if we had not wept with him, as we compared the way he looked now with that first sight we had had of him. For, as I have said, he was a very pleasant-mannered youth, and his courtesy and agreeable way of speaking showed him to be a person who was wellborn and well reared. Al-

though we were but countryfolk, his polite way of speaking was such
that it was not hard for us to grasp his meaning.

"As he was in the middle of his story, he stopped suddenly and fell
silent, fixing his eyes upon the ground for a good long while as we stood
there in suspense, waiting to see what the outcome of this fit of abstraction would be. We were more than a little sad as we gazed at him. He
would sit there for many minutes, staring down at the earth, his eyes
wide open and without batting a lash; and again he would close his eyes,
compress his lips, and arch his eyebrows, and we were then sure that some
kind of madness had come upon him. He soon convinced us that we were
right in thinking this. Rising furiously from the ground to which he had
fallen, he attacked the first person he encountered so boldly and in such a
rage that if we had not pulled him off, he would have slain his victim with
blows and bites. And as he did this he kept shouting, 'Ah, false Fernando!
Now, now you shall pay for the wrong you have done me! These hands
shall tear out your heart, abode and nesting place of every form of evil,
but, above all, of fraud and deceit!' He had more to say, and it was all
against Fernando, whom he accused of faithlessness and betrayal.

"With considerable difficulty we forced him to release his hold on
our companion, and he then, without saying another word, ran off and
hid himself among the brambles and the underbrush, so that it would
have been impossible to follow him. This led us to surmise that his madness seized him at intervals, and that someone named Fernando must have
done him a very great wrong indeed to have brought him to such a pass;
all of which later was shown to be the truth, for he has often come up
to the shepherds, sometimes to request them to give him something to
eat, and at other times to take it from them by force. When the fit is
on him, even though they may offer him food of their own free will, he
will not accept it but will attack them with his fists and appropriate it;
but when he is in his right senses, he politely and with courteous phrases
begs it of them in God's name, thanking them profusely and shedding
not a few tears.

"The truth is, gentlemen," the goatherd went on, "that only yesterday
I and four other lads, two of them my servants and the other two my
friends, made up our minds to keep on looking for him until we found
him; and we vowed that when we did find him, we would take him, either
of his own free will or by force, to the town of Almodóvar, eight leagues
from here, and there would have him given a cure, if there be any cure for
his disease, or at least we would find out who he is when he is in his right
mind and whether or not he has any relatives that we might notify. This,

gentlemen, is all that I can tell you in answer to the question you have asked me. You know now that the owner of those belongings is the same one whom you saw running over the mountains so nimbly and so lightly clad." For Don Quixote had told him of having glimpsed the man.

The knight marveled greatly at what he had just heard and was more eager than ever to learn who the poor madman was, being resolved now to carry out his first intention, which was that of seeking for him all over the mountain without leaving a corner or a cave unsearched until he had found him. Fate, however, arranged matters for him better than he could have hoped or expected, for at that very instant the youth whom he sought emerged from a ravine near where they stood and came toward them, muttering something to himself that could not be understood when one was close upon him, much less from a distance. His costume was such as has been described, except that, as he approached, Don Quixote noticed that the ragged doublet he wore was amber-scented,[13] which indicated that a person who wore clothes of such quality could not be of the lowest rank.

As the youth came up, he greeted them in a hoarse, discordant voice, but very courteously. Don Quixote returned his salutation no less politely, and, dismounting from Rocinante, he gently and gracefully went over and embraced the young man, holding him tightly in his arms for some little while, as if he had known him for a long time. The Ragged One of the Sickly Countenance, as we may call him—just as Don Quixote is the Knight of the Mournful Countenance—after permitting himself to be embraced, fell back a step or two and laid his hands upon Don Quixote's shoulders as if to see whether or not he knew him; for it may be that he was no less astonished at beholding the knight's face, figure, and suit of armor than the knight was at seeing him. To make a long story short, the first to speak was the Ragged One, and what he had to say will be set forth in the following pages.

CHAPTER XXIV. *In which is continued the adventure of the Sierra Morena.*

THE history tells us that Don Quixote listened to the Knight of the Mountain most attentively.

"Although I do not know you, sir," the latter went on, "I certainly thank you for the courtesy that you have shown me, and I only wish that I were in a position to repay with something more than good will the kind reception you have accorded me, but fate has given me nothing with which I might suitably requite your favors except the desire to do so."

"My own desire," said Don Quixote, "is to be of service to you, and it was for this reason that I resolved not to leave these highlands until I had found you and learned from your own lips if any remedy was to be found for the sorrow that, from the strange way of life you lead, appears to beset you. I accordingly had meant to leave no stone unturned in searching for you, had a search been necessary. Even though your misfortune might be of that kind that closes the door on any sort of consolation, I would, I thought, weep with you and share your grief in so far as I could. For when one is in trouble, it is consoling to find some person who can feel with one the weight of one's misfortunes.

"But if my good intentions do deserve to be repaid with any of that courtesy that I see you possess in so high a degree, I would beg you, sir, by all in this life that you love or have loved, to tell me who you are and what it is that has brought you to live and die like a brute beast amid these solitudes, for your person and your bearing show that the life you now lead is one that is alien to you. And I further swear, by the order of knighthood which I, though unworthy and a sinner, have received, and by my profession of knight-errant, that if you accede to my request, I will serve you in accordance with those obligations that I have assumed, either by helping you if there is any help to be had, or by weeping with you as I have promised."

The Knight of the Wood, upon hearing the Knight of the Mournful Countenance speak in this manner, could only stare at him long and hard, surveying him from head to foot, and it was not until after he had studied him intently that he replied.

"If you have anything that you can give me to eat," he said, "for the love of God, let me have it, for I have had nothing since yesterday. Give me food, and I will do all that you command, out of gratitude for your good intentions toward me."

Sancho then brought out from his bag, and the shepherd from his pouch, sufficient food to satisfy the Ragged One's hunger. The man ate like one who is stupefied, with no time between mouthfuls, gulping down the victuals rather than swallowing them. Meanwhile, the others watched him, saying nothing. When he had finished, he made signs for them to follow him, which they did. He then led them around the corner of a cliff to a little plot of green not far from there and dropped down upon the grass. The others did the same, and not a word was spoken by any of them until the Ragged One had settled himself to his liking.

"If, gentlemen," he said to them then, "you would like me to tell you briefly how enormous the misfortunes are that I have suffered, you must promise me that you will not interrupt with questions, or in any other manner, the thread of my mournful tale, for the moment you do so it will come to an end."

This remark reminded Don Quixote of the story his squire had told him, when the knight had been unable to remember the number of goats that had crossed the river and the tale had been left hanging in the air. But to come back to the Ragged One—

"If I make this stipulation," the latter continued, "it is for the reason that I desire to relate my misfortunes as briefly as I can, since the telling of them serves only to bring me fresh sorrows; and so, the fewer questions you ask of me the sooner I shall be done, it being understood, of course, that I shall leave out nothing of importance such as you might wish to know."

Don Quixote promised in the name of the others, and with this assurance, the Ragged One began.

"My name is Cardenio, my birthplace one of the finest cities in this province of Andalusia,[1] my lineage noble, my parents rich, my misfortune so great that my kin must have wept and grieved over it, without being able to alleviate it with their wealth; for when it comes to remedying the ills that Heaven sends us, the gifts of fortune are of little avail. In that same country there lived one who was Heaven to me, a Heaven that held all the glory I could desire. Such was the beauty of Luscinda, a damsel noble and rich as I, but more fortunate and with less constancy than was due to such a passion as mine. From my first and tenderest years I had loved, longed for, and adored this Luscinda, and she had cared for me with her simple, innocent, childlike heart. Our parents knew how we felt toward each other and were not disturbed, for they saw that later on our youthful affection must surely lead to marriage, a thing that was altogether fitting in view of the fact that our wealth and lineage were so evenly matched. As we grew older our love grew to such an extent that Luscinda's father felt obliged, out of respect for the conventions, to forbid me his house, thus imitating the example set him by the parents of that Thisbe so celebrated by the poets.

"This denial merely added flame to flame and desire to desire; for even though tongues may be silenced, pens cannot be, and the latter with more freedom than the former can make known to a loved one that which is locked in the heart, since very often the presence of the loved object disturbs the firmest resolution and ties the boldest tongue. Ah, good Heaven, how many letters I wrote her! How many charmingly modest answers did I receive! How many love verses did I compose in which my heart declared and translated its feelings, painted its kindled desires, feasted on its memories, and re-created its passion. In short, seeing myself wasting away like that, my soul consumed with longing to behold her, I determined to go through with what appeared to me to be the best plan for winning the prize that I coveted and deserved: I would ask her father for her hand in lawful wedlock; and this I did. He replied, thanking me for the honor I had shown him by telling him that I should feel honored in receiving such a treasure from him; but he added that, inasmuch as my own father was still alive, it was only right that he and not I should make this request, and if it was not my father's will and pleasure, then Luscinda was not a woman to be taken or given by stealth.

"I thanked him for his kindness, for it seemed to me that he was right, and I felt sure, as I have said, that my father would give his consent. I accordingly lost no time in going to my parent to make my wishes known to him. When I entered the room where he was, I found him with an open letter in his hand, and before I could say a word he began addressing me. 'From this letter, Cardenio,' he said, 'you will see how ready the Duke Ricardo is to do you a favor.' Now, this Duke Ricardo, as you gentlemen should know, is a Grandee of Spain whose estate lies in the best part of this province of Andalusia. I took the letter and read it, and the offer contained in it was so flattering a one that I myself felt my father would have done wrong in not accepting it; for the duke proposed that I should be sent to be the companion, not the servant, of his eldest son, agreeing to see to it that I should be provided for in accordance with that esteem in which he held me. I read the epistle and was silent, especially when I heard my father saying, 'You will be leaving in two days, Cardenio, to do as the duke desires; and I thank God that the way is now being opened for you to attain that which I know should be yours by merit.' To which he added other words of fatherly advice.

"As the time for my departure drew near, I spoke to Luscinda one night and told her all that had happened, and I also had a word with her father, begging him to wait a few days and not dispose of her hand until I could find out what Duke Ricardo wished of me. He promised, and she confirmed it with a thousand oaths and swoons. I then went to the duke's place and was so well received and treated that envy at once began to do its work, the old servants feeling that their master's eagerness to do me favors was to their own detriment. But the one who was most delighted by my arrival was the duke's second son, named Fernando, a gallant lad of gentle breeding, generous and loving by nature, who within a short while became so great a friend of mine that everyone was talking about it. Although the eldest son liked me well enough and was very kind to me, he did not treat me with the extreme show of affection that Fernando did.

"Between friends there is no secret that is not shared, and as my intimacy with Fernando grew into friendship, he told me all that was on his mind, one of his special confidences having to do with a love affair that was giving him some concern. He was enamored of a peasant lass, one of his father's vassals, whose parents were very rich and who was so beautiful, modest, virtuous, and discreet that none could say in which of these virtues she excelled or which outweighed the others. These good qualities on the part of the girl raised Fernando's desires to such a pitch that in order to possess her he determined to give her his word to marry her, since it was impossible to get what he wanted in any other way. I as his friend felt obliged to restrain and dissuade him from doing this, with the best arguments and most striking examples that I could find; and when I saw that my efforts were in vain, I decided to lay the matter before Duke Ricardo, his father.

"Don Fernando, however, being very clever and astute, feared and dreaded this, knowing that as a good servant I was bound to keep nothing hidden that might be prejudicial to the honor of my lord the duke; and, accordingly, by way of distracting and deceiving me, he told me that he could think of no better means of forgetting the beauty that so enslaved him than to absent himself for a few months, and he suggested that the two of us go to my father's house, under the pretext, which he would give to the duke, that he wished to buy a few of the very fine horses that are to be found in my city, which produces the best in the world.

"Upon hearing him say this I was pleased, since even if his resolve had not been so good a one, I still should have looked upon it as one of the most praiseworthy that could be conceived, inasmuch as it would provide me with a fine occasion and opportunity to see my Luscinda once again. With this thought in mind and animated by my own amorous desires, I approved his judgment and urged him to go through with the plan, telling him that he should set about it as soon as possible and assuring him that absence had its effect in spite of the firmest of attachments. But at the very time he told me this story, as I afterward learned, he had already had the peasant girl through a promise of marriage and was only waiting for a chance to reveal it with safety to himself, being fearful of what the duke his father would do when he learned of his son's foolish conduct.

"Now, love with young lads is for the most part nothing more than appetite whose ultimate aim is pleasure, and once that aim has been achieved, love disappears, being unable to pass beyond the bounds assigned it by nature, which on the other hand sets no limit to true love; and so it was that, once Don Fernando had had his way with the peasant lass, his desires were appeased and his ardor cooled, and if he pretended that he wished to go away in order to be cured of his love, it was in reality that he might not have to keep his promise. In any case, the duke having granted his permission and directed me to accompany his son, we came to my city, and Fernando was received by my father in a manner befitting his rank. I then saw Luscinda once more, and although they had never been dead or even deadened, my desires began to live again. To my sorrow, I took Fernando into my confidence, as it seemed to me that, by reason of the great friendship he had shown me, I ought to conceal nothing from him. I praised Luscinda's beauty, grace, and modesty until my words aroused in him the desire to see a young woman adorned with so many good qualities.

"Most unfortunately, I yielded to his wishes and showed her to him one night by the light of a candle at a window where we were accustomed to converse. As she appeared to him in her loose-flowing robe, she at once caused him to forget all the beauties that he had thus far seen. He was struck dumb and stood there in a daze as if he had lost his senses. In brief, as you will see in the course of my story, he had fallen in love with her. His passion, which he hid from me and revealed only to Heaven, was still further inflamed when, as chance would have it, he found one day a letter of hers begging me to ask her father to give her to me in marriage, a letter so modest and discreet and yet so filled with love that upon reading it he assured me that in Luscinda and in her alone were to be found all the grace, beauty, and wit that are divided among the other women of the world.

"As I heard Don Fernando bestowing such well-merited praise upon her, I must confess that I was disturbed and began to fear and distrust him, for not a moment went by without his wishing to speak of her and he would so direct the conversation as to drag her name into it somehow or other. This awakened in me a spark of jealousy, not because I doubted Luscinda's loyalty and virtue, but for the reason that, despite the trust that she inspired, I dreaded what fortune might have in store for me. Don Fernando always contrived to read the notes that I sent her and those that I received from her in reply, under pretense that he greatly enjoyed the wit that each of us displayed. And then it came about that Luscinda asked me for a book of chivalry to read, one of which she was very fond, the *Amadis of Gaul*—"

No sooner did he hear a book of chivalry mentioned than Don Quixote spoke up. "Had your Grace told me," he said, "at the beginning of your story that Señora Luscinda was fond of books of that sort, it would not have been necessary for you to add anything more in order to give me an idea of her superior qualities of mind; for I must say that I should not have found her all that you, sir, have painted her as being if she had lacked the taste for such pleasant reading as that. Consequently, so far as I am concerned, it is not necessary to waste any more words in assuring me of her beauty, worth, and understanding, since merely upon hearing of this preference of hers, I set her down as the most beautiful and modest woman that there is. I could only wish, sir, that along with the *Amadis of Gaul* you had sent her the worthy *Don Rugel of Greece*,[2] for I am sure the lady Luscinda would have liked Daraida and Garaya very much and would have enjoyed the shrewd observations of the shepherd Darinel [3] and those admirable Bucolics of his as sung and recited by himself; but all this can be remedied in time if your Grace will but come with me to my village, for there I can give you more than three hundred books which are the delight of my soul and the solace of my life—but come to think of it, I have not a single one left, thanks to certain evil and envious enchanters who robbed me of them.

"Pardon me, your Grace, if I have broken my promise not to interrupt your story, for in hearing of knights-errant and deeds of chivalry I can no more refrain from speaking of such things than the rays of the sun can help giving heat or those of the moon moisture. And so, forgive me and continue, for that is what matters now."

As Don Quixote was saying all this, Cardenio's head had sunk to his bosom and he gave evidence of being deeply lost in thought. Although the knight twice requested him to go on with his story, he did not raise his head nor utter a word in reply. Finally, however, after a good while, he did so.

"I cannot rid myself of the thought," he said, "nor will anyone in the world ever be able to rid me of it or make me believe anything else— indeed, he would be a blockhead who believed the contrary—no, I am convinced that great villain of an Elisabat was living in adultery with the Queen Madásima—"

"That," replied Don Quixote in high dudgeon, "is not true, I swear it is not!" And he turned upon him angrily as he always did in such cases. "That is pure malice, or, better, a most villainous assertion. The Queen Madásima was an illustrious lady, and it is not to be presumed that a princess of her high birth would commit adultery with a quack. Whoever says that she would lies like a villain himself, and I will give him so to understand, mounted or on foot, armed or unarmed, day or night, as he may prefer—"

Cardenio was now staring attentively at the knight, for his madness had come upon him again and he was in no condition to go on with his story, nor was Don Quixote capable of listening to it, so disgusted was he with what he had just heard regarding Queen Madásima. A strange thing! but he felt impelled to defend her as if she had been his own lady, to such a pass had those unholy books of his brought him. Cardenio, then, being mad as I have said, upon hearing himself called a liar and a villain, along with other epithets of the same sort, and not fancying the jest, picked up a stone that was lying near him and let Don Quixote have such a blow in the chest with it as to lay him flat on his back.

Seeing his master attacked in this fashion, Sancho Panza fell upon the madman with clenched fists, but the Ragged One received him in such a manner, having resort to his own fists, that the squire the next moment was lying at his feet, whereupon he leaped on his ribs and began crushing them with great zest. The goatherd, who sought to defend Sancho, suffered the same fate; and after he had beaten and mauled them all, the mad assailant left them lying there and calmly went away to his hiding place in the mountains.

Furious at having been thus set upon through no fault of his own,

Sancho when he arose ran to take vengeance on the goatherd, saying the shepherd was to blame for not having warned them that this man was subject to fits of madness; for had they known it, they would have been upon their guard and might have been able to protect themselves. The shepherd replied that he had told them this, and if Sancho had not heard it, that was no fault of his. One word led to another until the squire and the goatherd were pulling beards and exchanging such fist blows that if Don Quixote had not made peace between them they would have knocked each other to pieces.

"Leave me alone, your Grace, Sir Knight of the Mournful Countenance," said Sancho as he grappled with the shepherd, "for this one is a countryman like me and has not been dubbed a knight, and so I may take satisfaction for what he has done to me by fighting with him hand to hand like an honest man."

"What you say is true," replied Don Quixote, "but I am sure that he is not in any way to blame for what happened."

Having pacified them, the knight once more inquired of the goatherd if it would be possible to find Cardenio, as he was extremely desirous of hearing the end of the story. The shepherd repeated what he had told him before, to the effect that he was not certain as to the man's place of abode, but if they went about enough in those parts they would not fail to encounter him, whether in his right senses or not.

CHAPTER XXV. *Which treats of the strange things that happened to the valiant Knight of La Mancha in the Sierra Morena and of his imitation of Beltenebros's penance.*

Taking his leave of the goatherd, Don Quixote once again mounted Rocinante and ordered Sancho, who was now in a very bad humor, to follow him, which the latter did with his donkey.[1] They were gradually making their way into the most rugged part of the mountain, and the squire was dying to have a talk with his master, but he wished the latter to begin the conversation so that he would not have to disobey his command. At last, he was unable to endure the silence any longer.

"Señor Don Quixote," he began, "will your Grace give me your blessing and your permission, for I wish to return home at once to my wife and young ones. I can at least talk to them as much as I like; but to have to go through these lonely places day and night, as your Grace would have me do, without being able to speak when I feel like it, is a living death for me. If fate willed that the animals should talk as they did in Aesop's time, it would not be so bad, for I could then talk to my gray [2] about anything that I pleased and forget my troubles. It is a terrible thing, and too much to put up with, to go all your life seeking adventures and get nothing out of it but kicks and blanketings, brickbats and punches, and with all that to have to sew up your mouth and not dare to say what is in your heart, as if you were dumb."

"I know what is the trouble with you," said Don Quixote. "That interdict that I put on your tongue is killing you. Well, just regard it as lifted and say what you like, but with the understanding that it is only for the time it takes us to cross these highlands."

"So be it," said Sancho. "Let me speak now, for God knows what will happen afterward; and so, beginning at once to take advantage of this privilege, let me ask you: what led your Grace to stick up so for that Queen Magimasa or whatever her name was? And what difference did it make whether that abbot [3] was her friend or not? If your Grace had let that pass, seeing that you were not a judge in the matter, I believe the madman would have gone on with his story and we'd have avoided the blow from the stone, the kicks, and more than half a dozen good cuffs."

"Upon my word, Sancho," replied Don Quixote, "if you but knew what an honored and illustrious lady the Queen Madásima was, I am certain you would say that I have a great deal of patience not to smash the mouth from which such blasphemies come. For it is a very great blasphemy to say, or so much as think, that a queen would commit adultery with a surgeon. The truth is, that Master Elisabat of whom the madman spoke was a very prudent man and sound in his judgments, who served the queen as tutor and physician; but to imagine that she was his friend is nonsense and merits severe punishment. And in order to perceive that Cardenio did not know what he was saying, you have but to remember that he was out of his wits when he said it."

"And I say," Sancho insisted, "that it was not for you to make much of the words of one who is mad; for if luck had not favored your Grace and that stone had hit your head instead of your chest, we'd have been in a pretty pickle as a result of standing up for that lady of yours, may God confound her. And what would you wager that Cardenio would not have gone free as being insane?"

"Against the sane and the insane," said Don Quixote, "every knight-errant is obliged to defend the honor of women, especially when they are queens of high rank and dignity such as was Queen Madásima, for whom I have a particular affection by reason of her excellent qualities; for in addition to being comely, she was very prudent, and long-suffering in calamities of which she had many. And the counsels and companionship of Master Elisabat were of great help to her by enabling her to endure her troubles with patience and wisdom. All of which has given the ignorant and ill-intentioned mob an excuse for asserting that she was his mistress. And—I repeat it—all those who say and think so lie, and will lie two hundred times more."

"I neither say nor think it," said Sancho. "Let those that do, eat it with their bread.[4] Whether they were lovers or not, it is to God that they must give an account. I come from my vineyard, I know nothing. I am not fond of prying into other people's lives. He who buys and lies feels it in his purse. What is more, naked was I born and naked I find myself; I neither win nor lose. Supposing that they were, what's that to me? Many think to find bacon when there are no pegs.[5] Who can put doors to the open country? Moreover, they said of God—"

"So help me God, Sancho," said Don Quixote, "what are all these absurdities that you are stringing together? What has the subject of which we were speaking to do with those proverbs you are threading? As you value your life, keep quiet; confine yourself to prodding your ass, and do not meddle in what does not concern you. And understand with all your five senses that what I do, have done, and shall do, is the fruit of sound reason and wholly in conformity with the rules of chivalry, with which I am better acquainted than all the professed knights in this world."

"Sir," said Sancho, "is it a good rule of chivalry for us to be wandering lost in these mountains, without road or path, in search of a madman who, when we find him, may undertake to finish what he has begun—and I do not mean his story but your Grace's head and my ribs, by smashing them altogether this time?"

"I tell you once again, Sancho, be quiet; for I will inform you that it is not so much the desire to find a madman that leads me to traverse these regions as it is the hope of accomplishing here an exploit that will win for me perpetual renown and fame throughout the whole of the known world, one that will place the seal on all that there is that can make a knight-errant famous and perfect."

"And is it a very dangerous exploit, that one?" Sancho Panza asked.

"No," replied the Knight of the Mournful Countenance, "it is not—not if the dice fall right for us; but everything will depend on your diligence."

"On my diligence?" said Sancho.

"Yes," said Don Quixote, "for if you return quickly from where I mean to send you, my labors will soon be at an end and my fame will begin to spread. And in order not to keep you any longer in suspense with regard to the meaning of my words, I want you to know, Sancho, that the famous Amadis of Gaul was one of the most perfect of knights-errant. But I am not correct in saying that he was 'one of the'; he was the sole and only one, the very first, the lord of all those in the world in his time. A plague on Don Belianís and all the others who claimed to equal him in anything, for they are wrong, I swear they are! When a painter wishes to become famous, he strives to imitate the works of the most distinctive practitioners of his art; and the same rule holds for all the other arts and crafts that serve as the ornament of states and nations.

"Thus, he who would achieve a reputation for prudence and long-suffering must and does follow in the footsteps of Ulysses; for in describing his character and the hardships that he endured Homer gives us a lively picture of the virtues mentioned. Similarly, Vergil, in the person of Aeneas, portrays for us a dutiful son and the sagacity of a brave and intelligent leader. And these personages, be it noted, are not depicted or revealed to us as they were but as they ought to have been, that they may remain as an example of those qualities for future generations. In this same way, Amadis was the north star, the morning star, the sun of all valiant and enamored knights, and all those of us who fight beneath the banner of love and chivalry should imitate him. This being true, and true it is, I am of the opinion, Sancho my friend, that the knight-errant who most closely models himself upon Amadis will come the nearest to attaining the perfection of chivalry.

"One of the occasions upon which that knight most clearly displayed his prudence, true worth, valor, endurance, firmness of will, and loving devotion was when, having been rejected by the lady Oriana, he retired to do penance on Poor Rock,[6] having changed his name to Beltenebros,[7] one that was certainly significant and suited to the life he had voluntarily chosen. Accordingly, seeing that it is easier for me to imitate him in this than by cleaving giants, beheading serpents, slaying dragons, routing armies, sinking fleets, and undoing enchanters' spells, and seeing, also, that this place where we are is better adapted to such a purpose as the one I have in mind, I feel that I should not let slip the opportunity that now so conveniently offers me its forelock."

"To get down to the purpose," said Sancho, "what is it that your Grace proposes to do in this lonely spot?"

"Have I not told you," replied Don Quixote, "that I mean to imitate Amadis by playing the part of a desperate and raving madman, thus imitating Orlando at the same time, on that occasion when he discovered in a fountain the signs that Angélica the Beautiful had committed a villainy with Medoro, which so grieved him that he went mad, tore up trees, muddied the waters of clear-running springs, slew shepherds, destroyed herds, set fire to huts, tore down houses, dragged mares along after him, and did a hundred thousand other outrageous things that are worthy of eternal renown and record? I grant you, I am not thinking of imitating point by point Roland, or Orlando, or Rotolando—for he went by all three names—in every mad thing that he did, said, and thought; what I shall give, rather, is a rough sketch, containing what appear to me to be the essentials; or it may be I shall content myself with merely imitating Amadis, whose madness did not prompt him to do any damage of that sort but who confined himself to tears and sighs and yet gained as much fame as the best of them."

"It strikes me," said Sancho, "that those knights who did all that had provocation and some cause for such foolish penances, but what reason has your Grace for going mad, what damsel has rejected you, or what signs have you found that lead you to think the lady Dulcinea del Toboso has been up to some foolishness with a Moor or Christian?"

"That," said Don Quixote, "is the point of the thing; that is the beautiful part of it. What thanks does a knight-errant deserve for going mad when he has good cause? The thing is to go out of my head without any occasion for it, thus letting my lady see, if I do this for her in the dry, what I would do in the wet. Moreover, I have occasion enough in the long absence I have endured from the side of her who shall ever be my lady, Dulcinea del Toboso; for you have heard that shepherd Ambrosio saying, 'He who is absent, suffers and fears all evils.' And so, Sancho my friend, do not waste time in advising me to forego so rare, so felicitous, and so unheard of an imitation as this. Mad I am and mad I must be until you return with a letter which I mean to send by you to my lady Dulcinea. If that answer be such as my devotion merits, there will be an end to my madness and my penance; but if the contrary is the case, I shall truly go mad and, being mad, suffer no more. Thus, whatever the manner in which she responds, I shall emerge from the painful struggle in which you leave me, either by enjoying as a sane man the good news you bring me, or, as one who is insane, by ceasing to feel the pain of the bad news.

"But tell me, Sancho, were you careful to preserve Mambrino's helmet? For I saw you pick it up from the ground when that wretch tried to smash it to bits but could not, from which you may see how finely tempered it is."

"God alive, Sir Knight of the Mournful Countenance," said Sancho, "I cannot bear in patience some of the things that your Grace says! Listening to you, I come to think that all you have told me about deeds of chivalry and winning kingdoms and empires and bestowing islands and other favors and dignities is but wind and lies, all buggery or humbuggery, or whatever you choose to call it. For when anyone hears your Grace saying that a barber's basin is Mambrino's helmet, and after four days you still insist that it is, what is he to think except that such a one is out of his mind? I have the basin in my bag, all crushed and dented. I'm taking it home to have it mended so that I can trim my beard into it, if God is only good enough to let me see my wife and children again someday."

"Look, Sancho," said Don Quixote, "by that same God I swear that you have less sense than any squire in the world ever had. How is it possible for you to have accompanied me all this time without coming to perceive that all the things that have to do with knights-errant appear to be mad, foolish, and chimerical, everything being done by contraries? Not that they are so in reality; it is simply that there are always a lot of enchanters going about among us, changing things and giving them a deceitful appearance, directing them as suits their fancy, depending upon whether they wish to favor or destroy us. So, this that appears to you as a barber's basin is for me Mambrino's helmet, and something else again to another person.

"It was a rare bit of foresight on the part of the magician who is on my side to have what really is the helmet appear to all others as a mere basin; for if it were known that it is of so great a worth, everyone would pursue me and endeavor to deprive me of it. On the other hand, thinking that it is no more than what it seems, they do not care to have it, as was shown when that fellow tried to smash it and went off and left it lying on the ground. Believe me, if he had known what it was, he never would have done that. Take good care of it, then, my friend, for I do not need it at present. Indeed, it is my intention to lay aside all this armor and remain naked as when I was born—that is to say, if I decide to take Orlando rather than Amadis as a model in doing my penance." [8]

Conversing in this manner, they reached the foot of a tall mountain, which, standing alone amid a number of surrounding peaks, had almost the appearance of a rock that had been carved out of them. Alongside it flowed a gentle brook, while all about was a meadow so green and luxuriant that it was a delight for the eyes to behold. There were many forest trees and a number of plants and flowers to add to the quiet charm of the scene. And such was the spot which the Knight of the Mournful Countenance was to choose for his penance.

The moment he caught sight of it he cried out in a loud voice, as if he really had lost his senses, "This is the place, O ye heavens! which I select and designate; it is here that I will weep for that misfortune that ye yourselves have brought upon me. This is the place where the fluid from my orbs shall increase the waters of this little brook while my deep and constant sighs shall keep in incessant motion the leaves of these mountain trees, as a sign and testimony of the pain my tortured heart is suffering. O ye rustic deities, whoever ye may be, who make your abode in this uninhabitable place, hear the complaints of this unfortunate lover who, suffering from long absence and a jealous imagination, has come here to voice his laments amid these rugged surroundings and to bemoan the harshness of that fair but thankless creature who is the end and sum of all that humankind may know in the way of beauty!

"And O ye nymphs and dryads too, who are accustomed to dwell in groves and thickets—may the light-footed and lascivious satyrs, who cherish for you an unrequited love, never disturb your sweet repose, but may you join me in weeping for my sorrows, or at least not tire of hearing them! And thou, O Dulcinea del Toboso, day of my night, glory of my sufferings, guide of my every path, star of my fortunes, may Heaven grant thee all thou seekest, and wilt thou look upon the place and state to which absence from thee has brought me and be moved to repay with kindness the debt that is due to my fidelity! Ye trees also, ye solitary trees that from this day forth are to be the companions of my solitude, give me a sign by the gentle murmuring of your leaves that my presence is not displeasing to you! And, finally, thou, my faithful squire, my congenial comrade in prosperity and adversity, remember well what thou seest me do here that thou mayest relate and recite it afterward to the one who is the sole cause of it all."

With these words he dismounted from Rocinante and in a moment had removed saddle and bridle, after which he gave the hack a slap on the rump.

"Freedom," said the knight, "he now gives thee who himself is left without it, O steed as unexcelled in deeds as thou art unfortunate in thy fate! Go where thou wilt, and bear with thee inscribed upon thy forehead this legend: that neither Astolfo's Hippogriff nor the renowned Frontino that cost Bradamante so dear [9] could equal thee in fleetness of foot."

As he saw his master do this, Sancho said, "Good luck to him who has saved us the trouble now of stripping the ass; [10] for upon my word, if the gray had been here, he too would have had a slap on the rump and a few words of praise. I'd never consent to it, however, for there would be no occasion, since there was nothing of the despairing lover about him any more than there was about his master, which I happened to be so long as God willed it. The truth of the matter is, Sir Knight of the Mournful Countenance, if you mean what you say about my departure and your fit of madness, then you'd better saddle Rocinante again so that he can take the gray's place, as that will save me time coming and going. If I go on foot, I cannot tell how long I'll be, for, the short of it is, I'm a very poor walker."

"You may do as you like, Sancho," said Don Quixote. "It is not a bad suggestion that you have made. You will set out three days from now. In the meantime, I want you to see all that I do for her sake and make note of all I say in order that you may be able to tell her of it."

"What more is there for me to see," said Sancho, "than what I've seen already?"

"You do not know what you are talking about," said Don Quixote. "I have yet to rend my garments, scatter my armor about, knock my head against those rocks, and other things of that sort, all of which you must witness."

"For the love of God!" exclaimed Sancho. "I hope your Grace has a care how you go about that head-knocking, for you may come up against such a rock or in such a way that with the very first knock you will put an end to this whole business of your penance. If your Grace feels that it is absolutely necessary to do this, and that you cannot go through with your undertaking without doing it, then it seems to me that, since it is all a matter of pretending and in the nature of a joke, you ought to be satisfied with bumping your head in water or something soft like cotton, and just leave the rest to me; I will tell my lady that your Grace did it against a piece of jutting rock hard as a diamond."

"I thank you for your good intentions, Sancho," said Don Quixote, "but you must know that the things I do are not done in jest but very much in earnest. Otherwise, I should be violating the rules of knighthood, which command that we shall tell no lie whatsoever under pain of suffering the penalty that is meted out for apostasy; and to do one thing in place of another is the same as lying. My head-knockings, therefore, have to be real ones, solid and substantial, with nothing sophistical or imaginary about them. And it will be necessary for you to leave me a little lint to dress my wounds, since fortune would have it that we should be without that balm that we lost."

"It was worse losing the ass," said Sancho, "for with it we lost the lint and all.[11] And I would ask your Grace not to remind me again of that accursed potion; the very mention of it turns my soul, not to speak of my stomach. I also beg of you to regard those three days that you gave me for witnessing your deeds of madness as being past; for, so far as I am concerned, that is the truth; I have seen and judged everything and will tell my lady marvels. Write the letter, then, at once and send me on my way, as I have a great desire to return and rescue your Grace from this purgatory in which I leave you."

"Purgatory you call it, Sancho?" said Don Quixote. "Better say Hell, or even worse, if there is anything worse than that."

"He who is in Hell," said Sancho, "has no retention,[12] so I've heard it said."

"I do not understand what you mean by *retention*," said Don Quixote.

"*Retention*," said Sancho, "means that he who is in Hell never can, and never will, get out. But it will be just the opposite with your Grace, or else my legs will fail me—that is, if I have spurs to put a little life into Rocinante. Just set me down once in El Toboso and in my lady Dulcinea's presence, and I will tell her such things about your Grace's foolishness and madness (it is all one), and all the things you are doing and have done, that, even though I find her harder than a cork tree, I will make her softer than a glove. And then when I have her gentle, honeyed answer, I will come flying back through the air like a witch and snatch your Grace out of this purgatory which seems to you to be a Hell but is not, seeing there is hope of your getting out of it; for as I have just said, those in Hell do not come out, and I do not think your Grace will contradict me on that."

"You speak the truth," said the Knight of the Mournful Countenance, "but how are we going to write the letter?"

"And the order for the ass-colts too," added Sancho.

"All that will be inserted," said Don Quixote, "and since we have no paper, it would be well for us to write it as the ancients did, on the leaves of trees or a few wax tablets; although it would be about as hard to find anything like that now as it would be to procure paper. It would be a good idea, an excellent idea, for me to write it in Cardenio's memorandum book, and then you will take care to have it transcribed on paper, in a fair hand, in the first village where you find a schoolmaster, or, failing that, some sacristan; but do not give it to any notary to be copied, for they write a legal hand that Satan himself would not be able to make out."

"But what is to be done about the signature?" asked Sancho.

"The letters of Amadis were never signed," Don Quixote assured him.

"That is all very well," said the squire, "but that order you are to give me has to be signed, and if it is copied over, they will say the signature is false and I'll not get the ass-colts."

"The order, duly signed, will be in that same little book, and when my niece sees it, she will not give you any trouble about carrying out my instructions. As for the love letter, you will have them put as the signature: 'Yours until death, the Knight of the Mournful Countenance.' It will make little difference if it is in some other person's handwriting, for, as I recall, Dulcinea does not know how to read or write, nor has she ever in all her life seen a letter of mine or anything else that I wrote; for our love has always been platonic and has never gone beyond a modest glance. Even that happened but rarely, since in the course of the dozen years that I have loved her—more than the light of these eyes which the earth will one day devour—I can truthfully swear that I have not seen her four times, and even then, it may be, she did not once perceive that I was looking at her, such is the seclusion and retirement in which her father, Lorenzo Corchuelo, and her mother, Aldonza Nogales, have reared her."

"Aha!" said Sancho, "so the lady Dulcinea del Toboso is Lorenzo Corchuelo's daughter, otherwise known as Aldonza Lorenzo?"

"That is the one," said Don Quixote, "and she deserves to be mistress of the entire universe."

"I know her well," Sancho went on, "and I may tell you that she can toss a bar as well as the lustiest lad in all the village. Long live the Giver of all good things, but she's a sturdy wench, fit as a fiddle and right in the middle of everything that's doing. She can take care of any knight-errant or about to err [13] that has her for a mistress! Son of a whore, what strength she has and what a voice! They tell me that one day she went up into the village belfry to call some lads who were out in the field that belongs to her father, and although they were more than half a league away, they heard her as plainly as if they had been standing at the foot of the tower. And the best of it is, there's nothing prudish about her; she's very friendly with everybody and always laughing and joking. And so, I say to you now, Sir Knight of the Mournful Countenance, that you not only may and ought to play mad for her sake, but you have good reason to despair and go off and hang yourself, and anyone who hears of it will say you did exactly the right thing, even though the devil takes you.

"I'd like to be on my way just to have a look at her again, for it's been a long time since I saw her, and the sun and air do a lot to the complexion of a woman who's all the time working in the field. I must confess the truth, Señor Don Quixote, that up to now I have been laboring under a great mistake; for I thought, right enough, that the lady Dulcinea must be some princess with whom your Grace was smitten, or at least some personage that merited the rich presents which your Grace sent her, such as the Biscayan and the galley slaves, and many others as well, no doubt, for your Grace must have won many victories before I became your squire. But, come to think of it, what is there about Mistress Aldonza Lorenzo—I mean, Mistress Dulcinea del Toboso—that those conquered ones whom your Grace sends to her should bend the knee before her? For at the moment they arrived she may very well have been dressing flax or thrashing in the granary, and they would run away when they saw her and she'd be annoyed by the present."

"Sancho," said Don Quixote, "I have told you many times before that you are much too talkative; and although your wit is very dull, your tongue is all too sharp at times. In order that you may see how foolish you are and how sensible I am, I would have you listen to a brief story which I am about to relate to you. Once upon a time there was a beautiful widow, young, rich, unattached, and, above all, free and easy in her ways, who fell in love with a youthful cropped-headed lay brother [14] of large and sturdy build. When his superior heard of this, he took occasion to speak to the widow one day, giving her a word of brotherly reproof. 'I am astonished, Madam,' he said, 'and not without a good cause, that a woman of your standing, so beautiful and so rich as your Grace is, should be in love with a fellow so coarse, so low, so stupid as is So-and-So, in view of the fact that there are in this institution so many masters, graduates, and theologians from whom your Grace might have her pick as from among so many pears, saying, "This one I like, this one I do not care for." ' She however, answered him with much grace and sprightliness, 'You are mistaken, your Reverence, and very old-fashioned in your ideas, if you think that I have made a bad choice by taking So-and-So, stupid as he may appear to be, since so far as what I want him for is concerned, he knows as much and even more philosophy than Aristotle himself.'

"Similarly, Sancho, as regards my need of Dulcinea del Toboso, she is worth as much to me as any highborn princess on this earth. Not all the poets who praised their ladies under names of their own choosing actually had such mistresses. Do you think that the Amarillises, the Phyllises, the Sylvias, the Dianas, the Galateas, the Filidas, and all the others of whom the books, ballads, barbershops, and theaters are full were in reality flesh-and-blood women who belonged to those that hymned their praises? Certainly not; most of the writers merely invented these creatures to provide them with a subject for their verses in order that they might be taken for lovelorn swains and respected as individuals capable of an amorous passion. And so it is enough for me to think and believe that the good Aldonza Lorenzo is beautiful and modest. So far as her lineage is concerned, that is a matter of small importance; no one is going to look into it by way of conferring on her any robes of nobility, and, as for me, she is the most highborn princess in the world.

"For you should know, Sancho, if you do not know already, that the two things that more than any others incite to love are great beauty and a good name, and these two things are to be found to a consummate degree in Dulcinea; for in beauty none can vie with her, and in good name few can come up to her. But to bring all this to a conclusion: I am content to imagine that what I say is so and that she is neither more nor less than I picture her and would have her be, in comeliness and in high estate. Neither Helen nor Lucretia nor any of the other women of bygone ages, Greek, Latin, or barbarian, can hold a candle to her. And let anyone say what he likes; if for this I am reprehended by the ignorant, I shall not be blamed by men of discernment."

"I agree with all that your Grace says," replied Sancho. "It is true that I am an ass—although I don't know how that word ass happened to slip out, since you do not speak of the rope in the house of a gallows bird. But let us have that letter, and then, God be with you, I am off."

Don Quixote thereupon took out the memorandum book and, going off to one side, proceeded to compose the letter with great deliberation. When he had finished he called Sancho, telling him to listen while he read it to him and to memorize it, in case the original should be lost along the way, as he had reason to fear from the ill luck that seemed to pursue him.

"Just write it two or three times in that book, your Grace," Sancho said, "and then give it to me; for it is nonsense to think I am going to learn it by heart when my memory is so bad that I often forget my own name. But go ahead and read it to me; I'll enjoy hearing it very much, for it ought to be as smooth as if it were all set down in print."

"Listen, then," said Don Quixote. "This is what it says:

DON QUIXOTE'S LETTER TO DULCINEA DEL TOBOSO

SOVEREIGN AND HIGHBORN LADY:

He who is pricked by absence and wounded to the heart, O sweetest Dulcinea del Toboso, wishes thee the health that is not his. If thy beauty despise me, if thy great worth be not for me, if my lot be thy disdain, even though I am sufficiently inured to suffering I hardly shall sustain this affliction which, in addition to being grievous, is lasting in the extreme. My good squire Sancho will tell thee, O beauteous ingrate, my beloved enemy! of the state in which I now find myself on account of thee. Shouldst thou care to succor me, I am thine; if not, do as thou seest fit, for by putting an end to my life I shall pay the price exacted by thy cruelty and mine own desire.

Thine until death.

THE KNIGHT OF THE MOURNFUL COUNTENANCE"

"By the life of my father," exclaimed Sancho when he had heard the letter, "that is the most high-flown thing I ever listened to. Why, damn me, how your Grace does manage to say everything here just the way it should be said, and how well you work that Knight of the Mournful Countenance into the signature! To tell the truth, your Grace is the very devil himself, and there's nothing you don't know."

"In the profession that I follow," replied Don Quixote, "one needs to know everything."

"And now," said Sancho, "if your Grace will put the order for the three ass-colts on this other page and sign it very clearly so that they will recognize your signature when they see it—"

"With pleasure," said Don Quixote. Having written the order, he read it aloud:

Upon presentation of this first order for ass-colts, mistress my niece, you will turn over to Sancho Panza, my squire, three of the five that I left at home and in your Grace's charge. The said three ass-colts to be delivered in return for three others here received on account; upon presentation of this order and his receipt they are to be duly turned over to him as specified.

Done in the heart of the Sierra Morena on the twenty-second day [15] of August of this present year.

"That is very good," said Sancho, "and now sign it, your Grace."

"It is not necessary to sign it," said Don Quixote. "All I need do is to add my flourish, which is the same as a signature and will suffice for three, and even three hundred, asses."

"I will trust your Grace," said the squire. "And now, let me go saddle Rocinante, and do you be ready to give me your blessing, for I am thinking of leaving at once without waiting to witness the foolish things that your Grace has to do; but I will tell her that I saw you do so many of them that she will not want to hear any more."

"There is one thing at least that I should like to ask of you, Sancho," the knight said, "and if I do ask this, it is because it is necessary. I should like you to see me stripped and performing a couple of dozen acts of madness, which I can get through with in less than half an hour; for having seen them with your own eyes, you can safely swear to the other things that you may care to add, and I assure you I mean to do more than you will be able to relate."

"For the love of God, my master," Sancho replied, "let me not see your Grace stripped, for I'd feel so sorry that I'd never stop weeping, and I wept so much for the gray last night that I have no more tears left to shed. If your Grace wants me to witness some of your insane actions, please perform them with your clothes on and be brief about it and to the point. So far as I am concerned, all this is unnecessary; for as I have told you, it would save time if I were to leave now and I'd be back all the sooner with the news that your Grace desires and deserves. For if it is not such as you desire, let the lady Dulcinea be prepared; if she does not give me a reasonable answer, I solemnly swear I'll have one out of her stomach with kicks and cuffs. Why should a knight-errant as famous as is your Grace have to go mad without rhyme or reason for a— Her ladyship had better not force me to say it, or by God I'll speak out and lay them out by the dozen even though there's no buyer. I am pretty good at that sort of thing. She doesn't know me very well, or, faith, if she did, we'd have no trouble in coming to an understanding."

"And faith, Sancho," said Don Quixote, "you appear to me to be no sounder in mind than I am."

"I'm not as crazy as you are," said Sancho; "I've more of a temper, that's all. But leaving all this aside, what is your Grace going to eat until I return? Are you going out, as Cardenio did, and take it away from the shepherds?"

"Do not let that trouble you," said the knight, "for even if I had other food, I should eat nothing but the herbs and fruits with which this meadow and these trees shall provide me. The fine point of my undertaking lies in not eating and in putting up with other hardships of the same sort."

"And, by God," said Sancho, "there's another thing. Do you know what I am afraid of, your Grace? I'm afraid I'll not be able to find my way back to this place once I leave it, it's so out of the way."

"Get your bearings well," said Don Quixote, "and I will try not to stray far from this vicinity. I will also make it a point to go up on those high cliffs to see if I can catch a glimpse of you on your way back. But in order not to miss me and lose yourself, the best thing would be to cut a few branches of the broom plant that is so abundant around here and scatter them along the way at intervals until you come out onto the plain; these will serve you as signs and landmarks, like the clues in Perseus's labyrinth,[16] and will help you to find me when you return."

"I will do that," said Sancho, and cutting a few of the brooms, he asked his master's benediction; after which, each of them shedding not a few tears, he took his departure. Mounting Rocinante—Don Quixote had charged him to take as good care of the steed as he would of his own person—he set out in the direction of the lowlands, scattering the branches at intervals as he had been advised to do. And so he went his way, although the knight still insisted that he wait and watch him perform at least a couple of mad acts. He had not gone a hundred paces when he turned and looked back.

"You know," he said, "I believe your Grace was right. In order to be able to swear without a weight on my conscience, I really ought to see you do at least one mad thing, although your remaining here is mad enough in itself."

"Did I not tell you that?" said Don Quixote. "Wait, Sancho, and you will see me do them before you can say a Credo!"

With this, he hastily slipped off his breeches and, naked from the waist down, leaped into the air a couple of times, falling heels over head and revealing things that caused Sancho to give Rocinante the rein, that he might not have to see them again. The squire was satisfied now; he could swear that his master was quite mad. And so we shall leave him to pursue his journey until his return, which was not to be long delayed.

CHAPTER XXVI. *In which is continued the account of those refinements that Don Quixote practiced in playing the part of a lover on the Sierra Morena.*

BUT to come back to the Knight of the Mournful Countenance and what he did when he found himself alone, the history informs us that after Don Quixote, naked from the waist down and clothed from the waist up, had finished performing those somersaults of his, and after Sancho had departed without waiting to see any more of his master's mad antics, the knight betook himself to the top of a tall cliff and there began turning over in his mind a question which long had been troubling him but for which he had never been able to find a solution: namely, as to whether he should seek to imitate the monstrous things that Orlando did in his fits of madness or, rather, the melancholy actions of Amadis.

"If Orlando," he mused, "was so good and valiant a knight as they all say he was, what is so marvelous about that? After all, he was enchanted and no one could kill him save by running a tenpenny nail through the sole of his foot, and he always wore shoes with seven iron soles, although such wiles did not avail him against Bernardo del Carpio, who understood them very well and strangled him in his arms at Roncesvalles. However, leaving aside the question of his valor, let us consider his loss of reason, for it is certain that he did lose it on account of the evidence that he discovered in the fountain and the news which the shepherd gave him, to the effect that Angélica had slept for more than two siestas with Medoro, a young Moor with curly locks who was Agramante's page.[1] If he was convinced that this was true and that his lady had done him a wrong, it is small wonder that he went mad. But how can I imitate him in his acts of madness unless I have a similar occasion for committing them? I would swear that my Dulcinea del Toboso in all the days of her life has never seen a single Moor, as he is, in his native costume; she is today what she was when her mother bore her, and I should clearly be wronging her if, with any other idea in mind, I were to go mad in the manner of Orlando the Furious.[2]

"On the other hand, I note that Amadis of Gaul, without losing his mind or committing any acts of madness, achieved as much fame as a lover as any other knight; for, seeing himself scorned by his lady Oriana, who commanded him not to appear any more in her presence until she so willed it, what he did, according to the history that we have of him, was to retire to Poor Rock in the company of a hermit, where he had his fill of weeping and commending himself to God until Heaven came to his succor in the midst of his greatest agony and need. And if this be true, and true it is, then why should I go to the trouble of stripping myself stark naked? Why should I injure these trees which have done me no harm or disturb the clear water of these brooks which provide me with a drink when I desire it?

"Long live the memory of Amadis, then, and let him be imitated in so far as may be by Don Quixote de la Mancha, of whom it shall be said, as was said of the other, that if he did not accomplish great things, he died in attempting them. I may not have been scorned or rejected by Dulcinea del Toboso, but it is enough for me, as I have said, to be absent from her. And so, then, to work! Refresh my memory, O Amadis, and teach me how I am to imitate your deeds. I already know that what he did chiefly was to pray and commend himself to God; but what am I to do for a rosary, seeing that I have none with me?"

At this point a thought occurred to him, and, tearing a large strip from the tail of his shirt, which hung down over his buttocks, he made eleven knots in it, one bigger than the others, and this it was that served him as a rosary [3] as long as he was there, during which time he said a round million of Hail Marys. He was not a little put out at the fact that there was no other hermit there to hear his confession and offer him consolation; and so he spent his time walking up and down the little meadow, carving inscriptions on the bark of trees, and writing many verses in the fine sand, all reflective of his melancholy and some of them in praise of Dulcinea; but when he was found there later, the only ones that proved to be legible were the following:

> *Ye trees and shrubs, each plant*
> *In this place that grows,*
> *So tall and green, not scant,*

Do I tire you with my woes
As for my love I pant?
Let not my grief disturb
You, even though it be a
Thing that might perturb.
Don Quixote cannot curb
His tears for Dulcinea
del Toboso.

Here is the place to which
The lover most loyal far
Hath fled from a beauteous witch,
Under an evil star.
To wander he has an itch;
Love drags him every way,
Which certainly cannot be a
Very good thing, I should say.
Don Quixote his tears doth spray
By the kegful for Dulcinea
del Toboso.

Seeking adventure he goes
Among the barren rocks;
Cursing his many woes
And fortune's cruel knocks,
He flounders in Love's throes.
Held by no gentle rein,
It must ever be a
Lash that adds to his pain.
Don Quixote, sorrowful swain
Weeps for his Dulcinea
del Toboso.

Those who came upon the foregoing verses laughed no little at the addition of "del Toboso" to Dulcinea's name; for they assumed that Don Quixote must have thought that unless he added those words the stanza would be unintelligible, which was the fact, as he himself afterward admitted. He wrote many others, as has been said, but only these three could be deciphered in their entirety. Thus it was he spent his days, in sighing and in calling on the fauns and satyrs of these groves, and on the river nymphs and the dolorous and humid Echo, beseeching them to answer him, to hear his prayers and console him; and he also looked for herbs with which to sustain himself until Sancho should return—and if the squire had stayed away for three weeks instead of three days, the Knight of the Mournful Countenance would have worn so altered a look that the mother who bore him would not have recognized him.

But it will be as well to leave him wrapped up in his sighs and verses as we relate what happened to Sancho Panza on his mission. The latter, immediately upon reaching the highroad, had struck out for El Toboso, and the next day he came to the inn where that unfortunate affair of the blanketing had occurred. He no sooner caught sight of it than it seemed to him he was once again flying through the air; and he had no desire to enter, although it was an hour when he might well have done so, for it was dinnertime and he had a great desire to taste something hot, having existed on cold cuts for many days past. Irresistibly, he drew near the tavern, unable to make up his mind whether to enter or not, and as he stood there two persons came out who at once recognized him.

"I say, Señor Licentiate," one of them remarked to the other, "that fellow on the horse there—isn't that Sancho Panza, the one who, so our adventurer's housekeeper told us, went away with her master as his squire?"

"Yes," said the licentiate, "it is, and that is our Don Quixote's horse."

If they knew him so well, it was for the reason that these two were the curate and barber of his own village, the same ones that had scrutinized and passed sentence on the books. As soon as they recognized Sancho and Rocinante, being desirous of having news of Don Quixote, they went up to the squire, the curate calling him by name.

"Friend Sancho Panza," he said, "where is your master?"

Perceiving who they were, Sancho made up his mind not to tell them where he had left the knight or under what circumstances. He accordingly replied that Don Quixote was in a certain place, occupied with a very important matter the nature of which, by the eyes that he had in his head, he could not reveal.

"No, no," said the barber, "that will not do, Sancho Panza. Unless you tell us where he is, we shall imagine, as indeed we do, that you have slain and robbed him, since you come riding on his horse. The truth is, you are going to have to produce the owner of the hack or take the consequences."

"There is no need for you to threaten me," said Sancho. "I am not a man who robs and kills anybody. Let his own fate or the God who made him kill each one. My master is up there in the middle of those mountains doing penance and enjoying himself very much."

And then, all in one breath and without stopping, he proceeded to tell them of the state that Don Quixote was in, the adventures that had happened to him, and how he, Sancho, was at present carrying a letter to the lady Dulcinea del Toboso, who was the daughter of Lorenzo Corchuelo, with whom the knight was hopelessly in love. The pair from the village were greatly astonished at what they heard, for although they were familiar with the nature of their friend's madness, they never ceased to wonder at it. They then asked Sancho to show them the letter, and he informed them that it was written in a memorandum book and that he was to have it transcribed on paper in the first village at which he stopped; whereupon the curate said that he himself would make a fair copy of it. But when Sancho put his hand in his bosom to search for the book he could not find it, and he would not have been able to find it if he had searched until now, for the reason that Don Quixote still had it, the squire having forgotten to ask him for it.

Upon discovering that the book was not there, he turned deadly pale. Hastily feeling all over his person and still not finding it, he plunged both fists into his beard and tore out the half of it and then in rapid succession gave himself half a dozen blows in the face and on the nose until he was fairly dripping with blood. Seeing this, the curate and the barber asked what was the matter with him that he mistreated himself in this manner.

"What is the matter with me?" said Sancho. "I've just lost from one hand to the other, in a moment's time, three ass-colts, and each of them built like a castle."

"How is that?" inquired the barber.

"I've lost the memorandum book," said Sancho, "with the letter for Dulcinea and an order signed by my master directing his niece to turn over to me three ass-colts of the four or five that he has at home."

He then went on to tell them of the loss of the gray ass, whereupon the curate did what he could to console him by telling him that when he returned his master would give him another order and they would have it done on paper this time as was the usage and custom, for those that were made out in memorandum books were never accepted nor complied with. At this, Sancho felt relieved, remarking that the loss of the letter did not worry him greatly since he knew it almost by heart and so they would be able to transcribe it where and when they liked.

"Tell us, then, what was in it," said the barber, "and we will have it copied later."

With this, Sancho began scratching his head and standing first on one foot and then on the other, now staring hard at the ground and now looking up at the sky, in an effort to recall the contents of the note. Finally, after he had gnawed off half the end of one finger as the barber and the curate waited anxiously for him to begin, he turned to them and said, "In God's name, Señor Licentiate, may the devil take me if I can remember it! I know that it began, 'High and sufferable lady—'"

"He would not have said *sufferable*," the barber corrected him; "it must have been *sovereign* lady or something of that sort." [4]

"That's it," said Sancho. "Well, then, unless my memory fails me, it went like this: 'The pierced and wounded one, the sleepless one kisses your Grace's hands, O ungrateful fair one and most unrecognized,' and so on and so forth, all about health and sickness which he was sending her and a rigamarole that ended with 'Yours until death, the Knight of the Mournful Countenance.'"

The village pair were quite pleased with the good memory that Sancho Panza displayed and praised him not a little, asking him to repeat the letter a couple of times so that they themselves might memorize it and be able to copy it out when occasion offered. Repeat it he did, three times, and each time he uttered three thousand other absurdities; after which he went on to tell them other things about his master, but never a word did he say about how he had been tossed in a blanket at this inn which he now refused to enter. He also told how Don Quixote, in case he had a favorable reply from the lady Dulcinea del Toboso, was going to set out to make himself an emperor or at least a monarch, for so they had agreed between them, this being a very easy thing to accomplish in view of his personal worth and the might of his arm; and when he had achieved it, he was to marry off his squire, who would, of course, be a widower by that time, giving him as a wife one of the empress's damsels, the heiress to a large and rich estate on *terra firma*, for he wanted nothing more to do with islands of any kind.

He said all this with so much composure and so little show of judgment, wiping his nose from time to time, that his friends could not but marvel once more as they reflected how very infectious Don Quixote's madness must be to have turned the head of this poor man in such a fashion. They did not care to take the trouble of disabusing Sancho of his errors, for it seemed to them that, as they were doing no harm to his conscience, it was better to leave him his illusions and there would be all the more pleasure in listening to his nonsense. And so they told him that he should pray God for his master's good health, adding that it was a very likely and practicable thing for the knight in the course of time to become an emperor as he said, or at the least an archbishop or some other dignitary of equal rank.

"But, good sirs," said Sancho, "if Fortune should so bring things about that my master should decide upon being an archbishop in place of an emperor, what do archbishops-errant usually give to their squires?"

"They commonly give them," replied the curate, "some simple benefice or curacy, or else they make them a sacristan, which brings them in a sizable fixed income, in addition to the altar fees which are just so much more to the good."

"For that," Sancho reflected, "it will be necessary for the squire not to be married, and he must be able to serve mass, at any rate; and if that is so, poor unfortunate me, for I have a wife and I don't know the first letter of my ABC's! What will become of me if my master takes it into his head to become an archbishop and not an emperor as is the use and custom of knights-errant?"

"Do not let that trouble you, friend Sancho," said the barber, for we will entreat and advise him, even making it a matter of conscience, to decide to be an emperor, as that will be easier for him, since he is more a man of arms than he is a student."

"That's the way it looks to me," said Sancho, "although I can tell you that he has the ability for anything. What I mean to do, for my part, is to pray Our Lord to place him where it will be best for him and where he will be in a position to do me the most favors."

"Spoken like a wise man," said the curate, "and you will be acting like a good Christian. But the thing to be done now is to get your master out of that futile penance which you say he is engaged in performing; and as we think over what we have to do, it would be well for us to enter this inn and have a bite to eat, for it is now dinnertime."

Sancho thereupon told them to go in, saying that he would wait outside, adding that he would give them his reasons later for not wishing to set foot in the tavern. He asked them, however, to bring him out something to eat that was hot and also some barley for Rocinante. They did as he requested, and in a few minutes the barber was back with the food. The curate and his companion then set themselves to thinking how they might achieve the result they desired, and the former hit upon a plan that was very well adapted to Don Quixote's turn of fancy and to the purpose that they had in mind.

That plan, as he outlined it to the barber, was to put on the disguise of a wandering damsel while his friend would make himself up the best way he could as a squire, and the two of them would then go to Don Quixote, pretending that it was a maiden in deep affliction and distress who had come to ask a boon, one which he as a valiant knight-errant could not refuse her. The boon was to be that he should come with her wherever she might take him in order to right a wrong which a wicked knight had done her.

She would further entreat him not to ask her to remove her mask nor to make any inquiries concerning her affairs until the wrong done by the wicked knight had been repaired. There was no doubt, the curate thought, that Don Quixote would do anything they wanted him to when they put it in this way, and thus they would be able to get him out of that place and back home, where they would endeavor to see if there was any remedy to be had for the strange madness that possessed him.

CHAPTER XXVII. *How the curate and the barber carried out their plan, along with other things worthy of being related in this great history.*

THE curate's plan impressed the barber as not being a bad one at all. Indeed, it was so good that they at once set about putting it into execution. They asked the landlady for a skirt and a couple of hoods, leaving in pawn for them the curate's new cassock. The barber then made a great beard out of a reddish-gray oxtail into which the innkeeper was in the habit of sticking his comb. When the mistress of the house inquired as to why they wanted these things, the curate proceeded to describe Don Quixote's madness to her briefly, explaining that this disguise was necessary in order to get him down off the mountain where he was at present. At this point it dawned upon the landlord and his wife that the madman had been their guest, the one who had prepared the balm and whose squire had been tossed in the blanket; and she then told the curate all that had happened, not neglecting to mention the incident which Sancho had taken such pains to pass over in silence.

The short of it is, she dressed the curate up in a way that left nothing to be desired, in a cloth skirt with black velvet stripes as broad as your hand, all gored and flounced, and a bodice of green velvet with white satin trimming, both garments being of the kind that must have been worn in the days of King Wamba.[1] The curate would not consent to their putting a hood on him, but instead donned a quilted linen nightcap, binding his forehead with a strip of black taffeta, while out of another strip he fashioned a mask that served very well to cover his beard and face. He then put on his hat, which was big enough to serve him as an umbrella, and wrapping himself in his cloak he mounted his mule in lady-like fashion, his companion straddled the other beast, and they set out. The barber wore a beard, half red, half white, that fell all the way to his waist, for, as has been said, it was made of the tail of a reddish ox. They took their leave of all those in the inn, not forgetting the good Maritornes, who, sinner that she was, promised to say a rosary that God might grant them success in so arduous and Christian an undertaking as the one upon which they were now embarked.

No sooner had they left the inn, however, than the thought occurred to the priest that it was not right, but an indecent thing, for one of his calling to trig himself out like this, even though much might depend upon it. Accordingly, he asked the barber to change costumes with him, as it was more fitting for the latter to be the damsel in distress while the curate played the squire; in that way the dignity of the cloth would not be profaned to such an extent. He added that if the barber did not agree to this, he was determined to proceed no further and Don Quixote might go to the devil for all he cared.

At this point Sancho came up, and, seeing the two of them dressed in such a manner, he could not keep from laughing. The barber ended by acceding to the curate's wishes, and, changing the plot, the priest went on to school him as to what his words and behavior in Don Quixote's presence should be, in order that they might be able to persuade and compel the knight to come with them and to give up his fondness for the place that he had chosen for his vain and futile penance. The barber replied that he needed no lessons but would carry everything off all right. Meanwhile, he did not care to don his costume until they were near the place where Don Quixote was; and so he folded up the garments, the curate adjusted his beard, and they started off down the road with Sancho Panza as their guide, who was now engaged in telling them about the other madman who had been found upon the mountain, saying nothing, however, of the valise and the treasure it contained; for despite the fact that our young fellow's wits were none too sharp, they were sharp enough where money was concerned.

The next day they came to where Sancho had strewn the branches as a landmark to guide him to the spot where he had left Don Quixote. Recognizing the signs, he told his companions that this was the way into the place and they might put on their costumes if that was what was needed in order to save his master. For they had previously made it clear to him that their going in this manner and dressing in this fashion was of the greatest importance if they were to rescue the knight from the evil way of life that he had chosen; and they strongly charged him not to reveal their identity or let it appear that he knew them. If his master should ask him, as he was bound to do, if he had delivered the letter to Dulcinea, Sancho was to say that, not being able to read or write, she had replied by word of mouth, her message being that her lover was to come to her at once, under pain of her displeasure if he failed to do so. They explained that it meant much for Don Quixote's welfare, and by this means, with what they proposed to say to him, they felt certain that they would be able to bring him to a better life and at once put him on the road to becoming an emperor or a monarch, since no one need fear that he would end as an archbishop.

Sancho listened to it all, taking great pains to fix it in his memory. He was grateful that they intended to advise his master to become an emperor instead of an archbishop, for he still thought that emperors could do more favors for their squires than archbishops-errant could. He also suggested that it would be a good thing for him to go on ahead, hunt up his master, and give him my lady's answer, for it was possible that this would be enough to persuade him to leave and they would not have to go to so much trouble. The squire's advice seemed worth following, and so they decided to wait there until he returned with word of the knight.

Sancho then made his way into the mountain ravines, leaving the curate and the barber in a gully through which there ran a small and gently flowing brook, while other cliffs and a grove of trees that was there cast a cool and pleasing shade. The day on which they arrived at this spot was one in the month of August, which is usually a very hot month in these parts; and the heat and the hour of day—it was three o'clock in the afternoon—combined to render this an inviting spot in which to wait. And then, as they were taking their ease in the shade, they caught the sound of a voice, which, unaccompanied by an instrument of any kind, reached their ears with a sweet and regular cadence. They were quite astonished at hearing so good a singer in a place like this; for though it

is said that in the woods and fields one comes upon shepherds with super-
lative voices, this is an embellishment of the poets rather than the truth;
and they wondered still more when they discovered that these were not
such verses as rustic herdsmen compose but were, rather, the work of a
city-bred poet. The verses in question were the following, which confirm the truth of what has just been said:

> *What lessens all the good I gain?*
>   *Disdain.*
> *What is it augments my agony?*
>   *Jealousy.*
> *What tries my patience, keeps me tense?*
>   *Absence.*
> *Thus 'tis I'm always in suspense;*
> *No remedy ever do I find,*
> *Since all hope's killed within my mind*
> *By disdain, jealousy, and absence.*
>
> *Who sends this grief, what power above?*
>   *Love.*
> *Who at my glory casts a hateful glance?*
>   *Chance.*
> *Who consents to my woe without leaven?*
>   *Heaven.*
> *And so, I fear, to me 'tis given*
> *To die of this strange malady,*
> *Seeing that there's a conspiracy*
> *Of Love and Chance and highest Heaven.*
>
> *What can diminish my pain of breath?*
>   *Death.*
> *What can alter Love's humor strange?*
>   *Change.*
> *What can ever cure my sadness?*
>   *Madness.*
> *And so, since all of life is badness,*
> *'Tis not wise to seek a cure*
> *When the remedies most sure*
> *Are death and change and utter madness.*

The hour, the season, the solitude, the voice and skill of the singer
aroused admiration in the listeners and brought them contentment as

they waited to see if there was more of the song. When the silence had lasted for some little while, they decided to go out and look for the musician who had given them so much pleasure; but just as they were about to do so, the voice began again, the same one as before, and as they stayed their steps the following sonnet fell upon their ears:

> O sacred Friendship that on lightsome wing,
> Leaving thy counterpart with us below,
> Hast gone to dwell with the blest, amid the glow
> Of Heaven where the saints and angels sing,
> While lending us still thy semblance, signaling
> Thy true self 'neath a veil, thou mayest know
> That what we oft behold is a lying show,
> And from thy good works many evils spring.
> Quit Heaven, then, O Friendship, nor permit
> The hypocrite to don thy livery
> And mock the heart sincere; take back the life
> Thou gavest this shadow, for it is not fit
> To walk the earth; its artful treachery
> Will plunge the world once more in primal strife.

The song ended with a deep sigh, and the two once again waited attentively to see if there would be more; but when they perceived that the music had turned into sobs and mournful cries, they resolved to find out who the saddened singer was whose voice was as marvelous as his moans were lugubrious. They had not gone far when, in rounding the edge of a cliff, they saw before them a man with the same face and figure as Cardenio, according to Sancho Panza's description when he told them the story of the lovelorn swain. This man as they beheld him now was not leaping in the air, but stood with his head on his bosom like one who was deep in thought, and did not raise his eyes to look at them beyond a first glance when they suddenly came upon him.

The curate already knew of Cardenio's misfortune and recognized him from what Sancho had said, and, being a pleasant-spoken man, he now went up to him and with a few brief but well-chosen words endeavored to persuade him to give up this wretched life he was leading, lest by remaining there he lose life itself, which was the greatest misfortune of all. At that moment Cardenio was wholly in his right mind and free of those furious fits that so frequently took him out of himself. Seeing the two dressed in a manner that was so unusual among those who dwelt in these wilds, he could not but wonder somewhat, and he wondered still more when he heard them speaking of his personal affairs as of something that was well known to them; for such was the impression he derived from the curate's words, and he, accordingly, replied as follows:

"I can see plainly enough, gentlemen, whoever you may be, that Heaven, which is careful to succor the good, and the wicked as well very often, without my deserving it has sent to me here in this remote spot, so far from the ways of men, certain persons who with various and forceful reasons have shown me how unreasonable I am in continuing to lead the kind of life that I do, and who would induce me to leave it for a better one. But they do not know what I know, that in escaping from this evil I should but fall into a greater one, and so, they will perhaps take me for a weak-willed individual or one of little sense, and it would be small wonder if they did, for it is plain even to me that thinking about my troubles so intently as I do can lead only to my ruination, and without my being able to avoid it, I come to be like a stone, wholly lacking in consciousness and a proper sense of things.

"I am made aware of this truth when people at times tell me about, or show me, evidence of the things that I have done when that terrible madness rules me, in which case I can do no more than vainly grieve or futilely curse my fate, and by way of excuse can only tell the cause of it all to such as may care to hear it. For those who are sound of mind, when they behold the cause, will not marvel at the effects; if they can offer no remedy, they will at least not blame me, and the repulsion they feel at my waywardness will turn to pity for my woes. And so, if you, my dear sirs, have come here with the same intention as others in the past, before you go any further with your wise reasoning I would have you listen to the story of my misadventures, and perhaps when you have heard it you will spare yourselves the trouble of endeavoring to console a grief that is beyond all consolation."

The curate and the barber, who desired nothing more than to hear from Cardenio's own mouth the cause of his troubles, now begged him to tell them of it, promising him that they would do nothing that he would not want them to do by way of helping or consoling him. At this, the unfortunate gentleman began his pitiful tale with almost the same words and gestures that he had used in speaking to Don Quixote and the goatherd a few days before, when, owing to the dispute over Master Elisabat and the knight's punctiliousness in observing the code of chivalry, the narrative had been left unfinished, as has already been set forth in the course of this history. But this time, as good fortune would have it, the fit held off and gave him an opportunity to tell it to the end. Coming to the incident of the note which Don Fernando had found between the pages of *Amadis of Gaul*, Cardenio said that he could remember it very well and that it went like this:

LUSCINDA TO CARDENIO

Each day I discover in you qualities that persuade and oblige me to esteem you more; and if you would have me fulfill this obligation while leaving my honor intact, you can very easily do so. I have a father who knows you and who loves me well, and he without forcing my inclinations will grant whatever it is right that you should have, if you love me as you say and as I believe you do.

"By this letter I was led to ask for Luscinda's hand in marriage, as I have already told you, and it was by reason of it that she came to be looked upon by Fernando as one of the most discreet and prudent women of her age. It was this letter that gave him the desire to ruin me before my own desires could be gratified. I told Don Fernando that all that Luscinda's father was waiting for was my father's formal request for her, but that I dared not speak to my father about it, being fearful that he would not consent; not that he was unacquainted with her rank, graciousness, virtue, and beauty, for she had enough good qualities to ennoble any other line in Spain; it was simply that he had given me to understand that he did not wish me to marry so soon, until we had seen what Duke Ricardo meant to do for me. Finally, I confessed to my friend that if I had not ventured to tell my father, it was not on account of this difficulty alone, for there were many others that tended to make a coward of me, although I could not rightly say what they were; all I knew was that it seemed to me that I was destined never to attain the object of my desires.

"In reply to all this, Don Fernando told me that he would take it upon himself to speak to my father and have him talk to Luscinda's father. O ambitious Marius! O cruel Catiline! O wicked Sulla! O lying Galalón! [2] O treacherous Vellido! [3] O vengeful Julian! [4] O greedy Judas! O cruel, vengeful, lying traitor! What disservice did this unhappy one do you, he who so openly laid bare to you the contents and inmost secrets of his heart? How did he offend you? What words did he ever say to you, what counsel did he ever give you that were not all intended to augment your honor and advantage? But of what do I complain, poor wretched creature that I am? For it is certain that misfortunes, springing from the course of the stars and coming from on high, fall upon us with such fury and violence that there is no force on earth that can restrain them, no human ingenuity that can forestall them.

"Who would have believed that Don Fernando, a gentleman of illustrious birth and able wit, one who was under obligations to me for my services and who was in a position to take what he wanted in the way of love wherever his fancy might choose to roam—who would have believed that he would stoop so low, as the saying is, as to deprive me of my one ewe lamb which I had not as yet possessed? But let us leave all these considerations aside as being futile and profitless and resume the broken thread of my unfortunate history.

"To continue, then: Finding my presence an obstacle to the carrying out of his treacherous and wicked plan, Don Fernando determined to send me to his elder brother under pretext of asking him for money with which to pay for six horses that he had bought the very day he offered to speak to my father, all of this being a clever ruse on his part, designed solely to get me out of the way in order that he might better be able to put that damnable scheme of his into execution. Could I have foreseen this treason? Could I by any chance have imagined it? Most assuredly not; instead, it was with the greatest pleasure that I understood the errand, being quite happy over the good bargain he had made.

"That night I spoke to Luscinda, telling her of the arrangement with Don Fernando and adding that I now felt confident that our desires, which were right and proper, would be realized. She no more than I suspected Fernando's treason, but urged me to return as speedily as possible since she was convinced that the moment my father spoke to hers the fulfillment of our wishes would be delayed no longer. I do not know why it was, but as she said this her eyes filled with tears and a lump formed in her throat so that she was unable to put into words all the other things that she had to say to me. I was greatly surprised, for I had never seen her in such a mood before. On those occasions when good fortune and my own wits had brought about a meeting, we had always talked gaily and happily, and there had been no tears, sighs, jealousy, fears, or suspicions. At such times, I would thank my stars that Heaven had given her to me for my lady and would extol her beauty and praise her worth and understanding; and she would give me payment in kind by praising in me those qualities that most endeared me to her.

"We would then go on to speak of a hundred thousand trifles and happenings that concerned our neighbors and acquaintances, and the most daring thing I did was to take, almost by force, one of her white hands and raise it to my lips as best I could in those confined quarters, over the low grating that separated us. But on this night, preceding the sad day of my departure, she wept, moaned, and sighed, and then ran off, leaving me deeply bewildered and perturbed, for I still could not recover from my astonishment at seeing so many unwonted and distressing signs of grief and feeling on her part. However, in order not to slay my hopes, I attributed it all to the power of love and the suffering that absence causes in those who care for each other deeply.

"Finally, I set out, downcast and pensive, my heart filled with imaginings and suspicions without my knowing what it was that I suspected or imagined, which in itself was an ill omen of the sorrowful event and misfortune that awaited me. Arriving at my destination, I presented the letter to Don Fernando's brother and was well received, although, much to my disappointment, I was not sent back at once but was ordered to wait for the matter of a week in some place where the duke would not see me, for Fernando had asked his brother to send him a certain sum without their father's knowing anything about it. All this was a treacherous plot on his part, since his brother had sufficient money and there was no need for him to keep me waiting. I was of a mind not to obey the order, as it seemed to me an impossibility to spend so many days of my life away from Luscinda, especially in view of the unhappy state in which I had left her on that last night of which I have told you. Nevertheless, I did obey like a good servant, even though I realized it would have to be at the expense of my own welfare.

"I had not been there four days, however, when a man arrived with a letter for me bearing a superscription which I recognized as that of Luscinda, for the missive proved to be from her. I opened it with fear and trembling, thinking there must be something very wrong indeed that had moved her to write me at a distance, since she seldom wrote when I was near her. Before reading the message I inquired of the man as to who had given it to him and how long he had been on the road, and he informed me that as he chanced to be passing down a city street at midday a very beautiful lady had called to him from a window, her eyes full of tears, and had said to him, 'My brother, if you are a Christian as you appear to be, I beg you to take this letter at once to the place and person, both well known, that are indicated on the back of it and by so doing you will render a great service to Our Lord; and in order that it may not inconvenience you to do so, take what you find in this handkerchief.'

"The man then went on to explain, 'And saying this, she tossed me from the window a handkerchief in which were wrapped up a hundred reales and this gold ring that I hand you now along with the letter that I have already given you; after which, without waiting for any answer, she left the window, but not until she had observed me pick up the letter and the handkerchief and make a sign to her that I would do as she had commanded. And so, seeing that I was being well paid for my trouble in delivering it, and noting by the superscription that it was you, sir, whom I know very well, to whom it was addressed—not to speak of the tears of that beautiful lady and the obligation they laid upon me—I determined not to trust any other person with this communication but to come myself and place it in your hands. And in sixteen hours from the time it was given me, I have made the journey, which as you know is one of eighteen leagues.'

"As the newly arrived and grateful messenger told me all this, I hung on his every word, my legs trembling so that I could hardly stand. When I opened the letter, this was what I found:

"The promise that Don Fernando gave you to speak to your father and have him speak to mine has been fulfilled by him to his own satisfaction rather than to your advantage. You must know, sir, that he has asked to have me as his wife, and my father, looking upon him as being a more advantageous match than you, has acceded to his request with such alacrity that the marriage is to take place two days from now, with such secrecy and in such privacy that only Heaven and the household servants will be the witnesses. Picture the state that I am in and judge for yourself as to whether it is urgent for you to return, and from the outcome of this affair you will see if I love you dearly or not. Please God that this may reach you before my hands are joined to those of one who knows so little what it means to keep the promise he has made!

"Such, in brief, were the contents of the note, which caused me to take to the road at once without waiting any longer for the reply or the money which I was supposed to bring back with me; for I now knew that it was not the purchase of horses but his own wayward fancy that had prompted Fernando to send me to his brother. The resentment I felt against him, together with the fear of losing the prize which I had rightfully won through so many years of loving service, gave me wings, so that, almost flying, I reached home the next day, at the very hour when I was accustomed to go and speak to Luscinda. I entered secretly, leaving the mule on which I had come at the house of the good man who had brought me the letter. Fortune for once was kind, and I found

Luscinda at the grating which had been the witness of our love. She recognized me at once and I her, but it was not in the way that we ought to have recognized each other. However, who is there in the world who can flatter himself that he has known and fathomed a woman's confused mind and changeable disposition? [5] No one, certainly.

"As soon as she caught sight of me, Luscinda said, 'Cardenio, you see me in bridal dress. Waiting for me in the great hall at this moment are Don Fernando the traitor, my father the covetous one, and others who shall be the witnesses of my death rather than of my nuptials. Do not be perturbed, my dear, but, rather, try to be present at this sacrifice, and if it cannot be prevented by any words of mine, then this dagger that I have concealed here will forestall more determined violence by putting an end to my life and a beginning to the knowledge that will be yours of the love that I have and always have had for you.'

"Feeling pressed for time, I replied to her hastily and distractedly, 'May your deeds, O lady, make good your words. If you bear a dagger to affirm your honor, I have here a sword to defend you or to slay myself if fate should be against us.' I do not think that she could have heard all that I said, for I became aware that they were calling to her to come quickly as her bridegroom was waiting for her. Thus did the night of my sorrow close in upon me, thus did the sun of my happiness set; the light of my eyes was gone, my mind had lost the power to reason. At first, I could not bring myself to enter the house; indeed, I was not capable of any movement whatsoever; but then, reflecting on what was about to take place and how important my presence might be, I plucked up what courage I could and went in. I was very well acquainted with all the entrances and ways of egress in that house, and in any event, with all the confusion that secretly prevailed there, no one would have noticed me; and so, without being perceived, I contrived to conceal myself in the recess formed by a window in the hall itself, covered by the borders of two tapestries from behind which I could see without being seen and observe everything that went on in the room.

"Who can describe now the dread that was in my heart as I stood there, the thoughts that occurred to me, the things that went through my mind? They were such as cannot be told, and it is as well that they cannot be. I may merely say that the bridegroom entered the room dressed in his ordinary garments, without ornament of any kind. As attendant he had with him a cousin-german of Luscinda's, and there was not a person there from outside the family with the exception of the servants. After a little, Luscinda came out from a dressing-room, accompanied by her mother and her two damsels. She was made up and adorned as befitted her rank and beauty, as for a festive or ceremonial occasion. I had neither the time nor the presence of mind to note the details of her costume, but was conscious only of the colors that she wore, crimson and white,[6] and of the glitter of the gems and jewels on her headdress and all over her robe, which, however, could not vie with the striking beauty of her blond hair, which was such as far to outshine the precious stones and the light from the four torches that flared in the room.

"O memory, mortal foe to my peace of mind! What purpose does it serve to bring before me now the incomparable loveliness of my adored enemy? Would it not be better, O cruel memory, to remind me of, and picture for me, what she then did in order that, moved by so manifest a wrong, I may at least seek to end my life, now that vengeance is no longer mine to take?

"I hope, good sirs, that you will not tire of these digressions that I make, for my sorrow is not one of those that can be related briefly and succinctly, inasmuch as each circumstance appears to me to be worthy of a long discourse."

To this the curate replied that not only were they not tired of listening to him, but all the little things that he had to tell were of great interest to them and deserved not to be passed over in silence but to be narrated as attentively as the main body of the story.

"Well, then," Cardenio went on, "when they were all gathered in the great hall, the curate of the parish entered and, taking the two of them by the hand, performed the required ceremony. As he came to the words 'Do you, Señora Luscinda, take Señor Don Fernando here present to be your lawfully wedded husband as our Holy Mother Church commands?' —at that point I thrust my head and neck all the way out from behind the tapestries and, with deep perturbation of soul, strained my ears for Luscinda's response, feeling that upon her answer depended a death sentence or a grant of life for me. Oh, if then I had but dared to burst forth and cry, 'Ah, Luscinda, Luscinda, look well to what you are doing, think of what you owe to me, and remember that you are mine and cannot belong to another! Remember that if you say yes, my life at that instant will come to an end! Ah, traitorous Don Fernando, robber of my bliss, death of my life, what would you? Reflect that as a Christian you cannot accomplish your desires, for Luscinda is my bride and I her bridegroom!'

"Ah, fool that I am, now that I am far away and out of danger's reach, I keep telling myself that I should have done what I did not do. Now that

I have let him steal my jewel, I can but curse the thief on whom I might have avenged myself had I had the heart for vengeance in place of merely complaining as I do now. In short, I was both a coward and a fool, and it is little wonder if I am now dying a shamed and repentant madman.

"The curate, then, was standing there waiting for Luscinda's response, which was some while in coming; and just as I thought that she was about to take out her dagger to assert her honor or was trying to unloose her tongue to disabuse them and speak some truth that would redound to my advantage, I heard her saying in a weak, fainthearted voice, 'Yes, I do.' Repeating the same words, Don Fernando placed the ring on her finger, and they were bound by an indissoluble knot. The bridegroom then went to kiss his bride, but she with a hand to her heart fell back fainting in her mother's arms. It only remains now for me to tell you the state that I was in as I heard that yes making a mockery of my hopes, proving false Luscinda's words and promises, and rendering impossible for all time to come the attainment of the blessing which I at that moment had lost. I was stunned by it all, left unprotected as it seemed to me by all the heavens, while the earth was my sworn enemy, denying me breath for my sighs, moisture for my tears; it was fire alone that grew in strength until I was wholly aflame with rage and jealousy.

"They were all greatly agitated by Luscinda's fainting fit; and as her mother opened the bride's bodice to give her air, they found there a sealed note which Don Fernando promptly took. When he had read it by the light of the torches, he sat down in a chair with a hand to his cheek, in the attitude of a man who is thinking deeply, paying no attention to what they were doing to revive his bride. Perceiving that the entire household was in confusion, I ventured to slip out. It made little difference to me whether I was seen or not, for, in case I was, I had made up my mind to commit some insane act that would let the world know of the just indignation that burned in my bosom, through the punishment inflicted upon the perfidious Don Fernando and upon the fickle and swooning traitress as well. But my fate, which must have been reserving me, if possible, for still greater ills to come, if there be any such, ordained that at this moment I should have enough and to spare of that wit that I have lacked since then; and accordingly, without seeking to take vengeance on my greatest enemies—all thought of me being so far from their minds, it would have been an easy matter to slay them—I resolved instead to inflict upon myself the suffering that should have been theirs, employing even greater severity, it may be, than I should have shown toward them by killing them, for sudden pain is soon over but that which is marked by long-drawn-out torments always kills without putting an end to life.

"To be brief, departing from that house I returned to the one where I had left the mule. I had the man saddle it for me, and then, without so much as bidding him good-by, I mounted the animal and rode out of the city like another Lot, not daring to turn my face to look back. When I found myself alone in the open country and enveloped in the darkness of night, I was tempted to give vent to my grief without restraint or fear of being heard or recognized, and then it was I raised my voice and loosed my tongue, heaping curses on Luscinda and Don Fernando as if by that means I might obtain satisfaction for the wrong which they had done me. I called her cruel, ungrateful, false, and thankless, but, above all, I upbraided her for covetousness, seeing that my enemy's wealth had closed the eyes of her love and had taken her from me and handed her over to one with whom fortune had dealt more freely and liberally than it had with me.

"Yet even in the midst of this outburst of curses and vituperations I still found excuses for her, telling myself it was no wonder that a young girl reared in seclusion in her parents' house and brought up to obey them always should have seen fit to yield to their choice when they offered her for a husband a gentleman of such high rank and so rich and well bred that not to have readily accepted him would have led others to think either that she was lacking in sound judgment or that she had bestowed her affections somewhere else, a thing which would so have prejudiced her good name and reputation.

"And then again, I said to myself, supposing she had declared me to be her betrothed, they would have seen that she had not chosen so badly that she was not to be forgiven; for before Don Fernando had made his offer of marriage, they themselves, had their desires been tempered with reason, could not have wished a better husband for their daughter than I. And she, before letting herself be placed in that forced and final situation of having to give her hand to another, might very well have said that I had already given her mine, knowing that I would come forward to verify any assertion of this sort that she made. At last I reached the conclusion that little love, small judgment, much ambition, and great worldly longings had led her to forget the words with which she had deceived me and which had served to sustain my own firm hopes and honorable desires.

"Talking to myself in this manner, and deeply agitated, I journeyed all the rest of that night and at dawn found myself in a pass leading into the heart of these highlands. I traveled over the mountains for three days more, with no road or footpath to guide me, until I came to a halt in the meadows that lie on one side of this range, though I cannot tell you which side it is, and there I inquired of some shepherds as to which was the most rugged part of the region. They told me it was where we are now, and so I came here, meaning to end my life; and, upon entering this inhospitable land, my mule fell dead of weariness and hunger, or, I am more inclined to think, in order to be done with so useless a burden as the one he bore. I was left, then, without a mount, worn out, starving, with no one to give me aid and with no thought of seeking it.

"I cannot tell you how long it was I lay stretched out on the ground like that, but at last I arose, feeling no hunger, and found myself in the company of some goatherds, who must have been the ones who had aided me in my distress; for they told me of the condition I was in when they had found me, the nonsensical things I had said, the mad actions I had performed, all of which clearly indicated that I had lost my reason. And I myself since then have become conscious of the fact that I am not always in full possession of it and that it is so weak and decayed that I do a thousand mad things such as rending my garments and shouting at the top of my voice in these solitudes as I curse my fate and vainly repeat the loved name of my fair enemy, all with no other purpose than that of putting an end to my existence through such loudly voiced laments, and then, when I am myself once more, I am so tired and battered that I can barely move.

"My most common habitation is in the hollow of a cork tree large enough to shelter this wretched body. The cowherds and goatherds that frequent these mountains, moved by charity, bring me food, placing it along the paths and cliffs where they think that I may pass and find it; for though my wits may fail me, the necessities of nature teach me what I need in order to sustain the spark of life, awakening in me the desire to seek it and the willingness to accept it. At other times, so they tell me when they find me in my right senses, I go out on the roads and take by force, though they would gladly give it to me, the food which the shepherds are bringing back from the village to their folds.

"Such is the manner in which I spend my wretched life, what is left me of it until Heaven shall see fit to bring it to a close or so order things that I shall no longer remember the beauty of the treacherous Luscinda or the wrong done me by Don Fernando. If it does this without depriving me of life, I will then turn my thoughts to better things; if not, there is nothing left but to pray that it will have mercy on my soul, for I do not feel that I have the ability or the strength to retrieve my body from these straits in which I have placed it of my own volition.

"This, then, O worthy gentlemen, is the bitter story of my misfortunes. Tell me if it is such as could be related with any less feeling than you have seen me display. And do not trouble yourselves with persuading or advising me to take that remedy that reason says may be good for me, for it will do me no more good than the medicine prescribed by a famous physician for a patient who will have none of it. I want no health without Luscinda; and inasmuch as she chooses to be another's when she is or ought to be mine, let my choice be misfortune when it might have been happiness. She with her changeableness would make stable my perdition, and I, by seeking my own ruin, will gratify her wishes, thus serving as an example to those in days to come, of one who alone among men lacked that of which all the wretched have more than enough: that is, the ability to console themselves with the impossibility of any consolation; for this in my case only leads to greater sorrows and sufferings, since I do not believe that there will be an end to my pain even in death."

Here Cardenio brought to a close his long speech and a story as filled with misfortunes as it was with love. The curate was about to offer him a few words of sympathy but stopped short when a voice reached his ears, crying in pitiful accents what will be related in the fourth part of this narrative; for it was at this point that the wise and learned historian, Cid Hemete Benengeli, brought the third part to a conclusion.[7]

CHAPTER **XXVIII**. *Which treats of the new and pleasing adventure of the curate and the barber on the same mountain.*

MOST happy and most fortunate were those times when that boldest of knights, Don Quixote de la Mancha, came into the world; and it is by reason of his noble resolve to revive and restore to that same world the calling of knight-errantry, so long lost to memory and all but dead, that we now, in this age of ours which is so sadly lacking in merry entertainment, are able to enjoy not only the charm of his veracious history, but also the tales and episodes interpolated in it, which in a manner are no less pleasing, artful, and true than the history itself.

Pursuing, then, its hackled, twisting, winding thread of plot,[1] the work in question goes on to relate that just as the curate was beginning to offer Cardenio certain words of consolation, he heard a voice crying in mournful accents, "O God! Is it possible that I have found a place that may serve as a hidden grave for the burdensome weight of this body which I so unwillingly support? I have indeed, if the solitude that these mountains promise me is not a lie. Ah, unfortunate one that I am! How much more agreeable company do these crags and thickets afford me for my purpose—since here I may cry aloud my woes to Heaven—than would any human being, seeing that there is no one on earth to whom I may look for counsel in my doubts, a comforting answer to my lamentations, or a remedy for the ills that beset me."

Upon hearing and grasping the sense of these words, the curate and his companions rightly decided that the voice came from near by, and they accordingly arose to search for its owner and had not gone twenty paces when, behind a large rock, seated at the foot of an ash tree, they beheld a lad, dressed as a peasant, whose face they could not clearly see at the moment for the reason that his head was bent over as he bathed his feet in the rivulet that flowed there. They came up very quietly, giving no sign of their presence, while he devoted all his attention to what appeared to be two pieces of white crystal embedded among the stones of the brook, rather than feet. Feet they were, however, of a surprising whiteness and beauty, and, belying the lad's garb, they did not seem made to tread clods or follow the plow and the oxen.

Perceiving that the young peasant had not heard them, the curate, who had gone ahead, made signs to the others to crouch down and hide themselves behind some pieces of rock that lay scattered around, and this they all did, watching attentively, meanwhile, the actions of the one by the stream. The latter was clad in a gray-colored double-skirted jacket tightly bound about the waist by a girdle of white cloth, and he also had on breeches and gaiters of gray cloth and a cap of the same material on his head. His gaiters were rolled halfway up his legs, which, it seemed, must surely be of pure alabaster. Having bathed his feet, he took out a towel from beneath his cap and dried them; and in removing his *montera*,[2] he lifted his head, affording the onlookers a glimpse of a face of incomparable beauty.

"That," said Cardenio to the curate, "since it cannot be Luscinda, is no human being but a divine one."

Being now without his cap, the youth shook his head from side to side, and, as he did so, a mass of hair whose brightness the sun might have envied was unloosened and fell down over his shoulders. This told them that the one who had appeared to be a peasant lad was in reality a woman of exquisite loveliness, indeed the most beautiful that two of them had ever beheld, and the same might have been said of Cardenio if he had not looked upon and known Luscinda, for as he afterward observed, only her beauty could compete with that of the creature before them, whose long blond locks not only covered her shoulders, but were so abundant as to conceal the whole of her body with the exception of her feet. For a comb she made use of her two hands, and if her feet in the water had the appearance of crystal, her hands in her hair were like driven snow. All of which filled her beholders with admiration and made them more desirous than ever of knowing who she was.

They accordingly resolved to show themselves, and at the sound which they made upon getting to their feet the lovely lass raised her head and, parting her hair from in front of her eyes with both hands, gazed in their direction. No sooner did she see them than she rose, without pausing to put on her shoes or gather in her flowing locks, and, hastily snatching up something like a bundle of garments that was on the bank beside her, she started to flee in great fear and alarm. She had not gone six paces, however, when, her delicate feet being unused to the rough stones, she sank to the ground; whereupon the three of them ran up to her. The curate was the first to speak.

"Stay, my lady," he said, "whoever you may be, for we whom you see here only wish to be of service to you. There is no reason for you to take to importunate flight like this, for your feet will not suffer it, nor can we consent to it."

To this she replied not a word, being very much astonished and bewildered. They then came closer to her, and the curate, taking her by the hand, went on speaking.

"What your garb denies, lady," he began, "your hair has revealed to us; and we feel sure that the causes cannot have been slight ones that have led you to disguise your beauty in so unworthy a habit and come to so lonely a place as this where it has been our good fortune to find you. If we cannot remedy your griefs, we at least would offer you such comfort as we can; for no sorrow so long as life lasts can be so overwhelming or so far beyond the reach of human aid that the sufferer will refuse to listen to those words of comfort that are uttered with good intentions. And so, dear lady, or dear sir, whichever you prefer, try to overcome the fear which the sight of us has caused you and tell us of your good or evil fortunes, for in all of us together and in each of us individually you will find a sympathetic audience."

While the curate was saying this, the lass in boy's clothing stood as if spellbound, looking first at one and then at another, without moving her lips or saying a word, like a rustic villager who is suddenly shown some curious thing that he has never seen before. But as the priest went on with other arguments to the same effect, she gave a deep sigh and broke her silence at last.

"Inasmuch," she said, "as these mountain wilds have not been able to conceal me, while the sight of my loosened hair renders futile any lie my tongue might tell, it would be vain for me to go on pretending to be what I am not, since if you believed it at all, it would be out of politeness rather than for any other reason. In view of this fact, then, gentlemen, I would say that I thank you for the offer you have made me, which has put me under the obligation of granting your request by telling you all that you may wish to know; although I fear that the story of the misfortunes which I shall relate to you will cause you boredom as well as compassion, seeing that there is no remedy or comfort to be had for them. Nevertheless, I would not have my honor compromised in your sight, for you now know me to be a woman and see me, a young girl, alone here and in this costume, two things that well might drag in the dust any woman's good name. And so, I shall tell you what I would much rather keep secret if I could."

All this was uttered so gracefully and fluently and in so charming a voice that they could not but admire the cleverness as much as they did the beauty of this creature who stood revealed as one of the most entrancing of women. With this, they repeated their offers, begging her to fulfill her promise, and she, without further urging, after first very modestly putting on her shoes and gathering up her hair, seated herself upon a rock with the three about her. Doing her best to restrain her tears, she began the story of her life, in a calm, clear voice.

"In this province of Andalusia there is a village that lies within the domains of a duke, one of those who are known as Grandees of Spain. This duke has two sons: the elder, who is heir to his estate and, apparently, to his good morals as well; and a younger one, who is heir to— I cannot tell you what, unless it be the treasons of Vellido and the lying wiles of Galalón. My own parents are the vassals of this lord, and though of humble antecedents are so rich that if their lineage had been equal to their fortune they would have had nothing left to wish for and I should have had no fear of finding myself in my present plight. For it well may be that my misfortunes spring from theirs in not having been born to the nobility. It is true enough that they are not so lowly born that they need blush for their station in life, but, on the other hand, their rank is not so high that I can rid myself of the thought that it was their humility that brought my troubles upon me.

"They are, in short, plain country people without any admixture of disreputable blood; they are rusty [3] old Christians but so well off that, by reason of their luxurious mode of living, they have come to be known as *hidalgos* and even *caballeros*,[4] although the wealth and nobility that they most prized lay in having me for a daughter. They were fond parents and had no other son or daughter to be their heir, and, as a result, I was one of the most pampered young ladies that ever was. I was the mirror in which they beheld themselves, the staff of their old age, and the object toward which, by the grace of Heaven, all their wishes tended; and their wishes being such worthy ones, my own were in agreement with theirs. And just as I was the mistress of their hearts and minds, so was I of their estate as well. It was through me that they engaged and discharged servants, and it was through my hands that the accounts of the sowing and the harvest passed, of the oil mills, wine presses, herds, flocks, and hives, all the things that a rich farmer like my father might possess— I kept count of them all; I was at once the mistress and the major-domo, all of which duties were performed with such diligence on my part and such satisfaction on the part of my parents that I cannot well describe it to you.

"That portion of the day that was left me after I had dealt with the stewards, overseers, and laborers I devoted to those pursuits that are as proper as they are necessary for young ladies, commonly represented by the needle, the sewing-cushion, and the distaff. And if I occasionally, by way of recreation, forsook these tasks, it was to read some book of devotion or play upon the harp, for experience has taught me that music soothes the troubled mind and brings rest to the weary soul.[5]

"Such, then, was the life that I led in my parents' house. If I have pictured it for you in so great detail, it has not been for purposes of ostentation or by way of impressing upon you the fact that I am wealthy. My object, rather, is to show you how, through no fault of my own, I have fallen from that happy state of which I have told you to the one in which I now find myself. It was a busy life I led but one so cloistered that it

can be compared only to that of a convent. It seemed to me I saw no one
at all outside the servants; for on those days that I went to early morning
mass, accompanied by my mother and the women of the household, I
was so veiled and so closely attended that my eyes scarcely beheld more
of the ground than that on which I set my feet. Yet for all of that, the
eyes of love, or, it would be better to say, dalliance, with which those of
the lynx cannot compare, found me out through the persistency of Don
Fernando, for that is the name of the duke's younger son of whom I
spoke."

The moment he heard Fernando's name mentioned, Cardenio turned
pale and began perspiring all over, displaying such signs of deep emotion
as to lead the curate and the barber, who were watching him, to fear he
was about to have one of those fits that, so they had been told, came over
him from time to time. He did nothing more than sweat, however, and
sat there quietly, staring hard at the peasant lass, for by now he suspected
who she was. Without paying any attention to him, she went on with
her story.

"Those eyes of his had had no more than one good glimpse of my face
when, as he said afterward, he fell violently in love with me, as his later
actions proved. But to bring the tale of my misfortunes to as speedy an
end as possible, I will pass over all the means to which Don Fernando
had resort in making known his love. He bribed all the servants in the
house and gave and offered gifts and favors to my parents. Every day in
our street was an occasion for festivity and rejoicing, and at night one
could not sleep for the music that was played. The love notes that, without my knowing how, reached my hands were infinite in number and
were filled with amorous phrases and declarations. They contained more
oaths and promises than they did letters of the alphabet. All of which did
not soften me in the least, but, rather, hardened me against him to such an
extent that I came to look upon him as my mortal enemy, while all the
efforts that he made to win my love had just the opposite effect. It was
not that I disliked his courteous intentions or found them excessive; for
it gave me a certain satisfaction to be loved and held in such esteem by
a gentleman of his illustrious rank. Nor was I annoyed by reading his
praises of me in the notes that he sent me, for however ugly we may
be, I think we women always enjoy hearing ourselves called beautiful.

"No, it was simply that my sense of propriety was opposed to all this,
and my parents, moreover, were constantly advising me against him, as
they now very clearly perceived Don Fernando's purpose, and he did not
care if all the world knew it. My parents reminded me that my virtue was

the sole depository of their honor and good name and urged me to take into consideration the disparity of rank between him and myself, saying that if I did so, I would see that, whatever he might say, he was thinking more of his own pleasure than of my welfare. They added that if I cared to oppose in the slightest degree his unjust claims to my affection, they would marry me at once to anyone I might choose from among the leading families of our village or the neighboring ones, since in view of their wealth and my reputation for virtue, there was no limit to our expectations.

"These assured promises and the truths my parents told me greatly strengthened my resolution, and I never said a word in reply to Don Fernando that might have afforded him the remotest hope of attaining his desire. This reserved attitude on my part, which he must have mistaken for flirtatiousness, merely served to whet his lascivious appetite; for that is the only name that I can give to the feeling that he showed for me, since if it had been anything else, you would not be hearing of it now, as there would be no occasion for telling you of it.

"Finally, he learned that my parents were about to arrange another match by way of putting an end to his hopes of possessing me, or at least were going to have me more carefully watched over in the future, and it was this news or suspicion that led him to commit the act which I shall now relate. One night, being alone in my room, with the doors well locked and only my maid for company—for I feared that in some way, though I did not know how, my virtue might be endangered—I suddenly found him, in spite of all my modesty and precautions, standing before me there in the silence and seclusion of my chamber. The sight of him so perturbed me that I could not take my eyes off him and my tongue was tied.

"I was so frightened that I could not even cry out, and I do not believe that he would have permitted me to do so; for he at once came up to me and, taking me in his arms—as I have told you, I did not have the strength or presence of mind to defend myself—he began to say all sorts of things to me, making lies appear to be the truth in a manner that I should not have believed possible. And what is more, the traitor even managed a few tears and sighs by way of making his words sound plausible. As a result, poor young thing that I was, alone with my attendants who had had little experience in such cases as this, I came somehow to accept his falsehoods as the truth, although it was nothing more than a kindly compassion that his tearful protestations aroused in me.

"And so, when my first start of surprise was over, I began to recover somewhat of my self-possession and with more spirit than I should have believed myself capable of showing, I spoke to him.

" 'Sir,' I said,[6] 'if instead of being in your arms as I am at this moment I were in the grasp of a fierce lion and my liberation depended upon my saying or doing something which would prejudice my virtue, that thing would be as impossible for me as it is to undo that which has already been. Though your arms may hold me like this, my soul is firmly attached to worthy desires very different from yours, as you shall see if you endeavor by force to put your own into effect. I am your vassal, but I am not your slave, and your nobility of blood does not, and should not, give you the right to despise and dishonor my humble origins. As a peasant girl of the countryside I have as much self-respect as do you, a lordly gentleman. With me neither force nor your wealth nor any words that you may utter to deceive me nor all your sighs and tears shall be of any avail in softening my resolve.

" 'If I were to find any of these qualities [7] I have mentioned in the one whom my parents gave me for a husband, I would adjust my will to his and never go beyond the bounds of his wishes; and thus my honor would be left me even though my desires were not gratified, and I would give him freely that which you, sir, now seek to take so forcibly. I have told you all this in order that you may know that he who is not my husband never will obtain anything from me.'

" 'If that,' replied the faithless gentleman, 'is all that is troubling you, my loveliest Dorotea' "—for such was the name the unfortunate one bore—" 'then look, I give you my hand and promise to be yours, and Heaven itself from which nothing is hidden shall be my witness as well as that image of Our Lady that you have there.' "

When Cardenio heard the name Dorotea he was once more deeply agitated, for it appeared to him to confirm the opinion he had held from the start, but he did not wish to interrupt the story whose end, he felt almost certain, he already knew.

"So, Dorotea is your name, lady?" was all he said. "I know another of whom the same story is told and whose misfortunes, it may be, equal your own. But continue. When the time comes, I may tell you some things that will astonish you as much as they will excite your pity."

Listening attentively to what Cardenio had to say and studying at the same time his strange manner and shabby attire, Dorotea begged him if he knew anything else concerning her to tell her at once. For if Fortune had left her any blessing at all, it was that of being able to bear any calamity that might overtake her, inasmuch as, so it seemed to her, nothing could increase in the slightest degree the weight of suffering that she already carried.

"Lady," replied Cardenio, "I should not let the opportunity pass to tell you what I think if I felt that my suspicions had any basis in fact, but up to now there is nothing to show that they do have, and so it is not important that you should know of them."

"Be that as it may," said Dorotea, "and to go on with my story: Picking up a holy image that was in the room, Don Fernando took it to be the witness of our troth. With highly persuasive arguments and the most unusual oaths, he gave me his word that he would be my husband; although, before he said this, I warned him that he should take good care as to what he was doing and think of what his father would say of his being married to a peasant girl who was his vassal. I added that he should not let my beauty, such as it was, blind him, as it would not be a sufficient excuse for his error, and that if he really loved me he ought to let my fate take its course in accordance with my station in life, for marriages in which the parties were so unevenly matched never made for happiness, nor did the glow with which they began ever last for long.

"All this I told him, and many other things besides which I do not recall; but nothing that I might say could dissuade him from his purpose, since he who has no intention of paying does not quibble over the bargain. At this point, I thought things over, saying to myself, 'I certainly shall not be the first one to rise from a lowly estate to a high one by way of matrimony, nor will Don Fernando be the first whom beauty or, what is surely the better word, a blind passion has led to take a companion unsuited to his lofty rank. Accordingly, seeing that I am setting no new custom or fashion, it would be well to accept this honor that fate offers me even though the affection that he displays toward me lasts no longer than the achievement of his desires; for when all is said, I shall still be his wife before God. If I repel him with scorn, I can see that, fair means failing him, he is of a mind to use force, and then I shall be left dishonored and without excuse in the mind of anyone who did not know how blamelessly I came to be in such a position as this. For what could ever bring my parents to believe that this gentleman had thus come into my chamber without my consent?'

"To turn over all these questions and answers in my mind was the work of a moment. But it was, above all, Don Fernando's oaths, the witnesses to whom he appealed, the tears he shed, and, finally, his highbred manner, which, accompanied by so many manifestations of true love, well might have won over any heart, even one as free and shy as mine—it was these things that inclined me to what, without my realizing it at the time, was to be my ruin. I summoned my maid in order that she might be an earthly witness to go with the heavenly ones he had invoked. Don Fernando then began reiterating and confirming his previous oaths, calling upon yet more saints and invoking a thousand future curses upon himself in case he did not fulfill his promises. Once again his eyes brimmed with tears and his sighs grew in volume as he clasped me still more tightly in his arms which had never let go of me. As a consequence of all this and of my maid's leaving the room at that moment, I ceased to be a maid and he became a traitor and a faithless wretch.

"The day that followed the night of my dishonor did not come as quickly, I imagine, as Don Fernando would have liked; for once appetite has had its fill, the dominant impulse is to hasten away from the place where it has found satisfaction. By this I mean to say that he was in great haste to leave me, and through the cleverness of my maid, who was the one who had admitted him in the first place, he slipped out into the street before it was yet dawn. Upon bidding me farewell, he swore again, though not with so much earnestness and vehemence, that I might be assured of his good faith and that all his vows were stanch and true. By way of confirming what he said, he took from his finger a costly ring and put it upon my hand.

"With this, he departed and I was left neither sad nor happy. That is to say, I was pensive and bewildered, almost beside myself with what had just happened, and I either did not have the spirit or I forgot to scold my maid for the treachery of which she had been guilty by closeting Don Fernando with me; for the truth is, I could not as yet make up my mind as to whether what had befallen me was good or bad. I had told Don Fernando as he left that he might visit me on other nights by the same means that he had employed on this occasion, until such time as he should see fit to make it public, since I now belonged to him. With the exception of the following night, however, he came no more, and for a month and longer I was unable to catch a glimpse of him either in the street or in church. Vainly, I wore myself out waiting for some word, for I knew that he was in the town and that most days he went hunting, this being a sport of which he was very fond.

"Those days, those hours, I well remember, were sad and wretched ones for me. It was then that I began to doubt and disbelieve in Don Fernando's good faith, and it was then, also, that my maid had from me those words of reproof for her bold act that she had not heard before. I recall that it was all I could do to restrain my tears and maintain the composure of my countenance that I might not give my parents an excuse for inquiring as to the cause of my unhappiness, and the result was that I had to invent lies to tell them. But the time came when considerations of this sort and all thoughts of honor were abandoned, for as my patience gave out my secret thoughts became known. The occasion was the news that came, within a short while, of Don Fernando's marriage to an exceedingly beautiful maiden in a near-by city, the daughter of parents who enjoyed some rank, though she was not so rich that by reason of her dowry she might have looked forward to such a match as this. They tell me that her name was Luscinda and that at her wedding certain things happened that are truly cause for wonderment."

Upon hearing Luscinda's name, Cardenio did no more than shrug his shoulders, bite his lips, and arch his brows as a double stream of tears poured from his eyes. Dorotea, however, did not for this reason break off her story.

"When this news reached my ears," she went on, "in place of my heart's being congealed, the rage and desire for vengeance that was kindled in it was so great that it was all I could do to keep from running out into the street and crying aloud the perfidy and treason of which he had been guilty toward me. The only thing that stayed my wrath was the plan that came to me then, one that I put into execution that very night. The plan in question was to don this costume which I now have on and which was given me by one of those *zagales*,[8] as they are called in peasant homes. He was a servant of my father's, and I had told him all that had happened and had asked him to come with me to the city where I had heard that my enemy was. After reproving me for my bold scheme of which he sternly disapproved, he nevertheless, when he saw how bent I was upon carrying it out, offered to accompany me—to the end of the world as he assured me. I at once put into a pillowcase a woman's dress and a few pieces of jewelry along with a little money in order that I might be prepared for any eventuality; and that night when all was still, without saying anything to my treacherous maid, I left my home, and in the company of the servant lad and my many thoughts I set out on foot for the city, borne on the wings of desire as it were, being anxious, if not to prevent what was already done, at least to demand of Don Fernando how in all conscience he could have done it.

"I arrived at my destination in two days and a half, and, entering the city, I inquired at once for the home of Luscinda's parents. The first person to whom I put the question told me more than I sought to know. Pointing out the house, he informed me of all that had occurred at the marriage of the daughter, a thing so well known throughout the town that people formed in groups on the street to discuss it. It seemed that, after the ceremony had been performed and Luscinda had given him her promise to be his bride, she had been seized with a violent fainting fit, and when he had opened her bodice to give her air he had found there a letter in her handwriting in which she stated and declared that she could not be his bride for the reason that she belonged to Cardenio—the name, so the man assured me, of a leading gentleman of that same city—adding that if she had said yes to Fernando, it was to avoid having to disobey her parents.

"In short, as the story was told to me, the letter made plain her intention to kill herself following her marriage and went on to set forth the reasons why she was taking her life. All of which, they say, was confirmed by a dagger that they found somewhere or other on her person. In view of this, Don Fernando could not but feel that she had mocked and belittled him, and, accordingly, before she had been revived from her faint, he fell upon her and endeavored to stab her to death and would have done so if the parents and others present had not prevented him. It was further stated that Don Fernando went away at once and that Luscinda did not recover from her fit until the next day, when she informed her parents that she was in reality the bride of that Cardenio whom I have mentioned.

"Another thing: they say that Cardenio was present at the wedding and that upon seeing Luscinda given to another as a bride, something he had never thought would happen, he had flung himself out of the city in desperation, leaving behind him a note in which he spoke of the wrong that she had done him and announced his intention of going where people would never see him again. All this, as I say, was well known throughout the town and everyone was talking of it, and they talked still more when it was learned that she was not to be found either in her father's house or anywhere in the city, and that as a consequence her parents were frantic, not knowing what measures to take.

"These circumstances of which I had just learned gave me fresh hope, for it seemed to me better not to have found Don Fernando at all than to have found him married, as this meant that the door might not yet be wholly closed upon my chance for happiness. It might be that Heaven had placed this obstacle in the way of a second match as a means of bringing him to realize his obligations to the first one, and perhaps now he would come to reflect that he was, after all, a Christian and owed more consideration to his soul than to mundane matters.

"All these things I turned over in my mind, consoling myself without achieving consolation, pretending that I cherished certain faint and distant hopes of sustaining the life that I now abhor. Being in the city, then, and not knowing what to do since Don Fernando was not there, I chanced to hear a public crier who was promising a large reward to anyone that found me and was giving my age and a description of the clothes I wore. The crier went on to say that I had been taken from the home of my parents by the lad who was with me, a thing that cut me to the quick when I saw how low my reputation had sunk. It was not enough to tarnish my good name by reporting my flight, but they must add with whom I had fled, a person so low of station and so unworthy of my affections. Upon hearing the crier, I left the city immediately, along with my servant, who was already giving signs of wavering in the faith and loyalty that he had promised me, and that same night we entered this mountain fastness, being very much afraid of being discovered.

"But, as the saying is, one evil calls to another, and the end of one trouble is usually the beginning of a greater one. That was the way it was with me; for my servant, who up to that time had been loyal and dependable, upon finding himself with me in this lonely spot, moved more by his own vileness than by my beauty, sought to take advantage of the opportunity which, as he saw it, was offered him by these solitudes. With no shame and less fear of God or respect for me, he made advances to me, and when I replied to his disgraceful proposals with well-merited words of scorn, he left off the entreaties which he had at first employed and began to use force.

"But Heaven is just and seldom or never fails to regard and favor good intentions; and so, with the little strength that I had and no great amount of effort, I managed to push him over a precipice, where I left him, whether dead or alive I do not know. After which, with greater swiftness than I would have thought possible in my weariness and fright, I made my way into the heart of these mountains with no other thought, no other plan, than that of hiding myself here from my father and those whom he had sent out to look for me.

"I cannot tell you how many months ago it was that, animated by this desire, I came here. I ended by meeting a herdsman who took me as his servant to a place in the very heart of these mountains, where I have worked up to now as a shepherd, striving always to stay out in the meadows in order that they might not catch a glimpse of this hair of mine, which you, through no intention on your part, have chanced to discover. However, all my care and ingenuity were in vain, for my master found out that I was not a lad, whereupon there was born in him the same evil passion as in my servant; and inasmuch as fate does not invariably provide a remedy along with a misfortune, I now found no cliff or ravine where I might fling him down as I had done in the other instance. Accordingly, I decided that it would be better to leave him and hide myself once more in this rugged place than to risk trying my strength or force of arguments.

"And so, as I say, I came back here to look for a spot where, with nothing to prevent me, I might beseech Heaven to take pity on my woes and either give me the intelligence and the luck to escape them or else let me lay down my life amid these wastes, leaving no memory of one who, through no fault of hers, has given occasion for talk and gossip in her own and other provinces."

CHAPTER XXIX. *Which treats of the amusing artifice and means employed in extricating our enamored knight from the extremely harsh penance he had inflicted upon himself.*

"AND that, sirs, is the true story of my tragedy. Look now and judge if the sighs to which you listened, the words you heard, the tears that you saw starting from my eyes, might not well have been more in number. When you shall have considered the nature of my disgrace, you will see how vain is all consolation, how impossible is any kind of remedy. All that I ask—a thing that you can and should do—is that you advise me where I may spend the rest of my life without suffering from this deadly fear I have of being found by those who are searching for me. For even though the great love that my parents have for me is assurance that I shall be well received by them, so great is the shame that lays hold of me at the mere thought of appearing in their presence in so different a guise than what they expect, that I regard it as better to banish myself from their sight forever than to look them in the face with the thought that they are beholding my own countenance robbed of that decency that they had a right to expect of me."

Saying this, she fell silent, her visage taking on a hue that showed clearly enough the deep shame and feeling of her soul. The faces of those who listened to her, meanwhile, were filled as much with pity as with wonderment at her troubles, and although the curate was ready to console and counsel her, it was Cardenio who first addressed her.

"The short of it is, lady," he said, "that you are the beauteous Dorotea, only daughter of the rich Clenardo."

Dorotea was astonished at hearing her father's name mentioned, especially by so unprepossessing a person as this; for we have already spoken of the shabby manner in which Cardenio was clothed.

"And who are you, my brother, who thus know my father's name? For I up to now, unless my memory fails me, in all the course of my unhappy story have not mentioned it once."

"I," replied Cardenio, "am that luckless one whom, you tell me, Luscinda claimed for her bridegroom. I am the unfortunate Cardenio, who have been brought to the plight in which you now see me by the evil designs of the same one who is responsible for your being where you are. You behold me now, ragged, half-naked, lacking all human comfort, and, what is worse, lacking in reason as well, of which none is left me save when it pleases Heaven to restore it to me for a brief while. I, Dorotea, am he who was present when Don Fernando committed those wrongs, who waited to hear the yes uttered by his bride, Luscinda. I am he who did not have the courage to wait and see what came of her swoon or what resulted from the letter that was found in her bosom, for my soul did not have the power of suffering to endure so many misfortunes all at once. And so, I lost my patience and quit the house, leaving a letter with my host which I asked him to place in Luscinda's hands.

"After that, I came to these solitudes with the intention of spending the rest of my life here, a life which I hated as if it had been my mortal enemy. Fate, however, was not minded to end my existence, being content to deprive me of my reason, possibly with the object of preserving me for the good fortune of meeting you. If what you have told us is true, as I believe it is, it may be that Heaven has planned a better outcome for our calamities than we think. For since Luscinda, being mine as she openly declared herself to be, cannot marry Don Fernando, and Don Fernando, being yours, cannot marry her, we have a right to hope that Heaven will restore to us that which is ours, seeing that it still exists and has not been alienated or destroyed.

"And since we do have this comfort, not born of an exceedingly remote hope nor founded on the hallucinations of our own minds, I beg of you, lady, to adopt another resolution, letting your virtuous thoughts dwell upon it, as I myself mean to do: namely, to become used to looking forward to better times to come; for I swear to you by the faith of a gentleman and a Christian not to desert you until I see you possessed of Don Fernando. If words will not bring him to recognize his obligations to you, then I will make use of that privilege which my rank as a gentleman gives me and will justly challenge him, calling upon him to give an account of the wrong he has done you, without taking thought of those that I have suffered at his hands and which I shall leave to Heaven to avenge while I here on earth see to righting yours."

By the time that Cardenio finished speaking Dorotea had ceased to wonder at his appearance and, not knowing how to thank him for so great an offer, wished to take his feet and kiss them, but he would not consent. The licentiate replied for both of them, expressing approval of the fine sentiments that Cardenio had voiced, and then he begged, advised, and sought to persuade them to accompany him to his village where he could supply them with the things they lacked and where they could plan how to set about looking for Don Fernando and how to get Dorotea back to her parents, while making such other arrangements as might be necessary.

Cardenio and Dorotea accepted his offer with thanks, and the barber, who had been taking it all in without saying a word, now made a pleasing little speech, declaring his willingness as the curate had done to help them in any way in which he could best be of service. He also informed them what it was that had brought him and his companion to this place, and told them of Don Quixote's strange madness and how they were waiting for the latter's squire who had gone to look for him. Then it was that Cardenio recalled as in a dream the struggle he had had with the knight, and he related the incident to the others, although he no longer remembered what had occasioned the quarrel.

At this moment they heard a shout which the curate and the barber recognized as coming from Sancho Panza, who, not finding the pair where he had left them, was now calling to them at the top of his lungs. They thereupon went forward to meet him, and when they made inquiries concerning Don Quixote, he told them how he had found him clad only in his shirt, very lean, jaundiced-looking, near-dead with hunger, and sighing constantly for his lady Dulcinea. Sancho had told his master that Dulcinea had commanded him to leave this place and come to El Toboso where she was awaiting him, but the knight had replied that he was determined not to appear before his beauteous one until he should have performed such exploits as would render him deserving of her grace. And if all this kept up, the squire added, there was a danger that the poor man would never become an emperor as was his bounden duty, nor even so much as an archbishop, which was the very least that he ought to expect. And so, they must all put their heads together to see what could be done to get him away from there.

The licentiate replied by assuring Sancho that there was no cause for uneasiness, for they would rescue the knight whether he liked it or not. He then revealed to Cardenio and Dorotea the plan they had formed, by which they hoped, in any event, to be able to induce Don Quixote to return home with them. She thereupon remarked that she could play the part of the damsel in distress better than the barber; and what was more, she had with her the garments that would enable her to give a most lifelike semblance to the role. All they needed to do was to leave it all to her and she would see to everything that was necessary to the carrying out of their plan; for she had read many books of chivalry and was familiar with the mode of speech that was employed by afflicted maidens when they sought a boon of knights-errant.

"Well, then," said the curate, "it only remains for us to put our scheme into execution. Fortune is undoubtedly favoring you,[1] seeing that it has so unexpectedly opened the door for your relief, and by doing so it has at the same time facilitated our present task."

Dorotea then took from her pillowcase a skirt made of a certain rich woolen material and a *mantellina*[2] of elegant green cloth, and from a small box she drew forth a necklace and other jewels, and within a moment's time she was adorned as befitted a rich young lady of high estate. All these things and others too, she told them, she had brought with her from home in case of emergency, but up to then she had had no occasion to use them. They were all extremely pleased with her grace and beauty and highbred appearance, which led them to reflect that Don Fernando must have been a man of very little discernment to have cast aside such charms as these.

The one who admired her most of all, however, was Sancho Panza, for it seemed to him, which was indeed the truth, that he had never in all the days of his life beheld so ravishing a creature. He accordingly with great eagerness now inquired of the curate who this beautiful woman might be and what she was doing in these parts.

"This lovely lady, Sancho, my brother," replied the curate, "and let no one tell you otherwise, is heiress in the direct male line to the great kingdom of Micomicon,[3] and she comes here in search of your master to ask a favor of him, which is that he right the injury or wrong which a wicked giant has done her. By reason of the fame as a worthy knight which your master enjoys throughout the known world, this princess has journeyed all the way from Guinea to seek him out."[4]

"Happy search and happy find!" exclaimed Sancho upon hearing this. "And still more so if my master is fortunate enough to right the wrong and redress the injury by slaying that son of a whore of a giant that your Grace is speaking about. Slay him he will if he meets him and the giant is not a phantom, for against phantoms he can do nothing whatsoever. But there is one thing among others, Señor Licentiate, that I would ask of your Grace. In order that my master may not take it into his head to be an archbishop, which is what I am afraid of, I would have your Grace advise him to marry this princess and in that way it would be impossible for him to be ordained, and he would get his empire and I'd get my wish. For I have studied it all out very thoroughly and have come to the conclusion that it would not be a good thing for me if he took holy orders, since I, being married, am of no use to the Church, and it would be an endless business for me with my wife and children to set about trying to obtain a dispensation so that I could hold a benefice. And so, everything depends upon my master's marrying this lady—for as yet I am unacquainted with her Grace and cannot call her by name."

"Her name," said the curate," is Princess Micomicona, for inasmuch as her realm is Micomicon, it could not be anything else."

"I do not doubt that," replied Sancho, "for I have known many who took their name and title from the place where they were born, calling themselves Pedro of Alcalá, Juan of Ubeda, Diego of Valladolid, and so forth, and they must have this same custom in Guinea, that of calling queens after their kingdoms."

"Yes," agreed the curate, "that is the way it is. And as to marrying off your master, I will do all that lies within my power."

Sancho was as pleased with this as the curate was astonished at his simplicity. The priest could not but marvel still at the extent to which the master's mad whims had laid hold of his man's imagination, for there was no doubt that Panza had fully convinced himself that Don Quixote was going to be an emperor.

By this time Dorotea had seated herself upon the curate's mule and the barber had put on his oxtail beard, and they now directed Sancho to lead them to the place where the knight was, after first warning him to give no sign that he knew either the licentiate or his companion, since his master's becoming an emperor depended upon their not being recognized. However, neither Cardenio nor the curate wished to accompany them, the former fearing that Don Quixote would be reminded of their quarrel, while the latter felt that his presence was not called for as yet. They accordingly let the others go on ahead while they followed slowly on foot. The curate in the meantime had not failed to advise Dorotea as to how she was to conduct herself, but she replied that they should not worry about that, for she would do everything precisely as it should be done in accordance with the rules and descriptions in the books of chivalry.

They had gone about three-quarters of a league when they came upon Don Quixote amid a confused cluster of rocks. He was clothed now but did not have on his armor; and as soon as Dorotea had caught sight of him and had been assured that it was he, she applied the whip to her palfrey [5] and hastened toward him, followed by the well-bearded barber. As she drew near to where the knight stood, her squire leaped down from his mule and, taking her in his arms, assisted her to alight, which she did very gracefully. She then fell upon her knees in front of Don Quixote, and, though he did his best to lift her to her feet, she remained kneeling and addressed him in the following manner:

"I shall not rise from this spot, O brave and doughty knight, until you out of your courtesy and kindness shall have granted me a boon, one which will redound to your own honor and glory and which will be of advantage to the most grievously wronged and disconsolate maiden that ever the sun has looked upon. If your immortal fame is indeed borne out by the valor of your strong right arm, then you are bound to show favor to the hapless one who, brought here by the fragrance that attaches to your name of great renown, has come from distant lands to seek a remedy for her woes."

"I shall not answer you a word, beauteous lady," said Don Quixote, "nor will I hear anything more of your business until you rise."

"That, sir, I will not do," responded the afflicted damsel, "unless you first, out of your courtesy, grant me the boon I seek."

"I grant and bestow it," said the knight, "providing that it does no hurt or detriment to my king, my country, and the one who holds the key to the freedom of my heart."

"It shall not be to the hurt or detriment of any of those you mention, my good sir," was the grieving maiden's answer.

Sancho Panza then came up and whispered very softly in his master's ear, "Your Grace may very well grant her the boon she asks, for it is nothing at all: just killing a big giant, and she who asks it is the highborn Princess Micomicona, queen of the great kingdom of Micomicon, in Ethiopia."

"No matter who she may be." said Don Quixote, "I shall do my duty and follow the dictates of my conscience in accordance with the calling that I profess." And, turning to the damsel, he added, "Rise, most beautiful one; I grant you the boon you seek."

"What I ask, then," said the damsel, "is this: that your magnanimous person deign to accompany me at once to the place to which I shall conduct you, and that you further promise me not to concern yourself with any other adventure or request until you shall have taken vengeance on a traitor who, in defiance of all laws human and divine, has usurped my kingdom."

"I tell you again that I grant it," said the knight. "And so, lady, you may now lay aside the melancholy that oppresses you and let your fainting hope recover new strength and courage; for by the aid of God and my good arm you shall soon see your kingdom restored to you and shall sit once again on the throne of your great and ancient realm in spite of all the knaves who would forbid it. To work, then; for it is the common saying that there is danger in delay." [6]

The distressed lady stubbornly insisted upon kissing his hands, but Don Quixote, who in every respect was the courteous and obliging gentleman, would by no means consent to this. Instead, he made her rise and then embraced her with great affability and politeness. He thereupon ordered Sancho to see to Rocinante's girths at once and bring him his suit of armor, which was hanging like a trophy from the bough of a tree. The squire did as he had been commanded. Having taken down the armor, he helped his master on with it, and then, seeing his steed in readiness and himself in battle harness, Don Quixote spoke.

"Let us go," he said, "in the name of God, that we may succor this great lady."

The barber was still on his knees, doing his best to keep from laughing and to prevent his beard from falling off, for if that had happened they would not have been able to carry out their clever scheme. Upon hearing the boon granted and perceiving that Don Quixote was so ready to embark upon the enterprise, he arose and took his lady's other hand and between the two of them they helped her on the mule. The knight then mounted Rocinante and the barber his own beast, while Sancho came along on foot, which led him to think once more of the gray ass whose loss he now felt worse than ever, although he bore it all very cheerfully, being convinced that his master was on the road to becoming an emperor very soon; for there was no doubt that he would marry this princess and become at the very least king of Micomicon. The only thing that troubled Sancho was that the kingdom in question was in the land of the blacks, and his vassals accordingly would all be Negroes. But for this he at once thought of a good remedy.

"Does it make any difference to me if they are black?" he said to himself. "What more do I have to do than take a boatload of them to Spain and sell them for ready cash, and with the money buy some title or office and live at ease all the rest of my life? That is to say, unless I'm asleep and am not clever or shrewd enough to make the most of things and sell thirty or ten thousand vassals in the twinkling of an eye! By God, but I'd make them fly, the little with the big, or do the best I could at it; I'd turn the blacks into white or yellow men! But come, I'm making a fool of myself!" [7]

Occupied with these thoughts, he went along so contentedly that he forgot all about his annoyance at having to travel on foot.

Observing all this from behind a thicket, Cardenio and the curate did not know just how to set about joining the others, but the priest, who was a great schemer, at once thought up a means by which they could accomplish what they desired. Taking out a pair of scissors that he carried with him in a sheath, he very skillfully trimmed Cardenio's beard and then threw over his companion's shoulders a drab-colored cape that he wore, giving him in addition a black coat, while he himself remained in breeches and doublet; all of which so altered the young man's appearance that he would not have recognized his own image in a mirror. While they were thus engaged in disguising themselves, the others had gone on ahead, but they had little difficulty in reaching the highroad before Don Quixote and his party did, for owing to the brambles and the rough places it was impossible to make as good time mounted as on foot. They therewith took up their position on the plain at the entrance to the mountain passes, and as soon as Don Quixote and his companions appeared, the curate began staring at the knight from afar, making signs as if he recognized him. After he had stood gazing at him in this fashion for a little while, he went up to him with open arms.

"Why bless me!" he exclaimed, "what a fortunate thing that I should here encounter the mirror of chivalry, my good countryman, Don Quixote de la Mancha, the flower and cream of nobility, friend and protector of those in distress, the very quintessence of knight-errantry!"

Saying this, he embraced the knight's left knee. Startled at the man's words and behavior, Don Quixote studied him attentively for a moment or so and then, recognizing him at last and being very much taken aback at seeing him there, made a great effort to dismount. The curate, however, would not permit him to do so.

"But allow me, Señor Licentiate," Don Quixote protested. "It is not fitting that I should remain mounted while a reverend person like your Grace is on foot."

"To that," replied the curate, "I can by no means give my consent. Let your Excellency remain on horseback since it was on horseback that you accomplished the greatest exploits and adventures that this age of ours has known. As for me, unworthy priest that I am, it will be enough if I may ride the crupper of one of the mules belonging to these gentlefolk who are of your company—that is to say, if there is no objection to it. If you grant this, it will seem to me that I go mounted on the steed Pegasus, or upon the zebra, or else upon the charger that the famous Moor Muzaraque rode, the same Muzaraque who to this day lies enchanted beneath the great slope of Zulema, not far distant from the great Complutum." [8]

"That, Señor Licentiate, is something to which I in turn cannot agree," said Don Quixote. "I am sure that my lady the princess will do me the favor of commanding her squire to yield you his saddle upon the mule, and he can ride the beast's crupper if she will allow it."

"She will, I am sure," said the princess; "and as to commanding my squire, that will not be necessary, for he is so courteous and urbane that he would never think of letting a churchman go on foot while he himself was in the saddle."

"Indeed, I would not," said the barber. And, dismounting at once, he offered his seat to the curate, who accepted it without much urging.

The unfortunate thing was, however, that just as the barber was settling himself upon the crupper, the mule—which was one of those that are for hire, that is to say, a bad one—raised its hind quarters in the air and gave a couple of kicks which, had he received them in the head or chest, would have caused Master Nicholas to curse himself for ever having come in search of Don Quixote. As it was, the shock was such that he was thrown to the ground, and at the same time his beard, to which he was able to give little thought, fell off. Finding himself without it, he could think of nothing better to do than cover his face with both hands and moan that his grinders had been knocked out.

Seeing that heap of beard lying there, far from the squire's face but without any sign of jawbone or blood, Don Quixote cried out, "By the living God, this is a miracle! His beard has been knocked off and torn away from his face as cleanly as if he had deliberately shaved it off."

The curate, seeing that his scheme was in danger of being discovered, ran over and, snatching up the beard, took it over to where Master Nicholas still lay. Drawing the barber's head down to his chest, he quickly attached the oxtail once more, muttering certain words as he did so which he said were a psalm that was appropriate to the sticking-on of beards, as they would see for themselves. Then he stepped aside, and there was the squire as well bearded and sound of limb as he had been before. Don Quixote was tremendously impressed by this and begged the curate, when he had time, to teach him that psalm, since it must be possessed of virtues beyond the one just demonstrated, it being obvious that when beards are torn off the flesh must remain raw and bleeding, but there was nothing like that in the present instance. The psalm, then, must be good for something more than beards.

"That it is," said the curate; and he promised to teach it to him at the first opportunity.

It was agreed upon among them that for the present the curate should mount the mule and that he should take turns with Cardenio and the barber until they reached the inn, a distance of some two leagues from there.[9] There were, then, three of them in the saddle, namely, Don Quixote, the princess, and the priest, while the other three walked along beside them.

As they started out, the knight turned to the damsel. "My lady," he said, "will your Highness be so good as to lead the way?"

Before she could reply, the licentiate spoke up. "Toward what kingdom does your Ladyship mean to guide us? Is it by any chance the realm of Micomicon? I take it that it is, or I know little of kingdoms."

She, being well schooled in everything, understood that she was supposed to answer yes, and so she said, "Yes, sir, my road lies toward that realm."

"If that is so," said the curate, "then we shall have to pass through my village, and from there your Grace will take the highway to Cartagena, where with good fortune you will be able to embark; and if you have a fair wind and a calm sea without squalls, in less than nine years you should come within sight of the great Meona—I mean Meotides—lake,[10] which is only a little more than a hundred days' journey from your Highness's kingdom."

"Your Grace is mistaken," she replied, "for it is not yet two years since

I left there; and although the truth is that I never had good weather, nevertheless I am here to behold that which I so greatly desired: Señor Don Quixote de la Mancha, whose fame, reaching my ears the moment I set foot in Spain, has induced me to seek him out, commend myself to his courtesy, and entrust my cause to the might of his invincible arm."

"That will be enough!" said Don Quixote. "Let me hear no more words of praise! For I am opposed to any kind of adulation, and even though this be no fawning, such talk for all of that offends my chaste ears. But one thing I may tell you, my lady: whether my arm is or is not possessed of might, it shall be employed in your service until I yield my life in your behalf. But, leaving all this for the time being, I should like to ask the Señor Licentiate what it is that brings him to these parts, alone, unaccompanied even by servants, and so lightly clad that I am really amazed by it."

"I can answer that in a few words," said the curate. "I may inform your Grace that I and Master Nicholas, our friend and barber, were on our way to Seville to collect a certain sum of money which a relative of mine who went to the Indies many years ago had sent me. It was not so small a sum at that, since it came to more than seventy thousand pieces of eight duly assayed, which is something. And as we were passing through this region yesterday we were set upon by four highwaymen who stripped us of everything down to our beards and, as a result, the barber had to put on a false one. Even this young man here," and he pointed to Cardenio, "they so mistreated that you would not recognize him.

"And the best part of it is," the curate went on, "it is a matter of common rumor around here that those who set upon us were certain galley slaves who, so they tell me, had been freed on this very spot by a man so valiant that, in spite of the commissary and the guards, he was able to turn them all loose. He must undoubtedly have been out of his mind, or else he must be as great a villain as they, some soulless creature without a conscience; for one might as well think of turning the wolf loose among the sheep, the fox among the hens, the fly in the honey,[11] as to seek to defraud justice and go against the king, his natural liege lord, for this was indeed an act against his Majesty's just commandments. I tell you, that one has cheated the gallows of their feet, has aroused the Holy Brotherhood which for many years had been quiet, and, finally, has committed an act for which he well may lose his soul while his body gains nothing by it."

Sancho had told the curate and the barber about the adventure of the

galley slaves and the glory that his master had achieved thereby; and the
priest now thought that he would allude to it by way of seeing what Don
Quixote would say or do. The knight changed color at every word and
did not dare to tell them that he was the one who had freed those worthy
folk.

"And they," continued the curate, "were the ones who robbed us.
May God in His mercy pardon him who kept them from the punishment
they deserved."

CHAPTER XXX. *Which treats of the fair Dor-otea's ready wit and other matters very pleasant and amusing.*

THE curate had scarcely finished speaking when Sancho addressed
him.

"Faith, Señor Licentiate," he said, "the one who performed that deed
was my master. Not that I didn't warn him beforehand and advise him
to look to what he was doing, it being a sin to free them, for they were
all of them the greatest rogues that ever were."

"Blockhead!" cried Don Quixote upon hearing this. "It is not the
business of knights-errant to stop and ascertain as to whether the afflicted
and oppressed whom they encounter going along the road in chains like
that are in such straits by reason of their crimes or as a result of misfortunes that they have suffered. The only thing that does concern them
is to aid those individuals as persons in distress, with an eye to their sufferings and not to their villainies. I chanced to meet with a rosary, or string,
of poor wretches and merely did for them that which my religion demands of me. As for the rest, that is no affair of mine. And whoever thinks
ill of it—saving the dignity of your holy office and your respected person, Señor Licentiate—I will simply say that he knows little of the laws
of chivalry and lies like an ill-begotten son of a whore. All of which I
will make plain to him, to the fullest extent, with my sword."

Having said this, he settled himself in the stirrups and pulled down his morion; for the barber's basin, which to him was Mambrino's helmet, he carried hanging from the saddletree in front of him until such time as he could have the damage repaired that the galley slaves had done to it. Then Dorotea, who was a very discerning and witty young lady, perceiving the mad character of Don Quixote's fancies and noting that all the others with the exception of Sancho were making sport of him, decided that she would have her share of the fun; and observing how annoyed he was, she now spoke to him.

"Sir Knight," she said, "I would remind your Grace of the boon that you have promised me, and of the stipulation that you are not to engage in any other adventure however urgent it may be. And so, let your Grace calm that breast of yours, for had the Señor Licentiate known that it was by your unconquered arm those prisoners were liberated, he would have taken three stitches in his lip or would have bit his tongue three times before he would have spoken a disrespectful word of your Grace."

"That I would, I swear it," said the curate, "and I would even have lopped off a mustache."

"I will be silent, my lady," Don Quixote assured her. "I will repress the just wrath that has arisen in my bosom and will go along quietly and peacefully until I shall have rendered you the boon that I have promised. But in return for this good will on my part, I beg you, if it will not trouble you too much, to tell me what the nature of your grievance is and who, how many, and of what sort are the persons of whom I am to demand full satisfaction and upon whom I am to wreak an utter vengeance."

"That I will gladly do," replied Dorotea, "if it will not tire you to listen to my griefs and misfortunes."

"It most certainly will not, my lady," said Don Quixote.

"Very well, then," continued Dorotea, "pay attention, kind sirs."

As she said this, Cardenio and the barber came up alongside her, for they were curious to see how her ready wit would serve her in making up her story; and Sancho likewise drew near, though he was as much deceived by her as was his master. Having straightened herself in the saddle, she coughed a little and indulged in a few other mannerisms by way of gaining time and then with an easy grace began her narrative.

"In the first place, I would have your Worships know that I am called—" At this point she paused for a moment, for she had forgotten the name which the curate had bestowed upon her. He, however, seeing what her trouble was, promptly came to her rescue.

"It is no wonder, my lady," he said, "if your Highness in relating your misfortunes should become confused and embarrassed; for they are of the kind that very frequently deprive those who suffer them of their memory, so that they are unable even to remember their own names. That is what has happened to your exalted Ladyship, who has forgotten that she is the Princess Micomicona, legitimate heiress to the great kingdom of Micomicon; but with this reminder, your Highness will readily be able to recall all that she may desire to tell us."

"That is true enough," said the damsel. "And from now on, I do not believe that I shall require any more prompting but shall be able to bring this true story of mine safely into port. To continue, then: The king my father bore the name Tinacrio the Wise, being very learned in what is known as the art of magic. It was through this science that he learned that my mother, the queen Jaramilla, was to die before he did and that he himself shortly after would pass from this life, leaving me bereaved of father and mother alike. He said, however, that this did not cause him so much anxiety as did the certain knowledge of what a monstrous giant, the lord of a great island near our kingdom who was called Pandafilando of the Frowning Look, was to do when he heard that I was left an orphan. This giant was so called for the reason that, so it was asserted, though his eyes were straight enough, he always squinted as if cross-eyed by way of giving himself a malignant appearance and striking fear and terror in those who beheld him.

"But as I was saying: My father knew that this giant, upon learning that I was an orphan, was to overrun my kingdom with a powerful army and drive me out of it, without leaving me so much as a tiny village where I might take refuge. The only thing that could save me from all this ruin and misfortune was for me to consent to marry him, but my father predicted that I would never agree to so unsuitable a match, and in this he was quite right, for I never would have entertained the thought of taking this or any other giant for a husband, however powerful and lawless he might be.

"My father also said that when, following his death, I saw my realm being overrun by Pandafilando, I should not wait to put myself upon the defensive, since that would be sheer self-destruction, but that, if I would avoid the slaughter of my good and loyal vassals, I should leave the kingdom free and open to him, since it would be impossible to defend myself against his diabolic strength. What I rather must do was to take a few attendants and set out for Spain, where I would find relief for my troubles in the person of a certain knight-errant, whose fame at that time extended throughout the whole of our country and whose name, unless my memory plays me false, was Azote or Don Gigote—"

"Don Quixote it should be, lady," Sancho Panzo corrected her, "otherwise known as the Knight of the Mournful Countenance."

"Yes, that is it," said Dorotea. "My father told me more: that this knight was to be tall, with a lean face, and that on his right side, under his left shoulder, or somewhere thereabouts, he was to have a brown mole with a few hairs around it resembling bristles."

Upon hearing this, Don Quixote said to his squire, "Come here, Sancho, my son, and help me undress, for I wish to see if I am the knight that wise king meant when he made that prophecy."

"But why undress, your Grace?" asked Dorotea.

"To see if I have the mole that your father spoke of," Don Quixote replied.

"There is no need of your Grace's doing that," said Sancho, "for I happen to know that you have a mole with those markings in the middle of your backbone, which is the sign of a strong man."

"That will suffice," said Dorotea. "With friends, one does not look into little things, and whether it is on his shoulder or his backbone does not greatly matter; it is enough that he has it wherever it may be, seeing that it is all of the same flesh. There is no doubt that my father was right in everything, and I was right in throwing myself on the mercy of Don Quixote. I know that he is the one my father meant, for the signs of his face are in accord with the high repute which this knight enjoys not only in Spain but throughout La Mancha. Indeed, I had barely disembarked at Osuna when I heard of all his many exploits, and my heart at once told me that he was the one I had come to seek."

"But, my lady," said Don Quixote, "how is it that your Grace disembarked at Osuna when it is not a seaport?"

Before she could reply, the curate took a hand in the matter. "What the princess must mean," he said, "is that after she had disembarked at Málaga, the first place that she had news of your Grace was in Osuna."

"Yes, that is what I meant to say," said Dorotea.

"That is all natural enough," remarked the priest. "And now, if your Highness will continue—"

"There is nothing more to add, except that, in the end, fate has been kind to me and I have found Señor Don Quixote. As a consequence, I already account and look upon myself as the queen and liege lady of all my realm, since he out of his courtesy and splendid bounty has promised to grant me the boon of going with me wherever I may take him, and that will be nowhere else than to the place where he may confront Pandafilando of the Frowning Look, in order that he may slay him and restore to me those domains that the giant has so unjustly usurped. And all this is bound to come about, for my good father, Tinacrio the Wise, has prophesied it; and he also said, and put it down in writing, in Chaldean or Greek characters which I am unable to read, that if this knight, after having beheaded the giant, wished to marry me, I was to give myself at once, with not the slightest demurring, to be his legitimate bride, and I was to yield him possession of my kingdom along with that of my person."

"What do you think of that, friend Sancho?" said Don Quixote at this point. "Do you hear what is happening? What did I tell you? Just look, we already have a kingdom to rule over and a queen to wed."

"You're right, I'll swear you are," said Sancho, "and he's a whoring rascal who wouldn't slit that Señor Pandahilado's windpipe and marry her! Why, just see how homely she is! I only wish the fleas in my bed were like that!"

Saying this, he gave a couple of leaps in the air with a great show of satisfaction and then ran up to take the reins of Dorotea's mule; forcing her to come to a halt, he fell upon his knees before her, begging her to let him have her hands to kiss as a sign that he took her to be his queen and mistress. Who would not have had a good laugh over it all, at beholding the master's madness and his servant's simple-mindedness? Dorotea let him kiss her hand and promised to make him a great lord of her realm, whenever Heaven should be so kind as to let her recover and enjoy it. And Sancho thanked her for these favors in words that set them all to laughing once more.

"That, gentlemen," continued the princess, "is my story. It only remains for me to tell you that of the many subjects whom I brought along there is left me only this well-bearded squire, for all the others were drowned in a great storm which overtook us within sight of port. He and I by a miracle managed to reach land upon a couple of planks; but, for that matter, my entire life is at once a miracle and a mystery, as you will have observed. If in telling my story I have in any respect been too prolix or not as accurate as I should have been, the blame must be ascribed to the circumstance which the curate mentioned at the beginning: the tendency of constant and extraordinary troubles to deprive those who suffer them of their memory."

"They shall not deprive me of mine, O highborn and worthy lady!"

said Don Quixote. "And it makes no difference how many I shall have
to endure in serving you nor how great and unheard of they may be. And
so, once again I confirm the boon I promised you and swear to go with
you to the end of the world until I find myself face to face with that
fierce enemy of yours. God helping me, and my own good arm, I mean
to cut off his head with the edge of this—I cannot say good sword, thanks
to Ginés de Pasamonte who carried mine away with him." [1] (This was
uttered between his teeth.) "And after I have cut it off," he went on,
"and have placed you in peaceful possession of your country, it will then
be for you to make such disposition of your person as you may desire;
for so long as my memory is occupied, my will held captive, and my mind
enslaved by a certain lady—I say no more—it is out of the question for me
to think of marrying anyone, even the Phoenix herself."

This last remark on the part of his master, to the effect that he did not
wish to marry, displeased Sancho very much, and it was with a great deal
of annoyance that he now spoke to the knight.

"Señor Don Quixote," he exclaimed, "I swear and vow that you are not
in your right senses! How can your Grace hesitate about marrying so
highborn a princess? Do you think that fortune is going to offer you
behind every stone such a piece of luck as this? Is my lady Dulcinea more
beautiful, perchance? No, indeed, not by a half; and I will even say that
she does not come up to the shoe of the one you see in front of you. A
fine chance I have of getting that earldom I'm waiting for if your Grace
goes around looking for tidbits at the bottom of the ocean. [2] Marry, then,
marry, in Satan's name, and take this kingdom which is falling into your
hands with no effort on your part; [3] and then, when you are king, make
me a marquis or the governor of a province, and to the devil with all the
rest."

Unable to endure such blasphemies against his lady Dulcinea, Don
Quixote raised his lance and, without saying a word to Sancho or giving
him a warning of any kind, he let him have a couple of thwacks which
sent him sprawling on the ground; and if Dorotea had not cried out to
him to desist, the knight undoubtedly would have finished off his squire
then and there.

"Do you think, base lout," he said after a while, "that you can always
be meddling in my affairs and that you can do anything you like and
I will forgive you? If so, excommunicated knave, for that undoubtedly
is what you are, think it no longer, now that you have set your tongue
to wagging against the peerless Dulcinea! Do you not know, clodhopper,
drudge, scoundrel, that if it were not for the valor she infuses into my

arm, I should not have the strength to kill a flea? Tell me, rascal with a viper's tongue, what do you think it was that won this kingdom and cut off that giant's head and made you a marquis—for I regard all this as a thing settled and accomplished—unless it was Dulcinea's own valor making use of my arm merely as the instrument for the achievement of her own enterprises? She fights and conquers in my person, and I live and breathe and have my life and being in her. O knavish son of a whoring mother, how ungrateful you are! You see yourself raised from the dust of the earth to be a titled lord, and all this you repay by speaking ill of your benefactress!"

Sancho was not so badly stunned that he did not hear all his master was saying, and, scrambling to his feet with some agility, he ran and stood behind Dorotea's palfrey and from there answered the knight.

"Tell me this, sir," he said. "If your Grace is bent upon not marrying this great princess, then it is clear that the kingdom will not be yours, and if that is the case, what favors will you be in a position to do me? That is just what I am complaining about. Let your Grace marry this queen once and for all, now that we have her here as if she had been rained down from Heaven, and afterward you can go back to my lady Dulcinea. After all, there must have been kings in this world who kept concubines. So far as beauty is concerned, I'm not saying anything about that. To tell you the truth, I like them both, although I have never seen the lady Dulcinea."

"What do you mean, you have never seen her, blasphemous traitor?" said Don Quixote. "Did you not just bring me a message from her?"

"What I mean," replied Sancho, "is that I did not have a good look at her. That is to say, I did not have a chance to take particular note of her beauty and her good features, point by point, but in the bulk I liked her well enough."

"Then I forgive you," said Don Quixote, "and pardon me for having lost my temper, for it is not in the power of men to control their first impulses."

"I can see that," said Sancho. "My first impulse is always the desire to speak, and I cannot keep from saying for once at least whatever is on the tip of my tongue."

"Nevertheless," his master admonished him, "be careful of your words, Sancho; for the pitcher that goes to the well too often—I need say no more." [4]

"Ah, well," replied his squire, "God's in his Heaven and sees all our tricks, and He will be the judge of who is the greater sinner: I in not speaking as I should, or you in doing what you should not do."

"Let's have no more of this!" cried Dorotea. "Sancho, run over and kiss your master's hand and beg his pardon, and from now on be more careful of whom you praise and whom you vituperate, and do not be speaking ill of that lady Tobosa, whom I do not know but whose servant I am. Meanwhile, trust in God to raise you to that condition where you may live like a prince."

Hanging his head, Sancho then came up and asked for his master's hand, and Don Quixote extended it with great dignity and composure. After the squire had kissed it, the knight gave him his blessing and then suggested that they go on a little way together as he had something to ask him and some very important matters to discuss with him.

Sancho complied with this request, and when they were some little distance in advance of the others, Don Quixote said to him, "Since you returned, I have not had the time nor the opportunity to question you with regard to many of the details connected with your mission and the answer that you brought back with you; and now that fortune does provide the time and the place, do not deny me the pleasure that you can give me with such good news."

"Ask whatever you will, your Grace," said Sancho, "and I will find my way out of everything as well as I found my way in. But I beg your Grace not to be so revengeful after this."

"Why do you say that, Sancho?"

"I say it," he replied, "because those blows you gave me just now were more for the quarrel that the devil got us into the other night than for anything that I said against my lady Dulcinea, whom I love and reverence as I would a relic—not that I mean to say she is one; I was merely thinking of her as something belonging to your Grace."

"Upon your life, Sancho," said Don Quixote, "let us not go back to that subject, for it is one that causes me annoyance. I have pardoned you for it once, and you know the saying—'Fresh sin, fresh penance.'" [5]

[As they were proceeding in this manner, they saw coming down the road toward them a man mounted upon an ass, who, as he drew near, appeared to them to be a gypsy. But Sancho Panza, whose heart and soul were stirred every time he caught sight of a donkey, had no sooner laid eyes on the fellow than he recognized him as Ginés de Pasamonte, and in this case the gypsy served as the thread that led him to the yarn-ball of his stolen gray, for it was indeed the gray upon which Pasamonte was riding. That worthy, in order to dispose of the ass and avoid being identified, had got himself up in gypsy costume, for he knew how to speak their language and many others as if they had been his native tongue.

As soon as Sancho had seen and recognized him, he called out at the top of his voice, "Hey, Ginesillo, you thief! Release my jewel, my treasure, my life, the beast on which I take my rest. Flee, you whoring knave; begone, you robber, and leave me that which is not yours!"

All these words and insults were quite unnecessary, for at the first sound of Sancho's voice Ginés had leaped down and, trotting, or, better, running, away, had soon left them all behind. Sancho then went up to the gray and threw his arms around it.

"How have you been, old friend," he said, "joy of my life, apple of my eye?" With this, he kissed and caressed it as if it had been a person, the ass standing quietly all the while, submitting without a word to this show of affection. The others now came up and congratulated him on the recovery of the beast, especially Don Quixote, who assured him that he would not for this reason annul the order for the three ass-colts, for which Sancho thanked him very much.]

As the two [6] went along conversing in this manner, the curate remarked to Dorotea that she had shown a great deal of cleverness in the telling of her story as well as in keeping it so short and preserving so close a resemblance to the books of chivalry. She replied that she had often found entertainment in reading those books; but, unfortunately, she was unfamiliar with the various provinces and seaports and so had said, quite at random, that she had landed at Osuna.

"I suspected as much," said the curate, "and for that reason I came to your assistance by saying what I did, which smoothed everything over. But is it not a strange thing to see how readily this unfortunate gentleman believes all these falsehoods and inventions, simply because they are in the style and manner of those absurd tales?"

"It is indeed," said Cardenio, "so rare and unheard of a thing that if anyone desired to invent and fabricate it, in the form of fiction, I do not know if there would be any mind that would be equal to the task."

"But there is another aspect of the matter," the curate went on. "Outside of the nonsense that he talks where his madness is concerned, if some other subject comes up he will discuss it most intelligently and will reason everything out very calmly and clearly; and, accordingly, unless the topic of chivalry is mentioned, no one would ever take him to be anything other than a man of very sound sense."

While this conversation was in progress, Don Quixote was saying to Sancho, "Friend Sancho, let us make up our quarrel. And now, laying aside all rancor and irritation, tell me how and when it was you found Dulcinea. What was she doing? What did you say to her and what did she reply? What was the expression on her face when she read my letter? Who copied it out for you? Tell me all this and everything else that seems to you worth knowing or asking about or concerning which I might be curious, neither adding anything nor telling me anything that is not true merely to please me; and be sure that you do not shorten the story and thereby deprive me of any of it."

"Sir," replied Sancho, "if I am to tell the truth, the letter was not copied for me by anyone, for I did not have it with me."

"That is true enough," said Don Quixote, "for a couple of days after you had left I found the memorandum book in which I had written it out and was very much grieved about it, not knowing what you would do when you found you did not have it, though I felt sure you would return for it."

"That is what I'd have done," said Sancho, "if I hadn't learned it by heart while your Grace was reading it to me, so that I was able to recite it to a sacristan who copied it all down for me, point by point. And he said that in the course of his life he had read many a letter of excommunication but never a pretty one like that."

"And do you still remember it, Sancho?" Don Quixote asked.

"No, sir, I do not; for as soon as I had said it over to him, seeing that I had no further need of remembering it, I proceeded to forget it. If there is anything I do recall, it is that business about the sufferable—I mean, sovereign—lady, and the ending, 'Yours until death, the Knight of the Mournful Countenance.' And between those two I put in 'my soul,' 'my life,' and 'light of my eyes,' more than three hundred times."

CHAPTER XXXI. *Of the delectable conversation that took place between Don Quixote and Sancho Panza, his squire, together with other events.*

"ALL this does not displease me," said Don Quixote. "You may continue. What was my beauteous queen engaged in doing when you arrived? Surely you must have found her stringing pearls or embroidering some device in gold thread for this her captive knight."

"No," replied Sancho, "I did not. I found her winnowing two fanegas [1] of wheat in the stable yard of her house."

"If that is so," said Don Quixote, "then you may be sure that those grains of wheat were so many pearls when her fingers touched them. And did you observe, my friend, if the wheat was fine and white or of the ordinary spring-sown variety?"

"It was neither," Sancho informed him; "it was the reddish kind."

"Then I assure you," the knight insisted, "that without a doubt, when winnowed by her hands, it made the finest of white bread. But go on. When you gave her my letter, did she kiss it? Did she place it on her head [2] or accord it any ceremony such as it deserved? If not, what was it that she did?"

"When I went to give it to her," said Sancho, "she was busy swinging the sieve, with a good part of the wheat in it, from side to side. 'Lay it on that sack,' she said to me. 'I'll not have time to read it until I have finished sifting all that there is here.'"

"Discreet lady!" said Don Quixote. "That was in order that she might take her time in reading it and revel in it. Continue, Sancho. While she was thus occupied, what words passed between you? Did she ask after me? And what did you say in reply? Come, tell me all and do not leave the smallest part of it in the inkwell." [3]

"She asked me nothing," said Sancho, "but I told her how your Grace, in her service, was doing penance naked from the waist up, living in these mountains like a wild animal, sleeping on the ground, without eating bread off a tablecloth or combing your beard, and weeping and cursing over your unhappy fate."

"That was wrong to say that I was cursing my unhappy fate; the truth is, I bless it and shall do so all the days of my life, for having rendered me worthy of loving so highborn a lady as Dulcinea del Toboso."

"She is so high," said Sancho, "that she tops me by more than a hand's breadth."

"How do you come to know that, Sancho? Did you measure with her?"

"I measured in this way. When I went to help her lift a sack of wheat onto a mule's back, we stood so close alongside each other that I could see she was the taller by more than a good-sized palm."

"That may be true," said Don Quixote, "though her height is accompanied and set off by a thousand million spiritual graces! You will not deny one thing, Sancho: that when you come near her you are conscious of a Sabaean odor, an aromatic fragrance, an indescribable and pleasing something for which I can find no name? What I mean is, an exhalation or emanation, as if one were in the shop of some exquisite glovemaker."

"All I can tell you," said Sancho, "is that I did notice a sort of mannish smell about her—it must have been because she was working so hard and all in a sweat."

"No," said Don Quixote, "it could not have been that. You must have been suffering from a cold in the head, or else it was yourself that you were smelling; for I well know what the fragrance of that rose among thorns is like—that lily of the field, that bit of diluted amber."

"You may be right," said Sancho, "for very often that same smell comes from me that I then thought was coming from her Grace, the lady Dulcinea. There's nothing surprising in that, for one devil's like another, you know."

"Very well, then," continued Don Quixote, "she has finished sifting her wheat and sent it to the mill. What did she do when she read the letter?"

"She did not read it; for, as I have told you, she does not know how to read or write. Instead, she tore it up into small pieces, saying she did not want anyone else to see it and have her private affairs known in the village. It was enough what I had told her about the love your Grace has for her and the extraordinary penance you are doing for her sake. Finally, she said to tell your Grace that she kissed your hands and that she would rather see you than write to you. And she further begged and commanded you, upon receipt of this message, to leave off your foolishness, come out of these woods, and set out at once for El Toboso before something worse happened to you, for she was very anxious for a sight of your Grace. She had a good laugh when I told her that your Grace was known as the Knight of the Mournful Countenance. I asked her if the Biscayan that we met a long while ago had been there, and she told me that he had been and that he was a very fine man. I also asked after the galley slaves, but she said she had seen nothing of any of them as yet."

"All goes very well up to now," said Don Quixote. "But tell me, what jewel was it that she gave you when you took your leave, in return for the news of me that you had brought her? For it is the usage and ancient custom among knights- and ladies-errant to present to the squires, damsels, or dwarfs who bring them word of their mistresses or their champions some costly gem as a guerdon and token of appreciation of the message they have received."

"That may all be true," said Sancho, "and I think it is a very good custom myself; but that must have been in times past, for nowadays all that they commonly give you is a little bread and cheese, which is what I had from my lady Dulcinea. She handed it to me over the wall of the stable yard as I was leaving, and that it might be still more of a token, it was cheese made from sheep's milk."

"She is extremely generous," observed Don Quixote, "and if she did not give you a golden jewel, it was undoubtedly because she did not have one at hand, for sleeves are good after Easter.[4] I shall see her and everything will be taken care of. But do you know what astonishes me, Sancho? I think you must have gone and returned through the air, for it has taken you less than three days to make the journey from here to El Toboso and back, a distance of more than thirty leagues. Which leads me to think that the wise necromancer who watches over my affairs and is a friend of mine—for there must be someone of that sort or else I should not be a real knight-errant—I think he must have aided you without your knowing it. For there are cases in which one of those magicians will snatch up a knight-errant as he lies sleeping in his bed and, without his knowing how or in what manner it was done, the next morning that knight will find himself thousands of leagues away from where he was the evening before.

"If it were not for this, knights-errant would not be able to succor one another when in peril as they are in the habit of doing all the time. For it may happen that one of them is fighting in the mountains of Armenia with some dragon or other fierce monster or with another knight, and he is having the worst of the battle and is at the point of death when suddenly, just as he least expects it, there appears over his head upon a cloud or a chariot of fire another knight, a friend of his, who a short while before was in England and who has now come to aid him and save him from death; and that same evening he is back at his lodgings having a pleasant dinner, although from one place to the other is a distance of two or three thousand leagues. All this is done through the wisdom and ingenuity of those skilled enchanters who watch over valiant knights. And so, friend Sancho, it is not hard for me to believe that you have gone from here to El Toboso and back in so short a space of time, for, as I have said, some wise magician must have carried you through the air without your knowing it."

"That may be," said Sancho, "for 'pon my word, if Rocinante didn't go as if he had been a gypsy's donkey with quicksilver in his ears!" [5]

"Quicksilver indeed!" exclaimed Don Quixote; "and a legion of devils besides, for they are folk who can travel and cause others to travel without growing weary, whenever the fancy takes them. But, putting all this aside, what do you think I should do now about going to see my lady as she has commanded? On the one hand, I am obligated to obey her command, and on the other, this is rendered impossible by the promise I have given to the princess who accompanies us, and the law of knighthood requires that I should keep my word before satisfying my own inclinations. I am wearied and harassed with longing to see my lady, yet my pledged word and the glory to be won in this undertaking calls to me and spurs me on.

"What I plan to do, accordingly, is to go with all haste to where this giant is, and then, after I have cut off his head and restored the princess to the peaceful possession of her throne, I shall return at once to see the light that illuminates my senses, giving her such excuses for my delay that she will come to be glad of it, inasmuch as it all redounds to her greater fame and glory. All that I have ever achieved or shall achieve by force of arms in this life is due to the favor she bestows upon me and the fact that I am hers."

"Ah," cried Sancho, "what a sad muddle your Grace's brains are in! For tell me, sir, do you mean to go all that way for nothing and let slip the chance of making so rich and important a match as this, where the bride's dowry is a kingdom? A kingdom which in all truth, I have heard them say, is more than twenty thousand leagues around, which abounds in all the things that are necessary to support human life, and which, in short, is greater than Portugal and Castile combined. For the love of God, do not talk like that, but be ashamed of what you have just said. Pardon me and take my advice, which is that you get married in the first village where you find a curate; or, for that matter, here is our own licentiate, who would do a first-rate job. Believe me, I am old enough to be giving advice, and this that I now give you is very pat; for a small bird in the hand is worth more than a vulture on the wing,[6] and he who has the good and chooses the bad, let the good that he longs for not come to him." [7]

"See here, Sancho," said Don Quixote, "if the reason for your advising me to marry is that you wish me, when I have slain the giant, to become a king at once so that I shall be in a position to grant you the favors I have promised, I may inform you that without marrying I can very easily gratify your desires; for before going into battle I shall lay down the condition that, in case I come out victorious, whether I marry or not, they are to give me a part of the kingdom which I may bestow upon whom-soever I see fit, and to whom should I give it if not to you?"

"That is fair enough," said Sancho, "but let your Grace see to it that my part is on the seacoast, so that, if I don't like the life there, I can take ship with my Negro vassals and do with them what I have said. Mean-while, your Grace should not be seeing my lady Dulcinea just now, but should rather go and kill the giant and have done with this business; for, by God, it strikes me there's great honor and profit in it."

"You are quite right about that, Sancho, and I shall take your advice so far as going with the princess before I see Dulcinea is concerned. And I would impress upon you that you are to say nothing to anyone, includ-ing those who come with us, regarding the subject that we have just been discussing; for Dulcinea is of so retiring a disposition that she would not have her thoughts known, and it is not for me or any other to reveal them."

"Well, then," said Sancho, "how comes it that your Grace sends all those whom you conquer by the might of your arm to present them-selves before my lady Dulcinea, this being as good as a signature to the effect that you are lovers? And since those that go there have to kneel before her and say that they come from your Grace to yield obedience to her, how can the thoughts of the two of you be kept hidden?"

"Oh, what a simple-minded fool you are!" exclaimed Don Quixote. "Can you not see that all this redounds to her greater praise? For you must know that in accordance with our rules of chivalry it is a great honor for a lady to have many knights-errant who serve her and whose thoughts never go beyond rendering her homage for her own sake, with no ex-pectation of any reward for their many and praiseworthy endeavors other than that of being accepted as her champions."

"That," observed Sancho, "is the kind of love I have heard the preacher say we ought to give to Our Lord, for Himself alone, without being moved by any hope of eternal glory or fear of Hell; but, for my part, I prefer to love and serve Him for what He can do for me."

"May the devil take the bumpkin!" cried Don Quixote. "What a wit you show at times; one would think you had been a student."

"But, on my word," said Sancho, "I cannot even read."

At this point Master Nicholas called out to them to wait a while as the others wished to pause at a little roadside spring for a drink. Don Quixote accordingly came to a halt, and Sancho was by no means displeased with this, for he was tired by now of telling so many lies and was afraid that his master would catch him up, the truth being that, while he knew that Dulcinea was a peasant girl of El Toboso, he had never in his life laid eyes upon her.

Cardenio in the meantime had put on the clothes that Dorotea had worn when they found her. Though they were none too good, they were much better than the ones he took off. They then dismounted beside the spring, and with the food that the curate had procured at the inn, while it was not much, they all contrived to satisfy their hunger. As they were engaged in their repast, a lad came along the highway and, after studying them all attentively, ran over to Don Quixote and clasped him around the legs, weeping copiously.

"Ah sir! Do you not know me, your Grace? Look at me well, for I am the lad Andrés that your Grace freed from the oak tree to which he was bound."

The knight then recognized him and, taking him by the hand, he turned to the others and said, "In order that your Worships may see how important it is to have knights-errant in the world to right the wrongs and injuries done by the insolent and evil beings who inhabit it, you may know that some while ago, as I was passing through a wood, I heard certain pitiful cries and moans as from one who was afflicted and in distress. I then, as was my duty, went to the place from which the cries appeared to come, and there I found, bound to an oak tree, this lad who now stands before you. I am heartily glad that he is with us now, for he will be my witness that I do not lie in anything I say. He was, as I said, bound to that tree while a peasant who, I later learned, was his master lashed him unmercifully with the reins of his mare. The moment I saw this, I asked the man what was the reason for the flogging, and the lout replied that he was whipping the boy because he was his servant and had been guilty of certain acts of carelessness that indicated he was a thief rather than a dunce. At this, however, the lad spoke up and said, 'Sir, he

is whipping me because I asked for my wages and for no other reason.'
The master then made some excuses or other which, if I heard them, I
did not accept as valid.

"The short of it was, I compelled the peasant to release the boy and
made him promise to take him home and pay him every real of what he
owed him, and perfumed into the bargain.[8] Is not that all true, Andrés,
my son? Did you not note how imperiously I commanded him to do
that and with what humility he promised to carry out all my orders and
instructions? Speak up and tell these ladies and gentlemen, clearly and
in a straightforward manner, just what happened; for I would have them
see and be convinced that I was right when I said that it is very useful to
have knights-errant going up and down the highroads."

"All that your Grace has said is very true," the lad replied, "but the
end of the matter was quite different from what you think."

"What do you mean by saying that it was quite different?" Don
Quixote demanded. "Did not the peasant pay you?"

"He not only did not pay me," said the boy, "but the moment your
Grace had left the wood and we were alone, he tied me to that same tree
again and gave me so many fresh lashes that I was like St. Bartholomew
when they had done flaying him. And at each stroke he made some jest
or gibe about how he had fooled you, so funny that I would have laughed
myself if the pain had not been so great. In short, he mishandled me to
such an extent that I have been in a hospital up to now with the cuts that
wicked lout gave me. For all of which your Grace is to blame. If you had
gone your way and had not come where you were not called nor meddled
in the affairs of others, my master would have been satisfied with giving
me one or two dozen lashes and then would have untied me and paid me
what he owed me. But your Grace roused his anger by insulting him so
unreasonably and calling him all those names, and since he could not
avenge himself on you, the moment we were alone the storm burst on
me, and, as a result, I do not think I shall ever be a man again as long as
I live."

"My mistake," said Don Quixote, "was in going off and leaving you
like that. I should not have left until I had seen you paid; for I ought to
have known from long experience that there is no peasant who keeps his
word if he finds that it is not in his interest to do so. But you remember,
Andrés, I swore that if he did not pay you I would come looking for
him, and would find him even though he were hidden in the belly of the
whale."

"That you did," said Andrés, "but it was of no use."

"Well, we will see now whether it is of use or not," said Don Quixote. And, saying this, he hastily arose and ordered Sancho to put the bridle on Rocinante, for the hack had been grazing while they were eating. Dorotea then asked him what he proposed to do, and he replied that he meant to go look for the peasant and chastise him for his behavior, and he also intended to make him pay Andrés to the last maravedi, notwithstanding and in spite of all the clodhoppers in the world. She thereupon reminded him that in accordance with his promise he could not embark upon any enterprise until he had finished the undertaking with which she had charged him. After all, she added, he knew this better than anyone else and should restrain the fury in his bosom until he had returned from her realm.

"That is true," Don Quixote agreed. "As you say, lady, Andrés will have to be patient until I come back; but I hereby swear and promise him anew that I will not desist until I have avenged him and seen him paid."

"I do not believe in those oaths," said Andrés. "What I need now is enough to take me to Seville; I would rather have that than all the vengeance in the world. So, if you have here anything to eat that I can take with me, let me have it; and God be with your Grace and all knights-errant, and may they be as errant with themselves as they have been with me."

Sancho then produced a bit of bread and cheese and gave it to the lad.

"Take it, brother Andrés," he said, "for we all have a share in your troubles."

"Why, what share is yours?" Andrés asked.

"This portion of bread and cheese. God knows whether I am going to need it or not, for I may tell you, my friend, that the squires of knights-errant are greatly subject to hunger and misfortune and other things that are better felt than put into words."

Andrés accepted the food and, seeing that no one offered him anything else, lowered his head and, as the saying goes, took the road in hand. But, before leaving, he turned to Don Quixote.

"For the love of God, Sir Knight-errant," he said, "if ever again you meet me, even though they are hacking me to bits, do not aid or succor me but let me bear it, for no misfortune could be so great as that which comes of being helped by you. May God curse you and all the knights-errant that were ever born into this world!"

Don Quixote was about to arise and follow him, but the lad started running so swiftly that no one thought of trying to overtake him. The knight was exceedingly crestfallen over the story Andrés had told, and the others had to do their best to keep from laughing so as not to discomfit him entirely.

CHAPTER XXXII. *Which treats of what befell Don Quixote and all his company at the inn.*

HAVING had a good meal, they saddled their animals and set out once more, and nothing worthy of note happened until the following day, when they arrived at the inn, the place that Sancho Panza so feared and dreaded. He did not wish to enter, but there was no escape for him. When they saw Don Quixote and his squire approaching, the innkeeper and his wife, their daughter, and Maritornes came out to receive them most cordially. As for the knight, he greeted his hosts with great dignity and condescension, remarking to them that they should prepare him a better bed than the one he had had the last time. To this the landlady replied that if he paid better than he did the other time, she would give him one fit for a prince. He assured her that he would, and so they made a fairly comfortable pallet for him in the same garret where he had slept before; and as he was very much shaken up and weary in mind as well as body, he went to bed at once.

No sooner had the door closed upon him than the landlady fell upon the barber and seized him by the beard.

"By the sign of the holy cross!" she cried, "you are not going to make use of my tail as a beard any longer. Give it back to me at once. It is a shame the way that thing of my husband's is all the time on the floor—I mean the comb that I used to stick into that pretty tail of mine."

She tugged and tugged, but the barber would not give up until the licentiate told him to let her have it, as there was no further need to make use of that device. Instead, he should show himself in his own person and tell Don Quixote that after the galley-slave robbers had despoiled him, he had fled to this inn; and should the knight inquire after the princess's squire, they would tell him that she had sent the man on ahead to advise her subjects that she was on the way and was bringing with her one who would liberate them all. Upon hearing this, the barber readily enough let the landlady have her tail, and at the same time they returned all the other objects they had borrowed in connection with their scheme to rescue Don Quixote. All those of the inn were very much struck with Dorotea's beauty and the shepherd Cardenio's fine figure; and the curate then directed them to lay out whatever they had to eat, and the landlord, hoping to be better paid this time, set before them a very decent meal. Don Quixote all this while was still asleep, and they deemed it best not to awaken him, as slumber would do him more good than food just now.

At the dinner table, at which were present the landlord, his wife, his daughter, Maritornes, and all the guests, the subject of discussion was Don Quixote's strange madness and the state in which they had found him. The landlady told them of the incident between the knight and the carter, and then, looking around to see if Sancho was there and perceiving that he was not, she went on to describe for them the blanketing that the squire had received, a story that afforded them no little amusement. When the curate made the observation that it was books of chivalry that had unbalanced Don Quixote's mind, the innkeeper took exception to this statement.

"I do not know," he said, "how that can be; for, to tell the truth, so far as I can see, there is no better reading in the world. I myself have two or three of them along with some manuscripts, and they have been the very breath of life not only to me, but to many others as well. For in harvest time the reapers gather here in large numbers on feast days, and there are always some among them who can read. One of them will take a book in his hands and thirty or more of us will crowd around and listen to him with so much pleasure that we lose a thousand gray hairs. For my own part at least, I can say that when I hear of the terrible and furious blows the knights exchange with one another, I feel like dealing a few myself, and could sit there hearing of them day and night."

"That," said the landlady, "suits me well enough; for I never have a moment's peace in the house except when you are listening to them. Then you are so absorbed that you forget for once to scold."

"That is the truth," said Maritornes; "and I give you my word, I also like to hear about those things, for they are very pretty, especially when they tell about some lady or other being embraced by her knight under the orange trees while a duenna keeps watch over them, and she herself is dying of envy and fright. I say that all that is better than honey."

"And what do you think, young lady?" said the curate, addressing the innkeeper's daughter.

"I really cannot tell you, sir," she replied. "Although I do not understand them, I get a great deal of pleasure out of listening to them. The only thing is, I do not like those blows that my father speaks of; I prefer the laments which the knights utter when absent from their lady loves and which sometimes make me weep from sympathy."

"Well, young lady," said Dorotea, "would you console them if it was for you that they wept?"

"I do not know what I should do," the girl answered. "All I know is that some of those ladies are so cruel that they call their knights tigers and lions and a thousand other nasty things like that. Good Lord! I don't know what kind of creatures they can be, without soul or conscience, if they cannot give a decent man so much as a glance but leave him to die or go mad. I don't see how they can be such prudes. If it is their honor they are thinking about, let them marry, for that is all the poor knights desire."

"Be quiet, child!" said the landlady. "You appear to know too much about such things, and it is not good for young girls to know or talk so much."

"This gentleman asked me," said the lass, "and I could not refuse to answer him."

"That will do," said the curate. "And now, mine host, if you will bring out those books of yours, I should like to have a look at them."

"With pleasure," replied the innkeeper. And, going into his room, he came back with an old valise held closed by a small chain. When it was opened it was found to contain three large books and a number of manuscripts in a very good hand. The first book that the curate inspected was *Don Cirongilio of Thrace*. Another was *Felixmarte of Hircania*, and there was also the *History of the Great Captain Gonzalo Hernández de Córdoba, with the Life of Diego García de Paredes*.[1] As soon as he had read the first two titles, the priest turned to the barber and said, "What we need here now is our friend's housekeeper and niece."

"No, we do not need them," said the barber. "I am quite capable of carrying these books out into the stable yard or over to the hearth, for, in truth, there is a very good fire burning there."

"What!" said the innkeeper; "is your Grace going to burn more books?"[2]

"No more," said the curate, "than these two: the *Don Cirongilio* and the *Felixmarte*."

"Are these books of mine, then, heretics or phlegmatics that you should wish to burn them?" the landlord wanted to know.

"*Schismatics*, you mean, friend," the barber corrected him, "not *phlegmatics*."

"Be that as it may," said their host, "but if you are bent on burning any, let it be this one about the Great Captain and this other about Diego García, for I would rather see my own child sent to the flames than any of the rest of them."

"But, my brother," the curate remonstrated with him, "those two books are full of lies, foolishness, and nonsense, whereas this one about the Great Captain is a true history and has the deeds of Gonzalo Hernández de Córdoba, who by his many and mighty exploits deserves to be known as the Great Captain to all the world. And this Diego García de Paredes was a leading knight, a native of the city of Trujillo in Estremadura, a most valiant soldier and one endowed with such natural strength that with the finger of one hand he could stop a mill wheel turning at full speed. On one occasion, armed with a large two-handed broadsword,[3] he took up his post at the entrance to a bridge and prevented a large army from crossing. These and other feats he performed, and he writes of them with the modesty of a knight who is his own chronicler; but if some other free and dispassionate author had recorded them, they would have cast into oblivion the deeds of all the Hectors, Achilles', and Rolands."

"Go tell that to my father!" exclaimed the innkeeper. "What is there so astonishing about stopping a mill wheel? By God, your Grace should read what Felixmarte of Hircania did,[4] who with a single backward stroke cut five giants in two around the middle, as if they had been made of horse beans like the little friars that children fashion for themselves. Another time he attacked a huge and powerful army, with more than one million six hundred thousand soldiers all armed from head to foot, and he put them to rout like a flock of sheep.

"And then, what have you to say of the worthy Don Cirongilio of Thrace, a sturdy and courageous knight as you will see from that book. For it tells there how, as he was sailing on a river, a fiery serpent arose from the water, and as soon as he saw it he fell upon it, straddled its scaly back, and, grasping its throat in both his hands, choked it with such force that the serpent, perceiving that it was being throttled, had no choice but to sink to the bottom of the river, carrying with it the knight, who would not let go his hold? And, down there, he found himself among palaces and gardens so pretty that they were a marvel to behold; and then the snake turned into an old man who told him such things as were never heard before. Ah, sir, say no more! If you were to hear that one, you would be beside yourself with joy. And a couple of figs for that Great Captain and for that Diego García that you talk about!"

As she listened to this, Dorotea whispered to Cardenio, "Our host could almost play a second to Don Quixote."

"Yes, it would seem so," replied Cardenio, "for, according to all indications, he holds it as certain that everything happened exactly as it is set down in those books, and the barefooted friars themselves would never convince him of the contrary."

"See here, brother," the curate went on, "there never was in this world a Felixmarte of Hircania or a Don Cirongilio of Thrace, nor any such knights as those mentioned in the books of chivalry. It is all a fiction, a story made up by idle minds for the purpose you speak of: whiling the time away, which is what those reapers of yours do when they read them; for I swear to you once more, there never were such knights, such exploits, or such nonsensical happenings."

"Give that bone to another dog!" said the innkeeper. "As if I didn't know how much is five and where the shoe pinches me! And do not think you can feed me pap, for, by God, I am nobody's fool. A fine thing, your Grace's trying to make me believe that all these good books say is nothing but lies and foolishness, when they are printed with the license of the Royal Council! Do you mean to tell me they are the kind of folk who would consent to the printing of a lot of stories that are not true, with all those battles and enchantments and other things that are enough to drive a person crazy?"

"I have told you, my friend," the curate replied, "that this is done simply to amuse your idle hours. Just as in well-ordered states there are games of chess, handball, and billiards to amuse those that do not desire, are not obliged, or are unable to work, so do they consent to the printing and distribution of such books as these, in the belief—and they are right in so believing—that there is no one so ignorant that he would take any of them to be a veracious history. If this were the proper occasion and my listeners so desired, I might say something about the qualities which books of chivalry should possess in order to be good ones and such as would be to the profit of certain readers and would please their taste as well. However, I trust the time will come when I shall be able to communicate my ideas to someone who is in a position to remedy the situation. In the meanwhile, mine host, remember what I say. And now, take your books and make up your mind as to whether they are true or false. Much good may they do you, and, please God you do not go lame on the same foot as your guest Don Quixote."

"That I shall not," replied the innkeeper. "I could never be so mad as to turn knight-errant, for I am aware that the customs of those days when famous knights roamed the world no longer prevail today."

In the midst of this conversation Sancho Panza had entered the room. He was very downcast and bewildered when he heard them say that there were no more knights-errant and that the books of chivalry were full of lies and nonsense, and he secretly made up his mind that he would wait and see how this expedition of his master's turned out; if the result did not come up to expectations, he would part company with the knight and return to his wife and young ones and his accustomed toil.

The landlord was about to remove the valise with the books it contained when the curate stopped him. "Wait," said the latter, "I want to see what papers those are that are written in so fine a hand."

Their host then took out the manuscript and gave it to them to read, whereupon they saw that it was on eight sheets, with a title in large letters at the top of the first one which read: *Story of the One Who Was Too Curious for His Own Good.* Having glanced over three or four lines, the curate remarked, "The title of this certainly impresses me as being an excellent one, and I should very much like to read the tale itself."

"Very well," replied the innkeeper, "your Reverence may do so; for I may tell you that certain of my guests who have read it have greatly enjoyed it and have earnestly begged me to let them have it, but I would not give it to them, thinking that I would return it to the one who forgetfully went away and left the valise here with these books and papers in it; for its owner may well come back for it sometime, and although I should not like to part with them, upon my word, I shall restore them to him, for although I am an innkeeper, I am also a Christian."

"You are quite right in that, my friend," said the curate, "However, if the story pleases me, you must let me copy it."

"I shall be glad to do so," the landlord assured him.

While the two were conversing, Cardenio had picked up the story and begun reading it. He liked it as well as had the curate, whom he now begged to read it aloud in order that all might hear it.

"I should not mind reading it," said the priest, "if it were not that it would be better to spend our time sleeping."

"I shall have my fill of rest," said Dorotea, "in passing the time away by listening to some story; for my mind is not as yet sufficiently calm to permit me to sleep when I ought to do so."

"In that case," said the curate, "I will read it, if only out of curiosity, and we may find some enjoyment in it."

Master Nicholas and Sancho now joined in urging him, and, seeing that it would give so much pleasure to all of them as well as to himself, he said, "Very well, then. Pay attention, all of you. This is the way the story begins."

CHAPTER XXXIII. *In which is related the "Story of the One Who Was Too Curious for His Own Good."*

IN FLORENCE, a rich and famous city of Italy, in the province of Tuscany, there lived two gentlemen named Anselmo and Lotario. They were wealthy and of high station and were so closely bound together in ties of friendship that all who knew them commonly referred to them as "the two friends." They were bachelor lads of the same age and habits, which in itself was enough to explain the bond of affection between them. It is true that Anselmo was somewhat more inclined to amorous pastimes than was Lotario, the latter being very fond of the hunt, but when occasion offered, the one would leave off his own pursuits to devote himself to those favored by the other, and in this manner their inclinations kept pace better than the best-regulated clock.

Anselmo was greatly enamored of a certain beautiful and wellborn maiden of the same city. Her parents were so worthy, and she herself so estimable, that the youth, upon the advice of his friend, without whom he did nothing, made up his mind to ask for her hand in marriage. This plan he put into execution, with Lotario as his emissary, who concluded the business so satisfactorily that the suitor soon found himself in possession of that which he desired, while Camila was so happy at having him for a husband that she never ceased giving thanks to Heaven and to Lotario who had been the means of bringing her so much happiness.

The first days of marriage commonly being given over to merrymaking, Lotario continued to frequent his friend's house as was his wont, doing all in his power to honor him and help make the occasion a joyful one. But when the wedding days were over and congratulatory visits became less frequent, he was careful not to go so often; for it seemed to him, as it must to all men of good sense, that one should not continue visiting the homes of married friends with the same frequency as in their bachelor days. Good and true friendship neither can nor should be at all suspect; but, nevertheless, the honor of a married man is so delicate a matter that even blood brothers may give offense, to say nothing of those who are no more than friends.

Anselmo noted all this and was greatly put out, telling Lotario that if he had known that his marriage was to come between them in such a manner, he would never have gone through with it. Seeing that when they were single they had been so intimate as to win for themselves the pleasing epithet of "the two friends," he would not consent to so famous and agreeable an association as theirs being sacrificed for no other reason than that of a conventional circumspectness. He therefore entreated him, if such a manner of speaking was permissible between them, to resume his old place as master of his friend's household, coming and going as he liked. Camila, he added, had no other will or pleasure than his own, and when she had learned how fond the two were of each other, she had not known what to think of such coldness on Lotario's part.

To this and all the other things that Anselmo had to say in an effort to persuade him to resume his former habits, Lotario replied so wisely and discreetly that his friend was quite satisfied of his good intentions; and so they made an arrangement to the effect that two days a week and on feast days Lotario was to dine at Anselmo's house. Nevertheless, the former was determined to observe this agreement only insofar as it did not conflict with his friend's honor, whose reputation he valued more than he did his own. He maintained, and rightly, that the man to whom Heaven had given a beautiful wife should exercise as much care as to the friends he brought home with him as he did with regard to his wife's feminine acquaintances—for while it may be difficult to arrange a clandestine meeting in the market place, in church, at public festivals, or in connection with private visits to religious shrines (and husbands cannot always forbid their wives such opportunities), these things are readily managed in the house of a trusted female friend or relative.[1]

Lotario was also in the habit of saying that every married man should have some friend of his own sex who would call his attention to any negligence on his part; for it frequently happens that a husband who is very much in love with his wife either does not warn her or, in order not to annoy her, says nothing to her whatever about doing or not doing certain things, although his own honor or loss of reputation depends upon her conduct; whereas, if advised by a friend, he may easily set everything to rights. But where is so true a friend to be found, one so loyal and discreet as Lotario would have him be? I cannot tell you, certainly; for only he was of that sort, zealously and painstakingly watching over Anselmo's honor so that the wandering and malicious gaze of the idle throng might not find occasion for scandal in seeing a young gentleman as rich, well-born, and attractive as he frequenting the house of a woman as beautiful as Camila. Even though her modesty and worth might put a bridle on every gossiping tongue, he nonetheless did not wish to cast even the shadow of doubt upon her good repute or that of his friend; and for this reason, on most of the days when he was supposed to go there, he occupied himself with other matters which he pretended were unavoidable. As a consequence, a good part of the time was spent in complaints on the one side and excuses on the other.

And so it came about one day, as they were strolling in a meadow outside the city, that Anselmo said to Lotario, "You may think, my friend, that in return for the favors God has shown me by giving me such parents as mine and bestowing upon me with no stinting hand what are commonly known as the gifts of nature as well as those of fortune, I should never be able to thank Him enough, not to speak of what He has done for me by giving me you as a friend and Camila for my wife, two blessings which I esteem, if not at their full worth, as much as I am able. Yet with all these advantages, which are commonly all that men require to live happily, I lead the most boring and fretful existence of any man in this universe. For some time now I have been wearied and oppressed by a desire so strange, so out of the ordinary, that I marvel at myself. I blame and scold myself for it when I am alone and endeavor to silence it and conceal it from my own thoughts, but I have no more succeeded in keeping it a secret than if I had deliberately set out to tell everyone about it. And since it has to come out, I would entrust it to your safekeeping; for I am confident that by this means and through your readiness as a true friend to do what you can to help me, the joy I derive from your kind offices will be as intense as the unhappiness which my madness has caused me."

Lotario did not know what to think of Anselmo's speech, nor did he have any idea as to what the object of this long and ominous preamble was. Though he did his best to imagine what the desire could be that so harassed his friend, his guesses were far from the truth, and by way of relieving the anxiety which this uncertainty caused him, he remarked to his companion that to adopt so roundabout a way of revealing one's most secret thoughts was to commit a grievous offense against a friendship as deep as theirs. If Anselmo would but tell him his troubles, he felt sure that he would be able to give him some advice that would help him in allaying them or in taking such action as was necessary to remedy matters.

"That is the truth," replied Anselmo, "and so, in all confidence, I will inform you, friend Lotario, that the thing that so tortures me is the desire to know whether or not my wife Camila is as good and perfect as I think she is, for this is a truth that I cannot accept until the quality of her virtue is proved to me in the same manner that fire brings out the purity of gold. For it is my opinion, my friend, that a woman is virtuous only in the degree to which she is tempted and resists temptation, and that she alone is strong who does not yield to promises, gifts, tears, and the constant wooing of importunate suitors. What thanks does a woman deserve for being good if no one urges her to be bad? What wonder if she is reserved and timid who has no opportunity to abandon herself, and who, moreover, knows that her husband will slay her for the first false move that he discovers on her part? Accordingly, she who is virtuous out of fear and lack of occasion is one whom I cannot esteem as I do her who is solicited and beset and still emerges with the crown of victory.

"For this reason," he continued, "and many others which I could give you by way of verifying and confirming the opinion I have just expressed, I desire that my wife Camila meet this test and go through the fire of seeing herself longed for and sought after by one who is of sufficient worth to offer her his affections. If she comes out of this battle, as I am convinced she will, bearing the victor's palm, I shall consider myself the happiest man alive. I shall be able to say that my cup runneth over and that I have had the good fortune to come upon that virtuous woman of whom the Wise Man has asked, 'Who can find her?' [2] And if things should turn out contrary to my expectations, then I shall have the satisfaction of knowing the truth and shall bear without complaining the pain which so costly an experience will naturally cause me.

"Inasmuch as nothing you may say will dissuade me from carrying out my plan, I would have you, friend Lotario, consent to be the instrument for putting it into execution. I will provide you with the opportunity and will see that none of the conditions are lacking for paying suit to a woman who is respectable, honored, reserved, and without inclination to let her fancies roam. What leads me, among other things, to entrust you with so arduous an undertaking is the consideration that, in case Camila is over-come, you will not carry your conquest too far, but, instead, you will regard as done that which out of respect for me you will leave undone. Thus I shall be offended only by her intent, and the injury that I suffer will remain shrouded in your virtuous silence, which I know to be eternal as that of death itself. And so, if you would have me enjoy what may properly be called life, from now on you will enter into amorous battle, and neither lukewarmly nor slothfully, but with all the earnestness and diligence that I so greatly desire and with that trustworthiness of which our friendship assures me."

Such were the words that Anselmo spoke to Lotario. The latter listened to them all most attentively and, beyond the remarks he had already made, did not open his lips until his friend had finished. When he per-ceived that the speech was ended, he gazed at him for a good while as if at some strange and amazing object that he had never seen before.

"I cannot persuade myself, friend Anselmo," he said at last, "that you are not jesting in what you have just told me. If I were convinced that you are in earnest, I would never have permitted you to go so far but would have put an end to all this talk by refusing to listen to you. Surely, either I do not know you, or you do not know me. But that cannot be; for I am well aware that you are Anselmo, and you are conscious of the fact that I am Lotario. Unfortunately, however, I cannot regard you as the Anselmo that used to be, and you likewise must have thought that I am no longer the Lotario of old. For the things that you have said to me are not those that my friend Anselmo would say, nor are the things you ask of me such as you would ask of the Lotario that you know. True friends, as the poet has said, will prove and make use of each other *usque ad aras*, which is to say, they will not put their friendship to the test in a manner that is contrary to God's will. If this was the way a pagan [3] felt about it, how much stronger should be the feeling of a Christian, who knows that divine friendship must not be sacrificed for that which exists between human beings? And if the time does come when a man goes so far as to lay aside the respect he owes to Heaven, it will not be for little things of slight importance, but only those that concern the very life and honor of his earthly friend.

"Tell me, then, Anselmo," Lotario went on, "which of these—your life or your honor—is now imperiled that I at risk to myself should oblige you by doing a thing so detestable as that which you ask of me? Neither of them, certainly. What you are demanding of me is, rather, as I under-stand it, that I seek and endeavor to deprive you, and myself at the same time, of both honor and life. For if I take away your honor, it goes without saying that I am also robbing you of life, since the man without honor is in worse plight than a dead man; and if I am to be the instrument, as you would have me be, of bringing so great a misfortune upon you, shall I not then remain a dishonored and hence a lifeless man? Hear me out, friend Anselmo, and be so patient as not to answer me until I have finished telling you all I think of this wish of yours. There will be time later for me to hear what you have to say in reply."

"With pleasure," was Anselmo's response. "Say whatever you like."

"It seems to me that you are reasoning now as the Moors always do, who cannot be brought to see the error inherent in their sect, through citations from Holy Writ; nor are they to be moved by intellectual speculation or arguments based upon the articles of faith, but they demand palpable examples, readily understood and demonstrable, and such as admit of undeniable and indubitable mathematical proof, as when they say, 'If equals are subtracted from equals, the remainders are equal.' If they do not understand this from words, as indeed they do not, it has to be shown them with the hands and placed before their eyes, and with all this no one could ever succeed in persuading them of the truths of my holy religion.[4] And this same mode of reasoning I am going to have to use with you; for the desire that has been born in you is so mistaken and utterly unreasonable a one that it appears to me a waste of time to endeavor to bring you to an understanding of your simple-mindedness—for the present I will call it by no other name than that. I am inclined to leave you to your folly, as a punishment for having conceived such a wish, but the friendship that I have for you will not permit me to deal with you so harshly, nor will it consent to my deserting you in this imminent danger of self-destruction that now obviously threatens you.

"In order that you may see clearly how the matter stands, answer me this, Anselmo. Did you not tell me that I am to pay court to a woman of reserve, bring my persuasive wiles to bear upon a respectable matron, make advances to one who is not looking for anything of that sort, and offer my attentions to a lady who is noted for her prudence? Yes, that is precisely what you told me. Well, then, if you know that you have such a wife, reserved, respected, prudent, and retiring, what is it that you seek? And if you are convinced that she will emerge the victor from all my assaults, as she undoubtedly will, what better titles do you think to bestow upon her than those that she already possesses? Or is it that you do not believe her to be what you say she is, or that you do not realize what you are asking? If you doubt her virtue, why trouble to test it?

Why not treat her as guilty and take what action you may see fit? If, on the other hand, she is as good as you are convinced she is, it is a futile proceeding to put that truth to the trial since in the end you will be left with the same opinion that you held before.

"It is therefore obvious that to undertake things from which harm rather than good is likely to come is a senseless and foolhardy act, especially when one is not forced or compelled to do so, and when the madness that lies in such a course of conduct is evident from afar. Difficult feats are attempted for the love of God or the world's praise or for both. It is saints who undertake the former as they strive to live an angelic life in human bodies, while they who seek the respect of the world are those who traverse great bodies of water and visit many climes and strange peoples in order to obtain what are known as fortune's favors. And, finally, those deeds that are performed for God and man alike are the work of valiant soldiers who, the moment they sight a breach in the opposite wall no bigger than a cannon ball can make, cast aside all fear and, with no word or thought of the manifest danger that threatens them but borne on the wings of their desire to defend their faith, their nation, and their king, hurl themselves intrepidly into the midst of a thousand deaths that await them at the hands of the enemy. Such are the deeds that men commonly attempt for the reason that there are honor, glory, and profit in them, despite the accompanying hardships and perils.

"But this undertaking of yours, as you explain it to me, has for object neither the glory of God, fortune's favors, nor worldly fame; for, supposing that the outcome is such as you desire, you will be neither happier nor richer nor more honored than you are at present; while if the result is not what you hope for, you will find yourself in the greatest misery that can be imagined, and there will be no comfort in the thought that none knows of your misfortune, as the fact that you yourself know it will be the greatest of afflictions.

"By way of confirming the truth of this, I should like to recite to you a stanza by the poet Luigi Tansillo which occurs at the end of the first part of his *St. Peter's Tears*.[5] It runs like this:

> *Then Peter's sorrow and his shame did grow*
> *As the day dawned and morning drew on apace,*
> *And although none was there to see or know,*
> *He was himself aware of his disgrace;*
> *For with the magnanimous heart 'tis ever so:*
> *Its own self-knowledge nothing can efface.*

> *Though only Heaven and earth behold its shame,*
> *It still will never cease itself to blame.*

"Thus, you will not be able to shun your grief by keeping it secret, but, rather, you will weep endlessly—if not tears from the eyes, tears of blood from the heart of the kind that simple-souled doctor wept of whom our poet tells us, who submitted to the test of the cup,[6] something that the more prudent Rinaldo declined to do. Granted that this is poetic fiction, it nonetheless contains certain secrets of morality that are worthy of being noted, understood, and imitated. Moreover, by what I am about to say you will be brought to see the great mistake that you would be making if you carried out your plan.

"Tell me, Anselmo, supposing that Heaven or good fortune had made you the master and lawful owner of a very fine diamond to whose quality and purity all the lapidaries who had seen it had testified, stating in unison their common opinion that in quality, purity, and fineness it was the best that nature could produce in the way of such a stone; and supposing, further, that you yourself believed all this to be true, without knowing anything that would cause you to believe otherwise, would it be right for you to wish to take that diamond and place it between a hammer and an anvil and there by force of blows and strength of arm endeavor to see whether or not it was as hard and fine as they had said it was? And supposing that you went through with this and the stone withstood so foolish a test, would you thereby be adding anything to its worth and the esteem in which it was held? Whereas, if it should break, a thing that could happen, would not all be lost? It would indeed; for certainly its owner would be looked upon by everyone as a man of little sense.

"Well, then, friend Anselmo, you must realize that Camila is a very fine diamond, both in your own estimation and in that of others, and there is no sense in placing her in a situation where she may be broken; for even though she remain whole, she will not then be of greater worth than she is now; and if she should weaken and not hold out, you must take into consideration that from that time forth you would have to do without her, and with what good reason you would reproach yourself for having been the cause of her ruination and your own as well. Remember that there is no jewel in all this world of so great worth as a wife who is chaste and respected, and that the honor of women lies wholly in the good opinion which others have of them; and since you know how excellent your own wife's reputation is, why do you seek to cast doubt upon that truth? Bear in mind, my friend, that woman is an imperfect creature, and we should not put stumbling blocks in her way where she may trip and fall; rather, we should remove them and clear her path of all obstacles, so that, without any hindrances, she may run swiftly on toward the goal of that perfection that she lacks, which lies in the attainment of virtue.

"The naturalists tell us that the ermine is a small animal with a very white skin and that hunters when they wish to track it down make use of the following artifice: knowing the places where it passes, they block them off with mud, and then, rousing the little beast, they drive it toward those places; but the ermine, as soon as it comes to the mud, stops and lets itself be captured rather than go through the mire and lose or sully its whiteness, which it values more than it does its liberty or its life. Now, the chaste and respected woman is an ermine, and the virtue of modesty is something that is whiter and purer than snow, but he who would not have her lose it but keep and preserve it must adopt with her a different course than that which the ermine hunters employ. He must not put before her the mire of presents and the attentions of importunate suitors; for perhaps—and, indeed, there is no perhaps about it—she will not be possessed of sufficient virtue and native strength to enable her to tread under foot and pass over these obstacles, for which reason it is necessary to remove them and instead place before her the purity of virtue and the beauty that lies in a woman's good name.

"The good woman is like a crystal mirror, shining and clear but likely to be dimmed and darkened by any breath that touches her. The respectable woman has to be treated as one does relics: she is to be adored, not touched. She is to be guarded and cherished, like a fine garden full of roses and other flowers whose master permits no one to enter and handle the blooms—it is enough to enjoy their beauty and fragrance from afar, through an iron grating.

"Finally, I should like to quote you some verses that I happen to remember. I heard them in a modern comedy, and they appear to me to have a bearing on the subject we are now discussing. One wise old man was advising another, who had a young daughter, to take the girl, shut her up, and watch over her carefully, and among other reasons he gave the following:

> *Woman is made of glass,*
> *But do not the trouble take*
> *To see if she will break,*
> *For anything may come to pass.*

> *She is easy to shatter;*
> *And so, then, be not rash*
> *Or you the glass may smash,*
> *But mending's another matter.*
> *This truth all men will tell,*
> *For 'tis known everywhere:*
> *If in this world are Danaës fair,*
> *There are showers of gold as well.*[1]

"What I have said to you so far, Anselmo, has been with reference to yourself; it is time now that you should hear something of my part in the matter. If I seem to you to be speaking at too great length, forgive me. This labyrinth in which you have become involved and from which you would have me extricate you makes it necessary. You look upon me as a friend, and yet you would take away my honor, which is a thing contrary to all friendship; and, what is more, you wish me to rob you of yours at the same time. That you would deprive me of mine is obvious; for when Camila sees me paying suit to her as you ask me to do, she will certainly take me for a man without honor and of evil intentions, since I shall be undertaking to accomplish something that is entirely out of keeping with my character and the obligations of friendship. And that you would have me deprive you of yours is equally clear; for when I press my attentions upon her, she will think that I have discovered something frivolous about her that has emboldened me to reveal my evil desires, and she will then look upon herself as dishonored, and inasmuch as she belongs to you, her dishonor will be your own.

"All this explains what commonly happens with the husband of an adulterous wife. He may be in no wise to blame for her straying from the path of duty; indeed, he may not even be aware of it. Owing to his carelessness and lack of precautions, it may not have been within his power to prevent the unfortunate occurrence; but, nevertheless, he is called by a low, vile name, and to a certain extent those who are aware of his wife's misbehavior look upon him with contempt rather than with pity, even though they can see that his misfortune is not due to any fault of his own but to the waywardness of his faithless spouse.

"But I should like to tell you why it is that the husband of an erring wife is with good reason looked down upon even though he knows nothing of her misdeeds and has been in no way to blame, having given her no cause or provocation for what she did. And please do not become bored with listening to me, for all that I say is for your own good. When

God created our first male parent in the earthly paradise, the Holy Scripture tells us that, having put him to sleep, He took a rib from Adam's left side and out of it fashioned our mother Eve; and when Adam awoke and saw her, he said, 'This is flesh of my flesh and bone of my bone.' And God said, 'Therefore shall a man leave his father and his mother, and they shall be one flesh.' [8] Then it was that the holy sacrament of marriage was instituted, with bonds that are only to be put asunder by death. And this miraculous sacrament is possessed of such force and virtue that it does indeed make one and the same flesh of two different persons; and it does even more in the case of the happily married, for although they have two separate souls, they have but a single will.

"From this it follows that, the woman's flesh being one with that of her husband, the stains and blemishes that she incurs are reflected upon his flesh, even though, as has been said, he has given no occasion for her sinning. For just as a pain in the foot or in any other member is felt by the body as a whole (being all of the same flesh), and the head feels the pain in the ankle though it has not caused it, so the husband, by the fact of being one with her, shares in his wife's dishonor. For, since all worldly honors and disgraces are born of flesh and blood, and those of the erring wife are of this sort, it is inevitable that the husband should bear his part of them and be looked upon as dishonored whether or not he is aware of it.

"Consider, then, Anselmo, the risk you are running in thus disturbing that tranquillity in which your good wife spends her days. Think well before, out of vain and ill-advised curiosity, you seek to stir up the passions that are now slumbering in your chaste wife's bosom. Remember that what you stand to gain is little, and that what you will lose is so much that words fail me and I shall not even try to express it. If all that I have said is not sufficient to dissuade you from your unworthy purpose, then you will have to look for another to be the instrument of your dishonor and undoing, for I have no intention of being that instrument though I lose your friendship, which is the greatest loss that I can conceive."

With these words the virtuous and prudent Lotario fell silent. As for Anselmo, he was confused and thoughful and for some little while did not speak.

"Friend Lotario," he said at last, "you have seen how attentively I have listened to all you had to say to me, and your arguments, examples, and comparisons have shown me how wise you are and how fine and true a friend. I further perceive and admit that if I follow my own inclinations instead of your advice, I shall be fleeing the good and running after the evil. Granting this, however, you must take into consideration that I am suffering from that infirmity which some women have who are seized with the desire to eat earth, plaster, charcoal, and still worse things that are disgusting enough to look at and even more so to eat. In my case, it is necessary to employ a degree of artifice in curing me, and this can readily be done, but only if you begin, even though lukewarmly and in a feigned manner, to make advances to Camila, who will not be so susceptible that her virtue will be overthrown at the first encounter. With this beginning I will be content, and you will have done your duty by me as a friend, not only by giving me life but by persuading me not to part with my honor.

"This," Anselmo continued, "you are obliged to do for one reason only. Being resolved as I am to carry out this test, you surely cannot consent to my revealing my foolishness to another person, since I should thereby be risking that honor that you would have me keep. And if your honor does not appear in the proper light to Camila while you are pressing your suit, that makes little or no difference, since very soon, when we see that she is all that we expect of her, you will be in a position to tell her the whole truth concerning our scheme and your standing with her will be what it was before. As you are in reality risking so little and are offering me so much contentment by risking it, I trust you will not refuse me even if more serious obstacles should arise; for, as I have said, when you shall have made no more than a beginning, I will regard the point at issue as having been conclusively settled."

Seeing Anselmo's resolute attitude and not having any more examples to cite him or any more arguments to present as to why he should refrain from putting his resolve into effect—especially when he heard him threaten to confide to another his ill-omened scheme—Lotario, by way of avoiding a greater evil, decided to give in to him and do what he asked, with the object and intention of guiding the affair in such a manner that, without Camila's affections being altered in the least, his friend at the same time should be satisfied. He accordingly told him now that he should not communicate his plan to anyone else, as he, Lotario, would take charge of the matter and would begin to act upon this decision as soon as was desired.

Anselmo thereupon embraced him tenderly and affectionately, thanking his friend for the offer as if it had been some great favor, and it was agreed between them that they would begin carrying out the plan the very next day. Anselmo was to provide the opportunity for Lotario and Camila to be alone together, and he was also to furnish the money and jewels that were to be offered her. He advised Lotario to arrange for serenades and compose verses in her praise. If this was too much trouble, he would write the verses himself. And Lotario assented to it all, but with a different purpose in view than Anselmo thought.

Having settled the matter, they returned to Anselmo's house, where they found Camila dutifully and anxiously awaiting her husband, for he was later that day than was his wont. Lotario then went to his own home, being as troubled in mind as Anselmo was satisfied, for he did not know just what course to follow by way of extricating himself from this unpleasant business. That night, however, he thought of a means by which he could deceive Anselmo without offending Camila; and the following day he went to dine at his friend's house and was well received by the mistress, who entertained him most cordially since she knew the high esteem in which her husband held him.

When dinner was over and the cloth had been removed, Anselmo remarked that he had some urgent business to attend to but would return in an hour and a half, and in the meanwhile Lotario might stay with Camila. The latter begged her husband not to go, and their guest offered to keep him company, but he declined this offer and instead insisted that Lotario wait for him there as he had a matter of great importance to discuss with him, and at the same time he directed Camila not to leave Lotario alone until he returned. In short, he feigned it all so cleverly, making his absence appear necessary, that no one would have suspected it was but pretense. When he had gone, Camila and Lotario were left alone at the table, for the household servants were all engaged in having their own meal. And so it was that the husband's friend found himself in the amorous lists just as the husband had desired, with an enemy in front of him who by her beauty alone well might conquer an entire company of armed knights. Is it any wonder if Lotario was afraid?

What he now did was to lean his elbow upon the arm of his chair and rest his cheek upon his hand; and then, begging Camila's pardon for the discourtesy, he observed that he would like to take a little nap until Anselmo came back. She replied that he would be more comfortable in the drawing-room than in a chair and suggested that he go in there to sleep, but he did not care to do this. Instead, he remained sleeping there; and when Anselmo came in and found his friend dozing and Camila in her room, he thought that he had been away so long as to have given the pair time for talk and a little sleep besides, and was impatient for Lotario to awake so that he might take him outside and question him as to the result of his venture.

It all happened as he desired. Lotario awoke and the two then left the house together and he was able to put the questions which he was so anxious to ask. Lotario replied that he had not thought it a good thing to reveal the whole of his design the first time, and so he had done no more than praise Camila's beauty, assuring her that in all the city there was none other so lovely and discreet. This had seemed to him a good beginning, by way of winning her favor and disposing her to listen to him with pleasure on another occasion. In this he was employing the same stratagem that the devil makes use of when he wishes to deceive someone who is on the watch for him: what the Prince of Darkness does in such a case is to transform himself into an angel of light by putting on a good appearance; it is only at the end that he reveals himself and achieves his purpose, providing his ruse has not been discovered in the beginning. Anselmo was well pleased and declared that every day he would provide the same opportunity. He would not leave the house, however, but would find something at which to busy himself so that Camila would not come to learn of his scheme.

Many days then went by, and Lotario, without saying a word to Camila, kept reporting to Anselmo that he had talked with her but had never been able to obtain from her the least show of consent to anything that was dishonorable; she had afforded him no sign or shadow of hope, but had threatened that if he did not abandon his evil suggestions she would have to tell her husband about him.

"That is well," said Anselmo. "So far Camila has held out against words; it is necessary for us to see now how well she can resist deeds. Tomorrow I will give you two thousand gold crowns to offer or present to her, and as many more to buy jewels with which to tempt her; for women, particularly those that are beautiful, and however chaste they may be, are very fond of being sprucely attired, and if she resists this temptation, I shall be satisfied and will give you no more trouble." Lotario replied that, having entered upon this undertaking, he meant to go through with it, although he was certain that he would come out of it weary and vanquished. The next day he was forced to accept the four thousand crowns, and with them four thousand crowns' worth of embarrassment, for he was unable to think of any fresh lie to give his friend. Finally, he made up his mind that he would tell him that Camila had stood as firm against gifts and promises as she had against words, and there was no need of going to any further trouble since all this was time wasted. But fate, which directs things after its own fashion, was to ordain otherwise.

Having left Lotario and Camila alone together as on other occasions, Anselmo this time shut himself in a room and began listening and spying through a keyhole, only to discover that in more than half an hour the pair had not exchanged a single word, nor would they do so if they were to remain there for a hundred years. It was then he realized that all his friend had told him about Camila's replies was falsehood and fiction. By way of seeing if this was so, he came out of the room and, calling Lotario to one side, asked him what news there was and inquired as to Camila's state of mind. Lotario replied that he did not care to go on with this business, for she had answered him so harshly and angrily that he had not had the courage to say anything more to her.

"Ha!" exclaimed Anselmo, "Lotario! Lotario! How ill you have repaid the debt of friendship that you owe me and the confidence that I have reposed in you! I have been watching through this keyhole, and you did not say a single word to Camila, from which I gather that you have yet to utter your first ones. If that is the case, and it undoubtedly is, why have you deceived me? Why have you so ingeniously sought to deprive me of the means by which I might achieve my desire?"

Anselmo said no more, but he had already said enough to leave Lotario feeling confused and abashed. The latter upon being caught in a lie took it as a point of honor and swore to his friend that from that moment he would assume the responsibility of satisfying him and would lie to him no more, as he would see if he chose to spy upon them again. It would not be necessary, however, to resort to that, since what he proposed to do by way of gratifying him would remove all suspicion of laxity on his part. Anselmo took him at his word and, in order to afford him a safer opportunity and one less subject to surprise, he decided to absent himself from home for a week and go visit another friend who lived in a village not far from the city. And by way of presenting Camila with a more plausible excuse for his departure, he arranged with the friend in question to send him a pressing invitation.

Ah, unfortunate and ill-advised Anselmo! What is it that you are doing? What is it you are plotting? What do you seek to bring about? Behold what you are doing to yourself: plotting your own dishonor and bringing about your own ruin. Your wife Camila is a good woman, and you are in quiet and tranquil possession of her. There is none to disturb your happiness, her thoughts do not go beyond the walls of her home, you are her Heaven on earth, the object of her desires, the fulfillment of all that she could wish for, the measure of her will which she in every respect adjusts to yours and to the will of Heaven. If, then, the mine of her honor, beauty, modesty, and reserve yields you without any labor on your part all the wealth that it holds and that you could want, why do you wish to go deeper into the earth and seek out new veins of new and unheard-of treasure at the risk of bringing everything down, since when all is said it is supported only on the weak props of her frail nature? Bear in mind that when a man seeks the impossible, it is only just that the possible be denied him. But a poet has put it better when he says:

> Life in death I implore,
> In sickness health I would see,
> In prison I would be free,
> In the closed room I ask a door,
> In the traitor loyalty.
> From my fate I never should
> Hope for anything that's good;
> And since the impossible I would find,
> Fate and Heaven have combined,
> And I could not have the possible if I would.

The next day Anselmo set out for the village, having told Camila that during the time he was absent Lotario would come to look after the house and dine with her and that she was to take care to treat him as she would himself. She was pained at her husband's instructions as any discreet and modest wife would have been and reminded him that it was not well that anyone else should occupy his seat at table. If the reason for his doing this was that he had no confidence in her ability to direct the household, let him try her this once and he would see from experience that she was equal to greater tasks. Anselmo replied that he would have it so, and there was nothing for her to do but bow her head and obey. She promised him that she would do as he had ordered even though it was against her wishes.

And so Anselmo departed, and the next day Lotario came to the house, where he was received by Camila in modest and friendly fashion. But she never permitted him to see her alone, for she was always surrounded by her male and female servants, being closely attended, in particular, by her maid named Leonela, of whom she was very fond for the reason that the two of them had grown up together in the home of Camila's parents, and when she married Anselmo, she had brought the girl with her. During the first three days Lotario said nothing to her, although he might have done so when the cloth was removed and the servants in accordance with their mistress's orders went to make their own repast with as much haste as possible. She had even ordered Leonela to eat first in order that she might not have to leave her side, but the maid had her mind upon other things more to her taste and, needing the time and opportunity for her own concerns, did not always obey her mistress on this point, with the result that the pair were left alone as if they had deliberately sent her out of the room.

Camila's modest appearance, it is true, the serious look on her face, and her quiet and assured bearing, were such as to put a bridle on Lotario's tongue, but in the end her many virtues by the silence that they thus imposed were to prove harmful to both of them; for if his tongue was still, his thoughts were given free play and he had a chance to observe one by one all of her many fine qualities, her charms of mind and body, which were enough to inspire love in a marble statue, not to speak of a human heart. In place of conversing with her, he spent the time thinking how worthy she was of being loved, and this consideration began little by little to impair the respect that he had for Anselmo. A thousand times he felt an impulse to leave the city and go where his friend would never see him again and he would never see Camila, but the pleasure he found in gazing upon her prevented this and kept him there. Struggling with himself, he made an effort to reject and not to feel the happiness which the sight of her gave him.

When alone, he would indulge in self-reproaches for his folly, calling himself a bad friend and a bad Christian. He would argue the matter in his mind, making comparisons between himself and Anselmo, and he always reached the same concluson: to the effect that Anselmo's madness and rashness outweighed his own treachery, and if he could find an excuse before God as in the eyes of men for what he now thought of doing, then he need fear no punishment for his offense.

The short of it is that Camila's beauty and virtue, together with the opportunity which the foolish husband had placed in his hands, had proved too much for Lotario's loyalty as a friend. Unable to think of anything but her toward whom his affections were inclined, after Anselmo had been gone for three days, during which time he had waged a continuous battle in an effort to hold out against his own desires, he began making love to Camila so violently and in such amorous terms that she did not know what to do and could only rise and go to her room without giving him a single word in reply. This stern demeanor on her part, however, was not enough to discourage in Lotario the hope that is always born along with love. Instead, he was more bent than ever upon winning her.

As for Camila, this was a side of Lotario's character that she had never glimpsed nor suspected, and she was at a loss as to what course to adopt. It seemed to her that it was not safe nor the proper thing to give him an opportunity to speak to her again; and, accordingly, she resolved to send one of her menservants that very night with a note to Anselmo, a note that read as follows.

CHAPTER XXXIV. *In which is continued the "Story of the One Who Was Too Curious for His Own Good."*

It is commonly said that an army does not present a good appearance without its general nor a castle without its castellan, but in my opinion the young married woman without her husband creates an even worse impression unless there is a good reason for it. I find myself so badly off without you and so incapable of enduring your absence that unless you come quickly I shall seek refuge in my parents' house, even though I leave your own without a guardian. For the guardian that you left me, if he still deserves that title, I think is concerned rather with his own pleasure than with your interests; but since you are a discerning person, I shall say no more, nor is it fitting that I should.

Upon receiving this letter Anselmo thought that Lotario must have begun the undertaking and that Camila had responded as he would have wished. Being extremely happy over this news, he wrote his wife that she should by no means leave his house as he would return very shortly. Camila was greatly astonished at such a reply, which threw her into greater confusion than ever, since now she dared not remain in her own home nor go to that of her parents; for if she remained, she would be imperiling her virtue, and if she went, she would be disobeying her husband's express command.

Finally, she chose what was for her the worse of two possible courses by deciding to stay; and she further resolved that she would not shun Lotario's company, since she did not wish to occasion talk among the servants. She was sorry now that she had written her husband, for she was afraid he would think that Lotario had perceived in her some evidence of frivolity which had caused him to forget the decorum that he should have preserved. Confident, however, of her own virtuous conduct and good intentions, she made up her mind to put her trust in God and to offer a silent resistance to all of Lotario's pleas. In the meanwhile, she would say nothing more to her husband in order not to involve him in any quarrel or unpleasantness.

She even thought of how she might be able to excuse his friend's conduct in explaining things to him, when he should ask what had led her to write that letter. These thoughts of hers were honorable enough, but they were not of much help or to the point as she sat listening to Lotario the next day. He was now wooing her so ardently that her firmness was already beginning to waver and her virtue had to come to the aid of her eyes lest they give some sign of the amorous compassion that his words and tears had awakened in her bosom. Lotario noted all this and became more ardent than ever.

It seemed to him that he must take advantage of the opportunity afforded him by Anselmo's absence by pressing the siege of this fortress, and so he proceeded to attack her self-conceit with praises of her beauty; for there is nothing that more quickly lays low and levels the castled towers of lovely women's vanity than vanity itself on the tongue of adulation. In brief, he most diligently undermined the rock of her integrity with such devices that, even had she been made of bronze, she must have fallen to earth. He wept, entreated, promised, flattered, importuned, and pretended with such a show of real feeling that he ended by overcoming Camila's reserve and winning the victory that he least expected and most desired.

Camila surrendered, yes, Camila fell. Was it to be wondered at if friendship in Lotario's case could not keep its footing? Here we have an example which shows us clearly that the passion of love is to be conquered only by fleeing it. There is none may grapple with so powerful an enemy, for divine strength is needed to subdue its human power. Leonela alone knew of her mistress's weakness, the two false friends and new lovers being unable to conceal it from her. Lotario did not wish to tell Camila of Anselmo's purpose nor how the latter had provided the opportunity for him to reach this point, as he did not want her to underrate his love or derive the impression that it was purely by chance and unthinkingly that he had paid court to her.

Anselmo returned to his home a few days later but failed to perceive what was lacking there: namely, the thing that he had treated so lightly yet had treasured most. He then went to call upon Lotario and found him at his house. The two embraced and Anselmo at once asked for the news that meant life or death to him.

"The only news that I can give you, friend Anselmo," said Lotario, "is that you have a wife who is worthy to serve as the crowning example of all good women. The words that I spoke were borne away on the wind, my offerings were disdained, my gifts not accepted, while the feigned tears that I shed she regarded as a very enlivening jest. In a few words: just as Camila is the emblem of all beauty, so is she the treasure-house of modesty, good deportment, matronly reserve, and all the virtues that can render a respectable woman praiseworthy and happy. So, take your money, my friend. You see that I still have it, for I had no need of touching it, as Camila's integrity is something that is not to be laid low by gifts and promises.

"Be content now, Anselmo," he went on, "and do not seek for any further proof. Having passed dryshod over the sea of those doubts and suspicions that may be, and commonly are, held of women, do not think of embarking once again upon an ocean of fresh troubles or seek with another pilot to test the strength and seaworthiness of the good ship which Heaven has given you as your lot that you may cross the waters of this world. Rather, you should consider that you are now safely in port and should cast out the anchor of good sense, letting things be as they are until you are called upon to pay the debt that no human being however noble is dispensed from paying."

Anselmo was very happy at hearing Lotario's words and believed them as if they had been uttered by an oracle. Nevertheless, he begged him, if only out of curiosity and for the sake of amusement, not to abandon the undertaking, though he need not press his suit with as much fervor as he had shown up to now. All that he asked of him was that he write some verses in praise of Camila, alluding to her under the name of Chloris; for he would give Camila to understand that their friend was smitten with a lady on whom he had bestowed that name—this, in order that he might be able to praise her with that respect that was due to her virtue. If Lotario did not care to take the trouble to compose the verses, he himself would do so.

"That will not be necessary," said Lotario, "for the Muses are not such enemies of mine that they do not pay me a visit now and then in the course of the year. So, go ahead and tell Camila that story about my amours, and if my verses are not all that the subject deserves, they will at least be the best that I can produce."

Such, then, was the agreement reached between the one who was too curious and his treacherous friend; after which, returning to his own house, Anselmo asked Camila the question which she wondered that he had not asked before: as to what the occasion was for her having written the letter that she had sent him. Her answer was that it had seemed to her that Lotario was gazing at her a little more freely than when he, Anselmo, had been at home, but in this she had found that she was mistaken and was convinced that it had been her imagination, for now Lotario shunned her and avoided being alone with her. Her husband thereupon assured her that she might feel safe so far as any suspicion of that sort was concerned, for he happened to know that his friend was in love with a young lady in the city of very prominent family whose praises he was in the habit of singing under the name of Chloris; and even if this were not the case, their great friendship and Lotario's loyalty left nothing to fear.

Had not Camila previously been informed by her lover that his passion for Chloris was a feigned one and that he had merely told Anselmo this in order to be able to write an occasional poem to herself, she undoubtedly would have been desperately jealous; but, being forewarned, she was not taken by surprise and gave no sign of uneasiness. Another day, the three of them being together at table, Anselmo asked Lotario to recite for them some of the verses he had composed for his beloved Chloris; for since Camila did not know the young lady, he might feel free to do so.

"Even if she did know her," said Lotario, "I should make no effort at concealment; for when a poet praises his lady's beauty and calls her cruel, he does not thereby cast any reflection upon her good name. However, be that as it may, I will tell you that yesterday I did a sonnet on Chloris's ingratitude, which runs like this:

SONNET[1]

In the silence of the night when gentle sleep
Holds all the world beneath its soothing spell,
'Tis then that I am ever wont to tell
My many woes, the sorry score I keep
For Heaven and for Chloris. When the sun doth peep
From the rosy portals of the east, my hell
Begins once more, the plaint I know so well,
The broken words, the sighs—I can but weep.
And when from his burning, star-girdled midday throne

> *The sun sends down his rays to warm the earth,*
> *My moans are doubled 'mid a flood of tears.*
> *The night returns, and still the mournful drone*
> *Continues. Sorrow is of little worth*
> *When Heaven is deaf and Chloris hath no ears."*

Camila was well pleased with the sonnet, but Anselmo liked it even better. He praised it, remarking that the lady was exceedingly cruel not to show her appreciation of so much sincerity as was there expressed.

"Does that mean," said Camila, "that all poets who are in love are sincere in what they say and always speak the truth?"

"As poets," replied Lotario, "they may go beyond the truth, but as lovers they fall far short of it."

"That," Anselmo agreed, "is undoubtedly so." For he wished to support what his friend had to say in order to lend it weight with Camila. She, however, was as unconcerned with her husband's design as she was deeply in love with Lotario; and so, taking a pleasure in anything that had to do with the latter and knowing well that she herself was the object of his desires and poems and was the real Chloris, she asked him if he did not have another sonnet or bit of verse that he could recite to them.

"Yes, I have," said Lotario, "but I do not think it is as good as the other one, or perhaps I should say it is no worse. In any event, you may judge for yourselves, for here it is:

SONNET[2]

> *I'm dying, that I know—believest thou me?*
> *Dost not believe thou wouldst behold me dead*
> *Here at thy feet, cruel one, uncomforted,*
> *Before I should repent of loving thee?*
> *When I to oblivion shall go and see*
> *Life, fame, and fortune, all I valued, fled,*
> *Open then my bosom, look how I have bled,*
> *And find thine image carved in mimicry.*
> *This relic will I guard 'gainst the harsh fate*
> *That I to mine own obstinacy owe,*
> *Which thy severity doth but increase.*
> *The sailor on darkened seas must needs await*
> *His doom when no pole star there is to show*
> *Where lies the way unto some port's release."*

Anselmo praised this sonnet as he had the preceding one, and so went on adding link after link to the chain by which he was binding himself and assuring his own dishonor; for the more Lotario dishonored him, the more he held that he was being honored. As a consequence, each step that Camila descended toward the depths of scorn she mounted one, in the opinion of her husband, toward those heights of virtue and good repute that he wished her to attain. On a certain occasion, finding herself alone with her maid, Camila unburdened herself to the waiting woman.

"Friend Leonela," she said, "I am ashamed to see how cheaply I have held myself that I did not compel Lotario to purchase by an expenditure of time that complete possession of my will and affections that I so quickly yielded him. I fear that he will see only haste and frivolity on my part [3] without taking into consideration the irresistible pressure that he brought to bear upon me."

"Do not let that worry you, my lady," replied Leonela; "it does not diminish the value of the thing given to give it at once, providing it is a good thing and worthy of being esteemed. Indeed, there is a saying that he who gives quickly gives twice."

"And there is also a saying," Camila reminded her, "that what costs little is valued less." [4]

"That does not apply to you," observed Leonela, "for love, I have heard it said, sometimes flies and sometimes walks; it sometimes runs and sometimes loiters; some it chills and others it inflames; it wounds some and slays others. The course of its desires begins and ends at one and the same point. In the morning it lays siege to a fortress and by night the besieged will have surrendered, for there is no force that can withstand it. And since this is so, why then are you astonished or what do you fear upon seeing that the same thing has happened with you and Lotario, love having taken my master's absence as the means of overcoming us? [5] For it was essential that love's labor be accomplished within that time, before Anselmo should return and by his presence compel it to remain uncompleted. Love has no better minister to carry out his designs than opportunity, of which he makes use in all his undertakings, particularly at the beginning. All this I know very well, and more from experience than from hearsay. I will tell you all about it someday, my lady, for I too am made of flesh and my blood is young.

"What is more, my lady Camila," she went on, "you did not yield and give yourself so quickly, before you had seen in Lotario's eyes, in his words and sighs and in his gifts and promises, his whole soul laid bare, revealing all those virtues that render him worthy of being loved. This being so, do not trouble your thoughts with all these finical scruples and imaginings, but be assured that Lotario esteems you as you do him, and be content and satisfied with knowing that if you have fallen into the amorous net, it is one of worth and valor who has caught you in it, one who not only has the four S's that they say all true lovers ought to have, but a whole alphabet. If you do not believe me, just listen and I will repeat it for you. As I see it, it goes like this: Amiable, Bountiful, Courteous, Devoted, Enamored, Faithful, Gallant, Honorable, Illustrious, Loyal, Manly, Noble, Open, Princely, Qualified, Rich, and the S's that I have mentioned. And then, Trusty, Veracious—the X does not suit him, being too harsh a letter. The Y has already been given, and Z is for Zealous of your honor." [6]

Camila had to laugh at these ABC's and decided that her waiting woman was more experienced in affairs of the heart than she admitted. Leonela now confessed as much by telling of an affair she was having with a well-born youth of that same city. Her mistress was alarmed at this, fearing that her own honor would thus be endangered, and inquired as to whether the matter had gone beyond mere words, to which the maid, with little shame and much effrontery, replied that it had; for there is no doubt that the careless conduct of ladies renders their maids shameless, and the latter, when they see their mistresses stumble, think nothing of limping themselves, nor do they care who knows it.

All that Camila could do was to beg the girl to say nothing to the one who was supposed to be her lover, but to regard all such matters as strictly private in order that they might not come to the attention of either Anselmo or Lotario. Leonela assured her that she would do this, but she carried out her promise in such a manner as to make certain that Camila's fears of losing her reputation would be justified. For the brazen and dishonorable creature, upon seeing that her lady's conduct was not what it should be, had the audacity to bring her lover into the house, being confident her mistress, even though she might see him, would not dare say anything.

For one of the punishments that ladies must suffer for their sins is that of becoming the slaves of their own servants. This was what happened with Camila, who found herself obliged to cover up the immodesty and baseness of her serving woman. Although she more than once saw that Leonela was entertaining her gallant in a room of the house, she not only dared not reprove her, but even helped her conceal him and did all she could to keep her husband from catching a glimpse of him. She was unable, however, to prevent Lotario from seeing him as the man was stealing away at daybreak one morning. Not knowing who he was, Lotario thought at first that he must be an apparition of some sort, but when he saw him muffling himself in his cloak and taking great pains not to be observed, he at once had another idea which would have been the ruination of them all if Camila had not set things to rights.

It did not occur to him that this man whom he had seen leaving Anselmo's house at so untimely an hour had gone there to meet Leonela; as a matter of fact, he had forgotten that such a person existed. He believed, rather, that Camila, just as she had been light and easy with him, was now playing the same game with another. For there is yet another penalty that the erring woman must pay for her sin, and that is, to have her honor mistrusted even by the one to whom, upon his urgent entreaties and persuasions, she has given herself, for he is convinced that she will yield all the more readily to others, and so he will give unquestioning credence to any suspicion of this sort that occurs to him.

For what Lotario did at this point there would seem to be no other explanation than that he had lost his good sense entirely. He forgot all the words of wisdom that he had spoken on the subject, nor did he pause to consider what was proper or reasonable under the circumstances. Moved only by a blind impatience inspired by the jealous rage that gnawed at his entrails, he was dying to avenge himself on Camila, who had not offended him in the slightest; and, accordingly, without more ado, he hastened to the master of the house before the latter had risen.

"I want you to know, Anselmo," he said, "that for some time now I have been struggling with myself, trying to force myself to tell you that which it is neither possible nor right that I should any longer withhold from you. And so, I will inform you that the fortress that was Camila has already fallen and is now wholly at my disposition. If I have delayed in telling you this truth, it was in order that I might see if it was merely some passing whim on her part, or if, possibly, she was doing it to test those protestations of love that, with your permission, I had begun to offer her. I feel, moreover, that if she were all that she ought to be and all that we both thought she was, that she would already have told you of my advances. However, seeing that she has waited so long, I know now that the promises she made me were true when she told me that, the next time you were absent from home, she would talk to me in that closet where your jewels are kept." And it was true that Camila was in the habit of conversing with him there.

"I should not wish you," he continued, "to rush out at once and take some vengeance or other, for as yet the sin has been committed only by intent, and it is possible that between now and the time for carrying it out Camila's intention will change and repentance will spring up in its place. And as you have always wholly or in part followed my advice in the past, so be guided by it now in order that, without any mistake but with cautious deliberation, you may be able to decide upon the best course to follow. Pretend that you are going away for two or three days as you have done on other occasions, and arrange to hide in your closet, for the tapestries and other things there will make it easy for you to conceal yourself. You will then be able to see with your own eyes, and I with mine, what Camila's purpose is; and if it be an evil one, which is to be feared rather than expected, you may with silence, wisdom, and discretion exact punishment for the wrong done you."

Anselmo was amazed, bewildered, astounded at what Lotario had just told him. The news came at a time when he least expected to hear it, for he believed that Camila had already come out victorious in his friend's feigned assaults and he was beginning to revel in her glorious triumph. He was silent for some time, staring hard at the ground without batting an eyelash.

"Lotario," he said at last, "you have acted as I expected you to, in view of our friendship, and I will follow your advice in everything. Do as you see fit, and guard this secret as you know it should be guarded under circumstances as unlooked for as these."

Lotario promised that he would do so, but as he left Anselmo he began wholly to repent having said what he did, perceiving that he had been very foolish in what he had done, since he might have avenged himself upon Camila in some less cruel and dishonorable a fashion. He cursed his lack of sense and condemned the hasty impulse upon which he had acted, without knowing what means to adopt to undo the wrong or how he could fairly find a way out of it all. He finally made up his mind to tell Camila everything, and as it was not hard to find an opportunity for doing so, he sought her out that very day.

She was alone when he came upon her, and as soon as she saw that she might speak to him freely, she said, "Friend Lotario, I must tell you that there is something that pains me until it seems my heart will burst, and it will be a wonder if it does not. Leonela's shamelessness has reached such a point that every night she closets herself with a gallant here in this house and stays with him until daybreak, at great cost to my reputation, inasmuch as anyone seeing him leave my house at so unaccustomed an hour well might form his own opinion of the matter. What annoys me most is that I cannot punish nor scold her, for the fact that she is acquainted with our relationship puts a bridle on my tongue by way of silencing hers, and I very much fear that something unfortunate may come of all this."

When Camila first began speaking, Lotario had believed this to be an artifice on her part with the object of making him think that the man he had seen leaving was Leonela's lover and not her own; but her tears, her very real suffering, and her pleas to him to help her, ended by convincing him of the truth of what she said, and this at the same time completed his confusion and feeling of remorse. He nonetheless told her not to worry, that he would see to putting a stop to Leonela's insolence. At the same time he informed her of what he had said to Anselmo in his jealous rage and how they had arranged for her husband to hide in the closet that he might there see plainly how disloyal she was to him. He implored her forgiveness for this act of madness on his part and her advice as to what he should do to get out of the intricate labyrinth in which, through his impetuosity, he had become involved.

Camila was alarmed and very angry at what Lotario had told her and proceeded to scold him most sensibly, reproving him for his evil thoughts and for the wicked and foolish resolution that he had adopted. But woman naturally has keener wits than man, for good and evil, although they may fail her when it is a question of reasoning things out logically; and so it was that Camila at once found the means of remedying what appeared to be an irremediable situation, by telling Lotario he should see to it that Anselmo hid himself in the closet the next day as he had planned, as she meant to make good use of his presence there so that from then on they would be able to enjoy each other's company without fear of being taken by surprise. Without revealing to her lover all that was in her mind, she directed him to be sure to come when Leonela called him, after Anselmo was safely hidden away, and to reply to anything that she said to him exactly as he would have done if he had not known that her husband was listening. Lotario, however, insisted that she explain to him more fully just what it was that she intended to do in order that he might be able to act with greater certainty and take such precautions as were necessary.

"I assure you," said Camila, "that there are no precautions to take; all that you have to do is to answer the questions that I put to you." She would not give him any further account of her plan, for although it appeared to her to be an excellent one, she feared that he might not care to follow it and would start looking for another that would not be so good.

Lotario then took his departure, and the next day Anselmo, acting upon the excuse that he had to go to the village where his friend lived, left the house and returned to take up his hiding place, which he was able to do without any inconvenience, for Camila and Leonela made it easy for him. His feelings as he concealed himself behind the draperies may be imagined: they were those of a man who expected to see the entrails of his honor laid bare before his eyes and who was about to lose that supreme good that he had thought he possessed in his beloved Camila. Having made certain that Anselmo was there, Camila and Leonela now entered the closet, and no sooner had she set foot in the room than the former gave a deep sigh.

"Ah, Leonela, my friend!" she exclaimed, "before I do something of which I will say nothing to you lest you seek to prevent it, would it not be better for you to take Anselmo's dagger which I asked you to procure for me and run it through this infamous bosom of mine? But no, do not do that; for there is no reason why I should suffer the penalty for another's fault. First of all, I should like to know what it was that Lotario's bold and shameless eyes beheld in me that caused him thus rashly to reveal to me a passion as evil as that which he has disclosed, in contempt of his friend's honor and my own. Go to that window, Leonela, and call down to him; for without any doubt he is there in the street, waiting to carry out his wicked intentions. But my own intentions, as cruel as they are honorable, shall be carried out first."

"Ah, my lady!" replied the crafty Leonela, who had been well schooled in her part, "what is it that you mean to do with that dagger? Are you perchance thinking of taking your own life or Lotario's? Whatever it is, it will result in the loss of your good name and reputation. It would be better for you to say nothing of the wrong that has been done you; rather, you should see to it that this evil man does not enter our house and find us alone. Consider, my lady: we are weak women and he is a man, strong and determined, and, coming as he does, blindly and passionately bent upon that foul design of his, he may well put it into execution before you can carry out yours, and may do that which in your eyes would be worse than if he were to slay you. A plague on my master for having given this shameless fellow the upper hand in his household! But supposing, my lady, that you kill him, for such I think is your intention, what shall we do with the body?"

"What shall we do with it, my friend?" replied Camila. "Why, we shall leave it for Anselmo to bury; for he should regard it as no task at all to put the betrayer of his good name underground. Go, then, and call him; for every moment that I delay taking the vengeance that is due my wrong appears to me an offense against that loyalty that I owe to my husband."

Anselmo was listening to all this, and at each word that Camila spoke his thoughts underwent a change. When he heard that she was resolved to kill Lotario, his impulse was to come out and reveal his presence and prevent such a deed, but, wishing to see what the outcome of her noble and virtuous determination would be, he restrained himself, thinking that he would be able to appear in time to stop her. At this point she was seized with a violent fainting fit and threw herself upon a near-by couch, as Leonela began weeping bitterly. "Ah, woe is me!" she exclaimed, "how unfortunate I am that the world's flower of virtue, the crowning example of chastity for all good wives, should be dying here in my arms!" She went on uttering other similar lamentations, and anyone hearing her would have thought that she was the most loyal and woebegone lady's maid that ever was, while her mistress was another and persecuted Penelope.

Camila, however, was not long in recovering from her swoon. "Leonela," she said, as she regained consciousness once more, "why do you not go call that most disloyal [7] friend to his friend that ever the sun shone upon or the night covered with its darkness? Go, run, hasten, make speed, lest the fire of my wrath burn itself out with delay and the just vengeance that I hope for be consumed in threats and curses!"

"That I will, my lady," said Leonela, "but first give me the dagger that you may not do something while I am gone that will cause all those who love you to weep for the rest of their lives."

"You may rest assured, friend Leonela, that I shall do nothing of the kind; for however rash and foolish I may appear to you to be in thus defending my honor, I am not like Lucretia, of whom it is said that she slew herself without being guilty of any fault whatsoever and without first having slain the one who was the cause of her dishonor. I shall die if needs be, but only after I have had revenge and satisfaction from him who is responsible for my being in this state where I must weep over audacious proposals for which I can in no wise be held accountable."

It required much urging before Leonela could be persuaded to call Lotario, but finally she left the room, and while she was gone Camila went on talking to herself.

"God help me! Would it not have been better to send Lotario away as I have done many times before than to give him the opportunity as I am doing now to look upon me as evil and unchaste, even for the brief space of time that it takes to undeceive him? It would have been better, no doubt, but then I should not have had my vengeance, nor would my husband's honor have been satisfied if Lotario had been allowed to wash his hands of the matter and escape so easily from this situation into which his own wicked impulses have led him. Let the traitor pay with his life for his lewd desires. Let the world know if it must that Camila not only preserved her loyalty to her husband, but avenged herself on the one who had dared offend him.

"But after all, I imagine it would have been better to give Anselmo an account of everything that has happened; yet I informed him of it in the letter that I wrote to him while he was in the village, and it is my opinion that if he did not at once hasten back to remedy the wrong of which I told him, it must have been because, being so pure-minded and trusting, he would not or could not believe that so stanch a friend could ever think of thus dishonoring him. Indeed, I could not believe it myself for a long while, nor should I ever have done so if Lotario's insolence had not been carried to the point where his open gifts and lavish promises and constant tears made it all too plain. But why do I let myself run on like this? Does a noble resolve, perchance, stand in need of any counsels? No, certainly not. Away, traitorous thoughts! Come, vengeance! Let the false one approach and enter, let him die and end it all, and then come what may! Pure I came to him whom Heaven gave me as my own, and pure I will leave him; nay, more, I will leave him bathed in my own chaste blood and in the impure blood of one who in all the world has been the greatest betrayer of friendship that ever was."

As she said this, she paced up and down the room with the dagger unsheathed, swaying and staggering and making such wild gestures that she appeared to be out of her mind, and one would have taken her for some desperate ruffian rather than a woman who had been gently bred and reared. Anselmo watched her from behind the tapestries where he had hidden and was vastly astonished by it all. It seemed to him that what he had seen and heard was sufficient answer to the worst suspicions he had entertained, and he would have been well enough pleased if Lotario had not come now, fearing as he did some sudden untoward event. He was about to come out and embrace his wife and tell her the whole story but stopped short when he saw Leonela returning, leading Lotario by the hand. The moment she saw the latter, Camila took the dagger and with it drew a long line across the floor.

"Lotario," she said, "mark well what I tell you. If by any chance you are so bold as to cross this line that you see here, or even come up to it, the instant I see you intend to do so I shall pierce my bosom with this dagger that I hold in my hand. Before you utter a single word in reply, I would have you listen to a few words that I have to say to you, and afterward you may make such answer as you like. In the first place, Lotario, I would ask you if you know my husband, Anselmo, and what opinion you hold of him. And in the second place, I would likewise inquire if you know me. Answer me this, clearly and plainly and without stopping to think for long what you are going to say, for the questions I have put to you are simple enough."

Lotario was not so dull-witted but that, when Camila told him to have Anselmo hide there, he had at once surmised what she meant to do, and he was now so clever and prompt in helping her carry out her plan that the lie came to seem the truest truth.

"I did not think, beauteous Camila," he answered her, "that you were sending for me to question me about things so foreign to the purpose for which I come here. If you are doing this merely to defer the promised favor, you might have put it off still longer, for an ardent desire is most painful when the hope of its being fulfilled is nearest to realization. However, in order that you may not be able to say that I have not answered your questions, I will tell you that your husband Anselmo and I have known each other since our tenderest years. I need not tell you further what you already know concerning the friendship between us, merely by way of bearing witness [8] against the wrong that love compels me to do to my friend—love, the most powerful excuse that can be offered for greater misdeeds than this. Yes, I know you well and you are as much mine as his; for I can assure you that, if it were not so, I would not for any lesser reward have gone against that which I owe to myself and to the holy laws of true friendship, now broken and violated by me through the work of an enemy no less powerful than love itself."

"If you admit this," replied Camila, "O mortal enemy of all that justly deserves to be loved, how then do you have the countenance to appear before one whom you know to be the mirror in which Anselmo beholds himself, who should be in turn the glass in which you see the unjustifiable injury that you have done him. But, alas, I now realize that it must have been some frivolity on my part that caused you to show so little self-respect. I will not call it immodesty, since it was in no way deliberate but must have been due to that careless attitude into which women sometimes inadvertently fall when they think that there is no occasion for reserve. If this be not so, then tell me, O traitor, when did I respond to your entreaties with any word or sign that might have awakened in you the shadowy hope of being able to accomplish your infamous desires?

When were your amorous pleadings not repelled and reprehended? When did they not meet with stern, harsh words from me? When were your many promises believed, your still more lavish gifts accepted?

"Nevertheless," she continued, "inasmuch as it seems to me that no one could persevere for so long in a purpose of this sort if he were not sustained by a hope of some kind, I must seek to attribute to myself the blame for your impudence, since no doubt some careless act of mine has all this time been giving you ground for hope. And so, it is my intention to punish myself and assume the penalty that you deserve. And as I would have you see that, being so cruel toward myself, I could not but be the same toward you, I have brought you here to witness the sacrifice that I am about to make to the offended honor of my so honored husband, to whom you have done the greatest wrong that was in your power, while I as well have wronged him by failing to avoid the occasion, if any, that I have given you by appearing to encourage and sanction your designs.

"I will say again that the suspicion I have that some bit of carelessness on my part has engendered in you this mad passion is the thing that most harasses me, and it is this negligence that I desire to punish with my own hands; for if another were to be my executioner, my fault would perhaps become more widely known. Before I do this, however, I mean to slay even in death and take with me one who will satisfy the desire and hope of vengeance that I cherish; for there where I go, wherever it may be, I shall see a disinterested and unyielding justice inflicted upon him who has placed me in my present plight."

Saying this, with incredible strength and swiftness she fell upon Lotario with the unsheathed dagger, with so evident an intention of burying it in his bosom that he was half in doubt as to whether it was a false show or she really meant to do as she said. In any event, he had to employ all his own strength and dexterity to prevent her from stabbing him; for she was so very lifelike in acting out this strange drama of conjugal fidelity [9] that, by way of lending it the color of truth, she even wished to stain it with her own blood.

Seeing that she could not come at Lotario,[10] or pretending that she was unable to, she said, "Since fate is unwilling to satisfy wholly my just desire, it at least is not so powerful as to keep me from satisfying it in part."

With a great effort she freed the hand with the dagger which Lotario held and, directing its point to a place where it would not inflict a deep wound, she plunged it into her left side near the shoulder and then fell to the floor as if in a faint. Leonela and Lotario were dumbfounded by this unexpected turn of events, and as they beheld Camila lying stretched out there and bathed in her own blood, they were uncertain as to whether the act was real or feigned. Terrified and breathless, Lotario ran up and withdrew the dagger, and when he saw the small wound it had made he was greatly relieved and once more was led to admire the sagacity, prudence, and extreme cleverness of the beauteous Camila. By way of carrying out his own part, he then began to lament long and loudly over her body, as though she were already dead, heaping curses not only upon himself but upon the one who had placed him in such a position. And as he knew that his friend Anselmo was listening, he said things that caused the latter to feel much more pity for him than for Camila, who was supposed to be dead.

Leonela then took her mistress in her arms and laid her upon the couch, begging Lotario to go seek some trustworthy person to care for her wound. At the same time she asked his advice as to what they should tell Anselmo if by chance he should return before it was healed. He replied that they might say whatever they liked, as he was in no condition to give advice that would be of any value. All he could tell her was to try to stop the bleeding. As for himself, he was going where no one would ever see him again. And then, with a great show of grief and feeling, he left the house; and as soon as he was alone and safely out of sight, he began crossing himself any number of times as he marveled at Camila's ingenuity and the telling manner in which Leonela played her part. Anselmo, he reflected, would surely be convinced that he had a second Portia for a wife, and he was eager to be alone with him in order that they together might celebrate this mixture of falsehood and truth dissimulated in a fashion that never could be imagined.

Leonela stopped the flow of her mistress's blood as he had directed, there being no more of it than was necessary to lend credence to the fiction, and, having bathed the wound with a little wine, she bandaged it as well as she could, meanwhile keeping up such a flow of words as would have sufficed to convince Anselmo, if the ones already spoken had not done so, that he had in Camila a model of virtue.

Mingled with Leonela's words were those of her mistress, who reproached herself for being a coward and lacking in courage, which had failed her at the time she most needed it—the courage to take her life, which was so abhorrent to her. She asked her waiting woman's advice as to whether or not she should tell her beloved husband of all that had happened, and Leonela counseled against this since it would put him under the obligation of revenging himself upon Lotario, which he could do only at great risk to himself. It was the duty of a good wife not to involve her husband in quarrels over her, but rather to remove the occasion for such disputes. Camila replied that this advice impressed her as being very good and she would follow it; but, in any case, they must begin to think of something to tell Anselmo concerning the cause of this wound, which he could not help seeing. To this the maid answered that she was incapable of telling a lie even in jest.

"Well, then, my sister," said Camila, "how do you expect me to tell one, who should not dare invent or keep up a falsehood if my life depended on it? And so, the best thing will be to tell him the naked truth in order that he may not catch us in a lie."

"Do not trouble yourself, my lady," said Leonela. "Between now and tomorrow morning I will think up something that we can tell him; and possibly, the wound being where it is, it may be kept covered so that he will not see it, and Heaven will be thus pleased to favor our just and honorable intentions. In the meantime, calm yourself and try not to appear so excited, for it is not well that my master should find you in this state of agitation. Just leave it to my care and God's, for He always looks after the desires of the righteous."

Anselmo had most attentively watched and listened to this tragedy involving the death of his own honor which had been performed with such marvelous and effective realism that the actors appeared to have been transformed into the very parts they played. He was eager for night to come so that he might have an opportunity to leave the house and go see his good friend Lotario that they might rejoice together over the precious pearl he had found in thus establishing beyond a doubt the virtue of his wife. Mistress and maid were at pains to provide him with an opportunity to leave, and, taking advantage of it, he went at once to seek Lotario. It would be quite impossible to describe the affectionate embraces that he gave him when they met, the many things he said out of the happiness of his heart, or the praises that he bestowed on Camila. Lotario listened to it all without being able to give any sign of joy, for he kept remembering what a deceived man his friend was and how unjustly he had wronged him. Although Anselmo saw that Lotario was not in good spirits, he believed the reason was that he had left Camila wounded and felt that he was to blame.

Anselmo accordingly told him, among other things, that he should not worry about what had happened to her, since her wound undoubtedly was a slight one, seeing that she and Leonela had agreed to conceal it.

This being so, there was nothing to fear, but henceforth he should be glad and rejoice with his friend, who, through his capable mediation, now found himself raised to the greatest heights of happiness that could be desired, with no other ambition than that of spending his time in composing verses in Camila's honor such as would preserve her name for all the ages to come. Lotario praised this good intention and promised to do his part in helping to erect so illustrious a monument.

Thus did Anselmo remain the most delightfully deceived man that could possibly be found anywhere in the world. He himself led home by the hand the one who had wrought the destruction of his good name, in the belief that he was bringing with him one who had exalted it. As for Camila, she received her husband's friend with a wry look but a smiling heart. This deception lasted for a number of months until, at a turn of fortune's wheel, the guilty relationship that had been so artfully concealed finally became known and Anselmo paid with his life for his ill-advised curiosity.

CHAPTER XXXV. *In which the "Story of the One Who Was Too Curious for His Own Good" is brought to a close, and in which is related the fierce and monstrous battle that Don Quixote waged with certain skins of red wine.*

THE reading of the story was nearly completed when from the garret where Don Quixote was taking his repose Sancho Panza burst forth in great excitement, shouting, "Come quick, sirs, and help my master, for he is in the thick of the most stubborn and fiercest battle that ever my eyes beheld! By the living God but he gave that giant who is the enemy of my lady, the Princess Micomicona, such a slash that he cut his head off all the way around as if it had been a turnip!"

"What are you talking about, brother?" asked the curate as he paused in his reading. "Have you gone out of your head, Sancho? How in the devil could what you say be true when the giant is two thousand leagues from here?"

At this point there came a loud noise from the upper room and Don Quixote could be heard crying, "Hold, robber, scoundrel, knave! I have you now, and your scimitar will not avail you!" And then it sounded as if he were giving great slashes at the wall.

"Don't stop to listen," said Sancho, "but go on in and stop the fight or else help my master; although, come to think of it, that will not be necessary, for there is no doubt whatever that the giant is already dead by this time and is now giving an account to God of his past life and evil ways. I myself saw the blood running all over the floor and his head cut off and lying to one side, and it was big as a wineskin."

"May they slay me!" cried the innkeeper at this point. "I'll bet Don Quixote or Don Devil has been slashing at one of those skins full of red wine that are at the head of his bed, and it must have been the wine spilling over the floor that looked like blood to this good man."

He then made his way to the garret, followed by all the rest of them, and there they found Don Quixote in the strangest costume imaginable. He was clad in his shirt, which was not long enough in front to cover his thighs completely and was about six fingers shorter behind. His legs were very long, lean, and hairy and anything but clean. On his head he had a little greasy red cap that belonged to the innkeeper, and around his left arm he had rolled a red blanket—an object against which Sancho, for reasons of his own, had a special grudge—while in his right hand he held an unsheathed sword with which he was laying about him in every direction, and all the time he kept talking to himself as if he were really fighting with some giant. The best part of it was that he had his eyes shut, for he was still asleep and dreaming that he was doing battle with the giant, the adventure which he was about to undertake having so worked upon his imagination that he fancied in his dream that he had already reached the kingdom of Micomicon and was engaged in a struggle with his enemy.

Under this illusion he had given the skins so many thrusts, believing them to be the giant, that the entire room was filled with wine. Seeing what his guest had done, the landlord was so angry that he fell upon Don Quixote with clenched fists and began pommeling him so hard that if Cardenio and the curate had not pulled him off, he would soon have concluded the war with the giant. But in spite of it all they did not succeed in awakening the poor gentleman until the barber had brought a large pot of cold water from the well and they had dashed its contents over the knight, who then regained consciousness but not sufficiently to be able to realize what had happened.

Seeing how scantily and thinly he was clad, Dorotea would not come in to witness the encounter between her champion and his adversary; and Sancho, meanwhile, was looking all over the floor for the giant's head, which he was unable to find.

"I knew all along," he said, "that everything about this house was under a spell. The other time, in this very room where I am now, they gave me any number of cuffs and blows without my knowing from where they came, for I was never able to see anyone doing it; and now I can't find that head though I saw it chopped off with my own eyes, with the blood spurting from his body as from a fountain."

"What blood and what fountain, enemy of God and his saints?" cried the innkeeper. "Can't you see, you brigand, that the blood and fountain you are talking about are nothing other than these skins that have been punctured and the red wine from them that is flowing all over the room —and I only wish I saw the soul of him who pierced them swimming in Hell!"

"I know nothing about that," said Sancho. "All I know is that, if I don't find that head, it will be my bad luck to see my earldom melting away like salt in water."

For Sancho awake was worse than his master asleep, such had been the effect of the promises Don Quixote had made him. The innkeeper was in despair at seeing this lack of concern on the part of the squire and the deviltry wrought by the knight, and he swore that it was not going to be like the last time, when they had left without paying. This time the privileges of knighthood would not let either one or the other of them off, but they would have to reimburse him even for the cost of the plugs to patch up the punctured skins. The curate all this while was holding Don Quixote's hands, and the knight, thinking that the exploit had been accomplished and that he was now in the presence of the Princess Micomicona, dropped to his knees in front of the priest.

"O exalted and famous lady," he said, "your Highness from this day forth may live assured against any harm this lowborn creature could have done you; and I too am now free of the promise I gave you, since with the help of Almighty God and the favor of her in whom I live and breathe, I have so thoroughly [1] fulfilled it."

"There!" exclaimed Sancho upon hearing this, "what did I tell you? You see I was not drunk after all. Just look how my master has salted down that giant! You can depend on the bulls,[2] and my earldom is certain."

Who would not have laughed at hearing the nonsense the two of them talked, master and man? And laugh they all did with the exception of mine host, who was roundly cursing himself. At last, however, with no little effort, the barber, Cardenio, and the curate managed to get Don Quixote back into bed, and he at once fell asleep with every appearance of being utterly exhausted. Leaving him there, they then went down to the gateway of the inn to console Sancho Panza for not having found the giant's head; but they had a good deal more on their hands when it came to placating the landlord, who was in a rage over the sudden death of his wineskins. The landlady, for her part, was screaming and carrying on at a great rate.

"It was an evil moment and an unlucky hour," she shouted, "when that knight-errant entered my house. I had never laid eyes on him before, but he cost me dearly. The last time it was the price of a lodging, a dinner, a bed, and straw and barley, for himself, his squire, a hack, and an ass. He said he was a knightly adventurer—may God give him and all the adventurers in this world nothing but misadventures!—and for that reason was obliged to pay nothing, since that was the way it was written down in the tariff code of knight-errantry. And now, on account of him, this other gentleman comes along and carries off my tail and gives it back to me with more than two cuartillos'[3] worth of damage done to it, all stripped of its hair and of no further use for my husband's purpose. And as the finishing touch to everything, he punctures my wineskins and spills my wine—if I could only see his blood spilled instead! But let him not think he'll be able to do the same thing this time! By my father's bones and my mother's ghost, he's going to pay me every cuarto[4] that he owes me or my name is not what it is and I am not my parents' daughter!"

The innkeeper's wife had all this and many other things to say, for she was very angry indeed, and her slavey, the worthy Maritornes, joined in the scolding. The daughter, however, was silent and merely smiled quietly to herself from time to time. The curate finally settled matters by promising to make good the loss to the best of his ability. He agreed to pay them for the wineskins and the wine and especially for the damage done to that tail of which they were forever talking. Dorotea, meanwhile, was comforting Sancho Panza by telling him that, the moment it was definitely established that his master had cut off the giant's head and she had come into peaceful possession of her kingdom, she would bestow upon him the finest earldom that it contained. Sancho felt better upon hearing this and assured the princess that he had seen the giant's head, adding by way of further identification that the monster had a beard that came all the way down to his waist, and if he was not to be seen at the moment, it was for the reason that everything that happened in that house was directed by an enchanter, as he himself had found to be the case the other time that he had stopped*there. Dorotea said that she believed this to be true, but that he should not let it worry him, as things would come out all right in the end and he would have whatever he wished.

When they had all quieted down, the curate suggested that they finish reading the story, for there was still a little of it left. Cardenio, Dorotea, and the others thereupon begged him to continue, and by reason of the pleasure that he as well as they derived from it, he went on with the tale, as follows:

As a result of it all, Anselmo was so convinced of Camila's virtue that he went on living a happy and carefree life, while she was deliberately cool toward Lotario in order that her husband might think her feeling for his friend was the opposite of what it was. By way of confirming this impression, Lotario begged permission not to come to the house, since it was plain to be seen that his visits were an annoyance to Camila; but Anselmo, thoroughly deluded, would by no means hear of this, and thus in a thousand ways he became the creator of his own dishonor in place of what he took to be his happiness.

In the meantime, Leonela was so elated at finding herself free to carry on her amours [5] that she came to think of nothing else and gave free rein to her passion, being confident that her mistress would afford her concealment and even show her how to manage the affair with little fear of discovery. Finally, one night Anselmo heard footsteps in her room, and when he sought to enter to find out who was there, he found the door held against him, a circumstance that made him all the more determined to open it. Open it he did by main force and entered just in time to see a man leaping from the window to the street.

He was about to follow in an effort to overtake him or see if he could recognize him but was prevented from doing either by Leonela, who threw her arms about him as she cried, "Calm yourself, my master. Do not excite yourself and go running after the one who just leaped from that window, for he belongs to me; in fact, he is my husband."

Anselmo was unwilling to believe this and, blind with rage, drew a dagger and threatened to stab Leonela, assuring her that he would kill her if she did not tell him the truth. She was so frightened that she did not know what she was saying and could only stammer, "Do not kill me, master, for I can tell you things that are more important than you can imagine."

"Tell me, then," said Anselmo. "If you do not, you are a dead woman."

"It would be impossible for me to do so now," she replied. "I am so excited that I cannot think. Give me until tomorrow morning, and then you will learn from me something that will astonish you. Meanwhile, you may rest assured that the one who left by way of this window is a young man of this city who has promised to marry me."

Anselmo was mollified by this and consented to grant her the time for which she asked. It did not occur to him that he would hear anything against Camila, for he felt perfectly sure of her virtue; and so he went away and left Leonela locked in the room, telling her that she would not come out until he had heard her story. He then went to inform Camila of all that had passed between him and her waiting woman and how the latter had promised to reveal to him some things of very great importance. As to whether his wife was alarmed or not by all this, there is no need of our saying. A terrible fear came over her, for she really believed—and she had good reason to believe it—that Leonela meant to tell Anselmo everything that she knew concerning his wife's disloyalty.

As a result, she did not have the courage to wait and see if her suspicion was false or not, but that very night, as soon as she thought her husband had gone to sleep, she got together the best jewels that she had and a little money and, slipping out unnoticed, made her way to Lotario's house. There she told him all that had happened and begged him to put her in hiding or go with her to some place where Anselmo would not find them. But he was greatly confused by it all and could not give her a single word in reply, nor was he able to make up his mind as to what should be done.

At last he decided to take her to a convent the prioress of which was his sister; and this he did, with her consent and with all the haste that the situation called for, after which he at once left the city without notifying anyone of his departure.

When dawn came, Anselmo was so eager to hear what Leonela had to tell him that he did not even notice that Camila was missing from beside him, but arose and went to where he had left the maid locked in her room. Opening the door, he went in but found no Leonela there. All that he did find was some sheets knotted to the window, an obvious indication that she had let herself down and made her escape. Very much disappointed, he returned to tell Camila, and when he failed to discover her in bed or anywhere in the house, he was truly dumfounded. He made inquiries of all the servants but none could give him any explanation.

As he was looking for her, he chanced to see her jewel boxes lying open and noted that most of the gems were missing from them. Then it was that he began to realize the nature of his misfortune, of which Leonela was not the cause; and without waiting to complete his toilet, he sadly and pensively went to seek his friend Lotario that he might tell him of his sorrow. Lotario, however, was not at home, and his servants said that he had not been there all night long but had left the house with all the money that he had. At this point Anselmo began to feel as if he were losing his mind, and to crown it all, when he returned to his own house, he found it utterly deserted, with all the many servants, male and female, gone. He did not know what to think or say nor what to do; his reason seemed to be deserting him, little by little. As he contemplated his situation, he had an instant view of himself as a man without a wife, without a friend, without servants, left wholly unprotected as it seemed to him by Heaven—above all, left without honor; for in the loss of Camila he saw his own ruination.

Finally, after a considerable length of time, he resolved to go to the village where his friend lived and where he himself had been while this great misfortune was in the making. Locking the doors of his house, he mounted his horse and with fainting heart took to the road. He had gone barely halfway when, harassed by his thoughts, he found it necessary to dismount and tie his steed to a tree, at the foot of which he threw himself down with many piteous and mournful sighs, and there he remained until nightfall, when he saw a horseman coming along the road from the direction of the city. Having greeted the man, he inquired of him what the news in Florence was.

" 'Tis the strangest I have heard in many a day," the citizen replied; "for they are now saying openly that Lotario, that great friend of the rich Anselmo who lived at San Giovanni, last night carried off Camila, the wife of Anselmo, who likewise is missing. All this was learned from a maid of Camila's who was found by the watch last night as she was lowering herself by a sheet from a window of the house. The truth is, no one rightly knows just what did happen, but the whole city is astonished over it, since no one would ever have expected such a thing in view of the great and close friendship that existed between the men, a friendship so strong that the pair were commonly called 'the two friends.' "

"Is it by any chance known," asked Anselmo, "what road Lotario and Camila took?"

"There is not so much as a trace of them," said the citizen, "although the governor has instituted a most thorough search."

"God go with you, sir," said Anselmo.

"God be with you," responded the citizen as he rode away.

With such overwhelming news as this, Anselmo was not only near to losing his mind but to ending his life as well. He arose and mounted his horse as best he could and made his way to the house of his friend, who had not yet learned of his misfortune but who, when he saw him arriving in this state, looking so pale, haggard, and worn, realized at once that his guest must be laboring under some deep sorrow. Anselmo at once asked if he might go to bed and requested them to provide him with writing materials. They did so and then left him alone, for he would have it that way and even directed them to bar the door. When they were gone, he began once more to think about the misfortune that had befallen him, which weighed upon his mind to such an extent that he perceived clearly enough that his end was drawing near.[6] Desiring to leave some record as to the cause of his strange death, he thereupon started to write, but before he had finished setting down all that he wished to say, his breath failed him and he died a victim of the grief which his ill-advised curiosity had brought upon him.

When the master of the house saw that it was growing late and Anselmo had not yet called, he decided to enter the room and see if his guest's indisposition had grown worse. He found him there, lying on his face, half of his body in the bed and the other half upon the writing-table over which he had been leaning. The paper with the writing on it was spread out in front of him, and he still held the pen in his hand. His host first called to him, and when he did not answer, he took him by the hand and found that it was cold, and then he knew that his friend was dead. He was astounded and deeply dismayed by this and at once summoned the members of his household to come and witness Anselmo's sad end. Finally he read the paper, which he recognized as being in the dead man's handwriting. It contained the following words:

A foolish and ill-advised desire has robbed me of my life. If the news of my death should reach Camila's ears, let her know that I forgive her; for she was under no obligation to perform miracles and I had no right to ask them of her. Thus, I was the creator of my own dishonor, and there is no reason why

That was as far as Anselmo had gone with his last note; for it was plain that at this point, before he had finished what he had to say, death had overtaken him. His parents were notified the following day by the one in whose house he had breathed his last. They already knew of their son's misfortune, and they knew as well of the convent where Camila lay, almost on the verge of accompanying her husband on his inevitable last journey, owing not to grief over the news of his death but to sorrow over the word she had received of her lover's departure. And they say that, although she had been left a widow, she did not care to leave the monastery, nor, on the other hand, to adopt the calling of a nun—at least not until, some while afterward, news came that Lotario had been killed in a recent battle between Monsieur de Lautrec and the Great Captain, Gonzalo Hernández de Córdoba in the kingdom of Naples: [7] for it appears that her lover had tardily repented. Upon learning of this, Camila forthwith took the veil and died within a short while of sorrow and melancholy. And such was the end of all of them, the end that came of so foolish a beginning.

"I like this tale well enough," remarked the curate, "but I cannot persuade myself that it is true. If it is pure invention, then the author is to blame; for I cannot imagine a husband so foolish as to make such a costly experiment as Anselmo did. If it were the case of a gallant and his mistress, that might do, but as between a husband and wife it is lacking in plausibility. As to the method of telling the story, I have no fault to find with that."

CHAPTER XXXVI. *Which treats of other extraordinary events that occurred at the inn.*

JUST at that moment the landlord, who was standing in the gateway of the inn, cried out, "Here comes a fine lot of guests for you; if they stop here, we well may sing *Gaudeamus*."

"What kind of folk are they?" asked Cardenio.

"They are four men," replied the innkeeper, "riding high in the saddle and short in the stirrup,[1] with lances and bucklers and black masks, and with them is a woman clad in white; she is riding on a sidesaddle and her face, also, is veiled; and there are two servants on foot."

"Are they very near?" inquired the curate.

"So near," said the landlord, "that they are arriving now."

Upon hearing this, Dorotea covered her face and Cardenio went into the room where Don Quixote was, and they had barely had time to do this when all those persons whom the innkeeper had described came trooping into the hostelry. The four on horseback, who had the look and manner of the wellborn, at once dismounted and went over to assist the lady to alight. One of them then took her in his arms and seated her in the chair that stood beside the entrance to the room where Cardenio was hidden. During all this time neither she nor her companions had removed their masks nor had they uttered a single word. The only sound to be heard was the deep sigh that the lady gave as she let her arms drop to her side like one who was ill and faint. The two servants, meanwhile, had taken the horses out to the stable.

Having watched all this, the curate, being desirous of knowing who these people were who came in such a costume and preserved such a silence, went over to where the servants were and asked one of them for the information that he wished.

"Upon my word, sir, I can't tell you," the youth replied. "All I know is that they appear to be very important people, especially the one who, as you saw, just took the lady in his arms. My reason for saying this is that all the others show him respect and do only what he orders and commands."

"And the lady, who is she?"

"That also is something that I do not know; for all along the way I did not have a glimpse of her face. It is true, I heard her sigh many times, and once in a while she would moan as if she were about to give up the ghost. It is no wonder, however, if we do not know any more about them than what I have told you, for my companion and I have not been with them more than a couple of days. We met them on the highway and they begged and persuaded us to come with them as far as Andalusia, promising to pay us very well."

"And have you heard any of them called by name?" the curate persisted.

"No indeed," said the lad. "They all go along so silently that it is really amazing. You can hear nothing but the sighs and sobs of the poor lady, which make us sorry for her, and we feel quite certain that, wherever it is she is being taken, it is against her will. So far as can be gathered from the habit she wears, she is a nun or, what is more likely, is about to become one; and it may be that it is against her will that she is entering a convent, which is the reason why she seems so sad."

"That may all be true," said the curate; and, leaving the servants, he returned to where Dorotea was. She, having heard the veiled lady sigh, moved by a natural compassion now went up and spoke to her.

"What is it that is troubling you, my lady?" she said. "If it is anything that women by their knowledge and experience can remedy, I herewith gladly offer you my services."

The poor woman said nothing, and although the offer was repeated, more earnestly than ever, she still remained silent, until the masked gentleman whom the servant had said the rest of them obeyed came over and addressed Dorotea.

"Do not tire yourself, lady," he said, "by making any offers of assistance to this woman, for it is her custom to show no thanks for any favor that is done her; so do not seek to get an answer from her, unless you wish to hear some lie from her mouth."

"I have never told a lie," declared the one who up to that point had been silent. "Rather, it is because I have been so truthful and without any lying propensities that I am now placed in this unfortunate situation. I call upon you yourself to be my witness, for it is the simple truth I speak that has made you out a purveyor of falsehoods and a liar."

Cardenio heard these words as clearly and distinctly as if he had been standing beside the one who spoke them, for there was only the door of Don Quixote's room between them; and he at once gave a shout and cried, "My God! What is this I hear? What voice is this that reaches my ears?"

Very much startled, the lady turned her head, and, not seeing who it was that had uttered this cry, she arose and was about to enter the other room, but the gentleman stopped her, refusing to allow her to move a step. As a result of the stir and excitement the lady's veil now fell down, revealing a face of incomparable, truly marvelous beauty, though pale and frightened in appearance, with a pair of eyes that kept searching all around wherever their gaze could reach, with so much anxiety that it seemed as if their owner were out of her senses. Dorotea and all the others who beheld her were deeply moved by all this, though they did not understand the reason for it. The gentleman all the while was grasping her firmly by the shoulders and was so occupied in doing so that he was unable to lift a hand to prevent his own mask from falling off, as it did a moment later.

Dorotea, who was standing there with her arms about the lady, now looked up and saw that the gentleman was none other than her own husband, Don Fernando. No sooner was she aware of his identity than, giving vent to a prolonged and mournful cry that appeared to come from the very depths of her being, she fell back in a faint; and if the barber had not been there to catch her in his arms, she would have fallen to the floor.

The curate then came over to remove her veil and throw water on her face, and as soon as he saw her features Don Fernando recognized her even as he held the other woman in his arms, and at the sight of her his own face turned deathly pale. He could not, however, release his hold on Luscinda, who was struggling to free herself from his grasp, she and Cardenio having recognized each other by their voices. For Cardenio also had heard the cry that Dorotea gave as she fainted, and believing it to be his Luscinda, he had rushed out terror-stricken. The first thing he saw was Don Fernando with Luscinda in his arms, and Fernando now recognized him, while the three of them—Luscinda, Cardenio, and Dorotea—remained silent and bewildered, scarcely knowing what had happened. They all gazed at one another without saying a word: Dorotea at Don Fernando, Fernando at Cardenio, Cardenio at Luscinda, and Luscinda at Cardenio. Luscinda was the first to break the silence, by addressing Fernando in the following manner:

"Let me go, Señor Don Fernando, for the sake of what you owe to yourself, seeing that nothing else can prevail upon you to do so. Leave me here to cling to the wall of which I am the ivy, to the support from which neither your importunities nor your threats nor your promises nor your gifts can separate me. Take note how Heaven, by unaccustomed paths that are dark to us, has placed before me my true husband. You know well, by a thousand costly experiences, that only death would ever suffice to efface him from my memory. Let this plain declaration, then, lead you, since you can do nothing else, to turn your love into wrath, your affection into spite, that you may do away with my life which I will gladly render here in the presence of my husband; and perhaps, seeing me die in this manner, he will be satisfied that I have kept faith with him to the very end."

Dorotea, who had by now fully recovered from her fainting fit, had listened closely to all that Luscinda had to say, and the latter's words told her clearly who the speaker was. Perceiving that Don Fernando would not let his victim go nor give her any answer, she now summoned all the strength she could and, rising, went over and dropped to her knees at Fernando's feet.

"If, my lord," she began, "the rays of that sun in eclipse that you hold in your arms had not blinded your eyes, you would have seen that the unfortunate creature (so long as you will have it so) who now kneels at your feet is none other than the ill-starred Dorotea. I am that humble peasant girl whom you, out of graciousness or for your own pleasure, saw fit to lift to the height where she might call herself yours. I am she who, locked within the bounds of virtue, lived a happy life until, in response to your importunities and what appeared to be your proper and sincerely intended declarations of love, she opened the gates of her modesty and delivered to you the keys of her heart, a gift so ill appreciated that I now of necessity find myself in my present position and behold you under such circumstances as these.

"But, nevertheless, I would not have you think that it is my shame that has brought me here; it is only my feeling of sorrow at seeing myself forgotten by you. You insisted upon my being yours, and in such a way that, though you would have it otherwise now, you still cannot help being mine. Reflect on this, my lord: may not the incomparable affection that I bear you compensate for the beauty and nobility of birth for which you would leave me? You cannot belong to the lovely Luscinda for you belong to me, and she cannot be yours for she belongs to Cardenio. If you will think it over, you will see that it will be easier to bring yourself to love one who adores you than to force one to love you who now abhors you. You played upon my innocence and sought to undermine my virtue. You were not unaware of my station in life, and you well know how I gave myself to you wholly, so that you cannot say that you were deceived.

"If all this is so, and it is, and if you are a Christian as you are a gentleman, then why by all these subterfuges do you delay making me happy in the end as you did in the beginning? And if you would not have me for what I am, which is your true and lawful wife, at least show me enough affection to take me as your slave; for merely by being in your possession, I shall look upon myself as happy and fortunate. Do not, by leaving me unprotected, permit my shame to be the subject of gossip in the street. Do not inflict so wretched an old age upon my parents, for they do not deserve such treatment in view of the faithful services which they as vassals have always rendered to you and yours. And if you think your blood will be contaminated by mingling with mine, remember that there is little or no nobility in this world that has not traveled the same road, and that in the case of illustrious lineages it is not the woman's blood that counts. What is more, true nobility consists in virtue, and if you show a lack of this by denying me what is so justly my due, then I shall have shown myself in the end to be more noble than you.

"In short, my lord, when all is said, I would have you know that I am your wife, whether you like it or not. Your own words are my witnesses, which cannot be lying ones if you pride yourself on that nobility for the lack of which I am despicable in your sight. I have your signed pledge,[2] and Heaven also, which you called upon to witness the vows you made, will bear me out. Failing all this, your own conscience should raise its voice amid your merrymaking and remind you of this truth I have just spoken, thus disturbing your hours of greatest happiness and contentment."

These and other words were spoken by the woebegone Dorotea with such feeling and so many tears that even those who accompanied Don Fernando and all the others present wept with her. Fernando listened without making any reply until she had finished, whereupon she began sighing and sobbing so passionately that it would have been a heart of bronze that would not have melted at such a show of grief. Luscinda gazed at her with no less sympathy for her suffering than admiration for her wit and beauty, and she would have gone up to her and uttered a few words of consolation if Don Fernando's arms had not restrained her, for he still clasped her tightly. Greatly astonished and confused by it all, he stared fixedly at Dorotea for a good while and then, opening his arms, he let Luscinda go.

"You have conquered, O beauteous Dorotea," he said, "you have conquered. No one could have the heart to deny so many truths as you have uttered."

Luscinda, when Don Fernando released his hold of her, was so faint that she would have fallen; but, as it happened, Cardenio, in order to avoid being recognized, was standing behind his former friend, and now, casting aside all fear and risking everything, he came forward to support the one he loved.

"If merciful Heaven," he said, as he took her in his embrace, "is pleased to let you have a little rest at last, O my loyal, steadfast, and beautiful lady, I do not think you will find a safer haven than in these arms that now receive you as they did of old, when fortune willed that I might call you mine."

At these words, Luscinda gazed at Cardenio. She had begun to recognize him by the sound of his voice, and now, being assured by the sight of her eyes that it was indeed he, she forgot all about decorum and, flinging her arms around his neck, laid her cheek against his.

"Yes, my lord," she said, "you are the true master of this your captive one, even though an adverse fate should once more intervene and once again threaten this life which is sustained by yours."

It was a strange sight for Don Fernando and all the bystanders as they stood marveling at so extraordinary an occurrence. It seemed to Dorotea that Fernando changed color and made a gesture as if he meant to avenge himself upon Cardenio, for she saw him put a hand to his sword; and no sooner did this thought enter her mind than she threw her arms about his knees, kissing them and holding him fast so that he could not move as her tears all the while continued to flow.

"What is it that you think of doing in this unforeseen situation, O sole refuge that I have?" she cried. "Here at your feet is your own wife and she whom you would have for wife is in her husband's arms. Do you think that it would be well or even possible for you to undo that which Heaven has done or seek to take as your own one who, in spite of every obstacle, confirmed in her loyalty and stanchness of purpose, there before your eyes is now bathing with her loving tears the face and bosom of her cherished mate? In God's name and for your own sake I beg and entreat you not to let this open manifestation of their love increase your ire, but rather let it diminish your wrath so that these two lovers, quietly and in peace and without any interference on your part, may spend together the rest of the time that Heaven allots them. In this way you will be displaying the generosity that your noble and illustrious bosom harbors, and the world will see that reason with you is stronger than passion."

Cardenio had stood with his arm about Luscinda all the time that Dorotea was speaking. He did not take his eyes off Don Fernando, for he was resolved that, if his erstwhile friend made any move in his direction, he would actively defend himself to the best of his ability against any and all who might attack him, even though it cost him his life; but at that moment Don Fernando's companions and the curate, the barber, and all the others present, not forgetting the worthy Sancho Panza, came up and surrounded the irate lover, imploring him to have regard to Dorotea's tears, and if what she had said was true, and they believed that it undoubtedly was, not to permit her to be cheated of what she had every right to expect. Let him reflect that it was not by mere chance, as it might seem, but rather by a special providence of Heaven, that they had all been brought together in a place where they would never have thought they would meet. Let him remember also, the curate admonished him, that only death could part Luscinda and Cardenio, and that even though the edge of a sword were to come between them, they still would regard their end as a most happy one. In cases like this for which there was no remedy, it was the part of practical wisdom, by exerting an effort and overcoming one's inclinations, to show oneself generous-hearted; and so he ought of his own accord to permit this pair to enjoy the blessing which Heaven had conferred upon them.

Let him, moreover, but cast an eye on Dorotea's beauty and he would see that few if any could equal, much less excel, her. And in addition to her beauty, there was her meekness and the very great love she had for him. Above all, let him bear in mind that if he prided himself upon being a gentleman and a Christian, he could not do anything else but keep the promise he had made, and, keeping it, he would at the same time be fulfilling his duty to God and would win the approval of all right-minded folk, who would realize and admit that it is the prerogative of beauty, even though in humble guise, to be elevated to any height whatsoever when accompanied by modesty, and without any hint of detriment to the one who places it upon an equal footing with himself. What was more, no one was to be blamed for following the strong dictates of passion when there was no taint of sin involved.

The others then added their arguments, so many of them and such forceful ones that Don Fernando's manly heart could not hold out against them; for he, after all, was of noble blood. He thereupon relented and let himself be vanquished by the truth, which he could not deny however much he might have wished to do so; and as a sign that he had surrendered and yielded to their good advice, he now stooped and embraced Dorotea.

"Rise, my lady," he said to her, "for it is not fitting that she whom I hold in my heart should be kneeling at my feet. If up to now I have given no evidence of the truth of what I am saying, it may be that Heaven has ordered it so in order that, beholding the steadfast love that you have for me, I may be able to cherish you as you deserve. All that I ask is that you do not reprehend me for the ill I have done you and for my very great neglect, since the same cause and force that moved me to accept you as mine likewise impelled me to struggle against being yours. If you would perceive the truth of this, turn your eyes and see how happy Luscinda is, and in those eyes you will find an excuse for all my erring ways. And since she has found and attained that which she desired, and

I have found in you all that I need, may she spend many tranquil and happy years with her Cardenio, and I pray that Heaven grant the same boon to Dorotea and me."

Saying this, he turned and embraced her, laying his face against hers with so tender a display of feeling that it was all he could do to keep from weeping as the indubitable sign of his love and repentance. The rest of them, however, were not so successful in this regard, and Luscinda, Cardenio, and nearly all those present began shedding so many tears, by reason of their own happiness or that of others, that it was as if some grave misfortune had befallen them. Even Sancho Panza wept, although, as he said afterward, it was only at finding that Dorotea was not as he had thought Queen Micomicona, of whom he expected so many favors. It took them all some time to recover from their emotion and astonishment, and then Cardenio and Luscinda fell on their knees before Don Fernando, thanking him so courteously for the favor he had bestowed upon them that he did not know what to say in reply but raised them up and embraced them most graciously and affectionately.

He then inquired of Dorotea how she came to be in this place so far from her home, and she very briefly and clearly related all that she had previously told Cardenio, at which Don Fernando and his companions were so pleased that they wished the tale had been longer, such was her skill as a storyteller. When she had finished, Fernando informed them of what had happened to him in the city, after he had found in Luscinda's bodice the note in which she declared that she was Cardenio's bride and could not be his. He stated that he would have liked to kill her, and would have done so if her parents had not prevented him. He then had left the house in an angry and disgruntled mood, being determined to avenge himself as soon as he had a better opportunity. The next day he heard that Luscinda had disappeared from her parents' home and that no one knew where she had gone. After some months he had learned that she was in a convent, having expressed a desire to spend the rest of her days there if she could not be with Cardenio.

Upon receiving this news, he had chosen three gentlemen companions and had gone to the place where she was but had not spoken with her since he feared that, if they knew he was there, a closer watch would be kept in the convent. He accordingly had waited for a day when the porter's lodge was open, and then, leaving two of them to guard the gate, he and the other one had gone in to look for Luscinda, whom they found in a cloister, in conversation with a nun. Carrying her off without ceremony, they had taken her to another place where they could provide themselves with the things they needed for carrying out their plan. All of which they had been able to do in safety, owing to the fact that the convent was in the open country, at some little distance from the town.

He added that as soon as Luscinda saw that she was in their power, she had fainted away, and that all she had done after recovering from her swoon was to weep and sigh without uttering a single word. And thus, with silence and her tears for company, they had reached this inn, which for him was like attaining Heaven itself, where all the misadventures of earth are at an end.

CHAPTER XXXVII. *Wherein is continued the story of the famous Princess Micomicona, along with other droll adventures.*

IT WAS with no little sorrow in his heart that Sancho listened to all this, for he could see his hopes of a title going up in smoke and disappearing as the lovely Princess Micomicona turned into Dorotea, and the giant into Don Fernando, while his master was sleeping peacefully, wholly unconcerned with what was happening. As for Dorotea, she could not be sure that the happiness she possessed was not a dream, and Cardenio and Luscinda felt the same way. Don Fernando, meanwhile, was giving thanks to Heaven for having taken him out of that intricate labyrinth in which he had been wandering at the imminent risk of losing at once his good name and his soul. In short, all those in the inn were quite pleased and satisfied with the fortunate outcome of so complicated and desperate an affair.

It was the curate who, as a man of wisdom, made it all clear to them, congratulating each in turn on the good fortune he had achieved. But the one who was the happiest and most jubilant of all was the landlady by reason of the promise that Cardenio and the curate had made her to the effect that they would pay with interest for all the damage wrought by Don Quixote. Sancho alone, as has been said, was wretched, sad, and dejected, and it was with a melancholy air that he went in to speak to his master, who had just awakened.

"Sir Mournful Countenance," he said, "your Grace may as well go on sleeping. In fact, you may sleep as much as you like, without troubling to kill any giant or restore the princess to her kingdom, for it is all done and settled now."

"That I can well believe," replied Don Quixote, "for I have just had the most monstrous and terrible battle with that giant that ever I hope to have in all the days of my life; and with one back-thrust—whack!—I laid his head on the ground, and the blood ran in rivulets, like water, all over the earth."

"Like red wine, your Grace might better say," Sancho corrected him; "for I would have your Grace know, if you do not know it already, that the dead giant is a punctured wineskin and the blood was six arrobas ¹ of *vino tinto* that it held in its belly, and the head you chopped off is the whore who mothered me, and may the devil take it all!"

"What is this you are saying, you lunatic?" cried Don Quixote. "Are you in your right senses?"

"If your Grace will rise," said Sancho, "you will see the fine mess you have made and what we are going to have to pay for it all. And you will also see your queen converted into a lady in private life, by the name of Dorotea, along with other things that will astonish you if you can get them through your head."

"I should not wonder at anything of the sort," said Don Quixote, "for, if you remember, the last time we were here I told you that everything that happened in this place was the work of an enchanter, and so it would not be surprising if this were also."

"I could believe all that," said Sancho, "if my blanketing had been like that, but it wasn't; it was real and true. I saw the landlord, who is here right now, holding one end of the blanket and tossing me up to the sky as lustily and heartily as you please and laughing fit to burst all the while. When it comes to recognizing persons, so far as I'm concerned, and I'm only a poor sinner, there's no enchantment about it but only a lot of bruises and bad luck."

"Well, then," said Don Quixote, "God will set everything to rights. Come help me dress so that I can go out, for I wish to see what has happened and view these transformations that you are talking about."

Sancho helped him on with his clothes; and, in the meantime, the curate was telling Don Fernando and the others of the knight's strange madness and the stratagem they had employed to get him off Poor Rock, where he imagined that he was doing penance for his lady's sake. He repeated at the same time nearly all the adventures that Sancho had related, at which they were considerably astonished and laughed a good deal; for this seemed to them to be, as it did to all who heard of it, the weirdest sort of insanity that could ever lay hold of a disordered intellect. The curate added that, inasmuch as Dorotea's good fortune prevented their going on with their plan, they would have to find and invent another one in order to get him back to his native heath. Cardenio then offered to continue what they had begun, saying that Luscinda would be able to take Dorotea's part very well.

"No," said Don Fernando, "that will not be necessary, for I wish Dorotea to continue with it. The village where this good gentleman lives is not far from here, and I shall be happy to see something done for his malady."

"It is more than two days' journey," said the curate.[2]

"Even if it were more, I should be glad to make it in so worthy a cause."

At that moment Don Quixote came out in full panoply, with Mambrino's helmet, still dented, on his head and his buckler on his arm, and with his tree bough or lance serving him as a staff. Don Fernando and the others were amazed by his strange appearance: his lean and jaundiced-looking face, half a league long; his fantastic assortment of arms; his dignified bearing; and they all remained silent to see what he would have to say as he, very calmly and gravely, turned to the comely Dorotea.

"I am informed by my squire, lovely lady," he said, "that your Highness's very being has been undone and annihilated, and that from the queen and great dame that you used to be you have been transformed into an ordinary damsel. If this has been done on the order of that royal necromancer, your father, because he feared I would not give you the aid you need and which I owe you, I will say that he did not and does not know half the mass [3] and was little versed in the annals of chivalry; for if he had read and meditated upon them attentively, and for as long a time as I have, he would have found that other knights less famous than I were constantly achieving more difficult undertakings. After all, it is no great thing to slay a little giant, however insolent he may be. As a matter of fact, it is not many hours since I was in his presence and— I shall say no more, lest you think I am lying. But time, which brings all things to light, will tell the tale when least we think to hear it."

"That was a couple of wineskins you were fighting, not a giant," said the innkeeper at this point; but Don Fernando ordered him to be still and not interrupt Don Quixote in any way.

The knight then continued, "I was about to say, in short, highborn and disinherited lady, that if it was for the reason I have mentioned that your father worked this metamorphosis in your person, do not be misled by it; for there is no peril on this earth where my sword will not open a path; and with that sword I will shortly bring your enemy's head to earth and place upon yours the crown of your realm."

Pausing here, Don Quixote waited for the princess to answer him, and she, knowing Don Fernando's determination to go through with the deception until they had the knight back in his village, now replied with much gravity and ease of manner, "Whoever it was that told you, valiant Knight of the Mournful Countenance, that my being had been changed and transformed, was not speaking the truth. It is true that certain fortunate circumstances that have given me more than I could have wished for have worked a change of a sort in me; but I have not for that reason ceased to be the person that I was before, and I still have the same intention that I always did of availing myself of the might of your valiant and invulnerable arm.[4] And so, my dear sir, I beg you to be so good as to honor once more the father who begot me, and I trust that you will look upon him as a wise and foreseeing man, since with his science he found so ready and reliable a means of aiding me in my trouble. For I am convinced that if it had not been for you, sir, I should never have had the good fortune that is now mine, and in this I speak the veriest truth, as most of these worthy folk who are present can testify. It only remains for us to set out tomorrow morning, since we could not travel far today. As for the rest, I trust in God and in your own valiant heart for a happy outcome."

Thus spoke the clever Dorotea. Upon hearing her words, Don Quixote was very angry and, turning to his squire, he said, "I tell you right now, my little Sancho, that you are the greatest little rascal in all Spain. Vagabond thief, did you not inform me a moment ago that this princess had been turned into a damsel by the name of Dorotea, and that the giant's head which I am sure I cut off was that of the whoring mother that bore you, along with other nonsense that threw me into the greatest confusion I have ever known in all the days of my life? I swear"—and here he gazed heavenward and ground his teeth—"I have a mind to do something to you that will put salt in the pate of all the lying squires of knights-errant that there are in this world, from this time forth!"

"Calm yourself, my master," said Sancho. "It may be that I was deceived in what I took to be the transformation of my lady, the Princess Micomicona; but as to the giant's head, or, at any rate, the puncturing of the skins and the fact that the blood was red wine, I was not wrong in that, by the living God! For the wounded skins are still there at the head of your Grace's bed, and the red wine has made a lake of the room. If you don't believe it, you will see when you go to fry the eggs.[5] By that I mean, when the landlord presents your Grace with the score for all the damage you did. Otherwise, if my lady the queen is as she always was, I rejoice in my heart, for it concerns me as much as any neighbor's son."

"Once again, Sancho," said Don Quixote, "I tell you that you are a fool, and, begging your pardon, that will do."

"That will do," said Don Fernando, "and let us hear no more of it. And since my lady the princess has said that we travel tomorrow, seeing that today is far gone, so be it. The evening we may spend in pleasant conversation as we wait for tomorrow to come, when we will all accompany Señor Don Quixote, as we desire to be witnesses of the valorous and unheard-of exploits that he is to perform in the course of this great enterprise that he has undertaken."

"It is I who will serve and accompany you," replied Don Quixote. "I thank your Grace very much for the good opinion that you hold of me, and I shall endeavor to live up to it or it shall cost me my life—or even more than my life, if such a thing be possible."

Many courteous words and compliments were exchanged between the two of them; but they all fell silent as a traveler entered the inn, one who from his attire appeared to be a Christian recently returned from the land of the Moors. He had on a short-skirted coat made out of blue cloth, with half-sleeves and without a collar. His breeches were of the same shade and material, and he had a blue cap on his head. On his feet were date-colored buskins, and slung across his breast from a shoulder strap was a Moorish cutlass. Behind him, mounted upon an ass, came a woman dressed after the manner of the Moors. Her face was covered and she wore a little brocaded cap on her head and a mantle that fell from her shoulders to her feet. The man, who was a little more than forty years of age, had a robust and graceful figure, a somewhat swarthy complexion, long mustaches, and a well-tended beard. In short, if he had been well clad, one would have said from his appearance that he was a person of birth and breeding.

Upon entering the inn, he asked for a room and, when told that there was none to be had, seemed to be very much put out. Going up to the Moorish-looking woman, he took her in his arms and assisted her to dismount, as Luscinda, Dorotea, the landlady, her daughter, and Maritornes all gathered around, attracted by the novelty of her costume, which was of a kind they had never seen before. Being always gracious, courteous, and discerning, Dorotea perceived that the woman as well as the man was vexed at not being able to obtain a lodging, and she accordingly sought to console her.

"Do not be too much disturbed, my lady," she said, "by the lack of accommodations that you find here, for that is the usual thing in roadside taverns; but if you would like to share our lodgings"—and she nodded at Luscinda—"you will perhaps say that in the course of your journey you have found others that were not so good."

The veiled lady made no reply to this but merely rose from where she was sitting and, crossing her hands upon her bosom, bowed her head and bent her body from the waist down by way of thanks. From her silence, they decided that she must undoubtedly be a Moor and unable to speak a Christian tongue.

At that moment, the captive,[6] who had been busied with other matters, returned; and, seeing all the womenfolk gathered about his companion while she made no reply, he said, "Ladies, this damsel understands very little of my language, nor does she know how to speak any tongue other than that of her native land, and it is for this reason that she does not and cannot answer your questions."

"We have not asked her anything," said Luscinda. "We have merely offered to share with her our company and our lodgings, where we will provide her with all the comforts that we can; for we are under obligations to be of service to all strangers in need, especially when they happen to be women."

"On her behalf and on mine, my lady," the captive replied, "I kiss your hand and esteem very highly, as I ought, this proffered favor, which, coming from persons such as your appearance shows you to be and under such circumstances, is indeed a great one."

"Tell me, sir," said Dorotea, "is this lady a Christian or a Moor? For her costume and her silence lead us to believe that she is what we would rather she was not."

"A Moor she is in costume and in body, but in her soul she is thoroughly Christian, for she has a very great desire to be one."

"Then she has not been baptized?" inquired Luscinda.

"There has been no opportunity for that," replied the captive. "Since leaving Algiers, which is her fatherland, there has been up to now no near peril of death such as would render it obligatory to baptize her at once, before she had first learned all the ceremonies that our Holy Mother Church enjoins. But God willing, the rite will soon be administered to her with the solemnity that befits the quality of her person, which is more than her garb or my own would indicate."

Upon hearing this, they were all eager to learn who the captive and the Moorish damsel were, but no one cared to ask just then, as it seemed that at that moment they ought rather to be seeking to make them comfortable than to be questioning them about their past lives. Dorotea took the girl by the hand and led her over to a seat beside her, requesting that she remove her veil. The damsel looked at the captive as though inquiring what they were saying and what she should do, and he thereupon explained to her in Arabic that they wished her to uncover her countenance. This she now did, revealing a face of such rare loveliness that Dorotea and Luscinda each thought her more beautiful than the other, while all the bystanders agreed that if there was anyone who could equal those two, it was the Moorish lady, and there were some, even, who maintained that she held a slight advantage. And inasmuch as it is beauty's gracious prerogative to win the heart and arouse good will, the entire company from then on manifested a desire to serve the lovely Moor and do her favors.

When Don Fernando asked what her name was, the captive replied that it was Lela Zoraida; and as soon as she heard this, having divined what the Christian had asked, she spoke up hastily, with much vexation and spirit.

"No, not Zoraida," she cried, "Maria, Maria!" thus giving them to understand that her name was Maria and not Zoraida.

These words and the deep earnestness with which the Moorish damsel had uttered them caused more than one tear to be shed by some of the listeners, especially the women, since women by nature are tenderhearted and sympathetic. Luscinda embraced her most affectionately.

"Yes, yes," she said, "Maria, Maria!" To which the damsel replied, "Yes, yes, Maria; Zoraida *macange*" [7]—by which expression she meant to say *no*.

Night was now coming on, and by order of Don Fernando's companions the landlord had set about preparing with all care and diligence the best supper that he could give them. When the time came, they all sat down at a long table of the kind to be found in servants' quarters, for there was neither a round table nor a square one to be found in the hostelry. They gave Don Quixote the place of honor at the head of the table, though he was for refusing it at first; and he insisted that the Princess Micomicona take the place by his side, as he was her protector.

Luscinda and Zoraida then seated themselves, and opposite them were Don Fernando and Cardenio. Then came the captive and the other gentlemen, while the curate and the barber had places alongside the ladies. And thus they supped in great good humor, which was increased when they saw the knight stop eating and begin to speak; for he was now moved by an impulse similiar to that which had led him to hold forth at such length when he was having supper with the goatherds.

"Truly, ladies and gentlemen," he began, "when you stop to think of it, those who follow the calling of knight-errantry behold some marvelous and unheard-of things. By way of example, let me ask you: what living being is there in all the world who, coming through the gateway of the castle at this moment and seeing us as we are, would take or believe us to be what we are? Who would say that this lady at my side is the great queen who is known to all of us, or that I am the famous Knight of the Mournful Countenance? No, there is no doubt that this profession and employment excels all others that men have invented, and it is all the more to be esteemed by reason of the greater perils to which it is subject.

"Away with those who would tell you that letters have the advantage over arms. I will tell them, whoever they may be, they know not of what they speak. For the reason that such persons commonly give, the one upon which they base their arguments, is that the labors of the mind exceed those of the body and the profession of arms is a physical one exclusively, a common laborer's trade as it were, for which nothing more than a sturdy frame is needed. What they fail to take into consideration is the fact that in the profession that is known to us who follow it as that of arms, there are included many acts of fortitude that require for their execution a high degree of intelligence. Does not a warrior who is charged with leading an army or defending a besieged city work with his mind as well as his body? How otherwise, by physical strength alone, would he be able to divine the intentions of the enemy, his plans and stratagems and the obstacles to be overcome, since all these things call for mental activity in which the body plays no part?

"It being true, then, that the profession of arms as well as that of letters has need of mind, let us see whose mind does the greater amount of work, that of the warrior or that of the man of letters.[8] This may be seen from the end and goal that each has in view; for that intention is to be most esteemed that has for its end the noblest object. The end and goal of letters is—I am not here speaking of divine learning whose purpose is to lead souls heavenward, since with an end so endless as that no other can be compared—what I have in mind, rather, is human knowledge, whose object is to administer distributive justice and give to each that which is his and see that good laws are observed—such an end and goal is assuredly a generous and a lofty one and deserving of high praise, but not such praise as should be bestowed upon the warrior's purpose, for here the objective is peace, which is the greatest blessing that men can wish for in this life.

"For the first good news that mankind and the world received was that which the angels brought on the night that was our day: 'Glory to God in the highest, and on earth peace, good will toward men.' [9] And the salutation which the great Master of Heaven and earth taught his chosen disciples to use when they entered any dwelling was, 'Peace be to this house.' [10] And another time he said to them, 'Peace I leave with you, my peace I give unto you, peace be with you.' [11] It was as a jewel and a precious gift given and left by such a hand, a jewel without which there can be no blessing whatsoever either in Heaven or on the earth. This peace is the true end of war, and for 'war' you may substitute 'arms.' Accepting, then, this truth that the end of war is peace, let us turn now to the physical hardships of the scholar and those of the man of arms and see which are the greater."

This speech of Don Quixote's was delivered in such a manner and couched in such excellent terms that it was quite impossible for the moment for any of those who heard him to take him for a madman. Indeed, most of them being gentlemen to whom arms were a natural appurtenance, they listened to him with right good will as he continued speaking.

"I will begin by saying that the student's chief hardship is poverty— not that they are all poor, but by way of putting the case in the strongest possible terms—and when the word poverty has been uttered, it seems to me there is nothing more to be said of their misfortune. For he who is poor has nothing that is good. He must suffer his destitution under various forms: hunger, cold, nakedness, and all of them combined. But, still, his poverty is not so great that he does not eat some time, even though it be a little later than usual and even though he must feed on the leftovers of the rich. His greatest wretchedness lies in what they call 'going for soup,' [12] but still he will not fail to find some other's brazier or hearth which, if it does not warm him, at least will temper the cold. And, finally, of a night, they sleep beneath a roof. I shall not go into any further details, such as their lack of shirts and not too many shoes, their thin and threadbare garments, or the pleasure with which they gorge themselves when luck affords them a banquet of some sort.

"By this path, then, which I have described, a rough and difficult one, stumbling here, falling there, raising themselves up and falling once more, they finally obtain their degree. And then, after all this, how many of them have we seen who, having passed through these Syrtes,[13] between these Scyllas and Charybdises, as if borne on the favoring wings of fortune—how many of them, I say, have we seen later ruling and governing the world from a chair, their hunger turned into satiety, their cold into comfort, their nakedness into courtly attire, their sleep on a mat into repose on damask and fine linen, all of which is the justly merited reward of their virtue. But contrasted and compared with the hardships of the warrior, theirs fall far short of those that he endures, as I shall now show."

CHAPTER XXXVIII. *Which treats of the curious discourse that Don Quixote delivered on the subject of arms and letters.*[1]

CONTINUING his discourse, Don Quixote spoke as follows:

"Since in the case of the student we began with poverty and the things that go with it, let us see if the soldier is any better off in this regard. We shall find that he is the poorest of the poor, being dependent upon his wretched pay, which comes late or never, or upon such booty as he can amass with his own hands, to the grave peril of his life and conscience. At times his nakedness is such that a slashed doublet serves him at once as shirt and uniform; and in midwinter, in the open country, it is his habit to protect himself against the inclemencies of the heavens with nothing more than the breath from his mouth, which, inasmuch as it emerges from an empty place, must obviously, contrary to all the laws of nature, come out cold. True, he looks forward to the coming of night that he may find a respite from all these discomforts in the bed that awaits him, which, unless it is through some fault of his own, will never offend by being too narrow; for he may measure out upon the earth as many feet as he likes for his couch and then may toss and turn in it to his heart's content, without fear of the sheets slipping off.

"Comes then the day and hour when he is to take his professional degree; comes then the day of battle; and then it is they place upon his head a doctor's cap made of lint, by way of healing the wound inflicted by some bullet that may have passed through his temple or left him mutilated in an arm or a leg. And if this does not happen and a merciful Heaven keeps and preserves him safe and sound, he still may be as poor as he was before and must go through more engagements and more battles and come out victorious from them all before he has some chance of improving his fortunes. Miracles of that sort, however, are very seldom seen.

"But tell me, gentlemen, if you have ever given it a thought, by how far do those who have prospered in war fall short of those who have perished in it? You undoubtedly will reply that there is no comparison, that the dead are innumerable while those who have lived and thrived can be represented by some number less than a thousand. All of which is just the opposite of what happens with scholars, for, by means of skirts, to say nothing of sleeves, the latter all find a way of supporting themselves.[2] Thus it is evident that, although the soldier's work is far harder, his reward is far less. To this the answer may be made that it is easier to reward two thousand scholars than thirty thousand soldiers, for upon the former may be bestowed such posts as must of necessity be allotted to men of their calling, whereas if the latter are to be given any compensation at all, it can only be out of the property of the master they serve. But this objection merely strengthens my argument.

"However, let us leave all this to one side, for it is a labyrinth from which it is difficult to find one's way out, and, instead, let us turn to the question of the pre-eminence of arms over letters, one that up to now has not been settled, so many are the arguments put forth by either side. In addition to those that I have mentioned, letters say that without their help arms cannot support themselves, for war also has its laws to which it is subject and which fall within the domain of scholars. To this arms will reply that without them laws cannot be maintained, since it is by force of arms that states are defended, kingdoms preserved, cities guarded, highways rendered safe, and the seas rid of corsairs; and, finally, if it were not for them, states, kingdoms, monarchies, cities, highroads by sea and land would be subjected to the oppression and confusion that war brings with it, so long as it lasts and is free to make use of its privileges and powers. And it is a well-known fact that what costs most is and ought to be most highly valued.

"For anyone to attain eminence in letters costs time, loss of sleep, hunger, nakedness, headaches, indigestion, and other things that go with them, some of which I have already mentioned. But to become a good soldier costs all that the student has to pay and in so much higher a degree that there is no comparison, for such a one at every step runs the risk of losing his life. And what fear of want and poverty that can affect and harass the student is comparable to that fear which the soldier knows as he stands guard in some ravelin or bastion, knowing that the enemy is running a mine toward the place where he stands, and unable under any circumstances whatsoever to leave his post and flee the danger that so imminently threatens him? All that he can do is to notify his captain of what is happening in order that a countermine may be laid; and, meanwhile, he must remain there, fearing and expecting that he will suddenly fly up to the clouds without wings or descend into the lower depths against his will.

"And if this appears to be a small risk to run, let us see if it is equaled or exceeded when two galleys clash and lock prows in the middle of the ocean, leaving the soldier no more standing room than a couple of feet on the plank of the spur-beam. In such a case, he sees in front of him as many ministers of death as there are enemy cannon pointed at him, at no greater distance from his body than the length of a lance, and he further perceives that at the first false step he will go down to visit the depths of Neptune's bosom; yet, nevertheless, with intrepid heart, sustained by the sense of honor that incites him, he will make himself a target for the musketry and will endeavor to cross that narrow passageway to the enemy's ship. And the most marvelous thing of all is that one has no sooner fallen, never to rise again until the end of the world, than another steps forward to take his place, and if he too falls into the sea that hostilely awaits him, another and yet another will follow without any pause between their deaths, the whole constituting the greatest exhibition of valor and daring that is to be found in all the hazardous annals of warfare.

"Happy were the blessed ages that were free of those devilish instruments of artillery, whose inventor, I feel certain, is now in Hell paying the penalty for his diabolic device—a device by means of which an infamous and cowardly arm may take the life of a valiant knight, without his knowing how or from where the blow fell, when amid that courage and fire that is kindled in the breasts of the brave suddenly there comes a random bullet, fired it may be by someone who fled in terror at the flash of his own accursed machine and who thus in an instant cuts off and brings to an end the projects and the life of one who deserved to live for ages to come.

"And so, from this point of view, I could almost say that it grieves my soul that I should have taken up the profession of knight-errant in an age so detestable as this one in which we now live.[3] For, although no danger strikes terror in my bosom, I do fear that powder and lead may deprive me of the opportunity to make myself famous and renowned, by the might of my arm and the edge of my sword, throughout the whole of the known world. But Heaven's will be done. If I succeed in carrying out my design, I shall be all the more honored for it, inasmuch as I shall have confronted greater perils than the knights-errant of old ever did."

All this long discourse was delivered by Don Quixote as the others were having their supper; and he was so occupied with talking that he forgot to raise a single bite of food to his mouth, although Sancho reminded him a number of times that it would be better to eat now and say what he had to say afterward. Those who heard him were moved to fresh pity at seeing a man, who to all appearances was perfectly sensible and able to discuss any other topic quite rationally, so hopelessly lost whenever the subject of chivalry came up, for that was his dark, pitch-black obsession. The curate assured him there was much reason in what he had said on the warrior's behalf, and that, although he himself was a man of letters and a university graduate, he was of the same opinion.

When supper was over, they took the tablecloth away, and while the landlady, her daughter, and Maritornes were busy preparing Don Quixote's garret so that the ladies, as had been decided, might have it to themselves for the night, Don Fernando asked the captive to tell them the story of his life, which must be a tale quite out of the ordinary and one well worth hearing, if they were to judge from the hints he had dropped when he arrived with Zoraida. The captive replied that he would be glad to do as requested, adding that he was afraid his story would not give them the pleasure they hoped for, but in order to comply with their wishes he would tell it anyway. The curate and all the others thanked him for this, and they too begged him to begin. In response to their insistence, he remarked that so much urging was unnecessary where a mere command would suffice.

"And so, then, your Worships, pay attention and you shall hear a true tale which possibly cannot be matched by those fictitious ones that are composed with such cunning craftsmanship."

As he said this, they all settled themselves in their places and a deep silence fell; and, seeing that they were quietly waiting to hear what he had to say, he began speaking in a calm and pleasant voice.

CHAPTER XXXIX. *In which the captive narrates the events of his life.*

"IT WAS in a village in the mountains of León that the line of which I come had its beginnings, a family more favored by nature than by fortune, although amid the poverty that prevailed in that region my father had the reputation of being a rich man and indeed might have been one, had he displayed the same skill in conserving his property that he did in squandering it. His inclination to liberal spending came from his having been a soldier in his youth, for that is a school in which the miser becomes generous and the generous becomes prodigal; if there are some soldiers that are parsimonious, they may be said to be freaks such as are rarely to be met with.

"My father went beyond the bounds of liberality and came close to prodigality, which is not a profitable thing for a married man with children to bring up who are to succeed him and carry on his name. He had three of them, all of them males and of an age to decide upon their calling in life. Accordingly, when he saw that, as he put it, there was no use in his trying to overcome his natural propensity, he made up his mind to rid himself of the instrument and cause of his lavish spending; in other words, he would get rid of his property, for without his fortune Alexander himself would have appeared in straitened circumstances. And so, calling the three of us together one day and closeting himself alone with us, he proceeded to address us somewhat in the following manner: [1]

" 'My sons, there is no need of my telling you that I have your welfare at heart; it is enough to know and state that you are my sons. On the other hand, the fact that I am unable to control myself when it comes to preserving your estate may well give you a contrary impression. For this reason, in order that you may be assured from now on that I love you as a father should and have no desire to ruin you as a stepfather might, I have decided to do for you something that I have long had in mind and to which I have given the most mature consideration. You are of an age to enter upon your professions in life, or at least to choose the ones which, when you are older, will bring you profit and honor.

" 'What I have thought of doing is to divide my estate into four parts, three of which I will turn over to you so that each has that which is his by right, while the fourth part I will retain for my own livelihood and support for the rest of the time that Heaven shall be pleased to grant me. But after each of you has had his due share of the property, I would have you follow one of the courses that I shall indicate. We have here in Spain a proverb which to my mind is a very true one, as indeed they all are, being wise maxims drawn from long experience. This one runs, "The Church, the sea, or the Royal Household," [2] which in plainer language is equivalent to saying, "He who would make the most of himself and become a rich man, let him become a churchman, or go to sea and be a merchant, or enter the service of kings in their palaces." For there is another saying, "Better a king's crumb than a lord's favor."

" 'I tell you this because it is my wish that one of you follow the profession of letters, that another go into trade, and that the third serve his king as a soldier, seeing that it is a difficult thing to obtain service in his household; for if the military life does not bring much wealth, it does confer fame and high esteem. Within a week, I will give you your shares in money, without defrauding you of a single penny, as you shall see in due course. Tell me, then, if you feel inclined to follow my advice and precepts in relation to what I have suggested.'

"He then called upon me as the eldest to answer; and after having told him that he ought not to rid himself of his property in that manner but should spend as much of it as he wished, since we were young and able to make our own way, I ended by assuring him that I would do as he desired, my own choice being to follow the profession of arms and thus serve God and my king. My second brother, having made a similar declaration, announced his intention of going to the Indies and investing his share in commerce. The youngest one, and in my opinion the wisest, said that he preferred to enter the Church or to go to Salamanca to complete the course of study that he had already begun.

"When we had made our choice of callings, my father embraced us all, and within the brief space of time mentioned he carried out his promise by giving each of us his share, which as I remember amounted to three thousand ducats in currency; for an uncle of ours had purchased the estate and paid for it in cash in order to keep it in the family. On that same day the three of us took leave of our goodhearted father; but inasmuch as it seemed to me an inhuman thing for him to be left with so little money in his old age, I prevailed upon him to take two of my three thousand ducats, since the remainder would be sufficient to meet my wants as a soldier. Moved by my example, my two brothers each gave him a thousand, so that he had in all four thousand, plus the three thousand which, as it appeared, his share of the estate was worth; for he did not care to dispose of his portion but preferred to keep it in land.

"And so, then, as I was saying, we took our leave of him and of our uncle, not without much feeling and many tears on the part of all. They charged us to let them know, whenever it was possible for us to do so, as to how we were faring and whether we were meeting with prosperity or adversity, and we promised them that we would. When he had embraced us and given his benediction, we all departed, one setting out for Salamanca, another for Seville, while I made for Alicante, where I had heard there was a Genoese craft taking on a cargo of wool for that city.

"It is now twenty-two years since I left my father's house, and although in the course of that time I have written a number of letters, I have had no word either of him or of my brothers. As to my own experiences during those years, I shall relate them for you briefly. Embarking at Alicante, I had a fair voyage to Genoa, and from there I went on to Milan, where I fitted myself out with arms and a few accessories. For it was my intention to take service in the Piedmont, and I was already on my way to Alessandria della Paglia when I heard that the great Duke of Alva was starting for Flanders.[3] I then changed my plan and, joining his army, served with him in the three campaigns that he waged. I was present at the deaths of the Counts of Egmont and Hoorne and rose to the rank of ensign under a famous captain of Guadalajara, Diego de Urbina by name.[4] After I had been in Flanders for some while, news came of the league which his Holiness, Pope Pius V of blessed memory, had formed with Venice and Spain against the common enemy, the Turk, who about that time had taken, with his fleet, the famous island of Cyprus, which was then under the rule of the Venetians. This was a serious loss and one truly to be deplored.

"It was known for a fact that the commanding general of this league was to be his Most Serene Highness, John of Austria, brother of our good King Philip, and there was much talk of the great and warlike preparations that he was making. I was deeply stirred by all this and felt a desire to take part in the coming campaign; and although I had prospects and almost certain promises of being promoted to captain where I then served, on the first occasion that offered, I chose to leave all this and return to Italy. And as it happened, John of Austria had just arrived in Genoa on his way to Naples to join the Venetian fleet, as he afterward did at Messina.[5]

"In short, I may tell you that I was soon taking part in that most fortunate campaign,[6] having already been made a captain of infantry, an honor that I owed to my good fortune rather than to my merits. And on that day that was so happy a one for all Christendom, since it revealed to all the nations of the world the error under which they had been laboring in believing that the Turks were invincible at sea—on that day, I repeat, in which the haughty Ottoman pride was shattered, among all the happy ones that were there (and those Christians that died were even happier than those that remained alive and victorious), I alone was wretched; for in place of a naval crown such as I might have hoped for had it been in Roman times, I found myself on the night that followed that famous day with chains on my feet and manacles on my hands.

"The way in which it came about was this: El Uchali,[7] King of Algiers, a bold and successful corsair, had attacked and captured the flagship of Malta, on which only three knights were left alive and those three badly wounded; whereupon the ship of Giovanni Andrea,[8] on which I and my company were stationed, came to its assistance. Doing what was customary under the circumstances, I leaped aboard the enemy galley, which, by veering off from the attacking vessel, prevented my men from following me. Thus I was alone among the enemy, who so greatly outnumbered me that any hope of resistance was vain; and the short of it is, after I had been badly wounded, they captured me. As you know, gentlemen, El Uchali and all his fleet made their escape, so that I was left a prisoner in his hands; and that is the reason why it was that only I was miserable among so many who were happy, and a captive among so many who were free. For there were fifteen thousand Christians slaving at the oars in the Turkish fleet who that day obtained their liberty.

"They took me to Constantinople, where the Grand Turk Selim made my master commander at sea for having done his duty in battle so well and displayed his bravery by carrying off the standard of the Order of Malta. The following year, which was '72, I was in Navarino, rowing in the flagship with the three lanterns,[9] and there I saw and noted how the opportunity was lost for capturing the entire Turkish fleet in the harbor;

for all the sailors and Janizaries were convinced that they would be attacked while in port and had their clothing and their *passamaques*, or shoes, in readiness in order that they might be able to flee overland without waiting to give combat, so great was the fear that our fleet inspired in them. But Heaven ordained otherwise, not because of any fault or carelessness on the part of our commander, but as a punishment for the sins of Christendom, since it is God's will that we should have with us always the agents of his wrath.

"The upshot of it was, El Uchali withdrew to Modon, which is an island near Navarino, and there, disembarking his men, he proceeded to fortify the mouth of the harbor, after which he waited quietly until John retired. On this voyage one of the galleys, called the *Prize*, whose captain was a son of the famous corsair Barbarossa, was captured by the Neapolitan craft known as the *She-Wolf*, commanded by that thunderbolt of war, that father to his men, the fortunate and never-vanquished captain, Don Alvaro de Bazán, Marquis of Santa Cruz.

"I must not omit telling you what took place in connection with this capture. Barbarossa's son was so cruel and treated his captives so badly that the moment the rowers saw the *She-Wolf* bearing down and gaining upon them, they all at one and the same time dropped their oars and seized the captain, who was standing upon the gangway platform, urging them to row faster. Laying hold of him, they passed him on from bench to bench and from poop to prow, and so bit and chewed him that before he had gone much farther than the ship's mast his soul had already gone to Hell. Such, as I have said, was the cruelty with which he treated them and the hatred that they had for him.

"We then returned to Constantinople, and the next year, which was '73, we learned how John had captured Tunis, driven the Turks out of that kingdom, and placed Muley Hamet on the throne, thus cutting short the hopes that Muley Hamida, bravest and cruelest Moor in all the world, had of returning to rule there. The Great Turk felt this loss very keenly and, having resort to the cunning which all those of his line possess, he made peace with the Venetians, who desired it much more than he did; and the following year, in '74, he attacked the Goleta [10] and the Fort near Tunis which John had left in a state of semi-completion.

"During all this time I was at the oar, with no hope whatever of gaining my freedom. At least I had no hope of ransom, for I was determined not to write the news of my misfortune to my father. Both the Goleta and the Fort finally fell, for in front of them were massed seventy-five thousand Turkish regulars, while the number of Moors and Arabs from all over Africa was in excess of four hundred thousand; and this enormous force was equipped with so many munitions and engines of war and accompanied by so many sappers that the latter might readily have buried both their objectives under handfuls of earth.

"The Goleta, which had previously been looked upon as inexpugnable, was the first to succumb; and if it was lost, this was not the fault of its defenders, who did all that they should and could have done. It was rather due to the fact that, as experience showed, it was easy to throw up entrenchments in the desert sand; for water was commonly found there at a depth of two palms, but the Turks went down for a depth of two varas [11] without striking any, and as a result, piling their sandbags one on top of another, they were able to raise ramparts so high that they could command the walls of the fort and fire upon them as from a bastion, so that it was impossible to make a stand or put up a defense.

"It was the common opinion that our men did wrong in shutting themselves up in the Goleta instead of waiting for the enemy in the open, along the landing place; but those who say this speak from a distance and with little experience in such matters. If in the Goleta and the Fort there were barely seven thousand soldiers in all, how could so small a force, no matter how courageous, hope to sally forth onto the open plain and hold its own against so numerous an opposing one? And how could such a force fail to be lost unless reinforcements were sent to it, especially when surrounded by enemies that were not only so many in number and so determined, but that were fighting on their own soil?

"It seemed to many, and to me as well, that Heaven was doing Spain a special favor by mercifully permitting the destruction of that source and lair of so many woes, that glutton, sponge, and waster responsible for the profitless spending of an infinite amount of money which served no other cause than that of preserving the memory of its capture by the invincible Charles V—as if, to sustain that memory, which is and shall be eternal, those stones were necessary. The Fort likewise fell, but the Turks had to win it inch by inch, for the soldiers who defended it fought so stoutly and bravely that they slew more than twenty-five thousand of the enemy in the course of twenty-two general assaults. Of the three hundred of them that were taken prisoners, not one was without a wound, which is clear proof of their valor and determination and the ability with which they had defended and held their posts.

"A small fort or tower that stood in the middle of the lagoon also conditionally surrendered. It was under the command of a gentleman and famous soldier of Valencia, Don Juan Zanoguerra. Among those captured was Don Pedro Puertocarrero, commandant of the Goleta, who had done all that he could to defend his fort and felt the loss of it so keenly that he died of grief on the way to Constantinople, where his captors were taking him. Yet another was Gabriele Serbelloni, a Milanese gentleman, a great engineer and a very brave soldier.

"In the defense of these two strongholds there died many noteworthy persons, among whom was Pagano Doria, a knight of the Order of St. John, a man of generous disposition as was shown by the extreme liberality with which he treated his brother, the famous Giovanni Andrea Doria; and the saddest part of it all was that he died at the hands of some Arabs to whom, when he saw that the Fort was lost, he had entrusted himself when they offered to conduct him, disguised in Moorish costume, to Tabarca, a small coastal fort or station held by the Genoese, who there ply the trade of coral fishing. The Arabs cut off his head and took it to the commander of the Turkish fleet, who thereupon proved the truth of our Castilian proverb that asserts that 'although the treason may be acceptable, the traitor is abhorred'; for it is said that the general in question ordered those who had brought him this present to be hanged because they had not delivered their victim alive.

"Among the Christians in the Fort was one named Don Pedro de Aguilar, a native of some village in Andalusia, I cannot tell you which one; he had been an ensign and was looked upon as a most capable soldier, and in addition, he was a man of rare intellectual attainments, being especially gifted in what is known as poetry. I speak of him for the reason that fate brought him to my galley and my bench, since we were both slaves to the same master; and before we left port this gentleman composed two sonnets in the manner of epitaphs, one to the Goleta and the other to the Fort. As a matter of fact, I mean to recite them for you, for I know them by heart, and I do not think they will bore you, but quite the reverse."

When the captive mentioned Don Pedro de Aguilar's name, Don Fernando glanced at his companions and all three of them smiled; and when he came to read the sonnets, one of them interrupted him.

"Before your Grace goes any further," he said, "I beg you to tell me what became of that Pedro de Aguilar of whom you speak."

"All I know," replied the captive, "is that at the end of the two years he spent in Constantinople he disguised himself as an Albanian and made his escape in the company of a Greek spy. I cannot tell you if he succeeded in regaining his liberty or not, but it is my belief that he did, for a year later I saw the Greek in Constantinople but was unable to ask him what the outcome of their journey had been."

"I can tell you that," replied the gentleman, "for this Don Pedro is my brother and at this moment is in our village, in sound health, rich, married, and the father of three children." [12]

"Thanks be to God," said the captive, "for all His mercies; for in my opinion there is no happiness on earth that can equal that of recovering one's lost liberty."

"What is more," the gentleman went on, "I am familiar with those sonnets that my brother composed."

"Recite them, then, your Grace," said the captive, "for you will be able to do so better than I."

"With pleasure," said the gentleman; and he proceeded to recite the one on the Goleta, which was as follows:

CHAPTER XL. *In which the captive's story is continued.*

SONNET

Blest souls that have been freed of mortal guise
And by reason of your good deeds here below,
The noble exploits that ye have to show,
Have gone to a better home there in the skies,
How often 'mid the heat of battle cries
Have ye spilt the blood of many a doughty foe
As, staining sand and sea, ye did overthrow
The wicked in their pride, O high emprise!
'Twas life not valor failed the weary arm,
And even as ye died ye well might claim
The victory, thus wrested from defeat.
Ye fell, 'tis true, and suffered mortal harm
Between the blade and wall, yet still your fame
Lives on and rises to the glory seat.

"That is the way I remember it also," remarked the captive.

"And the one on the Fort," said the gentleman, "runs like this, if I am not mistaken."

SONNET

Out of the sterile earth, this rubble heap,
These tumbled ruins that now strew the ground,
Three thousand souls a better home have found;
Three thousand soldiers that once here did sleep
Have gone above, their guerdon fair to reap.
It was in vain their valor did abound;
Few and exhausted, suffering many a wound,
They gave their lives their honor bright to keep.
This bit of earth has ever been the haunt
Of mournful memories beyond man's count,
Both now and in the ages long since past;
But no more worthy souls can Heaven vaunt
Amongst the many that from this spot did mount
Than these brave ones that are Heaven's own at last.

The sonnets were not displeasing, and the captive was happy over the news of his comrade which he had received. He then went on with his story.

"Well, then, the Goleta and the Fort having fallen, the Turks ordered the former stronghold dismantled, there being nothing left of the Fort to raze; and in order to accomplish the task more speedily and with less labor, they mined three-quarters of it, but by no device could they succeed in blowing up what appeared to be the weakest part, namely the old walls. On the other hand, all that remained of the new fortifications that the Little Friar [1] had built was brought to the ground with the greatest of ease.

"Finally, the victorious fleet returned in triumph to Constantinople, and a few months afterward my master, El Uchali, died, the one who was known as 'Uchali Fartax,' which in the Turkish tongue means 'scurvy renegade'; for that is what he was, and it is the custom of the Turks to bestow names that signify some fault or virtue. This is for the reason that they have only four surnames altogether, which apply to those descended from the Ottoman line; [2] the others, as I started to say, take their names and surnames from bodily defects or moral characteristics. And this Scurvy One, being a slave of the Grand Seignior's, had slaved at the oar for fourteen years, being then more than thirty-four years of age when he turned renegade. The way it came about was this: as he was rowing one day a Turk had dealt him a blow, and in order to be revenged on the fellow he renounced his faith. After that, his valor proved to be so outstanding that he did not have to resort to the usual underhanded ways and means by which the Great Turk's favorites rise at court, but was made king of Algiers and later commander at sea, which is the office that is third in rank in that seigniory.

"El Uchali was a Calabrian by birth and a man of moral principle who treated his captives with great humanity. He came to have three thousand of them, and after his death they were divided in accordance with the provisions of his will between the Grand Seignior (who is heir to all who die and who shares with the offspring left by the deceased) and his renegades. I fell to a Venetian renegade who, as a cabin boy aboard a ship, had been captured by Uchali. His master grew so fond of him that the youth became his prime favorite, and he also came to be the cruelest one of his kind that was ever seen. His name was Hassan Aga,[3] and, amassing great wealth, he rose to be king of Algiers. I accompanied him there from Constantinople and was somewhat pleased at being so near to Spain. Not that I intended to write to anyone there concerning my misfortunes; but I wished to see if fortune would be more favorable to me here than it had been in Turkey, where I had unsuccessfully essayed a thousand different means of escape. In Algiers I thought to find other ways of attaining what I desired; for never once did the hope leave me of achieving my freedom; and when my plottings and schemings did not come up to expectations and my attempts were unsuccessful, I did not at once abandon myself to despair but began to look for or invent some fresh hope to sustain me, however faint and weak it might be.[4]

"In this way I managed to keep myself alive, shut up in a prison or house which the Turks call a bagnio, in which they confine their Christian captives, both those of the king and those belonging to certain private individuals, and also those that are referred to as being *del Almacen*, that is to say, captives that belong to the Council and serve the city in public works and other employment. It is very difficult for these last to obtain their freedom, for inasmuch as they are held in common and have no individual for a master, there is no one with whom to treat regarding their ransom even where they have the means for purchasing their liberation. In these bagnios, as I have said, they are accustomed to place captives belonging to certain private citizens of the town, chiefly the ones that are to be ransomed, since there they may keep them in safety and leisure. For the king's captives do not go out to labor with the rest of the galley crew, unless their ransom be late in coming, in which case, by way of inducing them to write for it more urgently, they put them to work and send them to gather wood with the others, which is no small task.

"I, then, was one of this group; for when they discovered that I was a captain, although I told them that I had no fortune and few prospects, they nevertheless insisted upon placing me among those gentlemen and others who were waiting for ransom. They put a chain upon me, but more as a mark of my status than in order to keep me from escaping; and thus I spent my days in that bagnio along with many important personages who had been designated and were being held for the purpose I have mentioned. And although we were at times harassed by hunger and the want of clothing, nothing distressed us so much as what we almost constantly saw and heard of the cruelties, such as never before were heard of or seen, which my master practiced upon the Christians. Each day he hanged his man, impaled one, cut off the ear of another; and all this with so little excuse, or with none at all, that the Turks had to admit he did it simply to be doing it, inasmuch as their natural bent toward the entire human race is a homicidal one.

"The only person who made out well with him was a Spanish soldier by the name of Saavedra,[5] for although this man had done things which will remain in the memory of that people for years to come, and all by way of obtaining his liberty, yet the Moor never dealt him a blow nor ordered him flogged; as a matter of fact, he never even gave him so much as a harsh word. And for the least of the many things that Saavedra did, we were all afraid that he would be impaled, and he himself feared it more than once. If time permitted, which unfortunately it does not, I could tell you here and now something of that soldier's exploits which would interest and amaze you much more than my own story.

"To continue: Overlooking the courtyard of our prison were the windows of a wealthy Moor of high rank. These, as is usually the case, more nearly resembled peepholes and were, moreover, covered with very thick and tightly drawn blinds. It happened, then, that one day I and three companions were on the prison terrace, amusing ourselves by seeing how far we could leap with our chains on; and, since we were alone, all the rest of the Christians having gone out to labor, I chanced to raise my eyes, when through one of those closed windows

I saw a reed appear with a piece of linen cloth attached to the end of it, and it was moving and waving as if signaling for us to come and take it. As we stood gazing up at it, one of those who was with me went over and placed himself directly beneath the reed to see if it would be released or what would happen; but the moment he did so, it was raised and moved from side to side as if someone were saying no by shaking the head. The Christian then came back, and at once it was lowered again and the person above began making exactly the same motions with it as before. Another of my companions repeated the performance, and the same thing happened with him. And a third man had a similar experience.

"Seeing this, I could not resist the temptation to try my luck, and as soon as I was beneath the reed, it was dropped. It fell at my feet there in the bagnio, and I immediately hastened to untie the linen cloth, whereupon I found knotted in it ten cianis, which are gold coins of base alloy in use among the Moors, each being worth ten reales in our money.[6] I need not tell you how happy I was over this windfall, and my happiness was equaled by my wonder as to how it had come to us, and to me in particular, since the unwillingness of the donor to release the reed to anyone other than me showed clearly that I was the one for whom the favor was intended. Taking the welcome money, I broke the reed and went back to the terrace, where I once more gazed up at the window. Then it was I saw a very white hand emerge, which opened and closed very quickly; and by this we understood or were led to imagine that it was some woman who lived in that house who had shown us this act of kindness. By way of thanking her, we salaamed after the fashion of the Moors, which is done by bowing the head, bending the body at the waist, and crossing the arms upon the bosom.

"Shortly afterward, through the same window, there came a little cross made of reeds, only to be at once withdrawn. This strengthened us in the belief that some Christian woman must be a captive in that house, and that it was she who had done us the favor; but the whiteness of the hand and the Moorish bracelets of which we had caught a glimpse inclined us to think otherwise, although we fancied that it might be some fair renegade, for such women are commonly taken as lawful wives by their masters, who are glad to do this, since they esteem them more highly than those of their own race.

"In all our discussions about the matter, however, we were very far from the truth; but from that time forth we were solely concerned with looking up at that window from which the reed had appeared,

as if it had been our north star. Two weeks went by in which we had
no further sight of it, nor of the hand, nor any signal whatsoever. And
although during that time we did our best to find out who lived in
the house and if there was any renegade Christian woman in it, we
found no one who could tell us any more about the matter than that
the house belonged to a rich and prominent Moor by the name of Hadji
Morato, a former alcaide of La Pata, which is a very important office
with them.

"But just as we had given up hope of a second rain of cianis, we unexpectedly saw the reed appear again with another knotted cloth on
the end of it, a thicker one this time. This happened at an hour when
the bagnio was all but deserted, as it had been on the previous occasion, and we made the same test, each of the others in turn going to stand
beneath the window before I did, but it was only when I came up that
the reed was released and dropped. I undid the knot and found forty
Spanish gold crowns and a message written in Arabic with the sign of
the cross beneath it. I kissed the cross, took the crowns, and returned
to the terrace, where we all again salaamed. Then the hand appeared
once more, and I made signs that we would read the message, after
which the window was closed. We were at once pleased and bewildered
by what had occurred, and as none of us understood Arabic, great was
our curiosity to know what the message contained, and greater still our
difficulty in finding someone who could read it for us.

"Finally, I decided to take a certain renegade into my confidence. He
was a native of Murcia who professed to be a good friend of mine and
who had promised to keep any secret that I might entrust to him; for
it is the custom of some renegades, when they intend to return to Christian territory, to carry about with them testimonials of one sort or another from important captives to the effect that So-and-So is a good
man, has always shown kindness to Christians, and is anxious to flee at
the first opportunity that offers. There are those who procure these
certificates with a proper object in mind, and there are others who
cunningly misemploy them in case of need. The latter, when they go
to commit depredations on Christian soil, if perchance they are lost
or captured, will produce their affidavits as evidence of the purpose
for which they came: namely, that of remaining in a Christian land;
and they will assert that it was for this reason they joined the Turks.
In such a manner they escape the immediate consequences of their
act and are reconciled with the Church before it can punish them; and

then, as soon as they are able to do so, they return to Barbary to become what they were before. But, as has been said, there are others who make honest use of these certificates and actually do remain with their coreligionists.

"It was one of these renegades who was my friend. He had testimonials from all of us in which we expressed our confidence in him as forcefully as we could, and if the Moors had found him with these papers on his person, they would have burned him alive. He was known to be well versed in Arabic, being able not only to speak it but to write it as well. And so, before I unbosomed myself to him, I asked him to read the message for me, telling him that I had accidentally come upon it in a hole in my cell. He opened it and studied it for some little time, muttering to himself all the while. I asked him if he understood it, and he assured me that he did, very well, and that if I wished him to give it to me word for word, I should provide him with pen and ink, as he could do it better that way. We gave him what he asked for, and he translated the message little by little. When he had finished he said, 'You will find set down here in Spanish absolutely everything that is written on this paper; and you are to remember that where it says Lela Marien, that means Our Lady the Virgin Mary.'

"Following is the message as he had transcribed it:

"When I was young, my father had a slave girl who taught me the Christian zala [7] in my language, and she also told me many things about Lela Marien. The Christian woman died, and I know that she did not go to the fire but is with Allah, for twice afterward I saw her and she told me to make my way to the land of the Christians to see Lela Marien, who loved me a great deal. I do not know how to do so. I have seen many Christians from this window, and only you have seemed to me to be a gentleman. I am very young and beautiful and have much money to take with me. See if you can arrange for us to go, and there you may be my husband if you wish. If you do not wish it so, it will not matter to me, for Lela Marien will provide someone to marry me. I myself have written this; have a care as to whom you give it to read; do not trust any Moor, for they are all treacherous. I am deeply concerned lest you show this to someone, for if my father knew of it, he would cast me into a well and cover me with stones. On the reed I shall put a thread. Attach your reply to it, and in case you have no one who can write Arabic for you, tell me by means of signs and Lela

Marien will make me understand. May She and Allah and this cross protect you. The cross I kiss many times, as the Christian slave woman bade me.

"You can imagine, gentle folk, how astonished and pleased we were by the contents of this message. Indeed, we showed our feelings so openly that the renegade realized it was not by chance that this paper had been found but that it was in reality addressed to one of our number. He accordingly now asked us if his suspicions were true, telling us that we should confide everything to him, as he would be willing to risk his life for our freedom. Saying this, he brought forth from his bosom a metal crucifix and with many tears swore by the God whom that image represented and in whom he, though a wicked sinner, still fully and faithfully believed, that he would loyally guard all the secrets we might see fit to reveal to him; for he felt—indeed, he was almost certain—that through the one who had written that message he and all of us would be able to gain our freedom and it would be possible for him to fulfill his dearest wish, that of returning to the bosom of Holy Mother Church, from which like a rotten limb he had been severed and separated through ignorance and sin.

"So many tears did the renegade shed, and so many signs of repentance did he show, that we all of us unanimously consented and agreed to tell him the truth of the matter; and so we proceeded to give him an account of everything, keeping nothing hidden. We pointed out to him the little window through which the reed had appeared, and he then and there made note of the house and announced his intention of taking special pains to find out who lived in it. We also decided that it would be well to reply to the Moorish damsel's note, and, seeing that we had someone there who was capable of doing this, the renegade at once wrote out the words that I dictated to him, which were exactly as I shall give them to you; for nothing of any importance that happened to me in the course of this adventure has slipped my memory, nor shall it escape me as long as I live. This was the reply that we sent to the Moorish lady:

"May the true Allah protect you, my lady, and that blessed Mary who is the true Mother of God and who has put it in your heart to go to the land of the Christians, because she loves you well. Pray to her to show you how you may carry out her command, for she is well disposed and will assuredly do so. Do not fail to write and advise me of your plans, and I will always let you have an answer. The great Allah

has given us a Christian captive who knows how to read and write your language, as you can plainly see from this message. Thus, with nothing to fear, we shall be able to know your wishes. You say that if you go to the land of the Christians, you will be my wife, and I as a good Christian promise you that you shall be, and you know that Christians keep their promises better than Moors. May Allah and Mary His Mother watch over you, my lady.

"Having written and sealed this message, I waited two days until the bagnio was deserted as usual, and then I went out to my accustomed place on the terrace to see if the reed would appear, which it did very shortly. As soon as I caught sight of it, although I could not see who was letting it down, I held up the paper as a sign the person above should attach the thread. This had already been done, however, and I now fastened the paper to it, and shortly thereafter our star once more made its appearance with the white banner of peace in the form of a little bundle. It fell at my feet, and, upon picking it up, I found in the cloth all sorts of gold and silver coins, more than fifty crowns, which more than fifty times doubled our happiness and strengthened our hope of obtaining our liberty.

"That same night our renegade came back and told us what he had learned. The one who lived in that house was the same Moor whose name, Hadji Morato, had been mentioned to us. He was enormously rich and had one daughter, the only heir to all his wealth; and it was the general opinion in the city that she was the most beautiful woman in Barbary. Many of the viceroys who came there had sought her hand in marriage, but she had been unwilling to wed; and it was also known that she had had a female slave who was a Christian and who was now dead. All of which bore out what was said in the note. We then took counsel with the renegade as to what we should do in order to rescue the Moorish damsel and make our escape to the land of Christians, and it was finally agreed that we should wait until we had further word from Zoraida, which was the name of the one who now wishes to be known as Maria. For we saw plainly enough that she and no other would be able to provide a way out of all these difficulties. When we had reached this decision, the renegade told us not to worry, that he would set us at liberty or lose his life in the attempt.

"For four days the bagnio was full of people, and as a result the reed did not appear, but at the end of that period, when the place was once more empty, the bundle was again let down, so pregnant-looking as to promise a very happy birth. The reed and the cloth descended to me, and I found in the latter a message and a hundred gold crowns, with no other money whatsoever. The renegade being present, we gave him the note to read inside our cell, and he translated it for us as follows:

"Sir, I do not know how to arrange for us to go to Spain, nor has Lela Marien told me, although I have asked it of her. The thing that can be done is for me to give you for this venture much money in gold. Ransom yourself and your friends with it, and let one of you go ahead to the land of the Christians, purchase a boat there, and return for the others. He will find me in my father's garden, which is at the Babazón gate,[8] near the seashore. I expect to be there all this summer with my father and my servants. You will be able to take me away from there by night and carry me to the boat with nothing to fear. And remember that you are to be my husband, or I shall ask Mary to punish you. If you can trust no one to go for the boat, ransom yourself and go; for I know that you are more trustworthy than any other, being a gentleman and a Christian. Make it a point to become familiar with the garden; and, meanwhile, when I see you out for a stroll, I shall know that the bagnio is empty and will give you much money. Allah protect you, my lord.

"Such were the contents of the second note; and when all had heard it read, each offered to be the ransomed one, promising to go and return with all haste; and I myself made the same offer. But the renegade opposed all this, saying he would by no means consent for anyone to go free until we all went together; for experience had taught him that men when freed were lax about keeping the word they had given in captivity. He added that many times certain important captives had had recourse to this expedient and had ransomed one of their number to go to Valencia or Majorca, providing him with sufficient money to fit out a boat and return for them, but he had never come back. For, the renegade observed, liberty recovered and the dread of losing it again would erase from their memories all the obligations that there are. By way of showing us the truth of this statement, he briefly related for us what had recently happened to some Christian gentlemen, one of the strangest cases that had ever been heard of in those parts where the most astonishing and terrifying things are all the time occurring.

"In short, he told us that what we could and should do was to give him the ransom money intended for one of us Christians, and he would buy a boat there in Algiers under pretext of turning merchant and trading with Tetuan and along the coast in that region. Being a ship's master, it would be easy for him to hit upon a way of rescuing us from the bagnio and putting us all aboard, especially if the Moorish lady, as she said, was to provide the money for ransoming the entire lot of us. As free men, it would be the easiest thing in the world to embark, even at midday. The greatest obstacle lay in the fact that the Moors would not permit any renegade to buy or own a boat, unless it was a vessel to go on pillaging expeditions; for they feared that if he purchased a small one, especially if he was a Spaniard, he merely wanted it for the purpose of escaping to Christian territory. He, our friend, could readily overcome this difficulty, however, by taking a Tagarin Moor [9] into partnership with him in the purchase of the boat and the profits to be derived from it, and under cover of this arrangement he could become master of the craft; and with that he regarded the rest of it as something already accomplished.

"Although it seemed to me and to my comrades that it would have been better to send to Majorca for the boat as the Moorish lady had suggested, we did not dare oppose him, being fearful that if we did not do as he said he would reveal our plans and put us in danger of losing our lives when our dealings with Zoraida were discovered, for whose life we would all have given our own. We accordingly determined to leave the matter in the hands of God and in those of the renegade, and we therewith replied to Zoraida that we would do all that she had counseled us, since the advice she had given us was as good as if it had come from Lela Marien herself, adding that it remained for her to decide as to whether the project was to be postponed or put into execution at once. I also, once more, made an offer to marry her. And so it came about that the next day, when there was no one in the bagnio, she on various occasions by means of the reed and the cloth conveyed to us two thousand gold crowns and a message in which she informed us that on the next *Jumá,* that is to say, Friday, she was leaving for her father's summer place and that before she left she would give us more money. In case this was not enough, we were to let her know and we might have anything we asked for; for her father had so much that he would never miss it, and, what was more, she held the keys to everything.

"We at once gave the renegade fifteen hundred crowns with which to buy the boat, while I took eight hundred to procure my own ransom, giving the money to a merchant of Valencia who was in Algiers at the time and who had the king release me on the promise that, when the next boat arrived from home, he would pay the ransom fee; for if he were to pay it at once, the king might suspect that the funds had been in Algiers for some time and that the merchant for his own profit had kept the matter secret. Moreover, my master was so captious that I on no account dared pay him immediately. And so, on the Thursday before the Friday that the beauteous Zoraida had fixed as the day for going to her father's summer place, she gave us another thousand crowns, at the same time advising us of her departure and requesting me, in case I was ransomed, to make myself acquainted with the site or, in any event, to seek to procure an opportunity for going there to see her. I replied in a few words that I would do this, urging her to be sure and commend us to Lela Marien by making use of all those prayers that the slave woman had taught her.

"When this had been done, it was arranged that my three companions likewise should be ransomed, so that they would be able to leave the bagnio; since if they saw me set at liberty while they remained behind, despite the fact that there was sufficient money to ransom them, they might create a disturbance and the devil might put it into their heads to do something that would injure Zoraida. It was true that, in view of their rank, I could feel reasonably safe in this regard, but, nevertheless, I did not wish to imperil the undertaking, and so I had them released at the same time as myself, paying over all the money to the merchant in order that he might with confidence and security pledge his word, although we never once divulged to him our secret plan, as there would have been too much danger in doing so."

CHAPTER XLI. *In which the captive's story is still further continued.*

"A FORTNIGHT had not gone by before our renegade had bought a boat capable of carrying more than thirty persons; and by way of rendering the project safer and allaying suspicion, he made a voyage, as he had suggested, to a place called Shershel which is thirty leagues from Algiers in the direction of Oran [1] and which does a large trade in dried figs. Two or three times he did this in the company of the Tagarin Moor I have mentioned; for *Tagarinos* is the name given in Barbary to the Moors of Aragon, while those of Granada are called *Mudéjares;* but in the kingdom of Fez the *Mudéjares* are termed *Elches,* and they are the ones whom that king chiefly employs in war.

"To go on with my story, then: Each time that he passed with his boat he anchored in a cove that was not two crossbow shots from the house where Zoraida was waiting, and there, with the two little Moors that served him as oarsmen, he would deliberately station himself, either to say his prayers or by way of acting out the part he was later to perform in earnest. Thus, he would go to Zoraida's garden and beg fruit, and her father would give it to him without recognizing him. As he told me afterward, he would have liked to have a word with Zoraida herself so he could tell her he was there on my orders to bear her off to the land of the Christians and at the same time urge her to feel safe and happy.

"This, however, was impossible, for Moorish ladies do not permit themselves to be seen by any of their own race or by any Turk unless their husband or father so commands them. With Christian captives, on the other hand, they are allowed to converse and have dealings to a rather surprising extent. For my part, I was just as glad that he had not spoken to her, for she might have been disturbed to find her plan being discussed by renegades.

"But God in any case had ordained otherwise, and our renegade did not have an opportunity of gratifying his laudable desire. Seeing how safely he was able to go to Shershel and return and anchor where he chose, and perceiving that the Tagarin, his companion, was wholly compliant with his wishes and that all that was needed now was a few Christians to man the oars, he told me to look about for some that I might take with me in addition to those that were being ransomed and to engage them for the following Friday, which was the date he had set for our departure. I accordingly spoke to a dozen Spaniards, all of them powerful rowers. They were chosen from among those that were best in a position to leave the city, and it was no small task finding so many of them at that particular moment, since there were then twenty ships at sea and they had taken all the available oarsmen.

"I should not have been able to find them if it had not been that their master that summer was not going on a cruise but was occupied with completing the construction of a galiot which he had on the stocks. All that I told these men was that the next Friday afternoon they should steal out one by one and wait for me in the vicinity of Hadji Morato's garden. I gave these directions to each one separately, instructing them that if they saw any other Christians in the neighborhood, all they were to say to them was that I had ordered them to stay there until I came.

"Having attended to this, I had something else to do that was still more important, and that was to let Zoraida know how far our plans had progressed in order that she might be forewarned and not be caught off guard if we suddenly decided to abduct her before, as she would think, the Christian's boat would have had time to return. I therefore resolved to go to the garden and see if I could speak with her; so on a day before my departure I went there under pretense of gathering a few herbs, and the first person I encountered was her father, who addressed me in the language that throughout Barbary and even in Constantinople is in use between captives and Moors, and which is neither Moorish nor Castilian nor the tongue of any other nation, but a mixture of all of them by means of which we manage to understand one another. It was in this language that he asked me who I was and what I was doing in his garden. I replied that I was Arnaut Mami's [2] slave—because I knew for a certainty that Arnaut Mami was a very great friend of his—and that I was looking for herbs to make him a salad. He then inquired as to whether I was a ransomed man or not and what price my master wanted for me.

"As I was thus engaged in answering his questionings, the lovely Zoraida came out of the garden house. She had caught sight of me some while before; and since Moorish women, as I have said, are not at all prudish about showing themselves to Christians and do not avoid their company, she thought nothing of coming up to where her father stood conversing with me. In fact, when her father saw her slowly approaching, he called to her to come. It would be too much for me to undertake to describe for you now the great beauty, the air of gentle breeding, the rich and elegant attire with which my beloved Zoraida presented herself to my gaze. I shall merely tell you that more pearls hung from her comely throat, her ears, her hair than she has hairs on her head. On her feet, which, as is the custom, were bare, she wore two *carcajes*—for that is what they call bracelets for the ankles in the Moorish tongue—made of purest gold and set with many diamonds whose value, as she told me afterward, her father estimated at ten thousand doblas, [3] while those upon her wrist were worth fully as much as the others.

"The pearls also were numerous, for the way that Moorish women have of displaying their magnificence is by decking themselves out in this manner.⁴ And so it is you find more pearls of one kind or another among the Moors than all the other nations combined have to show, and Zoraida's father was reputed to have an abundance of them and the best that there were in Algiers. In addition, he had more than two hundred thousand Spanish crowns, and the fair one I now call mine was mistress of all this wealth.

"If you would form an idea of how beautiful she was in her prosperous days and when so adorned, you have but to observe how much of beauty is left her now after all that she has suffered. For it is a well-known fact that the beauty of some women has its day and season and is diminished or heightened by accidental causes. It is, moreover, a natural thing that the passions of the mind should add to or detract from it, and most often they destroy it utterly. What I am trying to say is that, as she came toward me that day, she impressed me as being, both in herself and in her adornments, the most dazzling creature that I had ever seen, and when I thought of all that I owed to her, it seemed to me that I had before me a goddess from Heaven who had come to earth for my delight and comfort.

"As she came up, her father told her in their language that I was the captive of his friend, Arnaut Mami, and that I had come to look for a salad. She gave me her hand and, in that admixture of tongues that I have described, asked me if I was a gentleman and why it was I had not been ransomed. I replied that I already had been, and that from the price paid she could see the esteem in which my master held me, for the sum of one thousand five hundred soltanis ⁵ had been put up for me. To which she answered, 'In truth, had you been my father's slave, I would not have permitted him to let you go for twice as much, for you Christians always lie in everything you say and make yourselves out to be poor in order to cheat the Moors.'

" 'That may be, lady,' I said, 'but I dealt truthfully with my master, as I do and shall do with everybody in this world.'

" 'And when are you going?' Zoraida asked.

" 'Tomorrow, I expect; for there is a vessel here from France that sets sail then and I intend to go on it.'

" 'Would it not be better,' said Zoraida, 'to wait for one from Spain, seeing that the French are not your friends?'

" 'No,' I told her, 'although if I were certain that a ship from Spain was on the way, I would wait for it. It is more likely, however, that I shall go tomorrow, for the desire I have to see my native land and my loved ones is such that I cannot bear to wait for another opportunity, even though a better one, if it be late in coming.'

" 'You no doubt have a wife in your own country,' she said, 'and I suppose you are anxious to see her.'

" 'No,' I assured her, 'I am not married, but I have promised to wed as soon as I return.'

" 'And is the lady to whom you have given this promise beautiful?'

" 'She is so beautiful,' I replied, 'that by way of praising her and telling the simple truth, I will say that she very much resembles you.'

"Her father laughed heartily at this. 'In Allah's name, Christian,' he said, 'she must be beautiful indeed if she is like my daughter, who is the most beautiful in all this realm. If you do not believe me, look at her well and tell me if I do not speak the truth.'

"Throughout the greater part of this conversation, Zoraida's father acted as our interpreter, being the more adept at languages; for while she spoke the bastard tongue that, as I have said, is in use there, she expressed her meaning by signs rather than by words.

"As we were discussing these and other subjects, a Moor came running up, crying in a loud voice that four Turks had leaped the garden railing or wall and were picking the fruit although it was not yet ripe. Both the old man and Zoraida were alarmed at this; for the fear that the Moors have of the Turks is a common and, so to speak, an instinctive thing. They are especially afraid of Turkish soldiers, who treat their Moorish subjects more haughtily, insolently, and cruelly than if the latter were their slaves.

"Zoraida's father then said to her, 'Daughter, retire to the house and shut yourself in while I speak to these dogs. As for you, Christian, gather your herbs and go in peace, and may Allah bring you safely to your own country.'

"I bowed, and he went away to look for the Turks, leaving me alone with Zoraida, who made as if to go back into the house as her father had commanded her. He had no sooner disappeared among the garden trees, however, than she, her eyes brimming with tears, turned to me and said, 'Tamejí, Christian, tamejí?' [6] Which means, 'Are you going, Christian, are you going?'

"And I answered her, 'Yes, lady, but under no condition without you. Wait for me next Jumá, and do not be frightened when you see us, for we are surely going to the land of the Christians.'

"I said this in such a way that she understood everything very well; and, throwing her arm about my neck, she began with faltering step to walk toward the house. But as luck would have it—and it would have been very unlucky indeed for us if Heaven had not ordered it otherwise—as we were going along in this manner, her father, who was coming back from his encounter with the Turks, caught sight of us, and we knew that he had seen us and had seen her arm about me. But Zoraida, cleverly on her guard, did not remove her arm; instead, she clung to me more than ever and laid her head upon my bosom, swaying at the knees a little and giving every evidence of having fainted, while I pretended to be supporting her against my will. The old man ran up to us and, seeing his daughter in this condition, asked her what the matter was.

" 'Undoubtedly,' he said, when he received no reply, 'it was those dogs coming into the garden that did this to her.' And, taking her off my bosom, he pressed her to his own, as she, her eyes not yet dry from her tears, sighed deeply and said, '*Ameji*, Christian, *ameji!*' [1]

" 'It is not necessary, my daughter, for the Christian to go,' her father said. 'He has done you no harm, and the Turks have left. There is no cause for you to be frightened, for nothing is going to hurt you, since the Turks at my request have gone back to where they belong.'

" 'It is true, sir, as you have said,' I told him, 'that they have given her a fright; but since she says for me to go, I would not cause her any annoyance; and so, peace be with you, and with your permission I will return to this garden for herbs, if I find it necessary, for my master says there are no better ones for salad than those that grow here.'

" 'Come back for all that you need,' replied Hadji Morato. 'My daughter does not say this because you or any of the other Christians annoy her. She either meant that the Turks should go, not you, or else that it was time you were looking for your herbs.'

"With this, I at once took my leave of both of them, and Zoraida, who appeared to be suffering deeply, went away with her father, while I, under pretense of gathering my salad, was able to roam the garden at will. I carefully noted the entrances and exits, the means they used to secure the house, and everything that might facilitate our plan; after which, I went to give an account of what had happened to the renegade and my companions. In the meanwhile, I looked forward to the time when I should be able to enjoy undisturbed the boon which fate had bestowed upon me in the person of the beauteous and charming Zoraida.

"Time went by, and at length the day came that meant so much to us. With all of us following the plan which, after many long discussions and the most careful consideration, we had decided upon, we met with the success that we longed for. On the next Friday after the day on which I had spoken to Zoraida in the garden, our renegade at nightfall anchored his boat almost directly opposite the house where she was, the Christians who were to man the oars having been notified in advance that they might hide themselves in various places round about. As they waited for me, they were all of them anxious and elated, eager to board the vessel on which their gaze was fixed; for they were unaware of the arrangement with the renegade and thought that they would have to gain their freedom by force of arm, through slaying the Moors who were on the boat.

"Accordingly, as soon as I and my companions showed ourselves, those who were in hiding sighted us and came up. This was at an hour when the gates of the city were closed, and in the whole of the country-side not a soul was to be seen. When we were all together, we discussed the question as to whether it would be better to go first for Zoraida or to make prisoners of the Moorish oarsmen. Before we had reached a decision, our renegade arrived and asked us what was the cause of our delay, for it was now time, all the Moors being off guard and most of them asleep. I told him why we were hesitating, and he replied that the most important thing was to capture the vessel first of all, which could be done very easily and with no danger whatever, and after that we could go for Zoraida. We all agreed with him, and so, without waiting any longer and with him as our guide, we went to the vessel, where he was the first to leap aboard. Laying a hand on his cutlass, he cried in the Moorish tongue, 'None of you stir from here or it will cost you your lives!'

"By this time nearly all the Christians were aboard; and the Moors, who were possessed of little courage, upon hearing their captain address them in this manner, were thoroughly terrified. None of them dared reach for his weapons, and for that matter, they had few if any; and so, without saying a word, they let themselves be shackled by the Christians, who accomplished this very quickly, threatening them that if they raised any kind of outcry they would all die by the knife.

"When this had been achieved, with half our number remaining behind to guard the prisoners, the rest of us, again with the renegade as our guide, made our way to Hadji Morato's garden; and it was our good fortune that, as we went to try the gate, it swung open as readily as if it had not been locked. We then, very quietly and saying nothing, went on to the house without our presence being discovered by anyone.

Zoraida, fairest of the fair, was waiting for us at a window, and as soon as she heard the sound of people below, she asked in a low voice if we were *Nizarani*, that is to say, Christians. I answered in the affirmative, saying that she should come down. Recognizing me, she did not hesitate for a moment, but without a word she came down instantly and, opening the door, appeared there in the sight of all, so beautiful and so richly clad that I cannot possibly tell you how she looked.

"As soon as I saw her, I took one of her hands and began kissing it, and the renegade and my two comrades did the same, while the others, being unacquainted with the circumstances, followed our example, since it seemed to them that we were merely recognizing and thanking her as the lady who was responsible for our going free. The renegade asked in Moorish if her father was in the house, and she replied that he was sleeping.

" 'Then it will be necessary to wake him,' he said, 'for we must take him with us and everything of value that there is in this beautiful summer place.'

" 'No,' she answered, 'you must by no means lay hands on my father. In this house there is nothing for you save that which I bring with me, and it is enough to make you all rich and happy. Wait a moment and you will see.'

"She then went back into the house, saying she would return at once and bidding us meanwhile not to make any noise. I took this opportunity of asking the renegade what had passed between them, and when he told me, I made it clear to him that under no condition was he to go beyond Zoraida's wishes. She now reappeared with a small trunk filled with gold crowns, so heavy that she could hardly carry it. At that instant, unfortunately, her father awoke and, hearing a noise in the garden, came to the window and looked out. Recognizing us all as Christians, he began bawling at the top of his lungs in Arabic, 'Christians! Christians! Thieves! Thieves!' This frightened us very much and threw us into confusion; but the renegade, perceiving the danger we were in and how important it was to go through with our undertaking before being detected, ran up as fast as he could to where Hadji Morato was, being accompanied by some of the rest of us. As for myself I did not dare leave Zoraida unprotected, for she, half fainting, had fallen in my arms.

"In brief, those who went up handled the matter so expeditiously that in a moment they were back, bringing with them Hadji Morato, his hands bound and with a napkin over his mouth so that he could not speak a word—and they threatened him that if he tried to speak it would cost him his life. When his daughter saw him, she put her hands over her eyes, and her father in turn was horrified at sight of her, not knowing that she had placed herself in our hands of her own free will. But it was essential now for us to be on our way, and so we hastily but with due care boarded the ship, where those that we had left behind were waiting for us, fearful that some untoward accident had befallen us.

"It was a little after two in the morning by the time we were all on the vessel. They then untied Hadji Morato's hands and removed the napkin from his mouth, but the renegade again warned him not to say anything or they would kill him. As the old man looked at his daughter, he began sighing mournfully, especially when he saw her held tightly in my embrace, and when he observed that she did not struggle, protest, or attempt to escape me; but he nonetheless remained silent lest they carry out the renegade's threat.

"Finding herself on the boat now and perceiving that we were about to row away while her father and the other Moors remained bound, Zoraida spoke to the renegade, requesting him to do her the favor of releasing the prisoners, particularly her father, as she would rather cast herself into the sea than have a parent who loved her so dearly carried away captive in front of her eyes and through her fault. The renegade repeated to me what she had said, and, for my part, I was quite willing. He, however, replied that this was not the wise thing to do, for the reason that, if they were left behind, they would alarm the entire city and countryside, whereupon some fast-sailing craft would put out in pursuit of us and so comb the sea and land that there would be no possibility of our escaping. What we might do, he added, was to give them their freedom as soon as we set foot on Christian soil. We all agreed to this, and when the matter was explained to Zoraida, along with the reasons why we could not comply with her wishes, she also was satisfied. And then, gladly and silently, cheerfully and with alacrity, each one of our powerful rowers took up his oar, as, commending ourselves with all our hearts to God, we set out on our voyage to the island of Majorca, which is the nearest Christian territory.

"However, inasmuch as the tramontane wind [8] was blowing a little and the sea was a bit rough, it was impossible for us to follow the route to Majorca, and we were compelled to hug the coast in the direction of Oran. This worried us considerably, for we feared that we would be discovered from the town of Shershel, which is about seventy miles from Algiers. And we also were afraid that we might encounter in those waters one of the galiots that commonly ply the coast with merchandise of Tetuán, although each of us secretly felt that if we did meet with a merchant vessel of that sort, providing it was not a cruiser, we not only should not be captured but, rather, should be able to come into possession of a craft in which we could more safely complete our voyage. In the meantime, as we were sailing along, Zoraida buried her face in my hands in order not to see her father, and I could hear her calling on Lela Marien to come to our aid.

"We must have gone a good thirty miles when dawn came, and we found ourselves at a distance of something like three musket shots off land. The shore was deserted, and we saw no one who might descry us, but, nevertheless, by rowing as hard as we could we put out a little more to the open sea, which was now somewhat calmer. When we were about two leagues from the coast, the order was given to row by turns so that we could have a bite to eat, the ship being well stocked with food; but those at the oars said it was not yet time for them to take a rest—the others might eat, but they themselves did not wish on any account to relax their efforts. We were starting to do as they had suggested when a strong wind came up, which obliged us to leave off rowing and set sail at once for Oran, that being the only course left us. All this was done very quickly, and with the sail we made more than eight miles an hour, with no fear other than that of falling in with a vessel that was out cruising.

"We gave the Moorish rowers some food, and the renegade consoled them by telling them they were not captives but would be given their freedom at the first opportunity. He said the same to Zoraida's father, who replied, 'If you promised me anything else, O Christian, I might believe it and hope for it by reason of the generous treatment you have accorded me, but when it comes to setting me free, do not think that I am so simple-minded as to put any credence in that; for you would never have incurred the risk of depriving me of my liberty only to restore it to me so freely, especially since you know who I am and the profit you may derive from releasing me. Indeed, if you wish to name the sum, I hereby offer you whatever you ask for me and for this unfortunate daughter of mine, or for her alone, for she is the greater and better part of my soul.'

"As he said this, he began weeping so bitterly that we were all moved to compassion, and Zoraida could not resist stealing a glance at him. When she saw him weeping, she was so touched that she rose from my feet and went over to embrace him, and as she laid her cheek against his the two of them shed so many tears that a number of us could not but join them in their weeping. But when her father perceived that she was in festive attire and decked out in all her jewels, he spoke to her in their own language.

" 'How does it come, my daughter,' he said, 'that last night, at dusk, before this terrible thing happened to us, I saw you clad in ordinary household garb; and now, without your having had time to dress, and without my having brought you any good news to celebrate by thus adorning and bedecking your person, I nonetheless behold you wearing the best garments with which I was able to provide you when fortune smiled upon us? Answer me this, for I am even more astonished and bewildered by it than I am by this misfortune that has come to us.'

The renegade informed us of all that the Moor had said to his daughter, who did not utter a word in reply. And when the old man saw, over at one side of the boat, the small trunk in which she was in the habit of keeping her jewels, he was more bewildered than ever; for he knew very well that he had not brought it to the summer place but had left it in Algiers. He thereupon asked her how the trunk had come into our hands and what was inside it; and then the renegade, without giving Zoraida time to answer, spoke up.

" 'You need not trouble, sir, to ask your daughter Zoraida so many questions, for I can give you one answer that will serve for all. I would have you know that she is a Christian, and that it is she who has filed our chains for us and set us free from our captivity. She goes of her own free will and, I fancy, is as happy about it as one who emerges from darkness into light, from death into life, or from the pains of hell into glory everlasting.'

" 'Is it true, my daughter, what this man says?' asked the Moor.

" 'It is,' said Zoraida.

" 'So you are a Christian,' said the old man, 'and it is you who have placed your father in the hands of his enemies?'

" 'As to my being a Christian,' she told him, 'that is true enough, but it is not true that I am responsible for your being in this situation; for I never had any desire to leave you or to do you harm, but only to do good to myself.'

" 'And what good have you done yourself, daughter?'

" 'Put that question,' she said, 'to Lela Marien, for she can tell you better than I.'

"No sooner had he heard this than the Moor, with an incredibly swift movement, hurled himself head foremost into the sea; and he would undoubtedly have drowned if the long and cumbersome robe that he wore had not tended to bear him up. Zoraida screamed for someone to rescue him, whereupon we all ran forward and, seizing him by his robe, hauled him in, half drowned and unconscious, at which his daughter was so distressed that she wept over him as bitterly and mournfully as if he were already dead. We turned him face downward and he disgorged much water, and after a couple of hours he was himself once more.

"Meanwhile, the wind had changed and we had to make for land, exerting all our strength at the oars in order not to be driven ashore. Luck was with us, and we were able to put into a cove alongside a promontory or cape which the Moors call *Cava Rumia*,[9] signifying in our language 'the wicked Christian woman'; for it is a tradition among them that La Cava, through whom Spain was lost, is buried in that spot, '*cava*' in their tongue meaning 'bad woman,' while '*rumia*' is 'Christian.' They regard it as bad luck to be compelled to drop anchor there, and they never do so unless it is absolutely necessary. But for us it was not the 'bad woman's' shelter; rather, it was a haven in distress, as the sea was now raging.

"Stationing our sentinels on land and never once relinquishing the oars, we ate what the renegade had provided and prayed to God and Our Lady with all our hearts that they would favor and aid us in order that we might bring to a happy conclusion an undertaking that had begun so propitiously. Upon Zoraida's request, the order was given to set her father and all the other Moors ashore, for her tender heart could not bear to see her father thus bound and her fellow countrymen held prisoners in front of her very eyes. We promised her that this should be done as soon as it came time for us to depart; for we ran no risk by leaving them in this deserted place. Our prayers were not in vain; for, Heaven favoring us, the wind changed and the sea grew calm, inviting us to resume with cheerful hearts the voyage that we had begun.

"We then unbound the Moors and, one by one, set them on land, at which they were greatly astonished; but when it came to disembarking Zoraida's father, who had by now completely recovered his senses, he gave us a piece of his mind.

"'Why do you think, Christians,' he said, 'that this wicked female is happy at your giving me my liberty? Do you imagine that it is out of filial affection? Assuredly not. It is only because my presence is an impediment to the carrying out of her base designs. And do not think that what has led her to change her religion is a belief that yours is better than ours; it is because she knows that in your country immodesty is more freely practiced than in ours.'

"As her father spoke, another Christian and I held Zoraida's arms that she might not be tempted to some foolish act. The old man now turned upon her.

" 'O infamous and ill-advised maiden! Where do you think you are going, so blindly and foolishly, with these dogs, our natural enemies? Cursed be the hour in which I begot you, and cursed all the luxury in which I have reared you!'

"Seeing that he was likely to go on in this way for some while, I hastened to put him ashore; and from there he kept on shouting at us, pursuing us with his curses and lamentations as he implored Mohammed to pray to Allah that we be destroyed, confounded, and brought to an end. And when, having set sail, we could no longer hear his words, we could still see his gestures, could see him plucking out his beard, tearing his hair, and rolling on the ground. At one point he raised his voice to such a pitch that we could make out what he said.

" 'Return, my beloved daughter, return to land, and I will forgive you everything. Give those men the money that is yours and come back to comfort your brokenhearted father, who, if you leave him now, will leave his bones on these deserted sands.'

"Zoraida heard all this and was deeply grieved by it. Weeping, she could only say to him in reply, 'O my father, may it please Allah that Lela Marien, who has been the cause of my turning Christian, console you in your sorrow! Allah well knows that I could have done nothing other than what I did. These Christians are in no wise to blame, for even had I not wished to come with them, even had I chosen to remain at home, it would have been impossible, so eagerly did my soul urge me to do that which to me seems as good, my dear father, as it seems evil to you.'

"When she said this, her father could no longer hear her, for we had lost him from view; and so, while I comforted Zoraida, we all of us turned our attention to the voyage, as we now had a wind so favorable that we firmly expected to be off the coast of Spain by dawn the next day.

"Blessings, however, are almost never unmixed with some evil that, without our having foreseen it, comes to disturb them. It may have been simply our misfortune, or it may have been those curses that the Moor had heaped upon his daughter (for a curse of that kind is always to be dreaded, whatever the father may be like), but, in any event, our luck now changed. We were on the high seas, and the night was a little more than three hours gone. We were proceeding at full sail with the oars lashed, since the wind had relieved us of the necessity of using them, when by the light of the moon, which was shining brightly, we sighted alongside us a square-rigged vessel with all sails set that was luffing a little and standing across our course.[10] It was so close upon us that we had to strike sail in order not to run foul of her, while they swung their prow about to give us room to pass.

"They now came to the ship's rail to ask us who we were, from where we came, and where we were going. When these questions were put to us in French, our renegade said, 'Let no one answer, for they are undoubtedly French pirates who plunder everything in sight.' As a result of this warning, no one said a word in reply. We were a little ahead, and the other vessel was lying to leeward, when suddenly they fired two pieces of artillery, both of them, as it seemed, loaded with chain-shot; for with one they cut our mast in half and brought both mast and sail down into the sea, while the other cannon, discharged at the same moment, sent a shot into the middle of our craft, laying it wide open but doing no further damage to it. As we saw ourselves sinking, we began crying out for help, imploring those on the other ship to come to our aid as we were filling with water. They then struck their own sails, and, lowering a skiff or boat, as many as a dozen Frenchmen, all well armed, with matchlocks and matches lighted, came alongside us. When they saw how few we were and how our craft was going down, they took us in, telling us that this had come about through our discourtesy in not answering them.

"Our renegade, then, without anyone's seeing what he did, took the trunk containing Zoraida's wealth and dumped it into the sea. To make a long story short, we all went aboard with the Frenchmen, who, after they had learned everything they wished to know about us, proceeded to despoil us of all that we possessed as if we had been their deadly enemies. They even took Zoraida's anklets, but this did not grieve me as much as it did her. What I feared more was that, having deprived her of her exceedingly rich and precious gems, they would go on to steal that jewel that was worth more than all the others and which she most esteemed. Their desires, however, did not go beyond money, in which regard they were insatiable in their covetousness. They would even have taken the garments their captives wore if these had been of any use to them. Some of them were for wrapping us all in a sail and tossing us into the sea; for it was their intention, by passing themselves off as Bretons, to put in at certain Spanish ports, and if they brought us in alive they would be punished when the theft was discovered.

"But the captain, who was the one who had despoiled my beloved Zoraida, said that he was content with the prize that he had and did not wish to stop at any port in Spain. Instead, he preferred to slip through the Strait of Gibraltar at night, or any way he could, and go on to La Rochelle, the port from which he had put out. Accordingly, they agreed to let us take their small boat and all that we needed for the brief voyage that remained for us. This they did the next day, within sight of the Spanish coast, a sight that caused us wholly to forget all our sufferings and hardships, which were as if they had never been, so great is the joy that comes from recovering one's lost freedom.

"It may have been around midday when they put us in the boat, giving us two kegs of water and some biscuit. And as the lovely Zoraida went to embark, the captain, moved by some sympathetic impulse or other, gave her as many as twenty gold crowns and would not permit his men to take from her those same garments that she is now wearing. As we entered the small boat, we thanked them for their kindness, our manner being one of gratitude rather than indignation, and they then put out to sea, making for the Strait, while we, needing no other compass than the land that lay ahead of us, bent to the oars so lustily that by sundown we were, as we thought, near enough to be able to reach it before the night was far gone.

"But as there was no moon and the sky was darkened over and we were ignorant of our exact whereabouts, it did not seem wise to attempt a landing, although many of us thought that we should do so, saying that it would be better to run ashore even if it were on some rocks, far from any inhabited place, since in that way we would assure ourselves against the very likely danger of Tetuán corsairs, who at night are in Barbary and by morning off the coast of Spain, where they commonly take some prize and then return to sleep in their own houses. There were a number of conflicting suggestions, but the one that was finally adopted was that we should gradually draw near the shore and, if the sea was calm enough to permit it, land wherever we were able.

"This was the plan followed, and shortly before midnight we came to the foot of an enormous and very high mountain that was not so near the sea but that it afforded a convenient space for a landing. We ran up on the sand and leaped ashore, kissing the ground on which we stood and shedding many joyful tears as we gave thanks to God, Our

Lord, for the incomparable blessing that He had conferred upon us. Removing the provisions from the boat, we drew it ashore and then went a long way up the mountain; for even here we could not feel in our hearts or bring ourselves to believe that the land beneath our feet was Christian soil. The sun, it seemed to me, came up more slowly than we could have wished, and in the meanwhile we had climbed the entire mountainside in an effort to see if we could discover any village or even a few shepherds' huts; but however much we strained our eyes, we were able to descry no village, no human being, no path, no road.

"Nevertheless, we determined to keep on and go farther inland, since surely we could not fail to come upon someone who could give us our bearings. What distressed me more than anything else was seeing Zoraida go on foot over this rough country; for though I once tried carrying her on my shoulders, my weariness wearied her more than she was rested by her repose, and so she would not again consent to my making the exertion but went along very cheerfully and patiently, her hand in mine. We had gone, I imagine, a little less than a quarter of a league when there reached our ears the sound of a little bell, which showed plainly that we must be near some flock or herd, and as we all gazed about us attentively to see if we could discern any, we saw at the foot of a cork tree a young shepherd who very calmly and unconcernedly was engaged in whittling a stick with his knife.

"We called to him, and he, raising his head, got to his feet very nimbly. As we afterward learned, the first persons that he caught sight of among us were the renegade and Zoraida, and seeing them in Moorish costume, he thought that all Barbary must have descended upon him. Dashing with amazing swiftness into a near-by wood, he began raising a terrible din as he shouted, 'Moors! Moors! The Moors have landed! Moors! Moors! To arms! To arms!'

"We were quite perplexed by all this, not knowing what to do; but, reflecting that the shepherd's cries would arouse the countryside and that the mounted coast guard would soon be along to find out what the trouble was, we decided that the renegade should take off his Turkish clothes and put on a captive's jacket, which one of us now gave him though he himself was left with only his shirt. And then, commending ourselves to God, we proceeded along the same path that the shepherd had taken, expecting that the guard would be upon us at any moment. In this we were not wrong, for two hours had not gone by when, as we were coming out of a thicket onto a plain, we caught sight of all of fifty horsemen coming toward us at top speed.

"As soon as we saw them, we stopped and watched them, and they, when they came up and found, in place of the Moors they were seeking, a handful of poor Christians, were very much surprised. One of them asked if it was we who had caused the shepherd to sound the call to arms. 'Yes,' I replied, and was about to go on and tell him our story, who we were and from whence we came, when one of our number happened to recognize the horseman who had put the question and, without giving me a chance to reply, spoke up and said, 'Thanks be to God, sirs, for having brought us into such good hands; for unless I am mistaken, this region where we now are is in the neighborhood of Vélez Málaga—unless all the years of my captivity have so deprived me of my memory that I cannot recall that you, sir, who have just asked us our names, are Pedro de Bustamente, my uncle.'

"The Christian captive had no sooner said this than the horseman dismounted and came up to embrace the young fellow. 'My dearest nephew!' he cried. 'I recognize you now. I and my sister—your mother—and all your relatives who are still alive have wept for you as dead, and now it appears that God has been pleased to prolong their lives that they might have the pleasure of seeing you again. We had heard that you were in Algiers, but from the look of your garments and those of all this company I realize that you have been miraculously liberated.'

" 'That,' replied the young man, 'is the truth, and there will be time to tell you all about it.'

"As soon as the guardsmen realized that we were Christian captives, they dismounted, and each then offered us his own horse to carry us to the city of Vélez Málaga, which was a league and a half from there. We told them where we had left the boat, and some of them went back to get it and take it to the town. Others mounted behind us on the cruppers, Zoraida going with the young man's uncle.

"The entire town came out to receive us, for someone had ridden ahead and told them of our coming. They were not the kind of folk to be astonished at seeing captives free or Moors held prisoner, being quite accustomed to such a sight. What they rather marveled at was Zoraida's beauty. Despite the fact that she was weary from the journey, she looked her loveliest at that moment, so joyful was she at finding herself on Christian soil with nothing to fear any longer. Happiness had put so much color into her face that—unless it can be that my love for her deceived me—I shall venture to say that there never was a more beautiful creature in all this world, none that I have ever seen, at any rate.

"We went directly to the church to thank God for his mercy; and as soon as Zoraida entered the portals, she remarked that there were faces there that resembled that of Lela Marien. We informed her that these were images of the Virgin, and the renegade to the best of his ability then went on to explain what their meaning was and how she might worship them as if each were the same Lela Marien who had spoken to her. Being possessed of a good, clear mind, she understood all this very readily. After that, they took us to various houses in the town, and the Christian who had come with us brought the renegade, Zoraida, and me to the home of his parents, who were people in moderately comfortable circumstances and who entertained us with as great a show of affection as they did their own son.

"We were in Vélez for six days, at the end of which time the renegade, having ascertained what he had to do, departed for Granada in order that, through the mediation of the Holy Inquisition, he might be restored to the sacred bosom of the Church. Each of the other liberated Christians went his own way, Zoraida and I being left with no other means than the crowns which the French captain had courteously given her. With them I purchased the beast on which she now rides; and with me serving her up to now as father and squire, not as husband, we are at present on our way to see if my own father is still alive or if one of my brothers has prospered to a greater extent than I.

"Seeing that Heaven has seen fit to give her to me as my companion, I can imagine no other fortune, however good, that might come to me which I should hold to be of greater worth. The patience with which she endures the hardships that poverty brings with it, and her desire to become a Christian, are such as to fill me with admiration and induce me to serve her all my life long. My happiness, however, at knowing that I am hers and she is mine is marred by the fact that I am at a loss where to find a nook in my own country in which to shelter her. For it may be that time and death have wrought such changes in the life and fortunes of my father and my brothers that, if they should not be there, I shall hardly find anyone who is acquainted with me.

"Gentle folk, that is all there is to my story. As to whether it be a pleasing and a curious one, that is for you in your good judgment to decide. For my own part, I may say that I should like to have told it more briefly, although, as it is, the fear of tiring you has led me to omit a number of incidents."

CHAPTER XLII. *Which treats of further happenings at the inn and other things worthy of being known.*

WITH these words the captive was silent, whereupon Don Fernando addressed him.

"Most assuredly, Captain," he said, "your manner of relating this extraordinary adventure has been equal to the novelty and unusual character of the subject matter. Your story is a strange one indeed, filled with incidents such as cause those who hear it to marvel greatly. We have enjoyed listening to it so much that we should be glad if you were to begin it all over again, even though tomorrow should find us still taken up with the same tale."

Cardenio and all the others then spoke in turn, offering to serve the captain in any way that they possibly could, and their words were so warm and sincere that he was quite touched by these expressions of good will. Don Fernando in particular told him that if he wished to come back with him, he would have the marquis, his brother, act as godfather at Zoraida's baptism, while on his own part he would be glad to fit him out so that he would be able to return to his own province with the dignity and outward appearance that befitted his rank. For all these generous offers the captain thanked them most courteously, although he would not accept any of them.

Night was now coming on, and just as darkness fell a coach accompanied by a number of men on horseback drew up at the inn; but when the newcomers asked for a lodging, the innkeeper's wife replied that there was not a hand's breadth of space in the hostelry that was not occupied.

"That being the case," said one of the mounted attendants who had ridden into the courtyard, "room must be found for his Lordship the judge."

Upon hearing this, the landlady was all aflutter. "Sir," she said, "the truth of the matter is that I have no beds; but if his Lordship carries one with him, as I have no doubt he does, let him come in, and welcome, for my husband and I will be glad to give up our room to accommodate him."

"That will do very well," said the squire.

At that moment there descended from the coach an individual whose garb plainly indicated the office and rank he held; for his long robe with the ruffled sleeves showed him to be a judge, as his servant had said. By his hand he led a damsel who looked to be around sixteen years of age. She was in traveling attire and was so beautiful, well bred, and elegant in appearance that all who beheld her were struck with admiration. Indeed, had they not seen Dorotea and Luscinda and Zoraida, who were now inside the inn, they would have regarded this maiden's loveliness as being of a sort that was hard to find.

Don Quixote was there when the judge and the young lady came in, and as soon as he saw them, he said to his Lordship, "Your Grace may enter and take your ease in this castle; for though it is but poor and lacking in conveniences, there is no poverty or inconvenience in the world that cannot provide accommodation for arms and letters, especially when arms and letters have beauty for their guide and leader, as letters, represented by your Grace, have in this charming damsel, for whom not only should castle gates be thrown wide open, but cliffs should rend themselves and mountains divide and bow low to give her welcome. Enter, your Grace, I say again, into this paradise; for here will be found stars and suns to keep company with the Heaven that your Grace brings with you. Here you will find the bravest of the brave and the fairest of the fair, both arms and beauty at their highest point of excellence."

The judge was astonished by this speech of Don Quixote's and stared at him very hard, being no less amazed by the knight's appearance than by his words; and he was still further surprised when he beheld Luscinda, Dorotea, and Zoraida, who, having heard of the arrival of the new guests and having been told by the landlady how beautiful the damsel was, had come out to see and welcome the young lady. Don Fernando, Cardenio, and the curate greeted the judge in a manner that was at once more intelligible and more urbane, while the beautiful ladies of the inn were doing the honors to his fair companion; but with it all, his Lordship was not a little bewildered as he made his entrance.

He could see that they were all persons of quality, but he was wholly at a loss to account for the figure, face, and bearing of Don Quixote. When the polite exchange of greetings was over and the question of accommodations had been discussed, it was finally decided that the previous arrangement was to stand and that all the women should sleep together in the garret already mentioned, while the men should remain outside as a kind of guard for them. The judge was well pleased that the damsel who accompanied him and who was his daughter was to be lodged with the other ladies, and she accepted with right good grace. And so, sharing between them what the landlord could provide and his Lordship had brought with him in the way of beds, they made out that night better than they expected.

The moment he laid eyes upon the judge, the captive's [1] heart had given a bound, for something told him that this was his own brother. He accordingly now inquired of one of the attendants what his Lordship's name was and from what province he came. The servant replied that his master was the licentiate Juan Pérez de Viedma and that he had heard it said that he was from a village in the mountains of León. This information together with what he had seen of the man was enough to convince the captive that the new arrival was indeed his brother, the one who upon their father's urging had chosen the profession of letters.[2] Very happy and excited, he called Don Fernando, Cardenio, and the curate to one side and explained the situation to them, assuring them that he was certain he was right.

The attendant had further stated that his Lordship was on his way to the Indies, having been appointed a judge of the High Tribunal [3] of Mexico. The damsel accompanying him was his daughter, whose mother had died in childbirth, leaving her husband very rich through the dowry that came to him with the girl. And the captive was now asking advice as to the best way in which to reveal his identity and how he might first find out if his brother, seeing him poor like this, would be ashamed of him or would receive him warmly and affectionately.

"Leave that to me," said the curate; "although, Señor Capitán, there is no reason to think that you will not be well received, as the worth and wisdom of which your brother's bearing shows him to be possessed do not indicate that he would be arrogant or unfeeling or would be incapable of making due allowance for the reverses of fortune."

"Nevertheless," said the captain, "I should like to make myself known to him, not suddenly, but in a roundabout way."

"You may take my word for it," said the curate, "that I shall handle it in such a manner that we shall all be satisfied."

At this point supper was served [4] and the entire company sat down at table, with the exception of the captive, and the ladies, who were supping by themselves in the other room. It was in the middle of the meal that the curate spoke to the judge.

"Your Lordship," he began, "I had a comrade in Constantinople, where I was a captive for a number of years, who bore the same name that your Grace does. He was one of the bravest soldiers and captains to be found in the whole of the Spanish infantry. But he was quite as unfortunate as he was valiant and daring."

"And what, sir, was the name of this captain?" the judge asked.

"His name," replied the curate, "was Ruy Pérez de Viedma, and he was a native of some village in the mountains of León. He told me a story about his father and his brothers which, if I had not known him to be so truthful a man, I should have taken to be one of those tales that old women tell by the fireside in wintertime. According to what he said, his father had divided his property among his three sons and had given them a certain piece of advice that was better than any Cato ever gave.[5] And I may say that the choice my comrade made of going to the wars proved to be so fortunate a one that within a few years, by reason of his worth and courage and with nothing to aid him save his own merits, he rose to be an infantry captain and was well on his way to becoming a corps commander. Fortune, however, did not favor him; for just as it appeared to smile upon him, he lost everything by losing his liberty on that glorious day when so many recovered their freedom, at the battle of Lepanto. I lost mine at the Goleta, and after each of us had gone through a series of adventures, we met in Constantinople. From there he went to Algiers, where one of the strangest things in the world happened to him."

The curate then went on and briefly related the story of Zoraida and the captive, to all of which the judge gave such a "hearing" as he never before had accorded to any case before him.[6] The narrator did not go beyond the point where the French had despoiled the Christians on the boat, but he dwelt upon the poverty and extreme want in which his comrade and the lovely Moor had found themselves, adding that he had not been able to learn how they had come out, whether they had reached Spain or had been carried off to France.[7]

The captain, who was standing a little to one side, was listening to all the curate said and at the same time was watching his brother's every movement. Perceiving that the story was ended, his Lordship heaved a deep sigh and his eyes filled with tears as he said, "O sir, if you only realized what news you have brought me and what it means to me. It means so much that, in spite of all my reasoned efforts at self-control, the tears start from my eyes! This brave captain of whom you speak is my elder brother, who, being hardier and endowed with loftier ambitions than those that I and my younger brother cherished, chose the honorable and worthy calling of arms, which was one of the three paths in life that our father pointed out to us, as your comrade told you in relating what seemed to you to be a fairy tale. I chose the profession of law, and God and my own faithful application have brought me to the position in which you see me now. My younger brother is in Peru and is so rich that, with what he has sent back to my father and to me, he has well repaid the portion of the estate that he took with him and in addition has furnished my father with the means of gratifying fully his generous inclinations, while I too have been enabled to pursue my studies, lead a more self-respecting life, and attain my present station.

"My father is still living, though he is dying [8] to hear from his eldest son and prays God unceasingly not to close his eyes in death until in life they have rested on him once again. At all of this I cannot but wonder, for my brother is extremely sensible and I cannot understand why, in all his troubles and afflictions or in prosperity, he should have neglected to let his father have some word of him; for if any of us had known where he was and the straits he was in, it would not have been necessary to wait for the miracle of the reed in order to obtain his ransom. But what distresses me now is the uncertainty as to whether those Frenchmen will have let him go free or whether they may have murdered him by way of covering up their robbery.

"As a result of it all, I shall continue my journey, not with that satisfaction with which I began it, but filled with melancholy and sadness. O my dear brother, if I but knew where you are now, I would go seek you and free you of your sufferings, however much of suffering it meant for me! Oh, to bring word to our aged father that you are still alive, even though you might be in the most deeply hidden dungeon of Barbary! For my father's riches, my own, and those of my brother would speedily get you out! O beauteous and generous-hearted Zoraida, if I could but repay you for what you have done for my brother! If I could but be present at the rebirth of your soul, and at your wedding, which would give us all so much pleasure!"

The judge went on talking in this manner, for he was deeply moved by the news of his brother which he had received, and all the listeners joined in showing the sympathy that they had for him in his sorrow.

And then the curate, seeing that he had achieved his purpose and fulfilled the captain's wish, arose from the table and went to the room where Zoraida was; for he had no desire to prolong their mood of sadness. Taking her by the hand, he came back, followed by Luscinda, Dorotea, and the judge's daughter. The captain was waiting to see what he was going to do, when the priest came over and with his other hand took that of Zoraida's husband-to-be; after which, with one of them on either side of him, he walked over to where the judge and the other gentlemen were.

"Dry your tears, my lord," he said, "and let your heart's desire be gratified; for you have here in front of you your worthy brother and your equally worthy sister-in-law. He whom you see here is Captain Viedma, and this is the lovely Moor who was so kind to him. The Frenchmen of whom I told you are responsible for their being in this poverty-stricken state, which will afford you an opportunity of exercising the generosity of heart that we know is yours."

The captain then ran over to embrace his brother, who placed both hands upon his chest and held him off in order that he might have a good look at him; but when he finally recognized him, he clasped him so tightly and shed so many tears of joy and affection that most of those present also wept. The words which the two brothers exchanged, the feelings they displayed, were such, I think, as could hardly be imagined, much less described. There and then, each gave the other an account of his life during the past years, providing the best of examples of what good friends two brothers can be. The judge embraced Zoraida, putting all that he had at her disposal, after which he had his daughter embrace her, and the beautiful Christian and the loveliest of Moors once more brought tears to the eyes of all.

Don Quixote stood there all the while observing these happenings most attentively but saying not a word, for he associated them all with his chimerical fancies that had to do with knight-errantry. It was agreed that the captain and Zoraida should return with his brother to Seville, where they would advise his father that he had been set free and found, so that the old man might be able to come to the wedding and baptism, since it was not possible for the judge to defer his journey, as he had just heard that within a month a fleet was leaving Seville for New Spain and it would be a very great inconvenience if he missed sailing with it.

In short, they were all happy and joyful over the fortunate outcome of the captive's adventure; and as the night was now nearly two-thirds gone, they decided to retire and get what rest they could. Don Quixote

offered to stand guard over the castle lest they be attacked by some
giant or wandering rogue of evil intent who might be covetous of the
great treasure of feminine beauty within these walls. Those who knew
him thanked him for this and gave the judge an account of the knight's
strange fancies, which afforded him considerable amusement.

Sancho Panza alone was fretting over their delay in retiring, but he
was the one that ended by making himself the most comfortable of all,
for he simply threw himself down on the trappings of his ass, though
he was to pay for this dearly a little later, as will be told further on.

The ladies, then, having retired to their room while the others ac·
commodated themselves as best they could, Don Quixote left the inn
and went outside to stand sentinel as he had promised to do. And so it
was that, shortly before daylight, the womenfolk heard a voice so
sweet and musical that they were compelled to pay heed to it, especially Dorotea, who was lying there awake while Doña Clara de
Viedma, the judge's daughter, slumbered by her side. None of them
could imagine who the person was who sang so well without the accompaniment of any instrument. At times the singing appeared to come
from the courtyard, at other times from the stable; and as they were
straining their ears and wondering about it, Cardenio came to the door
of their room.

"Those of you who are not asleep," he said, "should listen, and you
will hear the voice of a mule driver who sings most charmingly."

"We hear it, sir," replied Dorotea. And with this Cardenio went
away. She then gave all her attention to the song, the words of which
were the following.

CHAPTER XLIII. *In which is related the pleasing story of the muleteer, with other strange events that took place at the inn.*

> "Love's mariner am I,
> Sailing Love's own deep sea,
> Bereft of hope, forlorn;
> No haven waits for me.
>   And yet, my course I steer
> By a bright and gleaming star
> Palinurus¹ never sighted—
> I behold its light afar.
>   I know not whither it leads;
> No other thought have I
> Than to fix my soul's gaze upon it,
> Let all the rest go by.
>   A maiden reserve uncalled for,
> An unheard of modesty:
> These the dark clouds that cover
> My star of ecstasy.
>   O star so bright and gleaming,
> I tell thee with bated breath:
> To lose forever the sight of thee
> Would surely be my death." ²

As the singer reached this point, it occurred to Dorotea that it would not be right to let Clara sleep through it all and miss hearing so fine a voice, and so, shaking her from side to side, she roused her from her slumbers.

"Forgive me for waking you, my child," she said. "I do it because I wish you to hear the best singing that you have ever heard in all your life, it may be."

Clara awoke, sleepy-eyed, without understanding at first what Dorotea was saying to her. She accordingly asked her to repeat what she had said, which Dorotea did, and she was then all ears. She had barely heard a couple of lines, however, as the singer went on with his ballad, when she was seized with a strange trembling, as if she were suffering from a sudden and severe attack of quartan fever.

"Ah, my dearest lady!" she exclaimed as she clung to Dorotea, "why did you wake me? The greatest boon that fortune could bestow upon me would be to keep my eyes and ears closed so that I might not see nor hear that hapless musician!"

"What are you saying, child? Why, they tell me that the one who is doing that singing is a mule driver."

"No," replied Clara, "that is not so. He is lord of many places,[3] and the place that he so securely holds in my heart shall never be taken from him for all eternity, unless he would have it so."

Dorotea was greatly surprised at hearing the girl express such sentiments as these, which so belied her years.

"You speak, Señora Clara," she said, "in such a way that I cannot understand you. Tell me more, and explain what you mean by the places which that musician, whose voice so disturbs you, holds, including the place in your heart. But do not tell me anything just now; for I would not forego, by listening to you, the pleasure I derive from that song. I think he is beginning again, with new words and a new air."

"Let him, in Heaven's name," said Clara. And in order not to hear him, she put both hands to her ears, at which Dorotea was more astonished than ever. The latter, meanwhile, was listening closely as the singer continued:

> "*Thou sweetest hope I know,*
> *Through impassable thickets thou dost wend thy way,*
> *Straight on dost go*
> *To the end thou hast set thyself. Let not dismay*
> *Come near when thou dost see*
> *How Death walks every step along with thee.*
>   *The faint of heart ne'er gain*
> *The hard won victory, the triumph dear;*
> *The slothful ne'er attain*
> *That happiness they seek, nor those who fear*
> *To come to grips with Chance*
> *That they their fortune may thereby enhance.*
>   *Love sells his favors high,*
> *But that is only just. What better gold*
> *Could anyone supply*

Than that which bears his stamp of worth untold?
For it would surely seem,
What costs but little is of small esteem.
    A lover's persistency
At times achieves the impossible, and thus
In all consistency
I take Love's way, of all most arduous.
But still my heart is stout:
That I shall win my Heaven, I do not doubt." [4]

With this the song stopped and the girl once more began sobbing, all of which kindled her companion's desire to know what lay behind a song so sweet and tears so bitter. Dorotea thereupon asked her what it was she had been going to tell her a while ago. Being afraid that Luscinda would hear what she had to say, Clara then threw her arms about the older woman and clasped her tightly, putting her mouth close to the other's ear to avoid being overheard.

"That singer, dear lady," she began, "is a gentleman's son, a native of the kingdom of Aragon. His father, who is lord of two villages, has a house opposite my father's in the capital. And although we had curtains to our windows in winter and blinds in summer, this gentleman, who was engaged in pursuing his studies, in some way or other had a glimpse of me, whether it was in church or somewhere else I cannot say. The short of it is, he fell in love with me, and gave me to understand as much from the windows of his own house, with so many tears and gestures that I could not but believe him. I even fell in love with him, without knowing what it was he wanted of me. Among the signs that he made to me was one that consisted in clasping one of his hands in the other, thus indicating that he wished to marry me; and while I was very happy over this, being alone and motherless I had no one with whom to talk it over, and the result was, I let matters stand as they were and gave him but small encouragement. The most that I did, when my father and his were away from home, was to raise the curtain or the blind a little so that he might have a good look at me, which made him so happy that he acted as if he were going mad.

"The time came for my father to leave, and the young man learned of it, though not from me, since I had had no opportunity to tell him. He then fell ill, and I believe that it was due to grief; and so it was that, on the day we left, I was not even able to see him from afar and say good-by to him with my eyes. But after we had traveled for a couple of days, as we were entering a wayside tavern one day's journey from here, I saw him standing at the gateway of the inn clad as a muleteer and looking the part so thoroughly that, had I not carried an image of him in my heart, it would have been impossible to recognize him. But I did recognize him and was at once astonished and overjoyed, and he would occasionally steal a glance at me; but he always keeps out of my father's way when he crosses my path on the road or at the inns where we stop. Since I know who he is, I feel very bad when I reflect that for love of me he has come all this way on foot, and wherever he goes my eyes follow him.

"I do not know what his purpose is in coming, nor how he has been able to slip away from his father, who is extremely fond of him, since he has no other heir and his son is fully deserving of his affection, as your Grace will perceive when you have had a sight of him. Another thing I can tell you is that he himself makes up those songs that he sings, for I have heard it said that he is a very fine student and also a poet. What is more, every time that I see him and hear him sing, I tremble all over and am terribly upset, for I am afraid that my father will recognize him and learn of our love. I have never spoken a word to him in my life, yet I love him so dearly that I cannot live without him. And that, my dear lady, is all that I can tell you about this musician whose voice has given you so much pleasure, and which alone should be enough to assure you that he is no muleteer as you say, but the lord of hearts and towns, as I have told you."

"Say no more, Doña Clara." For Dorotea had interrupted her; and, giving her a thousand kisses, she repeated, "Say no more, but wait until tomorrow comes, when I hope to God I shall be able to arrange this affair of yours so that it may have the happy ending that so innocent a beginning deserves."

"Ah, Señora!" cried Doña Clara, "what end can I hope for when his father is so rich and important a personage that it would seem I could not even be a servant much less a wife to his son? And as to marrying without my own father's knowledge, I would not do that for anything in the world. All I ask is that this young man leave me and return home, and perhaps with not seeing him and the great distance between us, my pain will be somewhat alleviated, although I dare say this remedy that I suggest would not do me much good. I do not know how in the name of Satan this came about or how this love found its way into our hearts, seeing that we are both so young; for we are really about the same age, and I am not yet sixteen but shall be on next St. Michael's day, my father tells me."

Dorotea could not help smiling as she heard Doña Clara talking so much like a child.

"Let us get some rest, Señora," she said, "for if I am not mistaken, morning will soon be here, and then everything will be all right or I shall be greatly disappointed."

With this they settled down for what remained of the night, and all the inn was wrapped in silence, the only ones not asleep being the inn-keeper's daughter and Maritornes the slavey, who, familiar with Don Quixote's whimsies and knowing that he was outside clad in his armor and on horseback, standing guard, decided to play some kind of prac-tical joke on him, or at least to have a little amusement by listening to his nonsense. Now, as it happened, there was not a window in the house that looked out over the fields, but only an opening in a straw-loft through which they used to throw out the straw. At this opening the two demi-damsels now stationed themselves. They could see Don Quixote in the saddle and leaning on his pike as he every now and then heaved such deep and mournful sighs that it seemed each one would tear his heart out; and they could also hear him talking to himself in a gentle, soft, and loving tone of voice.

"O my lady Dulcinea del Toboso," he was saying, "supreme model and ultimate goal of all beauty and discretion, treasury of grace, de-pository of virtue; in short, the ideal of all that is worth while, honor-able, and delectable in this world! And what would thy Grace be doing now? Art thou perchance thinking of thy captive knight who, merely to serve thee and carry out thy wishes, hath seen fit to expose himself to all these perils? Give me some word of her, O luminary of the three faces! [5] It may be that out of envy of her face thou lookest upon her even now as she paces some gallery of her sumptuous palace, or as, lean-ing from a balcony, she considers how, without detriment to her modesty and exalted rank, she may assuage the torment that this griev-ing heart of mine endures for her sake. Does she think of the glory that should compensate me for my sufferings, the repose that should be mine after all my exertions, or, in brief, what life should be bestowed upon this my death, what reward I should have for my services?

"And thou, O Sun, who must even now be harnessing thy steeds that dawn may soon come and thou mayest emerge to behold my mis-tress, I beg thee when thou dost see her to greet her for me. But have a care that, when thou dost see and greet her, thou dost not kiss her face; for I shall be more jealous of thee than wast thou of that swift-footed and ungrateful one that caused thee so to run and sweat over the plains of Thessaly and the banks of the Peneus—I do not rightly recall just where it was that thou didst run in thine amorous and jealous rage on that occasion." [6]

Don Quixote had gone as far as this with his lugubrious monologue when the innkeeper's daughter began signaling to him.[7] "Good sir," she called to him softly, "come over here, if your Grace is pleased to do so."

At this signal and the sound of her voice, Don Quixote raised his head, and by the light of the moon, which was then shining in all its brightness, he perceived that someone was summoning him from the opening in the loft, which to him appeared to be a window—a window with a gilded grating of the kind that a magnificent castle ought to have, for such he took the inn to be. And then, instantly, it occurred to his insane imagination that, as on a previous occasion, the daughter of the lord of this castle, overcome with love of him, was seeking to make a conquest. With this thought in mind and desiring not to be discourteous or unfeeling, he turned Rocinante and rode up to the opening where the two lasses were.

"It is a pity, lovely lady," he said as soon as he caught sight of them, "that thou shouldst have let thy affections roam where they can never be requited in a manner that befits thy great worth and high estate; but for this thou shouldst not blame this wretched knight-errant, for love hath rendered it impossible for him to yield his will to any other than her whom, the moment he beheld her, he made the absolute mistress of his heart. Forgive me, then, good lady, and withdraw into thy chamber, and do not display thy feeling for me any further, that I may not once more have to show myself ungrateful. If there is any other way, outside of love itself, in which I may gratify that love thou hast for me, thou hast but to ask it and I swear to thee by that sweet and absent enemy of mine that I will incontinently do thy bidding, even though the boon thou seekest be a lock of Medusa's serpent hair or the rays of the sun itself stoppered in a vial."

"My mistress has need of nothing of that sort," said Maritornes at this point.

"Then, discreet matron," replied Don Quixote, "what is it that she needs?"

"Merely one of your shapely hands," said Maritornes, "that she may vent upon it the consuming passion that has brought her to this loop-hole, at so great a risk to her honor that, if her father were to hear of it, the least slice of her that he would take would be her ear."

"I should like to see him do that!" said the knight. "Let him beware if he does not want to meet the most disastrous end of any father in this world for having laid hands upon the delicate members of his lovesick daughter."

Having no doubt that Don Quixote would offer his hand as she had asked of him, Maritornes at once began thinking what she would do now; and, climbing down from the opening, she went out to the stable and took the halter of Sancho Panza's ass, returning with it quickly just as the knight was getting to his feet on Rocinante's saddle in order to be able to reach the gilded window-rail where, so he imagined, the brokenhearted damsel was.

"Lady," he was saying, "take this hand, or better, this avenger of the world's evildoers. The hand of no other woman has ever touched it, not even that of her who holds entire possession of my body. I extend it to thee, not that thou shouldst kiss it, but that thou mayest study the contexture of the sinews, the network of the muscles, the breadth and spaciousness of the veins, from which thou canst deduce how great must be the might of the arm that supports such a hand."

"That we shall soon see," said Maritornes. And, making a slip-knot in the halter, she put it over his wrist; then, getting down from the open-ing, she tied the other end to the bolt on the door of the loft.

"But it seems to me," said Don Quixote, as he felt the rope grating on his wrist, "that thy Grace is scraping rather than caressing my hand. Do not treat it so harshly, for it is not to blame for my unresponsive will. It is not right that thou shouldst wreak all thy vengeance upon so small a part, for remember that one who loves well should not avenge herself in a manner so ill."

But there was no one to hear these words; for as soon as Maritornes had attached the halter, she and the other girl left, fit to burst with laughing, and they left Don Quixote tied in such a way that it was impossible for him to free himself. As has been said, he was standing on Rocinante's back and his entire arm was through the opening while his wrist was fastened to the bolt on the door; and he was very much afraid that if Rocinante should swerve to one side or the other, he would remain hanging there. For this reason, he dared not make the slightest movement, although Rocinante stood so quietly and patiently that he might have been expected not to stir for a century to come.

Finally, seeing that he was caught in this manner and the ladies had departed, the knight began imagining that all this was a kind of enchantment, like the last time when, in this very castle, that enchanted Moor of a carter had given him such a mauling. He now cursed himself for his lack of judgment and sound sense in having ventured to set foot there a second time after having fared so badly before; for it was generally accepted by knights-errant that, when they had essayed an adventure and had not succeeded in it, this meant that it was not for them but for others, and there was no necessity of trying again. Meanwhile, he kept pulling on his arm to see if he could loosen it, but it was well tied and all his efforts were in vain. It is true, he pulled very gently, lest Rocinante should move; but, in any event, he was unable to seat himself in the saddle, and there was nothing for it but to remain standing or wrench his hand off.

Then it was that he longed for the sword of Amadis, against which no enchantment whatever could prevail. Then it was that he cursed his ill fortune, exaggerating the loss which the world would suffer while he was held there under a spell, for he had no doubt that this was the case. Then he remembered once again his beloved Dulcinea del Toboso, and then too it was that he called for his good squire, Sancho Panza, who, lying stretched out on the packsaddle of his ass and dead to the world, was unmindful even of the mother who bore him. Then it was that he called upon the wise Lirgandeo and Alquife [8] to aid him, beseeching also his good friend Urganda to succor him. And then, at last, morning found him so despairing and bewildered that he brayed like a bull; for he had no hope that with the coming of day his sufferings would be ended; rather, he believed that, as a result of the magician's spell, they would be eternal. This belief was strengthened in him when he observed that Rocinante never so much as stirred. And so he was convinced that he and his steed would have to remain there in that condition, without eating, drinking, or sleeping, until the evil influence of the stars had waned or until another, more skillful enchanter came to disenchant him.

In this, however, he was greatly deceived; for it was no sooner daylight than four fully accoutered horsemen, their firelocks across their saddlebows, drew up at the inn. Finding the gateway closed, they pounded lustily upon it; and when he saw and heard this, even in his present position, Don Quixote did not fail to play the sentinel.

"Knights," he said to them, "or squires, or whoever you may be, you have no right to knock at the gates of this castle; for you should know that at such an hour those inside are asleep, or are not in the habit of throwing open the fortress until the sun is fully up. Withdraw, then, and wait for day, and we shall then see whether or not it is fitting that they open for you."

"What the devil kind of fortress or castle is this," asked one of them, "that we are obliged to stand on such ceremony? If you are the innkeeper, have them open the gate for us. We are travelers who desire no more than to give some barley to our horses and go on, for we are in a hurry."

"Do I impress you, gentlemen, as having the appearance of an innkeeper?" was Don Quixote's answer.

"I do not know what appearance you have," replied the man. "But I know that you are talking nonsense when you refer to this inn as a castle."

"A castle it is," Don Quixote insisted, "and one of the best in all this province. And there are those within who have held a scepter in their hands and have worn a crown upon their heads."

"It would have been better the other way around," said the traveler: "the scepter on the head and the crown in the hand; but it may be there is some company of actors inside, for they very often have those crowns and scepters that you are talking about, and I cannot believe that in a small tavern like this, where you cannot hear a sound, any persons would be lodged who are entitled to them in real life."

"You know little of the ways of the world," replied Don Quixote, "seeing that you are ignorant of the things that happen in connection with knight-errantry."

The companions of the one who asked the questions were by this time tired of the conversation between him and the knight, and they again began pounding so furiously that the innkeeper and all the others awoke and the landlord arose to inquire who was knocking. At that moment one of the horsemen's mounts came up to smell Rocinante as the hack, sad and melancholy, with his ears drooping, stood there motionless, supporting his well-stretched master's weight; and being, when all is said, only flesh and blood though he appeared to be of wood, Rocinante could not but weaken and in turn smell the one that had come to court him. In doing this, he moved ever so little, and at once Don Quixote's feet slipped from the saddle and he would have fallen to the ground if his arm had not been held fast, a circumstance which caused him so much pain that he thought his wrist would be cut off or his arm torn from his body. For he was left hanging so near the ground that he could touch the earth with the tips of his toes, which was all the worse for him since, being conscious of how little he lacked of being able to plant his feet firmly, he wore himself out by stretching himself as far as he could in an attempt to accomplish this. He was like those who, suffering the strappado and placed in the position of touch-without-touching, merely add to their pain by the effort they make to stretch their bodies, in the vain hope that with a little more straining they will be able to find solid footing.[9]

CHAPTER XLIV. *In which are continued the unheard-of adventures at the inn.*

DON QUIXOTE by now was bawling so loudly that the landlord, very much alarmed, ran out and threw open the gate to see what the matter was, while those outside were equally curious. Maritornes also had been awakened by the shouts, and, suspecting what the cause of it all was, she hastened to the straw-loft without anyone's seeing her and unfastened the halter by which Don Quixote was supported, whereupon he at once dropped to the ground as the innkeeper and the travelers looked on. Coming up to him, they asked why he was shouting in that manner; but he without saying a word removed the rope from his wrist, rose to his feet, mounted Rocinante, braced his buckler on his arm, fixed his lance, and, retiring down the field for some little distance, came back at a half-gallop.

"If there be anyone," he cried, "who says that I deserved to have this spell put upon me, providing the Princess Micomicona grant me permission to do so, I hereby give him the lie; I defy him and challenge him to single combat."

The new arrivals were amazed by Don Quixote's words, but the landlord explained matters to them by telling them who the knight was, adding that they were to pay no attention to him as he was out of his mind. They then inquired of him if a lad about fifteen years of age and dressed as a muleteer had stopped at the inn, the description they gave being one that fitted Doña Clara's lover; to which he replied that there were so many guests that he had not noticed the lad they mentioned. One of the travelers, however, had caught sight of the judge's equipage.

"He is undoubtedly here," he said, "for this is the coach that he is following. One of us will stay at the gate and the others will go in and look for him; and it would be well, also, to ride around the side of the inn to make sure he does not get away over the stable-yard wall."

"We will see to that," was the reply.

Two of them then went in while one remained at the gate and a fourth man rode to the back. The landlord, meanwhile, was unable to guess why they were making so thorough a search, although he believed they must be after that youth whose description they had given him. The sun was now up, and for this reason as well as on account of the uproar that Don Quixote had created, they were all awake and stirring, especially Doña Clara and Dorotea, neither of whom had slept much that night, the one being too excited by the near-presence of her lover, while the other was eager to see what he looked like.

When he perceived that none of the four travelers was paying the slightest attention to him nor would answer his challenge, Don Quixote was ready to die with rage and spite; and had he found by the ordinances of chivalry that a knight-errant could lawfully assume and undertake any other enterprise than the one for which he had given his word of honor, until his pledge had been fulfilled, he would have attacked them all and compelled them to answer him whether they wished to or not. As it was, he felt that he could not do this until he should have restored Micomicona's kingdom to her. In the meanwhile, he must keep silent, remain quietly where he was, and wait to see what the result of the horsemen's search would be.

One of them had by this time come upon the youth sleeping beside a mule driver, not dreaming that anyone was looking for him, much less that his whereabouts had been discovered.

"Well, Don Luis," said the man, taking him by the arm, "that garb you wear is certainly becoming to you, and the bed in which you sleep goes well with the luxury in which your mother reared you."

Rubbing his sleep-filled eyes, the youth stared for a moment at the one who had hold of him. Then he recognized him as a servant of his father's, which gave him such a shock that for some while he was not able to say a word.

"There is nothing for you to do now, Don Luis," the man went on, "but to come along quietly and return home, unless your Grace desires to be the death of your father and my lord, for no less than that is to be expected as a result of his grief over your absence."

"But," said Don Luis, "how did my father know that I had taken this road and in this disguise?"

"It was a student," the servant replied, "to whom you had revealed your plans who told him of them, for he was moved to pity when he saw how your father was suffering. And so, my lord dispatched four of us to look for you, and we are all here now at your service, happier than you can imagine at the thought that we shall speedily return and restore you to the gaze of him who so longs to see you."

"That," said Don Luis, "shall be as I decide or as Heaven may ordain."

"What is there for Heaven to ordain or you to decide, beyond your consenting to come with us, since there is no other possible course?"

This entire conversation was heard by the mule driver at Don Luis' side; and, rising from where he lay, he went to inform Don Fernando, Cardenio, and the others of what had happened, for they were by now up and fully clothed. The muleteer told them how the man had addressed the lad as "Don" and what they had said to each other, with the servant urging the youth to return home while the latter was unwilling to do so. When they learned of this and recalled what a fine voice Heaven had bestowed upon the young fellow, they were all of them eager to know more about him, and even to help him should an attempt be made to use force with him. They accordingly hastened out to where the two stood talking and arguing.

Dorotea at this point came out of her room, followed by Doña Clara, who was trembling all over. Calling Cardenio to one side, she related to him briefly the story of the musician and his love, and he in turn described how the father's servants had come looking for the lad. He kept his voice low, but not so low that Clara failed to hear what he said, and she was so beside herself that she would have fallen in a faint had not her friend supported her. Cardenio then advised Dorotea to go back to the room, saying that he would take care of everything, and this they now did.

All four of the servants were inside the inn, standing around Don Luis and endeavoring to persuade him that, without a moment's hesitation, he should return to console his father. His answer was that he could by no means do this until he had settled a matter on which his life, his honor, and his soul depended. The servants thereupon grew more insistent, impressing upon him that on no account would they go back without him, and that they meant to take him whether he liked it or not.

"That you will not do," said Don Luis, "unless you take me back dead; although whatever way you took me, there would be no life in me."

By this time all those in the hostelry were gathered around listening to the argument, including Cardenio, Don Fernando and his companions, the judge, the curate, the barber, and Don Quixote; for the knight deemed there was no further necessity of his guarding the castle. Knowing the youth's story, Cardenio asked the men why it was they wished to take this boy away against his will.

"Because," one of them said, "we wish to restore life to his father who, on account of this young gentleman's absence, is on the verge of losing it."

At this Don Luis spoke up for himself. "There is no necessity," he told them, "of going into my affairs here. I am a free being and shall return if it pleases me; if it does not, none of you is going to compel me."

"Reason should compel your Grace," the man went on, "and if reason does not suffice to persuade you, it is sufficient to persuade us to do what we came to do and what it is our duty to do."

It was now the judge's turn. "Let us hear what is at the bottom of all this," he said.

"Sir," replied the man, who recognized him as a neighbor, "does not your Lordship recognize this young gentleman, your neighbor's son, who has thus run away from his father's house in a guise that so ill befits his station, as your Grace may see for yourself?"

The judge studied the youth more attentively and, when he saw who it was, gave him an embrace. "What child's play is this, Don Luis," he asked him. "What motive could have been powerful enough to prevail upon you to come clad in this manner that is so unbecoming to you?"

At this the lad's eyes filled with tears and he was unable to make any reply. The judge then requested the four servants to be calm, assuring them that it would all be settled properly; after which, taking Don Luis by the hand, he led him off to one side and inquired of him what the reason was for his presence there.

While these and other questions were being asked and answered, a loud shouting was heard at the gateway of the inn. What had happened was this: two guests who had been lodged there that night, observing that everyone was occupied with questioning the four travelers, had attempted to leave without paying what they owed; but the innkeeper, who was more attentive to his own business than to that of others, had waylaid them as they went out the gate and was demanding that they pay the score. His language to them was such that they were led to reply to him with their fists, and they were laying it on so heavily that the poor landlord had to cry out for help. His wife and daughter looked about for someone to aid him, but the only person whose attention was not taken up was Don Quixote; so the innkeeper's daughter addressed herself to him.

"Sir Knight," she said, "by the power that God has reposed in you, I beg you to succor my poor father. There are two wicked men out there who are beating him to a pulp."

"Lovely damsel," was the knight's measured and phlegmatic response, "your request is at this moment out of place, for I am prevented from entering upon any other adventure until I shall have fulfilled my word and brought to a conclusion the one upon which I am at present embarked. What I may do, however, in order to serve you is this: run and tell your father to sustain this combat as best he may and in no wise to allow himself to be vanquished while I go beg permission of the Princess Micomicona to succor him in his distress. If she but grant me that permission, you may rest assured that I will rescue him."

"Sinner that I am!" exclaimed Maritornes when she heard this, "before your Grace obtains the permission you speak of, my master will be in the other world."

"I beg you, lady," replied Don Quixote, "to give me leave to obtain it. Once I have the princess's consent, it will make little difference if your father is in the other world, for I will have him out of it in spite of all that the world in question can do; or, at the least, I will take such vengeance on those who have sent him there that you will be more than moderately satisfied."

Saying no more, he went over and dropped to his knees in front of Dorotea, imploring her in the language of knight-errantry that her Highness be pleased to grant him permission to aid and succor the castellan of that castle, who was in grave peril. The princess gave her consent readily enough, and he then, bracing his buckler and grasping his sword, ran out to the gate of the inn, where the two guests were still mistreating the landlord. But as he came up, he stopped short as if perplexed, although Maritornes and the landlady kept urging him to help their master and husband, asking him why he hesitated.

"If I hesitate," said Don Quixote, "it is for the reason that it is not permitted me to lay hand to sword against those of the rank of squire;

but go call my own squire, Sancho, for me, for it appertains to him to undertake this defense and vengeance."

All this took place at the gateway of the inn, where many most effective blows and punches were being exchanged to the great detriment of the landlord as the wrath of Maritornes and of the landlady and her daughter increased; for they were now in despair over Don Quixote's cowardice and the beating that was being administered to their master, husband, and father.

But let us leave him there; for there will surely be someone to succor him; or, if not, let him bear it and hold his peace who is rash enough to attempt more than his strength will warrant. Let us, rather, fall back some fifty paces and see what was Don Luis' reply to the judge. It will be recalled that we left them conversing to one side, with his Lordship inquiring of the lad why he had come on foot and so vilely clad. At this, the youth wrung his hands, indicating that some great sorrow lay upon his heart.

"My dear sir," he said, his tears flowing freely. "I can tell you no more than this: that from the moment Heaven willed, through our being neighbors, that I should lay eyes upon Doña Clara, your daughter and my lady, I have made her the mistress of my will, and if your will, O true father of mine, is no obstacle, I would make her my wife this very day. For her sake it was that I left my father's house, and for her I donned this attire in order to be able to follow her wherever she went, even as the arrow seeks the target or the mariner the north star. She knows nothing more of my desires than what she may have learned from seeing me, on a number of occasions and from afar, weeping for love of her. You, sir, are acquainted with the wealth and noble lineage of my parents, and you also know that I am their only heir. If these be sufficient qualifications to lead you to risk making me perfectly happy, then accept me at once as your son; for if my father, having other plans of his own, should not approve of this blessing I have sought out for myself, time still is more potent than the human will when it comes to undoing and altering things."

Having said this, the lovelorn boy was silent, and the judge upon hearing it was at once astonished, agreeably surprised, and filled with uncertainty. He was surprised by the skillful manner in which Don Luis had declared himself, and uncertain as to the course that he as a father should pursue in so sudden and unlooked-for a situation. The only answer he could make was that the young man should put his mind at rest for the present and meanwhile arrange with his servants not to take him back that day, in order that there might be time to consider what was the best for all concerned. Don Luis insisted upon kissing his hands and even bathed them with his tears, a sight that might have melted a heart of marble, to say nothing of that of the judge, whose worldly wisdom told him how advantageous such a marriage would be to his daughter, although, if it were possible, he preferred to see it consummated with the consent of Don Luis' father, who, as he knew, was looking for a titled match for his son.

By this time the two guests out at the gate had made their peace with the innkeeper and, owing to Don Quixote's mild and persuasive reasoning rather than to any threats on his part, they had paid all that was asked of them. As for Don Luis' servants, they were waiting for him to finish his conversation with the judge and make up his mind what he was going to do, when at that moment—so the devil, who never sleeps, would have it—the very same barber from whom Don Quixote had taken Mambrino's helmet and Sancho the trappings for his ass, came up to the inn. The said barber, as he was leading his beast out to the stable, chanced to catch sight of Sancho Panza, who was engaged in tinkering with his packsaddle, and the instant that he saw him he recognized him.

"Hah! Sir Thief," he cried, "I have you now! Give me back my basin and my packsaddle and all the other things you stole from me."

Sancho, being unexpectedly assailed in this manner and hearing himself called such names, with one hand laid hold of the packsaddle and with the other dealt the barber such a blow that he drenched his teeth in blood. The barber, however, did not for this reason let go his prize in the form of the packsaddle, but began shouting so loud that everybody in the place came running out to see what was the cause of all the uproar and the fighting.

"Here, in the name of the king's justice!" he screamed. "Not satisfied with taking my property, he wants to kill me, this robber, this highway bandit!"

"You lie," said Sancho. "I am not a bandit. My master Don Quixote won those spoils in honorable warfare."

The knight was standing by while this was going on and was greatly pleased to see how well his squire could both defend himself and take the offensive. From that time forth, he was to look upon him as a man of mettle, and he resolved in his heart that upon the first occasion that offered he would have him dubbed a knight, for he felt sure that the order of knighthood might worthily be bestowed upon him. The barber, meanwhile, was running on.

"Gentlemen," he was saying, "this packsaddle is mine, as surely as I owe it to God to die someday. I know it as well as if I had given birth to it. And there is my donkey in the stable; he will not let me lie. If you don't believe me, try it on him, and if it doesn't fit him perfectly, then I'm a rogue. What is more, the same day that he took the packsaddle he also robbed me of a brass basin which I had not yet broken in and which was worth all of a crown."

At this point Don Quixote, unable to contain himself any longer, stepped between the two and parted them, and then, picking up the packsaddle, he placed it upon the ground where all could see it that it might lie there until the truth was established.

"In order," he said, "that your Worships may behold plainly and clearly the error into which this worthy squire has fallen, you have but to observe that he calls a basin that which was, is, and shall be Mambrino's helmet, a trophy won by me in honorable warfare and of which I took lawful and rightful possession! As for the packsaddle, I have nothing to do with that. All I can say is that my squire, Sancho, begged permission of me to strip the mount belonging to this conquered coward of its trappings. To this I consented, and he did so. As to how those trappings came to be converted into a packsaddle, I can give no explanation other than the usual one: namely, that such transformations frequently occur in connection with the practice of chivalry. And by way of confirming all this, run, Sancho my lad, and bring me that helmet which this good man says is a basin."

"Good Lord!" exclaimed Sancho, "if that is all the proof we have that what your Grace says is true, then that basin is just as much Malino's [1] helmet as this good man's trappings are a packsaddle."

"Do what I command you," said Don Quixote; "for surely everything in this castle cannot be controlled by enchantments."

Sancho went for the basin and returned with it, and as soon as Don Quixote saw it he took it up in his hands.

"Your Worships," he said, "can see what cheek this squire has to say that this is a basin and not the helmet of which I have told you. I swear by the calling of knighthood which I follow that this is the same one I took from him and that I have neither added anything to nor subtracted anything from it."

"There can be no doubt of that," remarked Sancho at this point;

"for from the time my master won it until the present he has fought but one battle in it, and that was when he freed those poor unfortunate ones that were going along in chains; and if it had not been for this basin-helmet, it would have gone hard with him that time, for there were certainly enough stones thrown."

CHAPTER XLV. *In which the dispute over Mambrino's helmet and the packsaddle is finally settled, with other events that in all truth occurred.*

"WELL, gentlemen," said the barber, "and what do your Worships think of that which these fine fellows have to say, who still insist that this is not a basin but a helmet?"

"And if anyone states the contrary," maintained Don Quixote, "I will have him know that he lies, if he be a knight, and if he be a squire, that he lies a thousand times."

Our own barber, who had witnessed all this and who was well acquainted with Don Quixote's fancies, now decided to fall in with them and carry the joke a little further so that they might all have a good laugh.

"Master barber," he said, addressing the other one, "or whoever you may be, I may inform you that I also am of your profession and have held a license for more than twenty years, being quite familiar with each and every tool that a barber uses. And in my youth I was a soldier for some little while, and I likewise know what a helmet is, and a morion, and a closed helmet, along with other things having to do with a soldier's life. And I can tell you—standing always to be corrected by those of better judgment—that the piece we have before us here, which that worthy gentleman holds in his hands, is as far from being a barber's basin as white is from black or truth from falsehood; and I further assert that it is a helmet, though not a whole one."

"No, certainly not," agreed Don Quixote, "for half of it is missing, that is to say, the beaver."

"That is right," said the curate, who had already divined the intentions of his friend the barber.

Cardenio and Don Fernando and his companions confirmed this; and even the judge, had he not been so preoccupied with Don Luis' affair, would have helped carry on the jest, but, as it was, the weighty matters that he had on his mind prevented him from giving his attention to such trifles.

"God help me!" cried the barber of whom they were making sport. "Is it possible that so many worthy folk can say that this is not a basin but a helmet? It is enough to astonish an entire university, however learned it may be. But enough; if this basin is a helmet, then this saddle-bag must be a horse's trappings, as this gentleman has just stated."

"It looks to me like a saddlebag," Don Quixote admitted, "but as I have said, it is something that does not concern me."

"As to whether it be a saddlebag or a horse's trappings," said the curate, "Don Quixote has but to give us his opinion, for in matters pertaining to chivalry, I and all these gentlemen bow to him."

"In God's name, my good folk," said Don Quixote, "so many strange things have happened in this castle on the two occasions that I have tarried here that I should not venture to give a positive reply to a question regarding anything that is in it, for it is my belief that all that takes place within its confines is the result of magic. The first time that I was here, there was an enchanted Moor who gave me a great deal of trouble, while Sancho did not make out any too well with some of his followers. And then, last night, I was strung up by this arm for nearly two hours without knowing how or why I came to be in such straits. And so, in a matter as far from clear as the present one, if I were to undertake to give an opinion, I should run the risk of rendering a rash decision. As to the charge that this is a basin and not a helmet, I have already answered that, but when it comes to declaring whether that is a saddlebag or a horse's trappings, I shall not venture to make any definite statement but shall leave it to your Worships' own good judgment. It may be that, inasmuch as you have not been dubbed knights as I have been, your Worships will not be subject to the enchantments of this place and, accordingly, your judgment being unimpaired, will be able to form an impression of things in this castle as they really and truly are and not as they appear to me to be."

"There is no doubt," said Don Fernando in reply to this, "that Don Quixote has put the case very well and that the decision rests with us; and in order that we may proceed upon firm ground, I will take the secret votes of these gentlemen and will announce the result plainly and fully."

To those acquainted with Don Quixote's mad whims, all this was very amusing indeed, but to the rest it seemed utter nonsense. This was especially true of Don Luis' four servants, and of their master as well, so far as that was concerned; besides whom there were three other travelers who had just arrived at the inn and who had the appearance of being patrolmen of the Holy Brotherhood, as in fact they were. The one, however, who was the most desperately bewildered of all was the barber, whose basin, there in front of his eyes, had turned into Mambrino's helmet, and whose packsaddle, also, he had not the slightest doubt, was due to turn into the rich caparison of a steed. The others, meanwhile, were laughing heartily as Don Fernando went around collecting the votes, whispering in the ear of each and asking him to give his private opinion as to whether the treasure over which there was so much dispute was a packsaddle or equine trappings.

Having obtained the votes of all those who knew Don Quixote, he turned to the barber and said, "The truth of the matter is, my good man, I am tired of gathering all these opinions; for there is not a one to whom I have put the question who has not assured me that it is nonsense to say that this is the packsaddle of an ass, when it is plain to be seen that it is the caparison of a horse and of a thoroughbred horse at that. And so there is nothing for you to do but yield, since in spite of you and your ass it is in fact a horse's trappings, and you have presented and proved your case very badly."

"May I forfeit my interest in Heaven!" cried the poor barber,[1] "if your Worships are not all mistaken. As my soul must appear before God, so does this appear to me to be a saddlebag; but 'laws go—'[2] I say no more; and I am not drunk, for I am fasting this morning—unless it be from sin."

These stupid remarks on the part of the barber aroused no less laughter than did Don Quixote's foolish talk; and it was now the knight's turn.

"There is nothing more to be done here," he announced, "except for each to take that which is his, and may St. Peter bless him to whom God has given it."

One of Don Luis' servants was the next to speak. "Unless this is a deliberate joke," he said, "I cannot believe that men of such good sense as all of those present are, or appear to be, would be so bold as to state and maintain that this is not a basin nor that a packsaddle; but inasmuch as I perceive that they do state and maintain it, I cannot but believe that there is some mystery behind their insistence upon something that is so contrary to what truth and experience teaches. For I swear"—and swear he did, a good round oath—"that all the people now living in the world will never convince me that this is not a barber's basin, and that, the packsaddle of an ass."

"It might be a she-ass," remarked the curate.

"It's all the same," said the servant. "That's not the point. The point is whether this is or, as your Graces say, is not a packsaddle."

Hearing this, one of the troopers who had come in and had been listening to the argument cried out angrily, "That is as much a pack-saddle as my father is my father, and he who says anything else must be drunk."

"You lie like a peasant knave!" replied Don Quixote. And, raising his pike, which he never let out of his hands, he aimed such a blow at the trooper's head that if the officer had not dodged, it would have left him stretched out on the ground. The pike as it struck the ground was shattered to bits; whereupon the other officers, seeing their companion assaulted in this manner, cried out for help in the name of the Holy Brotherhood. The innkeeper, who was one of the band, at once ran to get his staff of office and his sword and, returning, took his place alongside his comrades. Don Luis' servants surrounded their master that he might not escape amid the excitement; and the barber, perceiving that the household was turned upside down, once more seized his pack-saddle as Sancho did the same.

Drawing his sword, Don Quixote attacked the officers, while Don Luis cried to his servants to release him and go to the aid of the knight and of Cardenio and Don Fernando, both of whom were lending their support. The curate shouted, the landlady screamed, her daughter wailed, Maritornes wept, Dorotea was dumfounded, Luscinda terrified, and Doña Clara ready to faint. The barber cudgeled Sancho, and Sancho mauled the barber. Don Luis, when one of his servants seized his arm to keep him from running away, gave the fellow a punch that bloodied his mouth, and the judge came to the lad's defense. Don Fernando had a trooper down and was kicking him vigorously, and the innkeeper was again raising his voice to call for help for the Holy Brotherhood. In short, the entire hostelry was filled with shouts, cries, screams, with tumult, terror, and confusion, with sword slashes, fisticuffs, cudgelings, kickings, bloodshed, and mishaps of every sort. And in the midst of all this hubbub and labyrinthine chaos, Don Quixote came to imagine that he had been plunged headlong into the discord of Agramante's camp.[3]

"Hold, all of you!" he suddenly cried in a voice that rocked the inn like thunder. "Sheathe your swords, be calm, and hear me as you value your lives!"

At this mighty sound they all stopped short.

"Did I not tell you, gentlemen," he went on, "that this castle was enchanted and that it must be inhabited by some legion of devils? In confirmation of which, I would have you note how the strife that marked the camp of Agramante has been transferred and repeated here in front of your very eyes. Look you how here they fight for the sword, there for the horse, over there for the eagle, and there for the helmet. We are all engaged in fighting one another without knowing why. Come, then, your Lordship the judge and your Reverence the curate; let one of you take the part of King Agramante and the other that of King Sobrino, and make peace between us. For it is a very great shame for so many persons of high rank as are gathered here to be killing one another over causes so trifling."

The officers of the Brotherhood, who did not understand what Don Quixote was talking about, but who did know that they were being mishandled by Don Fernando, Cardenio, and their companions, were of no mind to calm themselves. The barber, however, was; for in the course of the fray both his beard and his packsaddle had suffered considerably. As for Sancho, he obeyed, as a good servant does, his master's slightest command, while Don Luis' four men likewise were quiet, seeing how little they had gained by not being so. The innkeeper alone was insisting that he had to punish the insolence of that madman who was all the time throwing his place into an uproar. But at last the tumult died down, the packsaddle remained a caparison and the basin a helmet until the Day of Judgment, and the inn was still a castle in Don Quixote's imagination.

When order had finally been restored and all of them, upon the persuasion of the curate and the judge, had become friends once more, Don Luis' servants began insisting that he go with them at once. While the lad went off to one side to discuss the matter with them, the judge took counsel with Fernando, Cardenio, and the curate as to what was to be done in the case, informing them of what Don Luis had told him. In the end, it was agreed that Fernando should reveal his identity to the men and say that it was his pleasure that their master should come with him to Andalusia, where his brother the marquis would show him the honor that was due to one of his rank; for it was plain to be seen that Don Luis had no intention of returning to his father just now, even though they hacked him to bits. Accordingly, when the four of them learned who Don Fernando was and saw how their master felt about it, they decided that three of their number should go back to inform the lad's father of how matters stood, while the fourth should remain to wait upon Don Luis, with the understanding that he was not to leave him until they returned or until it was known what the father's orders were.

In this manner, then, through the prestige of Agramante and the wisdom of King Sobrino, all the fighting at cross-purposes was finally quelled; but with this, the enemy of peace and concord, seeing himself thus despised and made sport of, and perceiving how little he had gained by setting them all against one another, resolved to try his hand once again by stirring up more strife and tumult.

As it happened, the officers of the Brotherhood had quieted down upon learning the rank of those with whom they were fighting and had been glad enough to retire from the fray, since it seemed to them that, whatever the outcome, they were bound to get the worst of it. One of them, however, the one who had been beaten and trampled by Don Fernando, chanced to remember that among the warrants he carried for the arrest of certain offenders was a writ for Don Quixote, whom the Holy Brotherhood had been instructed to apprehend on the charge of having freed the galley slaves, just as Sancho had rightly feared. An idea having come to him now, he wished to satisfy himself as to whether the knight answered the description that he had of him; and, taking a parchment out of his bosom, he found the document he was looking for and then began reading it slowly (for he was not a good reader), glancing up at every word to see if Don Quixote's features corresponded with those set down in the writ. Deciding that this was undoubtedly his man, he then took the parchment in his left hand and with his right seized Don Quixote by the collar so forcefully that he nearly choked him.

"Help for the Holy Brotherhood!" he cried in a loud voice. "And in order that you may see that I ask it in earnest, you have but to read this warrant where it is set forth that this highwayman is to be arrested."

The curate took the warrant and saw that what the officer said was true and that the description did indeed fit Don Quixote. But the knight, finding himself thus manhandled by this knavish boor, grew exceedingly angry and, with every bone in his body creaking, he seized the officer's throat with all the strength he could muster and would have choked the life out of him if the other troopers had not come to their comrade's rescue. The landlord, who was bound to render help to other members of the fraternity, now came running up, while his wife, believing her husband was again about to become involved in a fight, raised her voice and began screaming, in which she was at once joined by Maritornes and her daughter as all three of them called on Heaven and the others present to lend their aid.

"Good Lord!" cried Sancho, when he saw what was happening, "it is true what my master says about this castle being enchanted, for it is impossible to live an hour in peace here."

Don Fernando then separated the patrolman and Don Quixote, each of them being glad enough to have the other's firm grip released, on his jacket collar in the one case and on his throat in the other instance. The officers did not, however, for this reason give up their demand for the knight's arrest but insisted that the others help bind and deliver him into the hands of the law and thereby render a service to their king and to the Holy Brotherhood, in whose name they once more sought aid and assistance in effecting the capture of this highway bandit.

Don Quixote smiled as he heard these words. When he spoke, it was very calmly. "Come, now," he said, "you vile and lowborn wretches, do you call him a highwayman who gives freedom to those in chains, succors those who are in distress, lifts up the fallen, and brings aid to the needy? Ah, infamous rabble, by reason of your low and filthy minds you do not deserve that Heaven should reveal to you the true worth of knight-errantry and your own sin and ignorance when you fail to reverence the shadow, not to speak of the presence, of any knight-errant whatsoever! Come, come, you are a band of robbers, not of officers, footpads of the highway with the license of the Holy Brotherhood. Tell me, who was the ignorant one who signed that warrant for the arrest of such a knight as I am? Who is so ignorant as not to know that knights-errant are beyond all jurisdiction, their only law their swords, while their charter is their mettle and their will is their decrees?

"Who, I ask it again, is the stupid one who does not know that there are no letters-patent of nobility that confer such privileges and exemptions as those that a knight-errant acquires the day he is dubbed a knight and devotes himself to the rigorous duties of his calling? When did such a knight ever pay poll-tax, excise, queen's pattens, king's levies, toll, or ferry? What tailor ever took payment for the clothes he made for him? What castellan who received him in his castle ever made him pay his score? What king would not seat him at his board? What damsel but did love him, being ready to yield herself wholly to his will and pleasure? And, finally, what knight-errant was there ever, or ever will be in this world, without the mettle to deal singlehanded four hundred sturdy blows to any four hundred officers of the Holy Brotherhood that come his way?"

CHAPTER XLVI. *Wherein is concluded the notable adventure of the troopers, together with an account of the great ferocity of our good knight, Don Quixote.*

EVEN as Don Quixote spoke, the curate was endeavoring to convince the officers that the knight was not in his right mind, as they should be able to see from what he said and did, and that, accordingly, they ought to let the matter drop, since even though they did arrest him and take him away, they would only have to turn him loose again as being a madman. To which the one who held the warrant replied that it was not for him to judge Don Quixote's sanity but rather to carry out the orders of his superior, adding that once he had made the arrest, they might let him go three hundred times over if they chose.

"Nevertheless," said the curate, "for this once you are not going to take him, nor will he permit himself to be taken unless I miss my guess."

The short of it is, the curate was so very persuasive, and Don Quixote so very mad in his actions, that the troopers would have been even madder than he was had they not recognized his want of wit. And so they thought it best to allow themselves to be pacified and even to act as peacemakers between the barber and Sancho Panza, who were still engaged in a heated quarrel. As the representatives of the law they proceeded to arbitrate the dispute and did it in such a manner that both parties were, if not wholly, at least somewhat satisfied; for they exchanged the packsaddles but not the girths nor the headstalls. As for Mambrino's helmet, the curate quietly, and without Don Quixote's knowledge, gave the barber eight reales for it, obtaining from him a receipt with the understanding that he was to make no more mistaken demands, for the present or for all time to come, Amen.

These two disputes, which were the most important ones, having been settled, it remained for the three of Don Luis' servants to consent to take their departure while the fourth remained to accompany his master wherever Don Fernando might conduct him. And now that good luck and better fortune had begun to shatter lances and remove obstacles in favor of the lovers and the brave ones of the inn, fate appeared bent upon bringing everything to a happy conclusion; for the servants proved amenable to all that Don Luis asked of them, which gave Doña Clara so much satisfaction that none could look upon her face without being aware of the joy that was in her heart.

As for Zoraida, although she did not thoroughly comprehend all the happenings she witnessed, she nonetheless became sad or joyful to fit the mood of each of the others, and especially that of her beloved Spaniard on whom her eyes and heart were ever fixed. The landlord, in the meanwhile, had not failed to observe [1] the gift which the curate had made to the barber by way of recompense, and he now asked Don Quixote to pay for his lodging and also to reimburse him for the wine skins and the wine that had been spilled, swearing that neither Rocinante nor Sancho's ass [2] would leave the place until he had had the last penny that was due him. The curate, however, set everything to rights, and Don Fernando paid what was owing, with the judge very kindly offering to do the same. In this fashion peace was made between them all and quiet reigned, the inn no longer presenting the discordant aspect of Agramante's camp, as Don Quixote had put it, but rather suggesting the calm and tranquillity of the time of Octavianus.[3] And for this, all were agreed that thanks were to be given to the curate for his great eloquence and good will and to Don Fernando for his incomparable liberality.

Finding himself at last free and disembarrassed of all these disputes, those of his squire as well as his own, Don Quixote reflected that it would be a good thing to continue with the journey he had begun and bring to a conclusion the great adventure for which he had been called and chosen. With this firm resolve, he went and knelt before Dorotea, who would not permit him to say a word until he had risen, which he, to comply with her wishes, then did.

"Lovely lady," he said, "it is a common proverb that diligence is the mother of good fortune, and experience has shown in many and grave instances how the faithful application of the one engaged in it may bring to a successful close a doubtful undertaking. But in no case is this truth more apparent than in war, where swiftness and decision forestall the plans of the enemy and carry off the victory before he has had a chance to put himself upon the defensive. All this I say to you, O highborn and highly esteemed lady, for the reason that our stay in this castle appears to me to be a profitless one and may even result in very great harm to us as we shall someday discover. For who knows but that your enemy, the giant, through hidden spies who are ever at work, has already learned that I am coming to destroy him and is already fortifying himself in some inexpugnable castle or fortress against which all my efforts and the might of my tireless arm will avail me little? And so, my lady, let us with a show of diligence on our own part anticipate his designs by setting out at once in quest of that good fortune which your Highness desires and is only prevented from enjoying by my delay in confronting your foe."

The knight said no more but waited very composedly for the beauteous infanta's response; and she, with highbred manner that suited Don Quixote's own speech and bearing, thereupon spoke as follows:

"I thank you, Sir Knight, for the eagerness you have shown to aid me in my distress, as appertains to the calling of one whose duty it is to succor the orphan and the needy; and I pray to Heaven that your and my desire be fulfilled, so that you may see that there are women in this world who are capable of gratitude. As to what you say concerning our departure, let it be at once, for I have no will other than yours. Dispose of me as you may wish and deem best; for she who once has placed in your hands the defense of her person and the restoration of her royal holdings should not desire anything that is contrary to what you in your wisdom may ordain."

"Then let it be in the hands of God," said Don Quixote; "for when a lady [4] humbles herself to me, I would not lose the opportunity to raise her up and set her on her ancestral throne. Let us depart at once; the danger that lies in delay lends spurs to my eagerness to take the road. And seeing that Heaven hath not created nor Hell seen anyone who could frighten or make a coward of me, saddle Rocinante, Sancho, and harness your ass and the queen's palfrey, and let us bid farewell to the castellan and these gentlefolk and go hence immediately."

Sancho, who was taking all this in, wagged his head from side to side. "Ah, master, master," he said, "there's more mischief in the little village than you hear talked of,[5] begging the pardon of all good folks."

"What mischief could there be, you bumpkin, in any village or in all the cities of the world that could possibly harm my good name?"

"If your Grace is going to be angry," replied Sancho, "I shall keep still and leave unsaid that which I feel obliged to say and which a good servant ought to say to his master."

"Say whatever you like," Don Quixote told him, "for your words do not frighten me. When you are afraid, you are being yourself, and when I am not afraid, I am being the person that I am."

"That," said Sancho, "is not what I am talking about. I merely meant to tell you that I know it to be a fact that this lady who claims to be queen of the great kingdom of Micomicon is no more a queen than my mother is; for if she was what she says, she would not be rubbing noses with a certain one who is here, every time you turn your head, and behind every door."

Dorotea's face turned red at Sancho's words; for it was true that her husband, Don Fernando, when the others were not looking, had claimed with his lips a part of the reward that his affection merited, and Sancho, happening to espy them, had thought that such free and easy manners were more becoming in a courtesan than in a great and mighty queen. As a result, she did not know what reply to make, but let him run on.

"I tell you this, my master," he was saying, "for a very good reason. If after we have roamed the highways and the byways and spent bad days and worse nights, the one who is having his sport here in this inn is to come and gather the fruit of our labors, then I do not see why I should be in any hurry to saddle Rocinante, put the packsaddle on the ass, and get the palfrey ready; for it would be better if we stayed here and let every wench mind her spinning [6] while we go to dinner."

Heaven help me, what a rage was Don Quixote's when he heard these disrespectful words from his squire! So great was it that his eyes darted fire, as with stuttering, stammering tongue he turned on Sancho.

"O knavish lout!" he cried, "O villainous, insolent, ignorant, foul-mouthed, loose-tongued backbiter and slanderer! How dare you utter such words in my presence and that of these ladies? How dare you let such immodest and shameless thoughts enter that muddled head of yours? Go from my presence, O monstrous deformity of nature, depository of lies, storehouse of deceits, granary of villainies, inventor of iniquities, publisher of absurdities, and enemy of that respect that is due to royal personages! Begone and do not appear before me again under pain of my wrath!"

As he said this, Don Quixote arched his brows, puffed out his cheeks, glared all around him, and stamped on the ground with his right foot as hard as he could as a manifestation of the pent-up rage within him. Sancho was so intimidated and terrified by the knight's furious words and bearing that he would have been glad if at that instant the earth had opened beneath his feet and swallowed him up. He did not know what to do and was about to turn his back and leave the presence of his irate master when the clever-minded Dorotea, who by this time understood very well Don Quixote's whims, took a hand in the matter.

"Sir Knight of the Mournful Countenance," she began by way of appeasing his anger, "be not wroth at the foolish things your squire has just said. It may be that he has some reason for saying them, for his good sense and Christian conscience are such that he is not to be suspected of bearing false witness against anyone. And hence we are to believe, and indeed there is no doubt about it, since everything in this castle happens by way of enchantment as you yourself have stated, Sir Knight —we are to believe that Sancho must have been led by diabolic means to see that which he says he beheld and which is so great an offense to my honor."

"I swear by almighty God!" exclaimed Don Quixote at this point, "that your Highness has hit upon it, and that some evil vision must have appeared before this sinner of a Sancho that caused him to see what it would have been impossible to behold through any other means than those of magic; for I am well acquainted with the poor fellow's simplicity and goodheartedness, and I know that he would not willingly be guilty of slander."

"So it is and so it shall be," said Don Fernando; "and for that reason, Sir Don Quixote, your Grace ought to pardon him and restore him to the bosom of your favor, *sicut erat in principio*—as he was before such visions as these had deprived him of his senses."

The knight agreed to this, and the curate went in search of Sancho, who came back very humbly and, falling on his knees, asked for his master's hand to kiss, a request that was granted him.

"And now, Sancho my son," said Don Quixote as he gave him his blessing, "you will realize that it is true what I have told you so many times, that everything in this castle is under a magic spell."

"I can well believe it," said Sancho, "that is, everything except that business with the blanket, which happened in the ordinary way."

"Do not think that," said Don Quixote, "for if such were the case,

I should have avenged you, and should do so even now; but it was not possible then, and it is not possible now, to exact any vengeance for the wrong that was done you."

They all immediately wanted to know what this affair of the blanket was, and the innkeeper gave them the story in all its details, describing how Sancho had gone flying up in the air, at which they laughed not a little. The victim of the blanketing would have been quite as angry as they were amused, if Don Quixote had not once more assured him that it was all magic. His simple-mindedness, however, never reached the point where he could be brought to believe that it was not an established fact and the purest, unadulterated truth that he had indeed been tossed in a blanket by flesh-and-blood beings rather than by phantoms that he had dreamed or conjured up in his imagination as his master believed and maintained.

Two days had now gone by since all this illustrious company was gathered in the inn, and it seemed to them all that it was high time to be on their way. It was accordingly agreed that, without putting Dorotea and Don Fernando to the trouble of accompanying Don Quixote to his native village, under pretext of liberating the Queen Micomicona, the curate and the barber instead should take the knight with them as they had suggested, and once they had got him safely home, they would see what could be done about curing his madness. With this object in view, they proceeded to arrange with an ox-cart driver who chanced to be passing that way to bear their friend off in the following manner: first, they constructed a kind of cage with wooden bars, capable of holding him comfortably; after which, Don Fernando and his companions, along with Don Luis' servants, the troopers, and the landlord, all of them acting under the curate's direction, covered their faces and disguised themselves in one fashion or another so that Don Quixote would not recognize them as his acquaintances of the inn.

Having done this, they very quietly entered the room where he lay sleeping and resting from his recent frays, wholly unsuspecting of anything of this sort. Going up to him, they seized him firmly and bound him hand and foot, so that when he awoke with a start, he was unable to move or do anything except marvel at finding himself surrounded by so many strange faces. As a result, his disordered mind at once began to fancy that all these figures were phantoms of that enchanted castle and that he himself, without a doubt, was under a magic spell, seeing that he could not move nor defend himself. All of which was just as the curate, the originator of this scheme, had planned it.

Sancho alone of all those present was at once in his right mind and proper character, and while he was near to being as mad as his master, he did not fail to recognize these disguised figures; but he did not dare open his mouth until he saw what the outcome of this assault and capture would be. As for Don Quixote, he said not a word, for he too was waiting to see what was going to happen to him further. What happened was: they took him to the cage and shut him in it, nailing the bars so firmly that they could not easily be broken down.

As they lifted him on their shoulders and bore him from the room, there was heard an awe-inspiring voice—as much so as the barber (not he of the packsaddle but the other one) could make it.

"O Knight of the Mournful Countenance, be not grieved by the prison in which thou goest, for it is a fitting thing in order that thou mayest the sooner bring to a conclusion the adventure to which thy great courage hath impelled thee. That shall be when the raging Manchegan lion [7] and the white Tobosan dove shall have been made one, after they shall have bowed their proud necks to the gentle yoke of matrimony. And from this mating, of a kind that never was before, shall come forth into the light of this world brave whelps which shall emulate the ravening claws of their valiant sire. And this shall be ere the pursuer of the fleeing nymph in his swift and natural course shall twice have visited the luminous signs.

"And thou, O noblest and most obedient squire that ever girded on a sword, wore a beard on his face, or had a nose to smell with! be thou not dismayed nor unhappy at thus beholding the flower of knight-errantry borne away in front of your very eyes; for soon, if it be pleasing to Him who fashioned this world, thou shalt see thyself raised to so sublime a height that thou shalt not know thyself, nor shalt thou be defrauded of all the promises which thy good master hath made thee. And be assured on the part of the wise Mentironiana [8] that thou shalt be paid thy wages, as thou shalt see in due course. Do thou, then, continue to follow in the footsteps of this valiant and enchanted knight; for it behooves thee to go whither both of you are bound. It is not permitted me to say more; and so, may God be with thee, for I now return to the place that I well know."

As he concluded this prophecy, the barber raised and lowered his voice with so intense an emotional effect that even those who knew it to be a jest almost believed that it was the truth they heard. Don Quixote was greatly consoled by these predictions, for he at once grasped their purport, to the effect that he was to be united in holy and lawful bonds of matrimony with his beloved Dulcinea del Toboso, from whose fortunate loins should come forth whelps that were his sons, to the perpetual glory of La Mancha. Thoroughly imbued with this belief, he heaved a deep sigh and, lifting up his voice, he spoke as follows:

"O thou, whoever thou art, who hast prophesied all these blessings for me! I implore thee on my behalf to ask the wise enchanter who hath these things in his charge not to allow me to perish in this captivity in which they now bear me away before I shall have seen fulfilled all the joyful and incomparable promises that have just been made me. Let this be granted me and I shall glory in the sufferings of my prison house, my chains will be light indeed, and this bed upon which they lay me will be, not a hard-fought battlefield, but a soft and happy nuptial couch. As for the consolation that has been offered to Sancho Panza, my squire, I can only say that I rely upon his goodness and integrity, trusting him never to leave me in good fortune or in bad. And if by his or my own ill luck I should not be able to give him the island or some equivalent fief as I have promised, at least his wages shall not be forfeited; for in my will, which is already drawn up, I have declared that which is to be his, not in proportion to his many and faithful services, but in accordance with my means."

At this Sancho bowed most respectfully and kissed both his master's hands, it being impossible for him to kiss but one of them as they were tied together. Then those phantom figures put the cage upon their shoulders and carried it out and placed it on the ox-cart.

CHAPTER XLVII. *Of the strange manner in which a spell was laid on Don Quixote de la Mancha,*[1] *together with other remarkable occurrences.*

WHEN Don Quixote found himself caged in this manner and placed upon the cart, he spoke as follows:

"Many very grave histories have I read of knights-errant, but never have I read, seen, or heard of enchanted knights being borne away in this fashion and at the slow pace that these lazy animals seem likely to provide; for it is the custom to spirit them through the air, with marvelous speed, wrapped in some dark, dense cloud or upon a chariot of fire or some hippogriff or other similar beast. But that they should now be taking me upon an ox-cart, Heaven help me, that is something I cannot understand![2] However, it may be that chivalry and the art of magic in this our time must follow another path than the one it did in days gone by. And it may also be that, inasmuch as I am a new knight in this world, the first to revive the forgotten calling of knightly adventurers, they may likewise have invented other means of enchantment and other ways of carrying off the enchanted. What do you think of it, Sancho, my son?"

"I don't know what I think," replied Sancho, "not being as well read as is your Grace in the writings of errantry. But for all of that, I'd venture to swear and affirm that those apparitions are not altogether Catholic."[3]

"Catholic? My father!" said Don Quixote. "How can they be Catholic if they are all demons who have assumed fantastic shapes in order to do this thing and put me in this condition? If you would ascertain the truth, you have but to touch and feel them and you will perceive that they have none but an airy body and consist only of appearances."

"By God, sir," Sancho answered him, "I've already touched them, and that devil you see bustling along there is as plump as can be and it's real flesh that's on him; and there is something else about him that is very different from what I have heard tell of demons, for they say that they all stink of sulphur and other evil smells, but you can scent the amber on this one half a league away."

He was speaking of Don Fernando, who as a gentleman must of necessity give off the odor that Sancho had mentioned.

"You need not marvel at that, friend Sancho," said Don Quixote; "for I would have you know that the devils are very wise, and while they bear odors with them, they themselves smell of nothing, since, being spirits, they can emit no scent whatsoever, or if they do smell, it is not of anything pleasant but rather something evil and fetid. The reason for this is that, wherever they may be, they bring with them Hell itself and can receive no manner of comfort in their torments; and inasmuch as a pleasing fragrance is something that gives delight and happiness, it is obviously impossible for them to be possessed of such a thing. Accordingly, if this devil appears to you to smell of amber, either you are mistaken or he is trying to deceive you so that you will not take him to be a devil."

As this conversation occurred between master and man, Don Fernando and Cardenio began to fear that Sancho would discover the entire plot, for he had already gone a long way toward doing so. They therefore decided to hasten their departure and, calling the landlord to one side, they directed him to saddle Rocinante and put the packsaddle on Sancho's ass, which he did very quickly. The curate, meanwhile, had arranged with the troopers to accompany them as far as the village, promising to pay them so much a day. Cardenio then hung the buckler on one side of the saddletree and the basin on the other and made signs to Sancho to mount his ass and take Rocinante's rein, while the two troopers [4] with their muskets were placed one on either side of the cart. Before that vehicle could get under way, however, the landlady, her daughter, and Maritornes came running out to say good-by to Don Quixote, shedding feigned tears of sorrow over his plight.

"Do not weep, my good ladies," he now said to them, "for all these misfortunes are such as go with the calling that I profess; indeed, if they did not befall me, I should not look upon myself as a famous knight-errant. Such things never happen to knights of little name and reputation for the reason that no one in the world gives them a thought. With the valiant ones it is otherwise, for many princes and many other knights envy them their virtue and their valor and are bent upon destroying the worthy by foul means. But in spite of all this, virtue is omnipotent and, notwithstanding all the necromancy that Zoroaster, first inventor of the art,[5] ever knew, will emerge triumphant from every peril and bestow light on the world as does the sun in the heavens.

Forgive me, fair ladies, if, without meaning to do so, I have given you any offense, for I would not willingly and knowingly offend anyone. Pray, then, to God to rescue me from this captivity in which some enchanter of evil intent has placed me; and when I am free, I will by no means forget the favors which you in this castle have shown me, but will acknowledge, requite, and reward them as they deserve."

While the ladies of the castle were conversing with Don Quixote, the curate and the barber were taking their leave of Don Fernando and his companions, the captain and his brother, and all those happy damsels, particularly Dorotea and Luscinda. They all embraced one another and agreed to keep in touch by letter, Don Fernando telling the curate where to write to inform him of the outcome of Don Quixote's case, as nothing would give him more pleasure than this. For his part, Fernando promised to send back any news that might be of interest pertaining to his marriage as well as Zoraida's baptism, the upshot of Don Luis' affair, and Luscinda's return home. The curate gave his assurance that he would comply most faithfully with all that was asked of him, and then, with another exchange of embraces, they renewed their promises all over again.

The innkeeper at this point came up to the curate and handed him some papers, saying he had found them in the lining of the trunk where the *Story of the One Who Was Too Curious for His Own Good* had been discovered; and, seeing that their owner had not returned for them, he told the priest to take them all, as he himself did not know how to read and so did not care to keep them. The curate thanked him and, opening the manuscript at once, he saw that the title was *The Story of Riconete and Cortadillo,*[6] from which he gathered that it was a work of fiction; and since *The One Who Was Too Curious* had afforded such pleasant reading, he assumed that this must also be an interesting tale, as there was a possibility that they were by the same author, and so he kept it with the intention of reading it later when he had an opportunity.

He then mounted his horse and the barber did the same, both wearing their masks in order not to be recognized by Don Quixote; whereupon the entire party fell in, alongside and behind the ox-cart, in the following formation: first came the cart, driven by its owner; at the sides were the two officers of the Holy Brotherhood with their muskets, as has been stated; Sancho Panza then followed on his ass, leading Rocinante; and bringing up the rear were the curate and the barber upon their sturdy mules, their faces covered in the manner described as they solemnly rode along, suiting their pace to that of the oxen. Seated in the cage was Don Quixote, who with his hands bound and his feet stretched out, leaned patiently back against the bars, preserving a silence so complete that it seemed he was not a flesh-and-blood being but rather a stone statue.

They had proceeded thus slowly and silently for a matter of two leagues when they came to a valley which impressed the carter as being a good place to rest and feed his oxen, and he suggested to the curate that they halt there. The barber, however, spoke up and said that he thought they should go a little farther because he knew of a valley beyond a near-by slope where there was more and much better grass than was to be found here. And so, having decided to take his advice, they set out again.

Turning his head, the curate now saw six or seven horsemen, all of them well equipped and accoutered, riding up behind them. The cavalcade was soon upon them, for these men rode, not as those who must accommodate their pace to the sluggish gait of oxen, but rather as those do who go mounted on canons' mules, spurred by the desire to reach the inn as soon as possible for their noontide repose, for the hostelry was already in sight half a league away. In such manner did the ones who made haste overtake the ones who were compelled to lag. There was a courteous exchange of greetings, and then one of the newcomers, who was, as a matter of fact, a canon of Toledo and the superior of the others, upon beholding the slow and solemn ox-cart procession—the troopers, Sancho, Rocinante, the curate and the barber, and finally Don Quixote caged and imprisoned—could not refrain from asking what the purpose was in transporting the man in such a fashion, although he had already assumed from a sight of the officers' insignia that the fellow must be some villainous highwayman or other criminal who came under the jurisdiction of the Holy Brotherhood.

"Sir," replied one of the troopers to whom he had put the question, "he himself will have to answer that, for we do not know."

Hearing this, Don Quixote addressed the canon's party. "Gentlemen," he said, "are your Worships by any chance versed and skilled in what pertains to knight-errantry? For if you are, I can tell you of my misfortunes; but if you are not, there is no reason why I should put myself to the trouble."

In the meantime, seeing the travelers engaged in conversation with Don Quixote de la Mancha, the curate and the barber had come forward that they might answer the questions in such a way that their artifice would not be discovered.

"In truth, my brother," said the canon, for it was to him that the knight had directed his remarks, "I know more about books of chivalry than I do about Villalpando's *Compendium;* [7] and so, if that is the only thing that stands in the way, you may freely tell me anything that you desire."

"So be it, then, in Heaven's name," replied Don Quixote. "Sir," he went on, "I would inform you that I am being carried away enchanted in this cage as a result of the envy and deceit of wicked magicians; for virtue is more persecuted by the wicked than loved by the good. A knight-errant am I, and not one of those whom fame never thought of immortalizing in her annals. I am, rather, of that number who, in spite of the envy of which I have spoken, in spite of all the Magi that Persia has spawned, all the Brahmans that India has produced, all the gymnosophists [8] that have come out of Ethiopia, are destined to leave their names in the temple of immortality that they may serve as examples and as models for ages to come, wherein knights-errant may behold the paths they have to follow if it be their desire to attain the highest peak and pinnacle of honor in their pursuit of the calling of arms."

"Don Quixote de la Mancha speaks the truth," the curate put in, "when he tells you that he goes enchanted upon this cart, not through any fault or sin of his own, but owing to the ill will of those whom virtue annoys and valor angers. This, sir, is the Knight of the Mournful Countenance, whose name you may have heard upon occasion and whose brave deeds and great exploits shall be recorded in enduring bronze and eternal marble, no matter how tirelessly envy may seek to obscure them and malice endeavor to keep them hidden."

When the canon heard both the prisoner and the one who walked free beside him speak in this manner, he was ready to cross himself from astonishment and could not believe his own ears, while all his companions were equally amazed. Then it was that Sancho Panza, who had drawn near to listen to their talk, put the finishing touch on it all.

"Well, sirs," he said, "whether or not you like what I am going to say, the fact is that my master, Don Quixote, is no more enchanted than my mother, for he has all his senses about him and eats and drinks and attends to his necessities like the rest of us, just as he did yesterday before they put him in this cage. This being so, how would you have me believe that he is enchanted? For I have heard many people say that those that are under a magic spell neither eat nor sleep nor speak whereas my master, if you do not take him in hand, will do more talking than thirty lawyers."

Turning, then, to look the curate in the face, he went on, "Ah, Señor Curate! Señor Curate! So, your Grace thought I didn't know you and that I would not guess what the purpose of these new enchantments is? Well, then, I can tell you that I recognize you no matter how much you cover your face and that I know what you are up to no matter how cleverly and deceitfully you attempt to hide it. In short, where envy reigns virtue cannot live, nor generosity where there is miserliness. Devil take it all, if it wasn't for your Reverence, my master would be getting married to the Princess Micomicona right now and I would be a count at the very least, since I could expect no less from my kind-hearted master, him of the Mournful Countenance, after all that I have done for him. But now I see that it is true what they say hereabouts, that fortune's wheel turns faster than that of a mill,[9] and those that yesterday were up on top today are down on the ground.

"It grieves me to think about my wife and children, who rightly expect to see their father and husband returning home and coming through the door as governor or viceroy of some island or kingdom, and instead they will see him coming in as a stable boy. All this that I am saying to you, Señor Curate, is by way of urging your Paternity to have a conscience and not treat my master so badly as you are doing; for look well to it that God in the other life does not ask you to account for holding Señor Don Quixote a prisoner like this, and hold you responsible for all the good my master might have done and the aid he might have given others during all this time."

"Trim those lamps for me!"[10] cried the barber at this point. "So you, Sancho, are of the same confraternity as your master, are you? Good lord, but I'm beginning to think you ought to be in the cage there with him, for you're as much bewitched as he is when it comes to the subject of chivalry! It was an evil day for you when your brains became impregnated with all those promises that he made you and you got that island into your head that you've so set your heart on."

"I'm not pregnant by anybody," declared Sancho, "nor am I the man to let myself be put in that condition by any king that ever lived. I may be poor, but I'm an old Christian and I don't owe anyone anything. If I want islands, there are others who want worse things. Each one is the son of his own works, and being a man I may come to be pope,[11] not to speak of being governor of an island; for my master may win so many that there will not be people enough to give them to. Sir Barber, you had better watch what you say, for there is some difference between Peter and Peter.[12] I say this because we all know one another and it won't do to throw false dice with me. And as for my master's being enchanted, God knows the truth, so leave it as it is, for it is better not to stir it."

The barber did not care to answer Sancho for fear that the latter in his simple-mindedness would reveal what he and the curate were trying so hard to conceal. It was the same consideration that led the curate to suggest to the canon that they ride on a little way ahead, where he would explain to him the mystery of the man in the cage along with other things that would interest him. The canon accompanied by his servants accordingly did so and listened most attentively to all that was told him regarding Don Quixote's life, his madness, and his habits, along with a brief account of the beginning and cause of his derangement, the course of events which had led up to his being placed in that cage, and the plan they had for taking him back home to see if some remedy could be found for the form of insanity from which he suffered. Both the canon and his attendants marveled afresh at this strange history, and when it was finished, the churchman voiced his view of the matter.

"Truly, Señor Curate," he said, "it is my opinion that those so-called books of chivalry are harmful to the well-being of the state. And while it is true that, out of idle curiosity and a false sense of pleasure, I have read the beginning of nearly all that have been printed, I have never been able to read any of them from beginning to end, for it seems to me that they are all more or less the same and one is worth about as much as another. As I see it, this species of writing and composition is in the same class with what are called Milesian fables,[13] which are nonsensical tales designed solely to amuse and not to instruct, in which respect they are unlike those apologues which afford entertainment and instruction at one and the same time. Granting, even, that the chief purpose of such works is to amuse, I do not see how it can be achieved when they are so full of monstrous nonsense.

"For that beauty which the soul conceives," he went on, "must come from the beauty and harmony that it beholds or contemplates in those things that are presented to it by sight or by the imagination, and nothing that is ugly or inharmonious can give us any pleasure whatsoever. Well, then, I ask you, what beauty can there be, or what proportion of parts with the whole or of the whole with its parts, in a book or fable in which a seventeen-year-old lad slashes a giant tall as a tower and cuts him in half as if he were a sugar-pastry? And when they go to depict a battle scene for us, although we may have been told that there are a million fighting men on the enemy's side, nevertheless, let the hero of the book be against them and of necessity, whether we like it or not, we have to believe that the knight in question carried off the victory single-handed, by virtue of his mighty arm.

"Then, what shall we say of the readiness with which a hereditary queen or empress throws herself into the arms of an unknown knight-errant? Could any person, save one with a barbarous and uncultivated mind, find pleasure in reading that a great tower filled with knights goes sailing over the sea like a ship with a favoring wind and is tonight in Lombardy and tomorrow morning in the land of Prester John of the Indies,[14] or in other domains such as Ptolemy never discovered and Marco Polo never laid eyes on? And if you should answer me by saying that those who write such books offer them to us as fiction and hence are not obliged to observe the fine points of the truth, I should reply that the falsehood is all the greater when it appears in the guise of truth, and that as fiction, the more it contains of the pleasing [15] and the possible the more it delights us.

"For in works of fiction there should be a mating between the plot and the reader's intelligence. They should be so written that the impossible is made to appear possible, things hard to believe being smoothed over and the mind held in suspense in such a manner as to create surprise and astonishment while at the same time they divert and entertain so that admiration and pleasure go hand in hand. But these are things which he cannot accomplish who flees verisimilitude and the imitation of nature, qualities that go to constitute perfection in the art of writing.

"Never," concluded the canon, "have I seen any book of chivalry that held the body of a story completely with all its members so that the middle was consistent with the beginning and the end with the beginning and the middle. Rather, they are made up of so many disparate members that it would seem the author's intention was to create a chimera or a monster rather than a well-proportioned figure. In addition to all this, they are crude in style, unconvincing in the exploits that they relate, lascivious in the love affairs that they portray, uncouth in their efforts at courtliness, prolix in their descriptions of battles, absurd in their dialogue, nonsensical in their accounts of journeyings, and, finally, destitute of anything that resembles art; for which reason it is they deserve to be banished from the Christian state as not being of public utility."

The curate had listened to all this very closely, for the canon impressed him as being a man of sound understanding who was right in what he said. He now told him that he was of the same opinion and, having a grudge against such works, had burned all those that Don Quixote possessed, of which there were a great many. He then went on to relate how he had gone through all the books in the knight's library, mentioning those that he had condemned to the flames and those that he had let live, at which the canon laughed not a little.

But for all the harsh things that he had said of such books, the canon added, he had found one good thing about them, and that was the chance they afforded for a good mind to display its true worth, for they offered a broad and spacious field over which the author's pen might run without impediment, describing shipwrecks, tempests, battles, and encounters; depicting a valiant captain with all the qualities requisite to such a character, showing him as prudent, capable of anticipating the stratagems of the enemy, an eloquent orator in persuading or dissuading his soldiers, exhibiting a ripened wisdom in council, quick in making decisions, and as brave when it came to biding his time as he was in the attack; the author could relate now a lamentable and tragic event and now some joyful and unexpected occurrence; he could picture here a lovely lady, modest, discreet, and reserved, and there a Christian knight, gentle and brave, setting a lawless, barbarous braggart over against a prince, courtly, valorous, and benign, letting us see at once the loyalty and devotion of the vassals and the greatness and generosity of their lords.

The author might further show himself to be an astrologer, an excellent cosmographer, a musician, a student of statecraft, or even upon occasion, if he chose, a necromancer. He might take as his theme the astuteness of Ulysses, the filial piety of Aeneas, the bravery of Achilles, the woes of Hector, the treasons of Sinon,[16] the friendship of Euryalus,[17] the liberality of Alexander, the valor of Caesar, the clemency and truthfulness of Trajan, the fidelity of Zopyrus,[18] the prudence of Cato—in short, all those attributes that go to make an illustrious man perfect, as shown sometimes in a single individual and other times as shared among many. All of which being done in an easy-flowing style, with a skilled inventiveness that draws insofar as possible upon the truth of things, the result would surely be a web woven of beautiful and variegated threads,[19] one which when completed would exhibit such a perfected beauty of form as to attain the most worth-while goal of all writing, which as I have said is at once to instruct and to entertain. These books, indeed, by their very nature, provided the author with an unlimited field in which to try his hand at the epic, lyric, tragic, and comic genres and depict in turn all the moods that are represented by these most sweet and pleasing branches of poetry and oratory; for the epic may be written in prose as well as in verse.

CHAPTER **XLVIII**. *In which the canon continues his discourse on the subject of books of chivalry, with other matters worthy of his intelligence.*

"IT IS as your Grace has said, Señor Canon," remarked the curate, "and for that reason they are all the more deserving of reprehension who up to now have composed such books without giving any thought to good taste or the rules of art by which they might have been guided and thereby have rendered themselves as famous in prose as the two princes of Greek and Latin poetry are in verse."

"However that may be," replied the canon, "I myself was once tempted to write a book of chivalry, observing all the points that I have mentioned; and if I am to confess the truth, I have more than a hundred sheets already written. By way of putting them to the test and seeing if they were as good as I thought they were, I have submitted them to certain individuals who are passionately fond of this type of reading. Some of these persons were wise and learned, while others were ignorant, being concerned solely with the pleasure they derive from listening to nonsense, but all of them were warmly appreciative of my effort. I did not go on, however, for it seemed to me, on the one hand, that I was engaged in doing something that was foreign to my profession, and, on the other hand, the foolish impressed me as being more numerous than the wise; and while the praise of the discerning few offsets [1] the scorn of the unknowing many, I still did not care to subject myself to the confused judgment of that vapid public to which the reading of such works is for the most part confined.

"But what did most to stay my hand and even caused me to give up all thought of finishing what I had begun was an argument that I put to

myself, drawn from the comedies that are now being performed. It ran
as follows: All of these pieces, or the greater part of them at any rate,
whether purely fictitious or historical in character, are obviously nonsensical, without head or tail, yet the public takes pleasure in witnessing
them and regards them as worthy productions, though they are far
from good. And the authors who compose them and the actors who
perform them tell us that plays have to be of this sort, since the public
wants precisely that kind of thing and nothing else, whereas those pieces
that have a plot and develop the story in an artistic fashion will appeal
only to a handful of intelligent persons who are able to understand them,
while all the others will fail to perceive the art that is in them. This
being so, they—the authors and actors—prefer to gain their bread with
the many rather than subsist on the good opinion of the few. In which
case, my book, after I should have scorched my eyebrows in an attempt to observe the precepts I have mentioned, would meet with the
same fate as other works of merit, and I should end up by being the
tailor of Campillo.[2]

"Although I have a number of times endeavored to persuade the
actors [3] that they are wrong in the view they hold, and that they would
attract more people and win more fame for themselves by producing
comedies that follow the rules of art than they do by performing in
these silly ones, they are so firmly set in their opinion that no amount
of reasoning or evidence will convince them that they are wrong. I
remember saying to one of the stubborn fellows once upon a time: 'Do
you not recall that, only a few years ago, there were three tragedies
put upon the boards here in Spain, written by a famous poet of this
realm, which were so pleasing as to arouse the admiration and hold the
interest of all who heard them, the simple as well as the wise, the general public as well as the select few, and which brought in more money
to the performers—these three alone—than thirty of the best that up
to then had been produced?'

" 'You mean, of course,' the author [4] replied, 'the *Isabella*, the *Phyllis*,
and the *Alexandra?*' [5]

" 'Yes,' I said, 'those are the ones of which I am speaking; and see if
they do not well observe the rules of art, and if, superior creations that
they are, they are not still pleasing to everyone. The fault therefore lies
not with the public that asks for silly pieces, but with those who do not
know how to put on anything else. The *Ingratitude Avenged* was not
nonsense; neither was the *Numantia*, nor *The Merchant Lover*, and
certainly not *The Fair and Favoring Enemy;* [6] and the same might be

said of others composed by intelligent poets, to their own fame and renown and the profit of those who put on the plays.'

"I had other things to say along the same line, which left him, I thought, a bit embarrassed but by no means sufficiently convinced to give up his erroneous opinion."

"Señor Canon," said the curate, "by touching upon this subject you have awakened an old grudge of mine against the comedies of today, one that is equal to that which I hold against books of chivalry. For, according to Tully, a comedy should be a mirror of human life, an example of manners, and an image of the truth; [7] yet those that we see now are mirrors of nonsense, examples of foolishness, and images of lasciviousness. In connection with the subject of which we are speaking, what could be more absurd than for a character to appear as an infant in Act I, Scene 1, and in the following scene step out as a full-bearded man? What more out of place than to depict for us an old man parading his valor, a youth who plays the cringing coward, an eloquent lackey, a page wise in giving counsel, a king turned porter, or a princess serving as a kitchen wench?

"And what shall I say of the attention that is paid to the element of time in connection with the action that is represented? I may merely tell you that I have witnessed a comedy in which the first act takes place in Europe, the second in Asia, and the third in Africa—and if there had been a fourth act, the scene would have been laid in America and thus they would have encompassed the four quarters of the globe. If fidelity to life be the principal object which a comedy should have in view, how is it possible for the most mediocre intelligence to find any satisfaction in one where the action is supposed to take place in the time of King Pepin or Charlemagne, yet which has for its leading character the Emperor Heraclius entering Jerusalem with the Holy Cross and recovering the Holy Sepulcher like Godefroi de Bouillon, when there is a vast stretch of time between the two monarchs? Or in one which, essentially fictitious, makes a pretense at historical accuracy by mingling odds and ends of various events that happened to different persons at different times, and this with no attempt at verisimilitude but with obvious errors that are utterly inexcusable? And the sad part of it is, there are ignorant ones who say that this is the perfect thing and all the rest is affectation.

"And then, coming to religious dramas, what do we find? How many false miracles do their authors invent, how many apocryphal and erroneous incidents, with the wonders worked by one saint attributed to another! And even in those comedies that deal with human themes they dare to introduce miracles without rhyme or reason, merely because they think that such a scenic effect,[8] as they term it, will fit in well and serve to attract the ignorant, who will come to see the play and marvel at it. All of which is prejudicial to the truth, tending to corrupt history and cast opprobrium upon the Spanish genius; for those foreigners [9] that scrupulously observe the rules of comedy are led to look upon us as unschooled barbarians by reason of the absurdity and nonsense to be found in the productions of our theater.

"Nor is it a sufficient excuse for all this to say that the principal object which well-ordered states have in view in permitting the public performance of comedies is to provide the community with a little harmless recreation now and then and thus divert those evil impulses that idleness is wont to breed. It may be said that this end is attained by any comedy, good or bad, and that there is no necessity of laying down laws to govern the composition and performance of such pieces, since, as I have said, the same object is achieved by any kind of play. To this I would reply that it is, beyond any comparison, better achieved by good plays than by the other kind.

"For when he has witnessed a comedy that is well and artfully constructed, the spectator will come out laughing at its humor, enlightened by the truths it contained, marveling at the various incidents, rendered wiser by the arguments, made more wary by the snares he has seen depicted, and more prudent by the examples afforded him; he will leave the theater hating vice and in love with virtue; such are the effects that a good comedy has upon the mind of the listener, however boorish and dull-witted he may be. Nothing, in short, is more impossible than that the play that contains all these qualities should fail to provide more entertainment, satisfaction, and pleasure than the one lacking in them, as is the case with the majority of those that are at present to be viewed.

"It is not the dramatic poets who are to blame for this state of affairs; for many of them are fully conscious of their faults and know very well what ought to be done. But inasmuch as comedies have become salable commodities, the poets in question will tell us, and in this they are right, that their plays will not be bought unless they are after the accepted pattern, and, accordingly, the author seeks to adapt himself to what the actor who is to pay him for his work requires of him. That this is so may be seen from the countless number of comedies composed by one of the most fertile minds in this realm, plays so full of brilliancy and grace, marked by such polished versification, admirable dialogue, and profound wisdom, and, finally, so full of eloquence and so elevated in style, that his fame has gone out to all the world; and yet, owing to the necessity he has been under of having to adapt them to the taste of the players, not all his productions have attained that degree of perfection that is to be desired.[10]

"Still others compose their pieces without giving a thought to what they are doing; and, as a result, after the performance, the actors have to take to their heels and flee for fear of being punished, as they oftentimes have been, for having put something on the stage that was offensive to a certain monarch or that cast aspersions on some noble house. But all these improprieties would cease, and with them many others that I do not mention, if there were at court some wise and intelligent person to examine all the comedies before they are put on, not only those that are to be performed in the capital but those that are to be produced in other parts of Spain as well,[11] and without the approval, seal, and signature of that individual no local officer of the crown should permit any comedy to be staged. Under such a system, the performers would be at pains to forward their plays to the capital for inspection and then would be able to act in them with safety, while the authors, knowing that their works would have to pass a rigorous and intelligent censorship and being fearful of offending, would devote more care and attention to them, and as a consequence would produce good comedies, thus achieving in a felicitous manner the objectives for which they strive: the entertainment of the people and, at the same time, the furthering of the reputation of Spanish dramatists and of the interest and security of the performers, the necessity of punishing the latter having been removed.

"And if they were to charge some other person, or this same one, with the task of examining the newly published books of chivalry, we then undoubtedly should have some that would be possessed of that perfection that your Grace has described, works that would enrich our language with a pleasing and precious store of eloquence; and the luster of the older books would be dimmed by the light of these newer ones, whose purpose is to provide an innocent pastime, not for the idle alone, but even for the busiest of men. For it is not possible for the bow to be always bent, nor can weak human nature be sustained without legitimate recreation of some sort."

The canon and the curate had reached this point in their colloquy when the barber came up and spoke to the latter.

"Here, Señor Licentiate," he said, "is the place of which I was telling you; it is a good spot in which to take our noontide rest, and there is fresh and abundant pasturage for the oxen."

"It looks to me as if it would do very well," replied the curate.

When the canon was told of their intentions, he expressed a desire to make the halt with them, being attracted by the charming prospect which the valley afforded. He also wished to enjoy more of the curate's conversation, for he had become quite fond of him, and to hear of Don Quixote's exploits in greater detail. He accordingly ordered some of his servants to go to the inn, which was not far away, and bring back enough for them all to eat, as he meant to rest there in the valley that afternoon; to which one of them replied that the sumpter mule, which ought by this time to have reached the inn, carried sufficient provisions so that they would not have to procure anything from the hostelry except barley.

"In that case," said the canon, "lead all our mounts there and bring back the mule."

While this was going on, Sancho decided to take advantage of the opportunity to speak to his master without the constant presence of the curate and the barber, whom he looked upon with suspicion.

"Master," he said, going up to the cage, "I want to get a load off my conscience by telling you what goes on in connection with your enchantment. The truth of the matter is that those two with their faces covered are the curate of our village and the barber, and it is my belief that they have plotted to carry you off like this out of pure spite, because your Grace is so far ahead of them in famous deeds. If this is so, then it follows that you are not under a spell at all but have been hoodwinked and made a fool of. Just to prove this, I'd like to ask you one thing, and if you answer me as I think you will have to, then you'll be able to lay your hand on what's wrong and will see that you are not enchanted but simply out of your head."

"Ask me whatever you like, Sancho my son," replied Don Quixote, "and I will give you an answer that will satisfy you on every point. As to what you say about those who accompany us being the curate and the barber, our fellow townsmen whom we know very well, that is who they may appear to you to be, but you are not by any manner of means to believe that that is what they really and truly are. What you are rather to understand is that if they have, as you say, this appearance in your eyes, it must be for the reason that those who have put this spell upon me have seen fit to assume that form and likeness; for it is easy enough for enchanters to take whatever form they like, and so they must have assumed the appearance of our friends expressly for the purpose of leading you to think what you do, thus involving you in a labyrinth of fancies from which you would not succeed in extricating yourself even though you had the cord of Theseus.

"They also doubtless had another purpose, that of causing me to waver in my mind, so that I should not be able to form a conjecture as to the source of this wrong that is done me. For, if on the one hand you tell me it is the barber and the curate of our village who accompany us, and on the other hand I find myself shut up in a cage, knowing full well that no human but only a superhuman power could have put me behind these bars, what would you have me say to you or what would you have me think except that my enchantment, in view of the manner in which it has been accomplished, is like none that I have ever read about in all the histories that treat of knights-errant who have been laid under a spell? And so you may set your mind at rest as to the suspicions that you have voiced, for those two are no more what you say they are than I am a Turk. But you said that you had something to ask me; speak, then, and I will answer you, though you keep on asking until tomorrow morning."

"May Our Lady help me!" cried Sancho in a loud voice. "Is it possible your Grace is so thick-headed and so lacking in brains that you cannot see that I am telling you the simple truth when I say that malice has more to do than magic with your being in this plight? But since that is the way matters stand, I'd like to prove to you beyond a doubt that there is no magic about it. And now, tell me, as you would have God rescue you from this torment, and as you hope to find yourself in the arms of my lady Dulcinea when you least expect it—"

"Stop conjuring me," said Don Quixote, "and ask what you like. I have already told you that I will answer you point by point."

"What I ask is this," Sancho went on, "and what I would have you tell me, without adding anything to it or leaving anything out, but in all truthfulness, as you would expect it to be told, and as it is told, by all those who like your Grace follow the calling of arms, under the title of knights-errant—"

"I have said that I will tell you no lies," replied Don Quixote. "Go ahead and finish your question; for in truth you weary me, Sancho, with all these solemn oaths, adjurations, and precautions."

"I am sure," said Sancho, "that my master is kindhearted and truthful; and so, because it has a bearing on what we are talking about, I would ask your Grace, speaking with all due respect, if by any chance, since you have been in that cage and, as it seems to you, under a spell, you have felt the need of doing a major or a minor,[12] as the saying goes."

"I do not understand what you mean by 'doing a major or a minor,' Sancho. Speak more plainly if you wish me to give you a direct answer."

"Is it possible that your Grace doesn't know what 'a major or a minor' is? Why, lads in school are weaned on it. What I mean to say is, have you felt like doing that which can't be put off?"

"Ah, I understand you, Sancho! Yes, many times; and for that matter, right now. Get me out of this, or all will not be as clean here as it ought to be!"

CHAPTER XLIX. Of the shrewd conversation that Sancho Panza had with his master, Don Quixote.

"HA!" cried Sancho, "I have you there! That is what I wanted with all my life and soul to know! Come now, sir, can you deny the common saying around here when a person is out of sorts: 'I don't know what's the matter with So-and-So; he neither eats nor drinks nor sleeps nor gives you a sensible answer to any question that you ask him; he must be bewitched?' From which we are to gather that while those that do not do any of these things or attend to those duties of nature that I have mentioned are under a spell, the ones like your Grace, on the other hand, who feel a desire to do them, who eat and drink what is set before them and answer all questions, are not enchanted."

"You speak the truth, Sancho," replied Don Quixote, "but as I have told you before there are many ways of being enchanted, and it may be that the fashion has changed with the course of time and that today those who are in such a plight do everything that I do, although formerly such was not the case. So, there is no use arguing against custom or drawing inferences as you are doing. I know for a certainty that I am the victim of an enchanter, and that is all I need to know to set my conscience at rest, for it would hurt me sorely if I thought that, without being enchanted, I had slothfully and like a coward permitted myself to be put into this cage, thus cheating the wretched and the needy who at this very moment may be in great distress for want of my aid and protection."

"But for all of that," said Sancho, "I still insist it would be better, in order to satisfy yourself completely, if your Grace would try to get out of that jail. I promise to do everything I can to help you out of it and see if you can mount Rocinante once more, for he looks so sad and melancholy, I think he must be enchanted too. When you've done that, you can try your luck at seeking more adventures, and if they don't turn out well, there will be plenty of time for us to come back to the jail; in which case I promise you, as the law says a good and faithful squire should do, that I will shut myself up with your Grace, if by any chance your Grace should be so unlucky or I so foolish as not to be able to go through with what I've told you."

"I am willing to do anything you say, brother Sancho," Don Quixote assured him; "and when you find an opportunity to set me free, I will obey you in everything; but you will see, Sancho, that you are wrong in your explanation of my misfortune."

Conversing in this manner, knight-errant and errant squire arrived at the place where the curate, the canon, and the barber, who had already dismounted, were awaiting them. The carter then unyoked his oxen to let them graze in that pleasant pasturage, whose cool green proved alluring to persons not only as bewitched as Don Quixote but as shrewd and wide awake as his squire. The latter now begged the curate to allow his master to leave the cage for a little while, since otherwise it would not remain as clean as decency required in the case of such a knight.

The curate understood what he meant and told him that he would gladly grant his request, if it was not that he feared his master, once set at liberty, would be up to his old tricks and go off someplace where no one would ever see him again.

"I will answer for that," replied Sancho.

"And I for everything," said the canon, "especially if he but give me his word as a knight that he will not leave us against our will."

"I give it," answered Don Quixote, who had been listening to it all. "In any event, one who is enchanted as I am is not at liberty to do what he likes with his person, for the one who put the spell upon him may very well prevent him from stirring from a certain place for three whole centuries, and if he were to flee, he would be brought back flying."

He went on to say that, this being so, they might as well release him, as it was to the advantage of all of them; for, he protested, if they did not do so, he would not be able to avoid offending their sense of smell, unless they kept their distance from him.

The canon thereupon took the knight's hand, although it was bound to the other one, and, upon receiving his word and solemn promise, they let him out of the cage, which made him immeasurably happy. The first thing he did was to stretch his entire body, and then he went over to Rocinante and slapped him on the rump.

"O flower and mirror of steeds," he said, "I still trust in God and His blessed Mother that we shall both soon have our desire: you with your master on your back and I astride you, in pursuit of that calling for which God sent me into the world."

Having said this, he went off with Sancho to a remote spot, and when he came back he was greatly relieved and more desirous than ever of putting his squire's scheme into execution. Gazing at him, the canon could not but be struck by the strange nature of his madness and was astonished at the extremely sensible manner in which the knight talked and answered questions, losing his stirrups, so to speak, only when the subject of chivalry was mentioned. And so, as they all sat around on the green grass waiting for the meal which the canon had ordered, the churchman addressed him, saying:

"Is it possible, my good sir, that those disgusting books of chivalry which your Grace has read in your idle hours have had such an effect upon you as to turn your head, causing you to believe that you are being carried away under a magic spell and other things of that sort that are as far from being true as truth itself is from falsehood? How is it possible for any human mind to believe that there ever existed in this world all that infinite number of Amadises, or all that multitude of famous knights—all the emperors of Trebizond, all the Felixmartes of Hircania, all the palfreys, errant damsels, serpents, monsters, giants, all the adventures such as never before were heard of, all the battles and fearful encounters, all the splendid costumes, lovelorn princesses, squires turned into counts, facetious dwarfs, gallantries, warrior ladies—in short, all the absurdities to be found in the romances of chivalry?

"For myself, I can say that when I read such books without stopping to think how mendacious and frivolous they are, they do give me a certain pleasure; but when I reflect upon their real character, I fling the best of them against the wall and would even toss them into the fire if there happened to be one at hand; for they are deserving of the same punishment as cheats and impostors, who are beyond the pale of human nature, or as the founders of new sects and new ways of life, for leading the ignorant public to believe and regard as the truth all the nonsense that they contain.

"And these audacious works even upset the minds of intelligent and wellborn gentlemen like your Grace, as is plainly to be seen from the things that you have done, which have finally made it necessary to lock you up in a cage and convey you upon an ox-cart like some lion or tiger that is being taken from place to place to be exhibited for money. Ah, Señor Don Quixote, have mercy upon yourself, return to the bosom of common sense, and wisely make use of the many gifts with which Heaven has seen fit to endow you by applying your fertile mind to reading of another sort such as will be better for your conscience and for your good name as well.

"If, however, carried away by your natural inclination, you feel that you must read of knightly exploits, then turn to the Book of Judges in the Holy Scriptures, for there you will find great deeds recorded, and as true as they are valiant. Lusitania had a Viriatus,[1] Rome a Caesar, Carthage a Hannibal, Greece an Alexander, Castile a Count Fernán González, Valencia a Cid, Andalusia a Gonzalo Hernández, Estremadura a Diego García de Paredes, Jerez a Garci Pérez de Vargas, Toledo a Garcilaso, Seville a Manuel de León;[2] and in perusing the account of their feats of valor the loftiest intellect will find instruction and entertainment, diversion, and cause for wonderment. Here, my dear Señor Don Quixote, is reading matter worthy of your intelligence and which will leave you versed in history, in love with virtue, schooled in goodness of heart, and improved in manners and morals; it will render you valiant but not rash, prudent but not a coward; and all this to the honor of God and the fame of La Mancha, which, so I am informed, is your Grace's native province."

Don Quixote was all attention as the canon spoke, and when he saw that he had finished, after gazing at him for some little while, he replied as follows:

"It appears to me, my dear sir, that the purpose of your Grace's remarks is to lead me to believe that there have never been knights-errant in the world and that all the books of chivalry are false, lying, harmful, and lacking in public usefulness. You further imply that I have done wrong in reading them, worse in believing them, and worst of all in imitating them by setting out to follow the extremely arduous profession of errantry in accordance with the precepts to be found in such works. You would tell me that the world has never seen an Amadis, either of Gaul or of Greece, nor any of the other knights with whose names those books are filled."

"You have stated the case exactly," said the canon.

"Your Grace," said Don Quixote, "also went on to assert that such books had done me much harm, having turned my head and landed me in a cage, and that it would be better to mend my ways, change my reading matter, and turn my attention to other writings that are more truthful, pleasing, and edifying."

"That is right," said the canon.

"Whereas I," continued the knight, "find that it is your Grace who have had your head turned and have been bewitched. For to utter such blasphemies as your Grace has done against something that all the world knows to be true, by denying that it exists, is an offense deserving of the same punishment that your Grace says ought to be meted out to those books that so annoy you when you read them. For to endeavor to persuade anyone that Amadis never lived, nor any of the other knightly adventurers that fill the history books, is the same as trying to make him believe that the sun does not shine, that ice is not cold, or that the earth does not bear fruit. For who could ever be clever enough to convince another person that the story of the Princess Florípes and Guy of Burgundy is not true? And there is the story of Fierabrás and the bridge of Mantible,[3] which happened in the time of Charlemagne, and which I swear is as true as when I say it is daylight at this moment.

"But if all this is a lie, then it must be that there was no Hector nor Achilles nor Trojan War nor Twelve Peers of France nor King Arthur of England who to this day goes about in the form of a raven and is expected to reappear in his kingdom at any time. Similarly, they are so bold as to tell us that the history of Guarino Mesquino [4] is false as well as that of the quest of the Holy Grail, and that the love of Tristan and Queen Yseult is a fabrication, as is that of Guinevere and Lancelot, even though there are persons who can recall having seen Dame Quintañona,[5] who was the best cupbearer to be met with in all Britain. So true is this that I can remember how my grandmother on my father's side used to say to me, when she saw a lady in a venerable hood, 'That one, my grandson, looks just like Dame Quintañona.' From which I infer that she must have known her or at least have seen some portrait of her.

"And, then, who would deny the truth of the story of Pierres and the beautiful Magalona, seeing that to this very day, in the royal armory, one may behold the pin—a little bigger than a cart-pole—with which

the valiant Pierres guided his wooden horse through the air, while alongside it is Babieca's saddle? And at Roncesvalles there is Roland's horn of
the size of a beam.[6] From which it is to be inferred that the Twelve
Peers and Pierres and the Cid and other similar knights did of a truth
exist,

Of whom it is folks say,
They to adventures go.

"Furthermore, let them tell me whether or not it is true that there was
a brave Lusitanian knight-errant by the name of Juan de Merlo, who
went to Burgundy and in the city of Arras fought with the famous lord
of Charny called Monsieur Pierre, and afterward in the city of Basle
with Monsieur Henri de Remestan, emerging victorious from both encounters, with great fame and honor.[7] And what of the adventures and
challenges of those brave Spaniards, Pedro Barba and Gutierre Quijada
(from whom I am descended in the direct male line), who—likewise in
Burgundy—fought and overcame the sons of the Count of St. Paul?[8]
Let them tell me, also, that Don Fernando de Guevara did not go to
Germany in quest of adventures, where he engaged in combat with
Messire George, a knight of the Duke of Austria's line.[9] Let them tell
me that the joustings of Suero de Quiñones of the *Paso* were but a
hoax,[10] or the emprises of Monsieur Louis de Faux against the Castilian
knight, Gonzalo de Guzmán,[11] along with many other exploits performed by Christian knights of this and other realms, all of them so
true and authentic that, I say it once more, he who would deny them
is lacking in all reason and sound judgment."

The canon as he listened was amazed at the manner in which Don
Quixote jumbled truth and falsehood and also at the knowledge he
possessed of everything touching upon and pertaining to those feats of
knight-errantry of which he was so fond.

"Señor Don Quixote," he now answered him, "I cannot deny that
there is some truth in what your Grace has said, especially insofar
as pertains to Spanish knights-errant. I am willing to grant you that
there were Twelve Peers of France, although I cannot admit that all
the things that the Archbishop of Turpin has written of them are
true;[12] for the truth of the matter is, they were knights chosen by
the king of France, being called Peers to signify that they were equal
in worth, rank, and valor (or at least they were supposed to be, whether
they were or not). They constituted something like a religious order,
resembling the present ones of Santiago and Calatrava, in which it is

presumed that all those that take the vows are gentlemen, brave, worthy, and wellborn; and just as we speak of a Knight of St. John or a Knight of Alcántara, so in those days they would refer to someone as being a Knight of the Twelve Peers, for the reason that twelve equals were chosen for that military order.[18]

"That there was a Cid, and a Bernardo del Carpio [14] as well, there can be no doubt, but that they performed the feats attributed to them, I very much doubt. As to the Count Pierres' pin with which he guided his steed and which your Grace claims to have seen alongside Babieca's saddle in the royal armory, I must confess that I am either so stupid or so shortsighted that, although I have seen the former I have never laid eyes on the latter, even though it be as big as your Grace says it is."

"Yet there is not the slightest doubt that it is there, for all of that," replied Don Quixote, "and what is more, they say that it is encased in a cowhide sheath to keep it from rusting."

"That may all very well be," said the canon, "but I assure you by the holy orders which I have received that I cannot recall having seen it. But even assuming that it is there, that is no reason why I should believe the stories of all those Amadises and all the multitude of other knights that we read about; nor is it any reason why a man like your Grace, so worthy and respected and endowed with so fine a mind, should permit himself to believe that all the mad things described in those nonsensical books of chivalry are true."

CHAPTER L. *Of the weighty argument which took place between Don Quixote and the canon.*

"THAT," replied Don Quixote, "is a fine thing to say! Do you mean to tell me that those books that have been printed with a royal license and with the approval of the ones to whom they have been submitted and which are read with general enjoyment and praised by young and old alike, by rich and poor, the learned and the ignorant, the gentry and the plain people—in brief, by all sorts of persons of every condition and walk in life—do you mean to tell me that they are but lies? Do they not have every appearance of being true? Do they not tell us who the father, mother, relatives of these knights were, the name of the country from which they came, their age, the feats that they performed, point by point and day by day, and the places where all these events occurred? Your Grace had best be silent and not utter such a blasphemy; for let me give you a bit of advice, which is something that, as a sensible man, I ought to do: if you do not believe me, read them for yourself and you will see what pleasure you will derive from them.

"Tell me: could there be anything more fascinating than to see before us, right here and now, so to speak, a lake of bubbling pitch, with a host of snakes, serpents, lizards, and all sorts of fierce and terrifying animals swimming about in it, while from the middle of it there comes as mournful a voice as ever was heard, saying, 'Thou, O knight, whoever thou mayest be, who standest gazing upon this dreadful lake, if thou wouldst attain the boon that lieth covered beneath these dark waters, show then thy valor and thy stout heart by leaping into the midst of this black and burning liquid; for if thou dost not, thou shalt not be held worthy of looking upon the mighty marvels locked and contained in the seven castles of the seven fays that are situated beneath its ebony expanse.' And no sooner does the knight hear that awful voice than, without taking any further thought or pausing to consider the peril involved, he plunges into that seething lagoon, burdened with the full weight of his armor and commending his soul to God and Our Lady.

"And then, not knowing where he is or what the outcome is to be, he suddenly finds himself amidst flowering meadows to which the Elysian fields cannot compare. It seems to him that the heavens there are more transparent, while the sun is brighter than he has ever known it to be. His eyes behold a charming grove composed of leafy trees whose greenery is a joy to the sight, while his ears are delighted by the sweet and untaught song of an infinite number of little brilliant-hued birds, flying in and out through the interweaving branches. Here he discovers a brook whose clear-running waters, which have the appearance of molten glass, glide along over a bed of fine sand and white pebbles, giving the impression of sifted gold and the purest of pearls. Over there he sees an artfully wrought fountain of varicolored jasper and smooth marble; and there another of rustic design, with tiny clam shells and the twisted white and yellow houses of the snail arranged in a well-ordered disorder, mingled with bits of gleaming crystal and counterfeit emeralds, the whole forming a work in which art, imitating nature, would seem to have outdone the latter.

"In yet another place, his gaze unexpectedly comes to rest upon a strong-built castle or showy palace, with walls of solid gold, diamond turrets, and gates of jacinth—in short, of such marvelous construction that, though the materials of which it is built are nothing less than diamonds, carbuncles, rubies, pearls, gold, and emeralds, the workmanship in itself is of greater worth. But there is more to come. Having beheld all this, he now descries, trooping out of the castle gate, a goodly number of damsels so richly and festively attired that if I were to undertake to describe their costumes as the histories do, I should never be done with it.

"And the one who appears to be the leader of them all now extends her hand to the bold knight who has cast himself into the boiling lake and, without saying a word, conducts him into the splendid palace or castle, where she makes him strip until he is as bare as when his mother bore him, and then bathes him in lukewarm water, after which she anoints him all over with sweet-smelling unguents and clothes him in a shirt of finest sendal, all odorous and perfumed, as another maid tosses a mantle over his shoulders, one which at the very least, so they say, must be worth as much as a city and even more.

"And how pleasing it is when, after all this, we are told how they take him to another chamber, a great hall, where he finds the tables all laid in a manner that fills him with amazement. What must be his feelings as he sees them pouring over his hands water that has been distilled from amber and fragrant flowers? As they seat him upon a chair of marble? As all those damsels serve him in a deep and impressive silence? As they bring him a great variety of dishes so tastefully garnished that, tempted as his appetite may be, he is at a loss as to which he should reach for first? As he listens to the music that is played all the while, not knowing from whence it comes or who the musician may be? And then, when the repast is over and the tables have been cleared, as the knight leans back in his chair, picking his teeth, it may be, as is his custom, there enters unexpectedly through the doorway of the great hall a damsel far more beautiful than any of the others; and, seating herself at his side, she begins telling him to whom it is that castle belongs and how she is being held in it under a magic spell, along with other things that astonish him and amaze the one who reads his history. What, I ask you again, could be more charming than all this?

"I do not care to elaborate upon this point any further; from the examples I have cited it may be gathered that no matter what part of what history of a knight-errant one reads, it is bound to give pleasure and arouse wonderment. If, your Grace, you will believe me and, as I have said, read these books for yourself, you will see how they drive away melancholy and make you feel better in case you are out of sorts. As for myself, I may say that, since becoming a knight-errant, I am brave, polite, liberal, well-bred, generous, courteous, bold, gentle, patient, and long-suffering when it comes to enduring hardships, imprisonment, and enchantments; and although it was only a short while ago that I was shut up in a cage as a madman, I still expect, through the valor of my arm, with Heaven favoring and fortune not opposing, to find myself within a few days king of some realm or other where I may be able to display the gratitude and liberality that is in my heart.

"For take my word for it, sir, he who is poor cannot exhibit those virtues to anyone, no matter in how high a degree he may be possessed of them; and gratitude that consists only in the will to show it is a dead thing, just as is faith without works. For this reason it is, I wish that fortune would speedily provide me with the opportunity of becoming an emperor in order that I might make manifest the virtues of my heart by doing good to my friends and especially to this poor fellow, Sancho Panza, my squire, who is the best little man in the world; I should like to reward him by conferring upon him an earldom, which I promised him long ago. The only thing is I do not know if he has the ability to govern it."

These last words were no sooner out of his mouth than Sancho broke in upon his master. "Just you see to it that I get that earldom, Señor Don Quixote," he said, "the one you promised me and which I have been waiting for all this time, and I give you my word that I'll be able to govern it all right; and if I should fail, I've heard them say that there are men in this world who rent such estates from their lords, giving them so much a year, while they themselves take over the government, in which case all the lord has to do is to stretch out his legs and enjoy his income without worrying about anything else. That's what I'll do. I'll not haggle over a penny here and a penny there. I'll get rid of all the bother and live like a duke on what's coming to me."

"What you are speaking of, brother Sancho," said the canon, "is the matter of revenues; but the lord of a great estate also has to administer justice, and it is this that calls for ability and sound judgment and, above all, a right intention on his part in ascertaining the truth; for if this be lacking in the beginning, the middle and the end will always be wrong, whence it is that God is inclined to favor the simple when their hearts are in the right place and to frustrate the clever designs of the wicked."

"I don't understand those philosophies," replied Sancho. "All I know is that once I have that earldom, I'll be able to rule it; for I have a soul like anybody else and a body like the rest of them, and I'll be as much a king in my state as the others are in theirs. And when I'm king, I'll do as I please, and doing as I please, I'll be satisfied; and when you're satisfied, there's nothing more to be desired, so bring it on. God be with you and we shall see, as one blind man said to another."

"That is not a bad philosophy, as you call it, Sancho," observed the canon, "but there still remains much to be said on this subject of earldoms."

"I do not know what more there is to be said," Don Quixote answered him.[1] "I am guided simply by the example of the great Amadis of Gaul, who made his squire count of Firm Island;[2] and so, I, without any conscientious scruples, may make a count of Sancho Panza, who is one of the best squires that a knight-errant ever had."

The canon was astonished at Don Quixote's well-reasoned nonsense, at the vivid manner in which he had described the Knight of the Lake's adventure, and at the impression which the deliberate falsehoods contained in his books had made upon him; and he likewise marveled at the simple-mindedness of Sancho, who so eagerly longed to obtain that earldom that his master had promised him.

At this point the canon's servants, who had been to the inn for the sumpter mule, returned; and, spreading a carpet upon the green grass of the meadow, they sat down in the shade of some trees and made their repast there, in order, as we have said, that the carter might take advantage of the spot. As they were engaged in eating, they suddenly heard a loud noise and the sound of a small bell, which came from among some brambles and dense undergrowth near by, and at the same instant they saw coming out of the thicket a beautiful nanny-goat, its skin all speckled with black, white, and brown spots. Behind it came a goatherd, shouting at it, with such language as his kind customarily use and calling upon it to stop and come back to the fold. The fugitive goat, however, thoroughly frightened, ran up to where they were sitting, as if asking protection of them, followed by the goatherd, who, seizing it by the horns, spoke to it as if it had been capable of understanding.

"Ah, Spotty! Spotty!" he cried, "what a wild one you are! How comes it that you go limping around these days? What wolves have frightened you, my daughter? Won't you tell me what it is, my beauty? What else can it be than that you are a female and hence naturally restless? What ails you, anyway, and all those that you take after? Come back, come back, my dear; you may not be quite so happy there, but at least you'll be safer in the fold, along with your companions. For if you, who ought to watch over and lead them, go wandering off so aimlessly, what is to become of them?"

They were all quite amused by the goatherd's words, especially the canon. "As you live, brother," he said, "calm yourself a little and do not be in such haste to return this goat to the fold; for, seeing that she is a female, as you say, she must follow her natural bent no matter how much you try to stop her. Have a bite with us and take a drink; that will cool your anger and give the goat a chance to rest at the same time."

He therewith presented him with some cold loin of rabbit on the end of a knife and handed him a glass of wine. The goatherd accepted it with thanks, drank the wine, and grew calmer.

"I hope," he said, "that your Worships will not take me for a simpleton because I spoke the way I did to this animal; the truth of the matter is, there is a certain mystery behind the words I spoke. I may be a countryman, but I know how to treat both men and beasts."

"That I can well believe," said the curate, "for I know from experience that the woods breed men of learning and that many a philosopher is to be found in a shepherd's hut."

"At least, sir," replied the goatherd, "they shelter men who have some knowledge of life. And in order that you may be convinced of the truth of this and grasp it thoroughly, even though I may appear to speak without being invited, I should like you, gentlemen, if it will not tire you, to listen closely as I tell you a story which will confirm what this gentleman"—pointing to the curate—"and I myself have just been saying."

Don Quixote then spoke up. "Inasmuch," he said, "as this appears to me to savor somewhat of a knightly adventure, I for my part will gladly listen to you, brother, and so will all these other gentlemen; for they are extremely intelligent and fond of hearing new and strange things that astonish, divert, and entertain the mind as I am sure your story will. Begin, then, my friend, for we are all listening."

"I take back my stakes," [3] declared Sancho. "I'm going down to that brook that I see over there, with this pastry, and stuff myself for three whole days. I have heard my master Don Quixote say that a knight-errant's squire ought to eat all he can when he has the chance; for, likely as not, they will be getting into some wood or other and will not be able to find their way out for a week, and if his belly is not full or his saddlebags well stocked, he may remain there, as very often happens, dead as a mummy."

"In that you are right, Sancho," said Don Quixote. "Go wherever you like and eat as much as you like, for I have had my fill and it is only left for me to give my soul a little reflection as I shall do by listening to this good man's story."

"And we will all do the same," said the canon.

He then requested the goatherd to begin the tale that he had promised them; whereupon the man gave the animal a couple of slaps on the side, saying to it, "Lie down here beside me, Spotty; there will be time later for us to return to the fold." It seemed that the goat understood, for as soon as her master had said this she stretched out beside him very tranquilly, gazing up into his face as if to give him to understand that she was listening for the story he was about to tell. He then began as follows.

CHAPTER LI . *Which treats of the story the goatherd told to all those who were bearing off Don Quixote.*

"THREE leagues from this valley there is a village which, although it is a small one, is one of the richest to be found in all these parts. In it there lived a farmer who was highly respected, and while it is a common thing for the well-to-do to be treated with respect, he was held in even greater esteem for his virtue than for the wealth that he had acquired. But what made him happier than anything else, as he himself put it, was the possession of a daughter of such rare and exceeding beauty, grace, wit, and modesty, that any who knew and looked upon her could not but be astonished at the lavish gifts with which Heaven and nature had endowed her.

"She had been beautiful as a small child and had grown more so with the years until by the time she reached the age of sixteen she was the loveliest of creatures and her fame had begun to spread to the neighboring villages—what am I saying? to the far away cities—and had even reached the halls of royalty and the ears of persons of every class, who came from all around to behold her as if she had been some rare and curious thing or some miracle-working image.

"Her father watched over her and she watched over herself; for there are no locks, guards, or bolts that afford better protection to a maiden than does her own modesty. His wealth and her beauty led many of the villagers and others from distant parts to seek her hand in marriage, but, having so precious a jewel to dispose of, he was wholly unable to make up his mind as to which of her countless suitors he should give her. I was one of the many who were in love with her, and I had great hopes of being successful, since her father knew me as a native of the same village and I was of pure stock and in the flower of youth and in addition was very well off in this world's goods while my qualities of mind left nothing to be desired.

"But there was another suitor of the village possessing these same qualifications, and this caused the father to weigh his choice and hold it in suspense, since it seemed to him that either of us would be a good match for his daughter. By way of ridding himself of his perplexity, he resolved to speak to Leandra, for that was the name of the wealthy lass who had brought me to a state of misery. He accordingly told his beloved child that, inasmuch as we were equals in what we had to offer, he would leave the matter of choosing between us to her own good pleasure—a procedure that deserves to be imitated by all parents with children to whom they wish to give a start in life. I do not mean that the latter should be permitted to choose that which is evil and vile; what I am saying is that the good things should be set before them and from these they should make their own choice. I do not know which of us Leandra chose, but I do know that her father put us off with vague words, on the ground that the girl was so young, words that neither bound him to anything nor constituted an outright dismissal for us.

"My rival's name was Anselmo and mine is Eugenio; I tell you this to acquaint you with the characters in this tragedy, the end of which is not yet, although it is clearly bound to be disastrous.

"At this time there came to our village a certain Vicente de la Rosa, son of a poor peasant who lived there. Vicente had been a soldier in Italy and elsewhere, having been taken away when a lad of about twelve by a captain who chanced to be passing through the place with his company; and now, here he was back again, twelve years later, dressed in a soldier's gaudy uniform covered with any number of glass trinkets and fine steel chains. Today he would put on one uniform and tomorrow another, but all of them flimsy and showy, of little weight and less worth. The peasants, who are naturally malicious and, when time hangs heavy on their hands, can be malice itself, were quick to observe all this. They made an inventory of his jewelry and other finery piece by piece and discovered that he had, altogether, three uniforms of different colors with stockings and garters to match, but with these he effected so many combinations that, had they not counted them, they would have sworn that he had displayed more than ten different suits and more than a score of feathered bonnets. And do not think that, in enumerating the garments that he wore, I am straying from the point, for they have a considerable part to play in the story.

"He used to seat himself upon a bench that stood beneath a large poplar tree in the public square of our village, and there he would keep us all gaping as we listened to the story of the feats he had performed. There was no country on earth that he had not visited, no battle in which he had not taken part, and he had slain a greater number of Moors than there are in Morocco and Tunis put together. He had also been engaged in more singlehanded combats than Garcilaso,[1] Diego García de Paredes, and a thousand other knights whom he mentioned, and had emerged victorious from all of them without having lost a single drop of blood. What was more, he showed us the scars of wounds, and although they were so faint that we could not make them out, he gave us to understand that they were from gunshot and that he had received them in various battles and skirmishes. And to cap it all, he, with an unheard-of arrogance, addressed his equals, even those that he knew well, with the condescendingly formal pronoun *vos*, remarking that his father was his own good arm, his deeds his pedigree, and that by reason of being a soldier he owed nothing to the king himself.

"In addition to these arrogant attitudes, he was something of a musician and used to strum the guitar in such a way as to make it speak, according to some. His accomplishments did not stop here, however, for he was also a bit of a poet and would compose a ballad a league and a half long on any trifling event that occurred in the village.

"This soldier, then, whom I have described for you, this Vicente de la Rosa, this braggart, this gallant, this musician, this poet, was seen and admired by Leandra many times from the window of her house overlooking the square. She was charmed by the tinsel and glitter of his uniforms and by his ballads, for he gave away a score of copies of each one that he composed, and she had heard of his exploits as he himself had narrated them. The result was that finally—the devil must have had a hand in it—she came to fall in love with him before he had thought of paying court to her; and since no love affair runs more smoothly than the one in which the lady is enamored, Leandra and Vicente readily came to an understanding, and before any of her numerous suitors so much as suspected her plan, she had carried it through by leaving her father's house (she had no mother) and running away with the soldier, who came out of this undertaking more triumphantly than he had out of all the others of which he boasted.

"The entire village and all those who heard the news were very much shocked by it; I was dumfounded, Anselmo was thunderstruck, her father was deeply grieved, her relatives angry and ashamed, the law was invoked, and the officers of the Brotherhood held themselves in readiness. A thorough search was made of the highways, woods, and all the surrounding territory, and at the end of three days they found the wayward Leandra in a mountain cave, naked save for her chemise and without the large sum of money and extremely valuable jewels with which she had left home. Bringing her back to her grief-stricken father, they questioned her as to what had happened, and she freely confessed that Vicente de la Rosa had deceived her by promising that, if she would leave her father's house, he would marry her and take her to the richest and most luxurious city in all the world, which was Naples. Deluded by his words, she had foolishly believed him and, having robbed her father, had handed everything over to her lover on the night that she disappeared. He then had borne her away to a rugged mountain and there had shut her up in that cave where they had found her. She further told how the soldier, without depriving her of her honor, had robbed her of all her other possessions, after which he had gone off and left her alone, a circumstance that filled all who heard it with fresh amazement.

"It was hard for us to believe in the young fellow's continence, but she asserted it so emphatically that it did much to console the disconsolate father, who gave no thought to his material losses, seeing that his daughter had been left him with the one jewel which, once it is lost, is gone beyond hope of recovery. On the very day that Leandra returned, he removed her from our sight and took her to a convent in a near-by city, trusting that time would repair somewhat the damage to her reputation. The girl's youth served to excuse her for her fault, at least with those who had no interest in branding her as good or bad; but those who were aware of her excellent mind and sound judgment did not attribute her sin to ignorance, but rather to forwardness and the natural inclination of women, which for the most part is toward flightiness and irresponsibility.

"With Leandra shut away, Anselmo's eyes were blind, or at least had nothing to look upon that gave him any happiness, and my own also were in darkness, without a ray of light to guide them to anything that was pleasurable. With her absence our sadness grew, our patience became exhausted, and we cursed the soldier's fancy uniforms and railed at the carelessness of Leandra's father in not having kept a better watch upon her. Finally, the two of us decided to leave the village and come to this valley, and here, pasturing a large number of sheep which are his and a numerous herd of goats which are mine, we spend our lives amid the trees, giving vent to our sorrow as we sing together the praises of the fair Leandra and upbraid her for her fickleness, or go about, each by himself, sighing and sending up our complaints to Heaven.

"Imitating our example, a number of Leandra's other suitors have come to these inhospitable mountains, to practice the same mode of life as we. There are so many of them, indeed, that it would seem that this place has been converted into a pastoral Arcadia, being full of shepherds and sheepfolds, and there is no spot where the name of the beauteous Leandra is not heard. One curses her, calling her capricious, fickle, and immodest. Another condemns her as a woman of light and easy manners. One absolves and pardons, and another judges and reviles her. One hymns her beauty, another dwells on her bad qualities. In short, they all abuse her and all of them adore her, and their madness is carried to such a point that there are some even who complain of her scorn who had never had a word with her, while others moan and suffer all the rage and pangs of jealousy, although she never gave anyone cause to be jealous, for, as I have said, her misstep was known before we learned of her passion. And so, there is no cavity among the rocks, no brookside, no leafy shade where you will not find some shepherd lifting his voice to bewail his lot. Wherever there is an echo, it repeats the name of Leandra. The mountains resound with

'Leandra'; 'Leandra' murmur the brooks; and Leandra it is who holds us all under an agonizing spell, hoping without hope and fearing without knowing what it is we dread.

"Among all these foolish beings, the one who shows most and least sense is my rival Anselmo. Having so many other things of which he might complain, he laments only the fact that Leandra is far away, and to the sound of a rebec, which he plays admirably well, he goes about singing verses that display his fine abilities as a poet. As for me, I follow an easier and, as it seems to me, a wiser course, which consists in berating women for their frivolity, their inconstancy, their double dealing, their unkept promises, their broken troth, and, lastly, the want of sense they show in selecting the one upon whom they see fit to settle their affections. And there, gentlemen, you have the explanation of the words I used in addressing this goat as I came up to you; for, inasmuch as she is a female, I have little respect for her, even though she is the best of all my flock.

"Such is the story that I promised to tell you. If I have been tedious in the way I told it, that does not mean that I shall be slow in serving you. My hut is near by, and in it I have fresh milk and some cheese that you will like very much, along with ripe fruit that is no less pleasing to the eye than it is to the taste."

CHAPTER LII. *Of the quarrel that Don Quixote had with the goatherd, together with the rare adventure of the penitents, which the knight by the sweat of his brow brought to a happy conclusion.*

ALL those who had listened to it were greatly pleased with the goatherd's story, especially the canon, who was more than usually interested in noting the manner in which it had been told. Far from being a mere rustic herdsman, the narrator seemed rather a cultured city dweller; and the canon accordingly remarked that the curate had been quite right in saying that the mountain groves bred men of learning. They all now offered their services to Eugenio, and Don Quixote was the most generous of any in this regard.

"Most assuredly, brother goatherd," he said, "if it were possible for me to undertake any adventure just now, I would set out at once to aid you and would take Leandra out of that convent, where she is undoubtedly being held against her will, in spite of the abbess and all the others who might try to prevent me, after which I would place her in your hands to do with as you liked, with due respect, however, for the laws of chivalry, which command that no violence be offered to any damsel. But I trust in God, Our Lord, that the power of one malicious enchanter is not so great that another magician may not prove still more powerful, and then I promise you my favor and my aid, as my calling obliges me to do, since it is none other than that of succoring the weak and those who are in distress."

The goatherd stared at him, observing in some astonishment the knight's unprepossessing appearance.

"Sir," he said, turning to the barber who sat beside him, "who is this man who looks so strange and talks in this way?"

"Who should it be," the barber replied, "if not the famous Don Quixote de la Mancha, righter of wrongs, avenger of injustices, protector of damsels, terror of giants, and champion of battles?"

"That," said the goatherd, "sounds to me like the sort of thing you read of in books of chivalry, where they do all those things that your Grace has mentioned in connection with this man. But if you ask me, either your Grace is joking or this worthy gentleman must have a number of rooms to let inside his head."

"You are the greatest villain that ever was!" cried Don Quixote when he heard this. "It is you who are the empty one; I am fuller than the bitch that bore you ever was." Saying this, he snatched up a loaf of bread that was lying beside him and hurled it straight in the goatherd's face with such force as to flatten the man's nose. Upon finding himself thus mistreated in earnest, Eugenio, who did not understand this kind of joke, forgot all about the carpet, the tablecloth, and the other diners and leaped upon Don Quixote. Seizing him by the throat with both hands, he would no doubt have strangled him if Sancho Panza, who now came running up, had not grasped him by the shoulders and flung him backward over the table, smashing plates and cups and spilling and scattering all the food and drink that was there. Thus freed of his assailant, Don Quixote then threw himself upon the shepherd, who, with bleeding face and very much battered by Sancho's feet, was creeping about on his hands and knees in search of a table knife with which to exact a sanguinary vengeance, a purpose which the canon and the curate prevented him from carrying out. The barber, however, so contrived it that the goatherd came down on top of his opponent, upon whom he now showered so many blows that the poor knight's countenance was soon as bloody as his own.

As all this went on, the canon and the curate were laughing fit to burst, the troopers were dancing with glee, and they all hissed on the pair as men do at a dog fight. Sancho Panza alone was in despair, being unable to free himself of one of the canon's servants who held him back from going to his master's aid. And then, just as they were all enjoying themselves hugely, with the exception of the two who were mauling each other, the note of a trumpet fell upon their ears, a sound so mournful that it caused them all to turn their heads in the direction from which it came. The one who was most excited by it was Don Quixote; who, very much against his will and more than a little bruised, was lying pinned beneath the goatherd.

"Brother Demon," he now said to the shepherd, "for you could not possibly be anything but a demon, seeing that you have shown a strength and valor greater than mine, I request you to call a truce for no more than an hour; for the doleful sound of that trumpet that we hear seems to me to be some new adventure that is calling me."

Tired of mauling and being mauled, the goatherd let him up at once. As he rose to his feet and turned his head in the direction of the sound, Don Quixote then saw, coming down the slope of a hill, a large number of persons clad in white after the fashion of penitents; for, as it happened, the clouds that year had denied their moisture to the earth, and in all the villages of that district processions for prayer and penance were being organized with the purpose of beseeching God to have mercy and send rain. With this object in view, the good folk from a near-by town were making a pilgrimage to a devout hermit who dwelt on these slopes. Upon beholding the strange costumes that the penitents wore, without pausing to think how many times he had seen them before, Don Quixote imagined that this must be some adventure or other, and that it was for him alone as a knight-errant to undertake it. He was strengthened in this belief by the sight of a covered image that they bore, as it seemed to him this must be some highborn lady whom these scoundrelly and discourteous brigands were forcibly carrying off; and no sooner did this idea occur to him than he made for Rocinante, who was grazing not far away.

Taking the bridle and his buckler from off the saddletree, he had the bridle adjusted in no time, and then, asking Sancho for his sword, he climbed into the saddle, braced his shield upon his arm, and cried out to those present, "And now, valorous company, you shall see how important it is to have in the world those who follow the profession of knight-errantry. You have but to watch how I shall set at liberty that worthy lady who there goes captive, and then you may tell me whether or not such knights are to be esteemed."

As he said this, he dug his legs into Rocinante's flanks, since he had no spurs, and at a fast trot (for nowhere in this veracious history are we ever told that the hack ran full speed) he bore down on the penitents in spite of all that the canon, the curate, and the barber could do to restrain him—their efforts were as vain as were the pleadings of his squire.

"Where are you bound for, Señor Don Quixote?" Sancho called after him. "What evil spirits in your bosom spur you on to go against our Catholic faith? Plague take me, can't you see that's a procession of penitents and that lady they're carrying on the litter is the most blessed image of the Immaculate Virgin? Look well what you're doing, my master, for this time it may be said that you really do not know."

His exertions were in vain, however, for his master was so bent upon having it out with the sheeted figures and freeing the lady clad in mourning that he did not hear a word, nor would he have turned back if he had, though the king himself might have commanded it. Having reached the procession, he reined in Rocinante, who by this time was wanting a little rest, and in a hoarse, excited voice he shouted, "You who go there with your faces covered, out of shame, it may be, listen well to what I have to say to you."

The first to come to a halt were those who carried the image; and then one of the four clerics who were intoning the litanies, upon beholding Don Quixote's weird figure, his bony nag, and other amusing appurtenances, spoke up in reply.

"Brother, if you have something to say to us, say it quickly, for these brethren are engaged in macerating their flesh, and we cannot stop to hear anything, nor is it fitting that we should, unless it is capable of being said in a couple of words."

"I will say it to you in one word," Don Quixote answered, "and that word is the following: 'Set free at once that lovely lady whose tears and mournful countenance show plainly that you are carrying her away against her will and that you have done her some shameful wrong. I will not consent to your going one step farther until you shall have given her the freedom that should be hers.' "

Hearing these words, they all thought that Don Quixote must be some madman or other and began laughing heartily; but their laughter proved to be gunpowder to his wrath, and without saying another word he drew his sword and fell upon the litter. One of those who bore the image, leaving his share of the burden to his companions, then sallied forth to meet the knight, flourishing a forked stick that he used to support the Virgin while he was resting; and upon this stick he now received a mighty slash that Don Quixote dealt him, one that shattered it in two, but with the piece about a third long that remained in his hand he came down on the shoulder of his opponent's sword arm, left unprotected by the buckler, with so much force that the poor fellow sank to the ground sorely battered and bruised.

Sancho Panza, who was puffing along close behind his master, upon seeing him fall cried out to the attacker not to deal another blow, as this was an unfortunate knight who was under a magic spell but who had never in all the days of his life done any harm to anyone. But the thing that stopped the rustic was not Sancho's words; it was, rather, the sight of Don Quixote lying there without moving hand or foot. And so, thinking that he had killed him, he hastily girded up his tunic and took to his heels across the countryside like a deer.

By this time all of Don Quixote's companions had come running up to where he lay; and the penitents, when they observed this, and especially when they caught sight of the officers of the Brotherhood with their crossbows,[1] at once rallied around the image, where they raised their hoods and grasped their whips [2] as the priests raised their tapers aloft in expectation of an assault; for they were resolved to defend themselves and even, if possible, to take the offensive against their assailants, but, as luck would have it, things turned out better than they had hoped. Sancho, meanwhile, believing Don Quixote to be dead, had flung himself across his master's body and was weeping and wailing in the most lugubrious and, at the same time, the most laughable fashion that could be imagined; and the curate had discovered among those who marched in the procession another curate whom he knew, their recognition of each other serving to allay the fears of all parties concerned. The first curate then gave the second a very brief account of who Don

Quixote was, whereupon all the penitents came up to see if the poor knight was dead. And as they did so, they heard Sancho Panza speaking with tears in his eyes.

"O flower of chivalry," he was saying, "the course of whose well-spent years has been brought to an end by a single blow of a club! O honor of your line, honor and glory of all La Mancha and of all the world, which, with you absent from it, will be full of evildoers who will not fear being punished for their deeds! O master more generous than all the Alexanders, who after only eight months of service presented me with the best island that the sea washes and surrounds! Humble with the proud, haughty with the humble, brave in facing dangers, long-suffering under outrages, in love without reason, imitator of the good, scourge of the wicked, enemy of the mean—in a word, a knight-errant, which is all there is to say." [3]

At the sound of Sancho's cries and moans, Don Quixote revived, and the first thing he said was, "He who lives apart from thee, O fairest Dulcinea, is subject to greater woes than those I now endure. Friend Sancho, help me onto that enchanted cart, as I am in no condition to sit in Rocinante's saddle with this shoulder of mine knocked to pieces the way it is."

"That I will gladly do, my master," replied Sancho, "and we will go back to my village in the company of these gentlemen who are concerned for your welfare, and there we will arrange for another sally and one, let us hope, that will bring us more profit and fame than this one has."

"Well spoken, Sancho," said Don Quixote, "for it will be an act of great prudence to wait until the present evil influence of the stars has passed."

The canon, the curate, and the barber all assured him that he would be wise in doing this; and so, much amused by Sancho Panza's simplicity, they placed Don Quixote upon the cart as before, while the procession of penitents re-formed and continued on its way. The goatherd took leave of all of them, and the curate paid the troopers what was coming to them, since they did not wish to go any farther. The canon requested the priest to inform him of the outcome of Don Quixote's madness, as to whether it yielded to treatment or not; and with this he begged permission to resume his journey. In short, the party broke up and separated, leaving only the curate and the barber, Don Quixote and Panza, and the good Rocinante, who looked upon everything that he had seen with the same resignation as his master.

Yoking his oxen, the carter made the knight comfortable upon a bale of hay, and then at his customary slow pace proceeded to follow the road that the curate directed him to take. At the end of six days they reached Don Quixote's village, making their entrance at noon of a Sunday, when the square was filled with a crowd of people through which the cart had to pass.

They all came running to see who it was, and when they recognized their townsman, they were vastly astonished. One lad sped to bring the news to the knight's housekeeper and his niece, telling them that their master had returned lean and jaundiced and lying stretched out upon a bale of hay on an ox-cart. It was pitiful to hear the good ladies' screams, to behold the way in which they beat their breasts, and to listen to the curses which they once more heaped upon those damnable books of chivalry, and this demonstration increased as they saw Don Quixote coming through the doorway.

At news of the knight's return, Sancho Panza's wife had hurried to the scene, for she had some while since learned that her husband had accompanied him as his squire; and now, as soon as she laid eyes upon her man, the first question she asked was if all was well with the ass, to which Sancho replied that the beast was better off than his master.

"Thank God," she exclaimed, "for all his blessings! But tell me now, my dear, what have you brought me from all your squirings? A new cloak to wear? Or shoes for the young ones?"

"I've brought you nothing of the sort, good wife," said Sancho, "but other things of greater value and importance."

"I'm glad to hear that," she replied. "Show me those things of greater value and importance, my dear. I'd like a sight of them just to cheer this heart of mine which has been so sad and unhappy all the centuries that you've been gone."

"I will show them to you at home, wife," said Sancho. "For the present be satisfied that if, God willing, we set out on another journey in search of adventures, you will see me in no time a count or the governor of an island, and not one of those around here, but the best that is to be had."

"I hope to Heaven it's true, my husband, for we certainly need it. But tell me, what is all this about islands? I don't understand."

"Honey," replied Sancho, "is not for the mouth of an ass.[4] You will find out in good time, woman; and you're going to be surprised to hear yourself called 'my Ladyship' by all your vassals."

"What's this you are saying, Sancho, about ladyships, islands, and vassals?" Juana Panza insisted on knowing—for such was the name of Sancho's wife, although they were not blood relatives, it being the custom in La Mancha for wives to take their husbands' surnames.

"Do not be in such a hurry to know all this, Juana," he said. "It is enough that I am telling you the truth. Sew up your mouth, then; for all I will say, in passing, is that there is nothing in the world that is more pleasant than being a respected man, squire to a knight-errant who goes in search of adventures. It is true that most of the adventures you meet with do not come out the way you'd like them to, for ninety-nine out of a hundred will prove to be all twisted and crosswise. I know that from experience, for I've come out of some of them blanketed and out of others beaten to a pulp. But, all the same, it's a fine thing to go along waiting for what will happen next, crossing mountains, making your way through woods, climbing over cliffs, visiting castles, and putting up at inns free of charge, and the devil take the maravedi that is to pay."

Such was the conversation that took place between Sancho Panza and Juana Panza, his wife, as Don Quixote's housekeeper and niece were taking him in, stripping him, and stretching him out on his old-time bed. He gazed at them blankly, being unable to make out where he was. The curate charged the niece to take great care to see that her uncle was comfortable and to keep close watch over him so that he would not slip away from them another time. He then told them of what it had been necessary to do in order to get him home, at which they once more screamed to Heaven and began cursing the books of chivalry all over again, praying God to plunge the authors of such lying nonsense into the center of the bottomless pit. In short, they scarcely knew what to do, for they were very much afraid that their master and uncle would give them the slip once more, the moment he was a little better, and it turned out just the way they feared it might.

But the author of this history, although he has made a most thorough and diligent search, has been unable to come upon any account—at least none based on authentic sources—of the deeds performed by Don Quixote on his third sally. There is only the tradition, handed down in La Mancha, to the effect that in the course of this third expedition he went to Saragossa, where he was present at some famous tourneys that were held in that city and where he met with adventures such as befitted his valor and sound judgment. As regards his last days and his death, the present writer was unable to come upon any record whatsoever, nor would he have known anything at all about it if it had not been for an old physician who had in his possession a lead box which, so he said, had been found in the crumbling foundation of a very old hermitage that was being rebuilt. In this box were discovered certain writings on parchment, consisting of Castilian verses in Gothic characters, which had much to say of the beauty of Dulcinea del Toboso, of Rocinante's figure, Sancho Panza's loyalty, and the burial of Don Quixote himself, along with various epitaphs and elegies having to do with his life and habits.

Those verses that could be plainly read and made out were the following, as set down here by the author of this new and matchless history, who, in return for all the enormous labor that it has cost him to compile this book and all the research amid the archives of La Mancha, only asks of his readers that they give it the same credence that the discerning do to those books of chivalry that are so popular in the world today. Let them but do this, and he will regard himself as having been well repaid. And he will then endeavor to search out and bring to light others which, if not so true, will at least be equal to the present one in the matter of invention and the diversion they afford.

The first words written on the parchment that was found in the leaden box were these:

The academicians of Argamasilla,[5] a village of La Mancha, on the life and death of the valorous Don Quixote de la Mancha, HOC SCRIPSERUNT.

Monicongo,[6] academician of Argamasilla, for Don Quixote's tomb:

EPITAPH

The scatterbrain who was fair La Mancha's pride
And brought her more spoils than Jason brought to Crete;
The wit like a weathercock, pointed so neat,
That would have better been on the blunter side;
The arm whose might was celebrated wide—
From Cathay to Gaeta ran its fame so fleet;
Muse most horrendous, with wisdom most replete
That e'er her verses did to bronze confide;
He who left the Amadises behind him far,
Resting upon his love and gallantry;
Who held the Galaors to be but drab;
Whose calm the Belianises could not mar;
Who on Rocinante rode for chivalry:
Such the one now lies beneath this frigid slab.

Paniaguado,[7] academician of Argamasilla, *in laudem Dulcineae del Toboso:*

SONNET

She whom you here behold, with the chubby face,
With the high bosom and the vigorous mien,
Is the beauteous Dulcinea, Toboso's queen.
The great Quixote loved her regal grace,
And for her sake it was that he did trace
The slopes of the black Sierra, the famed demesne
Of Montiel's fields and the alluring green
Of Aranjuez' plain, on foot, with weary pace.
'Twas Rocinante's fault! O unkind star
Of this Manchegan lady and this bold
Knight-errant: she in the flower of her youth
Saw her beauty fade in death as he roamed far;
And though his fame in marble has been told,
He had to flee from love, spite, man's untruth.

Caprichoso,[8] a most learned academician of Argamasilla, in praise of Rocinante, steed of Don Quixote de la Mancha:

SONNET [9]

Upon the haughty adamantine throne,[10]
Which Mars with bloody footprints doth defile,
The mad Manchegan bravely all the while
Unfurls his standard with a strength unknown,
Hangs up his arms, the steel of finest tone
That shatters, rends, and razes with his bile.
Undreamed of prowess! Art invents a style
For the new paladin she calls her own.
If Gaul of its Amadis is justly proud,
Whose brave descendants brought triumph to Greece,
A thousand triumphs and a fame widespread,
Today it is Quixote the unbowed
Whom Bellona crowns there where the wars ne'er cease;
And proudest of all, La Mancha rears its head.
His fame shall live when others long are dead;
For Baiardo, Brigliador [11] did not exceed
In valor Rocinante, that gallant steed.

Burlador,[12] academician of Argamasilla, on Sancho Panza:

SONNET

Sancho Panza is this one with body small,
But big in valor, miracle how strange!
The simplest-minded squire that e'er did range
This world of ours, believe me one and all.
He'd have been a count if this age's biting gall
Had not prevented him; he could not change
The spite of men that gnawed them like a mange,
Pursuing even a donkey to its stall.
Upon the ass he went, if I'm not wrong,
Meekest of squires behind the very meek
And faithful Rocinante, and his lord.
Oh, the vain hopes we cherish all life long!
Thinking at last to find the rest we seek,
But shadow, smoke, and dreams are our reward.

Cachidiablo,[13] academician of Argamasilla, on Don Quixote's tomb:

EPITAPH [14]

Below there rests the knight,
Ill-errant, battered, sore,
Whom Rocinante bore
On his wanderings, left and right.
Sancho Panza, if you inquire,
Lies also within this span,
The most faithful little man
E'er followed the trade of squire.

Tiquitoc,[15] academician of Argamasilla, for Dulcinea del Toboso's tomb:

EPITAPH

Here Dulcinea doth lie,
Who was plump and high of bust;
Now she is ashes and dust,
For horrid death passed by.

> *She was of noble race,*
> *Truly a highbred dame,*
> *The great Don Quixote's flame*
> *And the glory of this place.*

Such were the verses that could be made out. The others, being worm-eaten, were turned over to an academician that he might decipher their meaning by conjecture. It is reported that he has done so, at the cost of much labor and many sleepless nights, and that it is his purpose to publish them, which leads us to hope that we may be given an account of Don Quixote's third sally.

> *Forse altri canterá con miglior plettro.*[16]

NOTES

Translator's Introduction

1. Aubrey F. G. Bell, *Cervantes* (Norman: University of Oklahoma Press, 1947). For two distinguished articles called forth by this book see "Knight-Errant from La Mancha, Anniversary Reflections on Don Quixote and the Literary Magic of His Creator," by T. R. Ybarra, *The New York Times Book Review*, August 17, 1947, p. 1; and "The Laughter and Sanity of Don Quixote; This Year Marks the 400th Anniversary of a Genius, Cervantes," by Bertram D. Wolfe, *The New York Herald Tribune Weekly Book Review*, August 17, 1947, pp. 1–2. Mr. Ybarra is himself the author of one of the best biographical-interpretative studies, entitled *Cervantes* (New York: Albert and Charles Boni, 1931).

2. See the article by Aubrey Bell, "The Wisdom of Don Quixote," *Books Abroad*, Summer 1947, pp. 259–63.

3. Ibid.

4. See the beginning of Chapter LXXIV, Part II.

5. Aubrey Bell is of the opinion that every one should read *Don Quixote* "not less than three times in his or her life," in youth, middle age, and old age. (*Cervantes*, p. ix.)

6. One thinks of Lang's Homer, Childs' *Beowulf*.

7. *Paradise Lost* is another classic on which the dust has for some time been gathering; but T. S. Eliot has recently called for a return to Milton (whom Ezra Pound violently condemns), and this may have its effects upon the intellectuals at least.

8. Bell makes the point that Cervantes in reality brought the Spanish Renaissance to the people of Spain, serving as a mediator between the culture of the elite and the great popular audience. (See the opening chapter of his book, "Cervantes and the Renaissance.")

9. On Cervantes and the art of fiction, consult *Five Masters, A Study in Imitations of the Novel*, by Joseph Wood Krutch (New York: Jonathan Cape and Harrison Smith, 1930).

10. Himself a native of the province, Rodríguez Marín was the first to stress the heavy Andalusian element in Cervantes' work. See his brochures, *Cervantes en Andalucía* (Seville, 1905), and *El Andalucismo y el Cordobesismo de Miguel de Cervantes* (Madrid, 1915). In the notes to his edition of the *Don Quixote* he is constantly pointing out traces of this influence. It was while serving as a tax collector that Cervantes became familiar with the speech and customs of the Andalusians, just as Rabelais while residing at Fontenay-le-Comte absorbed the idiom and the folklore of Poitou. On this, see what I have to say in my introduction to *The Portable Rabelais* (New York: Viking Press, 1946), p. 21.

11. His article cited in note 1.

12. Two of these appeared in Lisbon and one in Valencia early in 1605.

13. The first French translation of the *Don Quixote* was César Oudin's version, Paris, 1616. Pahsch Basteln von der Sohle's partial German version was published at Cöthen in 1621, and Lorenzo Franciosini's Italian rendering appeared at Venice in 1621.

14. For English-language versions see the Bibliography following this Introduction.

15. See the Introduction to Ormsby's translation of *Don Quixote*.

16. Filleau de Saint-Martin's *Histoire de l'Admirable Don Quichotte de la Manche*, in four volumes, was first published at Paris, 1677–78. It ran through numerous editions down to the 1890's. His *Continuation* appeared in 1713. In this latter work he has Don Quixote recover from his illness at the end of Part II and resume his adventures.

17. This will be referred to simply as the Motteux version from now on.

18. See the Bibliography. For convenient reference, Lockhart's notes, including his translation of numerous ballads, will be found in the two-volume revised edition of Motteux's *Don Quixote* published in Bohn's Popular Library (London: G. Bell & Sons, 1913). It is Ozell's revision of Motteux, with a notable Introduction by Herschel Brickell, that appears in the Modern Library edition (New York, 1930).

19. As Ormsby remarks, Motteux could hardly be worse than Phillips. Ticknor may be said to have damned Motteux with faint praise. See the constrained apology for the use of the Motteux version, by E. Bell, in the Editor's Preface to the Bohn's Popular Library edition cited in the preceding note.

20. In this respect Motteux is far from being an Urquhart, whose version of Rabelais he completed. When Urquhart expands upon his author he gives us a piece of English that is worth reading for its own sake, whereas Peter Anthony only becomes all the more dull and offensive. (He was a Frenchman by birth, who came to England in his midtwenties and afterward wrote in the language of that country.) It is well to bear in mind the admonition given to the Moorish translator in Part I, Chapter IX: "Add nothing and subtract nothing."

21. The works referred to are Edmund Gayton's *Festivous Notes on the History and Adventures of the Renowned Don Quixote, Pleasant Notes upon Don Quixote* (London, 1654); and Edward Ward's *The Life and Notable Adventures of that Renown'd Knight, Don Quixote de la Mancha, Merrily Translated into Hudibrastick Verse* (London, 1711-12). Gayton was an Oxford don.

22. He will be referred to as Jarvis hereafter.

23. See Pope's "Epistle to Jervas."

24. For example, E. Bell (see note 19 above) finds the Jarvis version "more precise but dull and spiritless," while in his view Motteux is "the best representative" of the "expressive language that Steele, Defoe, and Fielding used."

25. Jarvis has been worked over, touched up, by later editors in an effort to make him more readable, but, as Ormsby notes, they have only detracted from his chief merit, which is his fidelity to the original—the revisions obviously were made without reference to the Spanish text.

26. Ormsby: "A literary imposture of remarkable impudence."

27. Miss Smirke's version was compiled to accompany the engravings of her brother, Robert Smirke, R. A. Ormsby calls it "a patchwork version made out of previous translations," while E. Bell terms it "a careful revision of Jarvis's translation." On the title-page of the first three editions it is described as "translated from the Spanish," but in the fourth and last printing (New York: D. Appleton & Company, 1855) it is frankly announced as "a revised translation based on those of Motteux, Jarvis, and Smollett." In connection with the Smirke plates, see *Illustrations for Don Quixote, Engraved by C. Warren, F. Engleheart, R. Golding, I. Scott, A. Smith, and S. Noble, from Designs by Robert Smirke* (London, 1811?).

28. It may be observed in passing that the four translators cited by Professor Rudolph Schevill in the notes to his Spanish edition of the *Don Quixote* are Oudin, Franciosini, Ludwig Tieck, and Ormsby. (On Tieck and the importance of his German version see the Bibliography following.) It is the Ormsby translation of *Don Quixote* that was selected by Fitzmaurice-Kelly for Volumes III-VI of his seven-volume edition in English of *The Complete Works of Miguel de Cervantes Saavedra* (Glasgow, 1901-1903); and Robinson Smith in the Introduction to his new edition of 1932 pays tribute to his predecessor.

29. This despite the locutions that have been dropped from general usage.

30. In Part II, Chapter XXVI, this saying is put into the mouth of Master Pedro, the puppet showman, who is addressing his apprentice; in Part II, Chapter XLIII, it is Don Quixote who utters the aphorism.

31. See the valuable dissertation of Margaret J. Bates, *"Discreción" in the Works of Cervantes* (Washington: Catholic University of America Press, 1945). Dr. Bates here takes one word that has a large number of fine shadings and shows how important it is not only for the interpretation of Cervantes'

text but for an understanding of his view of life as well. For an interesting discussion of the problems of the Cervantes translator the reader may refer to the essay by F. B. Franz Biedermann, *Don Quichotte et la Tâche de Ses Traducteurs* (Paris, 1837); this is a treatise based upon the work of the French translator Louis Viardot.

32. Unfortunately, this edition has for some while been out of print. In his Cervantes bibliography (see note 63) Professor Grismer indicates there is some question as to the date of the first edition of the Smith version.

33. See Ormsby's note, Part II, Chapter VI, of his translation.

34. Part II, Chapter III.

35. For these works see the Bibliography.

36. In *La Lengua de Cervantes* Cejador has done for the creator of Don Quixote what M. Lazare Sainéan in *La Langue de Rabelais* (Paris, 1923) was to do a little later for the author of the *Gargantua* and *Pantagruel*.

37. Of the University of California.

38. The first two volumes, published in 1914, contain *La Galatea* and *Persiles y Sigismunda;* these were followed by six volumes of *Comedias y Entremeses,* 1915-22; the *Viaje del Parnaso* and the *Poesías Sueltas* (one volume each), 1922; three volumes of the *Novelas Ejemplares,* 1922-25; and, finally, Schevill's *Don Quixote,* the four volumes of which appeared in 1928, 1931, 1935, and 1941. Announced for future publication are a *Reseña Sucinta de la Vida de Cervantes* and an alphabetic index to the notes.

39. Such emendations, for instance, as are to be found in the edition of Juan Eugenio Hartzenbusch (1863), an editor whom Ormsby often follows. Hartzenbusch performed a valuable service by calling attention to the textual differences between the first and later editions, pointing out that these were not due to corrections made by the author; but he then proceeded to emend the first-edition text upon the basis of what he believed Cervantes "must have" written. Numerous examples of this will be found in the notes to the present translation.

40. See the editor's "Prólogo" to Tomo I of Schevill's *Don Quixote.*

41. See Chapter XXIII and note 2.

42. On this subject see Cortejón's brochure, *¿Corrigió Cervantes alguna de las ediciones del Don Quixote impresas por Juan de la Cuesta?* (Barcelona, 1907).

43. Compare Ormsby's remarks in the Introduction to his *Don Quixote.*

44. Duffield, Ormsby, and Watts all retain "ingenious" and the spelling "Quixote."

45. See Part I, Chapters XII-XIV.

46. This is the form that Cervantes regularly employs in place of the modern *Usted,* which, however, occurs in the *novela* of uncertain authorship, *La Tia Fingida.*

47. "Your Worship" is somewhat foreign to American ears. "Your Grace" has the advantage of being literal and the disadvantage of being commonly associated with a personage of ducal or archiepiscopal rank.

48. Here, the Schevill text has been used as a guide from which I have freely departed when there was reason for doing so.

49. An example of the kind of sentence that comes near to being the despair of any translator will be found in Part II, Chapter I (Schevill, Tomo III, pp. 45-46): *"Ya no ay ninguno que saliendo deste bosque entre en aquella montaña, y de alli, pise vna esteril y desierta playa del mar, las mas vezes proceloso y alterado; y hallando en ella y en su orilla vn pequeño batel sin remos, vela, mastil, ni xarcia alguna, con intrepido coraçon se arroge en el, entregandose a las implacables olas del mar profundo, que ya le suben al cielo y ya le baxan al abismo, y el, puesto el pecho a la incontrastable borrasca, quando menos se cata, se halla tres mil y mas leguas distante del lugar donde se embarco; y saltando en tierra remota y no conocida le suceden cosas dignas de estar escritas, no en pergaminos, sino en bronces."* Yet this is beautiful Castilian, with a classic dignity that puts one in mind of certain passages in Vergil. And it will be observed how that terseness within the sentence of which I have spoken is achieved. Not infrequently Cervantes is so very terse as to recall the famous *"Veni, vidi, vici"* attributed to Caesar, as in the closing lines of Chapter III, Part II: ". . . *tuuo el bachiller el em-*

bite, quedose, añadiose al ordinario vn par de pichones, tratose en la mesa de cauallerias, siguiole el humor Carrasco, acabose el banquete, durmieron la siesta, boluio Sancho y renouose la platica passada."

50. There is good precedent for this among the great Elizabethan translators: compare the practice of Philemon Holland in his translation of Livy; see F. O. Matthiessen's *Translation, An Elizabethan Art* (Cambridge: Harvard University Press, 1931), pp. 185-86.

51. Two examples at random: Part II, Chapter LX (Schevill, Tomo IV, p. 267): *Mandoselos boluer al punto Roque Guinart, y, mandando poner los suyos en ala, mandó traer alli delante . . ."* (the verb *mandar* used three times in two lines); and Part II, Chapter LXVI (Schevill, Tomo IV, p. 331): *". . . vn vezino deste lugar, tan gordo que pesa onze arrobas, dessafió a correr a otro su vezino, que no pesa mas que cinco. Fue le condicion que auian de correr vna carrera de cien pasos con pesos iguales, y, auiendole preguntado al dessafiador como se auia de igualar el peso, dixo que el dessaffiado, que pesa cinco arrobas, se pusiesse seis de hierro a cuestas . . ."* (note the repetition of *pesar—peso*, five times in six lines of text!).

52. Occasionally the synonyms have the effect of the rhetorical figure known as hendiadys, while the verbs may have an adjectival shading.

53. See the *Journey to Parnassus, Translated into English Tercets with Preface and Illustrative Notes*, by James Y. Gibson (London, 1883).

54. See *The Poetry of the "Don Quixote" of Don Miguel de Cervantes Saavedra* (London, 1887). I have not looked at the Gibson version while making this translation.

55. Compare M. Eloi Johanneau's Variorum edition of Rabelais.

56. See the Bibliography. The edition by the Spanish Royal Academy had appeared the year before (1780).

57. To suit his fancy, he even changed the title of the work to *Historia del Famoso Cavallero Don Quixote de la Mancha (History of the Famous Knight*, etc.).

58. See Appendix III to Ormsby's translation, "Bibliography of '*Don Quixote.*' "

59. This is essentially the stress of Rodríguez Marín. An annotator like Robinson Smith, on the other hand, is in the Bowle tradition.

60. See the introduction to the Rodríguez Marín edition in the Clásicos Castellanos series (see Bibliography).

61. See *Sancho Panza's Proverbs and Others Which Occur in Don Quixote; with a Literal English Translation, Notes, and an Introduction*, by U. R. Burke (London, 1872; third edition, 1892). Also, by the same hand, *Spanish Salt, A Collection of All the Proverbs Which Are to Be Found in Don Quixote* (London, 1877).

62. See the Bibliography under "Commentators and Lexicographers."

63. Raymond L. Grismer, *Cervantes: A Bibliography: Books, Essays, Articles, and Other Studies on the Life of Cervantes, His Works, and His Imitators* (New York: H. W. Wilson, 1946). See also, *Cervantes, A Tentative Bibliography of His Works and of the Biographical and Critical Material Concerning Him*, by Jeremiah D. M. Ford and Ruth Lansing (Cambridge: Harvard University Press, 1931).

A Note On the Author

1. For scholarly summaries of what is known about Cervantes the reader may be referred to the following works: *Cervantes*, by William J. Entwhistle (Oxford: Clarendon Press, 1940); *Cervantes*, by Rudolph Schevill (New York: Duffield & Company [Master Spirits of Literature series], 1919); *Miguel de Cervantes Saavedra: A Memoir*, by James Fitzmaurice-Kelly (Oxford: Clarendon Press, 1913); and *Two Essays* (I: "Don Quixote"), by William Paton Kerr (Glasgow: J. Maclehose and Sons, 1918).

2. It is in thinking of him as an old soldier that we are best able to understand Cervantes' psychology, his attitude on many questions. He is essentially an ardent patriot, a fervent Catholic, an impecunious *hidalgo*, and a life-battered man of letters.

3. What may be a description of the author's own Italian journeyings, resembling those of the ordinary tourist, will be found in the story "Man of Glass" (*El Licenciado Vidriera*) in the *Exemplary Novels*.

4. This is not to be taken as a literal account of Cervantes' experiences, but it is basically autobiographic.

5. In 1581, for example, he is in the service of the King as a messenger and in May and June of that year visits Tomar (Portugal), Oran, and Cartagena.

6. These were the *Numancia* and the *Pictures of Algiers* (*El Trato de Argel*). They were first printed in 1784, from newly discovered manuscript copies. On one occasion Cervantes is to be found contracting with a theatrical manager for six comedies at fifty ducats (about thirty dollars) each. When he published his dramatic works, in 1615, he entitled the volume *Eight Comedies and Eight Interludes, Original and Never Performed* (*Ocho Comedias y Ocho Entremeses Nuevos y Nunca Representados*). See the recent fine translation of the *Interludes* by S. Griswold Morley (Princeton: Princeton University Press, 1948).

7. See especially the *novela* "Rinconete and Cortadillo." Some of this argot is also to be found in *Don Quixote*, in such an episode, for example, as the freeing of the galley slaves (Part I, Chapter XXII). On the legend concerning the composition of Part I in prison, see the Prologue to Part I, note 1.

8. Valladolid was then the capital.

9. He may have been living in retirement at Esquivias, possibly at Valladolid.

10. "In any genre," says Lionel Trilling, "it may happen that the first great example contains the whole potentiality of the genre. It has been said that all philosophy is a footnote to Plato. It can be said that all prose fiction is a variation on the theme of *Don Quixote*. Cervantes sets for the novel the problem of appearance and reality . . ." See Trilling's essay on "Manners and the Novel," *The Kenyon Review*, Winter 1948.

11. See Part II, Chapter III. In the following chapter we are told that Cid Hamete (the supposed author of *Don Quixote*) is "more interested in the profit that may come to him from it than in any praise it may earn him." See also Part II, Chapter LXII, where another author says: "I do not write books to win fame in this world . . . it is money that I seek, for without it a good reputation is not worth a cent." I for one cannot accept the view put forth by Professor Joaquín Casalduero, to the effect that Cervantes had from the start, deliberately and carefully, plotted out a masterpiece of baroque art. See the paper by Casalduero, "The Composition of *Don Quixote*," in *Cervantes Across the Centuries, A Quadricentennial Volume*, edited by Angel Flores and M. J. Benardete (New York: The Dryden Press, 1947) pp. 56–93. Both the internal and the external evidence seems to me to be against it. Whatever else he may or may not have been, the author of *Don Quixote* was not an ivory tower dweller. (The Flores-Benardete collection, by the way, affords a good cross section of present day Cervantes scholarship and is the only one of its kind available in English.)

12. The idea was not original with Cervantes. In 1597 it had formed the subject of a dramatic piece of inferior quality, the *Entremés de los Romances* (*Interlude of the Ballads*, that is, the ballads of chivalry), the authorship of which is unknown—one critic has attempted to assign it to Cervantes himself. And in the fourteenth century the Italian novelist Franco Sacchetti had created a character whose adventures resemble those of the Knight of La Mancha.

13. In his *Five Masters: A Study in the Mutations of the Novel* (New York: Jonathan Cape & Harrison Smith, 1930), Joseph Wood Krutch compares certain aspects of Cervantes' thinking with the philosophy of "As If"; and in Part II, Chapter XXII, Don Quixote makes a statement that sounds as if it

were directly out of Sartre: "God knows whether or not there is a Dulcinea in this world . . . I contemplate her as she needs must be" ("*como conviene que sea*"). Today it is Kierkegaard and Sartre and the Existentialists. In Cervantes' time it was Augustine and Plato—Plato versus Aristotle.

14. See the essay by Frank, "The Career of the Hero," in *Cervantes Across the Centuries* (*op. cit.*, pp. 183–94).

15. Judging from what Cervantes has to say about publishers, one suspects that they may not always have been honest with him in their dealings.

16. It was formerly believed that the *Persiles* was written during the period under consideration here, but Professor Mack Singleton has put forward the somewhat heretical idea that it was a work of Cervantes' youth which he resurrected as he lay dying in order to provide a little revenue for his family. See Singleton's paper: "The 'Persiles' Mystery," in *Cervantes Across the Centuries* (*op. cit.*, pp. 256–63).

17. For some time the belief was current that Cervantes and Shakespeare had died on the same day; but the latter's death occurred on April 23 (Old Style).

NOTES

Part One

PROLOGUE

1. In the biographical sketch of Cervantes prefixed to his translation of the *Don Quixote*, John Ormsby writes: "The words in the preface to the First Part of 'Don Quixote' are generally held to be conclusive that he conceived the idea of the book, and wrote the beginning of it at least, in a prison, and that he may have done so is extremely likely. At the same time it should be borne in mind that they contain no assertion to that effect, and may mean nothing more than that this brain-child of his was begotten under circumstances as depressing as prison life. If we accept them literally, the prison may well have been that in which he was confined for nearly three months at Seville." A recent biographer, Mariano Tomás (*The Life and Misadventures of*

Miguel de Cervantes, translated from the Spanish by Warre B. Wells [Boston: Houghton Mifflin, 1934], pp. 160–161) states: "When . . . Miguel de Cervantes was released from the prison of Seville . . . he also carried with him . . . the first part of *The Ingenious Knight, Don Quixote de la Mancha*."

2. In its original form, this proverb reads: "*Al rey mando*—I give orders to the king"; compare "An Englishman's house is his castle."

3. From a fable, *De cane et lupo*, of the twelfth-century Walther [Gualterus] Anglicus. Compare Aesop and La Fontaine.

4. Horace, *Odes*, I, iv, 13–14.

5. For the first of these biblical quotations, see Matthew 5:44 and Luke 6:27, 35. For the second, Matthew 15:19 and Mark 7:21.

6. These lines are from Ovid's *Tristia*, I, ix, 5–6; the Cato referred to is Dionysius Cato, author of the *Disticha de Moribus*, a verse treatise on morals and manners widely used as a school text in the Renaissance era.

7. Reference here is to the valley of Elah, mentioned in I. Samuel 17:2; in the Vulgate, Elah is rendered as Terebinthus.

8. Noted thief of classical mythology, giant son of Vulcan, who dwelt on Mount Aventinus and disturbed the entire region round about with his depredations; he stole the cattle of Geryon from Hercules and was slain by him; see Ovid's *Fasti*, I, 543 ff., Vergil's *Aeneid*, VIII, 190 ff., and other Latin writers.

9. Allusion to the *Epistolae Familiares* (1539–45) of Antonio de Guevara. Orsmby finds this "a touch after Swift's heart."

10. Leon the Hebrew (died in 1520) was the author of the *Dialoghi d'Amore*, published in 1535.

11. The *Amor de Dios* of Cristóbal de Fonseca was published in 1594.

12. See Chapter II following and note 2.

PREFATORY VERSES

1. These pieces are burlesques on the laudatory poems which customarily prefaced the books that appeared in Cervantes' day. They are not to be taken as serious poetry. Urganda is a personage in the *Amadis of Gaul*, Lobeira's famous romance of chivalry (see Part I, Chapter VI). She in a manner combines the traits of Morgan the Fay, Vivien, and Merlin, the connotation here being that of "magic," which the author, in the original Spanish, playfully endeavors to suggest by means of a most unusual verse form. The epithet "*Desconocida*" (rendered as "Unknown") refers to Urganda's manifold disguises or transformations—"the Unrecognized." As for the verse form in question, it is a ten-line stanza with the rhyme scheme abbaaccddc; but its peculiarity consists in lopping off the final syllable of the last word in each verse, throwing the assonantal rhyme on the penultimate vowel. Thus:

> *De un noble hidalgo manche—*
> *contarás las aventu—*

a quien ociosas lectu—
trastornaron las cabe—

This passage from the beginning of the third stanza will serve to show how it is done. (It will be noted that the lopped-off syllables may or may not rhyme.) The invention of this form was commonly attributed to Cervantes, though it does him no great credit, but it probably was used before his time. It is one that in reality cannot be imitated in English, and there would seem to be little point in making the attempt. Accordingly, in this first piece I have ignored the lopped-line technique, but in two short ones later on in which it is again employed I have tried to give some idea of it.

2. Cervantes' patron; see the dedication of Part I.

3. Of La Mancha.

4. This is seen as a dig at Lope de Vega, whose portrait in a couple of early volumes of his work had beneath it a heraldic shield.

5. Alvaro (Alvarez) de Luna, Constable of Castile and favorite of John II, lost the royal favor and was beheaded at Valladolid in 1450.

6. Allusion to the Spanish captivity of Francis I of France, Charles V's prisoner.

7. Allusion to Juan Latino, Negro slave of the Duke of Sesa, who was made professor of Latin and Rhetoric at the University of Granada, a post that he held for sixty years.

8. This sonnet has reference to Don Quixote's penance in the Sierra Morena as narrated in Part I, Chapters XXV ff.

9. See Part I, Chapter XXV and note 6.

10. See Part I, Chapter I and note 4.

11. Heroine of the *Amadis of Gaul*.

12. Oriana's castle near London.

13. The lady's reputation had suffered from the too frequent visits which Amadis paid to her castle.

14. Reference has been seen to the author himself or to Lope de Vega.

15. The *buzcorona* consisted in cuffing a person over the head as he bent to kiss another's hand.

16. "Donoso" signifies gay, witty, or graceful. "Interlarded" is for "*entreverado*"—literally, "intermingled." On the verse form, see note 1 preceding. For the reader's convenience, the last word of each line has been given in full

in parentheses, which is not done in the original. The imitation is by no means an exact one, since in the Spanish it is not merely the final consonant or consonant and unaccented final vowel that is omitted but an entire syllable that is normally pronounced.

17. The allusion is not clear. No such character as Villadiego the Silent is to be met with in the comedy *Celestina*, referred to a few lines farther on.

18. *Celestina, or the Tragicomedy of Calisto and Melibaea*, by Fernando Rojas, published in 1499.

19. Babieca was the Cid's famous mount.

20. Hero of *Lazarillo de Tormes*, the well-known *novela* by Diego Hurtado de Mendoza. In this picaresque tale, Lazarillo steals his blind master's wine by means of a straw. Another allusion to the work will be found in Part I, Chapter XXII.

21. These sonnets are very inferior productions, and the first one, in particular, is so muddled at the end as to make little or no sense; it is only by adopting, as I have done here, Hartzenbusch's suggested emendation that one is able to extract a satisfactory meaning from the closing lines.

22. Orlando was one of the Twelve Peers (see Part I, Chapters VI and XLIX); there is, of course, a play on Peer and peer.

23. Angelica was Orlando's love who threw him over for Medoro; see Part I, Chapter X, and elsewhere following.

24. Hero of the romance *Knight of the Sun, Mirror of Princes and Knights (Caballero del Febo, Espejo de Príncipes y Caballeros)*, by Diego Ortuñez de Calahorra and Marcos Martínez, first printed at Saragossa in 1562.

25. Either an invented name or a printer's error for Solinan, a knight mentioned in the *Amadis of Gaul*.

26. The Cid's famous steed.

27. The name Rocinante is from *"rocin,"* a "hack."

CHAPTER I

1. In the past this village has been identified as Argamasilla de Alba, in La Mancha, and a legend grew up to the effect that Cervantes had been imprisoned there and hence had a grudge against the place "the name of which I have no desire to recall." Thus, Ormsby, in his biographical sketch of Cervantes, states emphatically: "That Argamasilla is Don Quixote's village does not admit of a doubt," and he goes on to point out that it is the only village in the region ("except perhaps its near neighbor Tomelloso") that satisfies the topographical exigencies of the narrative. More recent researches, however, have shown that down to the beginning of the seventeenth century there was no jail in Argamasilla and that Cervantes, in all probability, was never there. In the introduction to his edition of Ludwig Tieck's German version of *Don Quixote* (Strassburg, 1905, 1911), Wolfgang von Wurzbach compares this legend to the fiction of the Arabic "author" of the tale, Cid Hamete Benengeli. In his spurious continuation of *Don Quixote*, Alonso Fernández de Avellaneda named Argamasilla as the village in question, but it is more likely that Cervantes had no particular one in mind.

2. The phrase in the original, *"duelos y quebrantos,"* has given commentators and translators no end of trouble, and its meaning still remains uncertain (see the extended note in Schevill and Bonilla's edition of the *Obras Completas*, Vol. 15, *Don Quixote*, Tomo I, pp. 431–36). It does not seem to have occurred in literature before Cervantes, who was probably drawing upon the popular speech. It seems to have been a mixture of the scraps of fowl and pork, etc., which it was permissible to eat on Saturday, a day of semi-abstinence. Oudin in his French translation of 1614 rendered the expression as *"des oeufs et du lard,"* and Franciosini in his Italian version (1621) has *"frittate rognose,"* which he explains in a marginal note as being *"presciutto fritto con huova."* In other words, bacon and eggs, or ham and eggs, which Rodríguez Marín accepts as a good translation. Jarvis translates as "pains and breakings" and in his notes describes the dish as an "amlet" (omelet). Motteux: "griefs and groans on Saturdays." All in all, "scraps" appears to be the best, or at any rate the safest, rendering in English.

3. Feliciano de Silva was the author of the *Chronicle of Don Florisel de Niquea*, published in 1532, 1536, and

1551. The first passage quoted immediately below is from this work; the second is from Torquemada's *Olivante de Laura* (1564).

4. Reference is to the *History of Don Belianís of Greece*, by Jerónimo Fernández (1547).

5. Sigüenza was one of the "minor universities" (*universidades menores*), and a good deal of fun was poked at its graduates.

6. Protagonist of the ninth book of the *Amadis* series.

7. One of the principal personages in Boiardo's *Orlando Innamorato*.

8. Galalón (Ganelon) was the traitor of the Charlemagne legend.

9. The *real de vellón* was a coin worth about five cents. The cuarto, or four-maravedi piece, was the eighth part of a real.

10. "All skin and bones." The expression is common in classic literature; it will be found in Plautus and elsewhere. Gonela was an Italian jester in the service of the Duke of Ferrara (1450–1470).

11. In Spanish, *rocín*.

12. Quixote (*quijote*) literally means the piece of armor that protects the thigh. Quijada and Quesada were distinguished family names.

CHAPTER II

1. "*Armas blancas*" is properly "blank armor," but Don Quixote takes "*blancas*" in its literal sense—"white."

2. The Campo de Montiel was the scene of the battle, in 1369, in which Peter the Cruel was defeated by his brother Henry.

3. On Puerto Lápice and the windmills, see Chapters VIII and IX following.

4. Ormsby: "The particular *venta* [inn] . . . in this and the next chapter is said to be the Venta de Quesada, about two and a half leagues north of Manzanares, on the Madrid and Seville road. The house itself was burned down about a century ago, and has been rebuilt, but the yard at the back with its draw-well and stone trough are said to remain as they were in his [Cervantes'] day."

5. The sense of "*sanos de Castilla*" appears to be "thieves in disguise" (gypsy argot). "*Castellano*" means both "Castilian" and "a castellan."

6. These verses and the two quoted above are from an old ballad, "Moriana en un Castillo," possibly dating from the fourteenth century.

7. A parody of the opening lines of the ballad of Lancelot of the Lake. See Chapter XIII and note 2.

8. The first edition reads "*alzada la visera*"—"with his visor raised," but in that case, as commentators have pointed out, Don Quixote would have had no trouble in feeding himself. Hartzenbusch first emended "*visera*" to read "*babera*" ("beaver"), an emendation which Ormsby adopted, but later he decided that the correct reading was "*atada la visera*"—"with the visor fastened," and with this Fitzmaurice-Kelly agrees. Rodríguez Marín states that "*alzada la visera*" is obviously an error, though he does not suggest an emendation of his own. I have followed Hartzenbusch and Fitzmaurice-Kelly.

CHAPTER III

1. Percheles was the name of the place outside Málaga where fish were dried and sold; Isles of Riarán was the name of a disreputable suburb of the same city. The District of Seville was an open space on the river side of the town, near the Plaza de Toros, where fairs, etc., were held. The Olivera of Valencia was a small plaza in the center of the city. The Rondilla of Granada is said to have been in the Albaycín quarter. The Horse Fountain of Cordova refers to a section on the south side of the town that took its name from a stone horse standing over a fountain. The other expressions are self-explanatory. All these localities are said to have been the haunts of rogues and thieves.

2. This clause ("*como que era otra cosa de más importancia*") is none too clear.

3. An old plaza in Toledo.

CHAPTER IV

1. The barber was also the surgeon.

2. The word "*baldudo*" means "full-skirted."

3. A proverbial expression.

4. The sense of "perfumed" is "completely," "to perfection."

5. An obscure oath.

6. Alcarria was a sparsely populated region in the upper valley of the Tagus.

Estremadura was a province noted for its backwardness.

7. A proverb.

8. Civet, a favored perfume, was imported in cotton packing.

9. Another proverb. Guadarrama was known for its spindles.

CHAPTER V

1. Cervantes is here confusing two old ballads. According to the story, Carloto (or Charlot), Charlemagne's son, sought to kill Baldwin that he might marry his widow. Sorely wounded, Baldwin was found and succored by his uncle, the Marquis of Mantua.

2. The love of the Moor Abindarráez and the beautiful Jarifa (or Xarifa) was a favorite theme with Moorish and Christian minstrels and was incorporated by Jorge de Montemayor, referred to a few lines further on, in the second edition of his *Diana*.

3. See the following chapter and note 17.

CHAPTER VI

1. Fifth book of the Amadis of Gaul series, published in 1521.

2. Work by Feliciano de Silva (1535), ninth book of the Amadis series.

3. Work by Antonio de Torquemada (1564). The *Garden of Flowers* (1575) was translated into English in 1600 as *The Spanish Mandeville*.

4. Work by Lenchor Ortega de Ubeda (1556).

5. Fourth book of the Palmerin series (1533).

6. The first part of *The Knight of the Cross*, by an unknown hand, appeared in 1543; the second part, by Pedro de Luxan, in 1563.

7. Published in four parts, at Seville, 1533-50, one of the most popular of the Carolingian romances.

8. The *Fables* of Turpin (1527) belong to the Carolingian cycle. He was a monk of Saint-Denis and Bishop of Reims (mentioned by Rabelais). In *The Mirror of Chivalry* he is constantly cited for his veracity, and the Italian writers Ariosto, Boiardo, and Pulci speak of him as "Turpin who never lies in any place."

9. Matteo Maria Boiardo, fifteenth-century author of the *Orlando Innamorato*.

10. As a token of respect.

11. Allusion to Ariosto's Spanish translator, Gerónimo Jiménez de Urrea, whose version was published at Antwerp in 1549.

12. The works referred to are the *History of the Deeds of Bernardo del Carpio*, by Agustín Alonso of Salamanca (Toledo, 1585), and *The Famous Battle of Roncesvalles* by Francisco Garrido de Villena (Valencia, 1555).

13. The *Palmerin de Oliva* (Salamanca, 1511), of uncertain authorship, was the first of the Palmerin cycle. The first Spanish edition of the *Palmerin of England* appeared in 1547, translated from the first Portuguese edition (1544?). See W. E. Purser, *Palmerin of England* (London, 1904).

14. See Chapter 1, note 4.

15. This clause provided that when a person overseas was sued or indicted he might have a certain allowance of time in which to put in an appearance.

16. This work, by Johannot Martorell and Johan de Galba, was first published in the Catalan language at Valencia in 1490; a Castilian version appeared at Valladolid in 1511.

17. Jorge de Montemayor died in 1561, in which year the second edition of his *Diana* appeared (the date of the first is uncertain). Gil Polo's continuation was published at Valencia in 1564. This was the first and best of the Spanish pastoral romances. See H. A. Rennert, *The Spanish Pastoral Romances* (Philadelphia: University of Pennsylvania Press, 1912; originally published at Baltimore in 1892 by the Modern Language Association).

18. Published at Barcelona in 1573.

19. *The Shepherd of Iberia* is by Bernardo de la Vega (Seville, 1591); *The Nymphs and Shepherds of Henares*, by Bernardo González de Bovadilla, was published at Alcalá de Henares in 1587; *The Disenchantments of Jealousy*, by Bartolmé López de Enciso appeared at Madrid in 1586.

20. This pastoral by Luis Gálvez de Montalvo of Guadalajara was published at Madrid in 1582.

21. Work by Pedro de Padilla (Madrid, 1580).

22. López de Maldonado's *Cancionero* appeared at Madrid in 1586.

23. A proverb.

24. According to Ormsby, this "shows pretty clearly that until *Don Quixote* had made the author's name known, the *Galatea* had remained unnoticed."

25. There were three editions of the *Araucana*: Madrid, 1569, 1578, and 1590. The *Austriada* (Madrid, 1584) deals with John of Austria. The *Monserrate*, by the dramatist Virués (Madrid, 1588) gave M. G. Lewis the inspiration for his famous novel *The Monk*.

26. The work referred to is the *Angélica* of Luis Barahona de Soto (Madrid, 1586).

27. In connection with this chapter and the works mentioned in it, see Esther B. Sylvia, "Don Quixote's Library," *More Books, The Bulletin of the Boston Public Library*, April 1940, pp. 135–52.

CHAPTER VII

1. Reference to the *Carolea* of Gerónimo Sempere (1560), dealing with the victories of Charles V and the *León of Spain* of Pedro de la Vezilla, a poem on the history of the city of León.

2. No work by this title is known. Luis de Avila was the author of a prose commentary on the wars with the German Protestants.

3. Frestón was a magician; he was reputed to be the author of the *Belianís of Greece*.

4. A proverb.

5. Sancho's wife appears under various names.

CHAPTER VIII

1. That is, "the Pounder."

2. The Biscayans, or Basques, were supposed to speak broken Spanish. One characteristic of their speech was the use of the second person for the first. This can be brought out in English only if one is using the "thou" form. Thus Ormsby renders this passage: ". . . by the God that made me, unless thou quittest coach, slayest thee as art here a Biscayan." Like Motteux, I have represented this idiosyncrasy of dialect by substituting the objective for the nominative case—"me kill you."

3. A play on the double meaning of "*caballero*"—"knight" and "gentleman."

4. The proverbial expression is "carry the cat to the water"—"*llevar el gato al agua.*" The Biscayan inverts the saying.

5. The allusion is to the *Amadis of Gaul*. The expression is one used at the beginning of a fray. Agrajes is a bellicose personage in that romance.

6. This device of breaking off the tale between one part of a work and the following one is common in the romances of chivalry.

7. Reference here is to the four-part division of the first volume of *Don Quixote*, a division which the author ignored when he came to publish the second volume. The first part originally ended here.

CHAPTER IX

1. Reference is to the Hebrew language.

2. Two arrobas would be about fifty pounds; two fanegas, a little over three bushels.

3. That is, "Paunch and Shanks."

CHAPTER X

1. A tribunal, dating from the thirteenth century, for dealing with crimes on the highway and in the open countryside.

2. Play on the words "*homecidio*" and "*omecillo*"; the phrase "*no catar omecillo a ninguno*" means "not to bear ill will, or a grudge, toward anyone."

3. Allusion to Boiardo's *Orlando;* it was, however, not Sacripante, but another personage, Dardinel, who paid so dearly for the helmet of Mambrino, the Moorish king. Another allusion to the *Orlando* occurs a few paragraphs further on ("men of arms that came to Albraca to win the fair Angelica").

4. An imaginary realm.

5. In the *Amadis of Gaul* Firm Island is the promised land for the faithful squires of knights-errant.

CHAPTER XI

1. Reference to the *noria*, a machine with buckets attached used in irrigation.

2. The verse form here is trochaic tetrameter with assonant rhymes in the second and fourth lines, a variety of rhyme which is impossible to imitate in English but which in Spanish with its stressed vowels is adapted to singing. The ballad has accordingly been rendered with ordinary rhymes.

CHAPTER XII

1. Reference to the *autos,* or allegorical religious dramas.

2. Play on *sarna,* the itch, and Sarah, Abraham's wife. "Older than the itch" is a proverb of ancient lineage.

3. Ormsby: "Though Cervantes tries to observe dramatic propriety by making Pedro blunder, in the end he puts into his mouth language as fine and words as long as Don Quixote's."

4. Literally, "which had the sun on one side [one cheek] and the moon on the other." Compare Part II, Chapter XLVIII.

CHAPTER XIII

1. The name Quintañona is Spanish, meaning a woman with a hundredweight (*quintal*) of years, i.e., a centenarian.

2. These lines are from the ballad that was parodied in Chapter II preceding. The ballad will be found in the *Cancionero de Romances* (Antwerp, n.d.) and in Agustín Durán's *Romancero General* (Madrid: 1849–51), No. 352.

3. The *Felixmarte of Hircania* has been referred to in Chapter VI preceding as *Florismarte of Hircania* (see note 4 there).

4. The lines are translated from the *Orlando Furioso,* XXIV, 57.

5. The word *"Gachupín"* literally means a Spaniard living in or returned from the colonies.

CHAPTER XIV

1. This poem in the original is marked by an intricacy of structure (interwoven rhymes, etc.) that cannot be imitated in English. The rhyme scheme of the sixteen-line stanza is abcabccdbbdeefef.

2. Envied as the bird that witnessed the crucifixion.

3. The Tagus River.

4. The Guadalquivir River.

CHAPTER XV

1. Yanguas was a district in the north of Castile. In the first edition there is a confusion in the text between Yanguesans and Galicians.

2. Untranslatable word play on *"feo Blas"* ("ugly Blas") and *"Fierabrás"*; on Fierabrás's balm see Chapter X preceding.

3. Another pun that cannot be rendered literally, a play on *"sin costas"*—"without (court) costs," and *"sin costillas"*—"without ribs." Ormsby translates it: ". . . that my beast should have come off scot-free while we come out scotched."

4. The Greek city of Thebes.

CHAPTER XVI

1. The knight muttered his lady's name "between his teeth" as he went into the fray; see Chapter XIII preceding.

2. In the sense of "star-lit" (compare Ormsby); that is, with crevices in the roof through which the light of the stars could enter. The phrase has troubled translators. Shelton omits it; Jarvis renders it as "illustrious"; Motteux has "wretched apartment."

3. The work bearing the title *The Chronicle of the Noble Knights Tablante de Ricamonte and Jofre, Son of Count Donason,* etc., was published at Toledo in 1531; there is a copy in the British Museum. It is by an unknown hand. A later version is attributed to one Nuño Garay. Count Tomillas was a character in the *novela* entitled *Story of Enrique de Oliva, King of Jerusalem, Emperor of Constantinople* (Seville, 1498).

4. Allusion to a children's tale that is part of the European folklore heritage. (See Schevill and Rodríguez Marín.)

5. The highway police; see Chapter X preceding, note 1.

CHAPTER XVII

1. The phrase is from the beginning of one of the old ballads of the Cid.

2. Coin worth about a sixth of a maravedi.

3. The wool carders of Segovia were famous throughout Spain. On the Horse Fountain of Cordova, see Chapter III preceding, note 1. Fair of Seville was the name given to a low quarter of that city.

CHAPTER XVIII

1. "Ceca" (literally, "a mint") was the name given to a part of the Mosque of Cordova. A proverbial expression corresponding to our "from pillar to post."

2. The reference here is not to Amadis of Gaul but to Amadis of Greece.

3. The participle *"cuajada"* means "curdled," which Ormsby renders as "churned up." Clemencín substitutes *"causada"*—"caused."

4. Ormsby: "Suero de Quiñones, hero of the *Paso Honroso* at Orbiga in 1434, used to fight against the Moors with his arm bare."

5. The sense is either "trail my fortune" or "my fortune creeps." There may be a double meaning. The asparagus plant would suggest the latter interpretation.

6. As has been noted, the Betis (Baetis) is the present Guadalquivir River.

7. Granada is on the Genil River.

8. Tartessus was an ancient maritime city of Spain.

9. Jerez (Xerez), near Cadiz, is noted for its sherry wines; our word "sherry" is derived from the name.

10. River flowing down from the Cantabrian Mountains and emptying into the Douro River below Valladolid.

11. This river of Spain and Portugal, emptying into the Atlantic, flows underground for a part of its course.

12. The primary meaning of the word *"peladilla"* is "a sugar almond"; secondary meaning, "a small pebble." Ormsby: "Here came a sugar-plum from the brook."

13. *"Almendra"* is literally an almond.

14. Dr. Andrés Laguna translated Dioscorides with copious notes in 1570.

15. A proverb.

16. The original reads "I will send to the devil flock and shepherd's crook (*hato y garabato*)."

CHAPTER XIX

1. Allusion to the story of Mambrino's helmet; see Chapter x preceding and note 3. Malandrino (*"malandrín"*—"rascal") is a play on Mambrino.

2. *"Encamisados,"* that is, those wearing shirts (*camisas*) over their armor as in a *camisado*, or night attack.

3. There is a word play here on *"derecho"*—"right" or "straight," and *"tuerto"*—"wrong" or "crooked."

4. There is a confused text at this point in some of the editions; I have

followed the first edition. The latter part of the chapter in Ormsby is badly jumbled.

5. "Moreover, if any, persuaded of the devil . . ."

6. Reference to a ballad of which Lockhart has a version. See Sylvanus Griswold Morley's *Spanish Ballads* (New York: Henry Holt, 1911), pp. 118 ff.

7. A proverb; literally, "The dead man to the grave, the living to the loaf."

CHAPTER XX

1. The original has *"les aguó el contento del agua."*

2. A proverb.

3. A proverb.

4. The Horn is the constellation of Ursa Minor, with a curved shape somewhat like a hunting-horn. In this method of telling the time of night by the stars, the arms were extended in the form of a cross and the hour was indicated by the position of the Horn in relation to the arms.

5. Cato Censorino, or Cato the Censor; Sancho believes the name to be derived from *"zonzo"*—"a blockhead."

6. The story that Sancho undertakes to tell is an old one, probably of Oriental origin. It will be found in the Italian collection, *Cento Novelle Antiche*, and there are also Latin and Provençal versions.

7. Compare Swift's *Gulliver's Travels*, Part II, Chapter 1: "I was pressed to do more than one thing which another could not do for me."

8. As distinguished from a Moorish or Jewish convert, or "new Christian."

9. *"Todo saldrá en la colada."* We have the proverb today.

10. A proverb.

11. Compare the reference to Firm Island a little further on; see also Chapter x preceding, note 5.

12. "Turkish fashion."

13. Tag of a proverb: "Whether the pitcher hits the stone or the stone the pitcher, it will be bad for the pitcher."

CHAPTER XXI

1. The reading of the first edition, *"pesada burla,"* has been followed here. A later edition has *"pasada"* in place of *"pesada,"* which has led some translators

'o render the phrase as "the late joke," "the late jest," etc.

2. Allusion to a proverb: "Please God that it be marjoram and not turn out to be caraway."

3. The original is *"malandantes,"* meaning "unfortunate"; but there is a slight play on *"caballero andante"*—"knight-errant."

4. Earlier translators have "cuts off," in accordance with a later reading, *"corta"*; but the first edition has *"harta,"* an obvious misprint for *"harpa,"* from *"harpar (arpar)"*—"to tear" or "claw." This example and the one given in note 1 above will serve to show how a careful study of the original edition will provide the modern translator with a more accurate text as a whole, even though the variant in a particular case will often make little difference so far as the English-language reader is concerned.

5. A proverb.

6. Sancho means Mambrino.

7. Literally, a changing of hoods. Reference is seen to a seasonal change of hoods on the part of cardinals as provided for in an ecclesiastical manual which Professor Schevill discovered in the Central Library of Zurich: *Sacrarvm Ceremoniarvm, sive ritvvm ecclesiasticorvm Sanctae Romanae Ecclesiae, libri tres,* etc. (Rome, 1560). John S. Nainfa, S.S., in his *Costume of Prelates of the Catholic Church* (Baltimore, 1900), has a passage concerning a change of bishops' hoods, applicable also to cardinals.

8. Hartzenbusch, always free with his corrections of the author's text, would substitute "enigma" or "prophecy" for "adventure," and "explain" for "carry through *(acabar)."*

9. Ormsby: "Cervantes gives here an admirable epitome, and without any extravagant caricature, of a typical romance of chivalry. For every incident there is ample authority in the romances." John Gibson Lockhart, notes to the Motteux translation: "The reader of romance does not need to be told how faithfully Don Quixote . . . has abridged the main story of many a ponderous folio. The imaginary career of glory which he unfolds before the eyes of Sancho is paralleled almost *ad literatim* in the romance of Sir Degore.

. . . The conclusion of Belianís is almost exactly the same sort of adventure."

10. There is some question as to what is meant by this *"vengar quinientos sueldos."* According to the *Dictionary of the Academy,* the verb *"devengar"* signifies "to acquire the right to some . . . compensation by reason of labor performed, services rendered, or other qualifications." Others have seen an allusion to an old Castilian law providing damages of five hundred sueldos as compensation for injury to person or property. In any event, whatever its source, the gentleman of La Mancha's income was not a large one by modern standards, seeing that the sueldo was worth anywhere from one to three cents.

11. Two proverbs.

12. A proverb.

13. A proverb.

14. For the play on *"litado"* and *"dictado,"* Ormsby's rendering has been adopted.

15. Ormsby: "No doubt Pedro Tallez Girón, third Duke of Osuna, afterward Viceroy in Sicily and Naples; 'a little man but of great fame and fortunes . . .' "

CHAPTER XXII

1. Of La Mancha.

2. The first edition reading is *"tres precisos de gurapas"*; a later edition has *"tres años"*—"three years."

3. A proverb.

4. It is interesting to compare the term "sing" in our American underworld of today. The one who "sang" was as unpopular then as now. There are numerous specimens of rogues' dialect in this chapter and indeed throughout the pages of *Don Quixote.* *"Gurapas"* is one example.

5. A proverb.

6. Allusion to the ceremony of public flogging.

7. Proverbial expression.

8. This does not appear to agree with Don Quixote's belief in enchanters and their spells, but he is here speaking, apparently, of love sorcerers.

9. The first edition has *"no ay diablo"*; later editions have *"sumista"* in place of *"diablo,"* rendered by Motteux

as "casuist" and by Ormsby as "accountant."

10. A proverb.

11. Reference to the famous work by Diego Hurtado de Mendoza, one of the classics of Spanish literature.

12. The proverb properly reads: "Do not go looking for five feet on a cat."

13. At the beginning of the chapter it was stated that the two men on horseback carried muskets.

14. A proverb.

CHAPTER XXIII

1. A proverb.

2. The passage beginning here and ending a few paragraphs below with the words ". . . he thanked his master for this favor" is not found in the first edition but is given in the second. Professor Schevill says: "We shall never know (in the author's own words) 'if the historian made a mistake' or if it was 'carelessness on the part of the printer.' I believe that Cervantes, upon completing [the first edition] wished to introduce the incident of the theft and for that purpose wrote an [additional] sheet, leaving it with the manuscript, and then forgot the additions and the changes they necessitated. Obviously, the printer did not know what to do with the loose leaf and introduced it later, while the text of [the second edition] was on the press." (Translated from Schevill's note in Spanish.) This will explain why, later in the chapter, the author speaks of Sancho as still having his ass, while still further on he again alludes to the theft. As the text originally stood, the episode of the galley slaves and the one related here all occurred on the same day, which was too much action for so short a space of time. That was doubtless why Cervantes desired to insert an interlude. Ormsby, in the latter part of the chapter, rather bungles the matter by tampering with the text in order to cover the discrepancy. Compare Part II, Chapters III, IV, and XXVII.

3. The word "*pollinos*"—"ass-colts," missing in the original, has been supplied by the translator.

4. Ormsby has: "with what Dapple used to carry."

5. A proverb previously quoted: "The thread leads to the ball of yarn." "Thread" here has the sense of "clue."

6. That is, "thread."

7. That is, "Phyllis."

8. Cervantes seems to have thought well of this sonnet of his, as he later inserted it in one of his comedies, *La Casa de los Celos y Selvas de Ardenia.*

9. It will be noted that the theft of the ass is not mentioned here.

10. The ass is present again.

11. This passage is not found until the third edition. The edition of Brussels reads ". . . Sancho on foot, consoled for the loss of his donkey by the promise of the three ass-colts . . ." The thief's two names are here confused.

12. Proverbial expression.

13 Ormsby says: "This is the explanation commonly given of the phrase '*de ambar*,' and it is true that scented doublets were in fashion in the sixteenth century; but it seems somewhat improbable that a tattered doublet which had been for six months exposed to all weathers would have retained sufficient perfume to be detected."

CHAPTER XXIV

1. Clemencín believes that Cervantes wrote "in this province of Andalusia" for the reason that the interlocutors were actually in that province at the time; but Schevill remarks that "it is also possible that Cervantes had written this story and (then) interpolated it without altering these details introduced while the author himself was in Andalusia." (Translated from Schevill's Spanish note.)

2. Allusion to the eleventh book (third and fourth parts) of the *Amadis.*

3. The shepherd Darinel has been mentioned in Chapter VI preceding.

CHAPTER XXV

1. Ormsby, still trying to cover the textual discrepancy, has "bade Sancho follow him, which he, having no ass, did very discontentedly."

2. Ormsby: "could talk to Rocinante" (!).

3. Sancho confuses the name Elisabad with "*abad*"—an "abbot."

4. The squire here begins a barrage of proverbs.

5. That is, no pegs on which to hang the bacon.

6. Poor Rock (Peña Pobre) was so named because those who sojourned

there lived in extreme poverty; Clemencín suggests that it was Mont St. Michel, but Ormsby thinks the island of Jersey would be a better identification.

7. The sense of the name Beltenebros is "darkly fair."

8. It is at this point that the editor Hartzenbusch introduces the episode of the theft of the ass.

9. The Hippogriff was the winged horse on which Astolfo went to seek news of Orlando. Frontino was the steed of Bradamante's lover, Ruggiero.

10. This is the first reference in the first edition to the theft.

11. "According to this passage, the gray was lost *with the lint and all;* but the lint was kept in the saddlebags which were left in the innkeeper's possession; that Ginés stole the packsaddle along with the beast appears more likely than the *ad hoc* explanation later given (Part II, Chapter IV), where it is related that Ginés stole only the ass, leaving Sancho seated upon the packsaddle suspended on four stakes." (Translated from Schevill's Spanish note.)

12. Sancho means, of course, redemption.

13. Freely for *"caballero andante, o por andar."*

14. Reference to the lay brothers who acted as servants in schools and convents and who wore their hair cropped short but without the tonsure.

15. Reading of the first and second editions; the third edition has "twenty-seventh of August."

16. The first three editions have Perseus; the edition of Brussels has Theseus. Schevill prefers to leave the reading Perseus, believing that it may have been in the original manuscript as the result of a mistake on the part of the author.

CHAPTER XXVI

1. The allusions here are to the *Orlando Furioso:* Medoro, however, was Dardinel's page, not Agramante's (XVIII, 166); and it was Ferrau, not Orlando (Roland), who had the seven iron soles (XII, 48).

2. That is, in Italian, Orlando Furioso.

3. The second and third editions and the edition of Brussels have another reading: "And for a rosary he made use of the galls of a cork tree, putting them together to form a string of ten beads." This is the reading that Motteux and some of the other translators have followed; Ormsby has the one given here.

4. The word play on *"sobajada,"* *"sobrehumana"* (omitted in my rendering), and *"soberana"* is in reality untranslatable.

CHAPTER XXVII

1. Wamba was a king of the Gothic line in the Iberian peninsula (672–680).

2. Galalón, previously mentioned (Chapter I), was the traitor of Roncesvalles.

3. Vellido (or Bellido) Dolfos was the murderer of Don Sancho, King of Castile.

4. The story of Count Julian is well known (Southey has treated it in English). His betrayal of Spain to the Moors is related in an old ballad, "En Ceupta está Julián," which Lockhart has translated.

5. This, of course, is an old, old theme. Compare Vergil (*Aeneid,* IV, 569): *"varium et mutabile semper/ femina,"* or the popular grand opera aria "La Donna è mobile." One thinks also of Francis I's saying: *"Femme souvent varie."*

6. The colors crimson and white signified joy and happiness, and sometimes, apparently, cruelty and innocence.

7. Part III ends here in the first edition.

CHAPTER XXVIII

1. The image is that of a ball of yarn being wound.

2. The *montera* was a cloth cap worn by peasants.

3. The adjective *"rancio"* literally means "rancid"; its secondary meaning is, anything that has been kept for a long time—such as wine or bacon—and so has acquired the flavor of age.

4. The *hidalgo* (literally, "son of a somebody") was a gentleman by birth, the *caballero* one by social position.

5. This saying was a commonplace among Spanish writers of the Golden Age. On the effects of music in purifying the passions, Schevill suggests a comparison with the section on music in Aristotle's *Politics.* And, of course,

there is Shakespeare's "Music hath charms . . ."

6. The Motteux version in this passage strays widely from the text.

7. It is not too clear to what Dorotea is referring.

8. The *zagal* was a shepherd or swain.

CHAPTER XXIX

1. The first three Spanish editions have: ". . . *la buena suerte se muestra en favor mio*"—"is favoring me." The edition of Brussels and some modern ones have "*nuestro*"—"is favoring us," in place of "*mio*"; but if "*mio*" is not correct, Schevill prefers the reading "*vuestro*"—"is favoring you," which is the one that I have followed here. Ormsby has "in our favor"; Motteux, as frequently, slurs the passage.

2. A variety of mantilla.

3. Needless to say, an imaginary kingdom.

4. The edition of Brussels and that of the Spanish Academy (1780) punctuate the passage to read: "throughout the known parts of Guinea."

5. A palfrey ("*su palafrén*") is usually a horse, commonly a saddle horse for ladies, and Dorotea is mounted on a mule.

6. A proverb.

7. Literally, "Come, I am sucking my finger."

8. The reference is to Alcalá de Henares, Cervantes' birthplace. Rodríguez Marín: "The Zulema slope is a large hill to the southeast of Alcalá de Henares, on which was situated the Complutum of Ptolomeus." Complutum was the Latin name of the town.

9. Ormsby substitutes the reading "three leagues." He remarks: "The original says 'two leagues,' but the context shows it must have been at least thrice as far."

10. Bowle notes that this is reminiscent of a passage in *La Angélica* of Luis Barahona de Soto, Canto VIII: "*La gran laguna Meótide*"—"the great Meotides Lake," etc. Clemencín identifies Lake Meotis as the "gulf of the Black Sea into which the River Don or Tanais empties."

11. Two commentators, Clemencín and Hartzenbusch, point out that this would be worse on the fly than on the honey. Hartzenbusch substitutes "the bear."

CHAPTER XXX

1. The author has not previously referred to this incident.

2. Proverbial expression denoting an impossibility or something beyond one's reach: "*pedir cotufas en el golfo.*"

3. The first edition reads "*que se le viene a las manos de vobis, vobis*"; but Schevill remarks that the Latin "*vobis*" is out of place in Sancho's mouth and that Cervantes doubtless wrote "*bóbilis, bóbilis*" (meaning "easily," "without effort"), the mistake being one on the part of the compositor when the passage was dictated to him. This is borne out by the fact that the phrase "*bóbilis, bóbilis*" occurs later on, in Part II, Chapter LXXI.

4. The proverb runs: "The pitcher that goes to the well too often leaves either its handle or its spout behind."

5. A proverb. The bracketed passage that follows is not found in the first edition but occurs in the second La Cuesta edition of 1605.

6. That is, Don Quixote and Sancho. The passage goes on from the point at which the preceding one was introduced.

CHAPTER XXXI

1. A fanega is equivalent to 1.6 bushels.

2. As a token of reverence; the expression has occurred before.

3. A proverbial expression which the author has previously employed.

4. The sense is: "A good thing (gift) is good in any season." Ormsby cites the Scottish proverb: "A Yule feast may be done at Pasch." Rodríguez Marín points out that sleeves were originally given as presents and hence came to signify a gift.

5. Gypsy dealers were in the habit of putting quicksilver in the ears of a beast for sale, by way of quickening its pace.

6. Motteux gives the version: "A bird in hand is worth two in the bush."

7. Sancho misquotes the proverb, which runs: "He who has the good and chooses the bad, let him not complain of the bad that comes to him."

8. See Chapter IV and note 4.

CHAPTER XXXII

1. The *Don Cirongilio of Thrace*, in four books, by Bernardo de Vargas, was published at Seville in 1545. Copies are preserved in the Biblioteca Nacional of Madrid and the British Museum. The *Felixmarte of Hircania* has been referred to as *Florismarte of Hircania* (see Chapter VI, note 4). The *History of the Great Captain Gonzalo Hernández de Córdoba y Aguilar, with the Life of the Knight D. García de Paredes* was published at Seville in 1580 and 1582; there are copies in the British Museum and the library of the Hispanic Society. This is a later account based upon the *Chronicle Entitled the Two Conquests of the Kingdom of Naples* (Saragossa, 1559), copies of which are to be found in the Biblioteca Nacional and the library of the Hispanic Society. Gonzalo was the general in command against the Moors at Granada and the French at Naples. García de Paredes was his comrade-in-arms in both campaigns.

2. I follow here the reading of the first, second, and third editions, "more books," instead of "my books," the reading of the edition of Brussels which has been adopted by other translators. In Chapter XXVII preceding, the curate tells the innkeeper and his wife of Don Quixote's madness and may have mentioned the burning of the knight's books.

3. The *montante* was a broadsword with large *quillons*, requiring two hands to wield it.

4. I follow the readings of Hartzenbusch and Schevill, in place of "what I have read of Felixmarte of Hircania."

CHAPTER XXXIII

1. Schevill remarks that similar views of women are to be found in many of Cervantes' contemporaries. This was, as a matter of fact, a prolongation of the attitude toward the sex that was held at the close of the Middle Ages. Compare the "*Querelle des femmes*," or argument over the "woman question," among French writers of the sixteenth century, e.g., Rabelais. Ormsby observes that "among the scenes of the Italian and Spanish tales of intrigue the church plays a leading part." "Private visits to religious shrines" is a rendering of the

Spanish "*estaciones*" and refers to "attendance at church for private devotion at other hours than those of the celebration of the mass." (Ormsby)

2. Proverbs 31:10: "Who can find a virtuous woman? for her price is far above rubies."

3. Allusion to Pericles in Plutarch's *On False Shame*.

4. I follow the reading of the first two editions, instead of the later one, "our holy religion."

5. *Le Lagrime de San Pietro* by Luigi Tansillo (1510–1568).

6. The cup was supposed to be a magic one. If the wife of the one who drank from it was unfaithful, it would spill. There is a confusion here of two stories in the *Orlando Furioso*, XLIII.

7. Reference to the well-known classic myth which tells how Zeus visited Danaë in her prison tower in the form of a shower of gold.

8. Genesis 2:24: "Therefore shall a man leave his father and his mother, and shall cleave unto his wife: and they shall be one flesh." Lotario omits the central clause.

CHAPTER XXXIV

1. This sonnet, like the one in Chapter XXIII preceding, will be found in Cervantes' play *The House of Jealousy*.

2. Commentators have seen these sonnets as "isolated compositions," having nothing to do with the text. Schevill believes that the author composed them years before and simply inserted them in the *Don Quixote*.

3. This follows the reading of the first edition: "*ha de estimar mi presteza o ligereza*"; later editions have "*desestimar*" (Ormsby: "will think ill of my pliancy or lightness"). As will be seen, "*estimar*" makes sense.

4. Two proverbs.

5. Reading of the early editions is "*rendirnos*"; modern editions have "*de rendiros*"—"of overcoming you." As Schevill points out, the reference well may be to both Camila and Leonela.

6. The "four S's" were *Sabio* (knowing); *Solo* (single-hearted); *Solicito* (diligent); *Segreto* (secret). It goes without saying that this "alphabet" cannot be rendered with anything more than an approach to literalness.

7. The first edition has *"más leal"*—"most loyal"; later ones have *"más desleal"*—"most disloyal."

8. This is the reading of all the earliest editions: *"por me hazer testigo"*; the edition of the Academy (1780) has: *"por no hacerme testigo"*—"in order not to bear witness."

9. Reading of the early Spanish editions is *"fealdad"*; the edition of Brussels and certain modern ones have *"falsedad"*—"conjugal faithlessness."

10. First edition reads *"no podia aber a Lotario"*; edition of Brussels: *"no podia herir"*—"could not wound."

CHAPTER XXXV

1. The first edition reads *"tambien la he cumplido"*; the emendation of Pellicer and later editors, *"tan bien,"* has been followed here.

2. *"Ciertos son los toros"*—allusion to the sport of bull-fighting. Ormsby has: "There's no doubt about the bulls," and explains the saying as "expressive probably of popular anxiety on the eve of a bull-fight." Motteux and Jarvis have: "Here are the bulls," Lockhart's explanation being: "In allusion to the joy of the mob in Spain when they see the bulls coming." In connection with the battle of the wineskins, Lockhart draws attention to the well-known story in Apuleius's *The Golden Ass.*

3. The cuartillo was one fourth of a real.

4. The cuarto was a coin worth four maravedis.

5. The text of the first two editions is confused at this point: *"qualificada no de con sus amores,"* which does not make sense. As Schevill notes, something apparently has been inadvertently dropped. It has seemed best to follow a later emendation: *"calificada en sus amores"* (third edition), or *"cualificada con sus amores"* (edition of Brussels).

6. A later edition has the reading: "perceived clearly enough by the mortal symptoms that he felt . . ."

7. Odet de Foix, Sieur de Lautrec, was Marshal of France under Francis I. On the Great Captain, see Chapter XXXII, note 1. Reference here apparently is to the battle of Cerignola (1503) in which the Spaniards won a victory over the French that resulted in the loss to Louis XII of the kingdom of Naples.

CHAPTER XXXVI

1. The fashion of riding known as *"a la jineta,"* in which the stirrups are high and the horseman is compelled to bend his legs.

2. The original has *"la firma que hiziste"*; but Ormsby notes: "Don Fernando did not sign any paper, but gave Dorothea a ring"; he translates: "the pledge which thou didst give me."

CHAPTER XXXVII

1. The arroba was equivalent to 4.26 gallons; the amount of spilled wine represented here is, accordingly, about twenty-five and a half gallons.

2. The words "said the curate" are supplied by the edition of Brussels.

3. Proverbial expression.

4. The first two editions have: *"vuestro . . . inuenerable braço"*—"your unvenerable arm." The third edition and the edition of Brussels read: *"inuencible"*—"invincible," and the Academy edition accepts this emendation. Hartzenbusch and Rodríguez Marín would read: *"inuulnerable"*—"invulnerable." This last appears to be the most logical reading, although Schevill thinks the "unvenerable" may not have been an error but a witticism on Dorotea's part, which seems unlikely in view of the serious tone that she consistently maintains in addressing Don Quixote.

5. A proverb.

6. In referring to the "captive," the author is running ahead of the story.

7. *"Macange"* (ma-kan-shi) is an emphatic negative in popular Arabic.

8. *"Letrado"*: reference here, in particular, to the student of jurisprudence.

9. Luke 2:14.

10. Luke 10:5.

11. John 14:27.

12. That is, going to the monasteries where soup was given out to the poor.

13. Syrtis was the name given by the ancients to sandbars in the sea, especially off the northern coast of Africa.

CHAPTER XXXVIII

1. Schevill observes that "this discussion of the subject of arms and letters

has its roots in the ancient literature and comes to be a commonplace with authors of the sixteenth century." (Translated from the Spanish note.) Among other works, the reader may be referred to Castiglione's *The Courtier*.

2. Motteux appears to have the sense here when he translates "either by hook or by crook." Clemencín gives the meaning as "in one way or another." Ormsby says: "Another explanation is that by skirts (*faldas*) regular salary is meant, and by sleeves (*mangas*) douceurs, perquisites, and the like."

3. It may be of interest to compare Rabelais' treatment of this theme in his *Gargantua*. The Chevalier Bayard stood for the type of chivalry or knighthood to which the introduction of artillery put an end.

CHAPTER XXXIX

1. Schevill points out that this tale of the father sending his three sons out into the world to choose their careers is a common one in the folk literature of Europe. To each the father gives good advice and his blessing and sometimes a talisman to guard him against harm. "It is possible that Cervantes, influenced by the proverb, 'Church or sea or Royal Household,' took the formula of the father and his three sons and found in the saying an indication of what the careers were to be." (From the Spanish note.)

2. This proverb is found in Lope de Vega; a variant reads: "Three things cause a man to prosper: learning and the sea and the royal household."

3. The Duke arrived at Brussels on August 22, 1567, with ten thousand men.

4. Cervantes had served in Diego de Urbina's company. See J. Fitzmaurice-Kelly, *Miguel de Cervantes Saavedra* (London: Chapman and Hall, 1917), pp. 42 ff.

5. Schevill notes that it is possible Cervantes entered this port on September 2, 1571.

6. The campaign of Lepanto in which Cervantes took part. The battle of Lepanto occurred on October 7, 1571. Compare the allusion in the Prologue to Part II.

7. Proper form: Aluch Ali.

8. Giovanni Andrea Doria (died in 1606), nephew of the great Andrea Doria, Genoese naval commander.

9. Motteux has: "in the flag-galley *The Three Beacons*"; but the "*capitana de los tres fanales*" refers to the three lanterns that were the sign of the admiral's ship.

10. Fort at the entrance to the lagoon of Tunis.

11. The vara is a variable measure, equal to about 2.8 feet.

12. Pedro de Aguilar's *Memoirs* were published at Madrid in 1875.

CHAPTER XL

1. Nickname of Jacome Palearo, who served under Charles V and Philip II.

2. Schevill: Cervantes here may possibly be alluding to the sovereigns who from 1360 to 1603 occupied the Turkish throne: Murad, Bayazid, Mohammed, and Selim or Suleiman.

3. The reference should be to Hassan Pacha.

4. Ormsby: "The story of the captive, it is needless to say, is not the story of Cervantes himself, but it is colored throughout by his own experiences, and he himself speaks in the person of the captive."

5. The author is referring to himself. The story of Cervantes' captivity is told in the work by Diego de Haedo, *Topography and General History of Algiers*, etc., published at Valladolid in 1612.

6. The cianí was worth a little more than six pesetas.

7. The term means "salaam," or form of worship.

8. South gate of Algiers.

9. A *Tagarino* was a Moor who lived among Christians. See the chapter following.

CHAPTER XLI

1. Motteux has: "to the eastward of Algiers towards Oran"; but Oran is west of Algiers. Ormsby has: "twenty leagues from Algiers." The original is: "*treynta leguas*"—"thirty leagues."

2. It was Arnaut Mami who captured the ship on which Cervantes and his brother were returning to Spain.

3. The dobla was a gold coin worth around ten pesetas. It is not to be confused with the doblón, or doubloon,

worth twice as much. Ormsby has: "ten thousand doubloons."

4. The original is: *"de ricas perlas y aljófar,"* the *aljófar* being a small pearl of irregular shape. Ormsby has: "rich pearls and seed-pearls."

5. The soltani was a Turkish coin equivalent to about nine pesetas.

6. The first edition has the form *"Amexi?"* Schevill believes this was what the author wrote, and adds: "It is not likely that Cervantes wrote such words correctly, and I do not care to emend the copy." (From the Spanish note.)

7. Which means, "Go, Christian, go!"

8. Literally, the wind from the other side of the mountains (the Alps); generally equivalent to north wind.

9. "La Cava" is the name given in ballads to Florinda, daughter of Count Julian (see Chapter XXVII preceding, note 4), who is said to have been seduced by King Rodrigo. Ormsby: "Cervantes gives the popular name by which the spot is known. Properly, it is 'Kuba Rumia,' 'the Christian's tomb'; that being the name given to the curious circular structure about which there has been so much discussion among French archaeologists."

10. I have followed Ormsby here as his rendering appears to be the only possible one for the nautical terms involved.

CHAPTER XLII

1. In the present chapter this person is sometimes referred to as "the captain," at other times as "the captive."

2. Here, as before, "letters" refers to jurisprudence.

3. The Audiencia.

4. The author apparently forgets that most of them had previously had supper.

5. See the Prologue to Part I, note 6.

6. A play on the word for "judge": *"oidor,"* literally, "hearer."

7. If the curate did not know whether they had reached Spain or not, how could he have known of the attack by the French pirates?

8. Rodríguez Marín would alter the punctuation here to make this passage read: "my father still lives dying, with the desire," etc. Schevill rejects this emendation.

CHAPTER XLIII

1. Palinurus was the pilot of Aeneas: *". . . surgit Palinurus, et . . . sidera cuncta notat tacito labentia caelo";* see the *Aeneid,* III, 513-515.

2. In the original, this ballad has double assonant rhymes in the second and fourth lines of each stanza; no imitation of this has been attempted here. Ormsby does attempt it and the result is an interesting version.

3. There is a play here in the word *"lugar,"* which sometimes means "place" and sometimes "town" or "village." Compare below: "lord of hearts and towns."

4. This ballad is said to have been set to music by Don Salvadore Luis, in 1591, fourteen years before the *Don Quixote* appeared; Schevill cites in this connection the four-volume *History of Spanish Music* by M. Soriano Fuertes, published in 1855-59.

5. Allusion to Diana; see Vergil's *Aeneid,* IV, 511: *"Tria virginis ora Dianae."*

6. The reference is to Daphne. Schevill notes the frequency of this allusion in Cervantes; see his *Ovid and the Renaissance in Spain* (Berkeley: University of California Press, 1913), p. 184. Compare Pliny's *Natural History,* IV, 8.

7. The Spanish verb here—*"cecear"* —is untranslatable; it simply means the sort of sound that Andalusians make in pronouncing the sibilant *ce.*

8. Lirgandeo was the tutor and chronicler of the Knight of the Sun. Alquife was the chronicler of the Knight of the Flaming Sword, Amadis of Greece. For Urganda, see the prefatory verses, note 1.

9. An inconsistency has been seen here, since if Don Quixote had been tied as tightly as we were told, how could his feet have come so near the ground? As Ormsby observes, the simple explanation is that "Cervantes never gave a thought to the matter."

CHAPTER XLIV

1. Reading of the first edition; other editions have Mambrino.

CHAPTER XLV

1. The first three editions have *"sobrebarbero,"* which, it has been suggested, may possibly mean "supernu-

merary barber." Certain modern editions have *"pobre barbero,"* or "poor barber," the reading that has been adopted here. The edition of Brussels has *"dixo el barbero burlado"*—"said the barber who was being made sport of."

2. A proverb: "Laws go as kings like."

3. Agramante and King Sobrino are personages in Ariosto's *Orlando Furioso.* For the incident referred to here, see Cantos XIV and XXVII.

CHAPTER XLVI

1. Pellicer's reading has been followed here: *"no se le passó por alto,"* in place of that of the first and second editions: *"se le pagó por alto."*

2. "Aside from the mention of the 'trappings' of the ass (Chapter XLII) and of the 'halter' and the 'packsaddle' (Chapter XLIV), this is the first allusion since the beast was found to the existence of Sancho's gray; from which I am inclined to think that the account of the finding of it was interpolated hastily and inopportunely in Chapter XXX, thus leaving fifteen chapters in which no mention whatever is made of its presence." (From Schevill's Spanish note.)

3. Augustus Caesar—the Augustan Age.

4. I follow here the first edition reading, *"vna señora."* Schevill is inclined to adopt the emendation of the edition of Brussels, *"vuestra señoria"*—"your Ladyship."

5. A proverb.

6. A proverb.

7. The early editions all have *"león manchado"*—"spotted lion"; but later editors have adopted the reading *"manchego"*—"Manchegan," or "of La Mancha."

8. From *"mentir"*—"to lie."

CHAPTER XLVII

1. The chapter heading in the original is not quite accurate. Ormsby: "Of the Strange Manner in Which Don Quixote of La Mancha Was Carried Away Enchanted."

2. It was considered an utter disgrace for a knight to ride in such a vehicle. Schevill draws attention to a similar incident in the French *nouvelle* of the fifteenth century, *Lancelot du Lac.*

3. Motteux substitutes "orthodox" for "Catholic."

4. We have previously been told (Chapter XLV preceding) that the officers were three in number.

5. In Covarrubias's *Tesoro de la lengua castellana* (cited by Schevill) it is stated that Zoroaster, "King of the Bactrians, was the first inventor of the magic art."

6. Allusion to Cervantes' own work, of course; the third of the *Exemplary Novels,* published (later) in 1613.

7. The work referred to is the *Suma de las Súmulas,* a treatise on logic by the theologian Gaspar Carillo de Villalpando, published at Alcalá in 1557.

8. The gymnosophists were Hindu philosophers who led a hermit existence, practiced mysticism and asceticism, and wore little clothing. Alexander the Great found them in India upon his arrival there.

9. A proverb.

10. Proverbial expression.

11. A proverb.

12. A proverb.

13. The aesthetic ideas expressed by Cervantes here were more or less current in his day. See J. C. Dunlop, *History of Prose Fiction* (London, 1906; first edition, 1888), Vol. I, pp. 10 ff.; on Cervantes, see Vol. II, pp. 313-23.

14. Prester John was a legendary Christian priest and king who in the Middle Ages and early Renaissance was believed to reign over a country in the Far East, his realm being later identified with Abyssinia. He is mentioned in Rabelais and other sixteenth-century writers.

15. The original reads *"quanto tiene más de lo dudoso y possible"*—literally, "the more it contains of the doubtful and the possible," the word "doubtful" being here understood in the sense of "probable." But Schevill points out that Cervantes does not elsewhere employ *"dudoso"* in this sense. It accordingly seems best to adopt Hartzenbusch's emendation: *"gustoso"*—"pleasing." The *"dudoso"* was probably a typesetter's error.

16. Sinon was the Greek soldier who persuaded the Trojans to drag the wooden horse into their city.

17. Euryalus, in Vergil's *Aeneid,* was the faithful friend of Nisus.

18. Zopyrus was a Persian nobleman who mutilated himself and thereby helped to conquer Babylon; a celebrated general of Darius Hystaspis, he is mentioned in Herodotus (III, 153) and Justinus (I, 10 ff.).

19. The original has *"varios y hermosos lazos"*—literally, "variegated and beautiful knots"; but the reading of modern editions, *"lizos"*—"threads," seems preferable.

CHAPTER XLVIII

1. The original reads *"puesto que es mejor ser loado de los pocos sabios que burlado de los muchos necios"*—literally, "better to be praised by the discerning few than scoffed at by the unknowing many." The word *"burlado"* has given commentators and translators some little trouble, since it does not appear to make sense. Hartzenbusch suggests substituting *"vitoreado"*—"acclaimed." Ormsby reads *"alabado"* and translates "better to be praised by the wise few than applauded by the foolish many." But the translation given above will perhaps solve the difficulty.

2. The original has *"sastre del cantillo,"* which is meaningless. El Campillo was the name of a number of places in Spain. The proverb ran: *"El sastre del Campillo, que cosia de balde y ponia el hilo"*—"The tailor of El Campillo who threaded his needle and stitched for nothing." There were other versions, such as "The tailor of the crossroads," etc. *The Tailor of El Campillo* was the title of plays by Belmonte and Candamo and of a *novela* by Santos.

3. The third edition has *"autores"*—"authors."

4. The edition of Brussels has "actor."

5. These plays are by Lupercio Leonardo de Argensola. See Otis Howard Green's *The Life and Works of Lupercio Leonardo de Argensola* (Philadelphia. University of Pennsylvania Press, 1927).

6. *Ingratitude Avenged (La Ingratitud Vengada)* is by Lope de Vega; the *Numantia (Numancia)* is Cervantes' own piece; *The Merchant Lover (El Mercader Amante)* is the work of Gaspar Aguilar; and *The Fair and Favoring Enemy (La Enemiga Favorable)* is from the pen of Francisco Agustín Tárrega.

7. What Cicero said was: *"Comoedia est imitatio vitae, speculum consuetudinis, imago veritatis"*—"Comedy is an imitation of life, a mirror of manners, and an image of the truth." The words are quoted by Lope de Vega in his *New Art of Making Comedies (Arte Nuevo de Hacer Comedias)*.

8. *"Apariencia."*

9. There has been considerable discussion as to whom Cervantes meant by these "foreigners." Literary historians will tell us that the theater in both France and Italy at this time was in a state of decadence, and as Ormsby remarks, the English certainly did not "scrupulously observe" the rules of comedy. Schevill believes that the author, carried away by his desire to criticize the type of comedy produced in Spain, may have been thinking, rather, of certain poetic manuals and treatises such as were commonly discussed (possibly years before) by those associated with the playhouse.

10. The author referred to is Lope de Vega. This chapter had a good deal to do with the bitter feeling against Cervantes on the part of Lope and his followers. Lope himself, however, in his *New Art of Making Comedies*, gives expression to practically the same cynical views that are here under attack. Later, in the second act of his play, *The Fortunate Procurer (El Rufián Dichoso)*, Cervantes recanted the opinions set forth in this passage.

11. This proposal is characterized by Professor Schevill as a "reactionary doctrine" which would have rendered impossible the creation of a national and popular theater, and the same commentator further describes it as a "feeble imitation" of Plato's views as expounded in the seventh book of *The Republic*. Plato wrote: "The magistrate will appoint censors to judge the compositions [of the poet] and see to it that they do not stray from the eternal types or laws of the beautiful, but shall tend to preserve the power and prestige of constituted authority, of tradition, and of ancient customs, in songs, games, ceremonies, sacrifices, spectacles, and all that pertains to the giving of pleasure. Otherwise, the citizens will readily fall in with dangerous novelties of a more serious nature." Plato was frequently cited in the Renaissance by those who

favored a censorship. "These pages of *Don Quixote*," says Schevill, "lead us to believe that Cervantes, regarding the novelties of the school of Lope as dangerous, had to take refuge in Plato's doctrine of censorship, applying it to comedy in such a manner that only those pieces of which the author of Don Quixote approved would be performed." (From the Spanish note.)

12. The Spanish is *"hazer aguas menores o mayores."* "Major or minor" is a common American euphemism and seems appropriate here.

CHAPTER XLIX

1. Viriatus, celebrated leader of the Lusitanians in the war against the Romans, is mentioned by Livy and other historians.

2. Don Manuel Ponce de León, knight of the time of Ferdinand and Isabella, whose name occurs in ballads relating to the siege of Granada, is the hero who figures in the incident of the glove in Schiller's poem, "Der Handschuh"; compare Leigh Hunt's "The Glove and the Lions" and Browning's "The Glove." He is mentioned again in Part II, Chapter XVII. Count Fernán González was a tenth-century knight of Castile. On Gonzalo Hernández (Fernández) and Diego García de Paredes, see Chapter XXXII preceding and note 1. Garci Pérez de Vargas is another ballad hero, but it would appear that the author is referring to Diego Pérez de Vargas, known as "the Pounder" (see Chapter VIII preceding and note 1). Garcilaso was a famous soldier of Ferdinand and Isabella.

3. The Princess Florípes was the sister of Fierabrás and wife of Guy of Burgundy, Charlemagne's nephew. The bridge of Mantible was defended by a huge giant, Galafre, supported by Turks, and was taken by Charlemagne with the aid of Fierabrás. The incident is related in the Charlemagne chronicle.

4. Guarino Mesquino was the hero of an Italian romance of the Charlemagne cycle which had been translated into Spanish.

5. Queen Guinevere's waiting woman; see Chapter XVI preceding.

6. The story of Pierres and Magalona is a twelfth-century Provençal romance by Bernardo Treviez which had been translated into Spanish. Babieca was the Cid's steed. On Roncesvalles, see Chapter VI preceding and note 12.

7. Juan de Merlo (Melo) was a fifteenth-century knight of Portuguese descent, born in Castile in the reign of John II. At the tournament of Arras, held under the auspices of Philip, Duke of Burgundy, he overthrew Pierre de Brecemont, Sieur de Charny, and at Basle he vanquished the famous German knight, Heinrich von Rabenstein (Henri de Remestan). The original has *"Mosen Pierres"* and *"Mosen Enrique de Remestan,"* the *"Mosen"* (rendered as "Monsieur") being a shortened form of *"mio señor,"* my lord, and a common Aragonian prefix corresponding to the Castilian "Don."

8. Allusion to a tournament held at St. Omer in Burgundy, in 1435, at which Gutierre Quijada, Lord of Villagracia, jousted with Pierre, Sieur de Haburdin, natural son of the Comte de St. Paul. Barba was Quijada's friend who was prevented by illness from taking part in the tourney. The stories in this passage were possibly taken by Cervantes from the *Chronicle of King John II.* (Schevill)

9. Another knight of the reign of John II.

10. Suero de Quiñones was one of ten knights who in 1434 undertook to hold the bridge of Orbiga, near Astorga, against all comers for thirty days, a feat of great renown in the later Middle Ages and one that came to be known as the *"Paso Honroso,"* or "Passage of Honor."

11. These knights, also, are mentioned in the *Chronicle of King John II.* Louis de Faux was a knight of Navarre.

12. On Turpin, see Chapter VI preceding and note 8.

13. The title "Knight of the Twelve Peers" mentioned here is an imaginary one.

14. See Chapter VI preceding and note 12.

CHAPTER L

1. At this point the third edition has an inserted passage for which there is no authority.

2. The promised land of squires; see Chapter X and note 5.

3. Expression used by gamblers.

CHAPTER LI

1. The original has "Garcia y Luna," apparently an erratum. Hartzenbusch's emendation has been adopted.

CHAPTER LII

1. Previously we were told that they were armed with muskets.

2. With which they were flagellating themselves.

3. This speech of Sancho's seems somewhat out of character—for example, the reference to "the Alexanders"—but it is to be presumed that by this time he has picked up some of his master's phraseology as well as ideas.

4. A proverb.

5. Don Quixote's village, "the name of which I have no desire to recall." (See Chapter 1, note 1.)

6. The sense of the word is manikin, a puppet or ridiculous figure (compare the modern Spanish "*monigote*," from "*monachus*," "a monk").

7. The name signifies a parasite or hanger-on.

8. The meaning is whimsical, crotchety.

9. This "sonnet," it will be noted, is of seventeen lines, the rhyme scheme of the sestet and final tercet being cdecdeeff.

10. This is the reading of the original —"*trono*"; the second and third editions and the edition of Brussels have "*tronco*"—literally, "trunk," which Hartzenbusch rejects, but which may have reference to a "trophy" instead of a "throne."

11. In the *Orlando Furioso*, Brigliador was Orlando's horse and Baiardo was Rinaldo's.

12. The name means jester.

13. Signifying hobgoblin.

14. In this and the following piece the rhyme scheme, in place of the one followed here, is abbaabba.

15. The name is onomatopoeic.

16. This line from the *Orlando Furioso* (xxx, 16) is wrongly given in the first edition: "*Forsi altro canterá con miglior plectio.*" This is the end of the original Part IV.

PART TWO

The Ingenious Gentleman

DON QUIXOTE

DE LA MANCHA

PART TWO: CONTENTS

Certificate of Price

I, Hernando de Vallejo, scrivener of the Chamber of our master the King, in behalf of those who reside in his Council, do hereby certify that, those lords having seen a book which was composed by Miguel de Cervantes Saavedra, entitled *Don Quixote de la Mancha, Second Part,* the said book having been printed by his Majesty's license, they have estimated the value of each sheet at four maravedis, and inasmuch as the book contains seventy-three sheets, the value of the paper in it amounts to two-hundred-ninety-two maravedis; and they have commanded that this certificate of price be placed in the front of each volume of the said book, in order that it may be known and understood what is to be asked and received for it, the price in no wise to exceed this amount, as is plainly set forth in the original edict and decree upon this subject, which I am charged with enforcing and to which I do hereby refer; and upon the order of the said lords of the Council and at the request of the said Miguel de Cervantes, I do give this certificate in Madrid, on the twenty-first day of the month of October of the year one-thousand-six-hundred-and-fifteen.

HERNANDO DE VALLEJO

Certificate of Errata

I HAVE seen this book entitled *Second Part of Don Quixote de la Mancha,* composed by Miguel de Cervantes Saavedra, and there is in it nothing worthy of note that does not correspond to the original. Given in Madrid, on the twenty-first day of October, one-thousand-six-hundred-and-fifteen.

THE LICENTIATE FRANCISCO MURCIA DE LA LLANA

Approbation

BY COMMISSION and order of the lords of the Council, I have had submitted to me the book referred to in this memorandum. It does not contain anything contrary to the faith or good morals, but rather offers much wholesome entertainment intermingled with much moral philosophy. A license may be granted for the printing of it.

In Madrid, on the fifth of November, one-thousand-six-hundred-and-fifteen.

DOCTOR GUTIERRE DE CETINA

Approbation

BY COMMISSION and order of the lords of the Council, I have seen *The Second Part of Don Quixote de la Mancha*, by Miguel de Cervantes Saavedra. It does not contain anything against our Catholic faith or good morals, but rather offers much decent recreation and harmless amusement such as the ancients looked upon as being of utility to their States, seeing that even the Lacedaemonians reared a statue to Laughter while the Thessalians had festivals devoted to that god, as Pausanias (cited by Bosio, *De Signis Eccles.*, Book II, Chapter 10) informs us.[1] For laughter inspires and revives weary minds and melancholy spirits, as Tully notes in the first book of his *De Legibus*, and the poet as well when he says: *"Interpone tuis interdum gaudia curis."* [2] That is what the author does, by mingling jest with earnest, the pleasing with the profitable, and the moral with the facetious, dissimulating under the bait of wit the hook of reprehension. All this in pursuance of his professed aim, which is that of driving out the books of chivalry, from whose contagious and baleful influence he has done much to cleanse these realms through the employment of his fine and cunning wit. It is a work such as befits his great talent, being the honor and glory of our nation and the object of admiration and envy on the part of other peoples. Such is my humble opinion. In Madrid, on the seventeenth of March, 1615.

MAESTRO JOSEPH DE VALDIVIELSO

Approbation

BY COMMISSION of Dr. Gutierre de Cetina, vicar-general of this city of Madrid, his Majesty's capital, I have seen this book, the second part of the *Ingenious Gentleman, Don Quixote de la Mancha*, by Miguel de Cervantes Saavedra, and have found in it nothing unworthy of a zealous Christian nor anything that is opposed to decency, the setting of a good example, or the moral virtues. On the contrary, it contains much erudition and profitable reading in worthy pursuance of its aim, which is that of extirpating the vain and lying books of chivalry, whose contagious influence is far too widespread. It is likewise commendable by reason of the smoothness of the Castilian tongue as employed therein, which is here not adulterated with any tiresome and studied affectations such as are rightly abhorred by the wise. Moreover, in the correction of vices the author in the course of his astute reasoning observes so wisely the laws of Christian reprehension that the one who is infected with the disease which he sets out to cure will unsuspectingly and with pleasure drink the sweet and savory medicine that is thus provided, with no feeling whatsoever of surfeit or of loathing, and will in this manner come to hate his own particular vice. All of which, the combining of pleasure and reproof, is an exceedingly difficult thing to accomplish.

There have been many who, not knowing how to mingle the useful with the pleasing in the right proportions, have had all their toil and pains for nothing; and being incapable of imitating Diogenes the learned philosopher, they have audaciously, not to say licentiously and stupidly, endeavored to imitate the cynic by having resort to slander and inventing cases that never occurred in order to enlarge upon the vice which they would so sternly reprove. Such as these may even discover new ways of pursuing the said vice and thus become the teachers of it rather than its censors. As a result, they render themselves odious to those of sound understanding and lose their reputation, if they ever had any, with the public, while the vices which they have so brazenly and imprudently undertaken to correct are left more deeply rooted than before. Not all abscesses yield to the cautery, but some are much better treated by mild and soothing medicines through the application of which the discreet and skilled physician finally succeeds in curing them, with far more satisfactory consequences, frequently, than are to be attained through the use of such stern measures as the iron.

Quite different has been the effect produced by the writings of Miguel de Cervantes upon our own nation and upon foreign ones as well. For even as they would wish to behold a miracle, so do the men of other lands desire to lay eyes upon the author of those books that, by reason of their circumspection and propriety as well as their urbanity and other pleasing qualities, have met with general applause in Spain, France, Italy, Germany, and Flanders.[3]

I can truthfully certify that on the twenty-fifth of February of this year 1615, that most illustrious gentleman Don Bernardo de Sandoval y Rojas, Cardinal Archbishop of Toledo and my lord, having gone to repay the visit of the French ambassador (who had come to treat of things having to do with marriages between the royal house of his country and that of Spain), a number of the French knights who accompanied the ambassador and who were as courteous as they were intelligent and fond of good literature, came to me and other chaplains of my lord the Cardinal to make inquiries concerning the most worth-while books then current. We thereupon fell to discussing those that I was at the time engaged in censoring, and no sooner had they heard the name of Miguel de Cervantes than they at once began speaking most enthusiastically of the high esteem in which his works were held not only in France but in neighboring kingdoms. They mentioned in particular the *Galatea*, the first part of which one of them could almost repeat from memory, and the *Novelas*. So fervent, indeed, was their praise, that I offered to take them to see the author of those works, an invitation which they eagerly accepted. They went on to question me in great detail regarding his age, his profession, his rank and worldly state, and I was obliged to inform them that he was an old soldier and an impoverished gentleman, whereupon one of them replied to me most gravely, "How comes it Spain does not see to it that such a man is maintained in luxury out of the public treasury?"

One of the others then made this astute observation. "If," he said, "it is necessity that obliges him to write, then God grant that he never be possessed of abundance, in order that, while poor himself, he may continue to enrich all the world." [4]

I realize that, as a censor's report, this document is somewhat long, and some will say that it borders on flattery, but the truth that I have here briefly stated should be sufficient to relieve the critic of suspicion and me of all concern; for today it is the custom to flatter only the one that is able to stuff the maw of the flatterer, who, even though he speak affectedly, falsely, and in jest, none the less expects to be rewarded in earnest. In Madrid, on the twenty-seventh of February, one-thousand-six-hundred-and-fifteen.

THE LICENTIATE MÁRQUEZ TORRES [5]

Royal Privilege

INASMUCH as we have been informed by you, Miguel de Cervantes Saavedra, that you have composed *The Second Part of Don Quixote de la Mancha,* with a copy of which you have presented us; and inasmuch as this is a storybook that is both pleasing and decorous and one that has cost you much labor and study, and you have besought us to command that a license be granted for the printing of it, along with a Privilege for twenty years or such time as we in our good grace may see fit; and inasmuch as the said book has been duly scrutinized by the members of our Council in accordance with our decree upon the subject, it has been decided that we should grant you this our scroll for the said purpose, the which we do right willingly.

With this object in view, we do hereby grant you, or the person whom you shall employ and none other, for the time and space of ten years current from the date of this our scroll, license and authority to print and sell the said book, herein above-mentioned. And for the present, we grant license and authority to any printer of our realms whom you may name to print the said book for the space of time herein provided, from the original copy as seen by our Council and signed at the end with his flourish by Hernando de Vallejo, our scrivener of the Chamber, and one of those resident therein. And it is further provided that, before the book is placed on sale, you shall bring it before them, together with the said original, in order that they may see if the printed text is in conformity with the aforesaid original; or you shall take public oath that the said printing has been seen and corrected by the reader appointed by us.

And the said printer who shall print the said book shall not print the beginning nor the first sheet thereof, nor deliver more than a single book along with the original to the author and person who pays the cost of the printing, or any other person whomsoever, until, first and foremost, the said book shall have been corrected and its price fixed by the members of our Council. Only when this shall have been done and under no other circumstances may the beginning and the first sheet be printed. And in the front of the said book shall be placed this our license and approbation, together with the certificate of price and the errata, nor shall you or any other person sell the book until the above provisions have been complied with, under pain of incurring those penalties provided for in the aforesaid decree and the laws of our realm having to do with this matter.

It is further provided that, during the said space of time no person may without your permission print or sell the said book, and whosoever shall so print or sell it shall lose whatever copies of it he may have in his possession along with the type and the forms, and shall in addition incur the penalty of a fine of fifty thousand maravedis for each offense, one third of the said fine to go to our Chamber, one third to the judge who shall sentence him, and the remaining third to the plaintiff.

And we do further command the members of our Council, the Judges and Magistrates of our Courts, the Justices and Bailiffs of our Household and Court Chancelleries, and all other magistrates of all the cities, towns, and villages within our realm and seignories, each one in his own jurisdiction, both those that now are and those that henceforth shall be, to observe and comply with the provisions of this our scroll which we by our grace do hereby grant you, and we forbid them to go contrary to it or neglect to fulfill it in any manner whatsoever, under pain of our disfavor and a fine of ten thousand maravedis for our Chamber.

Given in Madrid, on the thirtieth day of the month of March, one-thousand-six-hundred-and-fifteen.

I, THE KING

By command of our master, the King,

PEDRO DE CONTRERAS

Prologue

TO THE READER [1]

G OD bless me, gentle or, it may be, plebeian reader, how eagerly you must be awaiting this prologue, thinking to find in it vengeful scoldings and vituperations directed against the author of the second Don Quixote—I mean the one who, so it is said, was begotten in Tordesillas and born in Tarragona.[2] The truth is, however, that I am not going to be able to satisfy you in this regard; for granting that injuries are capable of awakening wrath in the humblest of bosoms, my own must be an exception to the rule. You would, perhaps, have me call him an ass, a crackbrain, and an upstart, but it is not my intention so to chastise him for his sin. Let him eat it with his bread and have done with it.[3]

What I cannot but resent is the fact that he describes me as being old and one-handed, as if it were in my power to make time stand still for me, or as if I had lost my hand in some tavern instead of upon the greatest occasion that the past or present has ever known or the future may ever hope to see.[4] If my wounds are not resplendent in the eyes of the chance beholder, they are at least highly thought of by those who know where they were received. The soldier who lies dead in battle has a more impressive mien than the one who by flight attains his liberty. So strongly do I feel about this that even if it were possible to work a miracle in my case, I still would rather have taken part in that prodigious battle than be today free of my wounds without having been there. The scars that the soldier has to show on face and breast are stars that guide others to the Heaven of honor, inspiring them with a longing for well-merited praise. What is more, it may be noted that one does not write with gray hairs but with his understanding, which usually grows better with the years.

I likewise resent his calling me envious; and as though I were some ignorant person, he goes on to explain to me what is meant by envy; when the truth of the matter is that of the two kinds,[5] I am acquainted only with that which is holy, noble, and right-intentioned. And this being so, as indeed it is, it is not likely that I should attack any priest, above all, one that is a familiar of the Holy Office.[6] If he made this statement, as it appears that he did, on behalf of a certain person, then he is utterly mistaken; for the person in question is one whose genius I hold in veneration and whose works I admire, as well as his constant industry and powers of application. But when all is said, I wish to thank this gentlemanly author for observing that my *Novels* are more satirical than exemplary, while admitting at the same time that they are good;[7] for they could not be good unless they had in them a little of everything.

You will likely tell me that I am being too restrained and over-modest, but it is my belief that affliction is not to be heaped upon the afflicted, and this gentleman must be suffering greatly, seeing that he does not dare to come out into the open and show himself by the light of day, but must conceal his name and dissemble his place of origin, as if he had been guilty of some treason or act of lese majesty. If you by chance should come to know him, tell him on my behalf that I do not hold it against him; for I know what temptations the devil has to offer, one of the greatest of which consists in putting it into a man's head that he can write a book and have it printed and thereby achieve as much fame as he does money and acquire as much money as he does fame; in confirmation of which I would have you, in your own witty and charming manner, tell him this tale.

There was in Seville a certain madman whose madness assumed one of the drollest forms that ever was seen in this world. Taking a hollow reed sharpened at one end, he would catch a dog in the street or somewhere else; and, holding one of the animal's legs with his foot and raising the other with his hand, he would fix his reed as best he could in a certain part, after which he would blow the dog up, round as a ball. When he had it in this condition he would give it a couple of slaps on the belly and let it go, remarking to the bystanders, of whom there were always plenty, "Do your Worships think, then, that it is so easy a thing to inflate a dog?" So you might ask, "Does your Grace think that it is so easy a thing to write a book?" And if this story does not set well with him, here is another one, dear reader, that you may tell him. This one, also, is about a madman and a dog.

The madman in this instance lived in Cordova. He was in the habit of carrying on his head a marble slab or stone of considerable weight, and when he met some stray cur he would go up alongside it and drop the weight full upon it, and the dog in a rage, barking and howling, would then scurry off down three whole streets without stopping. Now, it happened that among the dogs that he treated in this fashion was one belonging to a capmaker, who was very fond of the beast. Going up to it as usual, the madman let the stone fall on its head, whereupon the animal set up a great yowling, and its owner, hearing its moans and seeing what had been done to it, promptly snatched up a measuring rod and fell upon the dog's assailant, flaying him until there was not a sound bone left in the fellow's body; and with each blow that he gave him he cried, "You dog! You thief! Treat my greyhound like that, would you? You brute, couldn't you see it was a greyhound?" And repeating the word "greyhound"[8] over and over, he sent the madman away beaten to a pulp.

Profiting by the lesson that had been taught him, the fellow disappeared and was not seen in public for more than a month, at the end of which time he returned, up to his old tricks and with a heavier stone than ever on his head. He would go up to a dog and stare at it, long and hard, and without daring to drop his stone, would say, "This is a greyhound; beware." And so with all the dogs that he encountered: whether they were mastiffs or curs, he would assert that they were greyhounds and let them go unharmed.

The same thing possibly may happen to our historian; it may be that he will not again venture to let fall the weight of his wit in the form of books which, being bad ones, are harder than rocks.

As for the threat he has made to the effect that through his book he will deprive me of the profits on my own,[9] you may tell him that I do not give a rap. Quoting from the famous interlude, *La Perendenga*,[10] I will say to him in reply, "Long live my master, the Four-and-twenty,[11] and Christ be with us all." Long live the great Count of Lemos, whose Christian spirit and well-known liberality have kept me on my feet despite all the blows an unkind fate has dealt me. Long life to his Eminence of Toledo, the supremely charitable Don Bernardo de Sandoval y Rojas. Even though there were no printing presses in all the world, or such as there are should print more books directed against me than there are letters in the verses of *Mingo Revulgo*,[12] what would it matter to me? These two princes, without any cringing flattery or adulation on my part but solely out of their own goodness of heart, have taken it upon themselves to grant me their favor and protection, in which respect I consider myself richer and more fortunate than if by ordinary means I had attained the peak of prosperity. The poor man may keep his honor, but not the vicious one. Poverty may cast a cloud over nobility but cannot wholly obscure it. Virtue of itself gives off a certain light, even though it be through the chinks and crevices and despite the obstacles of adversity, and so comes to be esteemed and as a consequence favored by high and noble minds.

Tell him no more than this, nor do I have anything more to say to you, except to ask you to bear in mind that this *Second Part of Don Quixote,* which I herewith present to you, is cut from the same cloth and by the same craftsman as Part I. In this book I give you Don Quixote continued and, finally, dead and buried, in order that no one may dare testify any further concerning him, for there has been quite enough evidence as it is. It is sufficient that a reputable individual should have chronicled these ingenious acts of madness once and for all, without going into the matter again; for an abundance even of good things causes them to be little esteemed, while scarcity may lend a certain worth to those that are bad.

I almost forgot to tell you that you may look forward to the *Persiles,* on which I am now putting the finishing touches, as well as Part Second of the *Galatea.*

To the Count of Lemos [1]

W̶HEN, some days ago, I sent your Excellency my *Comedies*, printed before being performed, I stated, if I remember rightly, that Don Quixote was then engaged in putting on his spurs to go kiss your Excellency's hands; and I may now add that he has put them on and has set out. If he arrives, it is my belief that I shall have been of some service to your Excellency; for I am being strongly urged on all sides to send him forth by way of getting rid of the loathing and nausea occasioned by another *Don Quixote* who, disguising himself under the name of Part Second, has been wandering about the world. The one who has shown himself most eager in this regard is the Emperor of China, who about a month ago dispatched to me by courier a letter written in the Chinese language, in which he requested or, more properly speaking, implored, me to send the Knight to him, since he wished to found a college where the Castilian tongue should be read and he desired that the book to be used should be the story of Don Quixote. At the same time he informed me that I was to be the rector of this college. [2]

I thereupon asked the bearer of the message if His Majesty had given him anything toward defraying my expenses, and the reply was that he had not even thought of it.

"Well, then, brother," I said to him, "you may go back to that China of yours at ten o'clock, at twenty, or whatever time it was that you were sent; for I am not in good enough health to undertake so long a voyage. Moreover, in addition to being ill, I am without money, and emperor for emperor, monarch for monarch, in Naples I have the great Count of Lemos, who, without all those college titles and rectorships, still supports, protects, and favors me beyond anything that I could desire."

With this, I sent him away, and I myself now take my leave by offering to your Excellency *The Trials of Persilis and Sigismunda*, a work which, *Deo volente*, I shall bring to a close within the next four months. It ought to be the worst or the best that has been written in our language—I am referring, of course, to books designed for entertainment. As a matter of fact, I repent having said "the worst," for according to the opinion of my friends it should be extremely good.

May your Excellency come back to us in that state of health in which all wish to see you. Persiles will be there to kiss your hands and I your feet, as your Excellency's humble servant that I am.

From Madrid, on the last day of October, one-thousand-six-hundred-fifteen.

Your Excellency's servant,
MIGUEL DE CERVANTES SAAVEDRA

The Ingenious Gentleman

DON QUIXOTE

DE LA MANCHA

Part Two

CHAPTER I. *Of the conversation which the curate and the barber had with Don Quixote concerning his malady.*

IN THE second part of this history, dealing with Don Quixote's third sally, Cid Hamete Benengeli tells us that the curate and the barber went nearly a month without seeing their friend, in order not to remind him of what had happened. But they did not for this reason leave off visiting the niece and housekeeper, whom they urged to treat the knight with the greatest of care by seeing to it that he had comforting things to eat and such as would be good for his heart and for his brain as well, the latter being to all appearances the seat of his trouble and the cause of all his misfortunes. The women replied that this was what they were doing, and would continue to do, with a right good will and most attentively; for they had noticed that the master of the house at moments seemed to be in full possession of his senses.

The curate and the barber were well pleased at hearing this, and concluded that they had done the wise thing in having Don Quixote borne away in an ox-cart, as has been related in the last chapter of the First Part of this great and painstaking chronicle. They accordingly determined to visit him and see for themselves what improvement he had made, although they believed it to be all but impossible that he could be any better. They agreed that they would not bring up any subject that had to do with knight-errantry, as they did not wish to run the risk of reopening a wound that was still so sore.

When the pair came to pay their visit, they found their host seated upon the bed, clad in a green baize waistcoat and a red Toledo cap, and looking as withered and dried up as an Egyptian mummy. He received them very well and, when they made inquiries regarding his health, discussed with them this and other matters of a personal nature most sensibly and in words that were very well chosen. In the course of their conversation they came to touch upon what is known as statecraft and forms of government, correcting this abuse, condemning that one, reforming one custom and banishing another, with each of the three setting himself up as a new lawgiver, a modern Lycurgus or newly fledged Solon. In this manner they proceeded to remodel the State, as if they had placed it in a forge and had drawn out something quite different from what they had put in. And all the while Don Quixote displayed such good sound sense in connection with whatever topic was broached as to lead the two examiners to feel that he must undoubtedly be fully recovered and in his right mind.

The niece and housekeeper were present at this conversation and could not thank God enough when they saw how clear-headed their master apparently was. It was then that the curate changed his mind about not bringing up anything that had to do with chivalry; for he wished to make the test complete and assure himself as to whether the knight's recovery was real or not. And so, speaking of one thing and another, he came to relate various items of news that had just been received from the capital, including a report to the effect that it was looked upon as a certainty that the Turk was bearing down with a powerful fleet, although nothing was known of his plans as yet, nor where so great a storm as this would break, but as a result all Christendom was stirred by that feeling of dread that almost every year summons us to take up arms, and his Majesty had seen to fortifying the coasts of Naples and Sicily and the island of Malta.

"His Majesty," remarked Don Quixote, "has acted like a most prudent warrior in providing for the safety of his dominions while there is yet time, in order that the enemy may not take him unawares; but if he were to follow my advice, I should counsel him to adopt a measure which I am sure is far from his thoughts at the present moment."

"Poor Don Quixote," said the curate to himself when he heard this, "may God help you; for it looks to me as if you have fallen from the high cliff of madness into the abyss of simple-mindedness."

The same thought had occurred to the barber, who now asked the knight what this measure was that in his opinion should be adopted, adding that perhaps it was one that would have to be added to the long list of impertinent suggestions of the kind commonly offered to princes.

"My suggestion, Master Shaver," replied Don Quixote, "is not an impertinent one but is very much to the point."

"That is not what I meant," said the barber, "but experience has shown that all or most of the expedients that are proposed to his Majesty are either impossible or nonsensical, or else would be detrimental to king and kingdom."

"But mine," Don Quixote insisted, "is not impossible nor is it nonsensical, but rather is the easiest, the most reasonable, the readiest, and most expeditious scheme that anyone could devise."

"It takes your Grace a long time to tell it," observed the curate.

"I do not care to tell it to you here and now," said the knight, "and, the first thing tomorrow morning, have it reach the ears of my lords, the councilors, so that some other person may carry off the reward and win the thanks that are rightly due me."

"For my part," the barber assured him, "I give you my word, here and before God, that I will say nothing of what your Grace may tell me, to king, rook, or earthly man.[1] That, by the way, is an oath I picked up from the ballad about the curate who, in the prelude, tells the king of the thief who had robbed him of a hundred doblas [2] and his fast-pacing mule." [3]

"I know nothing about such stories," said Don Quixote, "but I do know that the oath is a good one by reason of the faith that I have in this worthy man, our master barber."

"And even if he were not what you take him to be," the curate went on, "I would go bond and put in an appearance for him, to the effect that in this case he will be as silent as a mute, under pain of any sentence that might be pronounced upon him."

"And who will go your Grace's bond?" Don Quixote asked the priest.

"My profession," was the curate's reply, "which consists in keeping secrets."

"Then, damn it, sir!" exclaimed the knight, "what more need his Majesty do than command by public proclamation that all the knights-errant at present wandering over Spain shall assemble in the capital on a given day? Even if no more than half a dozen came, there well might be one among them who alone would be able to overthrow the Turk's mighty power. Pay attention, your Worships, and listen closely to what I am about to say. Is it by any chance an unheard-of thing for a single knight-errant to rout an army of two hundred thousand men, as if they all had but one throat or were made of sugar paste? Tell me, how many stories do we have that are filled with such marvels? If only, alas for me (I do not care to speak for any other), the famous Don Belianís were alive today, or any of the countless other descendants of Amadis of Gaul! Let one of these but confront the Turk, and my word, they would have the best of him. But God will look after his people and will provide someone who, if not so brave as the knights of old, will not be inferior to them in the matter of courage. God knows what I mean. I need say no more."

"Oh, dear," wailed the niece at this point, "may they slay me if my master doesn't want to go back to being a knight-errant!"

"A knight-errant I shall live and die," said Don Quixote, "and let the Turk come or go as he will, with all the strength he can muster. Again I say to you, God understands."

The barber now spoke up. "I beg your Worships to grant me permission to relate to you briefly something that happened in Seville. It is a story that is made for the present occasion, which is why I should like to tell it."

Don Quixote gave his consent, and the curate and the others prepared to lend him their attention.

"In the madhouse of Seville," he began, "was a certain individual who had been placed there by his relatives, as being out of his mind. He was a graduate of Osuna, in canon law; but it was the opinion of most people that even if he had been of Salamanca, he would have been mad all the same. After a few years of seclusion, this man took it into his head that he had been wholly cured, and, being so convinced, he wrote to the archbishop, begging that prelate, earnestly and in well-chosen words, to have him released from the misery in which he was living, since he had now recovered his lost reason, even though his family, which was enjoying his share of the estate, insisted upon keeping him there; for contrary to the truth of the matter, they would make him out to be a madman until his dying day.

"Impressed by the many well and sensibly written letters he had received from the man, the archbishop sent one of his chaplains to find out from the superintendent of the madhouse if what the licentiate had written was true or not. The chaplain was further directed to converse with the patient and if he found him to be sane, he was to take him out and set him at liberty. Following these instructions, he was informed by the superintendent that the man was as mad as ever, and that while he very frequently spoke like a person of great intelligence, he would suddenly burst out with so many absurdities that they more than made up, in quantity and in quality, for all the sensible things he had previously said, as was readily to be seen by talking with him. This the chaplain resolved to do, and, sitting down with the patient, he carried on a conversation with him for more than an hour, during all of which time the madman did not make one incoherent or foolish remark but appeared to be so rational in everything he said that his visitor was compelled to believe him sane.

"Among other things, the man stated that the superintendent had it in for him, being motivated by a desire not to lose the gifts that the relatives made him for saying that his ward was still insane with lucid intervals. The greatest misfortune that he had to contend with, the poor fellow added, was his large estate, since it was for the purpose of enjoying his wealth that his enemies belied and cast doubts upon the grace which Our Lord had shown him by turning him from a beast into a man once more. In short, he spoke in such a way as to make the superintendent's conduct seem highly suspicious, while his relatives were made out to be covetous and heartless creatures; all of which was uttered with such a show of reason that the chaplain made up his mind to take the man with him that the archbishop might see him and come at the truth of this business.

"With this worthy intention, he asked the superintendent to send for the clothes which the licentiate had worn when he entered the place, whereupon that official once more begged him to look well to what he was doing, as there was not the slightest doubt that the patient was still mad; but all these cautions and warnings were lost upon the chaplain, who was bent upon having the man released. Seeing that it was the archbishop's orders, the superintendent complied, and they then brought the licentiate his clothes, which were new and very presentable. When the latter saw himself dressed like one in his right senses and rid of his madman's garments, he begged the chaplain to be so kind as to permit him to take leave of his fellow patients. The chaplain consented, remarking that he would like to go along and see the others who were confined in the institution. They accordingly went upstairs, accompanied by some of those who were present, and came to a cell where one who was raving mad was lodged, though at that moment he was calm and quiet.

" 'Brother,' the licentiate said to him, 'think if there is anything that I can do for you. I am going home, God in His infinite goodness and mercy, and through no merit of my own, having seen fit to restore my reason to me. I am now cured and sane, since where the power of God is concerned, nothing is impossible. You must have a great hope and confidence in Him, who, just as He has restored me to my former state, will do the same for you if you trust in Him. I will make it a point to send you some good things to eat, and be sure that you do eat them; for as one who has gone through it, I may tell you that in my opinion all our madness comes from having our stomachs empty and our brains full of air. Pluck up your courage, then. Despondency in misfortune only impairs the health and brings death all the sooner.'

"Everything the licentiate said was heard by another madman in a cell across the way, and, rising from an old mat where he had been lying stark naked, this man now cried out in a loud voice, demanding to know who it was that was going away cured and sane.

" 'It is I, brother,' the licentiate replied. 'I am leaving you. There is no longer any need of my remaining here, thanks be to Heaven for having shown me this mercy.'

" 'Mind what you are saying, licentiate,' the other warned him, 'and do not let the devil deceive you. You had best not stir a foot but stay where you are and save yourself the trouble of coming back.'

" 'I know that I am all right,' was the reply, 'and that it will not be necessary for me to do the stations again.' [4]

" 'You are all right, are you?' said the madman across the way. 'We shall see as to that. May God go with you; but I swear to you, in the name of Jupiter whose majesty I represent on earth, that for this one sin which Seville today is committing by releasing you from this place as if you were cured, I shall have to inflict such a punishment upon it as will be remembered throughout all the ages to come. Amen. Do you not know, miserable little licentiate, that I can do this, seeing that, as I have said, I am Jupiter the Thunderer and hold in my hands the fiery bolts with which I am accustomed to threaten the world and by means of which I can destroy it? There is, however, only one way in which I wish to punish this ignorant town, and that is by not raining upon it or anywhere in the entire district and vicinity for three whole years, beginning with the day and moment when this threat is made. You free, cured, in your right senses, and I a madman, sickly minded and confined? I would no more think of sending rain than I would of hanging myself.'

"The bystanders all listened attentively to the madman's words and cries. Then our licentiate turned to the chaplain and seized his hands. 'Do not be disturbed, your Grace,' he pleaded, 'and pay no attention to what this fellow says. If he is Jupiter and will not rain, then I who am Neptune, father and god of the waters, will do so any time that I feel like it or whenever it may be necessary.'

" 'For all of that, Sir Neptune,' the chaplain answered him, 'it would be as well not to annoy Sir Jupiter. Stay here, your Grace, and another day, when we have more time and it is more convenient, we will return for you.'

"The superintendent and the others laughed at this, and the chaplain was greatly embarrassed. They then undressed the licentiate, and he remained where he was, and that is the end of the story."

"If that is the tale, Master Barber," said Don Quixote, "what did you mean by saying that it was made for the present occasion, for which reason you could not refrain from telling it? Ah, Master Shaver, Master Shaver, how blind is he who cannot see through a sieve! Is your Grace not aware that comparisons of mind with mind, valor with valor, beauty with beauty, birth with birth, are invariably odious and ill received? I, Master Barber, am not Neptune, god of the waters, nor would I have anyone take me for a wise man when I am not wise. My sole endeavor is to bring the world to realize the mistake it is making in failing to revive that happiest of times when the order of knight-errantry was in the field. But this degenerate age of ours does not deserve to enjoy so great a blessing as that which former ages knew, when wandering men of arms took upon themselves the defense of realms, the protection of damsels, the succor of orphans, the punishment of the proud, and the rewarding of the humble.

"The knights of the present time, for the most part, are accompanied by the rustling of damasks, brocades, and other rich stuffs that they wear, rather than by the rattling of coats of mail. There is none that sleeps in the field, exposed to the inclemency of the heavens and fully armed from head to foot. There is none who, as they say, snatches forty winks without taking foot from stirrup, merely leaning on his lance. There is none who, sallying forth from a wood, will go up onto yonder mountain, and from there come down to tread the barren and deserted shore beside a sea that is almost always angry and tempest-tossed; or who, finding upon the beach a small craft, without oars, sail, mast, or rigging of any kind, will leap into it with intrepid heart and entrust himself to the implacable waves of the stormy deep, waves that now mount heavenward and now drag him down into the abyss. Such a one, breasting the irresistible tempest, may find himself more than three thousand miles from the place where he embarked; in which case, bounding ashore upon the soil of a remote and unknown land, he will meet with such adventures as are worthy of being recorded, not upon parchment, but in bronze.

"Today, sloth triumphs over diligence, idleness and ease over exertion, vice over virtue, arrogance over valor, and theory over practice of the warrior's art. Tell me, if you will, who was more virtuous or more valiant than the famous Amadis of Gaul? Who more prudent than Palmerin of England? Who more gracious and reasonable than Tirant lo Blanch? Who was more the courtier than Lisuarte of Greece? Who was more slashed or slashing than Don Belianís? Who more intrepid than Perión of Gaul? Or who more forward in facing danger than Felixmarte of Hircania? Who was more sincere than Esplandián? More daring than Don Cirongilio of Thrace? Who was braver than Rodamonte? Wiser than King Sobrino? Bolder than Rinaldo? More invincible than Orlando? Who was more gallant and courteous than Ruggiero, from whom the present dukes of Ferrara are descended, according to Turpin in his *Cosmography*? [5]

"All these and many others whom I could mention, Señor Curate, were knights-errant, the light and glory of chivalry. It is these, or such as these, that I would have carry out my plan, in which case his majesty would be well served and would save himself much expense, while the Turk would be left tearing out his beard. For this reason, I do not propose to remain at home,[6] even though the chaplain does not take me out; and if Jupiter, as the barber has said, does not choose to rain, then I am here to do so whenever it pleases me. I say this in order that Master Basin may know that I understand him."

"Really, Señor Don Quixote," said the barber, "I did not mean it in that way. So help me God, my intentions were of the best, and your Grace ought not to take offense."

"Whether I take offense or not," replied Don Quixote, "is for me to decide."

With this, the curate took a hand in the conversation. "I have hardly said a word up to now, but there is one little doubt that gnaws and pecks at my conscience and that comes from what Don Quixote has just told us."

"You may go as far as you like, Señor Curate," said Don Quixote

"Feel perfectly free to state your doubt, for it is not pleasant to have something on one's conscience."

"Well, then, with your permission," the curate continued, "I will say that my doubt arises from the fact that I am unable to persuade myself by any manner of means that all the many knights-errant your Grace has mentioned were in reality flesh-and-blood beings who actually lived in this world. I rather fancy that it is all fiction, fables, and lies, a lot of dreams related by men just awakened from sleep, or, better, still half asleep."

"That," declared Don Quixote, "is another error into which many have fallen who do not believe that such knights ever existed; and I many times, with various persons and on various occasions, have endeavored to bring this all too common mistake to the light of truth. Sometimes I have not succeeded in my purpose, but other times, sustained upon the shoulders of the truth, I have been more fortunate. For the truth is so clear that I can almost assure you that I saw with my own eyes Amadis of Gaul. He was a tall man, of fair complexion and with a beard which, though black, was quite handsome. His countenance was half mild, half stern; his words were few, but he was slow to anger and quick to lay aside his wrath. And just as I have depicted Amadis for you, so I might go on, I think, to portray and describe [7] all the other knights-errant in all the storybooks of the world. For I feel sure that they were what the histories make them out to have been, and from the exploits that they performed and the kind of men they were it would be possible, with the aid of a little sound philosophy, to reconstruct their features, their complexions, and their stature."

"How big, Señor Don Quixote, was the giant Morgante as your Grace conceives him?" the barber asked.

"On this subject of giants," replied the knight, "opinions differ as to whether or not there ever were any in this world: but the Holy Scriptures, which do not depart from the truth by one iota, show us plainly that giants did exist, when they tell us the story of that big Philistine of a Goliath, who was seven cubits and a half in height, which is a very great size.[8] Moreover, in the island of Sicily they have found thigh and shoulder bones so large that they must have belonged to giants as tall as towers.[9] It is a matter of simple geometry. But for all of this, I should not be able to state with any certainty what Morgante's size was, although I imagine that he was not exceedingly tall, since I find in that history where special mention is made of his exploits [10] that he very frequently slept under a roof, and inasmuch as he found houses that were large enough to accommodate him, he could not have been too big after all."

"I agree with you," said the curate. And merely for the pleasure of listening to such utter nonsense, he went on to ask Don Quixote what he thought the countenances of Rinaldo of Montalbán, Don Orlando, and the other Twelve Peers of France must have been like, seeing that they were all knights-errant.

"Concerning Rinaldo," Don Quixote answered him, "I would venture to say that he had a broad face, a ruddy complexion, and twinkling, rather prominent eyes, and that he was punctilious, extremely choleric, and a friend of robbers and those beyond the pale of the law. As to Roldán, or Rotolando, or Orlando—for the histories give him all these names—I am of the opinion, indeed I would assert, that he was of medium stature, broad-shouldered, somewhat bowlegged, red-bearded, with a hairy body and a threatening expression, a man of few words, but very courteous and well bred."

"If Orlando," observed the curate, "had no more of a gentlemanly appearance than that, I do not wonder that the lady Angélica the Fair should have disdained him or that she should have left him for that downy-faced young Moor who was so gay, so sprightly, and so witty. It seems to me she did wisely in preferring the softness of Medora to Orlando's ruggedness."

"That Angélica," replied the knight, "was a giddy damsel, flighty and capricious, and filled the world with her whims as much as with the fame of her beauty. She spurned a thousand gentlemen of wit and valor and was satisfied with a smooth-faced pageling with no other wealth or claim to fame than his reputation for gratitude, due to the affection that he showed his friend.[11] The great poet who sang of her beauty, the famous Ariosto, either did not dare or did not wish to relate what happened to this lady following her disgraceful surrender, but her adventures could not have been any too edifying, and it is with these lines that the bard takes his leave of her:

> *How she received the scepter of Cathay,*
> *Another with better plectrum will sing someday.*[12]

There can be no doubt that this was a kind of prophecy; for poets are also called *vates*, which means 'diviners.' The truth of this is plainly to be seen in the fact that a famous Andalusian poet wept for her and sang of her tears, while another famous and exceptional one of Castile hymned her beauty." [13]

"But tell me, Señor Don Quixote," said the barber, "among all the poets who have praised her, has there been none to compose a satire on this Lady Angélica?"

"I can well believe," replied Don Quixote, "that if Sacripante or Orlando had been poets, they would have given the damsel a dressing-down; for when poets have been scorned and rejected by their ladies, whether the ladies in question be real or imaginary [14]—in short, when they have been spurned by those whom they have chosen to be the mistresses of their affection—it is natural for them to seek to avenge themselves by means of satires and libels, although, to be sure, this is something that is unworthy of generous hearts; but up to now I have not come upon any defamatory verses directed at the Lady Angélica, who set the world on end." [15]

"That is very strange," said the curate.

At that moment they heard the housekeeper and the niece, who had left the room a while ago, shouting at someone in the courtyard, and they all ran out to see what the uproar was about.

CHAPTER II. *Which treats of the notable quarrel that Sancho Panza had with Don Quixote's niece and housekeeper, along with other droll happenings.*

THE history tells us that the cries which Don Quixote, the curate, and the barber heard came from the niece and the housekeeper. They were shouting at Sancho Panza, who was struggling to get in to see the knight, while they were doing their best to keep him out.

"What is this vagabond doing here? Home with you, brother; for you and no one else are the one who puts these foolish notions into my master's head; it is you who lure him away to go wandering over the countryside."

"You devil's housekeeper, you!" exclaimed Sancho. "The one who has foolish notions put in his head and is lured away is I and not your master. He has taken me all over this world; and you do not know the half of it. It was through a trick that he persuaded me to leave home, by promising me an island which I am still waiting to see."

"May you choke on your cursed islands, Sancho, you wretch!" the niece replied. "What are islands anyway? Are they something to eat, glutton that you are?"

"No," replied Sancho, "they are not something to eat, but something to govern and rule over and better than four cities[1] or four judgeships at court."

"Well, in spite of all that," said the housekeeper, "you are not coming in here, you bag of mischief. Go govern that weedpatch of yours and let us hear no more talk of islands or drylands or what have you."[2]

The curate and the barber greatly enjoyed listening to the conversation of these three; but Don Quixote, fearing that Sancho would talk too much, blurt out a lot of mischievous nonsense, and touch upon certain subjects that would not redound to his master's credit, now called his squire over to him and at the same time ordered the other two to hold their tongues and let the unwelcome visitor come in. Sancho entered the house as the curate and the barber took their leave. They were in despair over Don Quixote's state of mind, for they could not help perceiving how firmly fixed his hallucinations were and how imbued he was with those foolish ideas of his about knight-errantry.

"You will see, my friend," remarked the curate, "our gentleman will be off again one of these days when we least expect it."

"I have not the slightest doubt of that," replied the barber. "But I do not wonder so much at the knight's madness as I do at the simple-minded-ness of his squire, who believes so firmly in that island that no matter what you did to disillusion him, you would never be able to get it out of his head. Such at least is my opinion."

"God help them," said the curate, "and let us keep a close watch to see what comes of all this falderal about knight and squire. It would seem they had both been turned out from the same mold and that the madness of the master without the foolishness of the man would not be worth a penny."

"You are right," agreed the barber, "and I would give a good deal to know what the two of them are talking about at this moment."

"I feel certain," replied the curate, "that the niece or the housekeeper will tell us all about it afterward, for it is not like them to fail to listen."

In the meanwhile Don Quixote had shut himself up in his room with Sancho.

"It grieves me very much, Sancho," he began as soon as they were alone, "to hear you saying that it was I who took you away from your cottage. You know very well that I did not remain in my own house. We sallied forth and rode away together, and together we wandered here and there. We shared the same fortune and the same fate, and if they blanketed you once, they flayed me a hundred times, that is the only advantage that I have over you."

"That is as it should be," Sancho told him, "for, according to what your Grace says, misfortunes are better suited to knights-errant than to their squires."

"That is where you are wrong, Sancho," replied the knight, "in accordance with the proverb '*Quando caput dolet*,' etc."

"I understand no other language than my own," said Sancho.

"I mean," said Don Quixote, "that when the head suffers, all the other members suffer also. Being your master and lord, I am your head, and you, being my servant, are a part of me; and so it is that the evil which affects me must likewise affect you and your pain must be my own."

"It may be so," Sancho answered, "but I know that when they were blanketing me, as a member, my head was on the other side of the wall, watching me fly through the air, without feeling any pain whatever. And it does seem to me that if the members are obliged to suffer with the head, the head ought to suffer with them."

"Do you mean to stand there and tell me, Sancho, that I felt nothing when they were tossing you in the blanket? You must not say or think such a thing as that, for I felt more pain in my mind than you did in your body. However, let us put all this to one side; for there will be time enough later for us to consider this point and reach a conclusion. Rather, Sancho my friend, tell me, what are they saying about me here in the village? What opinion do the people have of me, and what do the gentry think, the *hidalgos* and the *caballeros?* [3] What do they say of my valor, of my exploits, of my courtesy? What kind of talk is there about my having undertaken to restore to the world the forgotten order of chivalry? In brief, Sancho, I would have you tell me everything that you have heard on this subject; and this you are to do without adding to the good or keeping back any of the bad; for it is fitting that loyal vassals should tell the truth to their lords, just as it is, without magnifying it out of adulation or diminishing it out of a feeling of false respect. I may tell you, Sancho, that if the naked truth could only reach the ears of princes, stripped of the garments of flattery, the times would be quite different from what they are and other eras would be known as the age of iron, not ours, which indeed I hold to be a golden epoch among those of the modern world. Give heed to this advice, Sancho, in order that you may be able to answer my questions intelligently and faithfully and tell me what you know to be the truth about these things."

"That I will do right willingly, my master," Sancho replied, "on condition that your Grace will not be angry at what I tell you, seeing that you would have me give it to you stark naked, without putting any other clothes on it than those in which it came to me."

"Of course I shall not be angry," said Don Quixote. "You may speak freely, Sancho, without any beating around the bush."

"Well, in the first place, the common people look upon your Grace as an utter madman and me as no less a fool. The *hidalgos* are saying that, not content with being a gentleman, you have had to put a 'Don' in front of your name [4] and at a bound have made yourself into a *caballero*, with four vinestocks, a couple of acres [5] of land, and one tatter in front and another behind. The *caballeros*, on the other hand, do not relish having the *hidalgos* set up in opposition to them, especially those gentlemen who perform the duties of a squire by polishing their own shoes and darning their black stockings with green silk."

"That," said the knight, "has nothing to do with me, since I always go well dressed and never in patches. Ragged I well may be, but rather from the wear and tear of armor than of time." [6]

"So far as your Grace's valor is concerned," Sancho went on, "your courtesy, exploits, and undertaking, there are different opinions. Some say: 'Crazy but amusing'; others: 'Brave but unfortunate'; others still: 'Courteous but meddlesome'; and they go on clacking their tongues about this thing and that until there is not a whole bone left in your Grace's body or in mine."

"Look you, Sancho," replied his master, "wherever virtue exists in an outstanding degree, it is always persecuted. Few or none of the famous men of the past have escaped without being slandered by the malicious. Julius Caesar, a most courageous, wise, and valiant captain, was charged with ambition and with being none too clean either in his dress or in his morals. Alexander, whose deeds won him the title of Great, was reported to be somewhat of a drunkard. Hercules—he of the many labors—if we are to believe what they say of him, was lascivious and inclined to effeminacy. Of Don Galaor, brother of Amadis of Gaul, it was whispered about that he was far too quarrelsome, while Amadis himself was called a whiner. So you see, Sancho, when good men have been traduced in this fashion, what they say about me may be overlooked, if it is no more than what you have told me."

"Body of my father!" exclaimed Sancho, "but there's the rub."

"What?" Don Quixote asked. "Is there more then?"

"That there is," said Sancho. "The tail is yet to be skinned.[7] All so far has been tarts and fancy cakes;[8] but if your Grace really wants to know what they are saying, I can bring you here at once one who will tell you everything, without leaving out the least particle of it. Bartolomé Carrasco's son came home last night. He has been studying at Salamanca and has just been made a bachelor. When I went to welcome him, he told me that the story of your Grace has already been put into a book called *The Ingenious Gentleman, Don Quixote de la Mancha.* And he says they mention me in it, under my own name, Sancho Panza, and the lady Dulcinea del Toboso as well, along with things that happened to us when we were alone together. I had to cross myself, for I could not help wondering how the one who wrote all those things down could have come to know about them."

"I can assure you, Sancho," said Don Quixote, "that the author of our history must be some wise enchanter; for nothing that they choose to write about is hidden from those who practice that art."

"What do you mean by saying he was an enchanter?" Sancho asked. "Why, the bachelor Sansón Carrasco—which is the name of the man I was telling you of—says that the one who wrote the story is called Cid Hamete Berenjena."

"That," said Don Quixote, "is a Moorish name."

"It may be," replied Sancho; "for I have generally heard it said that the Moors are great lovers of eggplant."[9]

"You must have made some mistake," said the knight, "regarding the surname of this Cid, a title which in Arabic means 'Señor.'"

"Maybe I did," replied Sancho; "but if your Grace would like me to bring the man here, I will go for him in a jiffy."

"It would give me much pleasure, my friend," said Don Quixote, "for I am astonished by what you have told me and shall not eat a mouthful that sets well on my stomach until I have learned all about it."

"Very well, then," said Sancho, "I will go fetch him." And, leaving his master, he went out to look for the bachelor. He returned with him a short while later, and the three of them then had a most amusing conversation.

CHAPTER III. *Of the laughable conversation that took place between Don Quixote, Sancho Panza, and the bachelor Sansón Carrasco.*

DON QUIXOTE remained in a thoughtful mood as he waited for the bachelor Carrasco, from whom he hoped to hear the news as to how he had been put into a book, as Sancho had said. He could not bring himself to believe that any such history existed, since the blood of the enemies he had slain was not yet dry on the blade of his sword; and here they were trying to tell him that his high deeds of chivalry were already circulating in printed form.[1] But, for that matter, he imagined that some sage, either friend or enemy, must have seen to the printing of them through the art of magic. If the chronicler was a friend, he must have undertaken the task in order to magnify and exalt Don Quixote's exploits above the most notable ones achieved by knights-errant of old. If an enemy, his purpose would have been to make them out as nothing at all, by debasing them below the meanest acts ever recorded of any mean squire. The only thing was, the knight reflected, the exploits of squires never were set down in writing. If it was true that such a history existed, being about a knight-errant, then it must be eloquent and lofty in tone, a splendid and distinguished piece of work and veracious in its details.

This consoled him somewhat, although he was a bit put out at the thought that the author was a Moor, if the appellation "Cid" was to be taken as an indication, and from the Moors you could never hope for any word of truth,[2] seeing that they are all of them cheats, forgers, and schemers. He feared lest his love should not have been treated with becoming modesty but rather in a way that would reflect upon the virtue of his lady Dulcinea del Toboso. He hoped that his fidelity had been made clear, and the respect he had always shown her, and that something had been said as to how he had spurned queens, empresses, and damsels of every rank while keeping a rein upon those impulses that are natural to a man. He was still wrapped up in these and many other similar thoughts when Sancho returned with Carrasco.

Don Quixote received the bachelor very amiably. The latter, although his name was Sansón, or Samson, was not very big so far as bodily size went, but he was a great joker, with a sallow complexion and a ready wit. He was going on twenty-four and had a round face, a snub nose, and a large mouth, all of which showed him to be of a mischievous disposition and fond of jests and witticisms. This became apparent when, as soon as he saw Don Quixote, he fell upon his knees and addressed the knight as follows:

"O mighty Don Quixote de la Mancha, give me your hands; for by the habit of St. Peter that I wear [3]—though I have received but the first four orders—your Grace is one of the most famous knights-errant that ever have been or ever will be anywhere on this earth. Blessings upon Cid Hamete Benengeli who wrote down the history of your great achievements, and upon that curious-minded one who was at pains to have it translated from the Arabic into our Castilian vulgate for the universal entertainment of the people."

Don Quixote bade him rise. "Is it true, then," he asked, "that there is a book about me and that it was some Moorish sage who composed it?"

"By way of showing you how true it is," replied Sansón, "I may tell you that it is my belief that there are in existence today more than twelve thousand copies of that history. If you do not believe me, you have but to make inquiries in Portugal, Barcelona, and Valencia, where editions have been brought out, and there is even a report to the effect that one edition was printed at Antwerp. [4] In short, I feel certain that there will soon not be a nation that does not know it or a language into which it has not been translated."

"One of the things," remarked Don Quixote, "that should give most satisfaction to a virtuous and eminent man is to see his good name spread abroad during his own lifetime, by means of the printing press, through translations into the languages of the various peoples. I have said 'good name,' for if he has any other kind, his fate is worse than death."

"If it is a matter of good name and good reputation," said the bachelor, "your Grace bears off the palm from all the knights-errant in the world; for the Moor in his tongue and the Christian in his have most vividly depicted your Grace's gallantry, your courage in facing dangers, your patience in adversity and suffering, whether the suffering be due to wounds or to misfortunes of another sort, and your virtue and continence in love, in connection with that platonic relationship that exists between your Grace and my lady Doña Dulcinea del Toboso."

At this point Sancho spoke up. "Never in my life," he said, "have I heard my lady Dulcinea called 'Doña,' but only 'la Señora Dulcinea del Toboso'; so on that point, already, the history is wrong."

"That is not important," said Carrasco.

"No, certainly not," Don Quixote agreed. "But tell me, Señor Bachelor, what adventures of mine as set down in this book have made the deepest impression?"

"As to that," the bachelor answered, "opinions differ, for it is a matter of individual taste. There are some who are very fond of the adventure of the windmills—those windmills which to your Grace appeared to be so many Briareuses and giants. Others like the episode at the fulling mill. One relishes the story of the two armies which took on the appearance of droves of sheep, while another fancies the tale of the dead man whom they were taking to Segovia for burial. One will assert that the freeing of the galley slaves is the best of all, and yet another will maintain that nothing can come up to the Benedictine giants and the encounter with the valiant Biscayan."

Again Sancho interrupted him. "Tell me, Señor Bachelor," he said, "does the book say anything about the adventure with the Yanguesans, that time our good Rocinante took it into his head to go looking for tidbits in the sea?"

"The sage," replied Sansón, "has left nothing in the inkwell. He has told everything and to the point, even to the capers which the worthy Sancho cut as they tossed him in the blanket."

"I cut no capers in the blanket," objected Sancho, "but I did in the air, and more than I liked."

"I imagine," said Don Quixote, "that there is no history in the world, dealing with humankind, that does not have its ups and downs, and this is particularly true of those that have to do with deeds of chivalry, for they can never be filled with happy incidents alone."

"Nevertheless," the bachelor went on, "there are some who have read the book who say that they would have been glad if the authors had forgotten a few of the innumerable cudgelings which Señor Don Quixote received in the course of his various encounters." [5]

"But that is where the truth of the story comes in," Sancho protested.

"For all of that," observed Don Quixote, "they might well have said nothing about them; for there is no need of recording those events that do not alter the veracity of the chronicle, when they tend only to lessen the reader's respect for the hero. You may be sure that Aeneas was not as pious as Vergil would have us believe, nor was Ulysses as wise as Homer depicts him."

"That is true enough," replied Sansón, "but it is one thing to write as a poet and another as a historian. The former may narrate or sing of things not as they were but as they should have been; the latter must describe them not as they should have been but as they were, without adding to or detracting from the truth in any degree whatsoever."

"Well," said Sancho, "if this Moorish gentleman is bent upon telling the truth, I have no doubt that among my master's thrashings my own will be found; for they never took the measure of his Grace's shoulders without measuring my whole body. But I don't wonder at that; for as my master himself says, when there's an ache in the head the members have to share it."

"You are a sly fox, Sancho," said Don Quixote. "My word, but you can remember things well enough when you choose to do so!"

"Even if I wanted to forget the whacks they gave me," Sancho answered him, "the welts on my ribs wouldn't let me, for they are still fresh."

"Be quiet, Sancho," his master admonished him, "and do not interrupt the bachelor. I beg him to go on and tell me what is said of me in this book."

"And what it says about me, too," put in Sancho, "for I have heard that I am one of the main presonages in it—"

"*Personages*, not *presonages*, Sancho my friend," said Sansón.

"So we have another one who catches you up on everything you say," was Sancho's retort. "If we go on at this rate, we'll never be through in a lifetime."

"May God put a curse on *my* life," the bachelor told him, "if you are not the second most important person in the story; and there are some who would rather listen to you talk than to anyone else in the book. It is true, there are those who say that you are too gullible in believing it to be the truth that you could become the governor of that island that was offered you by Señor Don Quixote, here present."

"There is still sun on the top of the wall," [6] said Don Quixote, "and when Sancho is a little older, with the experience that the years bring, he will be wiser and better fitted to be a governor than he is at the present time."

"By God, master," said Sancho, "the island that I couldn't govern right now I'd never be able to govern if I lived to be as old as Methuselah. The trouble is, I don't know where that island we are talking about is located; it is not due to any lack of noddle on my part."

"Leave it to God, Sancho," was Don Quixote's advice, "and everything will come out all right, perhaps even better than you think; for not a leaf on the tree stirs except by His will."

"Yes," said Sansón, "if it be God's will, Sancho will not lack a thousand islands to govern, not to speak of one island alone."

"I have seen governors around here," said Sancho, "that are not to be compared to the sole of my shoe, and yet they call them 'your Lordship' and serve them on silver plate."

"Those are not the same kind of governors," Sansón informed him. "Their task is a good deal easier. The ones that govern islands must at least know grammar."

"I could make out well enough with the *gram*," replied Sancho, "but with the *mar* [7] I want nothing to do, for I don't understand it at all. But leaving this business of the governorship in God's hands—for He will send me wherever I can best serve Him—I will tell you, Señor Bachelor Sansón Carrasco, that I am very much pleased that the author of the history should have spoken of me in such a way as does not offend me; for, upon the word of a faithful squire, if he had said anything about me that was not becoming to an old Christian, the deaf would have heard of it."

"That would be to work miracles," said Sansón.

"Miracles or no miracles," was the answer, "let everyone take care as to what he says or writes about people and not be setting down the first thing that pops into his head."

"One of the faults that is found with the book," continued the bachelor, "is that the author has inserted in it a story entitled *The One Who Was Too Curious for His Own Good*. It is not that the story in itself is a bad one or badly written; it is simply that it is out of place there, having nothing to do with the story of his Grace, Señor Don Quixote."

"I will bet you," said Sancho, "that the son of a dog has mixed the cabbages with the baskets." [8]

"And I will say right now," declared Don Quixote, "that the author of this book was not a sage but some ignorant prattler who at haphazard and without any method set about the writing of it, being content to let things turn out as they might. In the same manner, Orbaneja, the painter of Ubeda, when asked what he was painting would reply, 'Whatever it turns out to be.' [9] Sometimes it would be a cock, in which case he would have to write alongside it, in Gothic letters, 'This is a cock.' And so it must be with my story, which will need a commentary to make it understandable."

"No," replied Sansón, "that it will not; for it is so clearly written that none can fail to understand it. Little children leaf through it, young people read it, adults appreciate it, and the aged sing its praises. In short, it is so thumbed and read and so well known to persons of every walk in life that no sooner do folks see some skinny nag than they at once cry, 'There goes Rocinante!' Those that like it best of all are the pages; for there is no lord's antechamber where a *Don Quixote* is not to be found. If one lays it down, another will pick it up; one will pounce upon it, and another will beg for it. It affords the pleasantest and least harmful reading of any book that has been published up to now. In the whole of it there is not to be found an indecent word or a thought that is other than Catholic." [10]

"To write in any other manner," observed Don Quixote, "would be to write lies and not the truth. Those historians who make use of falsehoods ought to be burned like the makers of counterfeit money. I do not know what could have led the author to introduce stories and episodes that are foreign to the subject matter when he had so much to write about in describing my adventures. He must, undoubtedly, have been inspired by the old saying, 'With straw or with hay . . .' [11] For, in truth, all he had to do was to record my thoughts, my sighs, my tears, my lofty purposes, and my undertakings, and he would have had a volume bigger or at least as big as that which the works of El Tostado [12] would make. To sum the matter up, Señor Bachelor, it is my opinion that, in composing histories or books of any sort, a great deal of judgment and ripe understanding is called for. To say and write witty and amusing things is the mark of great genius. The cleverest character in a comedy is the clown, since he who would make himself out to be a simpleton cannot be one. History is a near-sacred thing, for it must be true, and where the truth is, there is God. And yet there are those who compose books and toss them out into the world as if they were no more than fritters."

"There is no book so bad," opined the bachelor, "that there is not some good in it." [13]

"Doubtless that is so," replied Don Quixote, "but it very often happens that those who have won in advance a great and well-deserved reputation for their writings, lose it in whole or in part when they give their works to the printer."

"The reason for it," said Sansón, "is that, printed works being read at leisure, their faults are the more readily apparent, and the greater the reputation of the author the more closely are they scrutinized. Men famous for their genius, great poets, illustrious historians, are almost always envied by those who take a special delight in criticizing the writings of others without having produced anything of their own."

"That is not to be wondered at," said Don Quixote, "for there are many theologians who are not good enough for the pulpit but who are very good indeed when it comes to detecting the faults or excesses of those who preach."

"All of this is very true, Señor Don Quixote," replied Carrasco, "but, all the same, I could wish that these self-appointed censors were a bit more forbearing and less hypercritical; I wish they would pay a little less attention to the spots on the bright sun of the work that occasions their fault-finding. For if *aliquando bonus dormitat Homerus*,[14] let them consider how much of his time he spent awake, shedding the light of his genius with a minimum of shade. It well may be that what to them seems a flaw is but one of those moles which sometimes add to the beauty of a face. In any event, I insist that he who has a book printed runs a very great risk, inasmuch as it is an utter impossibility to write it in such a manner that it will please all who read it."

"This book about me must have pleased very few," remarked Don Quixote.

"Quite the contrary," said Sansón, "for just as *stultorum infinitus est numerus*,[15] so the number of those who have enjoyed this history is likewise infinite. Some, to be sure, have complained of the author's forgetfulness, seeing that he neglected to make it plain who the thief was who stole Sancho's gray;[16] for it is not stated there, but merely implied, that the ass was stolen; and, a little further on, we find the knight mounted on the same beast, although it has not made its reappearance in the story. They also say that the author forgot to tell us what Sancho did with those hundred crowns that he found in the valise on the Sierra Morena, as nothing more is said of them and there are many who would like to know how he disposed of the money or how he spent it. This is one of the serious omissons to be found in the work."

To this Sancho replied, "I, Señor Sansón, do not feel like giving any account or accounting just now; for I feel a little weak in my stomach, and if I don't do something about it by taking a few swigs of the old stuff, I'll be sitting on St. Lucy's thorn.[17] I have some of it at home, and my old woman is waiting for me. After I've had my dinner, I'll come back and answer any questions your Grace or anybody else wants to ask me, whether it's about the loss of the ass or the spending of the hundred crowns."

And without waiting for a reply or saying another word, he went on home. Don Quixote urged the bachelor to stay and take potluck with him,[18] and Sansón accepted the invitation and remained. In addition to the knight's ordinary fare, they had a couple of pigeons, and at table their talk was of chivalry and feats of arms. Carrasco was careful to humor his host, and when the meal was over they took their siesta. Then Sancho returned and their previous conversation was resumed.

CHAPTER IV. *Wherein Sancho Panza answers the bachelor's questions and removes his doubts, together with other events that are worthy of being known and set down.*

RETURNING to Don Quixote's house, Sancho began where they had left off.

"Señor Sansón has said that he would like to know who it was that stole my ass and how and when it was done. In answer to that, I can tell him that it was the same night that we went up onto the Sierra Morena, to get away from the Holy Brotherhood. It was after the adventure of the galley slaves and that of the dead man that they were taking to Segovia. My master and I had gone into a thicket; and there, with him leaning on his lance and me seated on my gray and the both of us bruised and tired from the scuffles we had been through, we dozed off and slept as if we had had four feather beds beneath us. As for me, I was so dead to the world that whoever it was that came along was able to put four stakes under the four sides of my packsaddle and leave me sitting astraddle of it while he took my gray out from under me without my knowing anything about it."

"That," said Sansón, "is an easy thing to do and has been done before. It happened to Sacripante when, at the siege of Albraca, the famous thief known as Brunello, employing the same device, took the horse out from between the knight's legs."[1]

"Well," Sancho went on, "morning came, and when I went to stretch myself the stakes gave way and I took a mighty tumble. I looked around for the ass and could not see it, and then the tears came to my eyes and I set up such a howling that if the author of the book did not put it in, then he left out something very good. After I don't know how many days, going along with her Ladyship, the Princess Micomicona, I caught sight of Ginés de Pasamonte coming down the road dressed like a gypsy and mounted on my beast—he was that big rogue and trickster that my master and I freed from the galley slaves' chain."

"That is not where the error lies," replied Sansón, "but rather in the fact that before the ass turns up again the author has Sancho riding on it."

"I don't know what answer to give you," said Sancho, "except that the one who wrote the story must have made a mistake, or else it must be due to carelessness on the part of the printer."

"No doubt that is it," said Sansón, "but what became of the hundred crowns? Did they vanish into thin air?"

"I spent them on myself and on my wife and young ones, and that is why it is she puts up with my wanderings along the highways and by-ways in the service of my master Don Quixote; for if after all that time I had come home without my gray or a penny to my name, I would have had one devil of a welcome. If there is anything else you would like to know about me, here I am, ready to answer in person to the king himself, and it is nobody's business whether I took it or did not take it, whether I spent it or didn't spend it. If all the whacks they gave me on those journeys had to be paid for in money, even if they valued them only at four maravedis apiece, another hundred crowns would not be enough to pay for the half of them. Let every man look after himself and not be trying to make out that white is black and black is white; for each one is as God made him, and a good deal worse a lot of times."

"I shall make it a point," said Carrasco, "to remind the author that if he has another edition printed, he is by no means to forget what the good Sancho has told us, which I am sure will greatly improve the book." [2]

"Are there any other corrections to be made in this work?" Don Quixote inquired.

"There probably are," the bachelor replied, "but the ones we have mentioned are the most important."

"And does the author by any chance promise a second part?"

"Yes, he does," said Sansón, "but he states that he has not yet come upon it, nor does he know in whose possession it is, and accordingly there is a doubt as to whether it will appear or not. Indeed, there is some question as to whether a second part is desirable. There are those who say, 'Sequels are never good,' while others assert, 'Enough has been written already about Don Quixote.' But certain ones who are more jovially inclined and not of so morose a disposition will tell you, 'Let us have more of these Quixotic adventures; let Don Quixote lay on and Sancho talk, and, come what may, we shall be satisfied.' "

"And how does the author feel about it?"

"If he finds the history he is looking for so diligently," said Sansón, "he will send it to the printer at once, being more interested in the profit that may come to him from it than in any praise it may earn him."

Sancho now put in his word. "So, he is interested in money, is he? Then it will be a wonder if he doesn't botch the job, for it will be nothing but hurry, hurry, hurry, as at the tailor's on Easter Eve, and work done in haste is never done as it should be. Let that Moorish gentleman, or whoever he is, pay attention, and my master and I will supply him with enough stuff,[3] ready at hand, in the way of adventures and other happenings, to make not only one second part but a hundred of them. The good man thinks, no doubt, that we are asleep here in the straw, but let him hold up our hoofs to be shod and he will see which foot is the lame one. All I have to say is that if my master would take my advice, we would be in the field this minute, avenging outrages and righting wrongs as is the use and custom of good knights-errant."

No sooner had Sancho said this than they heard the whinnying of Rocinante, which Don Quixote took to be a very good omen; and he resolved then and there that they would sally forth again within the next three or four days. Announcing his intention to Carrasco, he asked the bachelor to advise him as to what direction he should take; whereupon Sansón replied that in his opinion the knight ought to head for the kingdom of Aragon and the city of Saragossa, as they were to have some ceremonious joustings there very shortly, in honor of the feast of St. George,[4] in which tournament Don Quixote might win a renown above that of all the knights of Aragon, who in turn would be sure to vanquish all others in the world. Sansón went on to praise his host's highly praiseworthy and valiant undertaking, but warned him to be a little more careful in confronting dangers, since his life was not his own but belonged to all those who had need of his succor and protection in the misfortunes that befell them.

"That is what I don't like about it, Señor Sansón," said Sancho. "My master will attack a hundred armed men just like a greedy boy falling on a half-dozen melons. Body of the world,[5] Señor Bachelor, but there is a time to attack and a time to retreat! Everything is not 'Santiago, and close in upon them, Spain!'[6] For I have heard it said—and I think my master himself was the one who said it—that true bravery lies somewhere in between being a coward and being foolhardy; and, for this reason, I would not have him run away when there is not good reason for it, nor have him attack when the odds are all against him. But, above everything else, I want to warn him that if he is going to take me with him, it will have to be on condition that he does all the fighting, it being understood that all I am to do is to look after his person and see to keeping him clean and comfortable. When it comes to that, I will be at his beck and call; but to look for me to lay hand to sword, even against the most rascally villains of hatchet and hood, is a waste of thinking.

"I do not expect, Señor Sansón," he continued, "to win fame as a fighting man, but only as the best and most loyal squire that ever served a knight-errant; and if my master Don Quixote, as a reward for my many faithful services, sees fit to give me some island of all those that his Grace says are to be had, I will accept it as a great favor; but if he does not give it to me, well, I was born like everyone else, and a man should depend on no one but God, and what is more, my bread will taste as good, and it may be even better, without a governorship than if I was a governor. How do I know that in connection with governments the devil has not prepared some trap for me where I may stumble and fall and knock my grinders out? Sancho was born and Sancho expects to die; but, for all of that, if without much risk or trouble on my part Heaven should provide me with an island, fair and square, I am not such a fool as to refuse it. For they also have a saying, 'When they offer you a heifer, come running with a halter,' and, 'When good luck comes along, open the door and let it in.' "[7]

"Spoken like a professor, brother Sancho," said Carrasco. "Put your trust in God and in Señor Don Quixote, and your master will see to it that you are provided with a kingdom and no mere island."

"More or less, it is all the same to me," replied Sancho. "I may tell you, Señor Carrasco, that my master would not be tossing that kingdom he is going to give me into a sack that was full of holes. I have taken my own pulse, and I find that I am man enough to rule over realms and govern islands, and I have already told him as much any number of times."

"But see here, Sancho," said the bachelor, "manners change when honors come,[8] and it may be that when you get to be governor you will not know the mother who bore you."

"That may be true of those that were born in the mallows,[9] but not of one like me with the fat of an old Christian four fingers deep on his soul. Do I look to you like the kind of man who would be ungrateful to anyone?"

"God's will be done," said Don Quixote. "We can tell better when the governorship comes, and it seems to me I can see it already."

Having said this, he turned to the bachelor and inquired if that gentleman was a poet. If so, would he do him the favor of composing some farewell verses for my lady Dulcinea del Toboso, each line to begin with a letter of her name, so that when the poem was complete those letters would spell out the name. Carrasco replied that, although he was not one of the famous poets of Spain—of whom, he said, there were but three and a half altogether [10]—he would not fail to do as Don Quixote had requested, although he found the task rather difficult, seeing that there were seventeen letters to be accounted for; if he made four stanzas of four lines each, there would be one letter left over, while if he employed one of those five-line stanzas known as *décimas* or *redondillas*, he would be three letters short.[11] Nevertheless, he would try, some way or other, to drop a letter in order that he might get the name Dulcinea del Toboso into a set of four-line stanzas.

"You must manage it somehow," said Don Quixote; "for if the name is not plainly to be made out, no woman would believe that the verses were written expressly for her."

This point having been settled, it was decided that the knight's departure should be one week from that day. The bachelor was charged to keep it secret, especially from the curate and Master Nicholas, and from the niece and housekeeper as well, in order that they might not prevent the carrying out of this commendable and valorous undertaking. Carrasco gave his promise and took his leave, and as he did so he urged Don Quixote to keep him informed, whenever the opportunity presented itself, of any good or ill fortune that might come to master and man. Thus they parted, and Sancho went away to make the necessary preparations for the expedition.

CHAPTER V. *Of the shrewd and droll remarks that passed between Sancho Panza and his wife, Teresa Panza, with other matters of a pleasant nature that deserve to be recorded.*

As HE comes to set down this fifth chapter of our history, the translator desires to make it plain that he looks upon it as apocryphal, since in it Sancho Panza speaks in a manner that does not appear to go with his limited intelligence and indulges in such subtle observations that it is quite impossible to conceive of his saying the things attributed to him. However, the translator in question did not wish to leave his task unfinished; and the narrative is accordingly herewith resumed.

As Sancho approached his house, he was feeling so happy and so gay that his wife could tell it at the distance of a crossbow shot.

"What do you bring with you, friend Sancho," she asked, "that makes you so merry?"

"Wife," he replied, "if it was God's will, I'd be glad not to be as happy as I am."

"I don't understand you, husband," said she. "I don't know what you mean by wishing you were not as happy as you are. I may be a fool, but I fail to see how you can find pleasure in not having it."

"Look here, Teresa," said Sancho, "I am happy because I have made up my mind to go back to serving my master Don Quixote, who wants to go out a third time in search of adventures, and I mean to go with him. It is necessity that leads me to do this, and then, too, I like to think that I may be able to come upon another hundred crowns to take the place of those we've spent, although, naturally, it makes me sad to have to leave you and the young ones. If God would only let me eat my bread at home, dryshod, without dragging me through the byways and cross-roads—and it would not cost Him anything, all He has to do is will it—it goes without saying that my happiness would be more solid and lasting than it is, whereas now it is mixed up with my sorrow at leaving you.

That is what I meant when I said that I'd be glad if, God willing, I was not so happy."

"Listen to me, Sancho," his wife replied. "Ever since you joined up with a knight-errant, you've been talking in such a roundabout way that there's no understanding you."

"It is enough, wife, if God understands me; for He understands everything, and that is good enough for me. And I want to warn you, sister, that you are to keep an eye on the gray these next few days so that he will be in condition to take up arms. Give him double rations, and look after the packsaddle and the other harness, for it's not to a wedding that we're bound; we're out to roam the world and play give and take with giants, dragons, and other monsters. We'll be hearing hissings and roarings and bellowings and howlings. But all that would be lavender if we didn't have to count upon meeting with Yanguesans and enchanted Moors."

"I know well, my husband," said Teresa, "that the squires of knights-errant have to earn the bread they eat, and so I will keep on praying to Our Lord to get you out of all this hard luck."

"I can tell you one thing, wife," said Sancho, "that if I did not expect to see myself the governor of an island before long, I would die right here and now."

"No, not that, my husband," Teresa protested. "Let the hen live even though she may have the pip,[1] and in the same way you should go on living and to the devil with all the governorships in the world. Without a governorship you came out of your mother's belly, without a governorship you've lived up to now, and without a governorship you will go, or they will carry you, to your grave when God so wills. There are plenty of folk in this world who manage to get along without being governors, yet they do not for that reason give up but are still numbered among the living. The best sauce in the world is hunger,[2] and since this is something they never lack, the poor always have an appetite. But look, Sancho, if by any chance you do fall in with a governorship, don't forget me and your children. Remember that little Sancho is already turned fifteen, and it is only right that he should go to school, if his uncle, the abbot, means to have him trained for the Church. Remember, too, that your daughter, Mari-Sancha, would not drop dead if we married her off; for I have my suspicions that she is as anxious for a husband as you are to be a governor, and, when all is said and done, a daughter badly married is better than one well kept outside of marriage."

"I promise you, wife," replied Sancho, "that if God only sees to it that I get hold of any kind of an island at all, I will get Mari-Sancha a husband so high up in the world that no one will be able to come near her without calling her 'my Ladyship.' "

"No, Sancho," said his wife. "Marry her to someone who is her equal; that's the best way. If you take her out of wooden shoes and put her into pattens, if you take her out of her gray flannel petticoat and put her into silken hoop skirts, if you stop saying 'thou' to her and change her from 'Marica' into 'Doña So-and-So' and 'my lady,' then the poor girl will not know where she is and every step she takes she will be making a thousand blunders and showing the thread of the coarse homespun stuff she's made of."

"Be quiet, foolish woman," said Sancho. "All she will need is two or three years to get used to it, and, after that, dignity and fine manners will fit her like a glove; and if not, what does it matter? Let her be 'your Ladyship' and come what may."

"Better keep to your own station, Sancho," Teresa admonished him, "and not be trying to lift yourself up to a higher one. Remember the old saying, 'Wipe the nose of your neighbor's son and take him into your house.' ³ It would be a fine thing, wouldn't it, to have our Maria married to some great count or high and mighty gentleman who every time he happened to feel like it would call her an upstart, a clodhopper's daughter, a country wench who ought to be at the spinning wheel. No, as I live, my husband, it was not for this that I brought up my daughter! You bring home the money, Sancho, and leave the marrying of her to me. There is Lope Tocho, Juan Tocho's boy. He's a strong, healthy lad and we know him well, and I can see he rather likes our lass. He's our kind, and she'll be making no mistake in marrying him. That way, we'll be able to keep an eye on her, and we'll all be together, parents and children, grandchildren, sons-in-law and daughters-in-law, and peace and God's blessing will be upon us. So don't go marrying her off in those courts and grand palaces where she will be a stranger to others and to herself."

"Why, you stupid creature!" exclaimed Sancho. "You wife of Barabbas! ⁴ What do you mean by trying to keep me from marrying my daughter to someone who will give me grandchildren that will be called 'your Lordship' and 'your Ladyship'? Look, Teresa, I have always heard the old folks say that the one that doesn't know how to make the most of luck when it comes his way has no business complaining if it passes him by. And now that luck is knocking at our door, we don't want to shut it out. Let us go with the favoring breeze that fills our sail." (It was this way of speaking, and what Sancho has to say a little further on, that led the translator of the history to remark that he looked upon this chapter as apocryphal.)

"Can't you see, you ninny," Sancho went on, "what a fine thing it will be for me to fall into some nice governorship or other that will help us get our feet out of the mud? Just let me find the husband I choose for Mari-Sancha, and you'll see how they'll be calling you 'Doña Teresa Panza,' and you will sit in church on a rug and cushions and fancy drapes in spite of the highborn ladies of the village. But no, you'd better stay the way you are, neither bigger nor smaller, like a figure on a tapestry, and we'll say no more about it. Little Sancha is going to be a countess, no matter what you think." [5]

"Husband," said Teresa, "are you sure you know what you are talking about? For I am very much afraid that if my daughter becomes a countess it will be her ruination. You can do what you like, you can make a duchess or a princess of her, but I want to tell you it will be without my will or consent. I always did believe in equality, brother, and I can't bear to see people put on airs without any reason for it. Teresa was the name they gave me when I was baptized, without any tags, or strings, or trimmings; there were no 'Dons' or 'Doñas' in my family. My father's name was Cascajo. As your wife, I am now called Teresa Panza, though by rights I should be known as Teresa Cascajo. But kings go where the laws would have them go,[6] and the name I have is good enough for me without their putting a 'Doña' on top of it and making it so heavy I can't carry it. I don't want to give people a chance to talk when they see me dressed like a countess or a governor's wife and have them saying, 'Just see the airs that hog-feeder [7] puts on, will you? Only yesterday she was spinning flax and went to mass with the tail of her petticoat over her head in place of a mantle, and today she goes in hoops, with her brooches and her nose in the air, as if we didn't know her!'

"If God lets me keep my six or seven senses, or whatever number it is that I have, I don't propose to give them a chance to see me in such a predicament. You, brother, go ahead and govern your island and strut all you like, but I tell you in the name of my sainted mother that neither my daughter nor I is going to stir one step from our village. The respectable woman has a broken leg and stays at home, and to be busy at something is a feast day for the maid that is virtuous.[8] Go, then, to look for adventures with that Don Quixote of yours, and leave us to our misadventures; for God will make things better for us if we deserve it. I'm sure I don't know," she added, "who made him a 'Don,' for neither his father nor his grandfather was one before him."

"I do declare," said Sancho, "you must have a devil in you. God help you, wife, but what a lot of things you have strung together so that there's no making head nor tail of any of them! What do the name Cascajo and brooches and proverbs and haughty airs have to do with what I'm saying? Look here, you foolish, ignorant woman—for I have a right to call you that, seeing you won't listen to reason but run away from good fortune. If I had said that my daughter was to throw herself from a tower or go wandering about the world as the Infanta Doña Uracca threatened to do,[9] you would be right in not agreeing with me; but when I want to put a 'Doña' or a 'ladyship' on her back and in the blink of an eye take her out of the stubble and seat her on a dais under a canopy or on a divan with more velvet cushions [10] than the Almohades of Morocco had Moors in their family tree, why won't you give your consent and let me have it my way?"

"Do you want to know why, husband?" Teresa asked him. "It's on account of the proverb that says, 'He who covers you discovers you.' To the poor, people give only a passing glance, but the rich man holds their gaze; and if he was poor once upon a time, then it is that the whispering and the evil gossip and the spitework begin, for the slanderers in these streets are as thick as a swarm of bees."

"Pay attention, Teresa," said Sancho, "and listen to what I am about to tell you. It may be that you have never heard it in all the days of your life. I am not speaking for myself but am giving you the opinions of the reverend father who preached in this village during Lent, the last time. If I remember rightly, he said that all present things which our eyes behold make much more of an impression on us and remain better fixed in our memories than things that are past." (These remarks of Sancho's are another reason for the translator's saying what he did about the apocryphal character of this chapter, since they are beyond the mental capacity of the squire.) "Hence it is that when we see some person richly dressed and making a fine appearance, accompanied by a retinue of servants, we feel compelled to respect him, even though our memory at the moment may remind us of some lowly condition in which we had previously seen him. That condition, whether due to poverty or humble birth, being a thing of the past, does not exist, since the only thing that is real to us is what we have before our eyes. And—these were the padre's very words—if the one that fortune has thus raised up out of the depths to the height of prosperity is well bred, generous, and courteous toward all and does not seek to vie with those that come of an old and noble line, then you may depend upon it, Teresa, there will be no one to remember what he was, but instead they will respect him for what he is, unless it be the envious, for no good fortune is safe against them."

"I do not understand you, husband," replied Teresa. "Do as you like and don't be addling my brains with your flowery speeches. If you have revolved to do what you say—"

"You mean *resolved*, wife, not *revolved*."

"Don't dispute my word," said Teresa. "I talk the way God would have me talk without beating around the bush. What I say is, if you are determined to be a governor, take your son Sancho with you so that you can teach him how to govern also; for it is a good thing for sons to learn and follow their father's trade."

"As soon as I have a government," said Sancho, "I will send for him posthaste. I will send you some money too; for there are always plenty of people to lend it to governors that do not have it. And I want you to dress him up in such a way as to hide what he is and make him look like what he is not."

"You send the money," Teresa replied, "and I'll see to that." [11]

"So, then, it's understood, is it, that our daughter is to be a countess?"

"The day that I see her a countess," was Teresa's answer, "I'll feel that I am laying her in her grave. But I tell you again: do as you like; for we women are born with the obligation of obeying our husbands, however stupid they may be."

Saying this, she began weeping in earnest, as though she already saw her Sanchica dead and buried. Sancho consoled her by assuring her that, while he might have to make his daughter a countess, he would put off doing so as long as he could. Thus ended the conversation, and Sancho went back to see Don Quixote to make arrangements for their departure.

CHAPTER VI. *Of what took place between Don Quixote and his niece and housekeeper, which is one of the most important chapters in the entire history.*

WHILE Sancho Panza and his wife, Teresa Cascajo, were engaged in the irrelevant conversation that has just been reported, Don Quixote's niece and housekeeper were by no means idle, for they could tell by any number of signs that their uncle and master was about to slip away a third time and return to what they looked upon as being his ill-errant conception of knighthood. They accordingly strove in every way possible to get so evil a thought out of his mind, but all this was like preaching in the desert or hammering cold iron.

"In truth, my master," the housekeeper said to him in the course of their many talks on the subject, "if you do not make up your mind to stay quietly at home and stop wandering over mountains and valleys like a lost soul, seeking what I am told are called adventures but which I call misfortunes, there will be nothing for me to do but raise my voice to God and the king, as loud as I can, so that they may do something about it."

"My good woman," replied Don Quixote, "what answer God will make to your complaints, or his Majesty either, for that matter, I am sure I do not know. But I do know that if I were king, I would not trouble to reply to all the innumerable and foolish petitions presented to me every day. One of the greatest of the many trials kings have to endure is that of being obliged to listen to everybody and give everyone some kind of answer, and I do not care to add my troubles to the burden that his Majesty has to bear."

"Tell us one thing," said the housekeeper, "are there no knights at his Majesty's court?"

"There are, and many of them; and it is right and proper that there should be, to set off the greatness of princes and show forth the majesty of royal power."

"Well, then," persisted the housekeeper, "could not your Grace be one of those who, without stirring a foot, serve their lord and king at court?"

"Look, my friend," said Don Quixote , "not all knights can be courtiers, nor can all courtiers be, nor should they be, knights-errant. There have to be all kinds in this world, and even though we may all be knights, there is a great deal of difference between us. For the courtiers, without leaving their rooms or the threshold of the court, may travel all over the earth merely by looking at a map; it does not cost them anything and they do not suffer heat or cold, hunger or thirst. But those of us who are real knights-errant, we take the measure of the entire globe with our feet, beneath the sun of day and in the cold of night, out in the open and exposed to all the inclemencies of the weather. We know our enemies not from pictures but as they really are, and we attack them on every occasion and under no matter what conditions of combat. We pay no attention to the childish rules that are supposed to govern knightly duels; we are not concerned as to whether one has a longer lance or sword than the other or may carry upon him holy relics or some secret contrivance; we do not worry about the proper placing of the combatants with regard to the sun [1] nor any of the other ceremonious usages of this sort that commonly prevail in man-to-man encounters, with which you are unfamiliar but which I know well.

"And let me tell you something else. The good knight-errant, even though he may behold ten giants with heads that not merely touch but rise above the clouds; and even though each of these giants may have two tallest towers for legs while his arms resemble the masts of huge and powerful ships; even though each may have eyes that are like great mill wheels and that glow more brightly than any glass furnace—in spite of all this, he is not to be in the least frightened but with highborn mien and intrepid heart is to give them battle and if possible vanquish and destroy them in a moment's time. And this, though they bear armor made of the shells of a certain fish that are said to be harder than diamonds, and in place of swords carry keen-edged blades of Damascus steel or clubs studded with spikes of the same material such as I have more than once seen. I tell you all this, my good woman, in order that you may perceive what a difference there is between knights; and it would be well if there were no prince who did not more esteem this second, or, rather, first, variety of knight-errant. For the history books tell us that some of the latter have been the salvation not of one kingdom alone but of many."

"Ah, sir!" cried the niece at this point, "your Grace must remember that all this you are saying about knights-errant is a fable and a lie. And as for those history books, if they are not to be burned, they ought all to wear the *sambenito* [2] or some other sign to show how infamous they are and how they corrupt good manners."

"By the God who sustains me!" exclaimed Don Quixote, "if you were not my flesh-and-blood niece, being the daughter of my own sister, I would so punish you for the blasphemy you have uttered that all the world would hear about it. How comes it that a lass who barely knows how to handle a dozen lace bobbins should set her tongue to wagging and presume to criticize these knightly histories? What would my lord Amadis say if he could hear such a thing? To be sure, he would pardon you, since he was the most humble and courteous knight of his age, and was, moreover, a great protector of damsels. But there are others who might have heard you, and in that case it would not have gone so well with you. For they were not all courteous and circumspect; some of them were the most unmannerly of rascals.

"By no means all of those that call themselves knights, or gentlemen,[3] are what they pretend to be. Some are of pure gold, others are a base alloy. They all look the part, but not all can stand the touchstone of truth. Some there are of low degree who split themselves trying to appear gentlemanly. On the other hand, there are those of high station who, one would wager, were dying to be mistaken for their inferiors. The former pull themselves up through ambition or by reason of their merits, while the latter debase themselves by slothfulness or vice. And a good deal of wisdom is required to distinguish between these two kinds of gentlemen who are alike in name but whose conduct is so different."

"So help me God, uncle," said the niece, "your Grace knows so much that in a pinch you could get right up in the pulpit or go out and start preaching in the streets. And yet, to think that you could be so blind and foolish as to try to make out that you are a hero when you are really an old man, that you are strong when you are sick, that you are able to straighten out the wrongs of the world when you yourself are bent with age, and, above all, that you are a knight; for, while the real gentry [4] may become knights, the poor never can."

"There is much in what you say, my niece," replied Don Quixote. "I could tell you things having to do with family trees that would astonish you; but since I do not wish to mix the human with the divine, I shall not mention them. You see, my friends—and pay attention to what I say—so far as family is concerned, all the people in this world may be divided into four classes: those who from humble beginnings have grown and expanded until they have attained a pinnacle of greatness; those who were great to begin with and who have since consistently maintained their original state; those who have arrived at a pyramidal point, having progressively diminished and consumed the greatness that was theirs at the start until, like the point of the pyramid with respect to its base or foundation, they have come to be nothing at all; and, finally, there is the vast majority who had neither a good start nor a subsequent history that was in any way out of the ordinary and who accordingly will have a nameless end, like the ordinary plebeian stock.

"Of the first group, who rose from humble origins to a greatness which they continue to maintain, the House of Ottoman may serve as an example; for it was founded by a lowly shepherd and later attained the heights which we now see it occupying. Of the second class, those who have maintained their original greatness without adding to or detracting from it, I may cite the case of many princes who have been content to remain peacefully within the confines of their kingdoms. As for those that began great only to taper away in a point, there are thousands of examples. For all the Pharaohs and Ptolemies of Egypt, the Caesars of Rome, and the countless drove (if I may employ that word) of princes, monarchs, and lords, of Medes, Persians, Greeks, and barbarians—all these royal and noble lines have ended in the point of nothingness, both they and their founders, and today it would be impossible to find a single one of their descendants, or if one did come upon any of them, they would be in some low and humble station. Of the plebeians I have nothing to say, except that they serve to increase the number of the living without any other claim to fame, since they have achieved no form of greatness that entitles them to praise.

"My reason for telling you all this, my innocent ones, is that you may see how much confusion exists with regard to the subject of family descent. They alone impress us as being great and illustrious that show themselves to be virtuous, rich, and generous. I say this for the reason that the great man who was also vicious would be no more than an outstanding example of vice, and the rich man who was not generous would be but a miserly beggar. What brings happiness to the possessor of wealth is not the having but the spending of it, and by that I mean, spending it well and not simply to gratify his own whims. The gentleman who is poor, however, has no other means of proving that he is a gentleman than by following the path of virtue, by being affable, well bred, courteous and polite, and prompt to do favors for others; he will not be proud and haughty or a backbiter, and, above all, he will be charitable. With the two maravedis that he gives with a cheerful heart to the poor he will show himself to be as generous as the one who distributes alms to the ringing of a bell, and no one who sees him adorned with the virtues that I have mentioned, even though he may not know him, will fail to regard him as coming of good stock. It would be a wonder if it were not so, for praise has ever been the reward of virtue, and those who are virtuous are bound to be commended.

"There are two paths, my daughters, by which men may succeed in becoming rich and honored. One is that of letters, the other that of arms. For my part, I am more inclined to the latter than to the former. Indeed, so strong is my inclination that it would seem that I must have been born under the influence of the planet Mars. And so I am practically compelled to follow that path, and I shall keep to it in spite of all the world. It is useless for you to wear yourselves out trying to persuade me not to do what Heaven wills, fate ordains, reason asks, and, above all, my own will desires. Knowing as I do all the innumerable hardships that go with knight-errantry, I also know the infinite number of good things that are to be attained by it. I am aware that the path of virtue is a straight and narrow one, while that of vice is a broad and spacious highway. I realize that the ends and goals are different in the two cases, the highroad of vice leading to death, while virtue's narrow, thorny trail conducts us to life, and not a life that has a mortal close, but life everlasting. As our great Castilian poet has put it:

> *This is the rugged path, the toilsome way*
> *That leads to immortality's fair heights,*
> *Which none e'er reach who from that path do stray.*" [5]

"Oh, dear me!" said the niece, "my master is a poet, too. He knows everything and can do everything. I'll bet that if he chose to turn mason he could build a house as easily as he could a birdcage."

"I can tell you one thing, niece," replied Don Quixote, "that if my mind were not so wholly occupied with thoughts of chivalry, there is nothing that I could not do, no trinket that I could not turn out with my own hands, especially birdcages and toothpicks."

At that moment there was a knock at the door, and when they asked who was there, Sancho replied that it was he. No sooner did the housekeeper hear this than she ran and hid herself, so great was her abhorrence of the squire. The niece opened the door and Don Quixote came forward to meet the visitor with open arms, after which the two of them shut themselves up in the knight's room where they had another conversation that was in no way surpassed by their previous one.

CHAPTER VII. *Of what passed between Don Quixote and his squire, with other very famous incidents.*

SEEING her master and Sancho Panza closeted together, the housekeeper at once suspected what they were up to. Feeling certain that as a result of their consultation they would resolve to sally forth a third time, she snatched up her mantle and, full of anxiety and deeply distressed, went out to look for the bachelor Sansón Carrasco; for it seemed to her that, being a well-spoken young man and a new acquaintance of Don Quixote's, he might be able to persuade the knight to give up so insane an undertaking. She found the bachelor walking up and down the patio of his house, and the moment she caught sight of him she ran up to him and fell on her knees in front of him, sweating all over and giving every evidence of affliction. Carrasco was surprised to see her so upset and grief-stricken.

"What is the meaning of this, Mistress Housekeeper?" he asked. "What has happened to cause you to appear so heartbroken?"

"It is nothing, Señor Sansón," she replied, "except that my master is breaking out again, there's no doubt of that."

"Breaking out where, Señora? Has he burst any part of his body?"

"No," said she, "it's through the door of his madness that he's bursting. I mean to say, my dear Señor Bachelor, that he wants to leave home again, which will be the third time, to go roaming the world and looking for what he calls ventures, though for the life of me I can't see why he gives them that name.[1] The first time he came home to us slung over the back of an ass and nearly clubbed to death. The second time it was in an ox-cart, locked in a cage, where he said he had been put through some magic spell or other, and such a sorry-looking sight he was that the mother who bore him would not have recognized him. He was lean and yellow and his eyes were deep-sunken in his head, and in order to bring him around again to something of his old self I had to use more than six hundred eggs, as God knows, and all the world and my hens as well, for they wouldn't let me lie."

"I can well believe," the bachelor assured her, "that those hens of yours are so good, so fat, and so well brought up that they would not say one thing in place of another even if they burst. In short, Mistress Housekeeper, nothing has happened except what you fear that Señor Don Quixote may do?"

"Nothing else," she said.

"Well, then," he told her, "don't worry, but go on home and prepare me a warm breakfast, and on the way you might repeat St. Apollonia's prayer, if you happen to know it. I will be with you shortly, and you shall see miracles."

"Ah, poor me!" said the housekeeper, "so it's St. Apollonia's prayer that I should be saying, is it? That would be all right if my master had the toothache,[2] but his trouble is not in his teeth but in his brains."

"I know what I am talking about, Mistress Housekeeper; so run along and do not dispute my word, for, as you know, I am a bachelor of Salamanca and that means the best there is." [3]

With this, the housekeeper returned home and Carrasco went to hunt up the curate and make certain arrangements with him which will be duly narrated when the time comes.

When they were shut up together, Don Quixote and Sancho had a conversation which the historian has very minutely and truthfully reported.

"Sir," began Sancho, "I have reduced my wife to let me go with your Grace wherever you choose to take me."

"*Induced*, you mean to say, Sancho, not *reduced*."

"Once or twice before, if I remember rightly," said Sancho, "I have begged your Grace not to correct my words so long as you understand what I mean by them. When you don't understand, all you have to do is to say, 'Sancho, I don't know what the devil you mean'; and then, if I don't make myself plain, you can go ahead and correct me all you want to. You know how focile I am."

"I fail to understand you right now, Sancho," said Don Quixote, "for I'm sure I don't know what you mean when you say, 'I am so *focile*.'"

"So *focile*," replied Sancho, "means, 'I am so much that way.'"

"I understand you less than ever," said his master.

"Well, if you can't make it out," answered the squire, "I don't know what to say to you. That's the best I can do, so help me God."

"Ah! I get it. What you mean to say is that you are so *docile*, easygoing, and tractable that you will accept whatever I say to you and follow my teachings."

"I will bet you," said Sancho, "that you understood what I meant all the time and just wanted to mix me up so that you could hear me make a lot more blunders."

"You may be right," replied Don Quixote, "but tell me, exactly what was it that Teresa said?"

"She said that I should get everything down in black and white with your Grace, to let papers talk and beards be still,[4] since he who binds does not wrangle,[5] and one 'take' is worth a couple of 'I'll give you's.'[6] And I can tell you that a woman's advice is of little worth and he who won't take it is a fool."[7]

"And so say I," observed Don Quixote. "Go on, friend Sancho, you are in rare form today."[8]

"The fact of the matter is, as your Grace well knows," continued Sancho, "we are all of us subject to death, we are here today and gone tomorrow, and the lamb goes as soon as the sheep,[9] and no one can promise himself more hours of life in this world than God may see fit to give him, for death is deaf, and when it comes to knock at the door of our life it is always in a hurry, and neither prayers nor force nor scepters nor miters can hold it back, all of which is a matter of common talk and knowledge and we hear it from the pulpit right along."

"That is all very true," said Don Quixote, "but I can't see what you are getting at."

"What I am getting at," replied Sancho, "is that your Grace ought to give me a fixed wage to be paid to me every month during the time that I am in your service, out of your estate. I don't like to depend on favors that come late or never and may not be what you expect—God help me where those that I am expecting are concerned. The short of it is, I'd like to know what I am earning, however much or little it may be; for a hen will set on one egg, and many littles make a much, and so long as something's gained nothing's lost.[10] If it should turn out to be true—which I neither believe nor expect—that your Grace is going to give me that island you promised me, I am not so ungrateful nor would I go so far as to say that you shouldn't take what the income from the island amounts to out of my wages on a *pro cata* basis."

"Friend Sancho," remarked Don Quixote, "a cat may sometimes be as good as a rat."

"I get you," was Sancho's answer. "I'll bet you that what I should have said was *pro rata* and not *pro cata*, but it makes no difference, since your Grace understood me anyway."

"I understand you so well," said Don Quixote, "that I can read you like a book. I know what the bull's-eye is you're shooting at with all those proverbs of yours. Look, Sancho, I should be glad to give you a fixed wage if I could find in the histories of knights-errant any instance that would afford me the slightest hint as to what their squires used to receive by the month or by the year. I have read all or most of those histories, and I cannot recall any knight who paid his squire such a wage. Rather, they all served for the favors that came to them; and when they least expected it, if things had gone well with their masters, they would find themselves rewarded with an island or something else that amounted to the same thing, or at the least they would have a title and a seigniory.

"If for the sake of these hopes and inducements, Sancho," the knight went on, "you choose to return to my service, well and good; but you are wasting your time if you think that I am going to violate and unhinge the ancient customs of chivalry. And so, my good Sancho, go back home and tell your Teresa how I feel about it, and if she and you are willing to depend upon my favors, *bene quidem,* and if not, we will be as good friends as we were before; for if there is no lack of food in the pigeon house, it will not lack pigeons.[11] And remember, my son, a good hope is better than a bad holding,[12] and a good complaint better than bad pay.[13] If I speak in this manner, Sancho, it is to show you that I, too, can scatter proverbs like showers. In conclusion, I would say to you that if you do not choose to come with me on these terms and take the same chance that I do, may God keep you and make you a saint, for I shall not fail to find other squires who will be more obedient, more diligent, and not so stupid or so talkative as you."

When Sancho saw how firmly resolved his master was on this point, the heavens darkened over for him and the wings of his heart drooped; for he had felt certain that Don Quixote would not go without him for anything in the world. He was very much astonished and was still lost in thought when Sansón Carrasco, accompanied by the housekeeper and the niece,[14] entered the room; for the womenfolk wished to hear the arguments which the bachelor would employ in persuading their master not to go back to seeking adventures. Sansón, that famous wag, now came forward and embraced Don Quixote as he had done on the previous occasion, and, raising his voice, he addressed him as follows:

"O flower of knight-errantry, O shining light of the profession of arms, O honor and mirror of the Spanish nation! May it please Almighty God in His infinite power that the person or persons who would prevent or impede your third sally never find their way out of the labyrinth of their schemings nor ever succeed in accomplishing what they most desire."

Turning then to the housekeeper, he went on, "Mistress Housekeeper, you may just as well leave off saying St. Apollonia's prayer; for I now realize that it has been definitely determined by the spheres that Don Quixote shall carry out his new and lofty undertakings, and I should be laying a great burden upon my conscience if I did not urge and entreat this knight to keep his good right arm and valiant spirit curbed and confined no longer, since by his tarrying here he is cheating the wronged of their rights, orphans of his protection, damsels of the honor he might save for them, widows of the favors he might bestow upon them, and wives of the support with which he might provide them, along with other things of the sort that have to do with, appertain to, and are the proper appurtenances of, the order of knight-errantry. Come, then, my dear Señor Don Quixote, so handsome and so brave, let it be today rather than tomorrow that your Grace and Highness takes the road, and if anything be lacking for the carrying out of your plan, here am I to supply the need. My person and my fortune are at your disposal, and, if needs be, I will even serve your Magnificence as squire. Indeed, I should count myself most fortunate in being allowed to do so."

At this point Don Quixote spoke up. "Did not I tell you, Sancho," he said, "that I would have no trouble in finding squires? Look who is now offering to serve me. None other than the distinguished bachelor, Sansón Carrasco, the darling and perpetual delight of the Salamancan schools. He is sound in body, agile-limbed, and discreet, and can stand heat as well as cold, hunger as well as thirst. In brief, he has all the qualifications that are required of a squire to a knight-errant. But Heaven forbid that, to gratify my own inclinations, I should shatter this pillar of letters and vase of learning and cut down this towering palm of the fine and liberal arts. Let this new Samson remain in his own country, bringing honor to it and at the same time to the gray hairs of his aged parents. As for me, I shall make out with any squire that comes along, seeing that Sancho does not deign to come with me."

"I do deign to come," Sancho protested. He was deeply moved and his eyes were filled with tears. "It shall not be said of me, my master," he went on, "that 'once the bread is eaten, the company breaks up.' [15] I do not come of ungrateful stock; for all the world, and especially my village, knows who the Panzas were, and I am descended from them. What's more, I know from the many kind things you have done and the kind words you have spoken how much your Grace desires to show me favor. If I seem to have haggled a bit over my wages, that was to please my wife. When she undertakes to get you to do something, there's no mallet that drives in the hoops of a cask the way she drives you until you've done it. But, after all, a man has to be a man and a woman a woman; and, seeing that I'm a man wherever I am, which there's no denying, I mean to be one in my own house as well, whatever anybody says. So, then, there is nothing more to be done except for your Grace to draw up your will, with a codicil that can't be provoked, and we will set out at once. That way, Señor Sansón will not have to suffer any more, for he says his conscience is nagging at him to persuade your Grace to sally out into the world a third time. And I offer to serve your Grace faithfully and loyally, as well and better than all the squires that have served knights-errant in times past or present."

The bachelor was amazed at Sancho Panza's way of talking; for, although he had read the First Part of the history, he never would have believed that the squire was as droll as he was depicted there. But as he now heard him speaking of a will and codicil that could not be *provoked* (in place of *revoked*), he was convinced of the truth of it all and came to the conclusion that this was one of the greatest simpletons of the age. Never before in the world, he told himself, had the like been seen of such a pair of madmen as this master and his servant.

In the end, Don Quixote and Sancho embraced and were friends once more; and with the advice and approval of the great Carrasco, who for the present was their oracle, they set the date for their departure at three days from then, which would give them time enough to make the necessary preparations and look for a closed helmet, as Don Quixote insisted that he must by all means have one to take with him. Sansón offered to see to this, saying a friend of his had such a piece and would not refuse it to him, although, to be sure, it was not bright and clean as polished steel ought to be but was covered with rust and mildew.

The curses which the two women, the housekeeper and the niece, heaped upon the bachelor's head were innumerable. They tore their hair, clawed their faces, and, like the hired mourners of old, set up such a wailing over their master's departure that one would have thought it was his death they were lamenting. In thus persuading the knight to sally forth again, Sansón had a plan in mind which the history relates further on. All that he did was on the advice of the curate and the barber, with whom he had previously discussed the matter.

The short of it is, in the course of those three days Don Quixote and Sancho provided themselves with what they thought was necessary, and, the squire having pacified his wife and the knight having calmed his niece and housekeeper, the two of them set out at nightfall for El Toboso, without being seen by anyone except the bachelor, who expressed a desire to accompany them for a distance of half a league from the village. Don Quixote was mounted upon his good Rocinante and Sancho upon his ancient gray, his saddlebags stuffed with certain victuals and his pocket with money which his master had given him for whatever might come up. Sansón gave the knight a farewell embrace, urging him to send back word of the good or ill fortune that the pair met with, in order that he, Carrasco, as the laws of friendship demanded, might rejoice over the former or grieve over the latter. Don Quixote promised that he would do so, and the bachelor thereupon returned to the village while the other two took the highway for the great city of El Toboso.

CHAPTER VIII. *Wherein is related what happened to Don Quixote as he went to see his lady, Dulcinea del Toboso.*

"BLESSED be the mighty Allah!" exclaims Hamete Benengeli at the beginning of this eighth chapter; and he repeats it three times: "Blessed be Allah!" He goes on to tell us that the reason for the benediction is his thankfulness at seeing Don Quixote and Sancho together once more, and he wishes the readers of this pleasant chronicle to feel that the exploits and the drolleries of the knight and his squire really start at this point. Let them forget, he says, the chivalrous deeds which the Ingenious Gentleman has performed in the past and fix their eyes, rather, on those that are to come and that have their beginning here and now on the El Toboso highway just as the others began on the plains of Montiel. It surely is not much to ask in return for all he promises, and so he continues as follows:

No sooner had Sansón left Don Quixote and Sancho alone than Rocinante began neighing and the gray started sighing, which both knight and squire took to be a very good sign and most fortunate omen, even though, if the truth must be told, the sighings and brayings of the ass exceeded the whinnyings of the hack, which led Sancho to infer that his own good fortune was destined to surpass and overtop that of his master, in making which assumption it may be that he was relying upon some system of judicial astrology with which he chanced to be familiar, though the history is silent on this point. All that is known is that, when he stumbled or fell, he was heard to say that he wished he had not come out of the house, since nothing was to be had from it but a torn shoe or a set of broken ribs, and in this, fool that he was, he was not far wrong.

"Friend Sancho," remarked Don Quixote, "night is descending upon us and it is becoming so dark that we shall not be able to reach El Toboso while it is yet daylight; but I am determined to go there before embarking upon another adventure, for there it is that I shall receive the blessing and kind consent of my peerless Dulcinea, with whose favor I feel assured of bringing to a happy conclusion every dangerous undertaking, since nothing in this life inspires more valor in knights-errant than the knowledge that they are favored by their ladies."

"I can believe that," replied Sancho, "but if I am not mistaken, your Grace may have a hard time seeing or talking to her, at least in any place where she could give you her blessing, unless she was to toss it over the wall of the stable yard where I saw her the last time, when I took her the letter with the news about the mad and foolish things your Grace was doing in the heart of the Sierra Morena."

"And did you fancy that was a stable-yard wall," said Don Quixote, "where or at which you beheld that grace and beauty that never can be praised enough? It must have been in the gallery, corridor, or portico, or whatever you call it, of some rich and royal palace."

"That may all be true," said Sancho, "but it looked like a wall to me, if my memory serves me right."

"Nevertheless, Sancho, we are going there," Don Quixote insisted; "for so long as I see her, it is all the same to me whether it be over a wall, at a window, or through the chinks in a door or the railing of a garden. Let but one ray of the sun of her beauty fall upon these eyes and it shall illuminate my understanding and fortify my heart to such a degree that I shall be matchless and without an equal in wisdom and in valor."

"To tell you the truth," said Sancho, "when I saw the lady Dulcinea del Toboso's sun, it was not bright enough to shed rays of any kind. This must have been due to the fact that, as I told you, she was winnowing wheat at the time, and this raised a lot of dust which came before her face like a cloud and darkened it."

"What!" cried Don Quixote, "do you still persist, Sancho, in saying, thinking, and believing that my lady Dulcinea was winnowing wheat, when you know that this is a task and occupation that is at variance with everything that persons of high distinction do and are supposed to do, seeing that they are constituted and reserved for other employments and avocations such as make manifest their rank at the distance of a bowshot? I can see, O Sancho, that you have forgotten those verses of our poet in which he describes for us the labors performed, up there in their crystal dwellings, by the four nymphs that rose from their beloved Tagus and set themselves down in a verdant meadow to embroider those rich tapestries, of which the bard tells us, that were all worked and woven of gold and silk and pearls.[1]

"My lady, when you saw her, must have been busied at a similar task. The only thing is that some evil enchanter must be envious of me, since all things that give me pleasure he at once changes into shapes that are not their own. This leads me to fear that the history of my exploits, which they tell me has been printed, may be the work of some magician who is my enemy, in which case he would have set down one thing in place of another and, mingling a thousand lies with a little truth, would doubtless have amused himself by relating many things that have nothing to do with the true sequence of events. O envy, thou root of endless evils, thou cankerworm of the virtues! All the other vices, Sancho, have in them some element of pleasure, but envy brings with it only vexation, bitterness, and rage."

"That is what I say too," replied Sancho, "and I think that in this legend or history of our deeds which the bachelor Carrasco says he has seen, my honor must have been knocked around and dragged up and down in the mud;[2] they must have swept the streets with it. And yet, I give you my word as an honest man, I have never spoken ill of any enchanter, nor do I have so many worldly goods that anybody would envy me. It is true, I am somewhat sly, and I have certain marks of the rogue, but it is all covered over with the great cloak of my simplicity, which is always natural and never artificial; and if I had no other virtue than that of believing, as I always have believed, firmly and truly in God and in all that the holy Roman Catholic Church holds and believes, as well as that of being, as I am, a mortal enemy of the Jews, the historians ought to have mercy on me and treat me well in their writings. But let them say what they will, naked was I born and naked I find myself, and so I neither lose nor gain; and although I see myself being put into a book and going through the world from hand to hand, I still don't care a fig; let them say anything about me that they like."

"That reminds me, Sancho," said Don Quixote, "of what happened to a famous poet of these days who, having composed a malicious satire against all the court ladies,[3] failed to mention in it a particular lady as to whose standing there was some question. When she saw that she was not on the list with the others, she complained to the poet, demanding to know what he had seen in her that had caused him to leave her out. She further insisted that he add a sequel to his satire and put her in it, or, otherwise, let him beware of the consequences. The poet did so, making her out to be the kind of woman of whom duennas do not speak, and she was satisfied with the fame he bestowed upon her even though it was infamy. Then there is the story they tell of the shepherd who set fire and burned down the famous temple of Diana, accounted one of the seven wonders of the world, simply in order that his name might be remembered for centuries to come. And although it was commanded that no one should mention his name either by word of mouth or in writing, so that his ambition might not be fulfilled, it is nevertheless known that he was called Erostratus.

"Much the same thing happened in the case of the great emperor, Charles V, and a certain gentleman in Rome. The emperor was desirous of seeing the famous temple of the Rotunda, which in antiquity was known as the temple of all the gods [4] and today is more appropriately named All Saints'. Of all the pagan edifices in Rome, this is the one that comes nearest to being preserved in its entirety, and it constitutes a fitting tribute to the grandeur and magnificence of those who built it. It is constructed in the shape of a half-orange and is very large and well lighted, the only illumination being afforded by a window, or, better, a rounded skylight at the top, and it was from this point of vantage that the emperor surveyed the building. At his side was a Roman gentleman who explained to him all the beauties and fine points of the huge and intricate structure with its memorable architecture.

"As they made their way down from the skylight, the gentleman turned to the emperor and said, 'A thousand times, your Sacred Majesty, I had a desire to throw my arms about your Majesty and cast myself down from that dome in order that my fame might be eternal in this world.'

"'I thank you,' the emperor replied, 'for not having yielded to so wicked an impulse. From now on, I shall see to it that you have no further opportunity to put your loyalty to the test. I accordingly command you not to speak to me or enter my presence again.' And with these words he made him a handsome gift.

"What I mean to say, Sancho, is that the desire of achieving fame is a powerful incentive. What do you think it was that threw Horatius down from the bridge, clad in full armor, into the depths of the Tiber? What was it burned Mutius's arm and hand? What was it that impelled Curtius to hurl himself into the deep and flaming abyss that yawned in the middle of the city of Rome? What was it led Julius Caesar to cross the Rubicon in spite of all the auguries which had warned against it? To come down to more modern times, what was it, in the New World, that scuttled and beached the ships and cut off those valiant Spaniards led by the most courtier-like Cortés?[5] All these and other great deeds of various sorts are, were, and shall continue to be a manifestation of the mortal desire for fame as a reward for notable achievements that confer upon man a portion of immortality. We Christians, Catholics, and knights-errant, on the other hand, are more concerned with the glory that, in ages to come, shall be eternal in the ethereal and celestial regions than we are with the vanity of that fame that is to be won in this present and finite time; for however long such fame may endure, it needs must finally end with the world itself, the close of which has been foreordained.

"And so, Sancho, our deeds should not exceed those limits set by the Christian religion which we profess. In confronting giants, it is the sin of pride that we slay, even as we combat envy with generosity and goodness of heart; anger, with equanimity and a calm bearing; gluttony and an overfondness for sleep, by eating little when we do eat and by keeping long vigils; lust and lewdness, with the loyalty that we show to those whom we have made the mistresses of our affections; and sloth, by going everywhere in the world in search of opportunities that may and do make of us famous knights as well as better Christians.[6] You behold here, Sancho, the means by which one may attain the highest praise that the right sort of fame brings with it."

"I have understood very well," Sancho told him, "all that your Grace has said up to now; but still there is one doubtful point I happened to think of that I wish your Grace would dissolve for me."

"*Solve* is what you mean to say, Sancho," replied Don Quixote. "Speak out, and I will answer you as best I can."

"Tell me, then, sir," Sancho went on, "those Julys[7] or Augusts, and all those knights you mentioned that were always up and doing, seeing that they are dead, where are they now?"

"The heathen ones," said Don Quixote, "are undoubtedly in Hell; the Christians, if they were good Christians, are either in purgatory or in Heaven."

"That is all very well," said Sancho, "but what I want to know is this: do the tombs where the bodies of those great lords are preserved have silver lamps in front of them, and are the walls of their chapels decorated with crutches, shrouds, locks of hair, legs, and eyes made of wax? Or, if not, what kind of decorations do they have?"

"The pagan sepulchers," Don Quixote answered him, "were for the most part sumptuous temples. Julius Caesar's ashes, for example, were placed upon a stone pyramid of enormous size which in the Rome of to-day is known as St. Peter's Needle. The Emperor Hadrian's burial place was a castle as big as a good-sized town and was called the Moles Adriani, which at the present time is St. Angelo's Castle. The Queen Artemisia buried her husband in a tomb that was reckoned one of the seven wonders of the world. But none of the many pagan tombs was adorned with shrouds or offerings and tokens such as you commonly see where saints are buried."

"I am coming to that," said Sancho. "And now, tell me, which is the greater thing, to bring a dead man to life or to kill a giant?"

"The answer to that question is easy," replied Don Quixote. "To bring the dead to life, of course."

"Ah," said Sancho, "that is where I have you. Then the fame of those who resurrect the dead, who give sight to the blind, who heal cripples and bring health to the sick, and who have burning lamps in front of their tombs while their chapels are filled with kneeling worshipers who have come to adore their relics—will not their fame, both in this world and in the world to come, be a better one than that which all the heathen emperors and knights-errant that ever were have left or shall ever leave behind them?"

"I am willing to grant you that also," Don Quixote admitted.

"Well, then," continued Sancho, "seeing that this fame, these favors, these privileges, or whatever you call them, belong to the bodies and relics of the saints, who, with the approval and permission of our Holy Mother Church, have lamps, candles, shrouds, crutches, paintings, locks of hair, eyes, legs, and what not, to spread their Christian fame and make the worshipers more devout; and seeing that kings are in the habit of taking the bodies of saints, or saints' relics, upon their backs, while they kiss the bits of bone and use them to decorate and enrich their chapels and their favorite altars—"

"What are you getting at, Sancho, with all this you are saying?" Don Quixote asked.

"What I mean," said Sancho, "is that we ought to become saints, and that way we'd have the fame we are after all the sooner. You may know, sir, that yesterday or day before yesterday—in a manner of speaking, for it was only a short while ago—they canonized or beatified two little barefoot friars,[8] and it is now considered a great piece of luck to be able to kiss and touch the iron chains with which they girt and tormented their bodies. Those chains, so it is said, are more venerated than is Orlando's sword in the armory of our lord the king, God save him. And so, my dear sir, it is better to be a humble little barefoot friar, whatever the order he belongs to, than a brave knight-errant. With God, a couple of dozen penances will get you more than two thousand lance thrusts, whether they be given to giants, dragons, or other monsters."

"I agree with all that," said Don Quixote, "but we cannot all be friars, and there are many paths by which God takes His own to Heaven. Chivalry is a religion in itself, and there are sainted knights in glory."

"Yes," said Sancho, "but I have heard that there are more friars in Heaven than there are knights-errant."

"That," Don Quixote explained, "is for the reason that the number of religious is greater than the number of knights."

"There are many errant ones," observed Sancho.

"Many," his master assented, "but few that deserve the name of knight."

In talk of this kind they spent that night and the following day, without anything happening to them worthy of note, at which Don Quixote was not a little put out. On the day after that, at sunset, they sighted the great city of El Toboso. The knight was elated, but Sancho was downcast, for he did not know where Dulcinea lived nor had he ever in his life laid eyes upon her any more than his master had. As a result, each of them was uneasy in his mind, the one being anxious to behold her while the other was worried because he had not already seen her. Sancho could not imagine what he was going to do when his master should send him into the town; but Don Quixote finally decided that they would wait until nightfall to make their entrance, and in the meanwhile they tarried amid some oak trees that grew round about. When the time came, they made their way into the streets of El Toboso, where the things that happened to them were really something.[9]

CHAPTER IX. *A chapter in which is related what will be found set forth in it.*

It was midnight on the hour,[1]
a little more or less, when Don Quixote and Sancho left the wood [2] and entered the city of El Toboso. The town was wrapped in a peaceful silence, for all the good people were asleep, or were stretching a leg, as the saying goes.[3] The night was not wholly dark, though Sancho wished it had been, as that might have provided an excuse for his inability to find his way. Nothing was to be heard anywhere but the barking of dogs, which deafened Don Quixote's ears and troubled his squire's heart. Now and then an ass would bray, pigs would grunt, a cat would miaul, and these various noises grew in volume with the silence. All of which the lovelorn knight took to be an ill omen, but he nonetheless adhered to his purpose.

"Sancho, my son," he cried, "lead the way to Dulcinea's palace; it may be that we shall find her awake."

"Body of the sun!" cried Sancho, "to what palace should I lead you? When I saw her Highness, she was in a very small house."

"Then," replied Don Quixote, "she must merely have retired to some small apartment of her castle, to amuse herself in solitude with her damsels, as is the custom of highborn ladies and princesses."

"Sir," said Sancho, "seeing that, in spite of anything I say, your Grace will have it that my lady Dulcinea's house is a castle, are we likely at this hour to find the gate open? And would it be right for us to go knocking at the gate in order to arouse them so that they can let us in, thus creating an uproar and disturbing everybody? Do you think, by any chance, that we are going to the house where our concubines live, as those who keep such women do, who come and call out and go in at any time, however late it may be?"

"First of all," said Don Quixote, "let us find out where the palace is, and then, Sancho, I will tell you what we should do. Look you, either my eyes deceive me or that huge dark bulk that we see yonder must be it."

"Then lead the way, your Grace, for it may be you are right. But, though I see it with my eyes and touch it with my hands, I will believe it is a palace just as soon as I would that it is now day."

Don Quixote accordingly led on, and when they had gone some two hundred paces they came up to the dark object and saw that it was a great tower, and then they realized that this was not a palace but the principal church of the town. "It's the church we've lighted on," the knight remarked to Sancho.

"So I see," replied the squire, "and please God we don't light upon our graves as well. It's not a good sign to be wandering in cemeteries at this hour of the night; and what's more, I told your Grace, if I remember rightly, that this lady's house would be up a blind alley."

"May God curse you, you fool!" cried his master, "and when did you ever hear of castles and royal palaces being built in blind alleys?"

"Sir," was Sancho's answer, "every land has its own customs,[4] and it may be that the custom here in El Toboso is to put up their palaces and other great buildings in alleyways. And so I beg your Grace to let me look through these streets and lanes, and in some nook or corner I may come upon this palace, though I'd like to see it eaten by dogs right now for leading us on such a wild goose chase."

"I wish, Sancho," said Don Quixote, "that you would show some respect in speaking of those things that pertain to my lady. Let us keep the feast and be merry and not throw the rope after the bucket."[5]

"I will control myself," said Sancho, "but how can I be patient when your Grace expects me, though I only saw our mistress's house once, to remember it always, and to find her in the middle of the night when your Grace, who must have seen her thousands of times, is unable to do so?"

"Sancho," said Don Quixote, "you will drive me to despair. Look, you heretic, have I not told you any number of times that I have never in all the days of my life laid eyes upon the peerless Dulcinea, that I have never crossed the threshold of her palace but am enamored of her only by hearsay, as she is famous far and wide for her beauty and her wit?"

"I hear you say it now," replied Sancho, "and I may tell you that if your Grace has never seen her, neither have I."

"But that cannot be," said Don Quixote, "or at any rate you have told me that you saw her winnowing wheat, that time you brought me back the answer to the letter that I sent to her by you."

"Pay no attention to that, sir, for I would have you know that it was also by hearsay that I saw her and brought her answer to you. I could no more tell you who the lady Dulcinea is than I could strike the sky with my fist."

"Sancho, Sancho," said Don Quixote, "there is a time for jesting and a time when jests are out of place. Just because I tell you that I have never seen nor spoken to the lady of my heart is no reason why you should say the same thing when you know it is not true."

As they were engaged in this conversation, they saw a man coming toward them with a team of mules hitched to a plow, which made a loud noise as it scraped along the ground. They assumed that he must be some farmer up before daybreak and on his way to the field, and this proved to be the case. The farmer was singing the ballad that runs:

> *The day of Roncesvalles was a dismal day for you,*
> *Ye men of France . . .*[6]

"May they slay me, Sancho," said Don Quixote when he heard it, "if anything good is going to come of this night. Do you hear what that rustic is singing?"

"Yes, I hear it," replied Sancho, "but what has the pursuit of Roncesvalles to do with the business that we have in hand? It would be all the same if it was the ballad of Calainos."[7]

At this point the farmer came up to them, and Don Quixote proceeded to question him. "Can you tell me, my good friend," he asked, "and may God prosper you, where in this vicinity is the palace of the peerless princess Doña Dulcinea del Toboso?"

"Señor," the lad answered, "I am a stranger here. I have been in this town only a few days, in the service of a rich farmer whose fields I plow. In that house across the way the curate and the sacristan live, and either one of them can tell your Grace what you wish to know about this princess, for they have a list of all the good folk of El Toboso. But, for my part, I never saw any princess whatever anywhere in the entire city. There are many ladies of high rank, it is true, and each may be a princess in her own house."

"Then the one that I am inquiring about must be among them, my friend," said Don Quixote.

"It may be so," replied the lad, "and God be with you, for there comes the dawn." And, lashing his mules, he did not wait to be questioned any further.

Seeing the unhappy state of mind his master was in, Sancho now spoke to him. "Sir," he said, "it will soon be daylight, and it will not do for the sun to find us here in the street. It would be better for us to go outside the town and for your Grace to hide yourself in some near-by forest. I will then come back and look in every corner for my lady's house, castle, or palace. It will be too bad if I do not find it, and when I do I will speak to her Grace and tell her how your Worship is waiting for her to arrange for you to come and see her without damage to her honor and good name."

"Sancho," said Don Quixote, "you have uttered a thousand sentences within the compass of a few words. I thank you for the advice you have given me and I accept it with right good grace. Come, my son, let us go look for a place where I may hide; after which, as you say, you will come back to look for and to see and talk with my lady, from whose discretion and courtesy I expect favors that will be more than miraculous."

Sancho was in furious haste to get his master out of the town so that the knight would not discover the lie that had been told him regarding Dulcinea's answer which his squire had brought back to the Sierra Morena. They set out at once, and at a distance of two miles from the city they found a forest or wood where Don Quixote might hide himself while Sancho returned to talk to Dulcinea, in the course of which embassy things happened to the messenger that call for fresh attention and belief.

CHAPTER X. *Wherein is related the ingenuity that Sancho displayed by laying a spell upon the lady Dulcinea, with other events as outlandish as they are true.*

WHEN the author of this great history comes to relate the events set forth in the present chapter, he remarks that he would prefer to pass over them in silence, as he fears that he will not be believed. For Don Quixote's madness here reaches a point beyond which the imagination cannot go, and even exceeds that point by a couple of bowshots. Nevertheless, in spite of such fear and misgiving, the historian has written down the events in question just as they happened, without adding to the chronicle in any way or holding back one particle of the truth, being in the end wholly unconcerned with the objections that might be raised by those who would make him out to be a liar. And in doing so he was right; for while the truth may run thin, it never breaks, and always rises above falsehood as oil does above water.[1]

The history, then, goes on to state that, after he had hidden himself in the wood, forest, or oak grove near El Toboso, Don Quixote ordered Sancho to return to the city and not to appear in his master's presence again until he should first have spoken in person to the lady Dulcinea and begged her to be pleased to grant her captive knight a glimpse of her, that she might bestow her blessing upon him, which would enable him to hope for a most fortunate conclusion to all his difficult enterprises and undertakings. Taking upon himself this task that had been assigned him, the squire promised to bring back as fair a reply as he had on the previous occasion.

"Go, my son," Don Quixote said to him, "and do not let yourself be dazed by the light from that sun of beauty that you go to seek. Ah, happy are you above all the squires in the world! Be sure to remember, and do not let it slip your mind, just how she receives you. Note whether she changes color while you are giving her my message and if she is restless and perturbed upon hearing my name. It may be that you will find her seated in sumptuous and royal state, in which case she will perhaps fall back upon a cushion; or if she be standing, see if she rests first upon one foot and then upon the other. Observe if she repeats two or three times the answer she gives you and if her mood varies from mildness to austerity, from the harsh to the amorous. She may raise a hand to her hair to smooth it back, though it be not disordered.

"In short, my son, note her every action and movement. If you report to me faithfully all these things, I shall be able to make out the hidden secret of her heart and discover how she feels with regard to my love; for I may tell you, Sancho, if you do not know it already, that among lovers exterior signs of this sort are the most reliable couriers that there are, bringing news of what goes on inside the heart. Go, then, my friend and may a better fortune than mine be your guide. May you be more successful than I dare hope in this fearful and bitter solitude in which you leave me."

"I go," said Sancho, "and I will return shortly. In the meantime, my master, cheer up that little heart of yours; for right now you must have one no bigger than a hazelnut. Remember what they say, that a stout heart breaks bad luck, and where there is no bacon there are no pegs. And they also say that when you least expect it the hare leaps out.[2] I tell you this for the reason that, if we did not find my lady's palace or castle last night, now that it is day I expect to come upon it when I'm not looking for it; and once I've found it, leave it to me to deal with her."

"I must say, Sancho," replied Don Quixote, "that your proverbs always come in very pat no matter what it is we are talking about. May God give me luck and grant me that which I desire."

With this, Sancho turned his back on his master and, lashing his donkey, rode off, leaving the knight seated in the saddle, his feet in the stirrups, and leaning on his lance. We, too, shall leave Don Quixote there, full of sad and troubled thoughts, as we accompany his squire, who was quite as pensive and troubled as he. As soon as he was out of the wood, Sancho turned his head and looked back, and, perceiving that he was by this time out of sight, he dismounted from his ass and sat down at the foot of a tree, where he began talking to himself, as follows:

"Look here, brother Sancho, supposing that you tell us where your Grace is going. Is it to hunt for some ass that has strayed? No, certainly not. Then, what *are* you hunting for? I am going to hunt for a princess, nothing more nor less than that, and in her I am to find the sun of beauty and all the heavens combined. And where do you think you are going to find all this, Sancho? Where? In the great city of El Toboso. Well and good; and who sent you to look for her? The famous knight, Don Quixote de la Mancha, who rights wrongs and gives food to the thirsty and drink to the hungry. That is all very well; but do you know where her house is, Sancho? My master says it will be some royal palace or proud castle. And have you ever laid eyes upon her by any chance? Neither I nor my master has ever seen her. And supposing the people of El Toboso knew that you were here luring their princesses and disturbing their ladies, don't you think it would be only right and proper if they came and clubbed your ribs without leaving a whole bone in your body? And, to tell the truth, they would be right, if you did not take into account that I am sent here under orders and that

> *A messenger you are, my friend,*
> *No blame belongs to you.*[3]

But don't put your trust in that, Sancho, for the Manchegan folks are as hot-tempered as they are honest and will not put up with anything from anybody. God help you if they get wind of you, for it will mean bad luck. Out with you, villain! Let the bolt fall![4] Am I to go looking for a cat with three feet just to please another?[5] Hunting for Dulcinea in El Toboso is like trying to find Marica in Rávena or a bachelor in Salamanca.[6] It was the devil, it was the devil himself and nobody else, that got me into this."

Such was Sancho's soliloquy. It had led him to no conclusion thus far, and so he continued:

"Well, there is a remedy for everything except death, beneath whose yoke we all have to pass, however heavy it may weigh upon us, when life draws to a close. I have seen by a thousand signs that this master of mine is a madman who ought to be in a cell, yet I am not behind him in that respect, seeing that I am foolish enough to follow and serve him. That is certainly the case if there's any truth in the old saying, 'Tell me what company you keep and I'll tell you who you are,' or that other one, 'Not with whom you are bred but with whom you are fed.' [7] And seeing that he is a madman, and that he is there can be no doubt—so mad that he takes one thing for another, white for black and black for white, like the time when he insisted the windmills were giants and the monks' mules were dromedaries, and the flocks of sheep were enemy armies, and other things of the same sort—seeing that this is so, it will not be hard to make him believe that the first farm girl I fall in with around here is the lady Dulcinea. If he doesn't believe it, I'll swear to it; and if he swears that it isn't so, I'll swear right back at him; and if he insists, I'll insist more than he does, so that, come what may, I'll always have my quoit on the peg. If I keep it up like that, I'll bring him around to the point where he won't be sending me on any more such errands as this, when he sees how little comes of it. Or maybe, and I imagine that this will more likely be the case, he will think that one of those wicked enchanters, who, he says, have it in for him, has changed her form just to spite and harm him."

These reflections greatly calmed Sancho Panza's mind and led him to look upon his business as already accomplished. He accordingly remained where he was until the afternoon, in order that Don Quixote might think he had had time to go to El Toboso and return. Everything went off so well with him that when he arose to mount his gray again, he saw coming toward him from the direction of the city three peasant lasses astride three ass-colts or fillies—the author is not specific on this point, but it seems more likely that they were she-asses, on which village girls commonly ride. However, it is of no great importance and there is no reason why we should stop to verify so trifling a detail.

The short of the matter is, as soon as Sancho saw the lasses he hastened to where Don Quixote was, only to find the knight sighing and uttering a thousand amorous laments.

"What is it, Sancho, my friend? Am I to be able to mark this day with a white stone or a black one?"

"It would be better," replied Sancho, "if your Grace marked it with red ocher like the lists on the professors' chairs,[8] so that all could see it very plainly."

"That means, I take it," said Don Quixote, "that you bring good news."

"Good news it is," replied Sancho. "All your Grace has to do is to put spur to Rocinante and ride out into the open, and there you will see the lady Dulcinea del Toboso in person, who with two of her damsels has come to pay her respects to your Grace."

"Good Lord, Sancho my friend, what is this you are telling me? Take care that you do not deceive me or try to relieve with false joy my very real sadness."

"And what would I get by deceiving your Grace," Sancho wanted to know, "when you will soon enough discover for yourself whether I am speaking the truth or not? Come quickly, sir, and you will see the princess, our mistress, clad and adorned as befits one of her quality. She and her damsels are all one blaze of gold, pearls, diamonds, rubies, and brocade cloth with more than ten borders.[9] Their hair falling loose over their shoulders are so many sunbeams playing with the wind. And, what is more, they come mounted upon three piebald cackneys,[10] the finest you ever saw."

"*Hackneys,* you mean to say, Sancho."

"*Hackneys* or *cackneys,* it makes very little difference," replied Sancho. "No matter what their mounts, they are the finest ladies you could wish for, especially the Princess Dulcinea, my lady, who stuns your senses."

"Come, Sancho, my son," said Don Quixote, "let us go. As a reward for the news you bring me, as good as it is unexpected, I promise you the best spoils that I win in my first adventure; and in case this is not enough to satisfy you, I will send you the colts which my three mares will give me this year—as you know, they are now out on the village common and are about to foal."

"I will take the colts," said Sancho, "for the spoils from that first adventure are rather uncertain."

At this point they emerged from the wood close to where the three village lasses were. Gazing up and down the highway that led to El Toboso, Don Quixote was completely bewildered, since all he could see was these country maidens. He then asked Sancho if the princess and her damsels had left the city or were, perhaps, waiting there.

"What do you mean?" said Sancho. "Are your Grace's eyes in the back of your head that you cannot see that those are the ones coming there, as bright and shining as the sun itself at midday?"

"I see nothing," declared Don Quixote, "except three farm girls on three jackasses."

"Then God deliver me from the devil!" exclaimed Sancho. "Is it possible that those three hackneys, or whatever you call them, white as the driven snow, look like jackasses to your Grace? By the living God, I would tear out this beard of mine if that were true!"

"But I tell you, friend Sancho, it is as true that those are jackasses, or she-asses, as it is that I am Don Quixote and you Sancho Panza. At least, that is the way they look to me."

"Be quiet, sir," Sancho admonished him, "you must not say such a thing as that. Open those eyes of yours and come do reverence to the lady of your affections, for she draws near."

Saying this, he rode on to meet the village maids and, slipping down off his donkey, seized one of their beasts by the halter and fell on his knees in front of its rider.

"O queen and princess and duchess of beauty," he said, "may your Highness and Majesty be pleased to receive and show favor to your captive knight, who stands there as if turned to marble, overwhelmed and breathless at finding himself in your magnificent presence. I am Sancho Panza, his squire, and he is the world-weary knight Don Quixote, otherwise known as the Knight of the Mournful Countenance."

By this time Don Quixote was down on his knees beside Sancho. His eyes were fairly starting from their sockets and there was a deeply troubled look in them as he stared up at the one whom Sancho had called queen and lady; all that he could see in her was a village wench, and not a very pretty one at that, for she was round-faced and snub-nosed. He was astounded and perplexed and did not dare open his mouth. The girls were also very much astonished to behold these two men, so different in appearance, kneeling in front of one of them so that she could not pass. It was this one who most ungraciously broke the silence.

"Get out of my way," she said peevishly, "and let me pass. And bad luck go with you. For we are in a hurry."

"O princess and universal lady of El Toboso!" cried Sancho. "How can your magnanimous heart fail to melt as you behold kneeling before your sublimated presence the one who is the very pillar and support of knight-errantry?" [11]

Hearing this, one of the others spoke up. "Whoa, there, she-ass of my father!" she said. "Wait until I curry you down.[12] Just look at the small-fry gentry, will you, who've come to make sport of us country girls!

Just as if we couldn't give them tit for tat. Be on your way and get out of ours, if you know what's good for you."

"Arise, Sancho," said Don Quixote, "for I perceive that fortune has not had her fill of evil done to me but has taken possession of all the roads by which some happiness may come to what little soul is left within me. And thou, who art all that could be desired, the sum of human gentleness and sole remedy for this afflicted heart that doth adore thee! The malign enchanter who doth persecute me hath placed clouds and cataracts upon my eyes, and for them and them alone hath transformed thy peerless beauty into the face of a lowly peasant maid; and I can only hope that he has not likewise changed my face into that of some monster by way of rendering it abhorrent in thy sight. But for all of that, hesitate not to gaze upon me tenderly and lovingly, beholding in this act of submission as I kneel before thee a tribute to thy metamorphosed beauty from this humbly worshiping heart of mine."

"Just listen to him run on, will you? My grandmother!" cried the lass. "Enough of such gibberish. We'll thank you to let us go our way."

Sancho fell back and let her pass, being very thankful to get out of it so easily.

No sooner did she find herself free than the girl who was supposed to have Dulcinea's face began spurring her "cackney" with a spike on the end of a long stick that she carried with her, whereupon the beast set off at top speed across the meadow. Feeling the prick, which appeared to annoy it more than was ordinarily the case, the ass started cutting such capers that the lady Dulcinea was thrown to the ground. When he saw this, Don Quixote hastened to lift her up while Sancho busied himself with tightening the girths and adjusting the packsaddle, which had slipped down under the animal's belly. This having been accomplished, Don Quixote was about to take his enchanted lady in his arms to place her upon the she-ass when the girl saved him the trouble by jumping up from the ground, stepping back a few paces, and taking a run for it. Placing both hands upon the crupper of the ass, she landed more lightly than a falcon upon the packsaddle and remained sitting there astride it like a man.

"In the name of Roque!" [13] exclaimed Sancho, "our lady is like a lanner, only lighter, and can teach the cleverest Cordovan or Mexican how to mount. She cleared the back of the saddle in one jump, and without any spurs she makes her hackney run like a zebra, and her damsels are not far behind, for they all of them go like the wind."

This was the truth. Seeing Dulcinea in the saddle, the other two prodded their beasts and followed her on the run, without so much as turning their heads to look back for a distance of half a league. Don Quixote stood gazing after them, and when they were no longer visible he turned to Sancho and spoke.

"Sancho," he said, "you can see now, can you not, how the enchanters hate me? And just see how far they carry their malice and the grudge they bear me, since they would deprive me of the happiness I might derive from a sight of my mistress. The truth of the matter is, I was born to be an example of misfortune and to be the target and mark at which the arrows of ill luck are aimed and directed. I would further call your attention, Sancho, to the fact that, not content with merely transforming my Dulcinea, they must change her into a figure as low and repulsive as that village girl, robbing her at the same time of that which is so characteristic of highborn ladies, namely, their pleasing scent, which comes from always being among amber and flowers. For I would have you know, Sancho, that when Dulcinea leaped upon her hackney as you call it (though I must say, it seemed to me more like a she-ass), the odor that she gave off was one of raw garlic that made my head swim and poisoned my heart."

"O you scum!" cried Sancho. "O wretched and evil-minded enchanters! If I could but see you strung up by the gills like sardines on a reed! Great is your wisdom, great is your power, and greater yet the harm you do! [14] Was it not enough, O villainous ones, to have changed the pearls of my lady's eyes into cork galls [15] and her hair of purest gold into the bristles of a red ox's tail? No, you had to change all of her features from good to ill, and even alter her smell, since had you not done so we might have discovered what lay concealed beneath that ugly bark. And yet, to tell the truth, I never noticed her ugliness but only her beauty, which was set off to perfection by a mole that she had on her right lip—it resembled a mustache, being surrounded by seven or eight red hairs of more than a palm in length."

"As a rule," observed Don Quixote, "moles on the face correspond to those on the body, and Dulcinea must accordingly have one of the same sort on the flat of her thigh, on the same side as the other. But hairs of the length you mentioned are very long for moles."

"Well, all I can tell you," answered Sancho, "is that there they were as big as life."

"I believe you, friend," said Don Quixote, "for everything pertaining to Dulcinea is by nature perfect and well finished, and so, if she had a hundred moles of the kind you have described, upon her they would not be moles but resplendent moons and stars. But tell me one thing, Sancho: that thing that looked to me like a packsaddle which you were adjusting, was it a flat saddle or a sidesaddle?"

"It was neither one nor the other," replied Sancho, "but a *jineta*,[16] with a field-covering so rich that it must have been worth half a kingdom."

"Oh, if I could but have seen all that, Sancho! I tell you again, and I will tell you a thousand times, that I am the most unfortunate of men."

It was all that the rogue of a Sancho could do to keep from laughing as he listened to this foolish talk on the part of his master, who had been so ingeniously deceived. Finally, after much other talk had passed between them, they mounted their beasts once more and took the road for Saragossa, hoping to arrive there in time for a certain important feast that is celebrated in that illustrious city every year. Before they reached their destination, however, many strange and noteworthy things were to happen to them that deserve to be set down and read, as will be seen further on.

CHAPTER XI. *Of the strange adventure that befell the valiant Don Quixote in connection with the cart or wagon of the Parliament of Death.*

CONTINUING on his way, Don Quixote was deeply dejected as he thought of the cruel joke which the enchanters had played upon him by transforming his lady Dulcinea into the ugly form of the village girl, nor could he imagine any means of restoring her to her original shape. He was so absorbed in these reflections that, without noticing it, he let go Rocinante's rein, and that animal, taking advantage of the freedom granted him, now paused at every step to feed upon the abundant green grass that covered the plain. It was Sancho who awakened the knight from his daydreams.

"Sir," he said, "sorrows are made not for beasts but for men, but if men feel them too much they become beasts. Your Grace ought to pull yourself together and pick up Rocinante's rein; you ought to wake up and cheer up and show that gallant spirit that knights-errant are supposed to have. What the devil is this, anyway? What kind of weakness is it? Are we here or in France? Let Satan carry off all the Dulcineas in the world; the welfare of a single knight means more than all the spells and transformations on this earth."

"Hush, Sancho," replied Don Quixote, in not too wan a voice,[1] "hush, I say, and do not be uttering blasphemies against that enchanted lady, seeing that I alone am to blame for her misfortunes, which are due to the envy that the wicked ones bear me."

"That is what I say," agreed Sancho. "Who saw her once and saw her now, his heart would surely weep, I vow." [2]

"You, Sancho, may well say that," was Don Quixote's response, "for you beheld her in all the fullness of her beauty; the spell did not go so far as to disturb *your* sight or conceal her loveliness from you; it was solely against me and these eyes of mine that the force of its venom was directed. And yet, Sancho, there is one thing that occurs to me. It would seem that you have not well described her; for, unless my memory serves me wrong, you said that she had eyes like pearls, and eyes of that sort are more characteristic of the sea bream than they are of a lady. Dulcinea's eyes must be green emeralds, large and luscious, with two rainbows for brows. Take those pearls from her eyes and bestow them upon her teeth, for undoubtedly, Sancho, you must have mistaken the former for the latter."

"That may be," said Sancho, "for her beauty disturbed me as much as her ugliness did your Grace. But let us leave it to God, for he knows all that is to happen in this vale of tears, in this evil world of ours, where you scarcely find anything that does not have in it some mixture of wickedness, deceit, and villainy. But there is one thing, my master, that worries me most of all: what is your Grace going to do when you have overcome some giant or knight and wish to send him to present himself before the beautiful Dulcinea? Where is that poor giant or wretched knight going to find her? I can see them now, wandering like a lot of nitwits through the streets of El Toboso looking for my lady. Even if they were to meet her in the middle of the street, they wouldn't know her from my father."

"It may be, Sancho," said Don Quixote, "that the spell will not prevent them from recognizing her as it does me. But we shall see as to that after we shall have dispatched one or two of them to seek her out; for I shall command them to return and give me an account of what happened."

"I must say," replied Sancho, "that your Grace has spoken very much to the point, and by this means we shall be able to find out what we wish to know. And since it is only to your Grace that her beauty is hidden, the misfortune is more yours than hers. So long as the lady Dulcinea has health and happiness, we will make the best of it and go on seeking adventures, leaving it to time to work a cure, for he is the best doctor for this and other greater ills."

Don Quixote was about to make a reply but was interrupted by the sight of a cart crossing the highway, filled with the most varied and weird assortment of persons and figures that could be imagined. He who drove the mules and served as carter was an ugly demon, and the vehicle was open to the heavens and had neither awning nor framework of branches on which to stretch it.[3] The first figure that Don Quixote beheld was that of Death himself, with a human countenance. Next came an angel with large and painted wings. At one side was an emperor with what appeared to be a gold crown on his head, and at Death's feet was the god called Cupid, without a bandage over his eyes but with his bow, his quiver, and his arrows. There was also a knight in full armor, except that he had no morion or helmet but instead wore a hat decked with vari-colored plumes.

Such a sight as this, coming as it did so unexpectedly, somewhat startled Don Quixote and struck fear in Sancho's heart, but the knight was at once cheered by the thought that this must be some new and perilous adventure, and with a mind disposed to confront any danger he stepped in front of the cart and called out in a loud and threatening voice, "O carter, coachman, demon, or whoever you may be! Tell me at once who you are and whither you are bound and who the persons are whom you carry with you in that wagonette, which looks more to me like Charon's bark than the kind of conveyance in common use."

Stopping the wagon, the demon gave him a most civil reply. "Sir," he said, "we are strolling players of Angulo el Malo's company.[4] This morning, which marks the octave of Corpus Christi, we have performed a theatrical piece in the village which lies beyond that hill yonder. It was a play called *The Parliament of Death*,[5] and we have to give it this afternoon in another village which you can see from here. Since the distance is so short, and in order to save ourselves the trouble of undressing and dressing again, we are traveling in the garments that we wear on the stage. That youth there is Death, the other is an Angel. That woman, who is the author's wife, takes the part of a Queen. This one is a Soldier, that one an Emperor, and I am a Devil—in fact, I am one of the principal characters in the play, for I take the leading roles in this company. If there is anything else your Grace would like to know concerning us, you have but to ask me and I will answer you very precisely; for, being a demon, I am capable of anything."

"Upon the word of a knight-errant," said Don Quixote, "when I first saw this wagon, I thought that some great adventure must be awaiting me, but I perceive now that one must actually touch with his hands what appears to the eye if he is to avoid being deceived. God go with you, my good people; be off to your festival; and if I can serve you in any way, I will gladly do so, for as a lad I was very fond of masks and in my youth my eyes were fixed upon the stage."

Now, fate would have it that as they were engaged in this conversation one of the company should come up, dressed in a mummer's costume, with many bells and with three cow's bladders on the end of a stick. Approaching Don Quixote, the clown began brandishing his stick, beating the ground with the bladders, and leaping high in the air to the jingling accompaniment of his bells. This terrifying apparition so frightened Rocinante that, without his master's being able to restrain him, the hack took the bit in his teeth and started off on a run across the plain, more swiftly than one would ever have thought possible, viewing the bones of his anatomy. Perceiving that his master was in danger of being thrown, Sancho leaped from his gray and ran with all haste to help him; but by the time he reached the spot both horse and rider were on the ground, which was the way it usually ended whenever Rocinante showed any signs of life.

No sooner had Sancho quitted his mount to go to Don Quixote's assistance than the dancing demon of the bladders jumped upon the gray's back and began beating it with them. Frightened by the sound rather than pained by the blows, the animal promptly started off at full speed over the countryside, in the direction of the village where the festival was to be held. As he witnessed his donkey's flight and his master's fall, Sancho was at a loss as to which case merited his attention first; but inasmuch as he was a good squire and a good servant, love of his master prevailed in the end over affection for his beast. Nevertheless, as he saw the bladders rising in the air and coming down on the donkey's flanks, he experienced all the throes and terrors of death; he would rather have had those blows fall upon his eyeballs than upon the least hair of his gray's tail. He was still troubled and perplexed as he reached the spot where Don Quixote lay, in a good deal worse plight than was to his liking.

"Sir," he said as he helped his master up on Rocinante's back, "the Devil's run off with the gray."

"What devil?" asked Don Quixote.

"The one with the bladders."

"Then I will recover it for you," said the knight, "though it be shut up with him in the deepest and darkest dungeons of Hell. Follow me, Sancho, for the wagon proceeds at a slow pace and its mules will make up for the loss of your gray."

"There is no need to go to all that trouble, sir," replied Sancho. "Your Grace may calm himself; for if I am not mistaken, the Devil has turned the gray loose and the beast is coming back to its old haunts."

This proved to be the truth; for, having taken a fall with the donkey in imitation of Don Quixote and Rocinante, the Devil had made off on foot toward the village, leaving the ass free to return to its owner.

"But I still think," said Don Quixote, "that it would be well to punish the discourtesy of that demon by taking it out on one of those in the wagon, even though it be the Emperor himself."

"Put that out of your mind, your Grace," Sancho urged him. "You had best take my advice, which is never to meddle with players, for they are a favored lot. I knew one of them who was up for two murders, yet he went scot free. Your Grace must be aware that, being merry folk whose business it is to amuse, they are liked by everybody and everyone protects, aids, and esteems them. This is especially true when they happen to belong to a royal company with a king's patent.[6] In that case, you might think that all or most of them were lords, from the clothes they wear and the manners they affect."

"Nonetheless," said Don Quixote, "I am not going to let that player demon go away boasting, even if the whole human race is on his side." Saying this, he returned to the wagon, which by this time was very near the town. "Stop!" he cried. "Wait, you merry, clowning crew! I'll teach you how to behave toward the beasts that serve as mounts to the squires of knights-errant."

Don Quixote was shouting so loudly that those in the wagon were able to hear and make out what he said; and, judging from the knight's words what his intentions were, the figure of Death leaped down, followed by the Emperor, the carter-Devil, and the Angel, nor did the Queen or the god Cupid stay behind. Arming themselves with pebbles, they formed in line and waited to receive Don Quixote with their missiles. The latter, seeing them drawn up in this gallant formation, their arms uplifted and ready to let fly a powerful volley, drew in Rocinante's rein and fell to thinking what would be the best way of attacking them with the least danger to his person. At this point Sancho came up and, perceiving that his master was about to fall upon the well-formed squadron, began remonstrating with him.

"It would be the height of madness," he said, "to undertake such a thing. Bear in mind, your Grace, that against brook-sop,[7] and plenty of it in this case, there is no defensive armor in the world except to hide yourself under a brass bell. Remember, too, that it is foolhardiness rather than valor for one man singlehanded to attack an army when Death is on the other side, when emperors are fighting there in person, and when the enemy has both good and fallen angels to aid him. And if this cannot lead you to be calm, it should interest you to know that, for a certainty, that among all those facing you, though they appear to be kings, princes, and emperors, there is not one knight-errant."

"Ah," said Don Quixote, "you have hit upon something there, Sancho, something that can and should sway me from my resolve. For, as I have told you many times, I ought not to draw sword against one who has not been dubbed a knight. It is for you, Sancho, if you so desire, to avenge the wrong that has been done to your gray, and I will cheer you on and help you with sound advice."

"There is no reason," replied Sancho, "why I should take vengeance on anyone; for it is not for good Christians to avenge the wrongs that are done them. I will arrange with my ass to leave everything to me, and my advice to him will be to live out peaceably the days that Heaven has allotted to him."

"Since that is your resolve, my good Sancho, my wise Sancho, my sincere and Christian Sancho, let us leave these phantoms and go back to seeking better and more legitimate adventures; for I can see this country is such that we cannot fail to meet with many most miraculous ones."

With this the knight turned his steed, Sancho made for his own mount, and Death with the whole of his flying squadron returned to the wagon, after which they continued on their way.

Such was the happy ending of this bold adventure of the wagon of Death, thanks to the wise counsel which Sancho Panza gave his master, who the very next day fell in with another enamored and erring knight, an episode quite as thrilling as the one that has just been related.

CHAPTER XII. *Of the strange adventure that befell the valiant Don Quixote with the fearless Knight of the Mirrors.*

THE night following the encounter with Death was spent by Don Quixote and his squire beneath some tall and shady trees, the knight having been persuaded to eat a little from the stock of provisions carried by the gray.

"Sir," said Sancho, in the course of their repast, "how foolish I'd have been if I had chosen the spoils from your Grace's first adventure rather than the foals from the three mares. Truly, truly, a sparrow in the hand is worth more than a vulture on the wing." [1]

"And yet, Sancho," replied Don Quixote, "if you had but let me attack them as I wished to do, you would at least have had as spoils the Empress's gold crown and Cupid's painted wings; for I should have taken them whether or no and placed them in your hands."

"The crowns and scepters of stage emperors," remarked Sancho, "were never known to be of pure gold; they are always of tinsel or tinplate."

"That is the truth," said Don Quixote, "for it is only right that the accessories of a drama should be fictitious and not real, like the play itself. Speaking of that, Sancho, I would have you look kindly upon the art of the theater and, as a consequence, upon those who write the pieces and perform in them, for they all render a service of great value to the State by holding up a mirror for us at each step that we take, wherein we may observe, vividly depicted, all the varied aspects of human life; and I may add that there is nothing that shows us more clearly, by similitude, what we are and what we ought to be than do plays and players.

"Tell me, have you not seen some comedy in which kings, emperors, pontiffs, knights, ladies, and numerous other characters are introduced? One plays the ruffian, another the cheat, this one a merchant and that one a soldier, while yet another is the fool who is not so foolish as he appears, and still another the one of whom love has made a fool. Yet when the play is over and they have taken off their players' garments, all the actors are once more equal."

"Yes," replied Sancho, "I have seen all that."

"Well," continued Don Quixote, "the same thing happens in the comedy that we call life,[2] where some play the part of emperors, others that of pontiffs—in short, all the characters that a drama may have—but when it is all over, that is to say, when life is done, death takes from each the garb that differentiates him, and all at last are equal in the grave."

"It is a fine comparison," Sancho admitted, "though not so new but that I have heard it many times before. It reminds me of that other one, about the game of chess. So long as the game lasts, each piece has its special qualities, but when it is over they are all mixed and jumbled together and put into a bag, which is to the chess pieces what the grave is to life."[3]

"Every day, Sancho," said Don Quixote, "you are becoming less stupid and more sensible."[4]

"It must be that some of your Grace's good sense is sticking to me," was Sancho's answer. "I am like a piece of land that of itself is dry and barren, but if you scatter manure over it and cultivate it, it will bear good fruit. By this I mean to say that your Grace's conversation is the manure that has been cast upon the barren land of my dry wit; the time that I spend in your service, associating with you, does the cultivating; and as a result of it all, I hope to bring forth blessed fruits by not departing, slipping, or sliding, from those paths of good breeding which your Grace has marked out for me in my parched understanding."

Don Quixote had to laugh at this affected speech of Sancho's, but he could not help perceiving that what the squire had said about his improvement was true enough; for every now and then the servant would speak in a manner that astonished his master. It must be admitted, however, that most of the time when he tried to use fine language, he would tumble from the mountain of his simple-mindedness into the abyss of his ignorance. It was when he was quoting old saws and sayings, whether or not they had anything to do with the subject under discussion, that he was at his best, displaying upon such occasions a prodigious memory, as will already have been seen and noted in the course of this history.

With such talk as this they spent a good part of the night. Then Sancho felt a desire to draw down the curtains of his eyes, as he was in the habit of saying when he wished to sleep, and, unsaddling his mount, he turned him loose to graze at will on the abundant grass. If he did not remove Rocinante's saddle, this was due to his master's express command; for when they had taken the field and were not sleeping under a roof, the hack was under no circumstances to be stripped. This was in accordance with an old and established custom which knights-errant faithfully observed: the bridle and saddlebow might be removed, but beware of touching the saddle itself! Guided by this precept, Sancho now gave Rocinante the same freedom that the ass enjoyed.

The close friendship that existed between the two animals was a most unusual one, so remarkable indeed that it has become a tradition handed down from father to son, and the author of this veracious chronicle even wrote a number of special chapters on the subject, although, in order to preserve the decency and decorum that are fitting in so heroic an account, he chose to omit them in the final version. But he forgets himself once in a while and goes on to tell us how the two beasts when they were together would hasten to scratch each other, and how, when they were tired and their bellies were full, Rocinante would lay his long neck over that of the ass—it extended more than half a yard on the other side—and the pair would then stand there gazing pensively at the ground for as much as three whole days at a time, or at least until someone came for them or hunger compelled them to seek nourishment.

I may tell you that I have heard it said that the author of this history, in one of his writings, has compared the friendship of Rocinante and the gray to that of Nisus and Euryalus and that of Pylades and Orestes; [5] and if this be true, it shows for the edification of all what great friends these two peace-loving animals were, and should be enough to make men ashamed, who are so inept at preserving friendship with one another. For this reason it has been said:

> There is no friend for friend,
> Reeds to lances turn . . . [6]

And there was the other poet who sang:

> Between friend and friend the bug . . . [7]

Let no one think that the author has gone out of his way in comparing the friendship of animals with that of men; for human beings have received valuable lessons from the beasts and have learned many important things from them. From the stork they have learned the use of clysters; the dog has taught them the salutary effects of vomiting as well as a lesson in gratitude; the cranes have taught them vigilance, the ants foresight, the elephants modesty, and the horse loyalty. [8]

Sancho had at last fallen asleep at the foot of a cork tree, while Don Quixote was slumbering beneath a sturdy oak. Very little time had passed when the knight was awakened by a noise behind him, and, starting up, he began looking about him and listening to see if he could make out where it came from. Then he caught sight of two men on horseback, one of whom, slipping down from the saddle, said to the other, "Dismount, my friend, and unbridle the horses; for there seems to be plenty of grass around here for them and sufficient silence and solitude for my amorous thoughts."

Saying this, he stretched himself out on the ground, and as he flung himself down the armor that he wore made such a noise that Don Quixote knew at once, for a certainty, that he must be a knight-errant. Going over to Sancho, who was still sleeping, he shook him by the arm and with no little effort managed to get him awake.

"Brother Sancho," he said to him in a low voice, "we have an adventure on our hands."

"God give us a good one," said Sancho. "And where, my master, may her Ladyship, Mistress Adventure, be?"

"Where, Sancho?" replied Don Quixote. "Turn your eyes and look, and you will see stretched out over there a knight-errant who, so far as I can make out, is not any too happy; for I saw him fling himself from his horse to the ground with a certain show of despondency, and as he fell his armor rattled."

"Well," said Sancho, "and how does your Grace make this out to be an adventure?"

"I would not say," the knight answered him, "that this is an adventure in itself, but rather the beginning of one, for that is the way they start. But listen; he seems to be tuning a lute or guitar, and from the way he is spitting and clearing his throat he must be getting ready to sing something."

"Faith, so he is," said Sancho. "He must be some lovesick knight."

"There are no knights-errant that are not lovesick," Don Quixote informed him. "Let us listen to him, and the thread of his song will lead us to the yarn-ball of his thoughts; [9] for out of the abundance of the heart the mouth speaketh." [10]

Sancho would have liked to reply to his master, but the voice of the Knight of the Wood, which was neither very good nor very bad, kept him from it; and as the two of them listened attentively,[11] they heard the following:

SONNET

Show me, O lady, the pattern of thy will,
That mine may take that very form and shape;
For my will in thine own I fain would drape,
Each slightest wish of thine I would fulfill.

If thou wouldst have me silence this dread ill
Of which I'm dying now, prepare the crape!
Or if I must another manner ape,
Then let Love's self display his rhyming skill.
Of opposites I am made, that's manifest:
In part soft wax, in part hard-diamond fire;
Yet to Love's laws my heart I do adjust,
And, hard or soft, I offer thee this breast:
Print or engrave there what thou may'st desire,
And I'll preserve it in eternal trust.[12]

With an *Ay!* that appeared to be wrung from the very depths of his heart, the Knight of the Wood brought his song to a close, and then after a brief pause began speaking in a grief-stricken voice that was piteous to hear.

"O most beautiful and most ungrateful woman in all the world!" he cried, "how is it possible, O most serene Casildea de Vandalia, for you to permit this captive knight of yours to waste away and perish in constant wanderings, amid rude toils and bitter hardships? Is it not enough that I have compelled all the knights of Navarre, all those of León, all the Tartessians [13] and Castilians, and, finally, all those of La Mancha, to confess that there is no beauty anywhere that can rival yours?"

"That is not so!" cried Don Quixote at this point. "I am of La Mancha, and I have never confessed, I never could nor would confess a thing so prejudicial to the beauty of my lady.[14] The knight whom you see there, Sancho, is raving; but let us listen and perhaps he will tell us more."

"That he will," replied Sancho, "for at the rate he is carrying on, he is good for a month at a stretch."

This did not prove to be the case, however; for when the Knight of the Wood heard voices near him, he cut short his lamentations and rose to his feet.

"Who goes there?" he called in a loud but courteous tone. "What kind of people are you? Are you, perchance, numbered among the happy or among the afflicted?"

"Among the afflicted," was Don Quixote's response.

"Then come to me," said the one of the Wood, "and, in doing so, know that you come to sorrow's self and the very essence of affliction."

Upon receiving so gentle and courteous an answer, Don Quixote and Sancho as well went over to him, whereupon the sorrowing one took the Manchegan's arm.

"Sit down here, Sir Knight," he continued, "for in order to know that you are one of those who follow the profession of knight-errantry, it is enough for me to have found you in this place where solitude and serenity keep you company, such a spot being the natural bed and proper dwelling of wandering men of arms."

"A knight I am," replied Don Quixote, "and of the profession that you mention; and though sorrows, troubles, and misfortunes have made my heart their abode, this does not mean that compassion for the woes of others has been banished from it. From your song a while ago I gather that your misfortunes are due to love—the love you bear that ungrateful fair one whom you named in your lamentations."

As they conversed in this manner, they sat together upon the hard earth, very peaceably and companionably, as if at daybreak they were not going to break each other's heads.

"Sir Knight," inquired the one of the Wood, "are you by any chance in love?"

"By mischance I am," said Don Quixote, "although the ills that come from well-placed affection should be looked upon as favors rather than as misfortunes."

"That is the truth," the Knight of the Wood agreed, "if it were not that the loved one's scorn disturbs our reason and understanding; for when it is excessive scorn appears as vengeance."

"I was never scorned by my lady," said Don Quixote.

"No, certainly not," said Sancho, who was standing near by, "for my lady is gentle as a ewe lamb and soft as butter."

"Is he your squire?" asked the one of the Wood.

"He is," replied Don Quixote.

"I never saw a squire," said the one of the Wood, "who dared to speak while his master was talking. At least, there is mine over there; he is as big as your father, and it cannot be proved that he has ever opened his lips while I was conversing."

"Well, upon my word," said Sancho, "I have spoken, and I will speak in front of any other as good—but never mind; it only makes it worse to stir it." 15

The Knight of the Wood's squire now seized Sancho's arm. "Come along," he said, "let the two of us go where we can talk all we like, squire fashion, and leave these gentlemen our masters to come to lance blows as they tell each other the story of their loves; for you may rest assured, daybreak will find them still at it."

"Let us, by all means," said Sancho, "and I will tell your Grace who

I am, so that you may be able to see for yourself whether or not I am to be numbered among the dozen most talkative squires."

With this, the pair went off to one side, and there then took place between them a conversation that was as droll as the one between their masters was solemn.

CHAPTER XIII . *In which is continued the adventure of the Knight of the Wood,*[1] *together with the shrewd, highly original, and amicable conversation that took place between the two squires.*

THE knights and the squires had now separated, the latter to tell their life stories, the former to talk of their loves; but the history first relates the conversation of the servants and then goes on to report that of the masters. We are told that, after they had gone some little distance from where the others were, the one who served the Knight of the Wood began speaking to Sancho as follows:

"It is a hard life that we lead and live, *Señor mío*, those of us who are squires to knights-errant. It is certainly true that we eat our bread in the sweat of our faces,[2] which is one of the curses that God put upon our first parents."

"It might also be said," added Sancho, "that we eat it in the chill of our bodies, for who endures more heat and cold than we wretched ones who wait upon these wandering men of arms? It would not be so bad if we did eat once in a while, for troubles are less where there is bread;[3] but as it is, we sometimes go for a day or two without breaking our fast, unless we feed on the wind that blows."

"But all this," said the other, "may very well be put up with, by reason of the hope we have of being rewarded; for if a knight is not too unlucky, his squire after a little while will find himself the governor of some fine island or prosperous earldom."

"I," replied Sancho, "have told my master that I would be satisfied with the governorship of an island, and he is so noble and so generous that he has promised it to me on many different occasions."

"In return for my services," said the Squire of the Wood, "I'd be content with a canonry. My master has already appointed me to one—and what a canonry!"

"Then he must be a churchly knight," said Sancho, "and in a position to grant favors of that sort to his faithful squire; but mine is a layman, pure and simple, although, as I recall, certain shrewd and, as I see it, scheming persons did advise him to try to become an archbishop. However, he did not want to be anything but an emperor. And there I was, all the time trembling for fear he would take it into his head to enter the Church, since I was not educated enough to hold any benefices. For I may as well tell your Grace that, though I look like a man, I am no more than a beast where holy orders are concerned."

"That is where you are making a mistake," the Squire of the Wood assured him. "Not all island governments are desirable. Some of them are misshapen bits of land, some are poor, others are gloomy, and, in short, the best of them lays a heavy burden of care and trouble upon the shoulders of the unfortunate one to whose lot it falls. It would be far better if we who follow this cursed trade were to go back to our homes and there engage in pleasanter occupations, such as hunting or fishing, for example; for where is there in this world a squire so poor that he does not have a hack, a couple of greyhounds, and a fishing rod to provide him with sport in his own village?"

"I don't lack any of those," replied Sancho. "It is true, I have no hack, but I do have an ass that is worth twice as much as my master's horse. God send me a bad Easter, and let it be the next one that comes, if I would make a trade, even though he gave me four fanegas [4] of barley to boot. Your Grace will laugh at the price I put on my gray—for that is the color of the beast. As to greyhounds, I shan't want for them, as there are plenty and to spare in my village. And, anyway, there is more pleasure in hunting when someone else pays for it."

"Really and truly, Sir Squire," said the one of the Wood, "I have made up my mind and resolved to have no more to do with the mad whims of these knights; I intend to retire to my village and bring up my little ones—I have three of them, and they are like oriental pearls."

"I have two of them," said Sancho, "that might be presented to the Pope in person, especially one of my girls that I am bringing up to be a countess, God willing, in spite of what her mother says."

"And how old is this young lady that is destined to be a countess?"

"Fifteen," replied Sancho, "or a couple of years more or less. But she is tall as a lance, fresh as an April morning, and strong as a porter."

"Those," remarked the one of the Wood, "are qualifications that fit her to be not merely a countess but a nymph of the verdant wildwood. O whore's daughter of a whore! What strength the she-rogue must have!"

Sancho was a bit put out by this. "She is not a whore," he said, "nor was her mother before her, nor will either of them ever be, please God, so long as I live. And you might speak more courteously. For one who has been brought up among knights-errant, who are the soul of courtesy, those words are not very becoming."

"Oh, how little your Grace knows about compliments, Sir Squire!" the one of the Wood exclaimed. "Are you not aware that when some knight gives a good lance thrust to the bull in the plaza, or when a person does anything remarkably well, it is the custom for the crowd to cry out, 'Well done, whoreson rascal!' and that what appears to be vituperation in such a case is in reality high praise? Sir, I would bid you disown those sons or daughters who do nothing to cause such praise to be bestowed upon their parents."

"I would indeed disown them if they didn't," replied Sancho, "and so your Grace may go ahead and call me, my children, and my wife all the whores in the world if you like, for everything that they say and do deserves the very highest praise. And in order that I may see them all again, I pray God to deliver me from mortal sin, or, what amounts to the same thing, from this dangerous calling of squire, seeing that I have fallen into it a second time, decoyed and deceived by a purse of a hundred ducats that I found one day in the heart of the Sierra Morena. The devil is always holding up a bag full of doubloons in front of my eyes, here, there—no, not here, but there—everywhere, until it seems to me at every step I take that I am touching it with my hand, hugging it, carrying it off home with me, investing it, drawing an income from it, and living on it like a prince. And while I am thinking such thoughts, all the hardships I have to put up with serving this crackbrained master of mine, who is more of a madman than a knight, seem to me light and easy to bear."

"That," observed the Squire of the Wood, "is why it is they say that avarice bursts the bag.[5] But, speaking of madmen, there is no greater one in all this world than my master; for he is one of those of whom it is said, 'The cares of others kill the ass.'[6] Because another knight has lost his senses, he has to play mad too and go hunting for that which, when he finds it, may fly up in his snout."

"Is he in love, maybe?"

"Yes, with a certain Casildea de Vandalia, the rawest [7] and best-roasted lady to be found anywhere on earth; but her rawness is not the foot he limps on, for he has other and greater schemes rumbling in his bowels, as you will hear tell before many hours have gone by."

"There is no road so smooth," said Sancho, "that it does not have some hole or rut to make you stumble. In other houses they cook horse beans, in mine they boil them by the kettleful.[8] Madness has more companions and attendants than good sense does. But if it is true what they say, that company in trouble brings relief, I may take comfort from your Grace, since you serve a master as foolish as my own."

"Foolish but brave," the one of the Wood corrected him, "and more of a rogue than anything else."

"That is not true of my master," replied Sancho. "I can assure you there is nothing of the rogue about him; he is as open and aboveboard as a wine pitcher and would not harm anyone but does good to all. There is no malice in his make-up, and a child could make him believe it was night at midday. For that very reason I love him with all my heart and cannot bring myself to leave him, no matter how many foolish things he does." [9]

"But, nevertheless, good sir and brother," said the Squire of the Wood, "with the blind leading the blind, both are in danger of falling into the pit. It would be better for us to get out of all this as quickly as we can and return to our old haunts; for those that go seeking adventures do not always find good ones."

Sancho kept clearing his throat from time to time, and his saliva seemed rather viscous and dry; seeing which, the woodland squire said to him, "It looks to me as if we have been talking so much that our tongues are cleaving to our palates, but I have a loosener over there, hanging from the bow of my saddle, and a pretty good one it is." With this, he got up and went over to his horse and came back a moment later with a big flask of wine and a meat pie half a yard in diameter. This is no exaggeration, for the pasty in question was made of a hutch-rabbit of such a size that Sancho took it to be a goat, or at the very least a kid.

"And are you in the habit of carrying this with you, Señor?" he asked.

"What do you think?" replied the other. "Am I by any chance one of your wool-and-water squires? [10] I carry better rations on the flanks of my horse than a general does when he takes the field."

Sancho ate without any urging, gulping down mouthfuls that were like the knots on a tether,[11] as they sat there in the dark.

"You are a squire of the right sort," he said, "loyal and true, and you live in grand style as shown by this feast, which I would almost say was produced by magic. You are not like me, poor wretch, who have in my saddlebags only a morsel of cheese so hard you could crack a giant's skull with it, three or four dozen carob beans, and a few nuts. For this I have my master to thank, who believes in observing the rule that knights-errant should nourish and sustain themselves on nothing but dried fruits and the herbs of the field."

"Upon my word, brother," said the other squire, "my stomach was not made for thistles, wild pears, and woodland herbs. Let our masters observe those knightly laws and traditions and eat what their rules prescribe; I carry a hamper of food and a flask on my saddlebow, whether they like it or not. And speaking of that flask, how I love it! There is scarcely a minute in the day that I'm not hugging and kissing it, over and over again."

As he said this, he placed the wine bag in Sancho's hands, who put it to his mouth, threw his head back, and sat there gazing up at the stars for a quarter of an hour.[12] Then, when he had finished drinking, he let his head loll on one side and heaved a deep sigh.

"The whoreson rascal!" he exclaimed, "that's a fine vintage for you!"

"There!" cried the Squire of the Wood, as he heard the epithet Sancho had used, "do you see how you have praised this wine by calling it 'whoreson'?"

"I grant you," replied Sancho, "that it is no insult to call anyone a son of a whore so long as you really do mean to praise him. But tell me, sir, in the name of what you love most, is this the wine of Ciudad Real?"[13]

"What a winetaster you are! It comes from nowhere else, and it's a few years old, at that."

"Leave it to me," said Sancho, "and never fear, I'll show you how much I know about it. Would you believe me, Sir Squire, I have such a great natural instinct in this matter of wines that I have but to smell a vintage and I will tell you the country where it was grown, from what kind of grapes, what it tastes like, and how good it is, and everything that has to do with it. There is nothing so unusual about this, however, seeing that on my father's side were two of the best winetasters La Mancha has known in many a year, in proof of which, listen to the story of what happened to them.

"The two were given a sample of wine from a certain vat and asked to state its condition and quality and determine whether it was good or bad. One of them tasted it with the tip of his tongue while the other merely brought it up to his nose. The first man said that it tasted of iron, the second that it smelled of Cordovan leather. The owner insisted that the vat was clean and that there could be nothing in the wine to give it a flavor of leather or of iron, but, nevertheless, the two famous wine-tasters stood their ground. Time went by, and when they came to clean out the vat they found in it a small key attached to a leather strap.[14] And so your Grace may see for yourself whether or not one who comes of that kind of stock has a right to give his opinion in such cases."

"And for that very reason," said the Squire of the Wood, "I maintain that we ought to stop going about in search of adventures. Seeing that we have loaves, let us not go looking for cakes, but return to our cottages, for God will find us there if He so wills."

"I mean to stay with my master," Sancho replied, "until he reaches Saragossa, but after that we will come to an understanding."

The short of the matter is, the two worthy squires talked so much and drank so much that sleep had to tie their tongues and moderate their thirst, since to quench the latter was impossible. Clinging to the wine flask, which was almost empty by now, and with half-chewed morsels of food in their mouths, they both slept peacefully; and we shall leave them there as we go on to relate what took place between the Knight of the Wood and the Knight of the Mournful Countenance.

CHAPTER XIV. *Wherein is continued the adventure of the Knight of the Wood.*

IN THE course of the long conversation that took place between Don Quixote and the Knight of the Wood, the history informs us that the latter addressed the following remarks to the Manchegan:

"In short, Sir Knight, I would have you know that my destiny, or, more properly speaking, my own free choice, has led me to fall in love with the peerless Casildea de Vandalia. I call her peerless for the reason that she has no equal as regards either her bodily proportions or her very great beauty. This Casildea, then, of whom I am telling you, repaid my worthy affections and honorable intentions by forcing me, as Hercules was forced by his stepmother, to incur many and diverse perils; and each time as I overcame one of them she would promise me that with the next one I should have that which I desired; but instead my labors have continued, forming a chain whose links I am no longer able to count, nor can I say which will be the last one, that shall mark the beginning of the realization of my hopes.

"One time she sent me forth to challenge that famous giantess of Seville, known as La Giralda, who is as strong and brave as if made of brass, and who without moving from the spot where she stands is the most changeable and fickle woman in the world.[1] I came, I saw, I conquered her. I made her stand still and point in one direction only, and for more than a week nothing but north winds blew. Then, there was that other time when Casildea sent me to lift those ancient stones, the mighty Bulls of Guisando,[2] an enterprise that had better have been entrusted to porters than to knights. On another occasion she commanded me to hurl myself down into the Cabra chasm[3]—an unheard-of and terribly dangerous undertaking—and bring her back a detailed account of what lay concealed in that deep and gloomy pit. I rendered La Giralda motionless, I lifted the Bulls of Guisando, and I threw myself into the abyss and brought to light what was hidden in its depths; yet my hopes are dead— how dead!—while her commands and her scorn are as lively as can be.

"Finally, she commanded me to ride through all the provinces of Spain and compel all the knights-errant whom I met with to confess that she is the most beautiful woman now living and that I am the most enamored man of arms that is to be found anywhere in the world. In fulfillment of this behest I have already traveled over the greater part of these realms and have vanquished many knights who have dared to contradict me. But the one whom I am proudest to have overcome in single combat is that famous gentleman, Don Quixote de la Mancha; for I made him confess that my Casildea is more beautiful than his Dulcinea, and by achieving such a conquest I reckon that I have conquered all the others on the face of the earth, seeing that this same Don Quixote had himself routed them. Accordingly, when I vanquished him, his fame, glory, and honor passed over and were transferred to my person.

> *The brighter is the conquered one's lost crown,*
> *The greater is the conqueror's renown.*[4]

Thus, the innumerable exploits of the said Don Quixote are now set down to my account and are indeed my own."

Don Quixote was astounded as he listened to the Knight of the Wood, and was about to tell him any number of times that he lied; the words were on the tip of his tongue, but he held them back as best he could, thinking that he would bring the other to confess with his own lips that what he had said was a lie. And so it was quite calmly that he now replied to him.

"Sir Knight," he began, "as to the assertion that your Grace has conquered most of the knights-errant in Spain and even in all the world, I have nothing to say, but that you have vanquished Don Quixote de la Mancha, I am inclined to doubt. It may be that it was someone else who resembled him, although there are very few that do."

"What do you mean?" replied the one of the Wood. "I swear by the heavens above that I did fight with Don Quixote and that I overcame him and forced him to yield. He is a tall man, with a dried-up face, long, lean legs, graying hair, an eagle-like nose somewhat hooked, and a big, black, drooping mustache. He takes the field under the name of the Knight of the Mournful Countenance, he has for squire a peasant named Sancho Panza, and he rides a famous steed called Rocinante. Lastly, the lady of his heart is a certain Dulcinea del Toboso, once upon a time known as Aldonza Lorenzo, just as my own lady, whose name is Casildea and who is an Andalusian by birth, is called by me Casildea de Vandalia. If all this is not sufficient to show that I speak the truth, here is my sword which shall make incredulity itself believe."

"Calm yourself, Sir Knight," replied Don Quixote, "and listen to what I have to say to you. You must know that this Don Quixote of whom you speak is the best friend that I have in the world, so great a friend that I may say that I feel toward him as I do toward my own self; and from all that you have told me, the very definite and accurate details that you have given me, I cannot doubt that he is the one whom you have conquered. On the other hand, the sight of my eyes and the touch of my hands assure me that he could not possibly be the one, unless some enchanter who is his enemy—for he has many, and one in particular who delights in persecuting him—may have assumed the knight's form and then permitted himself to be routed, by way of defrauding Don Quixote of the fame which his high deeds of chivalry have earned for him throughout the known world. To show you how true this may be, I will inform you that not more than a couple of days ago those same enemy magicians transformed the figure and person of the beauteous Dulcinea del Toboso into a low and mean village lass, and it is possible that they have done something of the same sort to the knight who is her lover. And if all this does not suffice to convince you of the truth of what I say, here is Don Quixote himself who will maintain it by force of arms, on foot or on horseback, or in any way you like."

Saying this, he rose and laid hold of his sword, and waited to see what the Knight of the Wood's decision would be. That worthy now replied in a voice as calm as the one Don Quixote had used.

"Pledges," he said, "do not distress one who is sure of his ability to pay.[5] He who was able to overcome you when you were transformed, Señor Don Quixote, may hope to bring you to your knees when you are your own proper self. But inasmuch as it is not fitting that knights should perform their feats of arms in the darkness, like ruffians and highwaymen, let us wait until it is day in order that the sun may behold what we do. And the condition governing our encounter shall be that the one who is vanquished must submit to the will of his conqueror and perform all those things that are commanded of him, provided they are such as are in keeping with the state of knighthood."

"With that condition and understanding," said Don Quixote, "I shall be satisfied."

With this, they went off to where their squires were, only to find them snoring away as hard as when sleep had first overtaken them. Awakening the pair, they ordered them to look to the horses; for as soon as the sun was up the two knights meant to stage an arduous and bloody single-handed combat. At this news Sancho was astonished and terrified, since, as a result of what the other squire had told him of the Knight of the Wood's prowess, he was led to fear for his master's safety. Nevertheless, he and his friend now went to seek the mounts without saying a word, and they found the animals all together, for by this time the two horses and the ass had smelled one another out. On the way the Squire of the Wood turned to Sancho and addressed him as follows:

"I must inform you, brother, that it is the custom of the fighters of Andalusia, when they are godfathers in any combat, not to remain idly by, with folded hands, while their godsons fight it out. I tell you this by way of warning you that while our masters are settling matters, we, too, shall have to come to blows and hack each other to bits."

"That custom, Sir Squire," replied Sancho, "may be all very well among the fighters and ruffians that you mention, but with the squires of knights-errant it is not to be thought of. At least, I have never heard my master speak of any such custom, and he knows all the laws of chivalry by heart. But granting that it is true and that there is a law which states in so many words that squires must fight while their masters do, I have no intention of obeying it but rather will pay whatever penalty is laid on peaceable-minded ones like myself, for I am sure it cannot be more than a couple of pounds of wax,[6] and that would be less expensive than the lint which it would take to heal my head—I can already see it split in two. What's more, it's out of the question for me to fight since I have no sword nor did I ever in my life carry one."

"That," said the one of the Wood, "is something that is easily remedied. I have here two linen bags of the same size. You take one and I'll take the other and we will fight that way, on equal terms."

"So be it, by all means," said Sancho, "for that will simply knock the dust out of us without wounding us."

"But that's not the way it's to be," said the other squire. "Inside the bags, to keep the wind from blowing them away, we will put a half-dozen nice smooth pebbles of the same weight, and so we'll be able to give each other a good pounding without doing ourselves any real harm or damage."

"Body of my father!" cried Sancho, "just look, will you, at the marten and sable and wads of carded cotton that he's stuffing into those bags so that we won't get our heads cracked or our bones crushed to a pulp. But I am telling you, *Señor mio*, that even though you fill them with silken pellets, I don't mean to fight. Let our masters fight and make the best of it, but as for us, let us drink and live; for time will see to ending our lives without any help on our part by way of bringing them to a close before they have reached their proper season and fall from ripeness."

"Nevertheless," replied the Squire of the Wood, "fight we must, if only for half an hour."

"No," Sancho insisted, "that I will not do. I will not be so impolite or so ungrateful as to pick any quarrel however slight with one whose food and drink I've shared. And, moreover, who in the devil could bring himself to fight in cold blood, when he's not angry or vexed in any way?"

"I can take care of that, right enough," said the one of the Wood. "Before we begin, I will come up to your Grace as nicely as you please and give you three or four punches that will stretch you out at my feet; and that will surely be enough to awaken your anger, even though it's sleeping sounder than a dormouse."

"And I," said Sancho, "have another idea that's every bit as good as yours. I will take a big club, and before your Grace has had a chance to awaken my anger I will put yours to sleep with such mighty whacks that if it wakes at all it will be in the other world; for it is known there that I am not the man to let my face be mussed by anyone, and let each look out for the arrow.⁷ But the best thing to do would be to leave each one's anger to its slumbers, for no one knows the heart of any other, he who comes for wool may go back shorn,⁸ and God bless peace and curse all strife. If a hunted cat when surrounded and cornered turns into a lion,⁹ God knows what I who am a man might not become. And so from this time forth I am warning you, Sir Squire, that all the harm and damage that may result from our quarrel will be upon your head."

"Very well," the one of the Wood replied, "God will send the dawn and we shall make out somehow."

At that moment gay-colored birds of all sorts began warbling in the trees and with their merry and varied songs appeared to be greeting and welcoming the fresh-dawning day, which already at the gates and on the balconies of the east was revealing its beautiful face as it shook out from its hair an infinite number of liquid pearls. Bathed in this gentle moisture, the grass seemed to shed a pearly spray, the willows distilled a savory manna, the fountains laughed, the brooks murmured, the woods were glad, and the meadows put on their finest raiment. The first thing that Sancho Panza beheld, as soon as it was light enough to tell one object from another, was the Squire of the Wood's nose, which was so big as to cast into the shade all the rest of his body. In addition to being of enormous size, it is said to have been hooked in the middle and all covered with warts of a mulberry hue, like eggplant; it hung down for a couple of inches below his mouth, and the size, color, warts, and shape of this organ gave his face so ugly an appearance that Sancho began trembling hand and foot like a child with convulsions and made up his mind then and there that he would take a couple of hundred punches before he would let his anger be awakened to the point where he would fight with this monster.

Don Quixote in the meanwhile was surveying his opponent, who had already adjusted and closed his helmet so that it was impossible to make out what he looked like. It was apparent, however, that he was not very tall and was stockily built. Over his armor he wore a coat of some kind or other made of what appeared to be the finest cloth of gold, all be-spangled with glittering mirrors that resembled little moons and that gave him a most gallant and festive air, while above his helmet were a large number of waving plumes, green, white, and yellow in color. His lance, which was leaning against a tree, was very long and stout and had a steel point of more than a palm in length. Don Quixote took all this in, and from what he observed concluded that his opponent must be of tremendous strength, but he was not for this reason filled with fear as

Sancho Panza was. Rather, he proceeded to address the Knight of the Mirrors, quite boldly and in a highbred manner.

"Sir Knight," he said, "if in your eagerness to fight you have not lost your courtesy, I would beg you to be so good as to raise your visor a little in order that I may see if your face is as handsome as your trappings."

"Whether you come out of this emprise the victor or the vanquished, Sir Knight," he of the Mirrors replied, "there will be ample time and opportunity for you to have a sight of me. If I do not now gratify your desire, it is because it seems to me that I should be doing a very great wrong to the beauteous Casildea de Vandalia by wasting the time it would take me to raise my visor before having forced you to confess that I am right in my contention, with which you are well acquainted."

"Well, then," said Don Quixote, "while we are mounting our steeds you might at least inform me if I am that knight of La Mancha whom you say you conquered."

"To that our answer," [10] said he of the Mirrors, "is that you are as like the knight I overcame as one egg is like another; but since you assert that you are persecuted by enchanters, I should not venture to state positively that you are the one in question."

"All of which," said Don Quixote, "is sufficient to convince me that you are laboring under a misapprehension; but in order to relieve you of it once and for all, let them bring our steeds, and in less time than you would spend in lifting your visor, if God, my lady, and my arm give me strength, I will see your face and you shall see that I am not the vanquished knight you take me to be."

With this, they cut short their conversation and mounted, and, turning Rocinante around, Don Quixote began measuring off the proper length of field for a run against his opponent as he of the Mirrors did the same. But the Knight of La Mancha had not gone twenty paces when he heard his adversary calling to him, whereupon each of them turned halfway and he of the Mirrors spoke.

"I must remind you, Sir Knight," he said, "of the condition under which we fight, which is that the vanquished, as I have said before, shall place himself wholly at the disposition of the victor."

"I am aware of that," replied Don Quixote, "not forgetting the provision that the behest laid upon the vanquished shall not exceed the bounds of chivalry."

"Agreed," said the Knight of the Mirrors.

At that moment Don Quixote caught sight of the other squire's weird nose and was as greatly astonished by it as Sancho had been. Indeed, he took the fellow for some monster, or some new kind of human being wholly unlike those that people this world. As he saw his master riding away down the field preparatory to the tilt, Sancho was alarmed; for he did not like to be left alone with the big-nosed individual, fearing that one powerful swipe of that protuberance against his own nose would end the battle so far as he was concerned and he would be lying stretched out on the ground, from fear if not from the force of the blow.

He accordingly ran after the knight, clinging to one of Rocinante's stirrup straps, and when he thought it was time for Don Quixote to whirl about and bear down upon his opponent, he called to him and said, "*Señor mio,* I beg your Grace, before you turn for the charge, to help me up into that cork tree yonder where I can watch the encounter which your Grace is going to have with this knight better than I can from the ground and in a way that is much more to my liking."

"I rather think, Sancho," said Don Quixote, "that what you wish to do is to mount a platform where you can see the bulls without any danger to yourself."

"The truth of the matter is," Sancho admitted, "the monstrous nose on that squire has given me such a fright that I don't dare stay near him."

"It is indeed of such a sort," his master assured him, "that if I were not the person I am, I myself should be frightened. And so, come, I will help you up."

While Don Quixote tarried to see Sancho ensconced in the cork tree, the Knight of the Mirrors measured as much ground as seemed to him necessary and then, assuming that his adversary had done the same, without waiting for sound of trumpet or any other signal, he wheeled his horse, which was no swifter nor any more impressive-looking than Rocinante, and bore down upon his enemy at a mild trot; but when he saw that the Manchegan was busy helping his squire, he reined in his mount and came to a stop midway in his course, for which his horse was extremely grateful, being no longer able to stir a single step. To Don Quixote, on the other hand, it seemed as if his enemy was flying, and digging his spurs with all his might into Rocinante's lean flanks he caused that animal to run a bit for the first and only time, according to the history, for on all other occasions a simple trot had represented his utmost speed. And so it was that, with an unheard-of fury, the Knight of the Mournful Countenance came down upon the Knight of the Mirrors as the latter sat there sinking his spurs all the way up to the buttons [11] without being able to persuade his horse to budge a single inch from the spot where he had come to a sudden standstill.

It was at this fortunate moment, while his adversary was in such a predicament, that Don Quixote fell upon him, quite unmindful of the fact that the other knight was having trouble with his mount and either was unable or did not have time to put his lance at rest. The upshot of it was, he encountered him with such force that, much against his will, the Knight of the Mirrors went rolling over his horse's flanks and tumbled to the ground, where as a result of his terrific fall he lay as if dead, without moving hand or foot.

No sooner did Sancho perceive what had happened than he slipped down from the cork tree and ran up as fast as he could to where his master was. Dismounting from Rocinante, Don Quixote now stood over the Knight of the Mirrors, and undoing the helmet straps to see if the man was dead, or to give him air in case he was alive, he beheld—who can say what he beheld without creating astonishment, wonder, and amazement in those who hear the tale? The history tells us that it was the very countenance, form, aspect, physiognomy, effigy, and image of the bachelor Sansón Carrasco!

"Come, Sancho," he cried in a loud voice, "and see what is to be seen but is not to be believed. Hasten, my son, and learn what magic can do and how great is the power of wizards and enchanters."

Sancho came, and the moment his eyes fell on the bachelor Carrasco's face he began crossing and blessing himself a countless number of times. Meanwhile, the overthrown knight gave no signs of life.

"If you ask me, master," said Sancho, "I would say that the best thing for your Grace to do is to run his sword down the mouth of this one who appears to be the bachelor Carrasco; maybe by so doing you would be killing one of your enemies, the enchanters."

"That is not a bad idea," replied Don Quixote, "for the fewer enemies the better." [12] And, drawing his sword, he was about to act upon Sancho's advice and counsel when the Knight of the Mirrors' squire came up to them, now minus the nose which had made him so ugly.

"Look well what you are doing, Don Quixote!" he cried. "The one who lies there at your feet is your Grace's friend, the bachelor Sansón Carrasco, and I am his squire."

"And where is your nose?" inquired Sancho, who was surprised to see him without that deformity.

"Here in my pocket," was the reply. And, thrusting his hand into his coat, he drew out a nose of varnished pasteboard of the make that has been described. Studying him more and more closely, Sancho finally exclaimed, in a voice that was filled with amazement, "Holy Mary preserve me! And is this not my neighbor and crony, Tomé Cecial?"

"That is who I am!" replied the de-nosed squire, "your good friend Tomé Cecial, Sancho Panza. I will tell you presently of the means and snares and falsehoods that brought me here. But, for the present, I beg and entreat your master not to lay hands on, mistreat, wound, or slay the Knight of the Mirrors whom he now has at his feet; for without any doubt it is the rash and ill-advised bachelor Sansón Carrasco, our fellow villager." [13]

The Knight of the Mirrors now recovered consciousness, and, seeing this, Don Quixote at once placed the naked point of his sword above the face of the vanquished one.

"Dead you are, knight," he said, "unless you confess that the peerless Dulcinea del Toboso is more beautiful than your Casildea de Vandalia. And what is more, you will have to promise that, should you survive this encounter and the fall you have had, you will go to the city of El Toboso and present yourself to her in my behalf, that she may do with you as she may see fit. And in case she leaves you free to follow your own will, you are to return to seek me out—the trail of my exploits will serve as a guide to bring you wherever I may be—and tell me all that has taken place between you and her. These conditions are in conformity with those that we arranged before our combat and they do not go beyond the bounds of knight-errantry."

"I confess," said the fallen knight, "that the tattered and filthy shoe of the lady Dulcinea del Toboso is of greater worth than the badly combed if clean beard of Casildea, and I promise to go to her presence and return to yours and to give you a complete and detailed account concerning anything you may wish to know."

"Another thing," added Don Quixote, "that you will have to confess and believe is that the knight you conquered was not and could not have been Don Quixote de la Mancha, but was some other that resembled him, just as I am convinced that you, though you appear to be the bachelor Sansón Carrasco, are another person in his form and likeness who has been put here by my enemies to induce me to restrain and moderate the impetuosity of my wrath and make a gentle use of my glorious victory."

"I confess, think, and feel as you feel, think, and believe," replied the lamed knight. "Permit me to rise, I beg of you, if the jolt I received in my fall will let me do so, for I am in very bad shape."

Don Quixote and Tomé Cecial the squire now helped him to his feet. As for Sancho, he could not take his eyes off Tomé but kept asking him one question after another, and although the answers he received afforded clear enough proof that the man was really his fellow townsman, the fear that had been aroused in him by his master's words—about the enchanters' having transformed the Knight of the Mirrors into the bachelor Sansón Carrasco—prevented him from believing the truth that was apparent to his eyes. The short of it is, both master and servant were left with this delusion as the other ill-errant knight and his squire, in no pleasant state of mind, took their departure with the object of looking for some village where they might be able to apply poultices and splints to the bachelor's battered ribs.

Don Quixote and Sancho then resumed their journey along the road to Saragossa, and here for the time being the history leaves them in order to give an account of who the Knight of the Mirrors and his long-nosed squire really were.

CHAPTER XV. *Wherein is told and revealed who the Knight of the Mirrors and his squire were.*

DON QUIXOTE went off very happy, self-satisfied, and vainglorious at having achieved a victory over so valiant a knight as he imagined the one of the Mirrors to be, from whose knightly word he hoped to learn whether or not the spell which had been put upon his lady was still in effect; for, unless he chose to forfeit his honor, the vanquished contender must of necessity return and give an account of what had happened in the course of his interview with her. But Don Quixote was of one mind, the Knight of the Mirrors of another,[1] for, as has been stated, the latter's only thought at the moment was to find some village where plasters were available.

The history goes on to state that when the bachelor Sansón Carrasco advised Don Quixote to resume his feats of chivalry, after having desisted from them for a while, this action was taken as the result of a conference which he had held with the curate and the barber as to the means to be adopted in persuading the knight to remain quietly at home and cease agitating himself over his unfortunate adventures. It had been Carrasco's suggestion, to which they had unanimously agreed, that they let Don Quixote sally forth, since it appeared to be impossible to prevent his doing so, and that Sansón should then take to the road as a knight-errant and pick a quarrel and do battle with him. There would be no difficulty about finding a pretext, and then the bachelor knight would overcome him (which was looked upon as easy of accomplishment), having first entered into a pact to the effect that the vanquished should remain at the mercy and bidding of his conqueror. The behest in this case was to be that the fallen one should return to his village and home and not leave it for the space of two years or until further orders were given him, it being a certainty that, once having been overcome, Don Quixote would fulfill the agreement, in order not to contravene or fail to obey the laws of chivalry. And it was possible that in the course of his seclusion he would forget his fancies, or they would at least have an opportunity to seek some suitable cure for his madness.

Sansón agreed to undertake this, and Tomé Cecial, Sancho's friend and neighbor, a merry but featherbrained chap, offered to go along as squire. Sansón then proceeded to arm himself in the manner that has been described, while Tomé disguised his nose with the aforementioned mask so that his crony would not recognize him when they met. Thus equipped, they followed the same route as Don Quixote and had almost caught up with him by the time he had the adventure with the Cart of Death. They finally overtook him in the wood, where those events occurred with which the attentive reader is already familiar; and if it had not been for the knight's extraordinary fancies, which led him to believe that the bachelor was not the bachelor, the said bachelor might have been prevented from ever attaining his degree of licentiate, as a result of having found no nests where he thought to find birds.[2]

Seeing how ill they had succeeded in their undertaking and what an end they had reached, Tomé Cecial now addressed his master.

"Surely, Señor Sansón Carrasco," he said, "we have had our deserts. It is easy enough to plan and embark upon an enterprise, but most of the time it's hard to get out of it. Don Quixote is a madman and we are sane, yet he goes away sound and laughing while your Grace is left here, battered and sorrowful. I wish you would tell me now who is the crazier: the one who is so because he cannot help it, or he who turns crazy of his own free will?"

"The difference between the two," replied Sansón, "lies in this: that the one who cannot help being crazy will be so always, whereas the one who is a madman by choice can leave off being one whenever he so desires."

"Well," said Tomé Cecial, "since that is the way it is, and since I chose to be crazy when I became your Grace's squire, by the same reasoning I now choose to stop being insane and to return to my home."

"That is your affair," said Sansón, "but to imagine that I am going back before I have given Don Quixote a good thrashing is senseless; and what will urge me on now is not any desire to see him recover his wits, but rather a thirst for vengeance; for with the terrible pain that I have in my ribs, you can't expect me to feel very charitable."

Conversing in this manner they kept on until they reached a village where it was their luck to find a bonesetter to take care of poor Sansón. Tomé Cecial then left him and returned home, while the bachelor meditated plans for revenge. The history has more to say of him in due time, but for the present it goes on to make merry with Don Quixote.

CHAPTER XVI. *Of what happened to Don Quixote upon his meeting with a prudent gentleman of La Mancha.*

WITH that feeling of happiness and vainglorious self-satisfaction that has been mentioned, Don Quixote continued on his way, imagining himself to be, as a result of the victory he had just achieved, the most valiant knight-errant of the age. Whatever adventures might befall him from then on he regarded as already accomplished and brought to a fortunate conclusion. He thought little now of enchanters and enchantments and was unmindful of the innumerable beatings he had received in the course of his knightly wanderings, of the volley of pebbles that had knocked out half his teeth, of the ungratefulness of the galley slaves and the audacity of the Yanguesans whose poles had fallen upon his body like rain. In short, he told himself, if he could but find the means, manner, or way of freeing his lady Dulcinea of the spell that had been put upon her, he would not envy the greatest good fortune that the most fortunate of knights-errant in ages past had ever by any possibility attained.

He was still wholly wrapped up in these thoughts when Sancho spoke to him.

"Isn't it strange, sir, that I can still see in front of my eyes the huge and monstrous nose of my old crony, Tomé Cecial?"

"And do you by any chance believe, Sancho, that the Knight of the Mirrors was the bachelor Sansón Carrasco and that his squire was your friend Tomé?"

"I don't know what to say to that," replied Sancho. "All I know is that the things he told me about my home, my wife and young ones, could not have come from anybody else; and the face, too, once you took the nose away, was the same as Tomé Cecial's, which I have seen many times in our village, right next door to my own house, and the tone of voice was the same also."

"Let us reason the matter out, Sancho," said Don Quixote. "Look at it this way: how can it be thought that the bachelor Sansón Carrasco would come as a knight-errant, equipped with offensive and defensive armor, to contend with me? Am I, perchance, his enemy? Have I given him any occasion to cherish a grudge against me? Am I a rival of his? Or can it be jealousy of the fame I have acquired that has led him to take up the profession of arms?"

"Well, then, sir," Sancho answered him, "how are we to explain the fact that the knight was so like the bachelor and his squire like my friend? And if this was a magic spell, as your Grace has said, was there no other pair in the world whose likeness they might have taken?"

"It is all a scheme and a plot," replied Don Quixote, "on the part of those wicked magicians who are persecuting me and who, foreseeing that I would be the victor in the combat, saw to it that the conquered knight should display the face of my friend the bachelor, so that the affection which I bear him would come between my fallen enemy and the edge of my sword and might of my arm, to temper the righteous indignation of my heart. In that way, he who had sought by falsehood and deceits to take my life, would be left to go on living. As proof of all this, Sancho, experience, which neither lies nor deceives, has already taught you how easy it is for enchanters to change one countenance into another, making the beautiful ugly and the ugly beautiful. It was not two days ago that you beheld the peerless Dulcinea's beauty and elegance in its entirety and natural form, while I saw only the repulsive features of a low and ignorant peasant girl with cataracts over her eyes and a foul smell in her mouth.[1] And if the perverse enchanter was bold enough to effect so vile a transformation as this, there is certainly no cause for wonderment at what he has done in the case of Sansón Carrasco and your friend, all by way of snatching my glorious victory out of my hands. But in spite of it all, I find consolation in the fact that, whatever the shape he may have chosen to assume, I have laid my enemy low."

"God knows what the truth of it all may be," was Sancho's comment. Knowing as he did that Dulcinea's transformation had been due to his own scheming and plotting, he was not taken in by his master's delusions. He was at a loss for a reply, however, lest he say something that would reveal his own trickery.

As they were carrying on this conversation, they were overtaken by a man who, following the same road, was coming along behind them. He was mounted on a handsome flea-bitten mare and wore a hooded great-coat of fine green cloth trimmed in tawny velvet and a cap of the same material,[2] while the trappings of his steed, which was accoutered for the field, were green and mulberry in hue, his saddle being of the *jineta* mode.[3] From his broad green and gold shoulder strap there dangled a Moorish cutlass, and his half-boots were of the same make as the baldric. His spurs were not gilded but were covered with highly polished green lacquer, so that, harmonizing as they did with the rest of his apparel, they seemed more appropriate than if they had been of purest gold. As he came up, he greeted the pair courteously and, spurring his mare, was about to ride on past when Don Quixote called to him.

"Gallant sir," he said, "if your Grace is going our way and is not in a hurry, it would be a favor to us if we might travel together."

"The truth is," replied the stranger, "I should not have ridden past you if I had not been afraid that the company of my mare would excite your horse."

"In that case, sir," Sancho spoke up, "you may as well rein in, for this horse of ours is the most virtuous and well mannered of any that there is. Never on such an occasion has he done anything that was not right—the only time he did misbehave, my master and I suffered for it aplenty. And so, I say again, your Grace may slow up if you like; for even if you offered him your mare on a couple of platters, he'd never try to mount her."

With this, the other traveler drew rein, being greatly astonished at Don Quixote's face and figure. For the knight was now riding along without his helmet, which was carried by Sancho like a piece of luggage on the back of his gray, in front of the packsaddle. If the green-clad gentleman stared hard at his new-found companion, the latter returned his gaze with an even greater intensity. He impressed Don Quixote as being a man of good judgment, around fifty years of age, with hair that was slightly graying and an aquiline nose, while the expression of his countenance was half humorous, half serious. In short, both his person and his accouterments indicated that he was an individual of some worth.

As for the man in green's impression of Don Quixote de la Mancha, he was thinking that he had never before seen any human being that resembled this one. He could not but marvel at the knight's long neck,[4] his tall frame, and the leanness and the sallowness of his face, as well as his armor and his grave bearing, the whole constituting a sight such as had not been seen for many a day in those parts. Don Quixote in turn was quite conscious of the attentiveness with which the traveler was studying him and could tell from the man's astonished look how curious he was; and so, being very courteous and fond of pleasing everyone, he proceeded to anticipate any questions that might be asked him.

"I am aware," he said, "that my appearance must strike your Grace as being very strange and out of the ordinary, and for that reason I am not surprised at your wonderment. But your Grace will cease to wonder when I tell you, as I am telling you now, that I am a knight, one of those

> *Of whom it is folks say,*
> *They to adventures go.*[5]

I have left my native heath, mortgaged my estate, given up my comfortable life, and cast myself into fortune's arms for her to do with me what she will. It has been my desire to revive a knight-errantry that is now dead, and for some time past, stumbling here and falling there, now throwing myself down headlong and then rising up once more, I have been able in good part to carry out my design by succoring widows, protecting damsels, and aiding the fallen, the orphans, and the young, all of which is the proper and natural duty of knights-errant. As a result, owing to my many valiant and Christian exploits, I have been deemed worthy of visiting in printed form nearly all the nations of the world. Thirty thousand copies of my history have been published, and, unless Heaven forbid, they will print thirty million of them.[6]

"In short, to put it all into a few words, or even one, I will tell you that I am Don Quixote de la Mancha, otherwise known as the Knight of the Mournful Countenance. Granted that self-praise is degrading, there still are times when I must praise myself, that is to say, when there is no one else present to speak in my behalf. And so, good sir, neither this steed nor this lance nor this buckler nor this squire of mine, nor all the armor that I wear and arms I carry, nor the sallowness of my complexion, nor my leanness and gauntness,[7] should any longer astonish you, now that you know who I am and what the profession is that I follow."

Having thus spoken, Don Quixote fell silent, and the man in green was so slow in replying that it seemed as if he was at a loss for words. Finally, however, after a considerable while, he brought himself to the point of speaking.

"You were correct, Sir Knight," he said, "about my astonishment and my curiosity, but you have not succeeded in removing the wonderment that the sight of you has aroused in me. You say that, knowing who you are, I should not wonder any more, but such is not the case, for I am now more amazed than ever. How can it be that there are knights-errant in the world today and that histories of them are actually printed? I find it hard to convince myself that at the present time there is anyone on earth who goes about aiding widows, protecting damsels, defending the honor of wives, and succoring orphans, and I should never have believed it had I not beheld your Grace with my own eyes. Thank Heaven for that book that your Grace tells me has been published concerning your true and exalted deeds of chivalry, as it should cast into oblivion all the innumerable stories of fictitious knights-errant with which the world is filled, greatly to the detriment of good morals and the prejudice and discredit of legitimate histories."

"As to whether the stories of knights-errant are fictitious or not," observed Don Quixote, "there is much that remains to be said."

"Why," replied the gentleman in green, "is there anyone who can doubt that such tales are false?"

"I doubt it," was the knight's answer, "but let the matter rest there. If our journey lasts long enough, I trust with God's help to be able to show your Grace that you are wrong in going along with those who hold it to be a certainty that they are not true."

From this last remark the traveler was led to suspect that Don Quixote must be some kind of crackbrain, and he was waiting for him to confirm the impression by further observations of the same sort; but before they could get off on another subject, the knight, seeing that he had given an account of his own station in life, turned to the stranger and politely inquired who his companion might be.

"I, Sir Knight of the Mournful Countenance," replied the one in the green-colored greatcoat, "am a gentleman, and a native of the village where, please God, we are going to dine today. I am more than moderately rich, and my name is Don Diego de Miranda. I spend my life with my wife and children and with my friends. My occupations are hunting and fishing, though I keep neither falcon nor hounds but only a tame partridge [8] and a bold ferret or two. I am the owner of about six dozen books, some of them in Spanish, others in Latin, including both histories and devotional works. As for books of chivalry, they have not as yet crossed the threshold of my door. My own preference is for profane rather than devotional writings, such as afford an innocent amusement, charming us by their style and arousing and holding our interest by their inventiveness, although I must say there are very few of that sort to be found in Spain.

"Sometimes," the man in green continued, "I dine with my friends and neighbors, and I often invite them to my house. My meals are wholesome and well prepared and there is always plenty to eat. I do not care for gossip, nor will I permit it in my presence. I am not lynx-eyed and do not pry into the lives and doings of others. I hear mass every day and share my substance with the poor, but make no parade of my good works lest hypocrisy and vainglory, those enemies that so imperceptibly take possession of the most modest heart, should find their way into mine. I try to make peace between those who are at strife. I am the devoted servant of Our Lady, and my trust is in the infinite mercy of God Our Savior."

Sancho had listened most attentively to the gentleman's account of his mode of life, and inasmuch as it seemed to him that this was a good and holy way to live and that the one who followed such a pattern ought to be able to work miracles, he now jumped down from his gray's back and, running over to seize the stranger's right stirrup, began kissing the feet of the man in green with a show of devotion that bordered on tears.

"Why are you doing that, brother?" the gentleman asked him. "What is the meaning of these kisses?"

"Let me kiss your feet," Sancho insisted, "for if I am not mistaken, your Grace is the first saint riding *jineta* fashion [9] that I have seen in all the days of my life."

"I am not a saint," the gentleman assured him, "but a great sinner. It is you, brother, who are the saint; for you must be a good man, judging by the simplicity of heart that you show."

Sancho then went back to his packsaddle, having evoked a laugh from the depths of his master's melancholy and given Don Diego fresh cause for astonishment.

Don Quixote thereupon inquired of the newcomer how many children he had, remarking as he did so that the ancient philosophers, who were without a true knowledge of God, believed that mankind's greatest good lay in the gifts of nature, in those of fortune, and in having many friends and many and worthy sons.

"I, Señor Don Quixote," replied the gentleman, "have a son without whom I should, perhaps, be happier than I am. It is not that he is bad, but rather that he is not as good as I should like him to be. He is eighteen years old, and for six of those years he has been at Salamanca studying the Greek and Latin languages. When I desired him to pass on to other branches of learning, I found him so immersed in the science of Poetry (if it can be called such) that it was not possible to interest him in the Law, which I wanted him to study, nor in Theology, the queen of them all. My wish was that he might be an honor to his family; for in this age in which we are living our monarchs are in the habit of highly rewarding those forms of learning that are good and virtuous, since learning without virtue is like pearls on a dunghill. But he spends the whole day trying to decide whether such and such a verse of Homer's *Iliad* is well conceived or not, whether or not Martial is immodest in a certain epigram, whether certain lines of Vergil are to be understood in this way or in that. In short, he spends all his time with the books written by those poets whom I have mentioned and with those of Horace, Persius, Juvenal, and Tibullus. As for our own moderns,[10] he sets little store by them, and yet, for all his disdain of Spanish poetry, he is at this moment racking his brains in an effort to compose a gloss on a quatrain that was sent him from Salamanca and which, I fancy, is for some literary tournament." [11]

To all this Don Quixote made the following answer:

"Children, sir, are out of their parents' bowels and so are to be loved whether they be good or bad, just as we love those that gave us life. It is for parents to bring up their offspring, from the time they are infants, in the paths of virtue, good breeding, proper conduct, and Christian morality, in order that, when they are grown, they may be a staff to the old age of the ones that bore them and an honor to their own posterity. As to compelling them to study a particular branch of learning, I am not so sure as to that, though there may be no harm in trying to persuade them to do so. But where there is no need to study *pane lucrando*—where Heaven has provided them with parents that can supply their daily bread —I should be in favor of permitting them to follow that course to which they are most inclined; and although poetry may be more pleasurable than useful, it is not one of those pursuits that bring dishonor upon those who engage in them.

"Poetry in my opinion, my dear sir," he went on, "is a young and tender maid of surpassing beauty, who has many other damsels (that is to say, the other disciplines) whose duty it is to bedeck, embellish, and adorn her. She may call upon all of them for service, and all of them in turn depend upon her nod. She is not one to be rudely handled, nor dragged through the streets, nor exposed at street corners, in the market place, or in the private nooks of palaces. She is fashioned through an alchemy of such power that he who knows how to make use of it will be able to convert her into the purest gold of inestimable price. Possessing her, he must keep her within bounds and not permit her to run wild in bawdy satires or soulless sonnets. She is not to be put up for sale in any manner, unless it be in the form of heroic poems, pity-inspiring tragedies, or pleasing and ingenious comedies. Let mountebanks keep hands off her, and the ignorant mob as well, which is incapable of recognizing or appreciating the treasures that are locked within her. And do not think, sir, that I apply that term 'mob' solely to plebeians and those of low estate; for anyone who is ignorant, whether he be lord or prince, may, and should, be included in the vulgar herd.

"But," Don Quixote continued, "he who possesses the gift of poetry and who makes the use of it that I have indicated, shall become famous and his name shall be honored among all the civilized nations of the world. You have stated, sir, that your son does not greatly care for poetry written in our Spanish tongue, and in that I am inclined to think he is somewhat mistaken. My reason for saying so is this: the great Homer did not write in Latin, for the reason that he was a Greek, and Vergil did not write in Greek since he was a Latin. In a word, all the poets of antiquity wrote in the language which they had imbibed with their mother's milk and did not go searching after foreign ones to express their loftiest conceptions. This being so, it would be well if the same custom were to be adopted by all nations, the German poet being no longer looked down upon because he writes in German, nor the Castilian or the Basque for employing his native speech.

"As for your son, I fancy, sir, that his quarrel is not so much with Spanish poetry as with those poets who have no other tongue or discipline at their command such as would help to awaken their natural gift; and yet, here, too, he may be wrong. There is an opinion, and a true one, to the effect that 'the poet is born,'[12] that is to say, it is as a poet that he comes forth from his mother's womb, and with the propensity that has been bestowed upon him by Heaven, without study or artifice, he produces those compositions that attest the truth of the line: '*Est deus in nobis*,' etc.[13] I further maintain that the born poet who is aided by art will have a great advantage over the one who by art alone would become a poet, the reason being that art does not go beyond, but merely perfects, nature; and so it is that, by combining nature with art and art with nature, the finished poet is produced.

"In conclusion, then, my dear sir, my advice to you would be to let your son go where his star beckons him; for being a good student as he must be, and having already successfully mounted the first step on the stairway of learning, which is that of languages, he will be able to continue of his own accord to the very peak of humane letters, an accomplishment that is altogether becoming in a gentleman, one that adorns, honors, and distinguishes him as much as the miter does the bishop or his flowing robe the learned jurisconsult. Your Grace well may reprove your son, should he compose satires that reflect upon the honor of other persons; in that case, punish him and tear them up. But should he compose discourses in the manner of Horace, in which he reprehends vice in general as that poet so elegantly does, then praise him by all means; for it is permitted the poet to write verses in which he inveighs against envy and the other vices as well, and to lash out at the vicious without, however, designating any particular individual. On the other hand, there are poets who for the sake of uttering something malicious would run the risk of being banished to the shores of Pontus.[14]

"If the poet be chaste where his own manners are concerned, he will likewise be modest in his verses, for the pen is the tongue of the mind, and whatever thoughts are engendered there are bound to appear in his writings. When kings and princes behold the marvelous art of poetry as practiced by prudent, virtuous, and serious-minded subjects of their realm, they honor, esteem, and reward those persons and crown them with the leaves of the tree that is never struck by lightning [15]—as if to show that those who are crowned and adorned with such wreaths are not to be assailed by anyone."

The gentleman in the green-colored greatcoat was vastly astonished by this speech of Don Quixote's and was rapidly altering the opinion he had previously held, to the effect that his companion was but a crackbrain. In the middle of the long discourse, which was not greatly to his liking, Sancho had left the highway to go seek a little milk from some shepherds who were draining the udders of their ewes near by. Extremely well pleased with the knight's sound sense and excellent reasoning, the gentleman was about to resume the conversation when, raising his head, Don Quixote caught sight of a cart flying royal flags that was coming toward them down the road and, thinking it must be a fresh adventure, began calling to Sancho in a loud voice to bring him his helmet. Whereupon Sancho hastily left the shepherds and spurred his gray until he was once more alongside his master, who was now about to encounter a dreadful and bewildering ordeal.

CHAPTER XVII. *Wherein Don Quixote's unimaginable courage reaches its highest point, together with the adventure of the lions and its happy ending.*

THE history relates that, when Don Quixote called to Sancho to bring him his helmet,[1] the squire was busy buying some curds from the shepherds and, flustered by his master's great haste, did not know what to do with them or how to carry them. Having already paid for the curds, he did not care to lose them, and so he decided to put them into the headpiece, and, acting upon this happy inspiration, he returned to see what was wanted of him.

"Give me that helmet," said the knight; "for either I know little about adventures or here is one where I am going to need my armor."

Upon hearing this, the gentleman in the green-colored greatcoat looked around in all directions but could see nothing except the cart that was approaching them, decked out with two or three flags which indicated that the vehicle in question must be conveying his Majesty's property. He remarked as much to Don Quixote, but the latter paid no attention, for he was always convinced that whatever happened to him meant adventures and more adventures.

"Forewarned is forearmed," [2] he said. "I lose nothing by being prepared, knowing as I do that I have enemies both visible and invisible and cannot tell when or where or in what form they will attack me."

Turning to Sancho, he asked for his helmet again, and as there was no time to shake out the curds, the squire had to hand it to him as it was. Don Quixote took it and, without noticing what was in it, hastily clapped it on his head; and forthwith, as a result of the pressure on the curds, the whey began running down all over his face and beard, at which he was very much startled.

"What is this, Sancho?" he cried. "I think my head must be softening or my brains melting, or else I am sweating from head to foot. If sweat it be, I assure you it is not from fear, though I can well believe that the adventure which now awaits me is a terrible one indeed. Give me something with which to wipe my face, if you have anything, for this perspiration is so abundant that it blinds me."

Sancho said nothing but gave him a cloth and at the same time gave thanks to God that his master had not discovered what the trouble was. Don Quixote wiped his face and then took off his helmet to see what it was that made his head feel so cool. Catching sight of that watery white mass, he lifted it to his nose and smelled it.

"By the life of my lady Dulcinea del Toboso!" he exclaimed. "Those are curds that you have put there, you treacherous, brazen, ill-mannered squire!"

To this Sancho replied, very calmly and with a straight face, "If they are curds, give them to me, your Grace, so that I can eat them. But no, let the devil eat them, for he must be the one who did it. Do you think I would be so bold as to soil your Grace's helmet? Upon my word, master, by the understanding that God has given me, I, too, must have enchanters who are persecuting me as your Grace's creature and one of his members, and they are the ones who put that filthy mess there to make you lose your patience and your temper and cause you to whack my ribs as you are in the habit of doing. Well, this time, I must say, they have missed the mark; for I trust my master's good sense to tell him that I have neither curds nor milk nor anything of the kind, and if I did have, I'd put it in my stomach and not in that helmet."

"That may very well be," said Don Quixote.

Don Diego was observing all this and was more astonished than ever, especially when, after he had wiped his head, face, beard, and helmet, Don Quixote once more donned the piece of armor and, settling himself in the stirrups, proceeded to adjust his sword and fix his lance.

"Come what may, here I stand, ready to take on Satan himself in person!" shouted the knight.

The cart with the flags had come up to them by this time, accompanied only by a driver riding one of the mules and a man seated up in front.

"Where are you going, brothers?" Don Quixote called out as he placed himself in the path of the cart. "What conveyance is this, what do you carry in it, and what is the meaning of those flags?"

"The cart is mine," replied the driver, "and in it are two fierce lions in cages which the governor of Oran is sending to court as a present for his Majesty. The flags are those of our lord the King, as a sign that his property goes here." [3]

"And are the lions large?" inquired Don Quixote.

It was the man sitting at the door of the cage who answered him. "The largest," he said, "that ever were sent from Africa to Spain. I am the lionkeeper and I have brought back others, but never any like these. They are male and female. The male is in this first cage, the female in the one behind. They are hungry right now, for they have had nothing to eat today; and so we'd be obliged if your Grace would get out of the way, for we must hasten on to the place where we are to feed them."

"Lion whelps against me?" said Don Quixote with a slight smile. "Lion whelps against me? And at such an hour? Then, by God, those gentlemen who sent them shall see whether I am the man to be frightened by lions. Get down, my good fellow, and since you are the lionkeeper, open the cages and turn those beasts out for me; and in the middle of this plain I will teach them who Don Quixote de la Mancha is, notwithstanding and in spite of the enchanters who are responsible for their being here."

"So," said the gentleman to himself as he heard this, "our worthy knight has revealed himself. It must indeed be true that the curds have softened his skull and mellowed his brains."

At this point Sancho approached him. "For God's sake, sir," he said, "do something to keep my master from fighting those lions. For if he does, they're going to tear us all to bits."

"Is your master, then, so insane," the gentleman asked, "that you fear and believe he means to tackle those fierce animals?"

"It is not that he is insane," replied Sancho, "but, rather, foolhardy."

"Very well," said the gentleman, "I will put a stop to it." And going up to Don Quixote, who was still urging the lionkeeper to open the cages, he said, "Sir Knight, knights-errant should undertake only those adventures that afford some hope of a successful outcome, not those that are utterly hopeless to begin with; for valor when it turns to temerity has in it more of madness than of bravery. Moreover, these lions have no thought of attacking your Grace but are a present to his Majesty, and it would not be well to detain them or interfere with their journey."

"My dear sir," answered Don Quixote, "you had best go mind your tame partridge and that bold ferret of yours and let each one attend to his own business. This is my affair, and I know whether these gentlemen, the lions, have come to attack me or not." He then turned to the lion-keeper. "I swear, Sir Rascal, if you do not open those cages at once, I'll pin you to the cart with this lance!"

Perceiving how determined the armed phantom was, the driver now spoke up. "Good sir," he said, "will your Grace please be so kind as to let me unhitch the mules and take them to a safe place before you turn those lions loose? For if they kill them for me, I am ruined for life, since the mules and cart are all the property I own."

"O man of little faith!" said Don Quixote. "Get down and unhitch your mules if you like, but you will soon see that it was quite unnecessary and that you might have spared yourself the trouble."

The driver did so, in great haste, as the lionkeeper began shouting, "I want you all to witness that I am being compelled against my will to open the cages and turn the lions out, and I further warn this gentleman that he will be responsible for all the harm and damage the beasts may do, plus my wages and my fees. You other gentlemen take cover before I open the doors; I am sure they will not do any harm to me."

Once more Don Diego sought to persuade his companion not to commit such an act of madness, as it was tempting God to undertake anything so foolish as that; but Don Quixote's only answer was that he knew what he was doing. And when the gentleman in green insisted that he was sure the knight was laboring under a delusion and ought to consider the matter well, the latter cut him short.

"Well, then, sir," he said, "if your Grace does not care to be a spectator at what you believe is going to turn out to be a tragedy, all you have to do is to spur your flea-bitten mare and seek safety."

Hearing this, Sancho with tears in his eyes again begged him to give up the undertaking, in comparison with which the adventure of the windmills and the dreadful one at the fulling mills—indeed, all the exploits his master had ever in the course of his life undertaken—were but bread and cakes.

"Look, sir," Sancho went on, "there is no enchantment here nor anything of the sort. Through the bars and chinks of that cage I have seen a real lion's claw, and judging by the size of it, the lion that it belongs to is bigger than a mountain."

"Fear, at any rate," said Don Quixote, "will make him look bigger to you than half the world. Retire, Sancho, and leave me, and if I die here, you know our ancient pact: you are to repair to Dulcinea—I say no more."

To this he added other remarks that took away any hope they had that he might not go through with his insane plan. The gentleman in the green-colored greatcoat was of a mind to resist him but saw that he was no match for the knight in the matter of arms. Then, too, it did not seem to him the part of wisdom to fight it out with a madman; for Don Quixote now impressed him as being quite mad in every way. Accordingly, while the knight was repeating his threats to the lionkeeper, Don Diego spurred his mare, Sancho his gray, and the driver his mules, all of them seeking to put as great a distance as possible between themselves and the cart before the lions broke loose.

Sancho already was bewailing his master's death, which he was convinced was bound to come from the lions' claws, and at the same time he cursed his fate and called it an unlucky hour in which he had taken it into his head to serve such a one. But despite his tears and lamentations, he did not leave off thrashing his gray in an effort to leave the cart behind them. When the lionkeeper saw that those who had fled were a good distance away, he once more entreated and warned Don Quixote as he had warned and entreated him before, but the answer he received was that he might save his breath as it would do him no good and he had best hurry and obey. In the space of time that it took the keeper to open the first cage, Don Quixote considered the question as to whether it would be well to give battle on foot or on horseback. He finally decided that he would do better on foot, as he feared that Rocinante would become frightened at sight of the lions; and so, leaping down from his horse, he fixed his lance, braced his buckler, and drew his sword, and then advanced with marvelous daring and great resoluteness until he stood directly in front of the cart, meanwhile commending himself to God with all his heart and then to his lady Dulcinea.

Upon reaching this point, the reader should know, the author of our veracious history indulges in the following exclamatory passage:

"O great-souled Don Quixote de la Mancha, thou whose courage is beyond all praise, mirror wherein all the valiant of the world may behold themselves, a new and second Don Manuel de León,[4] once the glory and the honor of Spanish knighthood! With what words shall I relate thy terrifying exploit, how render it credible to the ages that are to come? What eulogies do not belong to thee of right, even though they consist of hyperbole piled upon hyperbole? On foot and singlehanded, intrepid and with greathearted valor, armed but with a sword, and not one of the keen-edged Little Dog make,[5] and with a shield that was not of gleaming and polished steel, thou didst stand and wait for the two fiercest lions that ever the African forests bred! Thy deeds shall be thy praise, O valorous Manchegan; I leave them to speak for thee, since words fail me with which to extol them."

Here the author leaves off his exclamations and resumes the thread of the story.

Seeing Don Quixote posed there before him and perceiving that, unless he wished to incur the bold knight's indignation there was nothing for him to do but release the male lion, the keeper now opened the first cage, and it could be seen at once how extraordinarily big and horribly ugly the beast was. The first thing the recumbent animal did was to turn round, put out a claw, and stretch himself all over. Then he opened his mouth and yawned very slowly, after which he put out a tongue that was nearly two palms in length and with it licked the dust out of his eyes and washed his face. Having done this, he stuck his head outside the cage and gazed about him in all directions. His eyes were now like live coals and his appearance and demeanor were such as to strike terror in temerity itself. But Don Quixote merely stared at him attentively, waiting for him to descend from the cart so that they could come to grips, for the knight was determined to hack the brute to pieces, such was the extent of his unheard-of madness.

The lion, however, proved to be courteous rather than arrogant and was in no mood for childish bravado. After having gazed first in one direction and then in another, as has been said, he turned his back and presented his hind parts to Don Quixote and then very calmly and peaceably lay down and stretched himself out once more in his cage. At this, Don Quixote ordered the keeper to stir him up with a stick in order to irritate him and drive him out.

"That I will not do," the keeper replied, "for if I stir him, I will be the first one he will tear to bits. Be satisfied with what you have already accomplished, Sir Knight, which leaves nothing more to be said on the score of valor, and do not go tempting your fortune a second time. The door was open and the lion could have gone out if he had chosen; since he has not done so up to now, that means he will stay where he is all day long. Your Grace's stoutheartedness has been well established; for no brave fighter, as I see it, is obliged to do more than challenge his enemy and wait for him in the field; his adversary, if he does not come, is the one who is disgraced and the one who awaits him gains the crown of victory."

"That is the truth," said Don Quixote. "Shut the door, my friend, and bear me witness as best you can with regard to what you have seen me do here. I would have you certify: that you opened the door for the lion, that I waited for him and he did not come out, that I continued to wait and still he stayed there, and finally went back and lay down. I am under no further obligation. Away with enchantments, and God uphold the right, the truth, and true chivalry! So close the door, as I have told you, while I signal to the fugitives in order that they who were not present may hear of this exploit from your lips." [6]

The keeper did as he was commanded, and Don Quixote, taking the cloth with which he had dried his face after the rain of curds, fastened it to the point of his lance and began summoning the runaways, who, all in a body with the gentleman in green bringing up the rear,[7] were still fleeing and turning around to look back at every step. Sancho was the first to see the white cloth.

"May they slay me," he said, "if my master hasn't conquered those fierce beasts, for he's calling to us."

They all stopped and made sure that the one who was doing the signaling was indeed Don Quixote, and then, losing some of their fear, they little by little made their way back to a point where they could distinctly hear what the knight was saying. At last they returned to the cart, and as they drew near Don Quixote spoke to the driver.

"You may come back, brother, hitch your mules, and continue your journey. And you, Sancho, may give each of them two gold crowns to recompense them for the delay they have suffered on my account."

"That I will, right enough," said Sancho. "But what has become of the lions? Are they dead or alive?"

The keeper thereupon, in leisurely fashion and in full detail, proceeded to tell them how the encounter had ended, taking pains to stress to the best of his ability the valor displayed by Don Quixote, at sight of whom the lion had been so cowed that he was unwilling to leave his cage, though the door had been left open quite a while. The fellow went on to state that the knight had wanted him to stir the lion up and force him out, but had finally been convinced that this would be tempting God and so, much to his displeasure and against his will, had permitted the door to be closed.

"What do you think of that, Sancho?" asked Don Quixote. "Are there any spells that can withstand true gallantry? The enchanters may take my luck away, but to deprive me of my strength and courage is an impossibility."

Sancho then bestowed the crowns, the driver hitched his mules, and the lionkeeper kissed Don Quixote's hands for the favor received, promising that, when he reached the court, he would relate this brave exploit to the king himself.

"In that case," replied Don Quixote, "if his Majesty by any chance should inquire who it was that performed it, you are to say that it was the Knight of the Lions; for that is the name by which I wish to be known from now on, thus changing, exchanging, altering, and converting the one I have previously borne, that of Knight of the Mournful Countenance; in which respect I am but following the old custom of knights-errant, who changed their names whenever they liked or found it convenient to do so." [8]

With this, the cart continued on its way, and Don Quixote, Sancho, and the gentleman in the green-colored greatcoat likewise resumed their journey. During all this time Don Diego de Miranda had not uttered a word but was wholly taken up with observing what Don Quixote did and listening to what he had to say. The knight impressed him as being a crazy sane man and an insane one on the verge of sanity. The gentleman did not happen to be familiar with the first part of our history, but if he had read it he would have ceased to wonder at such talk and conduct, for he would then have known what kind of madness this was. Remaining as he did in ignorance of his companion's malady, he took him now for a sensible individual and now for a madman, since what Don Quixote said was coherent, elegantly phrased, and to the point, whereas his actions were nonsensical, foolhardy, and downright silly. What greater madness could there be, Don Diego asked himself, than to don a helmet filled with curds and then persuade oneself that enchanters were softening one's cranium? What could be more rashly absurd than to wish to fight lions by sheer strength alone? He was roused from these thoughts, this inward soliloquy, by the sound of Don Quixote's voice.

"Undoubtedly, Señor Don Diego de Miranda, your Grace must take me for a fool and a madman, am I not right? And it would be small wonder if such were the case, seeing that my deeds give evidence of nothing else. But, nevertheless, I would advise your Grace that I am neither so mad nor so lacking in wit as I must appear to you to be. A gaily caparisoned knight giving a fortunate lance thrust to a fierce bull in the middle of a great square makes a pleasing appearance in the eyes of his king. The same is true of a knight clad in shining armor as he paces the lists in front of the ladies in some joyous tournament. It is true of all those knights who, by means of military exercises or what appear to be such, divert and entertain and, if one may say so, honor the courts of princes. But the best showing of all is made by a knight-errant who, traversing deserts and solitudes, crossroads, forests, and mountains, goes seeking dangerous adventures with the intention of bringing them to a happy and successful conclusion, and solely for the purpose of winning a glorious and enduring renown.

"More impressive, I repeat, is the knight-errant succoring a widow in some unpopulated place than a courtly man of arms making love to a damsel in the city. All knights have their special callings: let the courtier wait upon the ladies and lend luster by his liveries to his sovereign's palace; let him nourish impoverished gentlemen with the splendid fare of his table; let him give tourneys and show himself truly great, generous, and magnificent and a good Christian above all, thus fulfilling his particular obligations. But the knight-errant's case is different.

"Let the latter seek out the nooks and corners of the world; let him enter into the most intricate of labyrinths; let him attempt the impossible at every step; let him endure on desolate highlands the burning rays of the midsummer sun and in winter the harsh inclemencies of wind and frost; let no lions inspire him with fear, no monsters frighten him, no dragons terrify him, for to seek them out, attack them, and conquer them all is his chief and legitimate occupation. Accordingly, I whose lot it is to be numbered among the knights-errant cannot fail to attempt anything that appears to me to fall within the scope of my duties, just as I attacked those lions a while ago even though I knew it to be an exceedingly rash thing to do, for that was a matter that directly concerned me.

"For I well know the meaning of valor: namely, a virtue that lies between the two extremes of cowardice on the one hand and temerity on the other. It is, nonetheless, better for the brave man to carry his bravery to the point of rashness than for him to sink into cowardice. Even as it is easier for the prodigal to become a generous man than it is for the miser, so is it easier for the foolhardy to become truly brave than it is for the coward to attain valor. And in this matter of adventures, you may believe me, Señor Don Diego, it is better to lose by a card too many than a card too few,[9] and 'Such and such a knight is temerarious and overbold' sounds better to the ear than 'That knight is timid and a coward.' "

"I must assure you, Señor Don Quixote," replied Don Diego, "that everything your Grace has said and done will stand the test of reason; and it is my opinion that if the laws and ordinances of knight-errantry were to be lost, they would be found again in your Grace's bosom, which is their depository and storehouse. But it is growing late; let us hasten to my village and my home, where your Grace shall rest from your recent exertions; for if the body is not tired the spirit may be, and that sometimes results in bodily fatigue."

"I accept your offer as a great favor and an honor, Señor Don Diego," was the knight's reply. And, by spurring their mounts more than they had up to then, they arrived at the village around two in the afternoon and came to the house that was occupied by Don Diego, whom Don Quixote had dubbed the Knight of the Green-colored Greatcoat.

CHAPTER XVIII. *Of what happened to Don Quixote in the castle or house of the Knight of the Green-colored Greatcoat, along with other extraordinary things.*

DON QUIXOTE found Don Diego de Miranda's house to be a rambling one of the village type, with the gentleman's coat of arms in rough-hewn stone over the street door and with the storehouse in the patio and the cellar under the entryway. In the cellar were many wine jars, which, by reason of the fact that they came from El Toboso, served to revive the knight's memories of his enchanted and transformed Dulcinea; and without regard to what he was saying or the others present, he exclaimed:

> "*O treasures sweet, now saddening to the sight,*
> *Ye once were pleasing when God willed it so.*[1]

O ye Tobosan jars that have brought to mind my sweetest treasure and my greatest grief!"

Among those who heard this was the student poet, Don Diego's son, who with his mother had come out to welcome the guest. Both mother and son were astonished at the knight's strange appearance as he dismounted from Rocinante and, with a great show of courtesy, asked to kiss the lady's hands.

"Señora," said Don Diego, "I would have you receive with your customary kindness Señor Don Quixote de la Mancha, who stands before you here, a knight-errant and the bravest and wisest that there is in all the world."

The lady, whose name was Doña Cristina, was most courteous and affable in her greetings, and Don Quixote at once, with many polite and suitable protestations of regard, put himself at her service. Practically the same exchange of courtesies occurred between Don Quixote and the student, who, upon hearing the knight speak, took him for a sensible and sharp-witted person.

Here, the author goes on to give a minute description of Don Diego's house, describing everything which such an abode, that of a rich gentleman farmer, might be expected to contain. But the translator of the history appears to have passed over these and other similar details in silence, since they did not fit in with the chief purpose of the chronicle, the value of which lies in its truthfulness rather than in wearisome digressions.

They conducted Don Quixote into one of the rooms, and there Sancho proceeded to remove his master's armor, leaving him in his Walloon breeches and chamois-skin doublet, which was all stained with rust. He wore a falling-band collar after the student fashion, without starch or lace, his half-boots [2] were date-colored and his shoes waxed.[3] His trusty sword hung from a shoulder strap made of sea-wolf's hide, for it is said that he had suffered for many years from a kidney ailment.[4] He then donned a cloak of good gray cloth, but not before he had doused his head and face with five or six buckets of water (there is some difference of opinion as to the exact number)—yet the water still remained whey-colored, thanks to Sancho's greediness in purchasing those damnable curds that had made his master's face so white.[5]

Attired in the manner described and with a gallant and sprightly air, Don Quixote now entered another room, where the student was waiting to entertain him while the table was being laid; for Doña Cristina wished to show that she possessed the means and the ability to set a proper board for those who came to her house, and especially so distinguished a guest as this one. While Don Quixote was taking off his armor, Don Lorenzo (for that was the name of Don Diego's son) had put a question to his father.

"Sir," he had asked, "what are we to make of this gentleman whom you have brought home with you? My mother and I are quite astonished by his name, his appearance, and his calling himself a knight-errant."

"I do not know what to say in answer to that, my son," Don Diego replied. "I can only tell you that I have seen him do things that lead one to believe he is the greatest madman in the world, yet his conversation is so sensible that it belies and causes one to forget his actions. But speak to him yourself and sound him out.[6] You are a discerning young man; form your own opinion, then, as to how wise or foolish he may be; although, to tell you the truth, I am inclined to regard him as insane rather than sane."

Don Lorenzo had then gone in to converse with Don Quixote, as we have said, and in the course of their talk the knight remarked to him, "Your Grace's father, Señor Don Diego de Miranda, has told me of your rare ability and intellectual capacity, and, what interests me most of all, has informed me that you are a great poet."

"A poet I may be," replied Don Lorenzo, "but by no means a great one. The truth is, I am rather fond of poetry and of reading the good poets, but I do not deserve the title which my father has given me."

"I like your humility," said Don Quixote, "for there is no poet who is not arrogant and who does not think he is the greatest there is."

"There is no rule without an exception," Don Lorenzo reminded him. "There may be some who are poets without knowing it."

"Very few," was Don Quixote's answer. "But tell me, what are those verses that your Grace is working on at the present time, and which, according to your father, have rendered you rather restless and distracted? If it is a matter of glosses, I know something about that sort of thing and should enjoy hearing them. If by chance they are for some literary tournament, your Grace should strive to carry off the second prize, for the first is always awarded as a favor to someone of high rank, the second goes to the one who merits first place, and thus the third is in reality second, while the first, by this reckoning, would be third, after the manner of the licentiate degrees that are conferred in the universities. But for all of that, the first prize carries with it a great distinction." [7]

"Up to now," Don Lorenzo thought to himself, "I cannot take you for a madman; but let's go on." And, speaking aloud, he said, "It would appear that your Grace has attended the schools; what branches have you studied?"

"Knight-errantry," said Don Quixote, "which is the equal of poetry and even a fraction of an inch or so above it."

"That," said the young man, "is a branch of learning with which I am unfamiliar. This is the first time I have heard of it."

"It is a discipline," the knight went on to explain, "that comprises within itself all or most of the others in existence. For the one who professes it has to be skilled in jurisprudence; he must be versed in the laws of justice and equity in order to be able to give each that which is his by right. He must be a theologian in order that, whenever it is asked of him, he may give a clear and logical reason for his Christian faith. He must be a physician, and above all a herbalist, so that when he finds himself in a desert or some desolate spot he will know what plants possess the property of healing wounds, for a knight-errant cannot be looking at every step for someone to treat his injuries. He must be an astronomer in order that he may know from the stars how far the night has advanced, what part of the world he is in, and in what clime. He must have a knowledge of mathematics, for he will have need of it at every turn.

"But," continued Don Quixote, "leaving aside the fact that he should be adorned with all the theological and cardinal virtues, and coming down to details, I would say that he must be able to swim like Nicolao the Fish, as the story has it.[8] He must know how to shoe a horse and repair his saddle and his bridle. And to return to higher matters, he must keep faith with God and with his lady. He must be chaste in his thoughts, decorous in words, and must show himself generous in good works, valiant in his deeds, long-suffering under hardships, charitable toward the needy. And, lastly, he must uphold the truth though it cost him his life to defend it.

"All these qualities, great and small," he concluded, "go to make up a good knight-errant. Judge, then, Señor Don Lorenzo, as to whether this be a contemptible science which the knight-errant has to study, learn, and practice, or whether it may not rather be compared to the most elevated branches that are taught in the schools."

"If that is so," replied Don Lorenzo, "I would say that this science excels all the others."

"If what is so?" inquired Don Quixote.

"What I mean," Don Lorenzo continued, "is that I doubt that there have been or are today any knights-errant, and adorned with all those virtues."

"What I am about to say now," remarked Don Quixote, "I have said many times before. The majority of people in this world are of the opinion that knights-errant never existed; and it is my belief that if Heaven does not miraculously reveal the truth to them, by showing them that there once were such knights and that they are still to be met with today, then all one's labors are in vain, as experience has many times taught me. I do not care to take the time here to disabuse your Grace of this error which you share with so many others. Rather, I mean to pray Heaven to deliver you from it and to make clear to you how profitable and necessary to the world knights-errant have been in ages past, and how useful they would be at the present time if the custom were still maintained. But today, owing to the state of sin in which we live, idleness and sloth, gluttony and luxury, rule triumphant."

"Now our guest is breaking out on us," thought Don Lorenzo; "but all the same, he is a most unusual kind of madman, and I'd be a dull-witted fool myself if I did not admit it."

At this point they were called to dinner and their conversation came to an end. Don Diego took occasion to ask his son what he had made out regarding their guest's state of mind.

"His madness," replied the young man, "is a scrawl, and all the doctors and clever scribes in the world would not be able to decipher it. He is a streaked madman, full of lucid intervals."

They then sat down at the table, and the meal fully bore out what Diego had said upon the highway concerning his manner of entertaining those whom he invited to his home. It was well served, abundant, and appetizing; but what pleased Don Quixote more than anything else was the marvelous silence that prevailed throughout the house, a silence which was like that of a Carthusian monastery. When the cloth had finally been removed and grace had been said and they had washed their hands, Don Quixote earnestly requested Don Lorenzo to recite the verses that were intended for the literary tournament. To this the youth replied that, inasmuch as he did not wish to appear to be one of those poets who when asked to read their verses refuse to do so but who vomit them forth when they are not asked,[9] he would consent.

"I will let you hear my gloss," he said; "but I do not expect it to win any prize, for I composed it solely to exercise my ingenuity."

"A friend of mine," observed Don Quixote, "a man of intelligence, is of the opinion that the writing of poetic glosses is a waste of energy, and the reason he gave me was this: that the gloss almost never can come up to the text but very often or most of the time goes beyond the meaning and intention of the original lines. And, moreover, he added, the rules governing this form of composition are too strict; they do not permit of interrogations or any 'said he' or 'I will say'; they do not allow verbs to be turned into nouns or the general sense and construction of the passage to be altered, along with other restrictions by which those who write glosses are bound, as your Grace must know."

"Really, Señor Don Quixote," said Don Lorenzo, "I wish I could trip your Grace up now and then, but I cannot, for you slip through my fingers like an eel."

"I do not understand," said Don Quixote, "what your Grace means by that."

"I will explain myself later," replied the young man, "but for the present I would have your Grace listen attentively to the original verses and the gloss.[10] They run like this:

> Oh, could my 'was' an 'is' become,
> I'd wait no more for 'it shall be';
> or could I the future now but see,
> and not this present, dour and glum.

GLOSS

> All things must pass away at last,
> and so, the blessing that was mine,
> fair Fortune's gift, it also pass'd,
> ne'er to return, though I repine;
> my skies are wholly overcast.
> Long hast thou seen me at thy feet,
> O Fortune fickle, Fortune fleet;
> but make me happy once again
> and I'd forget my present pain,
> could but my 'was' and 'is' now meet.

> No other pleasure do I crave,
> no other palm or warrior's prize,
> such triumph as befits the brave;
> all that I ask: those happier skies
> to which my memory is a slave.
> Would'st thou but give this gift to me,
> O Fortune, then perchance I'd see
> this fire of mine—O priceless boon!—
> consume me less, and if 'twere soon,
> I'd wait no more for 'it shall be.'

> Impossible the thing I ask,
> since Time, once gone, none can recall;
> for to accomplish such a task,
> no power on earth but is too small.

No more beneath those skies I'll bask.
Swift doth he come and swiftly flee,
nor doth return, light-footed he!
and well I know it is not right
to seek to stay Time in his flight;
turn past to present—futile plea!

My life is anxious, filled with gloom;
and living thus 'twixt hope and fear,
is naught but death's familiar doom;
better to lie upon my bier
and seek the door to pain's dark room.
It seemeth me, it would be sweet
to end it now, thus life to cheat;
but living long and living longer,
the fear within grows ever stronger
of that dread 'shall be' I must greet."

As Don Lorenzo finished reading his gloss, Don Quixote rose to his feet and seized the young man's right hand. Raising his voice until he was almost shouting, he said, "By the highest heavens, O noble youth, you are the best poet on the face of the earth and ought to be crowned with laurel, not by Cyprus or by Gaeta, as a certain rhymester—Heaven forgive him!—said,[11] but by the Academies of Athens, if they were still in existence, and by those that now flourish at Paris, Bologna, and Salamanca. If the judges rob you of the first prize, may Phoebus, please Heaven, pierce them with his arrows, and may the Muses never cross the thresholds of their houses! Read me, sir, if you will, some of your verses in other forms, for I desire to have a complete impression of your admirable talent."

Is there any need to say that Don Lorenzo enjoyed hearing himself praised by Don Quixote even though he looked upon him as a madman? O power of flattery, how broad and far-reaching are the bounds of your pleasant jurisdiction! The youth proved the truth of this and acceded to the knight's request by reading the following sonnet, based upon the story or fable of Pyramus and Thisbe:

SONNET

"The beauteous maiden now bursts through the wall,
she who in Pyramus's gallant breast
hath left a gaping wound. Love cannot rest

> *but, leaving Cyprus, comes to see it all.*
> *Silence there speaks, there is no word or call;*
> *the language of the heart alone is best*
> *for the fulfillment of Love's fond behest,*
> *and he all obstacles doth soon forestall.*
> *Desire grows, rashly the amorous maid,*
> *seeking her pleasure, hastens to her death.*
> *Ah, what a tale is here for hearts that strive!*
> *Two lovers dying by a single blade*
> *to find a common grave, and yet the breath*
> *of memory doth keep them still alive."* [12]

"Blessed be God!" cried Don Quixote when he had heard this composition. "Thank Him that among the infinite number of consumed poets [13] I have found one consummate bard, in your person, my dear sir; for the skill you display in the sonnet you have just read is enough to convince me of that."

For four days Don Quixote was entertained most royally in Don Diego's house, at the end of which time he asked permission to take his departure, saying that while he was deeply grateful for the kind and courteous treatment he had received, he did not think it a good thing for a knight-errant to spend many hours taking his ease and being entertained if he meant to fulfill the duties of his calling by seeking adventures, which he had been told were plentiful around there. He added that he intended to pass the time in those parts until the day came for the tournament at Saragossa, which was really his destination. Meanwhile, he planned to make his way into the Cave of Montesinos [14] of which so many marvelous stories had been told in that region, and he also meant to look into the true source and headwaters of the seven lakes that are commonly known as the Lakes of Ruidera.

Don Diego and his son assured their guest that this was a highly laudable enterprise, and they urged that he take with him out of their house and possessions anything that he might desire, as they could do no less in view of his personal worth and the honorable profession that he followed. The day set for his departure came at last, a happy one for Don Quixote but sad and bitter for Sancho Panza, who was making out very nicely with all the good things that Don Diego's household afforded and was loath to go back to the hunger of forest and desert and the short rations of his ill-stocked saddlebag, which he now proceeded to fill and stuff with whatever seemed to him most necessary.

As they went to leave, Don Quixote turned to Don Lorenzo. "I do not know," he said, "if I have told you this before or not, but, if so, I will tell you again: that if you wish to spare yourself toil and trouble in attaining the inaccessible summit of the temple of fame, you have but to turn aside from the somewhat narrow path of poetry and take the still narrower one of knight-errantry, but wide enough for all of that to make you an emperor in the twinkling of an eye."

With these words Don Quixote closed the case so far as convicting himself of madness was concerned, and this impression was still further confirmed when he went on to say, "God knows, Señor Don Lorenzo, I should like to have taken you along with me,[15] in order to teach you how to spare the humble and trample the proud under foot,[16] these being virtues that go with my profession; but since neither your youth nor your praiseworthy pursuits will admit of this, I shall content myself with advising your Grace that you may become a famous poet provided you are guided more by the opinion of others than by your own; for there is no father or mother whose children look ugly to them, and this illusion is even more common with respect to the children of our brain."

Once more father and son marveled at the mixture of nonsense and wisdom that Don Quixote talked, as well as at the pertinacity he displayed in going through with his unfortunate adventures in spite of everything, for such was the end and aim of his desires. And so, with a fresh exchange of courtesies and offers of service and with the kind permission of the lady of the castle,[17] Don Quixote and Sancho took their leave, the one mounted on Rocinante, the other on his donkey.

CHAPTER XIX. *Wherein is related the adventure of the enamored shepherd, with other truly amusing incidents.*

DON QUIXOTE had gone some little way from Don Diego's village when he encountered what appeared to be a couple of priests or students accompanied by a couple of peasants, the party being mounted upon four animals of the ass variety. One of the students carried, wrapped up in a piece of buckram that served as a portmanteau, a small supply of linen [1] and two pairs of coarse ribbed stockings,[2] as nearly as could be made out. The other had only a pair of fencing foils with their buttons. As for the peasants, they were laden down with other things and were apparently taking them back to their village from some large city where they had purchased them.

Both the students and the peasants were as astonished as all persons were when they beheld Don Quixote for the first time, and were consumed with curiosity to know who this man was who looked so different from other men. The knight greeted them and, upon learning that they were going in the same direction as himself, offered them his company, begging them, however, to slacken their pace a bit as their young she-asses traveled faster than his horse. And then, to oblige them, he told them in a few words who he was and acquainted them with his calling and profession, that of a knight-errant who went seeking adventures in all parts of the world. He informed them that his right name was Don Quixote de la Mancha but that he was known as the Knight of the Lions. All of which was Greek, or at any rate gibberish, to the peasants but not to the students, who at once realized that Don Quixote must be weak in the head but who nonetheless looked upon him with admiration and respect.

"If, Sir Knight," one of them said to him, "your Grace is not bound for any place in particular, seeing that such is not the custom of knights-errant, you would do well to come with us and see one of the finest and richest weddings that up to this day has ever been celebrated in La Mancha or for many miles around."

Don Quixote thereupon inquired if it was the marriage of some prince that he was describing in such terms as these.

"No," replied the student, "it is that of a farmer and a farmer's daughter. He is the richest man in all this region, and she the fairest maid that ever was seen; and the ceremony, which is to be held in a meadow adjoining the town where the bride lives, is to be marked by a pomp that is out of the ordinary. By reason of her surpassing beauty, the bride is known as Quiteria the Fair, and the bridegroom as Camacho the Rich. She is eighteen years of age and he is twenty-two, and they are well matched, although certain prying ones, who know all the pedigrees in the world by heart, will tell you that the beauteous Quiteria's family tree is better than Camacho's. That, however, is something that is readily overlooked these days, for wealth can solder many a crack.

"However this may be," the student continued, "this man Camacho is one who spares no expense, and he has taken it into his head to screen and roof the entire meadow with branches, in such a manner that the sun, if it wishes to visit the green grass with which the ground is covered, will have a hard time doing so. There are also to be dances, not only sword-dances but bell-dances as well; for in his town there are some who are very adept at ringing and jingling the chimes. I shall not speak of the clog-dancers,[3] except to say that they will be there in large numbers. But none of the things I have mentioned nor many others I have neglected to mention will do more to make this a memorable occasion than will the actions of the despairing Basilio, if he behaves as I expect him to. This Basilio is a youth of the same village as Quiteria and lives next door to her parents. Love accordingly took advantage of this fact to revive for the world the forgotten romance of Pyramus and Thisbe; for Basilio became enamored of Quiteria from his earliest years, and she in turn gave him innumerable signs of affection, until the relationship between the two of them came to be the talk of the town.

"As the pair grew up, Quiteria's father decided to forbid Basilio the run of the house which the lad had previously enjoyed, and by way of relieving himself of fear and suspicion, he ordered his daughter to marry the wealthy Camacho, since it did not seem well for her to wed Basilio, whose fortune did not equal his native gifts; for to tell the truth without prejudice, he is the cleverest young fellow that we have, expert at throwing the bar, the finest of wrestlers, and a great ball player; he runs like a deer, leaps better than a goat, and bowls over the ninepins as if by magic; he sings like a lark and can make a guitar speak, and, above all, he handles a sword with the best of them."

"By reason of those accomplishments alone," remarked Don Quixote, "the lad deserves to wed not merely the fair Quiteria, but Queen Guinevere herself, if she were alive today, and this in spite of Lancelot and all those who might try to prevent it."

"Tell that to my wife," said Sancho Panza, who up to then had been listening in silence, "for she insists that each one should marry his equal, according to the old saying, 'Every ewe to her mate.'[4] I'd like to see the good Basilio—for I'm taking a liking to him already—marry this lady Quiteria, and eternal blessings—no, I mean just the opposite—on all those that would keep true lovers apart."

"If all those who love each other were to marry," said Don Quixote, "that would deprive parents of the right to decide with whom and when their children should wed.[5] If it were left to daughters to choose their husbands, one would take her father's servant and another some stranger she had seen going down the street who had impressed her as being gallant and haughty, even though he might in reality be nothing more than a rake and a bully. For love and natural inclination readily blind those eyes of the mind that are so necessary in making life's important decisions; and when it comes to choosing a mate there is an especial danger of going astray, and great caution and the grace of Heaven are needed if one is to be guided aright. Before one sets out upon a long journey, he will, if he is prudent, seek some dependable and agreeable companion to accompany him. Why, then, should he not do the same who must travel all his life long toward the destination of death and whose companion must be ever with him, in the bed, at table, wherever he may go, which is the relation of wife to husband?

"The companionship of one's own wife," Don Quixote went on, "is not an article of merchandise that, once bought, may be returned, bartered, or exchanged; for this is an unbreakable bond that lasts as long as life endures, a noose that, once placed upon the neck, turns into a Gordian knot which cannot be undone until death comes to cut it. I could say much more upon this subject if I were not so anxious to hear whether or not the Señor Licentiate has more to tell us regarding the story of Basilio."

To this, the student, bachelor, or, as Don Quixote had called him, the licentiate made the following reply:

"I have told you all there is, except that from the moment Basilio learned that the fair Quiteria was to wed Camacho the Rich, he was never again seen to smile or heard to utter a rational word but has remained sad and pensive and goes about talking to himself in a way that clearly shows he has lost his senses. He eats little and sleeps little. His diet is fruits, and as for sleep, if he sleeps at all, it is in the open, upon the hard earth like a brute beast. From time to time he will look up at the heavens, and again he will fasten his gaze upon the ground, with such an air of abstraction that he appears to be no more than a clothed statue whose draperies are stirred by the wind. In short, he gives evidence of being so heart-stricken that all of us who know him fear that when the fair Quiteria says 'yes' tomorrow, it will be his death sentence."

"God will do better than that," said Sancho. "God gives the wound and He will give the medicine.⁶ No one knows what is to come; from now until tomorrow is a long time, and at any hour or minute the house may fall. I have seen it rain while the sun was shining. Many a one goes to bed healthy at night and the next day cannot move. Tell me one thing: can anyone boast that he has driven a spoke into fortune's wheel? No, certainly not; and between a woman's 'yes' and her 'no' I wouldn't venture to put a pinpoint, for it couldn't be done. Tell me that Quiteria loves Basilio with all her heart, and I'll give him a bag of good luck; for love, so I've heard folks say, looks through spectacles that make copper seem gold, poverty riches, and a pair of bleary eyes like a couple of pearls."

"What are you trying to get at, Sancho, curses on you?" said Don Quixote. "When you start stringing together proverbs and sayings, Judas himself couldn't stop you, and I wish he would carry you off. Tell me, stupid creature, what do you know of spokes or wheels or anything else?"

"Oh," replied Sancho, "if you don't understand me, then it's no wonder that my sayings are taken for nonsense. But no matter; I understand myself, and I know there is not much foolishness in what I've just said. The trouble is, my master, your Grace is too crickety of everything I say and do."

"*Critical*, you mean," said Don Quixote, "not *crickety*, you corrupter of good language, may God confound you!"

"Don't be cross with me, your Grace. You know that I was not brought up at court, nor have I studied at Salamanca, that I should know whether I am adding or dropping a letter now and then. Why, God help me, it's not fair to expect a man from Sayago to speak like one from Toledo,[7] and there are Toledans who do not make so good a job of it when it comes to polished talk."

"That is true," said the licentiate; "those that are brought up in the Tanneries and the Zocodover [8] cannot talk as well as those that spend practically the entire day in the Cathedral cloisters,[9] yet they are all Toledans. For language that is pure, correct, clear, and refined one must look to men of courtly taste, even though they may have been born in Majadahonda.[10] I speak of *taste*, for there are many who do not possess that quality, yet it is the grammar of good speech when accompanied by practice. I, gentlemen, for my sins,[11] have studied canon law at Salamanca and pride myself somewhat on being able to express my meaning plainly and intelligibly."

"If you did not pride yourself more on being able to handle those foils you carry than you do on skill with your tongue," the other student put in, "you would have been first among the licentiates instead of at the tail end as you were."

"See here, bachelor," replied the licentiate, "you are as mistaken as can be if you think that dexterity with the sword is a vain accomplishment."

"It is no mere opinion on my part," said Corchuelo (for that was the other student's name),[12] "but the established truth. If you would have me prove it to you by experience, this is your opportunity. You have swords with you, and I have a steady hand and a strong right arm; and aided by my courage, of which I have not a little, they will force you to confess that I am in the right. Get down and look to your stance, your circles, and your angles; make the most of your science, for I hope to make you see stars at midday with my rude and recently acquired swordsmanship, in which, next to God, I put my trust that the man is yet to be born who can compel me to turn my back and whom I cannot make give ground."

"As to whether you turn your back or not is no concern of mine,"[13] replied the one who prided himself on his skill, "for it well may be that where you set your foot down for the first time, there they will dig your grave; that is to say, you will be lying there dead as a result of your contempt for the art of fencing."

"We shall see as to that," said Corchuelo. And, dismounting with great alacrity and in a towering rage, he drew one of the swords which the licentiate carried.

At that instant Don Quixote spoke up. "No," he said, "that is not the way it is to be. I propose to act as fencing master here and judge this much debated question." With these words he too dismounted and, lance in hand, took up his position in the middle of the road just as the licentiate with easy grace of feet and body bore down upon Corchuelo, who similarly advanced to meet his adversary with fire darting from his eyes, as the saying goes. Meanwhile, the two peasants who accompanied the students, sitting there upon their donkeys, provided the audience for the tragedy. The slashes, thrusts, down-strokes, back-strokes, and double-handed blows that Corchuelo dealt came thicker than liver[14] or hail. He attacked like a lion whose temper has been roused, but only to meet with a tap on the mouth from the button of the licentiate's sword that stopped him short in the middle of his furious onslaught and forced him to kiss the blade as if it had been a relic, though not with that degree of devotion that ought to be, and commonly is, shown to relics.

To make a long story short, the licentiate tore off, one by one, all the buttons of a short cassock which Corchuelo wore and ripped the skirt into shreds until it looked like a cuttlefish's tail. Twice he knocked off his adversary's hat and wore him out to such an extent that at last, in despair, anger, and rage, the bachelor seized his sword by the hilt and sent it sailing through the air with such force that one of the peasants, who happened to be a notary and who went after it, later made a deposition to the effect that it had landed nearly three quarters of a league away,[15] a statement which serves, and has served, to show how very true it is that brute strength is overcome by skill.

Corchuelo now sat down, for he was exhausted, and at this point Sancho came up to him.

"Upon my word, Señor Bachelor," he said, "if your Grace will take my advice, you won't challenge anyone to a fencing match from now on but will only wrestle or toss the bar. You are young and have the strength for that sort of thing, but I have heard it said that these experts,[16] as they call them, can run the point of a sword though the eye of a needle."

"I am satisfied," replied Corchuelo, "to have fallen off my donkey,[17] and am glad that experience has shown me how far I was from the truth."

Getting to his feet, he embraced the licentiate, and they were as good friends as they had been before. Not caring to wait for the notary who had gone after the sword, since it appeared that it would take him some little while, they then decided to ride on in order that they might arrive in good time at the village where Quiteria lived, of which they all were natives.[18] For the balance of their journey the licentiate held forth on the advantages of the art of swordsmanship, so convincingly and with so many mathematical proofs and demonstrations that every man of them was persuaded of the excellence of this science and Corchuelo gave up the opinion he had so stubbornly held.

Night had fallen, but before they reached the town it appeared to all of them as though the sky were filled with numberless gleaming stars. At the same time they could hear the mingled and pleasing notes that came from various musical instruments such as flutes, tabors, psalteries, rustic pipes, tambourines, and timbrels. And as they came nearer they perceived that the trees of an arcade of branches that had been erected at the entrance to the village [19] were all filled with lights which were motionless in the gentle breeze then blowing that did not even stir the leaves. It was the musicians who were providing the merriment for the wedding party as they went in little groups through the pleasant grounds, some of them dancing, others singing, and all of them playing upon one or another of the instruments mentioned. In brief, it seemed as if mirth were running wild over the meadow and happiness were gamboling there.

Many other persons were occupied in raising platforms from which people might watch the performances and dances that were to be given there the following day by way of solemnizing the marriage of the rich Camacho and the obsequies of Basilio. Don Quixote was unwilling to enter the village, although the peasant [20] and the bachelor urged him to do so. The excuse he gave, an all-sufficient one as he saw it, was that it was the custom of knights-errant to sleep in the fields and forests rather than in towns, even though the shelter offered them might be a gilded roof. He accordingly turned off the road a little way, much to the displeasure of Sancho, who remembered the good lodgings he had had in Don Diego's castle or house.

CHAPTER XX. *Wherein is contained an account of the wedding of Camacho the Rich* [1] *and of what happened to Basilio the Poor.*

SCARCELY had the fair Aurora given the glowing Phoebus an opportunity to dry the liquid pearls upon her golden locks with the warmth of his rays when Don Quixote, shaking off all sloth from his limbs, rose to his feet and called to his squire Sancho, who was still snoring. As he stood gazing down upon him and before awakening him, the knight uttered the following soliloquy:

"Blessed art thou above all those upon the face of the earth, seeing that, without envying or being envied by any person, thou canst sleep so calmly, with no enchanters or spells to trouble or alarm thee! Thou sleepest,[2] I repeat, and I will say it a hundred times, without any jealous thoughts of thy lady to keep thee awake, with no concern as to how thou art going to pay the debts thou owest or provide food on the morrow for thyself and thy needy little family. Ambition doth not disturb thee nor this world's empty show; thou thinkest only of that beast of thine, having placed upon my shoulders the burden of thine own support, that counterweight that nature and custom have decreed masters should bear. The servant sleeps and the master keeps watch, thinking how he is to feed him, improve his lot, and do him favors. When the sky turns brazen and withholds from the earth its fitting dew, it is the master not the servant who is distressed, it is he who suffers, since he it is who must support amid sterility and hunger the one who hath served him faithfully in fertility and abundance."

To all this Sancho made no reply, for the very good reason that he was asleep, nor would he have awaked as quickly as he did if Don Quixote had not prodded him with the butt of his lance. He finally did rouse himself, however, sleepy-eyed and lazy, and turned his face around in all directions.

"If I am not mistaken," he said, "there is a steam and smell coming from around that arcade that is more like that of broiled rashers than it is like jonquils [3] or thyme. Faith, and a wedding that begins with such a smell ought to be all right; there should be plenty to eat."

"That will be enough from you, glutton," said Don Quixote. "Come, we are going to those nuptials to see what the rejected suitor, Basilio, will do."

"Let him do what he likes," replied Sancho. "He's a poor man, and yet he is bent on marrying Quiteria. He hasn't a cuarto [4] to his name, and yet he'd put his head in the clouds to look for a bride. Is that all he wants? My word, master, but I think the poor should be content with what comes their way and not go looking for tidbits at the bottom of the sea! [5] I will bet you an arm that Camacho could bury Basilio under the reales that he has; and if this is so, as it must be, then Quiteria would be a fool to give up the jewels and finery that Camacho must have given her (for he is well able to give them to her) and choose instead Basilio's bar-throwing and sword-juggling. For a good toss of the bar or a neat feint with the sword they won't give you a pint of wine at the tavern. Let Count Dirlos [6] have those graces and accomplishments that are not salable,[7] but when the same graces go with someone who has plenty of money, then so help me if they're not as pretty as can be. Upon a good foundation you can raise a good building, and the best foundation in the world is cash."

"For God's sake, Sancho," Don Quixote broke in, "have done with your harangue; for I am of the opinion that if you were to be permitted to finish what you are every minute beginning, you would never have time for sleeping but would waste it all in talking."

"If your Grace had a good memory," said Sancho, "you would recall that one of the articles of our agreement before we left home this last time was that I was to be allowed to say whatever I wanted to, so long as it was not against my neighbor or disrespectful to you, and it seems to me I've kept my part of the bargain so far as that article is concerned."

"I do not recall any such article as that," said Don Quixote, "and even if what you say is true, I want you to be quiet and come along; for those instruments that we heard last night are beginning to make the valleys ring with merriment once more, and the nuptials will undoubtedly be celebrated in the cool of the morning and not in the heat of the day."

Sancho did as his master had commanded, and when he had saddled Rocinante and placed the saddlebag upon his gray, the two of them mounted and, at a slow pace, made their way into the arcade. The first thing that met Sancho's gaze was a steer spitted entire upon an elm tree, and upon the fire for roasting it was a small mountain of logs, while round about were six stew-pots, but not fashioned like ordinary ones, for they were in reality half-sized wine jars and each of them big enough to hold a slaughterhouse. These pots swallowed up and concealed in their insides whole sheep as if they had been pigeons; and there was a countless number of hares, already skinned, and plucked hens, which had been hung up on the trees until the time came for burying them in the pots, and a multitude of birds and much game of various sorts had similarly been suspended from the boughs so that the air might keep them cool.

Sancho counted more than sixty wine bags, each holding more than two arrobas [8] and all of them, as later became evident, filled with the best of vintages. There were stacks of the whitest bread, resembling piles of wheat on the threshing floor, and a wall of cheeses arranged like a latticed brickwork. The oil was contained in two caldrons larger than those in a dyer's shop and was used for frying fritters, which when done were taken out with two powerful shovels and dropped into another caldron, of prepared honey, that stood near by. There were more than fifty cooks altogether, male and female, and all were neat-appearing, busy, and cheerful. Sewed inside the steer's big belly, twelve delicate little suckling pigs gave it flavor and tenderness. The various kinds of spices seemed to have been bought not by the pound but by the arroba, and all of them were open to view in a huge chest. In a few words, it was a country-style wedding but with enough provisions to feed an army.

Sancho Panza looked everything over, studied it closely, and was delighted with what he saw. It was the stew-pots first of all that completely won his affections, and he would most gladly have helped himself to a fair-sized dish of their contents. Then the wine bags claimed his attention, and, lastly, the fruit of the frying pan, if such pompous caldrons as those could be termed frying pans. Finally, unable to bear it or to control himself any longer, he went up to one of the bustling cooks and politely but hungrily begged permission to dip a piece of bread in one of the pots.

"Brother," the cook replied, "this is not a day when hunger has any rights here, thanks to the rich Camacho. Get down and look about for a ladle and skim off a hen or two, and much good may it do you."

"I don't see any," said Sancho.

"Wait a minute," said the cook. "Sinner that I am, how helpless you are!" And taking a pail he dipped it into one of the jars and brought up three hens and a couple of geese. "Eat my friend, and break your fast on these skimmings until dinnertime comes."

"But I have no place to put it," said Sancho.

"Then," replied the cook, "take spoon and all and thank Camacho and his happiness for it."

While Sancho was thus engaged, Don Quixote was watching a group of about a dozen peasants who had entered the enclosure from one end. They were mounted upon very handsome mares fitted out with rich and showy field trappings and many bells, and all of them were attired in their holiday best. In regular file, they ran their mounts up and down the meadow, not once but a number of times, shouting jubilantly, "Long live Camacho and Quiteria, he as rich as she is fair, and she the fairest in the world!"

"Quite evidently," thought Don Quixote, "they have not seen my Dulcinea del Toboso, or they would be a little more restrained in their praise of that Quiteria of theirs."

Shortly afterward many and varied sets of dancers made their entrance from different sides of the arcade. Among them was a band of sword-dancers, made up of some twenty-four lads of gallant and dashing mien, all of them clad in the finest and whitest of linen and wearing fine silk kerchiefs embroidered in various hues. One of those upon the mares inquired of the sprightly youth who led the group if any of the dancers had been wounded.

"Not as yet, thank God," was the reply. "We are all sound and whole." And with this he and his companions began to execute any number of complicated maneuvers, with so many evolutions and such skill that, although Don Quixote was used to witnessing such dances, he thought he had never seen any to equal this. He also was pleased by another group that came in, consisting of very beautiful young girls, apparently between the ages of fourteen and eighteen. They had on dresses of palm-leaf green and some of them had their hair braided while others wore it loose-flowing, but their locks in every case were of a golden shade that rivaled the sun, and their heads were decked with garlands of jessamine, roses, amaranth, and honeysuckle. They were led by a venerable old man and an aged matron who, however, were more active and nimble than might have been expected of them, considering their years. The maidens were accompanied by the notes of a Zamora bagpipe, and, with modest gaze and light-treading feet, they proved to be the very best of dancers.

The next dance was an artistic one, of the sort known as "talking dances." It was performed by eight nymphs. There were two rows of them, one being headed by Cupid, the other by Worldly Wealth.[9] The winged god of love carried his bow and arrows and his quiver, while the other figure was richly attired in gold and silk of many colors. On the back of each of Cupid's followers was a white parchment with the bearer's name written upon it in large letters. Poetry was the first one's name, the second was Wit, the third one Birth, and the fourth Valor. Worldly Wealth's attendants were similarly identified, the first being Liberality, the second Bounty, the third Treasure, and the fourth Pacific Possession. The nymphs were preceded by a wooden castle drawn by four savages appareled in ivy and green-dyed hemp[10] and looking so lifelike that Sancho was almost frightened by them. On the front and each of the other sides of the structure was the inscription: "Castle of Wise Discretion." Accompanying this group were four skillful musicians playing upon the tabor and the flute, and Cupid thereupon began his dance. Having executed a couple of turns, he raised his eyes and drew his bow against a maiden who stood upon the battlements of the castle, addressing her in this manner:

> *"The God of love behold in me,*
> *mighty on land and in the air,*
> *and on the broad and tossing sea;*
> *great is my power everywhere,*
> *e'en though in Hell's dread pit it be.*
>   *Fear is a thing I never knew,*
> *all that I wish must needs come true,*
> *howe'er impossible it seem;*
> *for my will and word are still supreme,*
> *I command, enjoin, forbid, subdue."*

Having recited the foregoing stanza, he let fly an arrow at the top of the castle and retired. Worldly Wealth then performed a figure or two and, when the tabors had ceased, spoke as follows:

> *"More powerful I than Love's fair face,*
> *though Love himself is now my guide,*
> *for I am of the finest race*
> *that on this earth did e'er abide,*
> *far famed and great in every place.*
> *Wealth is my name, I bring delight,*
> *but few know how to use me right,*
> *and to do without me is harder still.*
> *Such as I am, I bend my will*
> *To serve you ever, day and night."*

As Worldly Wealth stepped back, Poetry came forward and, having done the customary figures, gazed up at the maid on the battlements and recited these verses:

> *"With many a fancy and conceit,*
> *that charming goddess, Poesy,*
> *in measures lofty and discreet,*
> *lady, her soul doth send to thee,*
> *wrapped in a myriad sonnets neat.*
> *Oh, do not let me importune;*
> *but accept my homage, and thou right soon,*
> *the envy of a host of eyes,*
> *shalt be borne upward to the skies,*
> *beyond the very rim of the moon."*

Poetry then withdrew and, from the side of Worldly Wealth, Liberality advanced and proceeded to declaim:

> *"What men call liberality*
> *consists in giving without excess:*
> *no weak-willed prodigality;*
> *no grudging hand or miserliness:*
> *such the giver's law in totality.*
> *Howe'er, by way of enriching thee,*
> *I today shall more prodigal be;*
> *for though 'tis a vice, 'tis a goodly one*
> *when from loving heart 'tis done,*
> *which in the giving itself doth see."*

In this manner all the figures from the two groups came forward and retired, each executing her steps and repeating her verses, some of which were polished while others were mere burlesque; but although Don

Quixote had an exceptional memory, the stanzas quoted are all that he was able to recall. The dancers now mingled together, weaving in and out with an easy and pleasing grace. As Cupid went past the castle he let fly his darts, and Worldly Wealth broke gilded pellets against it.

Finally, after they had danced a good while, Worldly Wealth took out a large purse, made of the skin of a striped cat and seemingly full of money, and hurled it at the castle with such force that the walls fell apart and came tumbling down, leaving the maiden exposed and with no protection whatsoever; following which, he and his followers advanced and cast a huge gold chain about the damsel's neck as if to subdue her and take her captive. Seeing this, Cupid and his band made a show of freeing her, all to the accompaniment of tabors and in the form of a dance. It was the savages who made peace between them and with great dexterity set the walls of the castle up once more. The maiden then took her place in it as before, and thus the dance ended to the great satisfaction of the spectators.

Don Quixote inquired of one of the nymphs who it was that had composed and arranged the performance and was told that a certain cleric of the town who had a neat gift for that sort of thing was responsible for it.

"I will wager," said the knight, "that the bachelor or cleric in question is a better friend of Camacho's than he is of Basilio's and that he must have more of the satirist in him than he has of the vesper spirit, for in this dance he has well portrayed the youth's accomplishments and the other's wealth."

Sancho Panza, who was listening, now spoke up. "The king is my cock," [11] he said. "I stick to Camacho."

"It is plain to be seen, Sancho," said Don Quixote, "that you are one of the rabble who cry 'Long live the conqueror!' "

"I don't know what I am," replied Sancho. "All I know is that from Basilio's stew-pots I'll never get such elegant skimmings as I have had from Camacho's." With this, he showed his master the pail filled with geese and hens, and, taking one of the fowls, he began to devour it with a hearty zest and great good humor.

"Basilio," he exclaimed, "is out of luck with his accomplishments! [12] A man is worth as much as he has and has as much as he is worth.[13] There are two kinds of people in this world, my grandmother used to say: the Have's and the Have-not's,[14] and she stuck to the Have's. And today, Señor Don Quixote, people are more interested in having than in knowing.[15] An ass covered with gold makes a better impression than a horse with a packsaddle. And so I tell you again, I'm sticking to Camacho, whose pots hold plenty of geese and hens, hares and rabbits; but if anything of Basilio's comes to hand, or even to foot, it will be no better than wine slop."

"Have you finished your speech, Sancho?" asked Don Quixote.

"I'll have to finish it, seeing that your Grace takes offense at it; but if it wasn't for that, I'd have my work cut out for me for three days to come."

"I hope to God," said Don Quixote, "that I see you struck dumb before I die."

"At the rate we're going," replied Sancho, "I'll be chewing clay before your Grace dies, and then maybe I'll be so dumb that I'll not have a word to say until the end of the world, or at least not until Judgment Day."

"Even if that should happen, Sancho," said Don Quixote, "you could never make up with your silence for all the talking you have done, are doing, and will do in the course of your life. It stands to reason that I shall die before you do, and so I never hope to see you dumb, not even when you are drinking or sleeping, which is the most I can say."

"In good faith, sir," said Sancho, "there's no trusting that one with no flesh on her bones who eats lamb as well as mutton, for I've heard our curate say that she treads both the tall towers of kings and the humble cottages of the poor.[16] The lady is powerful but not finical or squeamish; she devours everything that comes her way and fills her saddlebags with people of every sort, of every age and station. She is not one of those reapers who take a siesta; she works at all hours and mows down the withered grass and the green alike. She doesn't seem to chew her food but gulps down anything that is set in front of her, for she is as hungry as a dog that never has its fill; and although she has no belly, you would think she had the dropsy, so thirsty is she to drink the lives of all who live as one might drink from a jug of cold water."

"Stop where you are, Sancho," said Don Quixote, "and don't risk a fall. For, really, what you have said about death, in your own rustic way, might have come from the mouth of a good preacher. I tell you, Sancho, if you had [17] as much judgment as you have mother wit, you might take a pulpit in hand and go through this world delivering fine sermons."

"He preaches well who lives well," was Sancho's answer. "That's all the theology I know."

"And all you need to know," said his master. "But what I cannot make out is this: the fear of God, they tell us, is the beginning of wisdom, yet you are more afraid of a lizard than you are of Him."

"Sir," replied Sancho, "your Grace would do well to judge your own deeds of chivalry and not go meddling with the fears or bravery of other people. I'm as God-fearing a man as any neighbor's son; so will your Grace please let me finish these skimmings, for all the rest is idle talk and we'll have to answer for it in the life to come."

Saying this, he once more attacked his pail with so hearty an appetite as to awaken Don Quixote's, who no doubt would have helped him out had he not been prevented from doing so by a circumstance which must be related further on.

CHAPTER XXI. *In which Camacho's wedding is continued, with other delightful incidents.*

As Don Quixote and Sancho were engaged in the conversation that has been related in the preceding chapter, they heard loud shouts and a great din created by those on the mares, who now rode forward with welcoming cries to receive the bride and groom. The bridal pair were accompanied by a large number of musical instruments and pageants of various kinds, as well as by the priest, the relatives of both parties, and all the most distinguished gentry of the neighboring villages, in holiday garb.

"My word!" exclaimed Sancho when he caught sight of the bride. "She's not dressed like any farmer's daughter but rather like some fine lady of the court. Damn me if those medals [1] she's wearing aren't of rich coral, and that palm-green cloth of Cuenca is thirty-pile velvet! [2] And look at that white linen trimming—I'll swear it's satin! and those jet rings that she has on her hands, may I never have any luck if they're not gold, and fine gold at that, and set with pearls white as a milk curd, every one of them worth an eye of your head! Oh, the whoreson wench! What hair she has, if it's her own; I never in all my life saw any that was longer or brighter colored. Just see her shape and the way she carries herself and then try to tell me that she doesn't remind you of a palm tree loaded down with clusters of dates, for that is just what those trinkets are like that she has hanging from her hair and neck. Upon my soul, she's an up-and-coming lass and fit to pass the banks of Flanders." [3]

Don Quixote had to laugh at these rustic praises which Sancho was bestowing upon the bride; but it nonetheless seemed to him that, with the exception of his own lady, Dulcinea del Toboso, he had never beheld so fair a creature.[4] The beauteous Quiteria was a trifle pale, however, owing no doubt to the bad night she had spent, as is always the case with brides busied with preparations on the eve of their wedding day. The members of the bridal party made their way to a theater on one side of the meadow, decked out with carpets and boughs, where they were to plight their troth and watch the dances and the pageants; but just as they reached the place they heard someone behind them shouting in a loud voice, "Wait a moment, you who are as inconsiderate as you are hasty!"

At the sound of these words, all turned their heads and saw that the speaker was a man attired in what appeared to be a large loose-fitting black coat with flame-colored patches. Upon his head, as they presently perceived, was a wreath of funereal cypress, and in his hands he carried a long staff. As he drew nearer they all recognized him as the gallant Basilio and waited anxiously to see what would come of his words and cries, for they feared that some misfortune would result from his appearance there at such a time. He was exhausted and breathless as he arrived; and, taking his staff, which had a steel point on the end of it, he planted it in the ground in front of the betrothed pair. His face was pale and his eyes were fixed on the bride as he addressed her in a hoarse and trembling voice.

"Well do you know, O heartless Quiteria," he said, "that in accordance with the holy law which we acknowledge you cannot take a husband so long as I am alive; nor are you ignorant of the fact that, hoping time and diligence would improve my fortune, I never failed to observe that respect that was due your honor. But you, turning your back on all that you owe to my true love, would surrender what is rightfully mine to another, whose riches serve to bring him not merely prosperity but the greatest happiness there is. And now, to crown his happiness—not that I think he deserves it, but because Heaven has seen fit to bestow it upon him—I with my own hands will do away with the obstacle that might interfere with it, by removing myself from between you. Long live the rich Camacho! May he spend many long and happy years with the heartless Quiteria! As for the poor Basilio, let him die, seeing that his poverty has clipped the wings of his own happiness and has brought him to the grave!"

Saying this, he seized the staff which he had driven into the ground, and they could then see that it served as a sheath to a fairly long rapier that had been hidden in it. With what might be termed the hilt still planted in the earth, he swiftly, coolly, and resolutely threw himself upon it, and a moment later the crimson point and half the steel blade could be seen protruding from his back, as he lay there transfixed by his own weapon and bathed in blood.

His friends at once came running up to aid him, for they were grief-stricken at his sad fate. Dismounting from Rocinante, Don Quixote took him in his arms and found that he had not yet expired. They were about to withdraw the rapier, but the priest who was present was of the opinion that they should not do so until the dying man had confessed, since the removal of the blade would mean his immediate death. At this point Basilio revived somewhat.

"O cruel Quiteria," he said in a weak and sorrowing voice, "if in this last and fatal moment you would but give me your hand in marriage, I then might hope that my rash act would find pardon, since through it I had achieved the blessing of being yours."

Upon hearing this, the priest told Basilio that he should be thinking of the welfare of his soul rather than of his bodily pleasures and should beg God in all earnestness to forgive him his sins and the rash act he had committed. Basilio's reply was that he would by no manner of means confess himself unless Quiteria first became his bride as only that happiness would give him the will and strength to do it. Don Quixote then took a hand by loudly declaring that the wounded man's request was only just and reasonable and, moreover, very easy to comply with, and that Señor Camacho would be as much honored by marrying the brave Basilio's widow as he would be if he were to receive Señora Quiteria directly from her father.

"In this case," he explained, "it is merely a matter of saying 'yes' and no consequence will follow, for the marriage bed will be the grave."

Camacho was listening to it all and was very much bewildered and confused, not knowing what to say or do; but Basilio's friends were so insistent that he give his consent for Quiteria to marry his rival, in order that the latter's soul might not be lost as it quitted this life in desperation, that he was moved and even compelled to say that she might do so if she wished, adding that he would be satisfied since it only meant putting off for a moment the fulfillment of his desires. All then crowded around Quiteria and with tears, prayers, and convincing reasons endeavored to persuade her to give her hand to poor Basilio; but she, harder than marble and more imperturbable than any statue, appeared unable or unwilling to utter a single word in reply, nor would she have answered at all had not the priest told her that she must make up her mind quickly, as Basilio was at the point of death [5] and this was no time for hesitation.

Then the fair Quiteria, speechless still but now deeply disturbed and, as it seemed, sad and regretful, came up to where Basilio lay with eyes upturned, his breath coming in short, quick gasps as he muttered his loved one's name—to all appearances he was dying like a heathen and not like a Christian. Kneeling beside him, she indicated by signs, not by words, that she wished to take his hand, and at this Basilio opened his eyes and gazed at her with a fixed stare.

"O Quiteria," he said, "you have relented at last when your pity can serve only as a dagger to deprive me of life, since I have not the strength to enjoy the supreme happiness you bestow by choosing me as yours, nor am I able to mitigate this pain which is so rapidly closing my eyes in the dread shadow of death. What I ask of you, O fatal star of mine! is that this handclasp you offer be no mere act of compliance on your part nor intended to deceive me afresh; instead, I would have you state and confess that it is of your own free will and without coercion that you take me to be your lawful husband; for there is no reason why, at such a time as this, you should trifle with me or lie to one who has always dealt so honestly with you."

As he uttered these words he grew weaker and weaker, and all the bystanders feared that each sinking spell would be his last. Overcome with shame, the modest Quiteria now took his right hand in hers.

"Nothing," she assured him, "could force me to do a thing that was against my will; and so, as freely as possible, I give you my hand as your lawfully wedded wife and take your own in return, providing that you too are acting in accordance with your own free choice and not merely because your mind has been deranged as a result of this calamity which your rash deed has brought upon you."

"My mind," replied Basilio, "is not deranged, nor is my thinking confused, and so, with that power of lucid reasoning with which Heaven has seen fit to endow me, I do hereby give myself to be your husband."

"And I," said Quiteria, "will be your wife, whether you live many years or they carry you now from my arms to the grave."

"That young fellow," remarked Sancho Panza at this point, "talks a lot to be so badly wounded. They should make him stop this love-making and attend to his soul; for so far as I can make out, if it is leaving his body, it has got no farther than his tongue." [6]

As the pair continued to hold hands, the priest, moved to tears, gave them his benediction; and no sooner had he done so than Basilio nimbly leaped to his feet and, with an unheard-of brazenness, drew the rapier from his body which had served as its sheath. The bystanders were dumfounded, and some of the more simple-minded and less inquisitive among them began shouting at the top of their voices, "A miracle! A miracle!"

"No miracle," said Basilio, "but a trick." [7]

Astounded and bewildered, the priest ran up and, putting out both hands to examine the wound, discovered that the blade had passed, not through Basilio's flesh and ribs, but through a hollow iron tube filled with blood which he had placed there, the blood, as was afterward learned, having been especially prepared so that it would not congeal.

The short of it was, the priest, Camacho, and all the others found that they had been tricked and made sport of. As for the bride, she did not appear to be resentful. Indeed, when some were heard to say that, having been accomplished through fraud, the marriage would not be valid, she promptly spoke up and stated that she confirmed it anew; from which all present derived the impression that the whole thing had been arranged between the two of them. Camacho and his supporters, on the other hand, were so angry that they proceeded to take vengeance into their own hands. Unsheathing their swords, and there were many of them, they fell upon Basilio, but nearly as many blades were drawn with equal promptness in his defense.

Taking the lead on horseback, with his lance braced upon his arm and well protected by his shield, Don Quixote then made them all give way, while Sancho, who never did care for such doings, retired to the pots from which he had had such pleasant skimmings, this being for him a sacred place and one for which a proper respect was to be shown.

"Hold, gentlemen, hold!" cried Don Quixote. "It is not reasonable to take vengeance for the wrongs done us by love. Remember that love and war are one and the same thing; and just as in war it is permissible to use wiles and stratagems to overcome the enemy, so in amorous contests those deceptions that are employed in order to attain the desired object are looked upon as proper, providing they are not to the detriment or dishonor of the lady who is sought. Basilio and Quiteria belong to each other by favorable and just decree of Heaven. Camacho is rich and may buy his pleasure when, where, and as it suits him. Basilio has but this ewe lamb, and no one, however powerful he may be, is going to take it away from him. What therefore God hath joined together, let not man put asunder;[8] and whoever shall attempt it will first have to pass the point of this lance."

As he said this, he brandished his weapon with such strength and skill as to frighten all those that did not know him. The effect upon Camacho was to fasten his thoughts intently upon the scorn that Quiteria had shown him, and he accordingly determined to efface her at once from his memory and was ready to listen to the persuasions of the priest, who was a prudent, well-meaning individual. The upshot of it all was, Camacho and his followers became calm and peaceful and put their swords back in their scabbards; for all were now inclined to place the blame upon Quiteria's fickleness rather than Basilio's wiles, the spurned bridegroom reasoning that if she had loved his rival before marriage, she would go on loving him after she was wed, and he would do better to thank Heaven for having taken her from him than for giving her to him.

Camacho and those in his train being thus pacified and consoled, Basilio and his friends likewise quieted down; and by way of showing that he harbored no ill will for the trick that had been played on him, the host expressed a desire that the festivities should continue just as if the marriage were to take place. This, however, proved inacceptable to Basilio, his bride, and their attendants, and they now went off to the village where the groom lived. For the poor, if they be virtuous and discreet, have those who follow, honor, and defend them, just as the rich have those who accompany and flatter them.[9] They took Don Quixote along, for they regarded him as a man of valor, with hair on his chest.[10] Sancho alone was heartsick when he saw that he would not be able to wait for Camacho's splendid feast and entertainment, which lasted until nightfall; and thus, it was in deep dejection that he followed his master and Basilio's party, leaving behind him the flesh-pots of Egypt though he bore them with him in his soul, the few skimmings that remained in his pail representing for him the glory and abundance of the good cheer he had lost. In this manner, grief-stricken and pensive though for once not hungry, he plodded along in Rocinante's foot-tracks without dismounting from his gray.

CHAPTER **XXII**. *Wherein is related the great adventure of the Cave of Montesinos in the heart of La Mancha, which the valiant Don Quixote brought to a triumphant conclusion.*

MANY and great were the attentions that the newly married pair showered upon Don Quixote, for they felt under obligations to him for having shown his readiness to defend their cause. They were as much pleased by his wisdom as by his bravery and looked upon him as a Cid in the matter of arms and a Cicero in eloquence. The worthy Sancho enjoyed himself for three whole days at their expense, and in the course of that time it was learned that Basilio's pretense at wounding himself had been a scheme of his own and not a plot between him and the fair Quiteria, and he had expected it to turn out precisely as it did. He admitted, however, that he had confided his plan in part to a few of his friends who might assist him in carrying out the deception.

"Deception," observed Don Quixote, "is not the word where aims are virtuous." And he went on to point out that the marriage of lovers is an excellent purpose to be achieved, reminding them, however, that love has no greater enemy than hunger and constant want; for love is all joy, happiness, and contentment when the lover is in possession of the object of his affections, and want and poverty thereby become his open and relentless foes. All this was said in an effort to induce Señor Basilio to give up the practice of his accomplishments, since even though they brought him fame they would bring in no money, and to devote his attention instead to the acquisition of a fortune by legitimate means and his own industry; for those who are prudent and persevering always find a way.

The poor man who is a man of honor (if such a thing is possible) has a jewel when he has a beautiful wife, and when she leaves him, his honor at the same time departs and is slain. The woman who is beautiful and virtuous and whose husband is pure deserves to be crowned with laurels and garlands of victory. Her beauty in itself attracts the desires of all who look upon and know it, and royal eagles and birds of lofty flight swoop down on it as if it were an alluring bait; and when such loveliness is accompanied by want and straitened circumstances, it is then assailed by ravens, kites, and other birds of prey, and she who can stand firm against such an onslaught may well be called her husband's crown.[1]

"Let me remind you, prudent Basilio," Don Quixote continued, "of something which some wise man or other has said. It was his opinion that there was only one good woman in all the world, and his advice was for each man to bring himself to believe that this woman was his wife, and in that way he might live happily. I myself am not married, nor have I ever thought of marrying up to now,[2] but for all that, I should not hesitate to advise anyone who might ask me as to the proper method of looking for a woman of the sort one would want to have as his wife. First of all, he should look at her reputation rather than at her dowry, for a good name is something to be won, not alone by being good, but by appearing good in the eyes of others, and loose manners in public do more harm to a woman's honor than secret sins. If you bring a good woman into your house, it should be an easy matter to keep her so and even to improve her virtue, but if you bring a bad one, you will have a hard time of it correcting her, since it is not very feasible to pass from one extreme to another. I do not say that it is impossible, but I hold it to be difficult."

Listening to all this, Sancho was talking to himself. "This master of mine, when I say something that has some pith and body to it, is in the habit of telling me that I ought to take a pulpit in hand and go through this world preaching fine sermons; and I will say of him that when he begins stringing sayings together and giving advice, he not only could take a pulpit in hand, but two of them by each finger and go through the market places talking his head off.[3] The devil take you for a knight-errant, what a lot of things you know! I thought in my heart that he knew only those things that had to do with chivalry, but he has a finger in everything and is always putting in his spoonful."

He had muttered this loud enough [4] for his master to hear.

"What are you mumbling about, Sancho?" Don Quixote asked him.

"I am not mumbling anything," Sancho replied. "I was only telling myself that I wish I had heard what your Grace said just now before I was married. In that case I might be saying, 'The ox that's loose licks himself well.' " [5]

"Is your Teresa so bad as all that?"

"She's not bad, but she's not good, at least not as good as I could wish."

"It is wrong of you, Sancho," said Don Quixote, "to be speaking ill of your wife, who after all is the mother of your children."

"We're even, then," was the answer, "for she also speaks ill of me whenever she happens to feel like it, especially when she is jealous. Satan himself couldn't put up with her then."

At length, when three days had gone by, during which time they had been feasted and entertained like royalty, Don Quixote asked the swordsman-licentiate to provide him with a guide who would conduct him to the Cave of Montesinos, as he had a great desire to enter it and see with his own eyes if the marvelous tales they told of it throughout that region were true or not. The bachelor replied that he would acquaint him with a first cousin of his, a notable student and very fond of reading books of chivalry, who would be delighted to conduct him to the mouth of the said cave and show him the Lakes of Ruidera, which were famous throughout La Mancha and all Spain as well. He assured the knight that the youth would be found to be entertaining company, since he knew enough to write books of his own, books that were printed and dedicated to princes.

The cousin finally arrived leading an ass in foal, with a pack-saddle covered by a striped carpet or sackcloth; and Sancho thereupon proceeded to saddle Rocinante and get his gray ready, taking care to stuff his saddlebags to keep company with those the newcomer had brought with him. Being thus well provisioned, they commended themselves to God and, taking leave of all present, set out along the road that led to the celebrated cave.

On the way, Don Quixote inquired of the cousin what his pursuits were, his profession, and his studies. To this their companion replied that his profession was that of humanist, adding that his pursuits and studies had to do with composing books for the printers, all of them of great public utility and very entertaining. One of them, he stated, was entitled *The Book of Liveries*, in which were depicted seven hundred and three different liveries with their colors, mottoes, and ciphers, from which the gentlemen of the court might pick and choose the ones that suited them best for their feasts and revels without having to go begging for them from anyone or, as the saying has it, straining their wits to procure the costumes adapted to their purpose.

"For," he went on to say, "I provide the jealous, the scorned, the forgotten, the far-absent, with the garb that they should have and that becomes them very well. I have another book which I am going to call *Metamorphoses, or the Spanish Ovid,* an original and extraordinary work, for in it, imitating Ovid in burlesque style, I show who Giralda of Seville and the Angel of the Magdalena were, and I further identify the Vecinguerra Conduit of Cordova, the Bulls of Guisando, the Sierra Morena, and the Legitanos and Lavapies Fountains of Madrid, not forgetting El Piojo, the Caño Dorado, and La Priora,[6] together with the allegories, metaphors, and versions associated with them, and all in such a manner as to interest, amuse, and instruct the reader at one and the same time.

"I have another book which I call *Supplement to Virgilius Polydorus.*[7] It treats of the invention of things and is a very scholarly work and one that cost me much study. In it I set forth in a pleasing style, with due proof and explanation, certain things of great moment that Polydorus neglected to mention. He forgot to tell us who was the first man in the world to have a cold in the head, or the first to take unctions for the French disease,[8] all of which I bring out most accurately, citing the authority of more than twenty-five authors. From this your Grace may see how well I have labored and may judge for yourself as to whether or not such a work should be useful to everyone."

Sancho, who had been listening very attentively to what the cousin had to say, now put in his word. "Tell me, sir, and may God guide your hand well in the printing of your books, tell me if you can, seeing that you know everything, who was the first man that ever scratched his head? For my part, I believe it must have been Father Adam."

"So it would have been," replied the cousin, "seeing there is no doubt that Adam had a head with hair on it, and being the first man, he would have scratched it some time or other."

"That is what I think," said Sancho. "But tell me something else: who was the first tumbler [9] in the world?"

"Really, brother," said the cousin, "I cannot determine that just now, not until I have given it some study. I will look into it as soon as I go back to where I keep my books and will let you know the next time we see each other again; for this is not going to be the last time."

"Then look here, sir," said Sancho, "you needn't go to the trouble, for I have hit upon the answer to my question. I can tell you that the first tumbler was Lucifer when they cast him out of Heaven and he came tumbling down into Hell."

"Right you are, friend," said the cousin.

"Sancho," said Don Quixote, "that question and answer are not your own; you've heard them somewhere."

"Hush, master," replied Sancho. "Upon my word, if I started asking foolish questions and giving silly answers, I'd be at it from now until tomorrow morning. When it comes to that, I don't need any help from my neighbors."

"You have spoken more wisely than you know, Sancho," declared Don Quixote; "for there are some who wear themselves out in learning and verifying things which, after they have been mastered, are not worth a rap so far as mind or memory goes."

With this and other pleasing talk they spent the day, and when night came found lodgings in a little village which, as the cousin informed Don Quixote, was not more than a couple of leagues from the Cave of Montesinos; and their guide took occasion to remind the knight that if he was resolved to make the descent, he would have to find ropes with which to lower himself into the depths. To this Don Quixote's answer was that even if it was as deep as Hell, he proposed to see the bottom of it; and so they bought nearly a hundred fathoms of rope, and the following day, at two o'clock in the afternoon, they reached the cave, the mouth of which is broad and spacious, but clogged with boxthorn, wild fig trees, shrubs, and brambles, so dense and tangled an undergrowth as wholly to cover over and conceal the entrance. All three of them then dismounted, and Sancho and the cousin bound Don Quixote very stoutly with the ropes.

"Look well what you do, master," said Sancho as they were girdling him. "Don't go burying yourself alive or get yourself caught so you will hang there like a bottle that has been let down into the well to cool. If you ask me, I would say it is none of your Grace's affair to be prying into this cave, which must be worse than a dungeon."

"Keep on tying and keep still," Don Quixote admonished him. "It is just such an undertaking as this, Sancho, that is reserved for me." [10]

The guide then addressed him. "Señor Don Quixote," he said, "I beg your Grace to view thoroughly and inspect with a hundred eyes what you find down there; who knows, maybe it will be something that I can put in my book on *Transformations*."

"Leave the tambourine," Sancho advised him, "to the one who knows how to play it." [11]

By this time they had finished tying Don Quixote, passing the rope over his doublet, not over his battle harness.

"It was careless of us," said the knight, "not to have provided ourselves with a cattle bell to attach to the rope at my side so that you might be able to tell from the sound of it whether I was still descending and still alive. However, there is nothing for it now. I am in God's hands and may He be my guide."

He knelt and prayed to Heaven in a low voice, imploring God to aid him and grant him success in this adventure, which impressed him as being a rare and dangerous one. Then he raised his voice:

"O lady who dost inspire my every deed and action, O most illustrious and peerless Dulcinea del Toboso! If it be possible for the prayers and entreaties of this thy fortunate lover to reach thine ears, I do beseech thee to hear them. What I ask of thee is nothing other than thy favor and protection, of which I so greatly stand in need at this moment. I am now about to sink, to hurl and plunge myself into the abyss that yawns before me here, simply in order that the world may know that there is nothing, however impossible it may seem, that I will not undertake and accomplish, provided only I have thy favor."

Having said this, he went up to the chasm[12] and perceived that if he was to make a descent he would first have to clear an entrance by force of arm or by hacking away the underbrush; and accordingly, taking his sword, he began cutting and felling the brambles at the mouth of the cave, the noise of which caused a very great number of crows and jackdaws to fly out. There were so many of these birds and such was their velocity that they knocked Don Quixote down, and had he been as much of a believer in augury as he was a good Catholic Christian, he would have taken this as an ill omen and would have declined to bury himself in such a place as that. Finally, he arose and, seeing that no more crows or other night birds were emerging, such as the bats that flew out with the crows, he allowed himself to be lowered into the depths of the horrendous cavern, with Sancho and the cousin letting out the rope as the squire bestowed his benediction and crossed himself an endless number of times.

"May God be your guide," exclaimed Sancho, "and the Rock of France,[13] along with the Trinity of Gaeta,[14] O flower, cream, and skimming of knights-errant! There you go, daredevil of the earth,[15] heart of steel, arms of brass! Once more, may God be your guide and bring you back safe, sound, and without a scratch to the light of this world which you are leaving to bury yourself in that darkness that you go to seek!"

The cousin, meanwhile, was offering up practically the same prayers. Don Quixote then went on down, calling for them to give him rope and more rope, and they let it out for him little by little. By the time they could no longer hear his voice, which came out of the cave as through a pipe, they had let him have the entire hundred fathoms, all the rope there was, and were of a mind to pull him up again. They decided, however, to wait for half an hour, and then they once more began hauling in the line, with no effort whatever, for they could feel no weight on the other end, which led them to think that Don Quixote must have remained behind. Believing this to be the case, Sancho began weeping bitterly and started pulling with all his might in order to learn the truth of the matter; but when they had come to a little more than eighty fathoms, as it seemed to them, they once more felt a tug, which made them very happy indeed. Finally, at ten fathoms, they could see Don Quixote quite distinctly, and as he caught sight of him, Sancho cried out, "Welcome, master, we are glad to see you again. We thought you had stayed down there to found a family."

But Don Quixote said not a word in reply, and when they had him all the way up they saw that his eyes were closed and that, to all appearances, he was sound asleep. They laid him on the ground and untied him, but even this did not wake him. It was not until they had turned him over first on one side and then on the other and had given him a thorough shaking and mauling that, after a considerable length of time, he at last regained consciousness, stretching himself as if he had been roused from a profound slumber and gazing about him with a bewildered look.

"God forgive you, friends," he said, "you have taken me away from the most delightful existence mortal ever knew and the pleasantest sight human eyes ever rested upon. Now truly do I begin to understand how it is that all the pleasures of this life pass away like a shadow or a dream or wither like the flower of the field.[16] O unfortunate Montesinos! O sorely wounded Durandarte! O unhappy Belerma! O tearful Guadiana! And you, hapless daughters of Ruidera, who in your waters display the tears your eyes once wept!" [17]

The cousin and Sancho listened attentively to Don Quixote's words, which appeared to have been uttered in great pain, as though drawn from his entrails. They thereupon begged him to tell them the meaning of it all and what it was he had seen in that Hell he had visited.

"Hell do you call it?" said Don Quixote. "Do not call it that, for it does not deserve the name, as you shall see."

He then asked them to give him something to eat, as he was exceedingly hungry; and so they spread the cousin's sackcloth upon the green grass and laid out what fare the saddlebags could afford, and, sitting down together like the three good friends and companions that they were, they proceeded to make a meal of it, combining lunch and supper. When the sackcloth had been removed, Don Quixote de la Mancha spoke.

"Let no one arise," he said, "but both of you listen most attentively to what I have to say."

CHAPTER XXIII. *Of the amazing things which the incomparable Don Quixote told of having seen in the deep Cave of Montesinos, an adventure the grandeur and impossible nature of which have caused it to be regarded as apocryphal.*

IT WAS around four in the afternoon when the subdued light and tempered rays of the sun, which was now covered over with clouds, afforded Don Quixote an opportunity to tell his two illustrious listeners, without undue heat or weariness, what it was he had seen in the Cave of Montesinos. He began in the following manner:

"At a depth corresponding to the height of twelve or fourteen men, on the right-hand side of this dungeon, there is a concave recess capable of containing a large cart with its mules. A small light filters into it through distant chinks or crevices in the surface of the earth; and I caught sight of this nook just at a time when I was feeling tired and vexed at finding myself dangling from a rope in that manner as I descended into those dark regions without any certain knowledge as to where I was going. And so I decided to enter the recess and rest a little. I called to you, asking you not to give out any more rope until I told you to do so, but you must not have heard me. Accordingly, I gathered it in as you sent it to me and, making a coil or pile of it, I seated myself upon it, meanwhile thinking what I should have to do in order to let myself all the way down to the bottom, as I now had no one to hold me up.

"As I sat there lost in thought and deeply perplexed, suddenly and without my doing anything to bring it about a profound sleep fell upon me; and then, all unexpectedly and not knowing how it happened, I awoke and found myself in the midst of the most beautiful, pleasant, and delightful meadow that nature could create or the most fertile imagination could conceive. Opening my eyes, I rubbed them and discovered that I was not sleeping but really awake. Nevertheless, I felt my head and bosom to make sure it was I who was there and not some empty and deceptive phantom. And my sense of touch and feeling and the coherence of my thoughts were sufficient to assure me that I was the same then and there that I am here and now.

"It was at that moment that my eyes fell upon a sumptuous royal palace or castle, the walls and battlements of which appeared to be built of clear, transparent crystal. The two wings of the main gate were suddenly thrown open, and there emerged and came toward me a venerable old man clad in a hooded cloak of mulberry-colored stuff that swept the ground. Around his head and his bosom was a collegiate green satin sash, and on his head a black Milanese bonnet. His beard was snow-white and fell below his waist, and he carried no arms whatever, nothing but a rosary which he held in his hand, a string on which the beads were larger than fair-sized walnuts, every tenth one being as big as an ordinary ostrich egg. His bearing, his stride, the gravity of his demeanor, and his stately presence, each in itself and all of them together, filled me with wonder and astonishment. Upon reaching my side, the first thing he did was to give me a close embrace.

" 'It is a long time,' he said, 'O valiant knight, Don Quixote de la Mancha, that we in these enchanted solitudes have been waiting for a sight of you, that you might go back and inform the world of what lies locked and concealed in the depths of this cave which you have entered, the so-called Cave of Montesinos, an exploit solely reserved for your invincible heart and stupendous courage. Come with me, most illustrious sir, and I will show you the hidden marvels of this transparent castle of which I am the governor and perpetual guardian; for I am Montesinos himself, after whom the cave is named.'

"No sooner had he informed me that he was Montesinos than I asked him if the story was true that was told in the world above, to the effect that with a small dagger he had cut out the heart of his great friend Durandarte and had borne it to the lady Belerma as his friend at the point of death had requested him to do. He replied that it was all true except the part about the dagger, for it was not a dagger, nor was it small, but a burnished poniard sharper than an awl."

"It must have been such a poniard," said Sancho at this point, "as that of Ramón de Hoces of Seville." [1]

"I cannot say as to that," replied Don Quixote, "for Ramón de Hoces lived only yesterday and the battle of Roncesvalles, where this unfortunate affair occurred, was many years ago; and, in any case, it does not alter in any way the truth and substance of the tale."

"That is right," said the cousin. "Continue, Señor Don Quixote, for I am listening to your Grace with the greatest of pleasure."

"And mine in relating the story is no less," Don Quixote assured him. "And so, as I am saying, the venerable Montesinos took me into the crystal palace, where, in a low room that was made entirely of alabaster and very cool, I beheld a tomb fashioned out of marble with masterly craftsmanship, and upon it lay a knight stretched at full length. He was not a bronze knight, nor one of marble or of jasper, as you see on other tombs; he was of actual flesh and bone. His right hand, which seemed to me somewhat hairy and sinewy, a sign that its owner had been possessed of great strength—his right hand lay upon his heart; and before I could ask any questions, Montesinos, seeing how amazed I was, went on to explain.

" 'This,' he said, 'is my friend Durandarte, flower and mirror of the brave and enamored knights of his age. Merlin, that French enchanter, who they say was the devil's own son,[2] holds him here under a spell as he does me and many other knights and ladies. How or why he did it to us, no one knows; but time will tell, and it is my belief that the time is not far off. What astonishes me is the fact that it is as certain that Durandarte died in my arms as it is that it is now day; and there is likewise no doubt that after his death I took out his heart with my own hands. It weighed all of two pounds; for according to the naturalists he who has a large heart is endowed with greater valor than he who has a small one.[3] And if it is true, then, that this knight really died, how is it that he still sighs and laments from time to time as though he were alive?'

"As Montesinos said this, the wretched Durandarte cried out in a loud voice:

'O my cousin Montesinos!
the last request I made of thee

was that when I should be lying
cold in death, thou wouldst favor me
by bearing this my captive heart
to fair Belerma where'er she be,
and ripping it from out my bosom
with knife or dagger, set it free.' [4]

"Hearing these words, the venerable Montesinos knelt before the unfortunate knight and addressed him with tears in his eyes. 'Long since, O dearest cousin, Señor Durandarte, I did what you requested of me on that bitter day when we lost you. I took out your heart as well as I could, without leaving the smallest particle of it in your breast. I cleaned it with a lace handkerchief and set out for France with it, having first laid you in the bosom of the earth with enough tears to wash my hands of the blood that stained them after they had been in your entrails. What is more, beloved cousin, at the first village I came to after leaving Roncesvalles I put a little salt upon your heart so that it would not have an unpleasant odor but would remain, if not fresh, at least well preserved when I came to present it to the lady Belerma.

" 'That lady, like you and me and Guadiana your squire and the duenna Ruidera and her seven daughters and two nieces and many others among your friends and acquaintances, has been held here many a year through Merlin's magic art; and although more than five hundred years have passed, not a one of us has died. The only ones that are missing are Ruidera, her daughters and her nieces, for Merlin would seem to have taken pity on their tears and has transformed them into an equal number of lakes which today, in the world of the living and the province of La Mancha, are known as the Lakes of Ruidera.[5] Seven of them belong to the King of Spain, and the two nieces to the knights of a very holy order called the Order of St. John.[6]

" 'As for Guadiana, your squire, weeping for your sad fate, he was transformed into a river of the same name. When he came to the surface and beheld the sun of that other heaven, he was so grieved at thought of leaving you that he plunged down into the bowels of the earth once more; but inasmuch as he must needs yield to his natural current, he rises again from time to time where men and the sun may see him.[7] The said lakes supply him with their waters, and with these and many others that reach him he enters Portugal with great pomp. But, for all of that, wherever he goes he is still sad and melancholy and does not pride himself upon breeding dainty fish of the kind that are sought after, but only coarse ones lacking in flavor, quite different from those of the Tagus with its golden sands.

"'All this, O cousin, I have told you many times; and since you do not answer me, I am led to think that you do not believe me, or it may be you do not hear, all of which pains me, God only knows how much. But now I have some news to give you which, if it does not assuage your grief, will not add to it in any way. Know that here in your presence—you have but to open your eyes and you will see him—is that great knight of whom the wise Merlin prophesied so many things, I mean the famous Don Quixote de la Mancha, who once again and to better advantage than in past ages has undertaken to revive in this present age the long-forgotten profession of knight-errantry. It may be that, thanks to his favor and mediation, we shall be disenchanted; for great exploits are reserved for great men.' [8]

"'And even if it be not so,' replied the wretched Durandarte in a low, faint voice, 'and even if it be not so, O cousin, I say to you: patience, and shuffle.' [9] And, turning on his side, he relapsed into his accustomed silence without uttering another word.

"At that moment a great outcry was heard, accompanied by the sound of weeping, profound sighs, and anguished sobs; and I turned my head and saw, through the crystal walls, a procession of exceedingly lovely damsels passing through another chamber. There were two rows of them, and they were all clad in mourning with white turbans on their heads after the Turkish fashion. At the end of the procession came a lady, as was to be seen from her dignified appearance, who wore a flowing white veil so long that it touched the ground. Her turban was twice as large as the largest of the others, her eyebrows were so close together that they met, her nose was somewhat flat and her mouth wide, but her lips were red; her teeth, when she displayed them, were seen to be few and uneven but white as peeled almonds. In her hands she carried a fine piece of cloth, and wrapped in it, so far as could be made out, was a mummified heart, all dried and withered.

"Montesinos informed me that all these people in the procession were the attendants of Durandarte and Belerma who had been enchanted along with their master and mistress, and that the last one, with the heart in her hands, was the lady Belerma herself, who with her damsels was accustomed to parade like this four days a week, singing, or rather weeping, dirges over the heart and body of his unfortunate cousin. He added that in case she impressed me as being somewhat ugly, or at any rate not as beautiful as report would have it, this was due to the bad nights and worse days that she spent as an enchanted being, as I could see for myself from the circles under her eyes and her sickly hue.

" 'And do not think,' continued Montesinos, 'that her sallowness and those circles are due to an affliction that is common to women at a certain period of the month, for it has been many months and even years since she has had that experience. It is, rather, the grief that she feels in her heart for that other heart she holds in her hands, which but serves to bring back to memory and revive the misfortune that befell her ill-starred lover. If it were not for that, even the great Dulcinea del Toboso, so famous in these parts and throughout the world, would scarcely equal her in beauty, grace, and dashing manner.'

" 'Hold there, Señor Don Montesinos!' said I at this point. 'Your Grace should tell your story in the proper way for, as you know, all comparisons are odious.[10] There is no reason for comparing anybody with anybody. The peerless Dulcinea del Toboso is who she is and has been, and let the matter rest there.'

" 'Señor Don Quixote,' he replied to me, 'forgive me, your Grace. I confess that I was wrong in saying that Señora Dulcinea could scarcely equal Señora Belerma; for by some means or other I have learned that your Grace is her knight, and that is enough to make me bite my tongue out before comparing her with anything but Heaven itself.'

"And so the great Montesinos having given me this satisfaction, my heart recovered from the shock it had received when I heard my lady mentioned in the same breath with his."

"But," said Sancho, "I still can't help wondering why your Grace didn't jump on the old fellow and kick his bones to a pulp and pull his beard until there wasn't a hair left in it."

"No, friend Sancho," replied Don Quixote, "it would not have been right for me to do that, for we are all of us obliged to respect the aged, even though they be knights, and especially when they are under a magic spell. But I can tell you that we came off even in all the other questions and answers that passed between us."

The cousin now put in a word. "I do not understand, Señor Don Quixote," he said, "how your Grace in the short time you were down there could have seen so many things and done so much talking."

"How long has it been since I went down?" asked Don Quixote.

"A little more than an hour," Sancho told him.

"That cannot be," said the knight, "for night fell and day dawned, and it was day and night three times altogether; so that, according to my count, it was three whole days that I spent in those remote regions that are hidden from our sight."

"My master," averred Sancho, "must be speaking the truth; for since all the things that happened to him came about through magic, who knows? what seemed to us an hour may have been three days and nights for him."

"That is right," said Don Quixote.

"And did your Grace eat in all that time?" the cousin inquired.

"Not a mouthful," replied Don Quixote, "nor did I feel the least bit hungry."

"Then, those that are enchanted do not eat?" the student persisted.

"They neither eat nor are they subject to the major excretions," was Don Quixote's answer, "although it is believed that their nails, beard, and hair continue to grow."

"And do they sleep by any chance?" asked Sancho.

"No, certainly not," said Don Quixote, "or, at least, during the three days I was with them, none of them shut an eye, and the same was true of me."

"The proverb, 'Tell me what company you keep and I'll tell you what you are,' [11] fits in here," observed Sancho. "Seeing your Grace has been keeping company with the bewitched, who fast and stay awake, it is small wonder if you didn't sleep either while you were with them. But forgive me, master, if I tell you that God—I was about to say the devil—may take me if I believe a word of your Grace's story."

"How is that?" asked the cousin. "Do you mean to say that Señor Don Quixote is lying? Why, even if he wished to, he had no opportunity to imagine and invent such a lot of falsehoods."

"I do not think that my master is lying," said Sancho.

"Well, then, what do you think?" Don Quixote wanted to know.

"I think," replied Sancho, "that Merlin or those enchanters that laid a spell on the whole crew you say you saw and talked with down there have put into your noddle or your memory all this rigmarole that you've been telling us, and all that remains to be told."

"Such a thing could be," said Don Quixote, "but it is not so in this case; for I have simply told you what I saw with my own eyes and felt with my own hands. Montesinos showed me countless other marvelous things which I will relate to you in due time and at leisure in the course of our journey, for this is not the place to speak of them. But what will you say when I tell you he pointed out to me three peasant lasses who were gamboling and disporting themselves like goats in those lovely meadows; and no sooner did I see them than I recognized one of them as being the peerless Dulcinea del Toboso and the other two as the same girls who had come with her and with whom we spoke upon the El Toboso road.

"I asked Montesinos if he knew them and he replied that he did not, but that he thought they must be some highborn ladies with a spell upon them. He added that they had arrived but a few days ago, which to me was not surprising in view of the fact that many other ladies of the present time as well as of past ages were to be found there in various strange and enchanted shapes, among whom he said he recognized Queen Guinevere and her duenna Quintañona, she who poured the wine for Lancelot 'when from Britain he came.' " [12]

As he heard his master say this, Sancho Panza thought he would lose his mind or die of laughing. Knowing as he did the truth respecting Dulcinea's supposed enchantment, since he himself had been the enchanter and the concoctor of the evidence, he now was convinced beyond a doubt that the knight was out of his senses and wholly mad.

"It was an evil hour, my dear master," he said, "a worse season, and a sad day when your Grace went down into the other world, and an unlucky moment when you met that Señor Montesinos, who has sent you back to us like this. You would have been better off if you had stayed up here, with all your wits about you as God gave them to you, speaking in proverbs and giving advice at every step of the way, in place of telling us the most foolish stories that could be imagined."

"Knowing you as I do, Sancho," said Don Quixote, "I take no account of your words."

"Nor I of your Grace's," was the reply, "even though you beat me or kill me for those I have already spoken or those that I mean to speak, unless you correct and mend your own. But tell me, seeing that we are now at peace: how or by what sign did you recognize the lady who is our mistress? Did you speak to her, and if so, what did you say and what did she answer you?"

"I recognized her," said Don Quixote, "by the fact that she wore the same clothes that she did when you first made me acquainted with her. I spoke to her, but she did not answer a word; she merely turned her back on me and fled so swiftly that a bolt from a crossbow would not have overtaken her. I was for following her and should have done so had not Montesinos advised me not to waste my strength as it would be in vain; and, moreover, the hour had come for me to leave the cavern. He further assured me that, in the course of time, he would let me know how he and Belerma and Durandarte and all the others who were there had been disenchanted. What gave me the most pain, however, of all the things that I saw and observed, was this. Even as Montesinos was speaking, one of the damsels who accompanied the hapless Dulcinea came up to me from one side, without my having noticed her, and, her eyes brimming with tears, addressed me in a low and troubled voice.

" 'My lady Dulcinea del Toboso,' she said, 'kisses your Grace's hand and implores your Grace to do her the favor of informing her how you are; and being in great want, she also begs your Grace in all earnestness to be so good as to lend her, upon this new dimity petticoat that I am wearing, half a dozen reales or whatever your Grace may have upon you, and she gives you her word that she will pay them back just as soon as she can.'

"I was astonished to receive such a message as this, and, turning to Señor Montesinos, I asked him, 'Is it possible, sir, for the highborn who have been enchanted to suffer want?' To which he made the following reply:

" 'Believe me, your Grace, Señor Don Quixote de la Mancha, this thing that is called want is to be found everywhere; it extends to and reaches all persons and does not even spare the enchanted; and since the lady Dulcinea del Toboso has sent you a request for those six reales and has offered you good security, there is nothing to be done, as I see it, but to give them to her, for she must undoubtedly be hard pressed.'

" 'Security I will not take,' I told him, 'nor can I give her what she asks, for I have only four reales on me.'

"With this, I handed the coins to the damsel—they were the ones that you let me have the other day to bestow as alms upon the poor that I might meet with along the road.

" 'Tell your lady, my dear,' I said, 'that her sufferings weigh upon my heart, and that I only wish I were a Fugger [13] that I might cure them. And you may inform her, further, that there can be no such thing as health for me so long as I am deprived of the pleasure of seeing her and enjoying her discreet conversation. Tell her, also, that I most earnestly beg her Grace to permit herself to be seen and addressed by her captive servant and world-weary knight, and that when she least expects it she will hear that I have taken an oath and made a vow similar to that of the Marquis of Mantua, who swore to avenge his nephew, Baldwin, that time he found him expiring in the heart of the mountains,[14] his vow being not to eat bread off a cloth, along with other trifling stipulations which he added, until vengeance had been had. For I mean to take no rest but to roam the seven parts of the world more faithfully than did the prince Dom Pedro of Portugal [15] until I shall have freed her from this spell.'

" 'All this and more you owe my lady,' was the damsel's answer; and, taking the four reales, in place of dropping a curtsy she cut a caper, leaping more than two yards into the air."

"Holy God!" cried Sancho as Don Quixote reached this point of his story. "Can it be that there are in this world enchanters of such power that they have changed my master's good sense into such madness as this? O master, master! in God's name, think what you are doing, look to your Grace's honor, and do not go believing all this nonsense that has turned your head and left you short of wit."

"It is because you love me, Sancho, that you talk that way," said Don Quixote. "Since you are not experienced in worldly matters, everything that is a little difficult seems to you impossible; but, as I said before, I will tell you more later on of what I saw down there, and you shall hear things that will compel you to believe that what I have already told you is the truth and admits of neither question nor reply."

CHAPTER XXIV. *Wherein are related a thousand trifling matters as inconsequential as they are necessary to the proper understanding of this great history.*

HE WHO translated this great history from the original manuscript left by its author, Cid Hamete Benengeli, states that when he came to the chapter dealing with the adventure in the Cave of Montesinos, he found in the margin, in Hamete's own handwriting, these words:

"I cannot bring myself to believe that everything set down in the preceding chapter actually happened to the valiant Don Quixote. The reason is that all the adventures that have taken place up to now have been both possible and likely seeming, but as for this one of the cave,

I see no way in which I can accept it as true, as it is so far beyond the bounds of reason. On the other hand, it is impossible for me to believe that Don Quixote lied, since he is the truest gentleman and noblest knight of his age and would not utter a falsehood if he were to be shot through with arrows; and, furthermore, I must take into account that he related the story in great detail and that in so brief a space of time as that he could not have fabricated such a farrago of nonsense. Accordingly, I would state that if the episode has the appearance of being apocryphal, the fault is not mine, and so, without asserting that it is either false or true, I write it down. You, wise reader, may decide for yourself; for I cannot, nor am I obliged, to do any more. It is definitely reported, however, that at the time of his death he retracted what he had said, confessing that he had invented the incident because it seemed to him to fit in well with those adventures that he had read of in his storybooks."

After that, the chronicle continues.

The cousin was astonished at Sancho's boldness and his master's patience and concluded that the good humor which the knight displayed on that occasion came from the happiness he felt at having seen his lady Dulcinea del Toboso, even though she was enchanted. Otherwise, Sancho deserved a clubbing for the things he had said, for he had certainly been rather impudent. It was to the knight that the student now addressed himself.

"I, Señor Don Quixote de la Mancha," he said, "look upon this journey I have made with you as having been exceedingly worth while, since from it I have gained four things. In the first place, I have made your Grace's acquaintance, which I hold to be a great good fortune. In the second place, I have learned what lies hidden in this Cave of Montesinos and have heard of the mutations of Guadiana and of the Lakes of Ruidera, all of which will stand me in good stead in connection with my *Spanish Ovid* which I now have under way.

"Thirdly, I have discovered something about the antiquity of playing cards; [1] for so far as I was able to gather from Durandarte's words as your Grace quoted them, they must have been in use in the time of the Emperor Charlemagne. After Montesinos had been talking to him for some time, Durandarte awoke and said, 'Patience, and shuffle.' He could not have learned to speak in that manner after he had been enchanted, but only before the spell had been put upon him, that is to say, in France and in Charlemagne's time. And the verification of this point will come in very pat in another book which I am composing, called *Supplement to Virgilius Polydorus on the Invention of Antiquities;* for I believe that in his book he forgot to say anything about cards, and so, if I put it in mine, it will be of very great importance, especially when I am able to cite so distinguished and unimpeachable an authority as Señor Durandarte.

"And fourthly," he concluded, "I have established for a certainty what the source of the Guadiana River is, which up to now has not been known."

"Your Grace is right," said Don Quixote, "but what I should like to know is, if by God's favor they grant you a license to print those books, which I doubt, to whom do you propose to dedicate them?"

"There are lords and grandees in Spain," replied the cousin, "to whom they can be dedicated."

"Not many of them," said Don Quixote. "Not that they do not deserve such a tribute, but because they do not care to accept it, as they do not wish to feel obliged to give the authors the reward that is obviously due them for their courtesy and their pains. But I know a prince who could more than make up for the others—by how much more I should not venture to say, lest perchance I should arouse envy in more than one noble bosom.[2] But let us leave this subject for a more convenient time and see what we can do about finding a lodging for the night."

"Not far from here," said the cousin, "is a hermitage, and the hermit who makes his dwelling there is said to have been a soldier and is reputed to be a good Christian, and, moreover, he is very wise and charitable. Adjoining the hermitage is a little house which he has put up at his own expense, and, although small, it is large enough to accommodate guests."

"Does that hermit you are speaking of by any chance keep hens?" Sancho asked.

"Few hermits are without them," said Don Quixote; "for those of today are not like the ones that dwelt in the deserts of Egypt, who clothed themselves in palm leaves and lived on the roots of the earth. And do not think that by praising the latter I am disparaging the former. What I mean to say is that the penances they do now cannot compare in rigor and harshness with those performed in olden times. This is not to say that they are not all of them good men, for I look upon them as such; and if worst comes to worst, the hypocrite who pretends to be good does less harm than the flagrant sinner."

While they were engaged in this conversation, they saw approaching them a man on foot, walking along swiftly and beating a mule that was laden down with lances and halberds. As he came up to them, he greeted them and was about to pass on when Don Quixote spoke to him.

"Hold, my good man," said the knight. "You seem to be in more of a hurry than your mule."

"I cannot stop, sir," the man replied, "for the arms that you see here are to be used tomorrow and I cannot afford to lose any time. *Adiós.* But in case you would like to know more about the matter, I intend to put up tonight at the inn that is just beyond the hermitage, and if you happen to be going the same way you will find me there, where I will tell you marvels. And so, once more, *adiós.*"

With this he prodded his mule so hard that Don Quixote did not have a chance to ask him what kind of marvels he meant. Being more than a little curious and never able to rest when there was something new to be learned, the knight decided that they would set out at once and spend the night at the inn without stopping at the hermitage which the cousin had suggested as their lodging; and, mounting once more, they all three made straight for the hostelry (where they arrived a little before nightfall). The cousin, on the way,[3] had proposed to Don Quixote that they go up to the hermitage and have a drink, and no sooner did Sancho Panza hear this than he turned his gray's head in that direction, followed by Don Quixote and the student. But Sancho's bad luck would seem to have ordained that the hermit should not be at home, as they were informed by a feminine sub-hermit.[4] When they asked her for a little of the best, she replied that her master did not have any, but if they cared for some of the cheap water[5] she would give it to them with great pleasure.

"If I found any pleasure in water," replied Sancho, "there are wells along the road where I could have satisfied my thirst. Ah, that wedding of Camacho's and all the good things they had in Don Diego's house, how I miss you!"

They then left the hermitage and spurred toward the inn, and had gone but a short distance when they overtook a youth who was walking along leisurely in front of them. He had a sword over his shoulder, and attached to it was a bundle, consisting apparently of his clothes, in all likelihood his trousers or breeches, a cloak, and a shirt or two. He was dressed in a short velvet jacket that was shiny as satin in spots, his shirt was showing, his stockings were of silk, and his shoes were of the square-toed variety in use at court.[6] He was around eighteen or nineteen years of age, with a merry countenance and a seemingly agile body, and he was singing short-meter ballads [7] as he went along, to while away the tedium of his journey. He had just finished a song which the cousin proceeded to memorize and which went like this:

> My purse is lean, so to war I go;
> If I had money, more sense I'd show.

Don Quixote was the first to address the youth. "Your Grace is traveling very lightly, gallant sir," he said. "Whither are you bound, may we ask, if it be your pleasure to tell us?"

"My traveling so lightly," the young fellow answered him, "is to be explained by the heat and by my poverty, and as to where I am going, I am off to war."

"What do you mean by poverty?" asked Don Quixote. "The heat I can understand."

"Sir," the youth replied, "I carry in this bundle a few pairs of velvet breeches to go with this jacket. If I wear them out along the way, I'll have no decent clothes when I reach the city, and I have no money with which to buy others. For that reason, as well as to keep myself cool, I am traveling in this manner until I overtake some companies of infantry that are not twelve leagues from here. I intend to enlist, and there will be no lack of baggage trains in which to travel from then on until we reach the port of embarkation, which they say is to be Cartagena. I would rather have the king for a master and serve him in war than wait on some pauper at court."

"And does not your Grace have any allowance?" inquired the cousin.

"If I had served some grandee of Spain or other highly placed personage," said the youth, "you may be sure that I'd have one. That is what comes of having a good master: from the servants' hall you may rise to be a lieutenant or a captain or get a good pension; but it was always my luck to be attached to some upstart or fortune-hunter where the keep and wages were so wretchedly slim that by the time you paid for the starching of a collar, half of it would be gone, and it would be a miracle indeed if a luckless page was ever able to lay by anything."

"But tell me, friend, upon your life," said Don Quixote, "is it possible that during all the years of your service you have not been able to acquire a livery?"

"Yes," replied the page, "they gave me two suits of livery; but just as they take away the habit from a novice who leaves an order before making his vows, and give him back his own clothes, so did my masters return mine to me; for as soon as their business at court was finished, they went home, taking with them the liveries which they had given their servants merely for purposes of show."

"What *spilorceria!* [8] as the Italians would say," exclaimed Don Quixote. "But for all that, you are to be congratulated on having left the court with so worthy an object in view; for there is nothing on earth more honorable or useful than, first of all, to serve God, and, after that, one's king and rightful lord. This is especially true of the profession of arms, by which more honor if not more wealth is to be attained than by following that of letters, as I have said many times. [9] Granting it is true that letters have founded more great houses than have arms, nevertheless, arms have somewhat of an advantage over letters, being accompanied by a certain splendor with which nothing else can compare. Be sure that you remember what I am about to say to you now, as it will be of great profit and comfort to you under hardship: do not let your mind dwell upon the adversities that may befall you, for the worst of them is death, and if it be a good death, the best fate of all is to die.

"When they asked Julius Caesar, that valiant Roman emperor, what the best death was, he replied: that which comes unexpectedly, suddenly, without having been foreseen; and although he spoke as a pagan who did not know the true God, yet from the point of view of human feeling he was right. Supposing that they kill you in the first skirmish or encounter, or that you are struck down by a cannon ball, blown up by a mine, what does it matter? You die, and that is the end of it. According to Terence, the soldier who dies in battle is more to be admired than the one who lives and seeks safety in flight, [10] and the good soldier achieves fame through obedience to his captain and others in command.

"Remember, my son, that to a soldier the smell of gunpowder is more pleasing than that of civet, and if old age comes upon you while you are still engaged in that honorable calling, even though you be full of wounds and maimed and crippled, at least it will not find you bereft of honor of a kind that poverty cannot diminish. What is more, provisions are now being made for giving aid and relief to old and disabled soldiers; for it is not right to treat them after the manner of certain persons who, when their aged blacks can be of no further use to them, turn the poor creatures out of the house under pretense of freeing them, only to make them the slaves of hunger from which death alone can liberate them. For the present, I do not care to say anything more to you, except that you should get up on the crupper of my steed and accompany me to the inn where you will sup with me; and tomorrow you shall go your way and may God speed you in accordance with the worthiness of your intentions."

The page did not accept the invitation to mount behind Don Quixote, but he did consent to have supper with him; all of which led Sancho to indulge in a few reflections.

"God help you, what a master!" he thought to himself. "Is it possible that a man who can say as many wise things as you have just said could have told the nonsensical and impossible tale that you did of the Cave of Montesinos? Well, well, we shall see."

They had reached the inn by now, just as night was falling, and Sancho was pleased to see that his master took it for a real inn this time and not for a castle as was his wont. As soon as they entered, Don Quixote inquired of the landlord if the man with the lances and halberds was there and was informed that the fellow was in the stable looking after his mule. The cousin [11] and Sancho therefore proceeded to follow his example, seeing to it that Rocinante had the best stall and manger in the place.

CHAPTER XXV. *Wherein is set down the braying adventure and the droll one of the puppet master, along with the memorable divinations of the divining ape.*

DON QUIXOTE'S bread would not bake,[1] as the saying goes, until he had heard the marvels which the man conveying the arms had promised to relate to him, and he accordingly went out to look for the fellow where the innkeeper had said that he was to be found. Coming upon him there, the knight urged him by all means to give him an immediate answer to the question which he had asked of him upon the highway.

"Not so fast," said the man. "My tale of wonders is not one that can be told standing up; but if you will wait, my good sir, until I have finished bedding down my beast, you shall hear things that will astonish you."

"Don't let that detain you," said Don Quixote. "I'll lend you a hand." And so he did, by sifting out the barley and cleaning the manger, an act of humility which made the man feel obliged to tell the knight with good grace all that he wished to know. And so, seating himself upon a bench with Don Quixote beside him and with the cousin, the page, Sancho Panza, and the innkeeper as senate and audience, the one of the lances and halberds began his story in the following manner:

"Your Worships must know that in a village four leagues and a half from this inn there lives an alderman [2] who, through the scheming and trickery of a servant girl of his, came to lose an ass, and although he searched everywhere for it he was unable to find it. A couple of weeks or so, according to report, had gone by when, as he was standing one day in the public square, another alderman accosted him. 'Reward me for bringing you good news,[3] friend,' the other man said, 'your ass has shown up.'

" 'That I will, and gladly,' replied the owner of the ass, 'but tell me, where was he found?'

" 'In the woods,' was the answer. 'I saw him this morning, without a packsaddle or harness of any kind and so lean-looking that it was really pitiful. I wanted to drive him home for you, but he is already so wild and shy that everytime I went up to him he would run away into the thickest part of the forest. If you like, we will both go back and hunt for him. Just let me put this she-ass in the stable and I'll be with you in a moment.'

" 'You will be doing me a great favor,' said the owner of the ass that was lost, 'and I will try to pay you back in the same coin.'

"All those that know the truth of the matter," the man who was conveying the weapons went on, "tell the story in the same way that I am telling it to you, with all these details. In short, the two aldermen set out for the forest, on foot and arm in arm, but when they came to the place where they thought the ass would be, they discovered no trace of him, nor were they able, however much they searched, to find him anywhere around.

"Whereupon the alderman who had had a glimpse of the beast said to the other one, 'See here, my friend, I've just thought of a plan that will undoubtedly enable us to discover this animal even though he has hidden himself in the bowels of the earth, not to speak of the forest. As it happens, I know how to bray marvelously well, and if you are at all good at it, then regard the thing as accomplished.'

" 'Do I know how to bray?' said the other. 'By God, when it comes to that, I won't take second place to anybody, not even to the asses themselves.'

" 'We shall see as to that presently,' said the second alderman. 'It is my plan for you to take one side of the woods and I the other in such a way as to make a complete circuit; and every so often you will bray and I will bray, and the ass cannot fail to hear and answer us if he is in this forest at all.'

" 'I assure you, my friend,' replied the owner of the beast, 'your plan is an excellent one and worthy of your great intellect.'

"They then separated as they had agreed to do, and as it happened, they both brayed at practically the same moment, and each deceived by the other came running up, thinking that the ass had put in an appearance.

" 'Is it possible, my friend,' said the one who had lost the animal, 'that it was not my ass that brayed?'

" 'No,' said the other, 'it was I.'

" 'Well, in that case,' said the owner, 'there is not the slightest difference between you and an ass so far as braying is concerned, for I never in my life heard anything that sounded more like it.'

" 'That compliment,' replied the one who had thought up the plot, 'is one that is better suited to you than to me, my friend, for by the God that made me, you can give a couple of brays by way of odds to the best and most skillful brayer in the world. Your voice is deep, the tone sustained, the time and pitch are excellent, and the cadenzas are magnificent.[4] The short of it is, I yield you the palm and banner for this rare accomplishment.'

" 'In that case,' said the owner of the ass, 'I am going to have a little higher opinion of myself from now on, in the belief that I know something, seeing that I possess at least one talent. Although I thought that I brayed very well, I never knew I was as good as all that.'

" 'And I will further assert,' said the second alderman, 'that there are rare gifts going to waste in this world for the reason that those who possess them do not know how to make proper use of them.'

" 'Ours,' replied his friend, 'cannot be of much use save in cases like the present one; but please God it may aid us here.'

"Following this conversation, they parted once more and went back to their braying, but they continued to mistake each other for the ass and meet again. Finally, they hit upon a countersign to distinguish themselves from the donkey: it was agreed that each should bray twice in succession; and in this manner, repeating their calls at every step they took, they made the circuit of the entire wood, but the ass did not answer them or give any sign of his presence. Indeed, how could the poor unfortunate beast have done so? For at last they found him in the thick of the forest, devoured by wolves.

" 'I wondered why he did not answer,' said his owner, 'for if he had not been dead, he would surely have brayed when he heard us, or he would not have been an ass. However, in exchange for having heard you bray so prettily, my friend, I count all the trouble I have had in looking for him as worth my while, even though I find him like this.'

" 'After you, my friend,' [5] the other replied. 'If the abbot sings well, the acolyte is not far behind.' [6]

"Hoarse and disappointed, they then returned to their village, where they told their friends, neighbors, and acquaintances all that had happened as they were searching for the ass, each one extolling the other's skill at braying; all of which was rumored about and discussed in the neighboring hamlets. Now, the devil as you know never sleeps but is fond of sowing and spreading discord and resentments everywhere, carrying gossip on the wind and creating quarrels out of nothing; and the devil it was who ordained and saw to it that the people of the other villages, when they met someone from ours, should promptly start braying, as if they were throwing up to us the accomplishment of our aldermen. Then the small lads took to it, and that was worse than all Hell itself. Thus the braying spread from one town to another, until now the natives of our village are well known and stand out as much as blacks do from whites; and the sorry joke has been carried so far that the victims have on many occasions sallied forth in an armed band and well-formed squadron to give battle to the ones who mock them, and neither king nor rook, fear nor shame, can remedy matters.

"Tomorrow or the day after," the speaker concluded, "I think the people of my village—that is to say, the brayers—mean to take the field against another town which is two leagues from ours and which is one of those that persecute us most. And in order that they may go forth well prepared, I am taking them those lances and halberds that you saw. These are the marvelous things I was going to tell you about, and if you do not think they are wonderful, I don't know any others."

With these words the good man finished his story, and at that moment there came through the gate of the inn a man all clad in chamois skin, hose, breeches, and a doublet.

"Have you a lodging, mine host?" he asked. "Here comes the divining ape and the spectacle of the freeing of Melisendra."

"Body of so-and-so," exclaimed the innkeeper, "if it isn't Master Pedro! We're going to have a fine night of it."

(I neglected to mention that the said Master Pedro had a patch of green taffeta over one eye and the whole side of his face, showing that something ailed it.)

"Your Grace is very welcome, Señor Master Pedro," said the landlord, "but where are the ape and the show? I don't see them."

"They are near at hand," replied the chamois-clad arrival. "I came on ahead to find out if you could put us up."

"I'd turn out the Duke of Alva himself to make room for you," the innkeeper assured him. "Bring on the show, for there are those in the inn tonight that will pay to see it and to watch that ape's clever tricks."

"Very well," said the one with the patch. "I will lower my price and will consider myself well paid if I make expenses. I'll go back now and bring on the cart." And, with this, he left the inn.

Don Quixote then inquired of the innkeeper who Master Pedro was and asked, also, concerning the show and the ape.

"This man," replied the landlord, "is a puppet master [7] who for a long time now has been roaming this Mancha de Aragon region,[8] giving a performance that shows the freeing of Melisendra by the famous Don Gaiferos,[9] which is one of the most interesting and best-staged stories that has been seen in this part of the kingdom for many a year. In addition, he carries with him one of the cleverest apes that you ever saw; indeed, you cannot imagine his like among men, for if you ask him anything, after listening carefully to what you say, he will jump up on his master's shoulder and whisper the answer in his ear, and then Master Pedro will announce it. He can tell you a good deal more about past events than he can about those that are to come, and although he does not always hit the truth, in most cases he does not miss it, until we are forced to think that he has the devil in him.

"He gets two reales for every question if the ape answers it—I mean, if his master does after the ape has whispered it to him. And, as a result, it is believed that Master Pedro is a very rich man. He is a 'gallant man,' as they say in Italy, and a 'good companion,' [10] and leads the finest kind of life; he talks more than six men, and drinks more than a dozen, all at the expense of his tongue, his ape, and his puppet show."

At this point Master Pedro returned, bringing with him in a cart his puppet theater and a big tailless ape with hindquarters that were as bare as a piece of felt. It was not a vicious-looking animal, however.

"Sir Diviner," said Don Quixote the moment he caught sight of the beast, "can your Grace tell me what fish we are going to catch [11] and how we are going to make out? See, here are my two reales." And he ordered Sancho to give the coins to Master Pedro, who replied in the ape's behalf.

"Señor," he said, "this animal does not answer any questions concerning things that are to come, but he knows something concerning the past and more or less about the present."

"Pshaw!" [12] exclaimed Sancho. "I wouldn't give a penny to be told my past, since who can know it better than I? It would be foolish to pay you for that. But since he knows the present also, here are my two reales, and let this Sir Ape of Apes [13] tell me what my wife, Teresa Panza, is doing right now and how she is amusing herself."

Master Pedro, however, declined to take the money. "I accept no fees in advance," he said; "you can pay me when the service has been rendered." Saying this, he slapped his left shoulder a couple of times, and with a single bound the ape was there and with his mouth close to his master's ear began chattering his teeth very rapidly. Having kept this up for the time it takes to say a Credo, he gave another leap and was back on the ground once more. In great haste Pedro then ran over and threw himself upon his knees before Don Quixote, embracing the knight's legs.

"I embrace these legs as I would the columns of Hercules, O illustrious reviver of the now-forgotten profession of knight-errantry, O Don Quixote de la Mancha, thou who canst never be praised enough, bringer of courage to the faint of heart, support of those that are about to fall, arm of the fallen, staff and counsel of all the unfortunate!"

Upon hearing these words, Don Quixote was astounded, Sancho was amazed, the cousin was staggered, the page was astonished, the man from the braying town was dumfounded, the landlord was bewildered, and all present were filled with wonder.

"And thou, O worthy Sancho Panza," the puppet master went on, "the best squire to the best knight in the world, be of good cheer, for your good wife Teresa is well and at this moment is engaged in hackling a pound of flax. What is more, she has at her left hand a jug with a broken spout that holds a good sip of wine to cheer her at her work."

"That I can very well believe," said Sancho, "and if it wasn't that she is so jealous, I wouldn't change her for the giantess Andandona,[14] who, according to my master, was all you could ask for in the way of a barbed wire. Mines were put in this, and any Viets who ventured into it went up in a spurt of earth and smoke. But they dug another trench alongside, and the whole thing would begin all over again.

An artillery barrage would usually begin around six in the evening and then die down, to start again about eleven. From fifty to a hundred guns would hail down shells on a piece of ground only a few hundred square yards in extent. A shelter stood up to the first shell, crumbled at the second, and collapsed at the third, so that toward midnight half the shelters had fallen on their occupants and their weapons, which they could no longer use. Then the storm of metal would come to an end and the Viets, who all this time had been digging under the barbed wire, would burst suddenly into the middle of the support post, which was already shattered with half its men either wounded or dead.

That is how the Huguette positions, and the Dominique ones we still held, fell one by one.

The next day there was a counterattack with paratroops—always the paratroops. After grim battles in the trenches which were already strewn with our own and enemy corpses, they would get hold of the support post. But how could they stay there? Everything would have to be rebuilt: the shelters were no more, and the trenches had fallen in. The first Viet shell hit its target every time, and the general ordered the final abandonment of the post.

At the field hospital, while all this was going on, we endured the same nightmare as had accompanied the fall of Beatrice and Gabrielle and Dominique 3. Before each attack or counterattack, people said: "This will see the end of it. The Viets will give way. The 'Heartbreak' column will get through and relieve us . . . Another paratroop group is going to be dropped . . . Tomorrow, if the weather is good, there will be hundreds of planes in the sky . . . it seems that lots of them have just reached Hanoi and Haiphong."

None of these things happened; and after a couple of days of relative peace everything started again.

When a man was wounded, then he at least should have been out of it. That was the idea, but that was not how it worked out in practice. No, once he was lying on the ground, wounded, he had to begin a new and dreadful ordeal. First he would say: "Where are the rest of the fellows? I hope they won't forget me . . . Ah, here they are."

"There's no stretcher left. Come on, get on my back."

"But I can't; my leg's broken. I can't even feel where it is."

"Get a move on, or we'll both have had it."

He manages to haul himself up, and his leg dangles against the calf of the friend who is carrying him. It's not worth while crying out; it won't have any effect. But he has a right to curse and swear, even if he doesn't know whom he is cursing.

"Look out, here's the first-aid post." The man who is carrying him bends down to enter.

"Ow! My leg's knocking against the steps."

Now at last he is inside, but there are already thirty wounded in a shelter whose capacity is fifteen.

"Sit down on that chest over there."

"But what about my leg?"

"What on earth can I do about it?"

Here finally come the orderly, injections, and the doctor—a lieutenant, who treated him before when the battalion made a drop at Langson. He takes a look and pulls a rubber tourniquet tight above the wound, does the dressing, puts the whole thing in a wooden splint, and ties that up.

"Ow, that's too tight."

Then he gets the official card, "To be taken to the field hospital."

"Hello, Vidal, Rivier speaking. Can you take one of my wounded? It's a leg, rather nasty."

"I haven't a bed left, old man. Ring Major Grauwin."

"Hello, major, I've got a wounded . . ."

"No room left—I'm even sending some on to Le Damany this very moment. I'll call you back. But is it really urgent? Be sure only to send the most urgent cases, no others."

Then comes the promised call: "I've got two beds free now. Send your wounded man along."

The stretcher is lifted, but it is not easy to get it out of such a place, and it is banged against the walls. Ah, here's the ambulance; you can hear the engine. That's better.

"Quick now, they're beginning to come down heavily again."

The ambulance moves off, the stretcher lying on the floor, for there is no time to fasten it up properly. They pass through refuse dumps, jolt over shell holes, up and down, bouncing and jerking.

"Oh, my leg . . . Stop, stop!"

Suddenly they plunge down and come to an abrupt halt. His head strikes the back of the driver's seat.

"We've landed in a shell hole, but don't worry—we'll take you to the field hospital on a stretcher."

The stretcher is got out, and they start again; every minute or two, they have to go down flat on their stomachs—or rather the orderlies do—for the wounded man is simply dumped on the ground, where a stone strikes him in the back like a blow from a fist. As for his leg . . .

At last they are off again and reach the bridge.

"My God, we'll never get across."

"We've got to; can't leave the guy behind."

But they have to make a dash for it. The poor leg is jerked right and left on the canvas, which responds to every movement, stretched to breaking point—and the tourniquet, which is so terribly tight! And all around there are blinding flashes, sparks, and smoke.

They have crossed the bridge and come to the square in front of the field hospital.

"My God, the tank is firing. Get down!"

The tank is certainly firing, for the shells go whistling over their heads, and the Viets reply to its fire. Ultimately the tank turns and goes back, but still with those quick yellow and red flashes playing around it.

"Now we're all right—here we are." They enter the trench and get a few yards along it before they are stopped: "Put that stretcher down—it's not worth while going any farther."

"But there's a tourniquet on this man."

"A tourniquet? But there are ten of them waiting to be undone in the emergency-treatment room."

"What's the emergency-treatment room?"

"It's where they get you ready for the butcher's shop."

In front of him there is a waiting line of wounded on stretchers, just like himself. The line vanishes into a dark hole fifty yards away. He realizes that this is his destination. The stretcher bearers have said, "We'll go and see the major," and have gone off; now they are back. "He has agreed—he'll see you in another ten minutes."

Ten minutes, then twenty. Suddenly there is a stir and the whole line is moved forward, stretcher by stretcher. Here he is, faced with the black hole, on the ground again. "But he said, in ten minutes . . ." Another ten minutes pass, then ten more. "My leg . . . The tourniquet . . . It's hurting . . ."

Another stir. The major with a nurse, at last . . . Ah, it's Geneviève herself. He has never seen her before. She says, "You were wounded on Eliane 3?"

"Yes."

"Are you thirsty? Would you like a cigarette?"

He has some fruit juice from a hole in a tin, and it tastes good. He puffs at a cigarette, a Craven A.

Good, here's the major. He feels the pulse, looks into the eyes, removes the splint, cuts the bandages: "Take care, gently, there's a tourniquet."

"Remove that tourniquet."

Blood spurts out in a great gush.

"Put the tourniquet back . . . my poor boy, nothing can be done for your leg . . . Anyhow, it's more or less amputated already. I've only got to finish the job."

He looks at the major, who has splashes of dried plaster on his arms, blood and sweat on his bare chest, and he answers, "Oh, I don't give a damn."

Once more his stretcher is lifted up and taken into a tunnel dimly lit by a few bulbs. But what is all this? Why is it so hot? And what a stink!

They turn left, then left again, and he is set down on a cot. This must be the emergency-treatment room; there are more men, wounded, on other beds, and a good deal of mess. They are very pale, asleep, looking like death. There are dozens of bottles tied to the roof, some containing water, others blood. Delicate rubber tubes come down to a needle which is inserted in the skin. One of the men stirs, moves, and begins shouting; the orderlies come along and tie him down. Another vomits over the next man, without realizing it.

Then the major is called to the phone. He says, "I can't send anyone. The jeep has gone off to Huguette 2 . . . Ten wounded? Send them to the Eighth Assault and let Patrice have a look at them . . . He'll send the ones who require an operation on to me."

Next the major looks down and says, "Dolosal, Phenergan. Atropine and morphine in ten minutes' time."

What is that he is saying? This is it, injections in the thighs, the ankle, the elbow. He becomes pleasantly drowsy and wants to sleep. Soon he is actually asleep.

He wakes up on the operating table, in a dazzling light which hurts his eyes. Then he is stripped of his clothes.

"What's going to happen to me now?"

"Don't worry—just a prick in the arm."

He is dizzy, then suddenly there is a black hole—and that is all.

Now instead of a leg he has an enormous dressing; it doesn't hurt any longer, but it's queer—it's as if the leg were still there. He touches the damp gauze with his hand. He emerges from the abyss of emptiness as from a sleep that has lasted for days. He takes a look around. On his right there is earth; but there is also earth behind and above him, on all sides: "Where have they put me?"

Some bare legs pass by, on a level with his face. He catches hold of one of them and asks: "You're an orderly? Where am I?"

"In the field hospital, and you've got one of the best places, a recess of your own—you won't be bothered by your neighbors."

It is warm and he is sweating. There's a bottle of water alongside, and he drinks thirstily.

Here's that nurse again, Geneviève. "Feeling better?" she enquires.

"Yes. You haven't another cigarette?"

"Yes, here's the pack."

There are constant explosions overhead, an aircraft engine in a dive, bullets whistling.

"Good God, I thought I was done for."

He closes his eyes and falls asleep again; his cigarette, half-smoked, drops to the muddy ground and goes out with a gentle hiss.

It was pitch dark. I had just come out of Gindrey's shelter, where there were four Vietminhs captured in the course of an attack on one of the Huguette support posts; their wounds were not serious. They were quietly eating when I went in, dry crackers with a little jam. They regarded me with indifference. Their faces bore the marks of great exhaustion.

"All right? Cigarettes?"

I offered them my pack of Gauloises. They answered "Thank you" in Vietnamese, and one of them added it in

French. He looked at me and I asked, "Where are you from?"

"From Namdinh," he replied.

"What's your rank?"

"Lieutenant. I've been six years in the people's army."

"I know Namdinh. Where does your family live?"

"I'm the son of the photographer opposite the cathedral . . . I'm a Catholic."

He was wearing a cross on the end of a string round his neck. Then he turned and nibbled his cracker, indifferent once more.

I looked toward the Eliane positions, on which our fate depended. If they were to be lost, it would be all over. There were explosions here and there, with vivid flashes of light. Flare followed flare in the sky; every now and then there was a stray bullet.

But to the left I saw an explosion that I was unable to place. An ordinary shell makes a quick flash, followed by a cloud of smoke, and that is all. But this was a magnificent fountain of silvery sparks which rained gently down on the ground. Then came another, lower, on the Second Thai Battalion; then one to the right of the track. I suspected that it was a phosphorus shell, and it turned out that I was right.

A quarter of an hour later, Patrice rang me: "I've just had four cases of phosphorus burns, one of them serious. Can I send you this one?"

"Right."

In another quarter of an hour Patrice's orderlies, who were a good bunch, brought me the poor fellow, whose abdomen, chest, and thighs had been injured by the phosphorus. I didn't altogether like the look of things. I told Perez, who was at hand, "Don't touch him . . . get some Dolosal-Phenergan and a solution of Coramine. Let me have a dish with a couple of Kocher forceps, a dissecting forceps, and compresses."

I put on a pair of gloves and slowly cut the clothing, turning it back on each side. The pieces of phosphorus were encrusted in the skin, which had a brownish tinge at the point where they went in. The smell typical of burnt flesh spread through the shelter.

"Turn out the lights."

Perez and N'Diaye wondered what I was going to do in the dark; then suddenly they saw the brilliant little phosphorescent spots. All the orderlies watched, holding their breath. All these fragments had to be removed, one by one, with a dissecting forceps, and it had to be done gently, for the pain is frightful. Fortunately the drugs had had their full effect. The task took over half an hour, until at last the fragments of phosphorus were gathered in a bowl, looking like broken pieces of the moon.

"Lights up."

Then the burns and the skin were cleaned with saline solution and compresses with a copper sulphate solution were applied.

My reserves were fast diminishing; my dispensary was like the sieve of the Danaïdes; when I got in a hundred plaster straps, there were only half of them left by the evening. I had to let the battalion doctors, who had now become surgeons, have all that they required. More doctors had arrived with the battalions sent to reinforce us. First came Rivier, on March 16, the legendary "medicine man" of the Sixth Colonial Paratroops, tall, thin and tireless. The moment they reached the ground, the men of his battalion went into the thick of the battle. They were in the counterattacks on Gabrielle, on Dominique 3, on the Elianes, with the Eighth Assault and the First Foreign Paratroops. Then came Lieutenant Rouault, doctor to the Fifth Paratroops, who took up their position on the track between the Dominiques and the Elianes; their best company, commanded by Captain Bizard, held the "Opera" position close to the airfield runway; then there was Lieutenant Jourdan, doctor to the Second Battalion, First Colonial Paratroops, who held the chief hill of the Elianes.

One day Jourdan got some shrapnel in his right thigh, and he was brought to me, smiling, on a stretcher: "It's nothing much—you'll see, in a week I'll be back in my infirmary."

I cut away some eight pounds of muscle and dead flesh and later attempted a secondary suture, which luckily succeeded. But on the tenth day, as soon as the stitches were out, he asked to go back to his battalion. He was still unable to walk; he went back in the ambulance.

Another day Lieutenant Madelaine, doctor to the Second Foreign Paratroops, appeared; forty-eight hours after his arrival he lost his two orderly sergeants, one of them Vietnamese, the other French.

All these doctors came along every morning, following a route that was both complicated and dangerous; they came to see their wounded and take their names, for very often these came straight to the field hospital. It had become the accepted thing, for what was the use of making your way through more than a quarter-mile of trenches and then having to go back again?

According to the means at my disposal, I let them have medical supplies and tins of milk and fruit juice.

Usually I received ten of the thirty packages which were dropped by parachute. Our director at Hanoi was well aware of this and multiplied my orders by three. I imagine that those in command would have preferred—and quite rightly—to get ammunition instead of medical supplies.

I got streptomycin in cases of a hundred bottles when I really needed a thousand. I got ten gallons of alcohol when I really needed a hundred.

A thousand bottles of streptomycin and a hundred gallons of alcohol dropped from the sky all right, but the violent ack-ack fire forced the planes to fly at a great height. The area of the camp remaining in our hands was now very limited, something over half a mile by a mile; and the slightest breath of wind sent the capricious parachutes into Vietminh territory. Then came parachutes with a fuse attached, which allowed the packages to drop freely for six thousand feet, when the detonator went off and released the parachute, which opened out six hundred feet above us. But aiming them was still a difficult job; and sometimes the detonator failed to work, so that the package fell on our own trenches, killing some of our men.

One drop that was greatly welcome was when we received intravenous kits known as "Bernards." Our ordinary "Baxter" kits, or vaculiters, were used up, and we had no time to clean and sterilize them properly; moreover, pieces were lost and could not be replaced. The "Bernards" were made on the same principle, but of plastic, so that they could be thrown away after use. One day I got nearly three thousand of them —a great blessing. Right up to the final day, we could each of us undertake from five to ten intravenous treatments at a time, without having to worry about those that were to come next.

After a drop, the packages had to be collected from wher- ever they had fallen—in the trenches, in minefields, in the river, in the barbed wire. The Viets chose this moment to send over hundreds of mortar shells, preventing our getting the packages and destroying some of their valuable contents on the ground.

Waiting for the darkness and a lull in the shelling, those charged with collecting them dashed out like thieves in the night and gathered together all that they could. Units were responsible for all the packages which fell in the piece of ter- ritory they held; it was their duty to collect them. There had been a special company of coolies for the job, but at the end of a week, two hundred of them had been either killed or wounded.

The men in the more distant support posts and our own neighbors generally performed miracles to fetch me packages marked with a red cross, especially if they had the word BLOOD on them. A fair number of them paid with their lives for having tried to collect a container of medical supplies.

Ice was another problem. If it was dropped by day, it melted in the sun, and in the evening I was brought a dirty little block of ice, not more than eight or nine pounds of it; if it was dropped by night, it had to be found in the dark, which was far from easy, for it was out of the question to stroll about with a torch. But it was this ice which enabled me to keep blood fresh for days.

In March I used to get containers, or rather refrigerator cases which held flasks of blood and ice mixed. But it was impossible to send them back to Hanoi to be refilled; and in two weeks we had exhausted all the refrigerator cases they had at the depot.

In April the flasks of blood came in wooden containers attached to a parachute, with the ice attached to another. It was seldom that they both reached me together, with the result that the fresh blood went bad in twenty-four hours and was useless.

After the fall of Dienbienphu, I saw hundreds of packages still intact in the barbed wire, in the mine fields, beyond our forward positions, in the river: shells, ammunition, rations, medical supplies. Who could collect them? It would have taken a suicide squad.

"To rejoin his unit." How many are the times that I have written these words on the back of the yellow card known as the "discharge ticket," or at the bottom of the usual hospital form! But up to March 13 I used to add:

"A month's convalescence at Dosan."

Or: "A fortnight's rest at Vatchai."

Or: "To go to the rest center at Dalat."

In April I wrote, "To rejoin his unit," and that was the end of the matter. It was the normal practice for superficial wounds, once they had been carefully dressed and given some antitetanus toxoid and penicillin. But when I said that for the first time to a man with his leg amputated and well on the way to being healed, he looked surprised. He had reason to be, but what else could I do?

The problem of where to put the wounded now had priority over everything else; it preoccupied me all the time.

In the main-passage shelters I kept only those who had undergone a serious operation and those whose condition demanded constant supervision, from minute to minute.

The Airborne Commandos' shelters were for those whose amputated stumps were still not quite right, for those with thorax wounds which needed draining every five or six days, abdominal cases whose stitches had been removed, those who had lost an eye and whose orbital cavity was still suppurating a little, those with head wounds twenty days after they had undergone an operation, those with face wounds who could not feed themselves, and finally those who were imprisoned in plaster from the feet to the middle of the abdomen.

In the course of fifty-seven days, a large number of the wounded saw their wounds heal. Toward the middle of April, injuries dating from the Gabrielle, Beatrice, and Dominique attacks were well on the way to being healed, if not completely cured. They were taking up my precious beds, and I needed room for the wounded who were waiting in the passages, coming from the Huguettes, from the Elianes, from all over the place.

I first began by sending them on to Le Damany, but after ten days of it he had no more room; sometimes in the evening he was able to offer me five or six or even ten places. By "place" I simply mean either a stretcher or a corner of earth with a piece of canvas spread over it. After that I had to fall back on the battalion infirmaries.

These "infirmaries" originally had ten stretcher beds; then they spread into the messes and into shelters that were empty or being evacuated. The battalion doctor naturally had to direct the wounded I sent him back to their respective companies, with instructions to come to him for dressings every three or four days. The captain or lieutenant of their company would say to them, "You fellows had better go back to your old shelters; there's nowhere else we can put you."

So they returned to the spot where they had been wounded some weeks before, to find those of their comrades who were still whole and fit. They did not like to hang about doing nothing, watching the others fire from loopholes or go cracking off in a support party or a counterattack. The moment would come when they got up and said: "Let me have that machine gun. I've only got one leg . . . Give me a chest to sit on, and then you'll see what I can still do with my hands."

"I've still got one arm left, and I haven't forgotten how to throw a grenade."

"I've still got one eye—let me have that tommy gun. I won't have to close the other eye, so it will be easier for me."

So I had to send back to their fighting positions hundreds of wounded who were well on the way to being cured—men with abdominal wounds, amputations, limbs in casts, muscular wounds or thorax wounds, and men who had lost an eye. Nearly all of these were wounded a second time, and I am sure that a third of them were killed in the blockhouses in the course of the final week.

After May 7, I went with the Viets into the shelters looking for any who might still be saved; and as I had expected, I found men with their legs off or in casts blasted by the side of their automatic weapons or suffocated in the collapse of their shelters, destroyed by a bazooka or some plastic explosive.

I saw all this in the former positions of the Sixth Colonial Paratroops, the Second Battalion of the First Paratroops, the First Foreign Paratroops, and the Second Company of the Eighth Assault. The Viets with me were astounded.

One day one of them said to me: "You told me that you had operated and cured 102 abdominal cases; we have only found 45. Where are the rest?"

"Look in your prison camps," I replied, "or, more likely, among the dead, for those who have a bluish scar in the middle of the abdomen."

Besides, the wounded themselves were quick to ask if they could go back to their company or their section, once they knew that a dressing twice a week and a little supervision was all they required.

The search for more room was never-ending; it dominated everything. A square yard of earth has never cost such a price in any country in the world.

Altogether, in the whole fifty-seven days, nearly four thousand men were dropped by parachute to reinforce us, not counting isolated drops. They all had to be quartered somewhere after the fray, yet there was less and less room. Then their wounded came to swell the number already with us.

The day came when all those who were still healthy were turned out of their shelters into the trenches, where they dug themselves recesses or holes in the walls of the trench and slipped into them like animals hibernating underground.

The wounded moved into the shelters they vacated and the most able-bodied among them became the medical orderlies.

By the middle of April, two-thirds of the medical orderlies were either killed or wounded. After all, Hanoi could not send all its best orderlies to Dienbienphu; they were needed elsewhere. Twice reinforcements were dropped, to be quickly absorbed by the battalions. Then during the day those who were fighting at night did the work of orderlies, learning to give injections and renew dressings, coming to me for medical supplies, and distributing rations and cigarettes.

Those in command would, I suppose, have preferred these

men to do other work, such as repairing and strengthening the shelters or preparing themselves for battle.

Now I was in need of more urgent reinforcements than a dozen or so orderlies. It was becoming more and more difficult to get those who were wounded to the west and the south of us into the field hospital. Sometimes they had to wait for twenty-four hours before they could hope to be taken through the trenches, or at night in the truck during a short lull. Moreover, Le Damany now had nearly three hundred wounded under him; Rondy, Verdaguet, Stermann had two hundred of them.

It was becoming necessary to have another look at amputated stumps, to trim them again, to consider closing some colostomies, to suture large spreading wounds which were on the way to healing, to take another look at fractures under plaster. In other words, we needed another surgical team.

I had already received several enthusiastic letters from Bergeron, telling me how much he wanted to rejoin me and revive our collaboration of Namdinh days; so I asked our director, by radio, if he could be dropped by parachute.

This was agreed: one evening Captain Méhay told me that he was in a Dakota flying overhead, but at the last minute the jump was forbidden. The "T"—the five lights which guide planes dropping parachutes—was incomplete, as some of the men responsible had been wounded at the beginning of the drop.

Another letter, brought me by a Legionnaire dropped in the usual course of reinforcement, told me how disappointed Bergeron had been and how impatient he was to come.

The next day Méhay phoned me to say: "It's all right this time. You can get ready to receive him." We heard planes passing overhead followed by the usual whistlings and explosions. "There they are."

It was not Bergeron, but Captain Hantz of the medical

service, tall and thin, a very likable person. "They've kept Bergeron back for strategic reasons," he told me. "I bring you greetings from all your colleagues in Hanoi."

He and his team won us over at once. I sent them along to the Ninth Group, where they were given a shelter which had been a mess to use as an operating room. Windows of a sort had been fitted up between the earth walls and the roof; they were a little too big, and every day the orderlies collected shell splinters which ricocheted on the logs in the roof during operations.

Right up to May 7, Hantz did an astounding amount of work. "I want to make up for lost time," he said to me. "You must try to rest a little; you've got a right to it, and it's your duty." He operated day and night without respite, up to the last minute. In twenty days he successfully carried out more than 250 urgent surgical operations. That borders on the miraculous.

But half of the containers for his own medical supplies dropped in Viet territory, and I had to let him have everything I could. His orderlies, who were made of the same stuff as their chief, came to see me from five to ten times a day, taking the exposed passage which led from the Ninth Group past the command post and so to our west entrance.

So I had to share out the surgical section of my medical supplies into three parts, between Vidal, Hantz, and myself. My radio messages kept on worrying our director at Hanoi, who multiplied my orders by ten to ensure my receiving at least the minimum of what I required.

The camp limits became more and more constricted, the ack-ack more deadly; collecting the packages demanded constant heroism.

I had to sterilize all Hantz's materials in my own sterilizer, as his had fallen into the hands of the Viets.

Luckily my sterilizing team consisted of two courageous fellows who were both resourceful and tireless; I never found out how they managed to stock up with gallons and gallons of gasoline for the Primus, buried in a hole dug in their shelter. Jerry cans, like everything else, fell all over the place. Who had collected them?

Before April 15 a few showers fell from time to time, pleasantly refreshing the air, but warning us of the rainy season to come; and we wondered how our roofs and shelters would stand up to the heavy and torrential rains of May.

Since February, those in command had envisaged taking up fresh positions on the Eliane and Dominique hills. The field hospital was to have been quartered on the west side of Dominique 3; the engineers' officer and myself had already worked out a plan of the new position. The command post and the services with it were due to go to Eliane. But the fighting had already decided all that.

I considered that my quarters, dug out of the ridge which was above—but very little above—the river were safe against flooding, but I really had no protection against the rain itself. The roofing was made up of so many different materials, as a result of the successive improvements made to it, and their piling up at certain points—over the emergency-treatment room, for instance—had caused slight slopes to form with little channels at the base of them. Then the six feet of earth which covered the whole roofing had faults in it, bits of girders and old roots which made other channels for the rain, so that it could come through the whole roof and pour down on us, which was exactly what it did.

When the rain really pelted down you heard a sound like the trampling of a vast flock of sheep; when it was stormy you heard on top of that the howl of the wind as it shrieked down our vent holes, putting me in mind of the melancholy murmur of chimneys in old houses in France.

The rain first came through at the entry to the N.C.O. mess shelter. First there was a large damp patch; then a rivulet went slowly from beam to beam and fell to the ground drop by drop in endless crystal beads of water.

The pace quickened as the rain penetrated other shelters. Water dropped on beds and on tables spread with flasks and instruments, dripped quietly into corners, fell more heavily on Gindrey's back and on the wounded stretched out on the operating table, dampening plaster and bandages; in the end it had invaded all the shelters and the whole length of our main passage.

The engineers came and dug drains, aided by Buezek and his pioneers—holes eighteen inches square, six feet in depth—in the crossway leading to the operating room, in the dispensary, in front of the emergency-treatment room, in front of my shelter, and all along the passage in front of entrances to shelters where the water streamed down the steps. There were large damp patches on the walls where mushrooms grew with tropical luxuriance.

The damp did not evaporate, and long after the shower was over, drops of water went on falling from the roof for days; the time came when the earth floor could absorb no more and was covered with a soft, slippery mud. It became difficult to walk; our boots, which we kept on day and night, were always soaked with water; the skin of our feet, shut up in these damp boots, turned an alarming color and looked like drowned dogs. You could walk barefoot, but concealed in the mud there were broken needles and glass which cut the soles of the feet. The mud grew thicker every day, what with the extra mud brought in by visitors and stretcher bearers from neighboring trenches.

In the operating room and in the emergency-treatment room the layer of mud came over the ankles, and after standing without moving for an hour you had to make an effort to wrench your feet out of the muck.

Shells easily penetrated the upper layer of mud and exploded deeper down when they came into contact with harder earth or logs, sending fountains of mud up in the air. Soil infections, always a great anxiety to military surgeons, became disastrous. Every shell splinter took mud into the body with it. Gangrene and acute anaerobic infections became dangerous complications to be feared with all wounds. The scissors or the knife uncovered these splashes of mud all the way under the aponeurosis, deep in the fibers of muscles which seemed healthy enough.

In the field hospital the wounded, without realizing it, got dirt in their wounds after they had been dressed and treated. Their temperature would suddenly rise, and when the dressing was removed purulent sinuses would be disclosed, reaching right into the limbs. You had to use the knife and make an incision all over again.

Roofs and ceilings grew much heavier, weighing down on walls weakened by the rain, and a number of shelters hastily erected during a lull collapsed on their occupants. At the end of April, the whole end of the main passage in the Airborne Commandos' quarters had become a heap of rubbish; the recesses there had to be abandoned, many of them folding up of their own accord.

The mud increased a little more every day. When the rain stopped, this mud began to dry in a few days and changed into a thick paste which stuck to the shoes in huge clods.

The ground at Barraud's infirmary, two hundred yards on the other side of the river, was more or less on a level with our place. By May the mud had risen above the knees, and he could only put his wounded in stretchers hung from the roof; and in the evening Barraud himself, with the mud clinging to him, would hoist himself still clothed into one of these stretchers and sleep without undressing. By morning his clothes were almost dry, but he had to plunge down into the morass once more.

In the emergency-treatment room and in the operating room, dirty dressings disappeared into the ground, swallowed up with the blood and vomit. Heat fermented this mixture, which itself became a fresh source of heat. In these rooms the patches of damp grew larger and larger. When nobody was looking I touched one of these patches, and my fingers went in as if it had been a sponge. When I thought of the considerable weight of the roof, I became alarmed. Which of these two essential shelters would collapse first? I dared not say a thing; on the contrary, I constantly assured everybody of the strength of these places.

Of course the Viets took advantage of the weather. When it was raining, no plane could be risked over Dienbienphu, and their artillery had a field day; afterward they launched sudden attacks, shouting and yelling, on support posts which were paralyzed by the mud. Then we had to think of the procession of wounded coming our way through narrow and slippery passages, with the mud rising to their knees, and the stretcher bearers with their heavy loads, trying to avoid a sudden fall into the fearful mud.

Such journeys took hours and hours; it was a martyrdom for the wounded, and often when the stretcher bearers, utterly exhausted, at last reached the entrance to our passage, they only had a corpse to bring me. I remember that one day at the beginning of May Camus and Perraud took three hours to cover the six hundred yards of trenches between Eliane 2 and the field hospital, though they were not wounded and had only their cameras to carry.

One evening toward the end of April, the rain began pattering, and then we suddenly heard the rumble of thunder; the sky became the color of lead and rain fell more heavily than ever before throughout the night. Rivulets ran across the ceiling; but they slowly vanished into the drains, so that I was not unduly alarmed.

Toward two in the morning, I returned to my shelter and began going through the cards of those to be discharged. I now had 350 names, those who had undergone serious operations, recently or at an earlier date, all to be looked after in the shelters which made up the field hospital.

After two hours' careful consideration, I was able to select fifteen of the wounded who could be returned to their companies the next day, with instructions on their cards that they should be looked over every four days at the infirmary attached to their unit.

The rain went on falling. Water flowed gently down my vent hole and made a pool under Phu's bed and Phuc's stretcher. They were both asleep. Then suddenly an unusual sound reached my ears; it was like a waterfall—that was it—a regular cascade; I could not be mistaken.

In a moment I had dashed out into the main passage and found myself face to face with a torrent surging down from the north entrance on my left, passing beneath the wounded, who, awake and scared, tried to raise themselves by pressing their hands against the sides of their stretchers. The water then poured into the two drains in front of the N.C.O. shelter and my own. In a few moments, these drains would be full to overflowing and the water would relentlessly pour into the shelters and the operational block.

In a flash, in response to my summons, everybody available had turned out. Wading as best we could, we went upstream to find the source of the water. It was coming, not from the north entrance, but from the Airborne Commandos' quarters.

It was a fact that all the communication trenches, including those of the Eighth Assault, the command post, and the artillery, led down to the Airborne Commandos, whose main passage received the water from these trenches just as a river receives its tributaries.

Our stream crossed the road by the underground passage, passed through Courtade's shelter, and poured into the field hospital's main passage.

First we hastily erected a dam of earth at the entrance to the tunnel under the road. This was only a temporary expedient, as the water that was shut in was rising rapidly in the shelters and getting into the recess. The wounded had to be placed, two together, in the upper bunks, which of course aroused a good many protests.

I phoned the engineers, who soon sent along a section of Moroccans, armed with picks and shovels.

There was only one solution, to deepen that part of the passage between the Airborne Commandos' and the north entrance, then continue the channel this would make past Gindrey's shelter and the one where the electric plant was—but there we came up against the ridge which bounded the morgue. We had to drive a channel through this ridge, so that the water could cross the "field of the dead" and flow down into the river. This was a great undertaking, and it had to be done in a quarter of an hour.

Everyone lent a hand—engineers, orderlies, stretcher bearers, coolies, and myself. We struck anyhow, scattering the mud in all directions, ignoring the explosions close at hand and the whistling that went on over our heads.

Exactly at the end of a quarter of an hour, the last obstacle was overcome and we knocked down the dam we had made at the entry to the Airborne Commandos', so that the water was released and went pouring down to the river. We were exhausted, covered with water, mud, and sweat, but we had won.

Half an hour later there was only the usual slippery layer of mud in the passage.

Heat, damp, and rot gave birth to a final disaster—flies.

They came in the first place from the morgue. But gradually they found their way into the field hospital and all the neighboring shelters. They laid their eggs all over the place, in the warm earth walls, in the trenches which had the sun on them, in the bloody dressings which were scattered all around the field hospital, in the beds, in the casts and bandages of the wounded.

Then came the maggots—though every day we used quarts of disinfectant everywhere, pounds of D.D.T. and chloride of lime. Nothing did any good, and in a few days I had exhausted my stock of disinfectants. The aircraft had other things to drop besides cans of disinfectant.

Maggots began to swarm in dirty sheets and blankets, in dressings which had to be renewed more frequently, inside plaster casts. Then the wounded slipped a piece of bamboo between the cast and the skin, hoping to drive them away, but only infecting their wounds. In the end the cast had to be taken off, the wound cleaned, and a fresh cast put on; in the evening, it had to be done all over again.

At night it was an astonishing sight to see these repulsive white grubs moving over the hands, faces, and ears of the sleeping wounded men.

Those who were wounded in the morning came to the field hospital in the evening with dozens of grubs already inside their bandages.

At first there was panic, but I did my best to reassure everybody by pointing out, "It's a very good thing. These grubs eat everything dirty, even dead bone. So they leave you with a nice clean wound; they do a better job than a pad of ether."

And it was true enough.

In the days that followed the maggots became a never-failing subject for jokes and were borne with like friends who are rather a nuisance but nevertheless remain companions in adversity.

But I could only feel that the end was near. All this misery, this dirt, this mud, this rottenness, could not last, could not go on much longer.

The wounded were reaching the end of their powers of

resistance, both moral and physical. Some of them already showed signs of mental disturbance.

I had to ask myself why God had imposed this trial upon us and where it was that the men found strength to resist it.

9.

A Day of Happiness

Sunday Mass was usually said in the operating room or in front of the entrance to the dispensary, as this enabled the chaplain to face the emergency-treatment room, which was always full of wounded waiting for the last stage in their treatment—the operation they were to undergo.

Peace suddenly enveloped all the shelters around. We were in the presence of God. Ears became deaf to the constant explosions and the rhythmical whistling of bullets. Fear and anguish in expectation of the hour which would surely come vanished, to give place to complete physical relaxation, a sort of peace and a return of confidence, a mysterious new source of strength which made men square their shoulders and brought a look of resolution into their eyes.

Since He had come, since He was there in front of us, God could not abandon us to our fate.

The scene never varied: the altar was the little metal table which a few minutes before had been covered with surgical instruments and bandages stained with blood, now replaced by the few simple things the ceremony requires, spread out on a gleaming white oilcloth.

Father Heinrich, a stole thrown over his dun-colored combat uniform, celebrated the Mass with slow gestures and with exceptional concentration. Sweat trickled from his temples and vanished down the collar of his blouse. The spirit was uppermost in his expression, the other-worldly look which marks the presence of God.

Above him were the logs of wood coupled together in the roof, while on either side were the earth walls which showed green patches of damp and various underground growths, dark and livid. Behind was the operating room, brilliantly lit, a confused pattern in which red contrasted with the purest white and with the gleam of metal.

Here and there the dark-brown color of earth showed through. The black body of a Senegalese was lying on the table, a fine statue in ebony; his abdomen had been opened, examined, and patched up. The rectangular white dressing caught the eye.

Genty was on the stretcher in front of him, raising himself on his elbows; and then there were the rest of us, the able-bodied—some ten officers, twenty N.C.O.'s and privates, our neighbors from the central command post, and some engineers.

There were also some Vietnamese, from the dioceses of Buichu or Phatdiem. The rest of the Vietnamese were Buddhists, but they were there too and looked on in astonishment.

These Frenchmen were astonishing. At the very moment when their God abandoned them and refused them His protection, even to the point of appearing to help their enemies, they came to adore Him and give thanks. It was beyond all comprehension.

Their own God had long ceased to have any place in their hearts or minds. If He had permitted such disasters as pour daily out of the skies and the suffering which they were coming up against for the first time, the reason could only be that He was neither good nor just.

But perhaps the God of the French was different? Might He be better, more lovable, more indulgent? For there had to be some reason for the peace which spread over the faces of the wounded, in spite of the physical torments they were enduring.

So they came slowly closer, pressing against us, to gaze ardently at the ciborium, quite unremarkable in itself, which Father Heinrich raised toward the log roof.

Could such things be? For they stood motionless, overcome, and a look of ecstasy passed over their features, which were suddenly calmer. Had they felt the touch of grace?

In the terrible days at the beginning of May, Father Heinrich administered the last sacraments hundreds of times. I showed him the stretchers and the cots on which the dying and those for whom there was no more hope were moaning softly; and day and night, tirelessly, he spoke the same words, repeated the same gestures. My Vietnamese orderlies were constantly present on such occasions and of course asked me the inevitable questions: "Why does the Reverend Father do that?"

Or: "Why is he so satisfied, that man who is wounded? He's going to die, so there's no point."

Then one evening—it must have been after the 120 shell fell on the clearing station—at the very moment when I had a feeling of doubt and despair, face to face with the dead and the dying, I saw two Vietnamese soldiers kneeling with clasped hands in front of the priest.

At their request he was baptizing them.

How many times have I said, "Call the chaplain!" As often in Dienbienphu as in two years in the delta. By telephone one could always get him either at the central command post, in his shelter, or at some other unit. Five or six minutes later he would appear, red in the face and out of breath, but always with a smile.

You had to make a dash for it under a burst of shellfire, and crossing the gap between the command post and my west entry was a real feat. It was the most exposed position in the whole of Dienbienphu.

I felt remorse for having summoned him when, having performed his task, he decided to visit the other wounded who were in the shelters separated from the main group. He stopped at the foot of the steps before going out into the inferno again, and under my breath I too counted: 1, 2, 3, 4, 5, 6—go! Usually there was a lull of thirty seconds to a minute between the salvos of half a dozen shells.

One day he had to go down flat some ten times before reaching the west entry. Then I made up my mind to summon him only when there was a lull or at least a breathing space. So it was my fault if a number of wounded died without receiving the last sacraments.

The night before Easter had been a very bad one, particularly in view of the failure to get rations, water, and ammunition through to Huguette 6. It was a highly dangerous trip, with the flares dropping all around, and the men were at the mercy of any ambush which lay waiting, ready to take its implacable toll of lives. Those who set out on it were well aware that it would not work, but yet it had to be attempted. Since the day before, the radio of Huguette 6 had been saying. "We have no more water, and only one issue of rations for thirty men . . ."

The supply column forming up in the trench leading to the slope in front of Huguette 6 had ten jerry cans of water, fifty gallons for a hundred men, two quarts per man. When the heat is stifling, when you can't sleep for days and nights on end, you have to drink all the time. By noon the next day nothing was left of the two quarts drawn at midnight from the water detail, which was ready to hurry off again.

You had to wait in the clinging mud of the passage or in a recess dug in the wall, a narrow horizontal recess six feet long which would just take your body; at the entrance was your head with its steel helmet. You had to slip hastily into that under the hail of shells, or when grenades or mortar projectiles were being lobbed over. You could only be hit then if the shell fell just in front of your recess, and of course that would never happen! It could happen to your neighbor, but not to you. Or a delayed-action shell which would bury you in the earth. That was better not thought of . . .

Silently the column got under way, but then the feet started making an infernal din, squelching on the mud which was now like a kind of putty, as there had been no rain for two days. You had to make an effort to pull your boots out of this glue, and the strange sucking sound, repeated again and again, became a weird sort of music constantly in your ears.

Sometimes there was the clang of a weapon striking a can and a suppressed oath:

"Damn it, there's a hole."

"Get going, you jerk!"

"Look out, there's a stiff there on the left."

Shells sang high in the air, exploding in a quick flash down there toward the command post. Here there was a queer sort of lull.

Next came the end of the trench. Then you had to go out into the open and slowly and silently resume the column's marching order. You had the feeling of being naked and defenseless before the jaws of an immense machine gun concealed in the darkness and aiming straight at you.

Suddenly, right in front and close at hand, came flashes of red and blue, sharp and terrible whistlings, the explosion of grenades, fifteen or twenty at once, in front, behind, on both sides, while above there were flares, making the night as clear as day.

What could be done? Go down flat—the jerry can had been hit, and the water trickled down your neck and along your arms. You had to abandon it and clamber back into the trench you had just left.

"Down—get the machine guns up . . . Grenades—good God."

"Advance section, fire straight ahead."

There was an infernal din, then the shouts and yells of the wounded: "Help . . . over here . . . I'm bleeding all over the place."

"I've got a bullet in the belly . . . Where are the orderlies?"

"Good God, don't leave me to die. Where are you guys?"

"Ow, me wounded, ow," cries a Vietnamese.

It was no use going on. If the Viets attacked, it would be simply a massacre. No supplies for Huguette 6 this evening.

"Fall back on the trenches. Fall back as fast as you can."

"Get the wounded in."

The wounded had to be dragged along by an arm or a leg, or you sprawled beside them saying, "Get on my back," and then with your face in the mud you crawled back with them to the trench.

As always, the affair ended up at my place, with thirty wounded and fifteen killed.

What had happened? With extraordinary speed and skill the Viets had dug a trench across the route followed by the supply column.

The next day the men in Huguette 6 returned to the central command post and were not replaced.

Easter morning was fair, and the air was cool. A slight mist was draped like an immense veil over the tops of the Dominique and Eliane hills and floated gracefully over the Namyoum river. You could see that it would disappear at the first touch of the sun, and so it did, at half-past nine.

At half-past nine, too, Father Heinrich began his Easter Mass. Gindrey had been using the operating room since five in the morning, so I had asked Father Heinrich to say Mass in the shelter next to mine, which held more wounded. Lieutenants Rollin and Deflinne were there, and Khaï of the

Eighth Assault. Geneviève was wedged between a log of wood and a cot. Those who usually came and the rest of us stood around the entrance where the shelter joined the main passage; to right and left began the long line of stretchers which never ended, and from them rose the groans of the wounded.

A few minutes after the mist had cleared, the din of explosions started. It was a real holiday—we were well looked after, with ten mortars firing at us almost at the same moment, then a burst of shells from 75's. The shelter shook several times; dried earth burst from the sandbags and fell between the logs onto our heads, onto the wounded, or onto the poor communion table.

Father Heinrich went on, deaf to these noises. But I kept my ears pricked; luckily, there were no delayed-action shells. But suddenly there were voices at the north entrance, dreadful swearing, hurried footsteps and crashings.

"Careful now—easy does it."

"Oh, my arm, my arm!"

"I can't feel anything in my leg, but it hurts, it hurts!"

I slipped out into the passage and went to the entrance: "What's the matter?"

"It's the morning supply detail, major. A shell burst right on top of them . . . four killed, twelve wounded. Your operating-room boy has been killed."

That was Phong, a little Catholic from Buichu; he was devoted and intelligent, having the virtue of simplicity, not given to words. He always wore around his neck a crucifix that was really too big for him, attached to a cheap chain; it was made of iron and had been blackened by sweat.

"Try not to make so much noise. Father Heinrich is saying Mass." So I led them all, jostling and grumbling as they went, to the emergency-treatment room. Having examined the poor devils, I gave the necessary orders and went back to the Mass.

Then suddenly there was complete silence. Not a murmur

came down the vent holes from outside. But then there was a sound, a rumbling in the distance, which grew louder—aircraft.

The Viet guns had discreetly kept quiet. Now you could clearly make out the sound of the engines, the fighters with their rhythmic throbbing and the louder pulsations of the bombers. From the entrance someone called out, "They're Navy planes!" Then people dashed out and we heard them exclaiming joyfully: "Did you see that dive?"

"See those bombs falling?"

We were eager to go out and watch. Luckily, Father Heinrich was coming to the end of the Mass; and then we hastened to the light at the end of the passage.

There was a marvelously blue sky, and the sun was warm. They were rare enough, those moments in which we could breathe freely without any fear of Viet shells, without straining our ears for the shrill whistling which sends one flat on one's face.

Even the ack-ack had stopped, and we were able to admire the absorbing game that the fighters were having, diving, machine-gunning, firing, then regaining height and beginning all over again. While this was going on, the heavy bombers, three thousand feet up, were moving more slowly and dropping huge sticks of bombs, followed by heavy explosions. The earth quaked, and huge clouds of black smoke rose up behind Dominique and Eliane and in the direction of Gabrielle and Beatrice.

"They're getting it all right, the guys over there." I've heard this phrase uttered often enough, but never with any hatred in it.

Suddenly the ack-ack started up, the heavy machine guns and the 37's. It was the moment for caution—but the Corsaires paid no attention and dived straight on the battery which was firing. Our hearts were tense.

"It's all right—God, he's up again."

And quick as lightning the plane went straight up into the sky again, marvelous in its power and grace. A few seconds later we heard a noise like the sudden tearing of a thick cloth. The six machine guns in the wings were firing. Then came the dull explosion of heavy-caliber bombs.

The attack had lasted ten minutes. Was it over? No, next came the Packetts and the Dakotas, to drop supplies, rations, medical requirements, ammunition. There was great excitement in the camp: would it be a successful drop? They were above us, six thousand feet up, and thanks to the attacks made by the fighters they came lower in great spirals. Suddenly a cloud of red, white, and blue parachutes appeared in the sky, dropping slowly, swinging gracefully, and collapsing as they deposited their burdens on the ground. If I remember rightly, not a single parachute went up in flames that day.

We were happy, really happy. When I said this to Father Heinrich, he replied, "Naturally—don't forget it's Easter today."

The packages had to be collected quickly, for once the planes had vanished, the Viets returned to their harassing fire. We had to go back into our holes. I got ten boxes and ten other packages, which were opened at once: all the medical supplies needed for three hundred badly wounded men, cans of butter, chocolate, fruit, ham, bottles of brandy and rum, cigarettes. It was wonderful, and a feeling of well-being spread over the whole hospital.

Geneviève did the distributing; for many minutes her fresh young laughter sounded above the great shouts which greeted her arrival in each shelter.

Toward the end of the afternoon, I had a little rest, sitting on a small stool at the crossway in front of my shelter. Perraud and Schoendorfer, our roving camera reporters, and Gindrey were leaning against the wall beside me. We chatted together, discussing this Easter day and comparing it with three or four earlier ones spent out here. Would this one be the last? Where would we spend the next?

The vent hole was just above our heads. It was made up of four shell cases joined together, the outer ends crisscrossed with bits of wood which prevented earth falling in when there was an explosion above. Only a dim gray light filtered through.

"Wait a minute, I've got something I'd like to show you." I went into my shelter and returned with a piece of writing paper on which, drawn and painted, was a Virgin and Child, moving in its simplicity as a primitive, or a sketch by Matisse. "Rondeau gave me this when I went around this morning." Rondeau was a paratroop lieutenant who had undergone a serious abdominal operation; he had done the picture with pencil, a little mercurochrome, and methylene blue.

The others leaned over and looked amazed.

"I can't see much," Gindrey remarked. "Suppose we open the vent hole a bit more."

No sooner said than done. With a bamboo I pushed aside the wooden grating, and suddenly a blinding ray of sunshine burst into our gloomy cave, quite overwhelming us. It took the form of a long slanting cylinder, pure gold, lighting the entire crossway and the passages right up to the dispensary, restoring an almost human look to our faces.

Instinctively I held out my hands to it, dipping them in the warm golden stream of light. But then they seemed thin and white, almost transparent, and I could see the deep bluish veins.

Why did they suddenly make me feel afraid?

Péraud and Schoendorfer gazed around them again and again, taking in the walls of rotting earth, the logs covered with mushrooms, and, just at the corner of the operating room, Bacus applying a dazzling white dressing to a wounded man who was squatting with his back to the wall.

"What a marvelous picture!" exclaimed Camus. "I'm going

to take some sensational photographs." He dashed off to his shelter, returned with a Leica, and finished off his last roll of film.

"Yes," Gindrey summed up, "the sun is shining up there for everybody, for the whole world—but not for us."

10.

The Paratroops

As soon as Colonel Langlais put in an appearance at the west entry, a wave of optimism spread over the field hospital. He came to have a look at his men, who loved to see and hear him.

He was thin and bright-eyed, with strongly marked features, the firm chin and swift gestures of the born leader. He would only have officers in his command post who liked action; he was fond of remarking that he was in charge of an operational command post, so that there was no need to put a cover on the chair in front of the folding table.

It only took him a moment to sum up a man. You could see his sharp eyes probing him, then turning aside. The man was judged, once and for all. Nor did he ever make a mistake.

At Dienbienphu Colonel Langlais commanded the Second Airborne Group; that is, all the paratroops came under him. They could not have had a more determined or daring leader, nor a wiser one; he loved his men, whom he called "my boys."

At the beginning of March there were two battalions of

paratroops; five others were dropped later, making seven in all
—and they were the cream of the colonial paratroops and the
Legion.

The first battalion dropped to reinforce the others was the
Sixth Colonial Paratroop Battalion under Major Bigeard. His
coming aroused great enthusiasm and restored confidence to
the entire camp. Everything was going to be all right, because
Bigeard was there.

He came to see me the next day, limping and leaning on a
cane, accompanied by Rivier, his faithful doctor. He had
strained a calf muscle some time before and was still, up to the
preceding day, under treatment in Hanoi, where he had been
officially advised against making a parachute jump.

"But can you imagine my battalion jumping without me?"

It was certainly quite unthinkable.

I had a look at the calf: it was very swollen and painful to
touch; it looked like a strain which had been neglected. Possibly there was some inflammation underneath, a localized
phlebitis.

"Doctor, you must make me walk," he told me. "I need to
badly."

I injected a mixture of Novocain and penicillin into the
femoral artery. He came every morning to have this treatment, and I was fortunate enough to see the edema diminish
and his walking improve. So I risked asking, "Now that
you've got as far as that, will things be better, major?"

"Oh, I wasn't really needed . . . the boys could manage very
well by themselves. I jumped for the sake of morale, that was
all."

When he was made a lieutenant colonel, Colonel Langlais
took him as his adjutant, and they were both to be seen dashing about at a tremendous speed in a jeep, bareheaded, driving
on all the dusty roads and muddy tracks, making toward the
peaks at which the Viets were launching an attack. Their
presence alone was an inspiration to the men fighting, and it

was better for them to give their orders in person than over the telephone or the radio, talking direct to the commander of the support post and assuring him that if he was hard pressed "they would be there."

Then when the hill positions fell and the fighting strength diminished, the Fifth Vietnamese Paratroops, composed of French and Vietnamese, dropped, then the Second Battalion, First Paratroops, the Second Foreign Paratroops, and finally the First Colonial Paratroops. Then the paratroop element in the camp was outstanding, not only in numbers but in quality. They had a part in every incident, in every attack, in every counterattack.

Each time a battalion was dropped, enthusiasm and confidence mounted throughout the camp: "France and the higher command aren't going to let us fall; they're sending us the best fellows of the lot."

The last three battalions were dropped at night in the center of the camp; the first two had dropped by day on the Isabelle runway, which was not then under heavy fire from the Viets. After that, Saigon had no more organized paratroop battalions that we knew of. There were two Vietnamese battalions still, but they were looking after the airfields at Gialam and Catbi, where there was also heavy fighting.

What reinforcements were left to fall from the sky?

Then, toward the middle of April, a special order of the day, signed by General de Castries, informed us that, in response to a request from the commander in chief, thousands of men in all branches of the service had volunteered to drop on Dienbienphu, without making any preliminary drop or having any previous training.

It was unbelievable, unprecedented; we could hardly believe our eyes as we read. Our hearts were filled with relief; around me I could hear the soldiers, visitors, and wounded expressing their joy and enthusiasm. Now they were convinced that everything would be done for Dienbienphu, that the higher command had decided to hold on to the end—until victory.

I had never before lived through moments so wholly inspiring, nor ever been so aware of a fellowship between men of every rank and race, united in their wholehearted confidence and in their resolve to fight their way to victory.

The first of these fresh reinforcements to come were, I believe, Legionnaires of the Fifth and Third Foreign with gunners of the Thirty-fifth Light Airborne Artillery, who had already dropped some men after the first attack on the camp. They came each night, in groups of a hundred, whenever weather permitted.

It was usually nine at night when one heard the engine of the first plane, passing some six hundred feet above us, and drops went on all night, at intervals of twenty to forty minutes. It was not hard to imagine what some little corporal of the Sixth Colonial Infantry, who had been in Hanoi only a few hours before, felt when someone said, "Go!" and pushed him into a black gulf at the bottom of which he saw flashes, explosions, and the brilliant track of tracer bullets; after the sudden jerk of the parachute as it unfolded, he suddenly found himself among flares, whistling bullets, blinding flashes, and the explosion of shells, 37's. He did not see the ground coming, as he had not had time to learn how to judge distances, but he felt it all right when the barbed wire pricked his backside and he splashed into the cold water and mud of the trenches, in the fiery breath of fresh explosions, staged to welcome his arrival.

The men of the Second Airborne Group used to come and see me toward eight o'clock, an hour before the drop. They were already equipped with a huge bull's-eye lantern, for they had the job of collecting the reinforcements, which was no simple task. They went along the trenches trying to spot those who had dropped:

"Hey, over here!"

"I can't see a thing."

"Look over here—I'll show a bit of light."

Mortars and 105 shells were falling thick and fast around them, and the whole thing had to be done at speed, getting everybody together and then running, doubled up, to the nearest shelter. After the regrouping, they were told their destination—which was never far off, being always at the end of a trench or a passage.

These drops by night were of the greatest interest to N'Diaye and Lachamp, it must be admitted, as it was the only distraction they had. They helped to collect the reinforcements on their own account, for their own amusement, and I often had to reprimand them for being out when shells were falling.

Every night they brought in three or four who asked in astonishment, "Where am I?" when they found themselves surrounded by wounded—a remark which always roused Levasseur to laughter and Bacus to sarcasm. We made them sit down on the cases of blood at the entry to the emergency-treatment room; then they realized at last where they were and began to sweat. Then we had to revive their spirits, but really it was they who revived ours.

We looked at their clean uniforms and their healthy faces which formed such an odd contrast to our own, the daggers in their sheaths and the new leather, the tommy gun still gleaming with oil, their parachute boots straight from the shop.

Sometimes one landed on our roof; there was a dull thud, then hesitant footsteps, which, a few minutes later, came into the main passage, and then in the light at the crossways appeared a brand-new paratrooper with all the clatter of his equipment. He too would say: "Where am I? I saw a little light, so I came in. There was some stuff falling outside, so I thought I'd better go in somewhere."

It was always the same thing: he had to give us news of Hanoi, France, the Geneva Conference, and football games. At last after some minutes we let him go, once we had learned all that was of interest to us, and he was taken off to the regrouping point, relieved of his cigarettes, his bottle of brandy, his bar of chocolate, and his daily paper.

One of them gave me a fairly recent Paris daily and pointed out an article beginning with these words, "Dienbienphu was a blunder in tactics and in policy." This made me jump, and I asked him, "You still came, even after you had read that?"

"What? Do you think I'd get into a funk for a few lines in a rag like that?"

Patrice often came to these affairs, and the humor of his questions further increased our gaiety. One evening he spotted a little Vietnamese paratrooper who had fallen exactly at our west entry, and my Vietnamese orderlies had besieged him with questions. Patrice asked him, winking at me, "What's your unit?"

"Me paratrooper."

"Yes, I know, but what battalion?"

"Second."

"Yes, but second what? Second Reserves?"

"No, me no reserve."

"Second Vietnamese?"

At this the man sprang to his feet, stood at attention, gave Patrice a black look, stuck out his chin, and replied, "No, me not Vietnamese reserve. Me Legionnaire."

This reply recalled to me the stinging answer I had got from another Vietnamese paratrooper whom I asked, seeing a medal on his chest, "You're a Catholic?"

"Me, no, not Catholic, me Colonial."

Another time, in the course of one of these night drops, my reserves of rum were nearly exhausted. I was finishing a cast on a leg, when N'Diaye brought along a Frenchman and made him sit on a case of blood. His face was as white as the plaster on which I was working. "What's happened?" I asked N'Diaye.

"He dropped in the morgue."

"Yes, I fell on something soft; I didn't know what it was. I touched it with my fingers and I made out a mouth, teeth, a nose; it was ice cold. Then I realized where I was. I tried to walk, but it was the same thing to right and left, in front and behind. I didn't dare move. Then shells began exploding only a few yards away, so I had to lie down on your stiffs . . . So you see it was a good thing that your orderly heard me."

After this I took him into my shelter and let him have my bottle of rum, which he nearly emptied.

When Captain Martin came to see me for the third time on a stretcher, I thought it was his last visit; but he was like Bois-bouvier; after a few minutes, when he had got over the shock of the explosion, he stood up, stretched, grimaced as he moved his head, and began laughing: "God, only a few more little holes—that's nothing. I'll just say hello to Rollin and shove off."

At the end of April he was in command of a company which embraced the remains of the First Foreign Paratroops, that is to say nearly a hundred men, most of them still bandaged. The rest were either dead or wounded. The Eighth Assault and the Sixth Colonial Paratroops were also both down to a hundred men. The Second Foreign Paratroops still had two companies left. The Fifth Vietnamese Paratroops and the Second Battalion, First Paratroops, were cut up a few days after they came and quickly reduced to three hundred men.

The "night infantry" reinforcements were shared out among these battalions and those holding the Huguette and Claudine positions. Generally speaking, ten fresh men reached each support post every morning. In the evening or at night, during so-called lulls, these support posts sent me in some fifteen to twenty wounded. So there was addition and subtraction; and the answer was . . .

Reinforcements dropped to the artillery were rapidly swallowed up by the gaping jaws of the batteries. Every day dozens of men fell around their guns; the majority were killed outright; and the night's reinforcements were not enough to fill the gaps made the day before.

One day we were surprised to see some North Africans put in an appearance; some were thin, some fat, some had mustaches, some had shaven heads. They too had been caught up in the general excitement. We had never seen that before, North Africans with parachutes. They were shared out among the engineers, or went to reinforce companies of survivors from Gabrielle and Dominique.

Losses and injuries on landing were rare; I observed two fractured femurs, three fractured legs, six sprains. That was really the minimum to be expected, an accident rate no higher than in the course of a normal drop by professional paratroops. When these figures became known, those who were all for the paratroops had a surprise, and these drops made by untrained soldiers lessened the prestige of the paratroops a little; those who cared less for the paratroops smiled to themselves, as they had long maintained that a parachute was only an ordinary vehicle, no different from a truck or a river transport.

"Now just suppose, major, that the Heartbreak column takes up a position between here and Nambac. Suppose the Paratroop Group is dropped to the east. The Viets would be forced to relinquish their hold, and then what could stop us from landing aircraft? Six hundred seriously wounded cases could be evacuated within ten hours."

So spoke Patrice de Carfort, captain in the Eighth Assault, whose doctor he was. He was cultured and balanced in his outlook; I always enjoyed hearing him propound his personal views on the military situation. He revived my spirits and gave me confidence.

As a battalion doctor he was incomparable; he had an ironic indifference to danger, and his aristocratic sensibility joined to a complete knowledge of his profession made him a person altogether out of the common run. His courage was a legend, and it was impossible to think of the Eighth Assault without Patrice de Carfort.

We often had these little talks on the situation between ourselves, during the infrequent lulls, made still more agreeable by a shot of rum or a finger of absinthe from a bottle secretly buried in the ground under my cot. Those moments of peace are never to be forgotten.

One day, while we were chatting, the curtain over the entrance to my shelter was drawn aside to reveal a smiling giant in a steel helmet, with a virile expression and large bright eyes. He came in and stood at attention. I had to stare at him again and again. No, it was not possible—it couldn't be Bizard.

He laughed and said, "Yes, it's really me."

"But a few months ago you had your farewell party."

"Yes, and a week ago I was orderly officer to a general. But when the balloon went up at Dienbienphu I couldn't stand it. I soon realized that the last, decisive battle would take place here, and I would have disgraced myself if I didn't lend a hand."

"Are you a paratrooper now, then?"

"No, I've just made my first jump."

"Good God, but don't you realize that we've had it?"

"Oh, I don't know about that. Anyhow, we might as well all be together at the end—it'll be easier for us."

Captain Bizard was twenty-seven and already an officer of the Legion of Honor. I don't know how many times he had been mentioned in dispatches—over a dozen. That meant that at home he would be a major at thirty, a general at forty. His brilliant career had already assured him a wonderful future.

Bizard and Bigeard were men of the same stamp, alike in their names and in the size and brilliance of their eyes.

He often paid me a quick visit, on his way back from the day's briefing, and he was always reliable, never shaken.

One day the medical supplies dropped by parachute fell in the position he was holding, known as Opera, which guarded what remained to us of the airfield. Some of the boxes, not too well packed, burst open on reaching the ground, and through his field glasses Bizard could make out oranges, apples, cans of milk, and bottles of brandy. "For the Wounded" was written in red on one side of a box.

But there was a snag to it. Getting them in by daylight was suicidal, and at night the Viets kept up a fire with automatic weapons and mortars; their guns were trained on the spot, and there was no dodging them.

"The wounded are going to have apples and oranges to-night," Captain Bizard asserted.

He organized and carried out a real military operation. All his company played a part in it, and late at night I saw six fellows turn up at my place, red-faced and out of breath but quite contented, as they dropped at my feet sacks full of a manna that we had never even hoped for.

I was digging into this knee for the third time. It would have taken an X-ray to spot the shell splinter; and, alas, my apparatus had been destroyed on March 16 by a delayed-action 105.

"It's the splinter still in your knee that's causing this discharge. I don't know where it is, you see—and I don't want to open the joint."

"That's all right, major. Don't worry, I'll wait. There are men in worse shape than I am."

All of a sudden my attention was drawn to one side, and I noticed the usual muddy boots; but this time there were clean trousers above them which even had a crease. H'm, must be another man dropped during the night. What did he want?

"Greetings, major."

"Wait a minute. I'm just coming."

"Oh, I've got plenty of time."

I raised my eyes and saw a face I recognized beneath the helmet there—Schmidt.

"Yes, it's me all right."

"What are you doing here?"

Schmidt had been at the artillery command post at Namdinh. We knew each other very well. "How are the Ronflés," I asked him, "and Edith and old Nadaud?"

"All very well."

"And how are things at Namdinh?"

"Oh, very quiet, you know. Everything is happening here and nowhere else."

"But you've never been a paratrooper. Is this your first jump?"

"Yes."

"You know that we've had it? A few more days, and then . . ."

"Certainly I know that—but that's no reason for my staying in my bolt-hole at Namdinh, while the men promoted with me, the ones in my battalion and in my old command post, get smashed up. So I've come along to be smashed up with them, with you. You know, I'm far from being the only one."

And indeed the next day and the day after I found the men who had known me at Namdinh turning up with a broad grin; officers, N.C.O.'s, and privates, they all came to have a word.

Good God, was it possible that with their help we would be able to pull it off?

"I was with you at Vietri in '48, major, do you remember? The engineer paratrooper, who was a neighbor of yours. Ah, those were the days! I was courting one of your nurses . . ."

"Of course, Landois, I remember you well. And now you are battery sergeant major attached to the First Rifles at Gialam? Splendid. But what are you doing here? I thought you had chucked the paratroops?"

"Well, what could I do, with a couple of sprains, a fractured tibia, and a dislocated knee? They let me go. And then one day at Gialam they said, 'Men are wanted to drive tanks at Dienbienphu.' How could I dodge it? So here I am—it's simple enough."

Yes, it was simple enough, but all the same I could not find words to express the thoughts buzzing through my poor head.

It was only the next day that Landois was brought to me on a stretcher, dying, with a shell splinter in his head.

His last glance was at me, and I treasure it.

One little paratrooper was not much over twenty. Gindrey had cut off his left arm two days before; and I had noticed how silent he was, and how reserved; he seemed shy. He had been put into one of the recesses—tombs cut into the walls of the main Airborne Commandos' trench, running parallel to the passage and slightly raised above the ground.

Wrapped in a huge white parachute stained with blood, for two days he remained prostrate, silent, and even contemptuous.

I went to see him twice a day: "How's it going?"

"Quite well."

"Is there anything you need?"

"No."

"Courage, my boy."

"Oh." This was said ironically, in a disillusioned voice.

Yet on the third day he seemed to find some relief. I offered him a cigarette, which he accepted. Then I sat down on the upturned jerry can beside the recess and, raising my eyes, I saw that six logs in the ceiling were higher than the others and so allowed air and light to enter the passage. There was less than two feet of earth on these logs.

I at once decided to stay only a few minutes beneath this sword of Damocles, for shells were falling all the time. The little paratrooper noticed what I was looking at and said, "Scared, major?"

"No . . ." (What a lie!) "But forgive me; I didn't realize how weak the roof was here. I'll have you moved."

"No, no, major. I want to stay here."

He said that with such force that I turned toward him in surprise.

"You don't often come during the day," he went on, "so you don't know. But just above me, between the logs, I can see a little piece of blue sky. I only saw it this morning and already I feel better."

"But if a shell falls there, I can't answer for your life."

"My life! If you knew how little that matters!"

"But why?"

"Oh, I'm not going to tell you the story of my life."

He told it to me all the same, and it was shattering in its simplicity—I was going to say, its banality.

It began like the well-known song:

> "*Mein Vater, ich kenne nicht,*
> *Meine Mutter, ich liebe nicht.*"
>
> (I don't know my father,
> I don't love my mother.)

From early childhood he had had no father or mother, only an orphanage and public charity; as an adolescent he had worked on farms, then with a baker, a confectioner, whose father was a retired schoolmaster. The father befriended him and gave up a few hours every evening to educating him and ended by putting him through the high-school course.

At eighteen the boy escaped into the army and made a logical choice, in the secret hope of revenging himself on the wasted years—he chose a unit with a great reputation, the colonial paratroops. Yet he suffered, for there is no place for the feelings in such units: let the best man win, and the devil take the hindmost.

Others could write to their father and mother, to their family; the day's sufferings vanish at night while writing a letter into which you can put a little love.

Then there was the mail orderly, who never called his name when distributing the mail.

So he maintained his silence and his reserve, more than ever convinced that he was always to remain a social outcast.

Now he was lying in a sort of tomb, with an arm missing, and mud all around. From time to time a cookie, an orange, or a cigarette was brought to him by a smiling young girl in paratroop uniform; he would like to talk to her at length, but would she listen? And in any case, she hadn't the time.

Then the day came when he spoke to me of his own accord: "I want to go back to my company, major, like the other fellows, if you'll let me, tomorrow or even right away, since there's a lull; there's still an officer, two N.C.O.'s, and thirteen men left."

"All right. Lieutenant Rivier can do your dressing, and he'll phone me if there's anything wrong."

"But I'd like you to look after something for me. I write sometimes, and I've written something here with the hand I have left. Oh, it's nothing much, but it's a sort of souvenir. Can you take charge of it? Because when I'm back with the company there'll be mud everywhere and my paper will be lost. When it's all over, I'll come and ask for it back."

He gave me a crumpled piece of dirty paper folded up in an old yellow envelope. "All right, you can trust me. Good luck, my lad."

I went back to my job, as Gindrey was asking for me, and slipped the envelope in with my cards for the evacuation of the wounded, where I forgot it.

Five days later—it was May 4—Bacus told me, in the course of an operation, "You remember that little paratrooper, major, who had his arm cut off and went off on Monday night? Well, he's been killed. He went back to his fighting line and a 105 shell exploded bang on his shelter."

Suddenly I remembered his last words and the yellow envelope. I searched among my three hundred cards and found it. Then I read this remarkable sonnet, written in an inferno:

MAY'S PATH

Why was this path, Suzanne, the one you chose?
   You know there is white hawthorn all the way?
   That my lips to your slender hand display
Jonquils' and clovers' contrast to the rose?
Don't you see the sweet-smelling branch disclose
   The quick birds flying, tender in song and gay?
   Where do they go? And why, can you not say,
Is grass more tender, sweeter, as each goes?
Tell me desires which check your laughter's ring,
   So short and sweet, yet strong to drive me mad,
   Seeking my thoughts and their most subtle thread.
You lay your arm on mine and gently sing.
   You know your beauty and my love? You're glad,
   Suzanne, that love is where the path has led?

Rondeau was a paratroop lieutenant and commanded a company of the Fifth Vietnamese Paratroops. It was during the counterattack on Dominique 2 that he appeared at the entry to the emergency-treatment room, erect and in full equipment, as if he had come to consult me about nothing worse than a skin eruption. "Doctor, a few minutes ago I got a small shell splinter in the skin of my belly. I'm sure it's nothing at all, but I'd like to have your opinion before going back to the top of the hill."

There was in fact a very small hole in the right iliac fossa. But I have learned to be suspicious of these little abdominal wounds which seem to be nothing at all. "Lie down for a few minutes," I told him.

I warned my orderlies not to give him any soothing injection, such as morphine or Dolosal. It did not take long, and after ten minutes Rondeau began to groan, "Oh, doctor, it's hurting like hell in the lower abdomen. I can't understand it. I came here on foot and didn't feel a thing."

Now it was beyond a doubt: the splinter was really in the abdomen.

Gindrey was taking a rest after twelve solid hours of amputations and cutting away great chunks of dead tissue. The operating table was therefore free, and I had Rondeau placed on it. His blood pressure was good, and there were no signs of serious shock. So the hemorrhage was only beginning; peritoneal infection had not had time to develop. It all augured well for the operation.

As soon as he was under, I opened up the abdomen and found multiple wounds of the small intestine on a twelve-inch segment. I did an intestinal resection and an ordinary anastomosis. But the cecum also had a two-inch tear; I had to bring it out and then close the abdominal wall above and below it.

It was all over in less than an hour, and soon Rondeau was installed in what was known as the "abdomens" shelter. There were ten there altogether; the stretchers were almost touching, but you had to leave somewhere to put your feet.

For three days, as was customary, his mind was clouded; from time to time, he was given a dose of Phenergan-Dolosal, and saline solution was constantly flowing through needles inserted in the thighs or in a vein at the ankle.

The third day he was in better condition. The abdomen was soft, the temperature normal, the pulse was 80. I was entitled to be optimistic; he could be put among those who were on the way to recovery. But the other shelters were full, and he had to stay a few days longer in the same shelter. On his left was a Cambodian who was reluctant to die; on the right was a North African who was talking all the time in his own tongue and preventing the others from snatching a little sleep, sleep which was anyhow so soon interrupted by sudden shooting pains which arose for no reason from deep within them.

On the fourth day I had no saline solution left, as was only to be expected. Those who had recently undergone abdominal operations had to have two to three quarts of saline solution every twenty-four hours and required a daily total of twelve quarts, or a hundred and twenty flasks. And I never got a hundred and twenty flasks at one time: a third of them were destroyed on the ground by the Viet artillery, and another third fell on enemy territory.

What could be done, then? Peritonitis was obviously the most dangerous complication, but next came dehydration, which is swift and relentless. There was only one way to alleviate the lack of saline solution—make the man drink. But that was forbidden; the intestinal tract would not yet tolerate the introduction of liquid, and vomiting would immediately follow, dangerous because it provoked violent contractions of the abdominal muscles which risked tearing open the sutures.

Now Rondeau, after many warnings, had to start drinking before the proper time. He looked at me with his bright and intelligent eyes and did not miss one of my words: "A teaspoonful every twenty minutes."

Everything went well for twenty-four hours; then he too began to vomit. It was painful, and it could not be checked. Luckily, one evening a case of saline solution was recovered from the barbed wire beside the river bank, at the cost of unprecedented efforts. The fluid which was to save them flowed once more in the veins of Rondeau and his unfortunate fellow-sufferers.

On the eleventh day I removed the clips from the wound.

Everything was going well; the colostomy was working; he was even allowed a normal clearance of the bowels, but three times a day Geneviève had to renew the nauseous dressing and smooth the abdominal wall with ointment to protect it against irritation from the intestinal juices, then clean the skin with alcohol to avoid sloughs.

Then he was taken to the convalescent shelter.

One evening without any apparent reason his temperature went up to 104°. Geneviève called me. I examined all the incisions but could find nothing wrong. At most there was a slight rattle at the base of the lungs. His dose of antibiotics was doubled; perhaps an abscess was forming in the abdominal wall? That happened often enough. But now antibiotics too were in short supply. I needed a hundred million units a day for those recently operated on, and another hundred million for those who followed one another into the emergency-treatment room from morning to evening and from evening to morning.

So I had to diminish doses of penicillin and streptomycin and inject sulfonamide or give it in tablet form to those who had been operated on more than ten days before, as was the case with Rondeau.

Every evening his temperature stayed around 102. Then one morning all became clear: it was a terrible complication which is often fatal—a suppurating parotid gland, that is to say an acute infection of the salivary gland which is in front of and below the ear. The swelling became huge, red, and shiny; the temperature went up to 104°, 105°; he got so thin that I was worried. I did not dare say to Geneviève that he was finished, but I told Father Heinrich, who came to see him more often.

But Rondeau did not share my opinion, and I could read in his eyes his resolve to live and conquer.

Toward the sixth day of this complication, delirium set in; he had to be watched all night, to prevent his getting up and tearing off his dressings. The next morning he was in the same state, but I received—what a blessing it was—a large supply of antibiotics. Among them were typhomycin and aureomycin.

Rondeau was at once given injections of aureomycin mixed with saline solution; the temperature began to go down, then lower still; the swelling in front of the ear burst, and from a small hole came streams of pus. I enlarged the hole with the knife. The temperature went down to 98.6°, and everything seemed to be going back to normal. However, I feared a return of this complication and ordered him tablets of typhomycin. I gave the bottle to Rondeau and explained to him, "One every two hours, don't forget. Above all at night, when you can't always be sure of the duty orderly; he has to look after those who have been operated on during the day."

Yet he slept, helped by some tablets of gardenal, and I wondered how he managed to wake up just at the minute when he had to take his typhomycin tablet.

In the other beds were more abdominal cases who, like him, had a colostomy. There were five of them in all, and the place was always smelling of fresh feces. When the rain began, the ground here became muddy, as everywhere else, and canvas had to be stretched over the bunks to catch and divert the water which trickled between the beams.

But Rondeau went on getting thinner, I could not tell why; for he took his soup in the evening with a good appetite; he often had a bar of chocolate, candy, condensed milk, and sometimes hot rice dishes. His abdomen remained soft, and his intestines were working well. There must have been some other complication, tucked away in the background somewhere. Perhaps the urea content of his blood was getting excessive? But I had no means of finding out. He was receiving the best drugs: but nothing did any good.

On Easter morning when I came into his shelter, he handed

me a sheet of paper, saying, "I've been thinking of you and have allowed myself to offer you a small present."

On the paper was the "Virgin and Child," which I showed to Gindrey, Perrard, and Mehrendorfer. Drawn and painted, as I have said, with the only materials he had, an ordinary pencil, a little mercurochrome, and methylene blue, it was a magnificent thing, a miracle of tenderness and sweetness. It was just like a sketch by Matisse.

I wondered where he had found the moral courage to lift himself out of all this wretchedness and suffering, the warm stinking smell, and the mud.

On the morning of May 1 he gave Geneviève and me the traditional bouquet of lilies of the valley, which he had made up out of the green paper wrappings of compresses, a few pieces of absorbent cotton, and a scrap of brass wire.

It was then I realized that he was a person quite out of the ordinary.

The dark hours of May 7 came along. The Viets broke into the field hospital, entered his shelter, and demanded his evacuation with the others, for the wounded had to be laid out on the terrace under parachutes spread over bamboos.

They put the stretcher on the ground near Rondeau and went to take him up and put him on it. He made a gesture: "Don't touch me."

He got up of his own accord, hoisting himself by clenching his hands on the sides of the bunk above him, then fell back on the canvas. He was naked, with only his dressing around his abdomen. The Viets took the stretcher out into the passage.

"Where are you taking me?"

"Outside, to the platform."

"I'll go by myself."

With a superhuman effort, clutching at the earth walls, he got to his feet and, slipping in the mud, made his way out.

All my life I shall remember the sight of Rondeau rising

out of the darkness of the passage, coming out into the sudden light of the blazing sun, staggering, dazzled, fearfully thin and pale, his feet in the mud, feces seeping from his dressing and trickling down his legs.

He went a little farther, climbed the slippery steps one by one, hoisted himself on to the platform, stood erect for a few seconds, looking up at the sky, then collapsed.

Under the canvas of the Viet field hospital, he refused all treatment and would not allow the Viet orderlies to touch him. I often went to see him; his filthy bed was surrounded with flies; every minute I expected to see him die.

In the end he was evacuated to Hanoi, then to Dalat; and there one night, alone, in the peace of a starry night which he could see from his window, he at last consented to die.

Colonel Langlais had invited me to lunch one day. "Come on, now," he had said, "it will be a change for you."

There were sardines from Madagascar, peas and cheese both out of cans, the usual meal, what we had every day, ending up with a little watered wine, also out of a can.

Some wounded officers, whom the colonel had taken into his command post, were also at the table. They squeezed up a bit, that was the only difference. Lieutenant Colonel Bigeard was also there; his leg was quite better, and his clear gaze expressed his gratitude to me.

At the end of the meal, I took a look at the staff maps covered with arrows and blue, red, and green circles; and my eyes alighted on a notice headed "Paratroops Available for Action."

On the left was a column showing the men originally available; in the middle, those available that very morning; on the right, the dead, wounded, and missing. It was a testimonial more effective than any words could be.

"Colonel," I said, "if this goes on, you will soon be left with nobody to command."

"Oh, well, there will always be the command post at least. By the way, talking of that, are you sure there are no laggards in your passages and shelters?"

"I would be very surprised if there were," Lieutenant Colonel Bigeard put in.

"Take a look around when you get back. One can never be quite sure . . ."

These few words were still in my head when I got back to the field hospital. It was not easy for me to make a proper investigation of all my quarters, and it was not a job I could entrust to anybody else, as it was really a confidential matter. So I set about it in a different way. I realize it was rather clumsy.

There were a few N.C.O.'s and men of the Sixth Colonial Paratroops in the emergency-treatment room, waiting to have their dressings renewed. "I've just come from your colonel," I told them, "and Colonel Langlais. It seems that with those who are still able-bodied in your battalion there's just enough to form another company . . . I was wondering whether some of you who are less seriously wounded would care to volunteer to go back to the forward shelters . . ."

My words spread like a trail of gunpowder through the whole field hospital, and I soon had reason to regret them: "Volunteers . . . Sixth Paratroops . . . Bigeard . . ."

Three magic words—no more were needed, and there was no explaining to be done. Within ten minutes the emergency-treatment room was besieged by paratroopers of the Sixth from all over the hospital. There were men with only one leg, leaning on their comrades with two; others with only one arm, their chests still encased in dressings; others with only one eye, asserting that they could see perfectly; others with limbs in casts; gasping thorax cases with feverish eyes; and last of all Lombardi, thin, naked, unhappy, and staggering. He was orderly with the Sixth, and while he was dressing a wounded man under a light bamboo roof a shell had exploded on it, a foot or two above his head. The blast had flung him down and knocked him out. In the field hospital he had lain for days unconscious, forgetting to drink, eat, or even sleep.

He too had heard the call, "Volunteers . . . Sixth Paratroops," and there he was. I was annoyed and said, "No, not all of you."

But the answer came: "The others are expecting us; now that we know, we've got to go. If they're going to be wiped out, we'll be wiped out with them."

11.

Still More Men

I think I have known all the men with the tanks, from their captain down to the privates; but however much I try, I can't remember seeing one of them without a dressing, a splint, or a limb in a cast.

Before March 13 I had got to know Captain Hervouet well. We had made friends on St. Isabelle's Day at the support post, commanded by Colonel Lalande, which bore her name.

The moment fighting started he was in command of operations in support of the infantry on the field of battle. At the end of March, when he was in his command tank, directing the fire himself from an open turret, he had both forearms smashed.

He was at my place a few moments later. His two forearms and his hands were rolls of flesh which had turned blue—double fractures in the radius and ulna, fractures in the four metacarpi of the right hand. An hour later I had encased his two arms in several pounds of plaster.

"How long before you can remove all that, doc?"

"Forty-five days."

"But that's out of the question! There are my tanks, my crews; they go out day and night, and I have to be there."

Forty-five days—exactly the period from that day to the fall of Dienbienphu. All this time he was to stay at Colonel Langlais' command post, refusing to go to the hospital and waste his time to no purpose in one of my shelters. He was to continue in command of his heroic detachment.

On May 4 he said to me, "Now you can remove this cast. It's the right time, isn't it?"

I removed the cast on the right arm. The bones were in position, and there was no deformity. We congratulated each other on the result. "In three days," I told him, "I'll take the cast off your left forearm."

"Right."

On May 6 a desperate breakaway toward the southeast was planned. It was to be carried out with all the able-bodied men and volunteers from units in the garrison.

Suddenly Captain Hervouet appeared, to say, "I want to go with them, whatever happens; I want to follow Colonel Langlais. Look, I can lean my tommy gun on my cast and fire with my good hand."

I hesitated, for it was madness—a tumble in a ditch or a shell hole and he had had it. He would be laid up, and we would have to start on him all over again in the worst possible conditions. He was risking the use of his arm for the rest of his life. "Listen," I said, "if the breakaway is really coming off, come to see me ten minutes before you form up and I'll remove the last of the cast."

"O.K. I'll be seeing you." And off he went in the best of spirits. I watched his aristocratic figure vanish into the gloom.

This bold plan had to be abandoned; it would have risked a great deal for a very uncertain result.

I saw Captain Hervouet in the days following May 7 at the Vietminh field hospital. He was confident and full of hope, but in a rage. Toward the end of May, he went off with other wounded officers to the airfield.

"You're off to Hanoi," the Viets were saying. But I saw the little column reach the crossways by the bridge, then turn suddenly to the right, cross the bridge, and disappear toward the road which led to Beatrice, to Road 41, to the prison camps.

One April afternoon Rondy suddenly appeared covered with dressings and adhesive tape. A 120 shell had exploded just in front of the entrance to his infirmary. Fortunately it was nothing serious, as none of the splinters had penetrated very deeply. Four doctors had already been wounded; not one had been killed; it was a piece of luck, and a great blessing. But death had exacted a heavy toll among the medical orderlies. By April 20, nearly two-thirds of the medical staff were gone.

I needed men to replace them, men to replace those splendid men, Mitry, Geay, Moret, De Cia, Mathy, and so many others.

The first drop landed eight medical orderlies, who were immediately absorbed into the Eighth and the Sixth Colonial Paratroops.

Faced with the growing number of wounded in my shelters, my staff was not large enough to cope with all the work. I asked Hanoi to send trained medical orderlies to reinforce us, but for three days there was no reply.

Bacus and Levasseur could not get over their indignation: "It's not surprising—those guys skulking at Lanessan . . . they've got white sheets and ventilators and their girl friends . . ."

Reinforcements arrived all the same. There were two sergeants, Alonso and Camara, Corporal Yahia, and Pfc. Florés; but there was one missing, Dumondelle. We searched for him. He had simply landed on our terrace, just in front of the north entry, but he had fractured a femur and came into the field hospital on a stretcher. I immediately put him in a cast and found a bed for him; and there he remained until May 7.

Most of them were hospital orderlies, used to a quiet time and regular hours of work. They had jumped for the first time in their lives.

Levasseur and Bacus could not get over their astonishment.

We had already received some reinforcements: the airmen stranded at Dienbienphu in the early days of the attack, and then some military police—yes, real military police. There were nine of them. Before the attack they policed the road and the airfield and drew up correct reports on breaches of military discipline. On March 13 their chief, Sergeant Major Salaun, came to see me and said, "We've got nothing left to do, major, so we've come to put ourselves at your disposal."

I rang the command post and got their consent. So they became the most daring of stretcher bearers, devoted and conscientious medical orderlies, intelligent and effective in the help they gave. Reliable, calm, scornful of danger, they were liked by all the wounded. One of them, Sergeant Arnone, was killed at his post.

His post was the kitchen, installed in a hole covered with a piece of canvas. After all, they had to eat, these poor fellows, and you could not make a fire in the passage. One day he got a piece of shell right in his chest. Another of them, Sansus, was seriously wounded.

Every morning and evening they distributed hot coffee or a thick soup which smelled very good. And each time it was a feat to accomplish.

"Good God," said Julot, who in civilian life had had trouble with the police, "the cops bring me coffee in bed every morning, can you believe it? The world has gone mad. My father will never believe it."

Jimmy was the dentist's boy, fifteen years old, always laughing and bounding about, the field hospital's mascot, paying no heed to danger. Every morning, around seven, whether I was up or still in bed, he used to bring me hot coffee, which I shared with Phu, Phuc, and Sergeant Yann, the other occupants of my shelter: "Hot coffee, very hot, very good, this morning."

I always noticed that he was in a hurry and short of breath. I could not help smiling, knowing that he had to run quickly down the passage leading to the kitchen, for it was open to the sky.

One day a 105 shell exploded just in front of him: he had an arm torn off and the left thigh opened and fractured. He was brought to me at once, a poor bleeding puppet whose joints would no longer work: "Poor me, major, poor me."

His eyes were frenzied, and the nails of his cold hand dug into my arm: "Stay with me, major, stay with me, major."

The stream of usual orders issued from my mouth: Dolosal, Phenergan, antitetanus toxoid, antigangrene, hemostatics, blood.

The needles went quickly into what remained of the skin. The blood pressure was dropping; his angel's face became waxen.

"Increase the blood, keep the leg straight. Coramine, Syncortyl."

An hour later the blood pressure was satisfactory. Gindrey operated on him, amputating the left arm, encasing the pelvis and the left leg in plaster.

I saw him again the next day; he was terribly pale, but conscious; a quiet little voice, toneless and almost extinguished, said, "It hurts, major, but all the same it's all right."

The one hand left to him, warm and transparent, was

placed on mine as he said, "Who'll bring your coffee in the morning, major?"

What am I to say about the Vietnamese? Their faces and gestures showed their pride in being paratroopers or Legionnaires. They modeled their attitude, their daring, courage, and fighting qualities on those of the white friends who were in command of them.

On stretchers or cots they lived side by side with their brothers-in-arms, sharing the same sufferings with the same silent resignation.

On only two occasions did I have to amputate both legs at once, first for a Chinese paratrooper, the second time for a Vietnamese paratrooper. They had been cut down as they stood erect, facing the enemy.

Every day I saw the courage of my medical orderlies, my stretcher bearers, my water carriers, my coolies who fetched the rations. At the beginning there were thirty of them; by May 7, there were nineteen.

Clip, clop! Two bare feet stopped in the mud beside me. The trousers were turned up to the knees, and there was a layer of dried mud around the calves. I raised my eyes to see a tall, thin Chinese in a paratrooper's combat uniform—torn, of course, and dirty and covered with blood. He was supporting his right elbow with his left hand; it did not seem to be very serious. There was a gentle smile on his pale face.

I called for N'Diaye, for I was out of sorts: "I've told you to ring every first-aid post and tell them only to send me men who are seriously wounded and need to be operated on at once."

"I did, major."

"Then what's this man doing here?"

Then I heard a faint voice saying, "It's me, forgive me, major—me wounded in the side here with Vietminh shell. Me know, major too much work, but if major look a little, me got much pain here. Then me go—forgive me very much."

Then I got up and had a look at the poor fellow. A piece of shell had smashed up his right arm; only the skin on the inner side of the arm was untouched—the rest was a gory mess. Blood was pouring between the fingers of his left hand and disappearing between his skin and the belt of his trousers.

"Quick, a stretcher," I called out, "Dolosal, Phenergan. Get out a flask of blood."

I just had time to get hold of him before he lost consciousness, still with that embarrassed little smile on his face. An hour later he had been operated on; Gindrey could do it by then in seven minutes. I was present when he came to.

"Where do you come from?" I asked. "Where's your family?"

"Moncay," he answered.

"How many *Ti gno?*"

"Three."

"Wife? Children?"

"One wife, two children."

"How will you manage now when you're back in civilian life?"

"Oh, that's nothing—work with one arm—maybe army give me a few piasters."

"Yes, you can be sure of that. Now, go to sleep. You're to stay here with me."

"No, major, not right. Want to go back to comrades. To-day, still tired—tomorrow back to company."

Right up to the last day, our cook and his two assistants gave us a hot meal every evening—made from canned stuff, of course. The coffee was always good and sweet; from time to time they even managed to give us a fancy dish or a chocolate custard.

It was a real feat, when I consider the kitchen shelter,

which had half collapsed and been flooded, while one side of the passage to it was smashed up and mortars were constantly lobbing shells over.

Can I ever forget Phu, who saved my life at Thaibinh, or my orderly Than, who saved it a second time at Namdinh?

When I went to Namdinh for the first time in 1947, nearly all the wounded were Europeans. Of a hundred wounded, only five were Vietnamese. By 1953 it was the other way round: of a hundred wounded, five were Europeans, and ninety-five were Vietnamese.

The first reinforcements that General de Castries got were airmen.

A few pilots had been able to get away, the day after Gabrielle fell. We knew that they had come back overhead with new machines, and I was sure that they had no need of instructions from the command post to attack and machine-gun the Viet positions.

The rest of the men were left at Dienbienphu; those in the observation group were attached to the artillery and took part in the defense of the batteries; others of the air detachment, radio operators, mechanics, clerks, general service men, who were left without a job, were grouped in a company under Captain Charnod, also of the air force. This company was quartered at the Junon support post, at the extreme south of the main camp, between the river on the east and the ammunition dump on the west. This support post was in the area of the First Foreign Paratroops, commanded by Major Guiraud.

Charnod's company took part every time in opening up the Isabelle road during the second half of March, and then in the attacks and counterattacks on the Eliane and Dominique positions. The company also formed a workshop unit, sections for collecting material dropped by parachute, and sections of workers who restored shelters.

A few minutes later, Gindrey and I were poring over an abdomen that was open from the sternum to the pubis when suddenly the strains of a German song that I knew well came floating to us:

Wenn alle Brünnlein fliessen,
So muss man trinken.

(When all the springs are flowing,
That's when you have to drink.)

In 1932, at a summer camp in Potsdam, I had learned this song with young Germans of my own age.

The voice was serious and extremely musical:

Sie hat zwei blaue Augelein . . . (She has two blue eyes.)

"That's pretty good, but tell him to shut up," I told Bacus. "I've told him to, major, but he won't. It's Sturm, the one to be amputated next."

For an hour he sang without stopping.

Gindrey and I exchanged glances from time to time—no need to say anything. The fellow was going mad. Exhaustion, then the shock of the explosion and the wound, the injection of morphine . . . it was the old story. Often they had to be tied down, but this one was the quiet type.

After the operation I went and had a look at him. I leaned over him and put my hand on his forehead: "Why are you singing?"

His face was quite serious and his voice was calm and reasonable as he replied in German, "If I don't sing, major, I think of that—" he glanced at his side—"and then the pain comes back. Don't worry—once all this mess is taken off I won't trouble you again."

It was quite true, for I saw him every morning afterward. As soon as he caught sight of me, he came correctly to attention with his one good arm firmly at his side, eyes front, his face rigid. There were eight of them in his shelter, and he was the most silent of them and the one who gave least trouble; on the fifth day he too said, "Major, I want to go back to my company. There are still twenty-seven of them, that's all—I can still be some help."

Sitting on the edge of Yann's stretcher—he was my Chinese friend who had had both his legs amputated—with my head bowed down and my hands on my ankles I had a look at the celebrated ray of sunlight which Camus and Perraud got so excited about. From there I could see in front of me the passage leading to the operating room and the dispensary, on the right the one leading to the abdominal cases, and on the left the one leading to the north exit—or rather entrance.

It was almost the only place where you could breathe properly. A slight draft laden with stench ran through the passage; if it came from the north, you smelled rotting corpses; if from the west, it brought the putrid stink of urine —but at least there was a little change of atmosphere, and you did not have the foul and stagnant smell of the shelters perpetually in your nostrils, throat, and head.

There, toward four in the morning, a Legion paratrooper had died—right leg smashed, splinters in the left eye socket, a complex wound in the abdomen.

He was the most traditional type of German, pale, blond, and blue-eyed, I could still hear his long, rhythmic howls and his rapid, irregular gasps: "*Meine Mutter, meine Mutter!*" Why is it that this wild cry for a man's mother, at the point of death, is always so shattering?

"*Ich kann nicht hier crepieren, ich muss nach Hause geben, ich muss.*" (I can't die here, I must go home, I must.)

All were suddenly silent in the passage, from the coolie to the sergeant major; and the rest of the wounded, waiting on their stretchers, checked their low moans. Even N'Diaye omitted to shout his usual rebuke.

No drug, even the strongest, had had any effect. Was the

tonic wine he had taken at the root of this power of resistance? No, it was not the first time that I had come across a case of this sort. With some men the will to live is so strong that their consciousness is proof not only against exhaustion but even against drugs freshly administered.

The will to live or the fear of death? How should I know?

I could have given him another injection of Phenergan-Dolosal, but that was out of the question, as I only had fifty phials left; or an intravenous injection of Pentothal, but that would be to kill him outright.

He had to be tightly bound down, hands and feet tied to the sides of the stretcher, and he made fantastic efforts to free himself. His muscles became as hard as stone, swelling under the skin as if they would burst. The one eye he had left seemed to rise from its socket in a most terrifying way, as if it were already fixed on a vision of the other world. Then suddenly he fell back, his breathing stopped, all his muscles relaxed and stretched out under the skin like so many small animals relieved to find rest at last. With his deeply marked features in a face the color of ivory, he became a magnificent figure in repose.

As I gently closed the eye he had left, I thought of this mother he had been calling for, the mother whom I never knew and shall never know.

12.

Last Round of Inspection

It was the fifth of May, the night of the fifth. Work in the operating room had just stopped. The last man to be operated on was still lying on the table. Without a word Gindrey and his team had dropped down here and there and fallen asleep right away.

Work was to start again at five in the morning; my duty orderly was to call the whole staff at a quarter to five.

I only heard the footsteps of the assistants and coolies who were awake, and the calls of the wounded from the farther shelters: "Orderly, give me a drink . . . I'm thirsty . . . It hurts."

All of a sudden there was a rumbling sound, explosions, whistlings, and rain—rain which we now feared more than anything else.

I went through my discharge cards. In the morning there would be seven to move on, making room for seven more wounded. My feet were in water and mud. We had to put boxes under Phuc's stretcher.

I had an urge to sleep that I could not resist; so I went and lay down on my cot.

Suddenly I was awake again. What was wrong? I had heard nobody cry out, so why had I wakened? I heard the dull, slow sound of something slipping—something collapsing, that was it.

In a moment I had sprung to my feet. Phu was sleeping peacefully. Phuc called out, "Major, I'm scared."

I tore aside the piece of canvas which cut off my corner of the shelter, to find that the whole of the left wall had collapsed. I woke Phu with a thump: "Quick, get up—we've got to get Phuc and Yann Phu out." I carried them out in my arms; they were not very heavy. Then I went out into the passage and shouted, "N'Diaye, Lachamp!"

Soon we were all there, staring at the disaster. The fall of earth had overturned my basin, covered my little office table and the box of discharge cards. On the left we were faced with the menace of a great gloomy hole in place of a wall; water oozed gently in. You could see the white ends of the bamboos which no longer had anything to support them.

At once my thoughts turned to Fleury. The props that he had erected were sustaining the whole weight of the ceiling. If it had not been for him, Phu and Phuc and I would all have been buried beyond hope of rescue. "Well, that's over; you can go back to sleep. I'll get the engineers in tomorrow," I told them.

Phu lay down on a stretcher in the passage; we had found a couple of places for Phuc and Yann in the emergency-treatment room.

I was alone once more, but all desire for sleep had left me. So I was going to make my round of inspection that I had not had time for that day. Besides, it was easier now; except when big attacks were being launched, the nights were always a little quieter than the days.

I went out into the main passage, wading and slipping; the water oozed and glided past, at one moment black as mud, then with a gleam in it. There was a line of stretchers on either

side, a wounded man, then an orderly, then more wounded . . .
On the right were three paratroopers with chest wounds; they
had been put there because the air was a little better; they
were propped up, head and back leaning against the earth
wall.

Two stretchers slung from the logs in the roof held N'Diaye,
so good and reliable, overwhelmed with fatigue, and Sioni,
asleep with his mouth wide open; his left leg dangled peril-
ously over the edge of the stretcher.

I went to the shelter which housed my ten most recently
operated abdominal cases. It was always the same inside. At
the entrance five coolies were lying bunched together. In a
corner were pots full of urine and feces; it was a problem to
empty them: you had to go outside, throw away the contents,
and clean them; but shells were falling all the time. Two days
before, a man engaged in this task had been struck down just
above the steps of the west exit; his hand was still clenched
on the handle of the chamber pot.

There were always flasks of plasma, saline solution, and the
tubes of new vaculiters, strapped to the roof; then there were
always the same cries:

"Major, let me have a mouthful."

"*Ong tu nhoc.*"

"*Louk sak boun, Toek.*"

"*Si ra koun, nhoc!*"

"*Kommandant, bitte Wasser.*"

"Major, *d'lou*, give me *d'lou*."

All that boils down to: "Water, major."

Tomorrow I would be left once more without any saline
solution. I had to give some to Hantz, Vidal, Patrice, and
Rondy. Then my abdominal cases would have to drink, which
was forbidden, but we had to get water into them; and they
would vomit and groan. Phu would summon me to see to
another laparotomy that had burst open.

One day a shell exploded just on the right-hand corner of

the shelter. Luckily it did not penetrate, but the explosion made a hole in the ceiling through which you could see a patch of gray sky. The earth cascaded down onto the stretcher, and clouds of black smoke mingled with the dust. The wounded burst out into the passage, naked, terrified, moaning. The passage was already full to overflowing, and they squatted down there in the mud. They had to be washed, and their dressings, which were befouled through and through, had to be changed. The engineers came and patched up the shelter—a hasty, makeshift job.

On emerging I had to take care not to tread on the hands and feet of the sleeping coolies. I had got into the habit by now of getting quickly along the passage by placing my feet, one in front of the other, in the space between the stretchers and the wall, with my right hand pressed against the wall.

I went into the shelter next to my own. Lieutenant Deflinne was in the shadows on the left: compound fractures in the left thigh, which was in a cast. His eyes wide open in the gloom, he said, "It's getting along all right, but it's painful inside all this plaster, and then I'm hot and thirsty."

"Don't worry. Your temperature's down to normal—that's a sure sign you'll be all right."

But it was high time to have an X-ray and a transtibial stirrup for applying traction—which could only be done at Hanoi. After the fall of Dienbienphu the two weeks in the open, waiting for the plane, was fatal to this poor leg. A few days after Deflinne's arrival at Lanessan, the leg was amputated.

On the right was Lieutenant Rollin. His condition was serious—compound fracture of the right leg; he too needed an X-ray. The shell fragment was still inside. I had to confine myself to a large débridement, and there was still a nasty edema in the leg.

The Vietminhs did not evacuate him. He went off in a

truck with thirty other wounded officers toward Road 41 on May 26.

In the bunk above Deflinne, Khai, a corporal in the Eighth Assault, gratified me with a large and friendly smile: right knee pierced by a bullet.

At the back, on the ground and in bunks, were Bacus, who saw to my instruments, Levasseur, my anesthetist, Deudon, assistant at the operating table; they were asleep, worn out, still wearing their blouses and rubber aprons stained with blood and dried plaster. Their cheeks were deathly pale. In half an hour I would wake them up brutally: "Quick now, there's a fellow with a tourniquet on the operating table."

In the next shelter were Geneviève's favorites. These were abdominal cases on the way to recovery. Nearly all had a piece of the large intestine protruding, with a slit in it through which feces gently flowed. Their dressings were constantly fouled and had to be changed two or three times a day. Geneviève did this with Sioni; she was always smiling and reassuring.

Then there was Hamiri; I had to perform a tracheotomy on him. A bullet went through his neck. He was cured, but unable to speak.

Abdelkader, Phuong, both with an arm off as well.

Genty of the Sixth Colonial Paratroops; a bullet had cut his urethra. He had a drainage tube through the abdominal wall into the bladder. The free end of the tube was in a flask on the ground. "When are you going to remove this contraption, major?"

"Soon; just wait a little while. You can see how much work there is to be got through."

I dared not tell him that he must soon undergo another operation.

A few days after the surrender, as he lay under his white strip of parachute, his bladder became inflamed; his drainage tube had got choked up. He suffered agonies, curled up, groaning and howling with pain. The Vietminh orderlies tried something or other, without any success. At that time, I was allowed to visit all my wounded, but not to attend them; I could only give them "moral attention."

When I passed by his parachute, Genty was able to recognize my bare legs, and he always cried, "Major, major . . ."

"But why do you appeal to me? You know quite well that I'm only allowed the use of my own hands."

"But it hurts, it hurts like hell, major. I'm going to die, I know I am . . ."

"Be patient, you only have to wait for the plane. They're going to evacuate you; your name is on the list."

It was a lie, but as a matter of fact he was evacuated quite soon. After that I tried to avoid going by his parachute.

Heinz, the one who had had three amputations, was asleep. His vitality and his gaiety never varied. Every morning he nearly broke my heart by saluting me with his right stump. One afternoon he welcomed me with a radiant smile, sitting on a stool in the main passage. All my life I shall wonder how he moved fifteen feet unaided to get there.

One bunk was empty. The day before it had held Nicolle, a nineteen-year-old paratrooper from the North of France. He had two shell splinters in the lung. Every three days we had to drain a pleural effusion, and for weeks his breathing was painful, but he was always smiling and confident. A few days ago, he had heard that there were only seventeen men left in his company: "Major," he said, "I want to return to my company. There are only seventeen of them left, and if they're going to be killed off I want to be with them."

"But after three minutes' walking you're like an old man with asthma. How will you manage?"

"Oh, it's only a quarter of a mile. I'll take my time, but I'll get there."

All my persuasions were in vain. After a handshake, Nicolle

went off and joined his company like the rest of them. I never saw him again.

I went into the last shelter before the north exit. It was always a bit fresher in there, or rather better ventilated, for it communicated with the Airborne Commandos' quarters, which were now an annex to the field hospital, by means of the tunnel which passed under the road leading to the command post, at the crossway.

There were eight of them there, fast asleep, almost naked, and covered with sweat. On the ground or flopped down on stretchers were the orderlies and coolies.

At the back, to the right, under the vent hole, was Courtade, N.C.O. in the paratroops, his spinal cord cut by a bullet. Spinal cord cut—that means complete paralysis in both legs. There they were, you could see and touch them, they were quite warm, but they could not feel anything and they were lifeless as blocks of wood, refusing to obey the orders that came from above. "Curse it, why am I not like that Senegalese below, who's been amputated? He can get up and walk. He's of some use. Is there any hope, doctor?"

I came to see him every night, toward three in the morning, when—sometimes—all was quiet in the hospital.

The shells were now falling constantly, the dull explosions from mortars; the quick crack of the 75's; the deeper impressive sound of the 105's. Then our guns started up, uncertain and isolated at first, then suddenly all of them, quick and angry bursts. Then the Viet counter-barrage replied, heavy and varied, but terribly accurate.

The Dakotas which dropped rations, ammunition, and men passed overhead again and again, accompanied by the whistling of large-caliber bullets and the explosion of shells from 37's.

With his eyes fixed on the ceiling, Courtade followed all this: "That's for Eliane 4; listen, that's Dominique 3; now the balloon's going up on the Huguettes."

"To be here, stuck to a damp bed, while the rest of the guys out there, not far off . . ."

Every sound coming through the vent holes, which were made of shell cases, echoed and was transformed reaching the ears as an odd sort of music.

"You haven't got a cigarette, doctor?"

We smoked together in silence, while the others slept.

"I think it's going to be all right; I can feel a tingling in my legs . . ."

The next day, or the day after, following a difficult time, I reached him later, at five in the morning: "God, doctor, I've been waiting for you since midnight. You can't imagine— great news!"

Surprised, I waited.

"I can move my big toe!"

And it was a fact that he could move this little fellow who seemed comically apart from him, at the end of this column of lifeless flesh.

His eyes, dancing with hope, gazed into mine: "That's a beginning, isn't it? It's going to work out?"

"Yes, I never doubted it for a moment."

He pressed my hand, but it was the look in his eyes which really expressed his gratitude.

Endowed with superhuman courage and will power, Courtade was to move his feet at Hanoi and his legs at Saigon, and receive me standing erect at Val-de-Grace.

Two other N.C.O.'s were in the same boat as Courtade— Hay and Gréa.

Being short of room, I had to send Hay back to a shelter in his own battalion, where Patrice looked after him. Every day he told me what he was going through, the sores which grew daily, the difficulty he had in urinating, the paralysis of his bladder. A drainage tube had to be fixed up for him, as for Genty. But he also really required a decent bed and a proper mattress, fresh air and sunshine.

I also had to send Gréa back to his battalion. Barraud took charge of him, and he was put in a stretcher slung from the ceiling, as there was nearly three feet of mud and water on the ground.

After May 7, the orderlies with me, under instructions from the Viets, visited all the distant shelters and brought to the terrace in front of the field hospital—which thus became a new scene of martyrdom—all the wounded who had had to be left by their comrades when they were taken off to the prisoner-of-war camps.

But Gréa was forgotten. Still I could not forget him and kept asking, "Where is Gréa?"

"We haven't been able to find him."

He was found on May 9; someone dared to go down into the cesspool which Barraud's infirmary had become and saw the stretcher hanging from the ceiling. Gréa was brought back to the field hospital, and when he saw me he began to cry. He was terrifyingly thin and in great distress, having been alone two days, without any attention or anything to eat or drink. He was getting ready to die like a pariah dog.

I left Courtade and went into the tunnel under the road. This morning the weight of a tank had made a huge piece of earth fall and scatter on the ground. I turned a little to the left, then to the right. In front of the entry to the main Airborne Commandos' passage, I had to watch out for the drain, which was four or five feet deep. There had been a board covering it, but this had floated off somewhere. A large stone would do the trick, but who was going to the riverside to get one?

Some twenty shelters opened to right and left of the mass of mud of which the passage consisted; they were not lit, as our electric plant was not strong enough to take electricity to all the shelters.

I went into the first, where a few candles were flickering in a little recess dug into the earth wall; their feeble light gave a glimpse of a Biblical scene—the halt and the lame—stretchers, limbs in casts, heads in turbans of bandages, dirty coverlets, bottles, and empty cardboard boxes. The wounded here were not naked, but clothed in blue American pajamas, distributed long ago and now covered with dirt, spots of dried blood, and pus. They ought to be washed, but what about the water? Who would dare to go down to the river and spend ten minutes there? And even supposing they could be washed, how could they be dried?

The walls were damp and sticky. My fingers went right in, and I slipped with every other step.

As soon as I went into another shelter I bumped up against a bed or a stretcher. There was the same dreadful disorder as in the other, and the same smell of decay; I could sense a horde of grubs preparing to attack and prey on wounds they had not yet investigated. The wounded were fast asleep. It was a long time since explosions, worms, or even pain had been capable of waking them. They had reached saturation point.

I went out carefully, lowering my head so as not to hit it on the beam in the ceiling.

I entered the third shelter, to find the same scene spread before me, and the twentieth was just like the first. I went farther down the passage, to the part which was covered with a thin layer of logs, where you could clearly hear the whistle of explosions. The recesses had collapsed right and left. Debris had filled up the bottom of the trench, making a heap which you had to cross crouching down. We had been able to get the wounded out in time. Farther on, the whole of the right wall was down, and just as in my own shelter there was a dark, oozing hole.

I passed in front of Geneviève's shelter, where a little light was showing, so I risked a glance through the hanging over the entrance. What was the meaning of this? On the bed there was a man covered with gauze and adhesive tape, and two more on the floor, one with a splint on the left leg, the other with a huge dressing on his head. Geneviève had given up her shelter to her friends the wounded. Since when? She had never said a word to me about it.

I had to know where she was and where she had found a place to sleep. I went on through the mud, looking left and right, lifting a hanging made of a piece of parachute. She was not there; perhaps she was in the bottom shelter. I took a few more steps and stumbled suddenly into a muddy hole up to my knees. It was a drain. I knew it was there, but I wasn't thinking. I turned around to see, in one of the still-intact recesses, a Legionnaire with both legs in casts, wrapped in a parachute.

"All right?"

"Yes, all right."

"Have you seen Geneviève?"

"She went down there. . . ." He indicated the exit to the Airborne Commandos' quarters.

I went on my way, just avoiding a quagmire at the exit, through Courtade's shelter, then found myself in the other passage again. On the left, in front of the entrance, was a gray hanging. I had a sudden desire for fresh air. Shells were falling every ten minutes or so.

I raised the blanket and stuck out my chest, thinking I would get a gulp of fresh air. But I was suddenly suffocated by a putrid smell which stopped my breathing. It could only be a dead man there; in the morning I would have to make a row about it. Why hadn't he been taken to the morgue?

I went forward in the moonlight, and there, on a stretcher in the passage leading to our shattered clearing station, I saw

a wounded man stirring and groaning softly. I was forgetting
—it was the Moroccan.

He had been found lying in a distant shelter toward the
Junon support post with compound fractures of the left leg.
He was operated on, and after some days was considered to be
on the way to recovery, so he was removed to this distant
shelter which the orderly only visited every other day.

One morning Rondy went by and sniffed the typical smell
of gangrene. He phoned me at once.

It was indeed gangrene. But the poor fellow only reached
us in the evening, and at once a dreadful stench spread into
the passage and on into the shelters. His leg, from the toes to
top of the thigh, was enormous, swollen to bursting and blue
in color—the blue of rotting flesh.

His general condition was very serious, that of a man gravely
infected, his temperature steadily at 104; his leg should have
been cut off, or rather disarticulated between the thigh and
the pelvis. But this would be an exceptionally serious operation, and he could not survive the shock, which would simply
be an assassination; it would also be a dangerous source of
infection to the operating room.

So I decided to do nothing. I gave orders that he should be
kept permanently unconscious, helped by injections of morphine from time to time, and that he should be kept as far
away as possible in order to avoid infecting our shelters.

The stretcher bearers therefore placed him there, in the
open trench. It was impossible to put him anywhere else. I
thought he would be dead in a few hours, but in the evening
he was still alive.

He lived another two days, to my great amazement. We
had to rig up some canvas to protect him from the sun; hundreds of flies swarmed around him, and grubs began to con-
sume his dead limb, which was already rotting. Why didn't he
die? He asked for a drink, and it was impossible to refuse.
One afternoon he was found crawling toward the entrance to

the passage, dragging his dead limb with him. Every two hours the orderlies used to say to me, "What about the Moroccan, major?"

All I could answer was: "Well, I can't kill him."

The following evening he at last consented to die, and I must admit that I was very relieved.

Next I went down the passage to the mess. The mud there was so thick that it went up to the calves; it was no longer a passage but the bed of a torrent, the one we made the day we were flooded. Gindrey's shelter was crammed. There were Viet soldiers mixed up with wounded Legionnaires and Vietnamese, sleeping anyhow, on bunks and on the ground.

I passed by Julot's department, the shelter housing the electric plants; of the three of them, two had given out, burnt out. They had had to do much more than they were ever designed for. The third, the one of five kilowatts, was working all the time and now supplied light to the command post. A little farther and I had a look at the shelters where the men used to eat and sleep; there everything was upside down and there were holes choked up with every sort of debris; the canvas roof had vanished into thin air. A few more steps brought me in front of the sterilizer shelter.

Kabbour was at work. His stove was hissing under the Poupinel and under the other sterilizer. The heat was terrible. He was surprised to see me. He was so thin that there seemed to be little more to his face than the eyes. Hoang, beside him, had also got very thin. At the back, asleep on the ground, were Corporal Arriba, one of the orderlies who had been wounded, and Lahcen, the ambulance driver, who had also been hit by some shell splinters. Now they were helping Kabbour in his work.

Kabbour and Hoang had not stopped work for fifty-seven days and fifty-seven nights, hard at their sterilizing in the suffocating heat of their shelter. We had never been short of surgical dressings, gloves, instruments, all sterilized.

It was Hoang and Kabbour who had to go from the sterilizer shelter to the operating room. To get there they had to make their way along this shattered passage that I had just come down. But even under the heaviest artillery barrage, all that we needed there always reached us.

At first Hoang was frightened. In the end, just like the others, he no longer paid any attention; and I used to see him go off toward the exit, his arms laden with drums of dressings and rectangular boxes of instruments.

We had used up nearly fifteen hundred surgical dressings. To begin with we only had two hundred and fifty, and after the Dominique attack we exhausted this supply, so Kabbour cut new surgical dressings out of the shrouds which were parachuted down to us. The majority of those killed in the fighting were now buried where they fell, wrapped in tent canvas so that we were able to make use of these shrouds that were no longer required.

I stayed a few minutes with Kabbour, as my visit seemed to have given him pleasure. His devotion to duty was of the quiet and unobtrusive type. Without the work he undertook on our behalf, it would have been impossible for us to operate.

I clasped his hand, then went out into the mud again to visit the mess where, before March 13, Barraud, Patrice, Marant, and I used to spend such enjoyable evenings.

Inside, there was apparent disorder, but it was a methodical disorder; this was no longer the mess, but the cookhouse, which supplied meals for everybody—wounded, orderlies, visitors, and even neighbors outside.

Looking for the cook and his coolies, I could see no sign of them, though the bulb in the ceiling gave plenty of light. At last, after looking around a bit, I discovered a hole under the table covered with white parachute silk, beneath which these three ingenious fellows were bunched up asleep. That was the best of protection against shells, a hole inside the shelter.

On my way back, I again ran into Kabbour, who said, "Oh, major, I was looking for you. Do you think N'Diaye could have this hole filled in behind my shelter?"

I followed him; I knew what he was talking about—the "amputation" hole, which was six feet across and six feet deep. It was there that the limbs cut off in the operating room were chucked away. Going closer, I saw a weird scene in the moonlight which no writer of thrillers could improve on. Shriveled legs, arms, and hands, grotesque feet, all mixed up as in some witches' cauldron. The lime scattered freely over it added a further note of unreality to the scene. I had asked N'Diaye not to cover these poor remains with earth each day, as this would have filled the hole too quickly and we would have had to dig another, and yet another.

Everybody knew of this spot, and I was not surprised when wounded men, reaching the field hospital with tourniquets on them, said to me:

"Major, you'll let me keep my leg?"

"*Bitte, mein Kommandant, nicht abschneiden?*"

"*Ong*—not cut?"

"Please, major, no cut, please."

I turned to Kabbour, who was also fascinated by the sight, and said, "No, have a little patience. In a few days, it will be finished."

Wading and slipping, leaning on the damp and dirty walls of the trenches, I went back to my shelter and came face to face with the operating room. There was Geneviève, lying down fully dressed on a stretcher wedged between the operating table and the wall. Her mouth was slightly open, and there were dark rings around her eyes; her face was very thin; her right hand hung down from the stretcher into the mud.

The last man to be operated on was strapped down on the table.

The saline was flowing drop by drop. Under the harsh light of the operating lamp he was fast asleep; his femoral artery had been hit. I felt the foot; it was not cold, and he would keep his leg. He was a little engineer. A minefield had had to be laid at midnight in front of the Opera position, the airfield's support post. The Viets were only fifty yards away, concealed in their trenches. Suddenly a flare went up, and twenty grenades rained down in a few minutes. Three dead, six wounded.

At the foot of the operating table were Bescond and Florés, lying on oilcloth spread on the blood-soaked ground; their blouses were stained with blood and dried plaster, their boots coated with foul mud.

I went on to the dispensary, a matter of constant anxiety. How much penicillin, streptomycin, saline, Pentothal was there left? Vidal had no more streptomycin, and I had to let him have all he needed.

Hantz had no more plasma; I still had fifty flasks.

Patrice had asked for plaster.

Rondy had no more Coramine. Had I any left?

Between the demijohns of drinking water, our emergency reserve, three orderlies were asleep, coiled up on the ground.

Next I went into the emergency-treatment room, the heart of my hospital, with room for fifteen seriously wounded men into whose veins was going blood which had come from the veins of unknown people in Hanoi, Haiphong, Saigon, and France. All the wounded realized that this was the place where their survival, their very life, was decided. But admission to it was the result of a remorseless selection which I had to make with a feeling of death in my heart.

This sorting out used to take place in the main passage and those adjoining it where the men were put on stretchers, one after another. Those wounded in the arms had to sit on the ground, their chins on their knees. All waited for my verdict. White, black, or yellow, privates and officers, they all knew.

"A tourniquet here, quick now."

"Good—take him off to the emergency-treatment room."

"He can wait."

"An ordinary seton for him—the usual dressing, then back to his unit."

"The drugs for him . . . double morphine—Pento-Novo in a quarter of an hour."

The stretcher bearers understood just from a gesture. I tried to avoid the wild look of those who stared at me.

I moved aside a little and murmured, "You had better call the chaplain to him." Every day I had to do this, twenty, thirty, a hundred times. Poor fellows!

"It's all right, isn't it, doc?"

"Yes, you've had the devil's own luck."

"Attaboy!"

"*Lebès*, major?"

"*Lebès, chouya.*"

"Major, me soon *lam?*"

"Soon, soon *lam.*"

"*Prima, mein Kommandant, das tut weh aber das geht gut.*"

"*Ja, bestimmt, das geht gut.*"

I did this sorting out with Geneviève and Sioni, her colleague. I know no more exhausting work.

Regulations insist that this work should be done by the senior surgeon of highest rank. Like a way of the cross the procession wound on into the emergency-treatment room. For every wounded man there, on a cot, on a stretcher, on a piece of canvas, or just lying on the ground, the same order had to be given, to relieve their pain with the latest drugs.

In a few minutes a sleep they could not resist had taken possession of them and handed them over to us like helpless children. This is an advance in medicine beyond anything known to the veterans of 1914–18. The wards containing wounded are now quiet and peaceful. This quiet makes for better and more careful work, brings a certain sense of well-being both to the wounded and to those treating them, allowing smiles and an atmosphere of confidence to return.

"Undress him." This order had to be carried out with scissors, and the clothes were shorn off, taking care of fractured limbs, feet injured by the explosion of mines, an unsuspected fracture of the humerus, or a piece of combat uniform adhering to burns.

"Wash him, but don't waste any precious water."

"Disinfect him with Dakin's solution."

Now they were bare to the skin, like victims ready for sacrifice. An orderly put a temporary dressing on the wound.

"Fix a splint—gently now, gently."

"Begin the intravenous therapy."

"Cut down on a vein at the ankle."

"Blood here."

"Plasma there."

"Subtosan * over there."

Then the miracle began, the lips regained their color, the pulse was perceptible, breathing became easier and less hectic, the extremities got warmer.

"Perez, cut down on a vein of the other foot; two bottles of blood must flow in simultaneously here."

Perez, undersized anyhow, was now lean as a stray cat as well. He had nearly died a week ago: he had a nasty jaundice and a temperature fluctuating between 102 and 104. Laid out in a sort of stall, greenish in hue, he said, "I've had it, major. I can't go on."

"Look here, my lad, those three fellows with you are waiting in the emergency-treatment room. If you don't get up, then they've certainly had it."

"But I'll go, major. I never said I wouldn't go."

For three days I watched over him all the time. Would he

---

* A blood plasma substitute. (Translator's note.)

be able to stick it out? He stuck it out all right, helped by Minh and Mhion, who were skilled and tireless, and by Lahcen and Abbour, who were courageous and reliable.

Orderlies were asleep on the ground, on the table, sprawled over a chest of blood, utterly exhausted.

Lachamp, my heroic secretary, was worn out, bowed over his little office table. I thought of the dangerous expeditions he used to make to get the wounded to the Dakotas, when they were still able to land. How far away all that seemed!

Our devoted Julot, always the life and soul of the party, was lying on a stretcher, his uniform dirty, torn, and covered with mud. Ten times a day he had to take a message across to the command post.

"Good morning, doctor," an officer would say, laughing.

"Oh, there's nothing wrong in being a doctor, sir," he used to answer.

Every three or four days one of the telephones or light wires was cut by Vietminh shells: "Hurry up, Julot, get it fixed. Look, we're in the middle of an operation."

Julot put on his helmet and went off to contact the other signal men and return half an hour later, covered with mud, red-faced, and out of breath. He had done the trick. No need to ask any questions: all this time shells had been falling every half-minute.

Julot was also a great friend of Simon Marie. Simon was blind. He was only eighteen and also had both hands badly injured. He had two fingers remaining on the right hand and three on the left, and I was uncertain what could be done even with these, as they were gradually becoming ankylosed in the course of healing.

It was the stretcher bearers of the Sixth Colonial Paratroops who brought him to the field hospital, along those fearful trenches which started at Eliane and came out at the bridge. When they reached the terrace, mortar shells were falling in salvos of six at a time. The trench was already full of stretchers. Somebody said, "Put him in the shelter here."

It was Lieutenant Gindrey's shelter. They went in, put the stretcher down somewhere near the others, and went off.

A bullet had touched off the pin of a grenade which he had tied to a buttonhole in his combat uniform. He had torn it off at once, to throw it away, but he was too late and it exploded in his hands.

He was waiting for somebody to talk to him, but there was only silence. After ten minutes, he began to speak himself: "Isn't there anybody here? Hey, orderly!"

Of course he could see nothing. If he could at least have touched something with his fingers, that would have helped, but the men had put two huge dressings around his hands. He tried to feel the way a little with his elbow. There was nothing to the right, but there was someone on the left.

"Oh," he said, "are you wounded too?"

There was still silence from his companion, though shells went on exploding and bullets whistling.

"What's the matter—don't you want to talk?" he went on. "Or are you wounded in the throat or the mouth?"

Someone came in for a moment and then went out again.

"I was wounded by a grenade. My eyes are in a mess, but the lieutenant says that the left eye is still all right. My hands are smashed too . . . but modern surgery can find a way around everything . . . Now I'm thinking about when I'll get to Hanoi . . . What about you?"

He pressed with his elbow again, and then an idea came to him. By rubbing his forearm against the side of the stretcher, he managed to roll up his sleeve. Soon he had bared his elbow, and with that could feel the body beside him, even make out a nose and mouth. But still the other man never uttered a word.

"But, good God, you're frozen . . . Don't you feel terribly

cold?" It was at this point that Simon Marie realized that he was lying beside a corpse, and he began to yell.

It was Julot who, coming out of the electric-plant shelter, heard his cry and came to look for me, very agitated: "Quick, major, there's someone yelling in the lieutenant's shelter."

He was taken at once to the emergency-treatment room, where he said, "I can't understand it—I don't know why I got scared. I've seen enough dead men. I think it was because I was alone in that hole."

Simon's eyes were a mess, and the eyelids were torn. After the damaged tissue had been cleaned and cut away, there were only two bloody holes left in place of eyes. I had him put in the emergency-treatment room and wondered whether he would have to stay there, for he could not do a thing for himself. He had to be constantly looked after and helped. In that room there was always somebody about.

His morale was first-class, his gaiety unfailing, despite his terrible wounds. He frequently asked for Julot: "Julot, give me a cigarette . . . Give me a drink . . . Tell me a story."

I remember one night having played a little trick on him. I was alone in the room when I heard him call, "Orderly!"

I went over to him and said, "Yes?"

"Give me a drink."

I went to the chest which also contained bottles of blood, opened it, and took out a can of pineapple juice. Having pierced a hole in it, I gave it to him to drink.

"Oh, that's good . . . You haven't got a cigarette?"

I went to my shelter and fetched him an English cigarette.

"Oh, but it's a Craven A . . . Wherever did you get that?"

"Sh, not a word—I pinched it from the major's room."

"You've got a nerve, haven't you?"

Later, I told him about this little trick. He went very red and said, "Oh, I was rather familiar, wasn't I?"

I wonder whether he has really forgiven me even now.

I was going back to my shelter when the orderly on duty,

a Vietnamese, called me: "Major, the last two men to be operated on are dead."

I was astounded, for they had not been seriously wounded: large wounds to be sure, but not affecting either bones or arteries. They were both lying on a stretcher in the muddy passage, terribly pale and thin. They had not died of their wounds, nor of any accident arising out of the anesthetic. They were dead simply because the heart and the vital functions had stopped as a result of complete physiological exhaustion, for which there was no remedy.

I had never witnessed that before. After all, food was seldom lacking. Sometimes it was impossible to collect the packages of foodstuffs, and the can of rations had to be shared out among ten, twenty, occasionally but not often thirty men. But that never went on for more than two days at the outside.

Supplies were collected during a lull, and rations once more became normal—if you can call canned stuff normal. Always canned stuff, cans of meat paste, carrots and other vegetables, cans of crackers . . . After a time the stomach categorically refused to absorb all this canned stuff. But you had to eat something.

I had seen accidents in the emergency-treatment room through the ordinary use of Dolosal-Phenergan—men not seriously wounded suddenly dying a few minutes after it had been injected. I had thereupon given orders to halve the dose and inject it into a muscle instead of a vein, spacing ten injections out over the same number of minutes, and there had been no more of these accidents.

Major Liesenfeld, who commanded the Second Foreign Paratroops, told me of some queer accidents in his battalion. In the course of a difficult supply detail, two Legionnaires collapsed in the mud with their burdens. Others hurried to them, but they were dead, dead from inanition, complete endocrine exhaustion as we would call it, brought on by the constant and extreme physical effort which was being demanded of the men. On top of that there was also the lack of sleep for units manning the support posts and the outer hills, which were constantly in action against the Viets.

Nothing could be done about that, nothing at all.

On another occasion a Vietnamese was brought to me on a stretcher, slightly wounded in both arms: it was a multiple wound, that is to say he had been peppered with microscopic fragments of a grenade. I went over to him and, in my irritation, ordered him to be sent back to his unit at once. But the stretcher bearers told me, "We tried to make him walk, major, but he can't stand up."

So I bent down and examined him. His skin was thin and wrinkled like an old man's, and had lost its elasticity. His muscles were soft and flaccid, on the way to degenerating; for instance, they did not react at all to an injection. All reflexes had gone; the lips were pale and dry. The eyes were wide open but quite expressionless; a profound anemia had reached the brain, and as an inevitable result, the mind was clouded.

I had him taken into the emergency-treatment room and tried a very cautious treatment, saline under the skin and a slight cardiac stimulant. Then I tried a very gradual injection of plasma with Novocain, but he died with the first drops which passed into his blood. The change was visible only in the sudden absence of movement in his ribs, which stuck out under the skin. The organism had not even been able to stand the introduction of the nourishing fluid which might have saved him.

It was nearly four in the morning when I got back to my shelter, and my legs felt like lead. My thoughts wandered—or rather, I forced myself not to think. But in place of this strange hospital which would have been appropriate on the banks of the Styx, I could see in my mind's eye the neat and clean one which I had found on my arrival at Dienbienphu.

I heard more footsteps in the passage—the squelch of many feet in the mud, and lowered voices. I went back to the entrance of my shelter to find myself face to face with curious beings covered with mud, carrying packages on their shoulders. At the sight of me, they halted. "And where are you going?" I asked.

An N.C.O. slipped through and approached. "It's the supply detail, major, ammunition and rations. I apologize for making use of your passage."

"But you'll disturb the stretchers . . . There are wounded men all along here . . . Didn't you realize that?"

"We've come from the ammunition depot, major, by way of the trenches, and when we reached your entrance, we had to go out on the road to get to the bridge. Well, you can hear they're coming down fairly heavily just now. By going this way, we can rejoin the Second Airborne's trench and be a little more under cover."

"O.K., I see. Consider that I haven't said a thing. Go ahead."

Then in the half-darkness there passed before my eyes a procession that I shall never forget. The men in the detail moved slowly, one by one. They were almost naked, with nothing but a pair of shorts which had lost any color they had had; they were completely covered with mud, drying in patches on their chests, wet and shiny on their legs, thighs, and abdomens. Their feet were also bare, as their boots had long ago been sucked down by the mud.

On the left shoulder, some carried a case of ammo, others a box of rations, others a jerry can of water. They leaned against the wall with their right hands. The same expression of utter weariness and deadly resignation was visible on all their faces.

Sometimes they stopped a moment, glancing at me like dead men, then turned toward the shelters on the other side from which came the smells of blood and ether, which they did not recognize. Then they started off again, mechanically, with the same slow and uncertain steps, through the slippery mud.

I saw the play of muscles beneath the mud on their legs. Sometimes, under this sheath of mud, there was the thickness made by a field dressing.

Not one of them spoke. Their lips were sometimes half-opened, but only to let out a quick raucous breath.

I seemed to be living in some evil dream. Long after the last of them had gone by, I stood motionless, gazing at the waste of mud in front of me, where hundreds of naked feet had left their mark—and once more I wondered what these men had done that God had sent them such an ordeal to face.

I returned to the emergency-treatment room. Always this hot and fearful stench! I had to rouse my orderlies and above all dear old Gindrey, my assistant.

He was asleep and he too was pale, with large blue rings around his eyes, mouth half-open. He had not had time to take off his nylon operating apron, nor to remove his glasses, which were now askew on his forehead.

As usual, I brought him a cup of hot coffee and a shot of rum: "Get up, old man, your work is ready—there's an abdomen on the table waiting for you."

The heavy lids were raised; at once he regained consciousness and became terribly aware of where he was.

There was all the weariness in the world in his face. He stretched his limbs, stiff with fatigue, got up, took four steps, and at once began to operate, returning to a nightmare which he thought had been interrupted by three hours' heavy sleep.

Courage, will power, unselfishness, the spirit of sacrifice—such words are simply not enough. It's like sticking a label on the crown jewels to say that they are worth a few francs.

13.

The General

Following a phone call from the command post, Lachamp was making out a list, and he was far from easy in his mind about it.

"Make out a list of those seriously wounded," the call had said, "who can be considered for awards. For officers, the Legion of Honor and the Croix de Guerre. For other ranks the Military Medal and also the Croix de Guerre."

Now we had nothing but seriously wounded men in the field hospital, so there was surely no problem: all their names had to be set down, without exception.

I was in my shelter when the hanging over the entrance was drawn aside and Lieutenant Colonel Trinquart appeared.

We were very fond of Lieutenant Colonel Trinquart; he was a real friend. His courage was of the calm and unspectacular sort, for he was one of those men who stroll along the trenches as if they were tourists visiting the trenches of World War I.

He often came to see me. His words had a calming effect, and his presence was a comfort. He was in charge of intelligence, and among the things that came under him was this question of awards.

"The general is coming shortly," he told me. "He wants to hand the awards himself to the men who are most seriously wounded."

"But they're all seriously wounded. And what about those who have only just come—in the passage? And those who are still coming in?"

"Well, the visit will last until six this evening. The general won't have time to see them all, because the briefing takes place at six."

Usually when a general comes to make awards to the wounded in a field hospital close to the front, it is customary to spruce up a bit and have a general clean-up. But N'Diaye was surprised and smiled ironically when I said to him: "All the orderlies must be in clean uniforms." I had said it simply out of habit.

"But, major, it's so long since we've had any uniform. We've got nothing left but a pair of shorts. We've given our shirts and trousers to the wounded who came in naked."

"Still, try to tidy the shelters up a bit."

There is always a cover to spread over things, cans and bottles to hide out of the way, a clean bandage to put over a dirty one.

As for myself, I asked Phu to get ready for me a clean pair of shorts and a uniform shirt.

Colonel Trinquart was to ring me at the moment when the general left the command post.

Since the day before, the Vietminh artillery had been harassing us almost without stopping. One attack followed another. After a few hours' respite for our eastern posts on the Elianes, they attacked all our western positions at once, the Huguettes and the Claudines.

To the north they were getting hold of trenches yard by

yard; and we were all waiting for the final onslaught, the last great battle.

It rained all day without stopping, and no aircraft could be heard in the sky. But the nights were fair and allowed rations, ammunition, and reinforcements to be dropped.

The passages were constantly full of stretchers. Others were waiting outside, in the rain, under fire, in the mud. Every now and then it was reported to me that one of the men had died, and that meant that each stretcher could move forward one—that happened roughly every quarter of an hour.

It was the same with Hantz. Vidal had only one place free —his operating table.

The wounded and the stretcher bearers brought me the news minute by minute. The Viets had suddenly multiplied by ten and were showing themselves everywhere. They literally rose up out of the mud and the water. They were in their element, infiltrating everywhere, into passages, trenches, shell holes, crossing seas of mud.

Our guns could no longer fire accurately on their positions; the Viets were constantly in contact all the way around.

A Viet N.C.O. told me how they blew up our blockhouses: a nine-foot bamboo with some plastic explosive on the end was gradually advanced toward a loophole; suddenly there was a great explosion, and the blast was strong enough to bring the blockhouse down on its occupants.

Around me I could see nothing but mud, mud everywhere, on the ground, on the beds, on clothes and dressings, on tables, in wounds, and on faces and hands. It would have taken plenty of water simply to clean the wounded when they were undressed, but the water tank was always empty.

The water carriers who set off for the river did not come back until hours later; sometimes several of them did not come back at all.

Gindrey was operating all the time, tirelessly. His feet were in the mud and sweat streamed off him, and all his men were utterly worn out.

Then the phone rang to say, "The general's on his way."

I didn't have time to put on my clean shirt and shorts, but it couldn't be helped. I made my way along the main passage toward the steps at the west entry, but there was a long line on the left: "What's this?"

"Wounded from Eliane, major. Vidal has sent them, as he can't take any more."

Alonso, orderly of the Airborne Commandos, summoned me: "One of our shelters has collapsed, major. I'm bringing four of the wounded whom I was able to get out, but the passage is already full. What's to be done?"

I waited at the foot of the steps. Here was the general. Thin and pale, he was wearing a khaki shirt and shorts. On his shoulders were the stars of rank on a square of red cloth. His red forage cap was on his head, ordinary walking shoes on his feet, and he was smoking.

"Good afternoon, Grauwin," he replied to my salute. "I'm coming to see the wounded with you, one by one. I haven't any awards, for they were dropped on the Viets during the night. It doesn't matter—we'll put that all in order later . . . I'll follow you."

Behind him came Colonel Trinquart, Captain Le Damany, and a few N.C.O.'s. Lachamp was already at hand with the necessary papers.

But Lahcen was missing, Lahcen who was the general's devoted servant for many years. Three days earlier a shell splinter had hit him in the head when he was going by trench from the command post to the mess, and he came back to die in the field hospital.

I had first got to know him at the beginning of March, when he asked me, hesitantly, whether he could bring the general's dog for me to look at, as he was getting very thin and wouldn't eat. Of course there was no vet at Dienbienphu, and

I had no scruples about giving my professional attention to a dog, so I agreed. He went off and came back with a German shepherd, a few months old, with a soft grayish coat. I put him behind the screen of the fluoroscope and found that he had double pneumonia; in spite of the care given him, he died in the night.

We had only to take a few steps to reach the first of the wounded in the passage, a paratrooper with a chest wound.

"Corporal Lary, general, of the Eighth Assault, Second Company, wounded in the counterattack on Huguette 4."

"How are you feeling? How many are left in your company?"

"I don't know now, general. There were still twenty of us the day I was wounded."

"I award you the Croix de Guerre. I haven't got it with me, but you'll get the official notice tomorrow."

"Thank you, sir."

Then came a Vietnamese paratrooper with a tourniquet on a smashed leg. He was asleep under the influence of drugs.

"Take his name, Trinquart."

Beside him was a Legionnaire from Huguette 5. He had lost an eye and a hand from the explosion of a 120 shell: "I was in my shelter with two other guys and the machine gun. I was firing through the loophole and saw them fall, five and ten at a time. Suddenly they got into the shelter, and that's all I can remember."

Then a Legion paratrooper: "I was wounded during the counterattack on Huguette, general. I got a shell splinter in the leg."

"And what about your arm?"

"That was in the counterattack on Eliane 1."

"I award you the Military Medal and the Croix de Guerre."

"Thank you, sir." The arms instinctively stiffened along the body.

We reached the crossway, and I took the general into my own shelter and presented its two occupants to him. "Yann, sergeant in the Sixth Colonial Paratroops. A shell exploded at his feet when he was taking part in the third assault to recapture a blockhouse occupied by the Viets on Dominique 2. I had to cut both his legs off."

"Phuc, orderly in the Second Battalion of the First Colonial Paratroops. Right arm amputated. The Viets took him prisoner while he was treating wounded in the first-aid post and made him look after their own. The Sixth counterattacked and threw a grenade into the shelter before going in."

The general listened, then said, "I award you both the Military Medal and the Croix de Guerre."

We left my shelter and went back into the main passage. The general slipped and steadied himself with a hand on the wall like the rest of us. His shoes were already covered with mud; he was wading in it, and sweat had begun to pour down his face. We entered a shelter close to mine: "Lieutenant Deflinne of the Eighth Assault, Second Company. I went out with my company to stage an ambush at the end of the runway. The Viets spotted us and sent over a salvo from their mortars."

Rollin was on the other side: "Lieutenant Rollin of the First Foreign Paratroops. I was wounded in the attack on the main Dominique position. We had almost reached the top, and the Viets were retreating down the farther slope. Then a shower of grenades came over."

The general said, "My friends, the awards fell into the hands of the Viets, but all the same I award you the Legion of Honor and the Croix de Guerre."

Above Deflinne there was Khai of the Eighth Assault. He also went out on the night of the ambush, for the twelfth time. His section was already down to seven men, and that night reduced it to three. A machine gun mowed them down at twenty yards.

We went out, and I led the group, struggling through the mud, toward the emergency-treatment room. Just at the crossway, in front of the dispensary passage, Alonso had placed a stretcher which he had managed to get out when the Airborne Commandos' shelter collapsed: the man was Carnot, paratroop N.C.O., whose spinal cord had been cut by a bullet. His abdomen had begun to swell dreadfully; it was distended to the point of bursting, and you could clearly see the blue network of the surface veins. He was dying, and his eyes were already dead. His chin contracted with a final effort . . . It was all over.

"Take his name, Trinquart. I award him the Military Medal and the Croix de Guerre—but not posthumously."

Near the operating room there was a pitiful object, stark naked and terribly thin, lying on a stretcher. His round eyes, filled with terror, stared at us. His body was stiff and arched, so that only the heels and shoulders were touching the canvas. He had been there for two days, and he had yelled so much that now he had quite lost his voice.

"What's that?"

"Tetanus, sir. He has no wound. I can only suppose that the mud must have infected a scratch in his leg."

All gazed at this distressing sight, and we went on into the emergency-treatment room. The heat was terrible. The general took a long look at the terrible mess, the mud rising from the ground to the beds, the water oozing everywhere, the great patches of damp on the walls, the flasks hanging from logs in the ceiling, the bloodstained dressings, the wounded lying naked on the canvas, the dozens of boots, useless now, under the beds. Mud . . . blood . . . stench!

On the left was Lieutenant Sylvestre, an artillery officer attached to an infantry battalion at a support post whose job it was to observe and regulate fire, by correcting it in radio contact with his battery's command post. A few days before, a Viet shell had exploded close to Sylvestre, who was standing in the open watching the fire he was directing through his field glasses. A shell splinter went into his left eye, and I was anxious about the other one. Since the operation he had not moved and had spoken only to ask for a drink.

The general looked at him: "How are you feeling?"

He heard nothing, so I said, "The general is here and talking to you." Then what we had been awaiting for over three days happened at last: Sylvestre pulled himself together, sat up, and tried to bring his arms to attention at his sides.

"I award you the Legion of Honor and the Croix de Guerre."

"Thank you, sir."

On the other side, against the oozing wall, Simon Marie was waiting.

"Simon Marie, corporal in the Sixth Colonial Paratroops. A bullet hit a grenade tied to my tunic, during the counter-attack on Eliane 1 . . . I'm doing very well, general. The major has said there is some hope for my left eye . . ."

I made a sign to the general with my hand, indicating that this hope no longer existed.

"How old are you?"

"Eighteen."

"Don't worry. You'll be looked after. Soon you'll go off to Hanoi. Meanwhile, I award you the Military Medal and the Croix de Guerre."

I saw Simon's face flush violently beneath the dressing. Certainly it is not everyone who gets the Military Medal at eighteen.

It's a pity that for fellows such as Simon there is no higher award than the Military Medal. He was a volunteer in every attack and counterattack, night ambushes, collecting packages dropped by parachute, repairing shelters under mortar fire. Every day he took part in the supply detail. All his company were made of the same stuff too.

The general wanted to shake hands with him. But his two

hands were simply two huge dressings, so he gave him a friendly pat on the arm instead.

"Thank you, sir."

In other beds there were three men with tourniquets under the influence of drugs, two Legionnaires and a Vietnamese. They had come from the counterattack on Huguette, as had all those waiting in the passage.

Then in stretchers on the ground were two Vietminhs captured that morning, paratroopers from Eliane wounded during the water detail, and three others wounded only last night while mining the ditch, the famous Opera ditch, where Captain Bizard was in command.

"Take their names, Trinquart. I'll send them the official notice tomorrow. They'll get it when they come to."

"The dispensary, sir. Be careful," I added, as the ground there was very slippery.

A Legionnaire was lying on a strip of canvas on the ground. He was a survivor from Beatrice, handed over by the Viets on March 14. He had been wounded that morning with a company of the Third Battalion.

"Have you received any awards? The Military Medal?"

"Not the Military Medal, sir."

"Very well, I now give it to you."

We had a look at four coolies beside him, each with a limb smashed. A shell had fallen in the middle of them while they were collecting material dropped by parachute. But regulations did not provide for any award to them.

We went into the operating room, where Gindrey was at work with his assistants and orderlies, weariness on all their faces, though their eyes were alert and watchful.

The general had a long look at the scene. Before turning and following me, he put a fresh cigarette in his mouth, and I think I saw his hand shaking.

We went into the third shelter in the main passage.

"Lieutenant Rondeau, of the Fifth Paratroops, wounded on Dominique 3, sir."

The general turned toward me, and I explained, "An abdominal wound, sir." He bent down and held out his hand: "I'm sorry, old man, but the awards went to the Viets. But you get the Legion of Honor and a mention in dispatches."

"Thank you, sir."

Heinz was at the back, overshadowed by the bunk above: "Legionnaire Heinz, of the Second Foreign Paratroops, wounded during the second counterattack on Huguette." The general held out his hand and waited for Heinz's, as I hadn't had time to say, "Both arms and the left leg amputated."

The same scene was repeated by each bed. The wounded man stiffened and kept his eyes to the front, then told his story, always short, but none the less moving.

On one side was a Senegalese infantryman wounded in the abdomen. He was taking ammunition up to the Second Battery, Fourth Colonial Artillery. Mortar shells were coming down, but it was essential to supply the covering fire demanded by the support post under attack. They were Legionnaires. The Senegalese got the Military Medal.

Once more we were in the passage and going to the first shelter. "Careful, sir, lower your head. A delayed-action 105 fell here yesterday."

"Nobody hurt?"

"I'm afraid so, sir, a sergeant in the Legion, Miotto. The shell fell a yard from the side of the passage, ripping open the metal plate and smashing the logs; a great block of earth fell into the trench, burying a stretcher, which was luckily rescued in time."

Buezek and his pioneers had hastily patched it all up, but there had not been time to sweep away all the rubbish.

"Miotto is the first on the right, general."

At the beginning of April, he had had a shell splinter in the forearm, which had exposed the radius and the ulna, broken in several places. I had not amputated it, but had enclosed the whole arm in a cast. Toward the middle of April, he had rejoined his unit like the rest of them.

Then a shell fell in front of his battalion infirmary, killing two of the men with him, who had also just rejoined their unit. He dashed back like a madman to the field hospital with more shell splinters in him and begged me to let him stay in one of my shelters. He was in such a state that I agreed, and he found a place in the farthest part of the Airborne Commandos' quarters. But whenever the shells were falling close at hand, Miotto could not stop himself from coming back to the emergency-treatment room where I was, and I pretended not to see him. This morning he had made one more attempt to dodge the explosions as they came nearer, each more deafening than the last, and lay down in an unoccupied shelter in the main passage—and there suddenly found himself buried.

The general spoke to him, but he made no reply. He stared hard at the ceiling, puzzling how it was that fate had placed him face to face with death three times in succession.

Courtade was down at the back. "Sergeant major Courtade of the Second Foreign Paratroops." I explained his case.

"I have every confidence, general. He is already doing very well." Another Military Medal.

On the left was Lieutenant Bouillé, another paratrooper. When he reached the field hospital, he was a company sergeant major. His battalion gave him the Military Medal and mentioned him in dispatches. Both of his legs had been smashed by a mortar explosion when his section was storming a Viet trench. Then he was specially promoted to second lieutenant. On this occasion the general conferred the Legion of Honor on him.

The man with phosphorus burns was groaning in the bunk above. He was going to die: the toxic poisoning had been too severe, the burns too deep. Some of them were like pieces of anthracite buried in the flesh.

On one side were two paratroopers: one with an amputation and a head wound, the other with a chest wound. Two more Military Medals.

Ty, of the Fifth Vietnamese Paratroops, over there on the left, was not forgotten. He had been in my shelter for two weeks, but it was too hot there. He asked to be in Courtade's shelter, where there was a little more air.

I had had to retrim his stumps. By then he must have weighed about sixty-five pounds.

He greeted the general, who held out his hand, with a splendid smile. He was eighteen, just like Simon Marie, but he looked no more than fourteen.

"Shall we go to the Airborne Commandos' shelters now, sir? Perhaps I had better go in front." We passed through the tunnel under the road. "Careful on the right there, sir— there's a hole, a drain." He just managed to avoid it. "Do you want to see all the shelters, general?"

"Of course."

"But there are twenty of them."

"Well, we'll see. Go ahead . . ."

There was no electricity beyond this point, and I had to ask Julot to go in front with a hurricane lamp.

The general had to stop at the entrance of each shelter, because the first bed was there, right at his feet. He tried to peer into the gloom, uncertainly lit by candles and the hurricane lamp. He could see only large eyes and faces turned toward him, faces which were pale and serious-looking beneath hair which had just been damped and combed. The men tried to press their hands to their sides just as if they were standing at attention.

He had a word or a friendly pat on the shoulder for each one of them. His hands were trembling slightly. Never before had I heard him talk so much. He came out into the passage again, slipped and waded in the mud once more. The mud had by now got well inside his shoes.

"Soon it will be all over," he told them. "Soon you will be at Hanoi . . . I don't yet know how it will be done, but I promise you that it will be managed somehow."

"You've only got to be patient a little longer," he told another and conferred more Military Medals.

There were recesses cut into the walls of the trench to the right and left of us, on a level with our knees. Hamiri was in one of them. He had been on the Dominique position, but had left before the Viets got there, a bullet having gone right through his neck and shoulders. When he reached the field hospital he was swollen up like an old leather bottle, and quantities of air were escaping from his lungs and getting in between the skin and the muscles. As he was threatened with suffocation, he had to have a tracheotomy. Now he was cured, but unable to speak.

The general spoke to him in his own tongue, having recognized him as a Berber, many thousands of whom he had had under his command in the past. Hamiri made desperate gestures, so anxious was he to reply.

We next reached a shelter larger than the others, crammed with some twenty wounded. It smelled foul.

Laniez, of the Sixth Colonial Paratroops, wounded on Eliane.

Halter, of the Third Battalion, Thirteen Demi-Brigade of the Legion, wounded in the counterattack on Gabrielle.

Mallet, of the Eighth Assault, wounded in the same counterattack.

Da, a reserve from the Second Battalion, Fourth Composite, wounded on Dominique.

Xung, of the Sixth Colonial Paratroops, wounded in the night ambush on the runway.

Carlotti, of the First Foreign Paratroops, wounded during the counterattack on Eliane 3.

Then came men of the First Battalion, Second Foreign Infantry, the Second Foreign Paratroops, the Second Battalion, First Colonial Paratroops, the Fifth Battery, Seventh Artillery. Gunners, engineers, black, white, and yellow—all branches of the service, all races, all countries, brought together there, side by side, on a piece of ground three yards square.

"Lieutenant Lécué is in the next shelter." He was from the First Colonial Paratroops, and he was lying among seven other paratroopers of his battalion, corporals and privates who had put their lieutenant down among them because his right side was paralyzed and he was unable to feed himself. Nor could he talk. He had a shell splinter in the skull.

Each of them had lost an arm or a leg or some piece of themselves. But they looked after their lieutenant better than the most tenderhearted mother could look after her favorite child.

The general had a long look at them, and they also stared at him. Lécué's eyes were large, dark, and expressive.

"Soon you will be in Hanoi. I promise you that."

I had taken from Lécué's skull a piece of bone as large as the palm of the hand; with a curette I had removed nearly a teacupful of damaged brain tissue. At the end of the operation I had said, "Call the chaplain"; and he survived. Then he was put in a recess in the passage. He categorically refused to stay there, and he protested, making vigorous gestures with his good arm. Several times he was found lying in the mud of the passage.

I saw him again much later at Saigon, where he was learning to talk again just as when he was a small child. I asked him why he had always refused to stay in that recess. His answer was: "It—was—like—a—tomb." For he had no wish to die.

In the recess opposite his was a man wounded in the face. His upper and lower jaws had been smashed; and what remained of the jaw and bone had been held together by steel wire. It was Geneviève who fed the poor devil by slipping a feeding tube up a nostril.

There was a very foul smell in the passage here.

This man was in the First Colonial Paratroops, and one evening he had set out with the others to ambush the Viets, which they managed most successfully, bringing down so many with tommy guns and Colts that the affair went off just like a military exercise. Then suddenly he felt something on his back; a Viet had hurled himself on him, not knowing that he was a judo expert. In a few moments the Viet had his neck broken, but not before he had just time to take the pin out of a grenade and hold it between them, so that it exploded. The man was awarded the Military Medal.

We went next toward the end of the passage where there was only a thin layer of logs above. Whistlings and explosions sounded louder and closer here. I wished the visit would come to an end, as I had no desire to see the general on my operating table: "It's getting late, sir."

"But there are still some shelters to visit?"

"Yes, but . . ."

"Come along, then."

Those in casts had been put together in this gloomy shelter, which was uncertainly lit by Julot's lamp. The stench was frightful. The wounds were developing sores under the plaster. Healing went on, but pus and grubs issued from the edges. Pieces of absorbent cotton were placed here and there, but they should really have been changed every five minutes.

The grubs were swarming all over the place, constantly active. They had been scattered a little in honor of the general's visit, but like the Viets they only returned in greater strength.

Here there were engineers and gunners and men who had been dropped by parachute only a few days ago, or even yesterday. At the back I recognized Bertéas. Like Lécué, he had received a shell splinter in the skull, but his story was quite a different one.

When he was brought in, he was in a state of complete coma. I already had several other cranial wounds on my hands; he was the fifth. His blood pressure was down to nothing, his pulse barely perceptible. It was a terrible wound from which issued brain tissue and blood all mixed up together.

I made a sign to Sioni and said, "The usual thing." This meant that Bertéas was to be considered moribund.

But he could not be left to die in the passage. Other wounded men were waiting. So the stretcher bearers took him out with others in similar case to what remained of the men's sleeping quarters, which was simply a large hole open to the sky. Whether he died here or there was of no consequence, as he was completely unconscious.

In the evening Cortés went out to attend to a call of nature. All of a sudden he came back, pale and wild-eyed: "Major, one of the dead men out there has lodged a complaint!"

He had reached this hole for the dying when he saw a ghostly movement and heard a voice say, "Is nothing going to be done for me, then?"

I told N'Diaye to go and have a look. Twenty minutes later he brought Bertéas to me—he had come back to life and was smiling and happy to see us all in the full light again: "Major, oh, major, I had been quite forgotten."

Like Lécué, he survived. It was a very remarkable event, if not a miracle.

But when the shells dropped too close, he used suddenly to lose his wits and before he could be stopped would go off into the trenches—anywhere, just following his nose. In the evening a Legionnaire or a paratrooper would bring him back to me. He never remembered a thing.

At that moment he looked at the general with his eyes open in an expression of grave astonishment; then he turned toward me and smiled.

Skirting the heap of rubble caused by the trench wall that had collapsed, we went into another shelter. I sincerely hoped this would be the last visit we had. There was no roof at all above our heads. You could see the smoke of explosions close at hand, both right and left.

There were two officers in this very narrow shelter, Ruyter and de Cacqueray, both paratroop lieutenants. They had taken part in the attacks and counterattacks on Eliane, Dominique, the Huguettes, and the end of the runway. They were both wounded at the same time by Viet shells, just when they had got possession of a trench.

"I award you the Legion of Honor," said the general.

We went back into the roofless passage. The aircraft were making an infernal din, and Viet shells were whistling dangerously. Once more I reflected that I did not want to have the general on my operating table.

Colonel Trinquart was close beside me. "It's six o'clock, colonel," I said. "There is the briefing . . ."

The general looked at me and said, "What's along there?"

"There are still seven shelters, but we would have to go out and then down again. Besides, they are just in front of your command post—and the wounded there are not serious cases."

I was lying, but I would get their names put on Lachamp's list.

Larriand, limping out of his shelter with the help of a stick, came to meet us: "Sergeant Major Larriand, radio operator. I got a shell splinter in the knee while getting the wounded in on a stretcher . . ." He got the Military Medal.

At last Colonel Trinquart came forward and intervened between the general and me: "It's getting late, sir. The battalion commanders are waiting for you."

"Right. We'll go back now. I'll see the rest of the wounded another day."

I heaved a sigh of relief as we retraced our steps. Once more we passed the heaps of rubble and the recesses which had collapsed into mud and water. We reached the tunnel under the road. "Look out for the drain, sir."

We went past one by one, trying not to slip, leaning against the damp wall.

"Hell!"

Our heads all jerked around at this unexpected turn to the proceedings. Lachamp was the one who had failed to skirt the drain and had gone in up to his waist—he who had managed to find a clean shirt and shorts. He remained there, dumfounded and furious, holding up the list in one hand and his pencil in the other.

Julot, who was in front of me, could not help bursting out laughing.

We came out into the main passage. More wounded had come in and were waiting for me—paratroopers from Eliane. I heard one say, "The Viets have got 75's which don't recoil up on Bald Hill."

We reached the west entrance. I had forgotten my abdominal cases, my favorites: "This way, general, men who have undergone an abdominal operation." There were ten of them, as usual, as there had been the day before and would be again the next day.

There was that constant smell of fresh feces and urine. The general went and saw them one by one. He carefully placed his shoes, which were now great clods of mud, between the stretchers and avoided the rubber tubes hanging from the roof. Ten Military Medals were awarded.

"Right. Good-by, Grauwin. Thank you for all that you have done and all that you are doing." He shook my hand twice. Did I see aright? His chin was trembling a little and there was a sudden gleam in his eyes which I had not seen there before. "Tomorrow you will have the official notices for all your wounded. Right, Trinquart?"

"Yes, sir."

He turned and slowly climbed the first steps of the slippery stairway, turned left into the Second Airborne's trench, and so vanished.

14.

Prisoner

It was the night of May 6. Staub was sitting on the side of the bed where Sylvestre was moaning softly and asking for a drink. I was sitting opposite, on the bed beneath Simon Marie's bunk.

Simon Marie was listening to us. In the other beds there were eight wounded, still to be operated on, and at the moment they were asleep. The orderlies had just brought two stretchers and placed them on the muddy ground. On the first one was a paratrooper with an abdominal wound. His blood pressure hovered around 40. I wondered if it would be any use giving him intravenous therapy.

Other stretchers had been put in the exit passage, in the infirmary in the main passage, and in the entrance to the operating room.

I was hot, and my limbs were heavy with fatigue.

Staub was a lieutenant, a doctor, who had just dropped by parachute with his battalion's first company—the First Colonial Paratroops under Captain de Bazin. He came to see me at once and held out his water bottle, saying, "That's come straight from Hanoi, major. There's still ice inside."

I had a drink. It was absinthe, and I took another gulp. It was very good.

"So the whole battalion is here now?" I asked.

"Yes. I came today with the last of them who were left. Do you know where we'll be put?"

"Oh, on the Elianes, of course."

We had had the sound of gunfire in our ears all day long. Every gun of every caliber, from the 37 to the 155, had been firing. The two tanks no longer needed to leave their positions to fire their machine guns toward Eliane, and their bullets skimmed over our vent holes, as did the Viet bullets.

I knew that it had been a tough day for the Elianes, even a critical one. You could still hear the mortars exploding and quick bursts of fire.

"What are people saying in Hanoi?"

"That it will soon be all over."

"Then why were the First Colonial Paratroops dropped here?"

"You know how it is with the paratroops: they like to win or get wiped out together."

I had known that for some time, for fifty-six days in fact.

Cassou came in, tall and comically appealing with his little mustache and his good-natured ways. He was with the Second Airborne and always close to Colonel Langlais. He was a real friend who had never let half a day pass without coming to see us. "Excuse me," he said, "but are you Lieutenant Staub?"

"Yes."

"Then you'd better get a move on. Your battalion is just going off into the trenches toward the Elianes. You'll have to get over there at once."

Staub jumped to his feet and grasped my hand: "Good-by, major, I'll be seeing you again soon."

"Yes, soon." But I was never to see him again.

"Well, Cassou, what's happening?"

"The balloon's going up. The Viets have managed to occupy half of Eliane 1 and 2. It may even be that they have complete control of Eliane 1. But the boss is going to counter-attack with what remains of the First Foreign Paratroops, the Eighth Assault, and the Second Foreign Paratroops. If only you could have heard old Langlais and Bigeard shouting orders. They're both back now. It seems that the boys got a bit of blast . . . they went everywhere and shells burst all around them."

"They went on foot?"

"Of course—in the last two days there hasn't been a jeep that can function in the whole of Dienbienphu."

I knew that the last of the jeeps had been given the job of carrying stretchers. It was now lying overturned in a shell hole full of mud.

I wondered what was left of the Eighth Assault, the Sixth Paratroops, the First Foreign Paratroops, and the Second Battalion, Colonial Paratroops: perhaps a hundred men in each battalion—and then I was over the mark. Of these hundred, only fifty were able to take the field in the end, and that was all.

The next to last support post on Huguette had fallen the day before. No wounded managed to get back to the field hospital.

At dawn, Legionnaires of the Thirteenth Demi-Brigade and the First Battalion, Second Foreign, recaptured the support post—it was simply a pile of mud and rubble. They found no trace of the wounded. It was a mystery.

I had been obliged to ask that Vidal be allowed to retreat. This was on May 3. First of all, he rang me to say, "Major, it's getting impossible. I'm up to my ankles in mud, and the wounded are piling up beside one another. I can't even move . . . my electric plant has packed up, and I only have a dozen candles left. I haven't any more gas for the Primus . . ." His tired voice made a dull echo on the phone.

I had tried to get supplies to him, but it was out of the question, suicidal.

The Viets had advanced relentlessly, yard by yard, along the dip between Dominique 2 and Eliane 1. Their dead were constantly being replaced by fresh companies which were waiting in the rear. Our dead were only replaced by wounded men, those who still had two legs.

The Viets were now only three hundred yards from Vidal: mortars and grenades were constantly raining down on him.

"Nobody dares to go outside any longer," he said.

I phoned the command post and found myself talking to Colonel Langlais: "Colonel, Vidal is now in the front line."

"My dear Grauwin, we're all in the front line now."

There was nothing to say to this dry answer, which was quite true; still, I made another attempt: "But, Colonel, there are fifty wounded in his shelter, waiting for treatment from him. And he can't even make a dressing."

"What do you propose?"

"Let him fall back on my place. Then ask him to work with Hantz, who is at the end of his tether."

"You'll take charge of everything?"

"Yes, colonel."

I summoned N'Diaye and told him to get ready the N.C.O. shelter in the Airborne Commandos' quarters for the Sixth Surgical Unit, which was coming along. Then I rang Vidal: "It's all fixed up. Come along here with your team and the walking wounded. We'll fetch the other wounded with a truck in the course of the night. Barraud will take charge of them for the time being."

"Oh thank you, major. I'll be along. We'll stow as much valuable material into our haversacks as we can."

It took him an hour to thread his way through the maze

of trenches, which were collapsing and filled with mud, heavily burdened as he was with over sixty pounds of stuff.

I don't know how he managed to get across the bridge. He must have run. At last he appeared, very much thinner and with great blue rings around his eyes; he had aged ten years. He was covered with mud, and sweat dripped slowly down onto his chest.

His whole team was behind him in the same condition, then the unhappy line of wounded men. They were put in shelters, in an odd corner, on a piece of canvas spread out in the mud.

After a few minutes' rest, I sent him to help Hantz, who first of all replied, when I told him of this unexpected relief: "No, no, let him stay with you. I'll manage this on my own."

We heard more squelching in the mud: six stretchers, each with its bloodstained burden—Legionnaires of the Thirteenth Demi-Brigade from the Claudine support post. "There are hundreds and hundreds of them, major," they told me. "We killed masses of them, but always more came on, jumping over the bodies of the others. They took the support post, but we got it back with the fellows of the Thirteenth. Then they came back again: there were a thousand of them. Now it's all over."

There were more explosions, shells whistling, and mortars in action. Then came shouts and groans—more stretchers at the north entrance. A stretcher bearer had just been wounded. The first body on the canvas was a paratrooper; he had his right arm torn off and then got a shell splinter in his back on our terrace.

There were no more stretcher bearers left, and it was the fighting men who had to carry the stretchers, returning at once to the scene of the fighting.

The other wounded were also paratroopers of the Second Battalion, First Colonial. "The captain is dead . . . the lieutenant too," I heard one say. "I'm the last man left in my company; the rest are wiped out. When I got away, the Viets were yelling around Major Brechignac's command post."

"Thousands and thousands of them . . . Their dead and their wounded tip over into our trench, falling on our machine guns and even on our shoulders."

Stretchers were pouring in from all sides. We had to cram them in everywhere—in the dispensary, in the operating room. Another procession, more men of that Second Battalion.

"It's all right, we've got Eliane 2 back. It was marvelous. Men from the Eighth Assault and the Second Foreign Paratroops—if only you could have seen them, major. It all went off like an exercise—it was sheer butchery. All the same, if that goes on, the major will soon be the only man left."

I turned to Cassou, who had just come in: "It's true enough, major," he said, "at the moment it's full steam ahead, according to the boss on the 'bigophone.'"

"Bigophone" was Cassou's word for the radio.

A wild hope entered our hearts. They were hanging on. But I had to ask: "How many men are there left in your company?"

"Oh, about fifteen. The lieutenant was killed right away. The sergeant major's in command now . . . if only you had seen it all, major. Langlais and Bigeard came along the trench. I knew it was them with their red forage caps. No helmets! And the stuff was coming down like hell!"

They said to the remains of the battalion which had fallen back on the shelters below the hill: "Come on, fellows. We must put this right. It's the last blow. If we get the hill back, we've won. Let's go, paratroops!"

They went into each shelter and right along the trench, not ducking to avoid shell splinters or bullets. They went into the holes dug by the Sixth Colonial Paratroops, now under the command of Major Thomas: "As soon as the counterattack begins, you'll push in behind. We must get them this time."

Galvanized into a mad rush, they swept up to the top of the

hill. The Viets were flung down the opposite slope in an inferno of explosions, blood, and smoke, down into the barbed wire, holes, and trenches.

A fresh procession arrived. "Put that first one on the chest with the bottle of blood in it. The next on the office table—it's big enough to take a Vietnamese. Put one in my shelter—there's room on the ground beside Phuc."

These are Legionnaires from Huguette. A German says: "Everything's smashed up; it was frightful. I was in Russia in 1944, but I have never yet seen anything like this."

There too Langlais and Bigeard went with their red forage caps, and the Legionnaires could hardly believe their eyes. After their visit, the counterattack took place with grenades and tommy guns: they retook the support post, the one just in front of their commanding officer's command post, shelter by shelter and trench by trench, advancing over the dead bodies of the enemy and those of their own men.

All of a sudden Rivier rose up before me covered with mud, thinner than ever. His face was deathly pale. Behind him I could make out a dozen more heads with eyes fixed on me.

"I've come to you, major," he said, "as my infirmary has just collapsed. The battalion is wiped out. It's the end. I've come with all those who were able to follow me."

The Sixth Colonial Paratroops, his battalion, had held a position at the foot of Eliane 1, which had been retaken some twenty minutes ago. The hundred and fifty able-bodied men who were left took part in the counterattack. Only the wounded were lying in the shelters, those whom in the past two weeks I had sent to rejoin their unit.

Then to the south hundreds and hundreds of Viets poured down from Bald Hill. "I heard them coming," Rivier went on, "but I hadn't realized that they were as close as that. I came out of my infirmary, and already the wounded were shrieking in the trenches. At the same moment a shell, a 120, exploded on my infirmary, when they were only a few yards away. They had their own mortars firing on them, major. You could hardly believe it."

So the western slope of Eliane 1, visible from our entry, had had it now.

"I was more or less pushed along by the Viets, with my ten men behind me. I really don't know why we're still alive."

He was utterly worn out. I told him to rest a moment in my shelter. He was thirsty and began to drink with immense relief. I had one or two oranges left, which he devoured. "If you could only know how good that is," he said. "I've eaten nothing for a couple of days. And I've only had a little rain water to drink, some that had trickled down into empty basins . . . The poor old battalion. Bigeard mustn't hear about this . . . It will be too cruel a blow for him."

On the cards of the wounded who were still coming in I saw the name of Rouault, doctor of the Fifth Vietnamese Paratroops. They said that the rest of the battalion had fallen back on the Second Thai Battalion, just opposite the field hospital, across the river.

This meant that the other slope of Eliane had had it. It was encircled now. There was no doubt that the Viets were going to take it. It was their usual procedure, and if they were to take it they would be on the river bank in a few minutes, on the bridge, some fifty yards from the field hospital.

The wounded from Bizard's company were coming in now. I had no more room, not a square yard even. But at that very moment N'Diaye told me, "Three have just died."

"Good, then Bizard's men can have their place."

"No, major," one of them said, "they won't get the Opera position . . . they'll be held up in the ditch. We let them come up their trenches, which run parallel, then give it to them at twenty yards. You should see how they jump!"

Now Huguette, Claudine, the white Thais, who were the last left to the south, and the Second Thai Battalion were each of them sending us nine or ten wounded.

I rang Barraud. "It's hell, major," he said. "Another two hundred yards and they're here. I can't get out. It's not worth trying . . . when I feel that the end is near, I'll say good-by."

Cassou came in—the first time I had ever seen him serious. There was fury in his eyes: "Eliane 1 has fallen, major. Major Brechignac said good-by to us over the 'bigophone.' He was alone with ten of his fellows, all men who had been wounded before—amputated, in casts, or with only one eye left. He said, 'It's the end. The Viets are on a level with my command post. In a few seconds the grenades will be here . . . Good-by, colonel. Good-by, all.' "

Cassou had been weeping, and his eyes were still swollen with tears.

The Fifth Vietnamese Paratroops' command post hadn't time to say good-by. The Viets swept over it in an avalanche.

Cassou went on: "The colonel wants to know if you have any wounded from the Sixth Paratroops. He'd like to question them."

"There is one, only one. I think he can walk." So Cassou took him off.

Eliane must have cost some thousands of lives to both sides. After the fall of Dienbienphu the Viets piled their dead and ours together in the trenches at the foot of the hill and covered them with earth. Above this they erected a sort of cenotaph thirty feet high, made out of bamboos and pieces of white parachute silk.

There was nothing else to be done.

I got through to Le Damany, whose voice was also sad and lifeless as he said, "I don't know where to put them all."

Hantz and Vidal were operating without a break. I had forgotten Gindrey—he too was operating all the time. On either side of the operating table were a couple of stretchers with wounded men waiting their turn and gazing apprehensively at what went on over their heads.

I considered that I ought to report to the command post, so on the phone I asked for Colonel de Pazzis, the general's chief of staff. "Colonel," I told him, "I can't keep this up."

"I'm coming over."

He was there a few minutes later, tall, pale, and distinguished. He stared again and again at the scene around him.

"In a few moments," I told him, "I will be hemmed in in the emergency-treatment room. Nobody will be able to come in or go out."

"I understand, doctor. It's terrifying. I'll report the situation to the general."

Yet I knew that the general could do nothing for me. Only a miracle . . . But perhaps I was wrong. Perhaps what Colonel de Pazzis said would lead the general to make a decision. One which he would afterward regret.

Suddenly I heard gasps and protests in the main passage and saw a long line of muddy statues—but they were moving, groping their way along the walls, trying not to disturb the poor fellows lying on the stretchers in the passage. I went closer and recognized them: they were the wounded who had still been in my shelters a couple of weeks ago. Under their layers of mud they were quite naked. "Where have you come from?" I asked.

They were from the Sixth, the Eighth, the Fifth, from the Second Battalion, First Colonial Paratroops, from the First and Second Foreign Paratroops, from Claudine, and from Huguette. There were twenty of them, fifty—I could no longer keep count of them.

One of them had a leg missing. How had he managed to get here? Another had an arm missing. Another had only one eye—he it was who only yesterday asked me if he could go back to his unit; I had operated on him only the evening before. Then men with casts on their shoulders, their chests, their legs. There was mud over everything, dressings and plaster. It got in between the plaster and the skin and was bound to reach the wound underneath. In the thick of all this mud I saw eyes with a question in them: "Why is this happening? Will it be over soon?"

I felt that my mind was giving way. Was it possible that God would permit this final ordeal?

The Viets had made these men leave the trenches and shelters where they were side by side with their dead comrades. They got them together and said: "Go back to your field hospital. We will see you again later. Tell your doctor that we are on our way." So they came along, supporting one another.

"So here we are. What do you want us to do, major?"

I summoned Alonso and told him, "Put them anywhere you can, in the Airborne Commandos' quarters and beyond that. Give each of them some absorbent cotton and alcohol, so that they can clean themselves a little, and then cigarettes, canned stuff, and rations."

There were more wounded behind them, from those of the First Colonial Paratroops who had been dropped on the previous night. The battalion was broken up all over the place, and each company tried to force its way out as best it could. But these did not know their way about the camp. How could they, when they were dropped in the darkness? Somebody took them off to their positions, and when daybreak came they did not even know where their own side or where the enemy were.

They were told, "The field hospital is straight ahead."

"There are wounded everywhere, major, nothing but wounded, all over the place." They could not get any farther, many of them. "We got through, because we can still walk."

Then I suddenly realized that for an hour I had not seen a stretcher come in, although the fighting was at its height and the din had reached paroxysms of violence. Every weapon, every gun was firing. I heard the four-barreled affair firing calmly—I heard her deep singing note. Suddenly there came some ten explosions and she stopped. She must have had it. No, she started up again, firing short, quick bursts.

Deudon asked me, "Would you like some hot coffee, major?"

"What time is it?" I countered.

"Six in the morning."

Time had never gone so quickly. For me the night had lasted only for five terrible minutes. It was surely daybreak by now. I went toward the main passage, leaning against the wall, and reached the north entry.

Geneviève was tirelessly distributing drinks in the shelters, giving injections, talking softly.

I risked a glance toward Eliane, but all I could see was a great cloud of smoke, nothing more. Between Eliane and the river, some thirty shells were bursting at the same moment. Numbers of bullets whistled close at hand, and the crack of their impact echoed again and again.

Then Lachamp and N'Diaye appeared, covered with mud: "Major, we can't do any more. We've tried to do the dressings and give at least an injection of antitetanus toxoid to everybody, but if you go right to the end of the line you come up against the Viets. We've got to stop somewhere, major."

In our trench and in the Second Airborne's and the Eighth Assault's, in the passage leading to the command post, in all the trenches which ended in the center of the camp, the wounded were squeezed together in an endless line, some sitting, some lying down, right in the mud—and this line only stopped at the point where it was in contact with the Viets.

There were some dead among them; they sank into the mud, and those who came in from the support posts walked over them, and they sank in a little deeper . . .

There were no more stretchers, no more canvas, nothing.

There were not only the wounded, but also those who had nothing more to do because they had no idea where to go nor where to take refuge. They were unarmed, so they stopped dead, worn out, at the end of their strength, joining the long line in the mud and falling asleep.

"There's nothing more that one can do," they said.

At ten o'clock Patrice came over, quite his usual self. I took him off to my shelter, where Rivier was sitting, unable to sleep, his hands still trembling all the time.

"It's a massacre, major. It must be stopped. Something must be done." It was the first time that I had seen Patrice really serious; he was staring at Phuc's stump of arm. "Huguette is no more. The Eighth Assault's second company has fallen back, and those in the Opera position too."

My thoughts turned to Bizard. The Viets never got hold of a yard of his drain; he only fell back under direct orders, with rage in his heart, firing right up to his last cartridge.

"One of our last support posts was captured an hour ago."

"What's left?"

"Nothing much—the central area of the camp, half caved in. Major Cheynel, commanding the Second Thai Battalion, and Barraud are getting it now."

At noon we were nibbling a few crackers in silence, when suddenly the sound of aircraft engines reached us from the vent holes; at once the ack-ack went into action, putting up a heavy barrage. Numbers of automatic weapons fired at the same moment. Their sound was cut short by bursts ripping from the guns of the fighters ending in the powerful throb of their climb back into the sky.

Then we heard bombs falling close at hand. The shelter shook several times. Phuc opened his eyes in terror. The incident lasted ten minutes, then it was all over.

All was quiet, for the Viets too were silent. It was an

odd sort of silence which suddenly embraced us. What was happening? Or rather, what was going to happen?

"They're regrouping and getting ready," said Patrice. "The final assault will take place in a few hours' time."

"May God protect us!"

It was I who said that. The hanging over the door was raised and Major Touret came in, his face a picture of utter exhaustion, his legs thick with mud up to the knees: "I'm going to the briefing, doc. All the battalion commanding officers who are left and those commanding support posts have been summoned to it. The final decision will be made in an hour's time. It's the last round."

He left, and I went into the passage. There were ten or twenty dead. Some of them had no visible wound—more deaths from the extreme limit of physical exhaustion. No, they had gone beyond the known limits, as expressed in formulas and equations.

These matters will have to be gone into all over again, for "new facts have appeared." People will give lectures to a delicate-minded and indifferent audience and say, "At Dienbienphu the men's physical resistance was . . ." What's the good of all that? These things happened at Dienbienphu, and they can only happen once, not again.

The dead were taken away, and I had them placed on our roof, anyhow, one on top of another. They had become great clods of mud, and the flies swarmed all over them.

Now there were ten places free, but they were quickly filled. Gindrey summoned me. The blood from the last man to be operated on had poured down on the wounded waiting their turn on the ground below.

Patrice was still at my side. "You know, major," he said, "I don't want to be made prisoner by the Viets. We ought to have got away last night."

Last night he had come to say good-by, as had Buezek and

some others, men in the Second Group and the Eighth Assault. They were going to regroup toward the Junon position. There were nearly two hundred of them, headed by Bigeard and Langlais. The general had decided to remain with the survivors, with the wounded, with us.

The idea was a desperate attempt to break out along the river to the south, get hold of the first Viet trench, and try to link up with Isabelle. Then, with the Isabelle garrison, they would strike toward the south, toward the Thai mountains and scrub. But at two in the morning, they all had to go back to their positions; it was out of the question. A Thai report had come in to say that after the first trench there was a second, then a third, and still more beyond that. It was no good simply to invite a massacre.

Nothing had really been known about the Isabelle position since April; only a few uncertain items had come over the radio, nothing definite. Today they must have been going through the same sort of hell as we were.

Now it was a quarter past four in the afternoon, and there was still this silence that we could not get used to. My orderlies had got through a fantastic amount of work.

"Who went to the river to get water?" I asked.

"I'm afraid we did, major," said N'Diaye, Lachamp, and Sioni almost apologetically. "We did as many dressings as we could in the passages, but we haven't been beyond the river."

Geneviève's uniform was stained with blood and mud. She had had no sleep for two days, and her shelter was crammed with paratroopers and Legionnaires.

Then I saw Major Touret come in. It was his habit to call and see me after the briefing. He paused in front of me, an expression of extreme gravity on his face: "Well, doc, it's all over . . . at half-past five we cease fire; there's to be no further resistance. Those who can are to destroy their weapons and blow up ammunition dumps."

He grasped my hand hard, tears in his eyes. The muscles

under his cheeks were violently contracted. I too was almost overcome with emotion.

"Good-by, doc." He turned and went off. Patrice followed him saying, "Good-by, major. I don't want to be taken prisoner by the Viets. I shall try to get away and take Major Touret with me."

The men from the Second Airborne came to see me one by one, an expression on their faces that I had not seen before; their eyes were gleaming with suppressed rage. They too had come to say good-by.

Now I was alone, beyond any hope of relief, alone with my misery, my mud, my sweat, my dead and dying, my wounded . . .

It was going to be June, 1940, all over again. I should be a prisoner for the second time.

I went off to the operating theater to tell Gindrey and his team the news. They stared at me, their eyes wide open, then turned to look again at the flesh which was waiting to be saved from rotting away.

In the emergency-treatment room my words were greeted with silence. My orderlies stopped dead. A few began to cry. Simon Marie sat up and said, "What are they going to do with me?"

Then I announced the news to the wounded, shelter by shelter, passage by passage. Eyes were turned on me in astonishment. Those who were still capable of it, turned paler.

"In one hour all resistance ceases. Keep calm. You will be quite unharmed."

Courtade too said, "What are they going to do with me?"

A few were alarmed, especially the Vietnamese. But on the whole, after the first shock of surprise had worn off, they seemed relieved, as if I had removed a great burden which had been weighing on them for a long time. Heads were raised, then fell back on the damp and dirty beds, staring at the logs in the roof.

But a paratroop sergeant major, wounded a few hours before, said, "But, major, there are still men around. We could still put up some sort of show before surrendering."

"Perhaps—but then fighting would take place in mud strewn with the dead and wounded . . . No, the general is right."

Geneviève said nothing and her eyes were dry, though her hands trembled slightly. What would they do with her?

I would have liked to say good-by to my colleagues, Barraud, Stermann, and Rondy: "Hello, give me the Second Thai Battalion."

"The line's cut, major."

"Then give me the First Foreign Paratroops."

"That line's cut too, major."

At last I got through to Le Damany and said, "You've heard the news?"

"What news?"

"In one hour it's all over. Fighting is at an end."

"No, it's not possible."

Then there was a long silence.

"Good-by, Le Damany."

"Good-by, Grauwin."

I would have liked to hear the voices of Major Méhay and Major Léost for the last time, but it was not possible. The whole command post was busy destroying documents, papers, and secret codes.

A wounded man turned up with his arm in a sling. I recognized him as Lieutenant Le Boudec of the Sixth Colonial Paratroops. He was specially promoted to captain on the occasion of his first wound. "I was wounded this morning at nine o'clock," he told me, "but I've only just been able to come over. A bullet went through my forearm, and I can't move my fingers."

I took him off to the operating room; he was to be the last man we operated on.

Suddenly a number of explosions broke the silence. Everyone looked up, and a wounded man said, "Some fathead is still firing."

Our guns fired a last salvo, the final salute.

Then we heard more explosions, duller but more powerful —the ammunition dumps being blown up—followed by short bursts and a few isolated shots. Then once more there was silence.

No, some aircraft had appeared in the sky; again we heard the engines of the fighters, their angry clamor cut into by bursts from machine guns and the explosion of bombs. Our shelters quivered beneath our feet. We could not grasp what was happening.

"It's coming down like a lot of gravel," said Julot.

"I suppose you refer to the defeat at Gravelotte," * said Bacus peevishly, in no mood for this sort of thing.

In a quarter of an hour the noise gradually lessened and died away. The air force too had been making its final salute. We were never to hear them again.

Now we had to get ready for the arrival of the Viets.

I gave my last orders. The uniform was to be shorts or trousers with khaki shirts showing a man's rank and the insignia of the medical service. An armlet with a red cross on the left arm. I did not have enough of these, so each man had to make his own from a piece of bandage and some mercurochrome.

Gindrey's team were to stay in the operating room. The emergency-treatment team would wait in its own room. There would be an orderly in every shelter. I would wait with the rest in the main passage, with Geneviève by my side.

Now we were prepared. The time was twenty-five past five. There was complete silence, inside and out, broken only by occasional dull explosions—ammo dumps going up.

Suddenly we heard a number of voices and phrases rapped out in Vietnamese. They reached us through the vent holes

---

* In the Franco-Prussian War of 1870. (Translator's note.)

and were followed by the tramp of feet thundering over our roof and the clash of arms.

How would they come, by the north or the west entry?

I went toward the west entry and took a step up. There were the Viets in their green uniforms, their helmets striped with shreds of green and yellow parachute silk. There they were, passing rapidly across the little square of blue sky which was all that I could see.

We heard a number of hoarse voices. The field hospital held no interest for them, at least for the time being. They retraced their steps. But among them I saw a red forage cap—the general. I could only see his head and shoulders, which were held very erect. He was very pale, and there was a cigarette in his mouth.

Behind him came Colonel Ducruix, Major Léost, Major Méhay, and the rest of the command post. I only caught sight of them for a few seconds.

I returned to the crossway in the passage. Some of the orderlies were pale with fright, and I had to reassure them: "Don't worry, they won't do anything to you. They're just taking off General de Castries."

Le Boudec came to on the operating table, still under the influence of Pentothal. He laughed and asked, "So they've brought up reinforcements?"

Slowly I went toward the north entrance, slithering on the muddy ground for the last time. I went into my shelter and said good-by to Phuc and Yann. In the emergency-treatment room I said good-by to Sylvestre and Simon Marie. In the shelter close to my own I shook hands with Rollin, Deflinne, and Rondeau.

I reached the muddy steps at the entrance and suddenly saw two legs appear encased in mud, but I caught a glimpse of green cloth. The legs were followed by a belt, grenades, and a tommy gun held in the firing position. A face appeared beneath a helmet covered with greenery, and there were slanting eyes in this pale oval face. The man made a gesture and said, "*Di ve*," which means "come out."

I turned to Geneviève and told her, "Keep close behind me."

Then I said to the others, "Follow me, all of you."

I passed by Courtade's shelter and heard a heart-rending cry, "Major?" I pretended not to hear and went on, staring hard at the square of blue sky which came to meet me. Then I climbed the steps, which were thick with mud. Suddenly the sun blinded me, and I was forced to shut my eyes. I took great breaths of air, but it smelled infected. The sound of our electric plant echoed in my ears.

"Come on, keep going!"

At one glance the new Dienbienphu appeared before me. It was a complete wreck. Great clouds of smoke were floating slowly over the hills. The sky was of the purest blue.

I went out onto our terrace, which was covered with wounded, sitting or lying down. Their dressings were all stained with mud; with drawn faces they watched us go by.

A dead body, thick with flies, was lying on the sloping roof of the mess. On the left, near the barbed wire, was another, swollen to the point of bursting, with thousands of grubs swarming over it.

We reached the crossway. I knew that I was to go toward the bridge, and anyhow we were swept up into a column coming down from the Claudine position and the central camp—Legionnaires, gunners, and some paratroopers of the First and Second Foreign Paratroops. Their faces showed their weariness, but there was always that gleam of suppressed rage in their eyes.

As for the Viets, within my entire range of vision, right out to what had been the farthest boundaries of our Dienbienphu, I could see nothing but men clad in green, going from shelter to shelter or marching in orderly ranks. There were hundreds, thousands of them; they seemed to have risen up out of our own trenches.

We went down toward the bridge, and they climbed to the center of the camp. Some of them cast curious glances at me; others had completely expressionless eyes. I heard a few words of Vietnamese which I understood. There was nothing offensive in them. Their trousers were turned up to the knees, and their scanty sandals of canvas and rubber were covered with mud.

We crossed the bridge, which was still in position, though I could see traces showing how often it had been hit.

Geneviève followed me in silence, and suddenly I thought of Odette, who had been beside me in the winter of 1947, on the march from Tuyenquang to Hanoi. But she had been in front of me, with a Colt on her right thigh. I had had my rifle with a bullet in the breech, which was against orders.

It was astonishing, this immense silence which came down from the sky and the mountains.

We crossed the Second Thai Battalion's positions; side by side with shell holes were those left by gaping shelters. There were arms lying about in the mud all over the place—rifles, tommy guns, grenades by the hundreds.

The Eliane and Dominique hills were closer now, and on their slopes were spread a number of white parachutes and gutted shelters. There were hundreds of bodies lying in the sun on the slopes of Eliane 2.

Suddenly a green helmet appeared in front of me, with keen, black, slanting eyes beneath it. I stopped dead, and my little group came to an abrupt halt behind me.

A voice said in French, "You are Major Grauwin?"

"Yes."

"You are to go back to your hospital and continue looking after your wounded. That's an order from the higher command of our army."

A tide of joy swept over me and filled my breast. My wounded! I had forgotten them. How could I ever do that?

I about-faced, so that I was at the rear of our little procession. Geneviève said, "Oh, I'm so glad."

Bacus, Levasseur, and Gindrey turned and gave me a fine smile. Soon we met our friends, the other prisoners, unhappy without their arms. Nobody would tell them to go back.

I could see Sioni's head, just in front of Geneviève. It didn't seem possible—his hair had been red and he was still a young man, barely twenty-five—but I saw many strands of white: "Sioni, have you seen your hair?"

"Yes, major, but have you seen yours? It's all white."

My little column went merrily back, and I took a look around with different eyes. There were packages of medical supplies and rations scattered all over the place, by the river bank, in the barbed wire. I would ask the Viets to salvage them. I could see cans of gas for the electric plant. There were cases of plasma, packed in netting, close to the bridge.

Someone said, "Look, there's a box of canned milk."

There were cases of ammunition sunk in the mud, and shells for the 105's. We crossed the bridge and returned toward the square, passing the two rotting bodies covered with blue and green flies. The horrible stench filled our nostrils. We reached the terrace. The wounded had not moved; one might have thought they were waiting for us. Now they welcomed us with joy in their eyes.

The large electric plant was still working away in its shelter. I paused before the muddy steps of our northern entry, from which the black hole sent up its hot and noisome breath. Slowly I went down, slithering, pressing my hands against the sticky sides of the trench. Once more my feet sank into the mud, and my thoughts turned to that smashed leg with a tourniquet on it, which I had had a last look at just before, and the thorax which ejected blood with each breath, and the man with an abdominal wound who groaned as he stared at me.

I reflected that I was going back to my work as a doctor—but this time as a prisoner.